The whatis?com
Encyclopedia
of Technology
Terms

Whatis?com

A Division of Pearson Technology
201 W. 103rd Street
Indianapolis, Indiana 46290

Trademarks

Warning and Disclaimer

Associate Publisher

Greg Wiegand

Acquisitions Editor

Greg Wiegand

Proofreader

Juli Cook

Team Coordinator

Sharry Lee Gregory

Interior Designer

Anne Jones

Cover Designer

Alan Clements

Page Layout

Michelle Mitchell

About the Author and Whatis.com

This book is based on a Web site, whatis.com, created by Lowell Thing in September, 1996, as an experiment in hypertext and also as a place for some information he was always forgetting. The original idea was to see how many useful hypertext links could fit on a Web page, and he wrote the first few topics in order to see what the idea would look like. One topic led to another and, by mid-2001, Lowell and some freelance contributors had written 3,500 definitions.

In February 2000, Whatis.com was purchased by TechTarget, a diversified media company providing targeted IT media to technology professionals. Lowell continues to play an active role as Editor of the site. Whatis.com currently serves more than one million visitors each month.

Lowell lives in Kingston, New York, with his wife, Suzanne. Their daughter, Emily, created the logo that was used during whatis.com's first three years, and their daughter, Hillary, contributed some of the first definitions. Lowell was formerly a technical writer and information planner for IBM. He is a senior member of the Society for Technical Communication.

Credits

TechTarget Co-Founders: Greg Strakosch and Don Hawk

Editor-in-Chief, TechTarget: Paul Gillin

Editor, whatis.com: Lowell Thing

Assistant Editor: Margaret Rouse

Cover Copy: Lisa Johnson

Cover Design: Frank Remick

Project Coordinator: Ed Montes

Senior Contributing Writers: Stan Gibilisco, Ivy Wigmore, and Sherri Wilson

Other Contributors: Megan Brady, Sean Brooks, Teresa Buday, Christine Campbell, Gordon Carrolton, Joyce Chutchian, Marilyn Cohodas, William W. Collier, Jim Connolly, Patricia Ellis, Crystal Ferraro, Sean Ford, David Gabel, Cathy Gagne, Kara Gattine, Joda Glossner, Karen Guglielmo, Paul Healey, Michele Hope, Jennifer Hubley, Laura Hunt, Joann Ives, Steve Jacobs, Dick Kennedy, Catherine Ketcher, Mark Lewis, Heather McCarthy, Fred McIntyre, Mary Michaud, Joseph Oliver, Jon Panker, Eric Parizo, Borys Pawliw, BJ Rama, Matt Savage, RJ Schille, Jeremy Selwyn, Jim Shaughessy, Stephen Simpson, Simon Smith, David Spenard, Sean Tierney, Steven Vagle, and many others.

Acknowledgements

I'd like to thank Deborah Kaufman, Greg Correll, and Joseph Flanigan for being the first great fans of whatis.com and for helping to build a Web site that became something of an institution. I also seize this opportunity to hug and kiss my wife, Suzanne, in print for her absolute support, love, and good humor without which even the first 10 definitions would never been written.

I would also like to thank Jim Connolly for being the first to see how whatis.com could fit into TechTarget; Ken Berquist and Bob Taylor for making it happen; Paul Gillin, Editor-in-Chief, for his overall guidance; and Don Hawk and Greg Strakosch for folding whatis.com into their own great idea while extending its possibilities. I would also like to thank Margaret "Peggy" Rouse for demanding that I hire her and for making our jobs so much fun.

Finally, I would like to thank the thousands of people worldwide who contributed to whatis.com during the first five years of its existence. In the first days, it was users from such places as Riga, Nairobi, and Ulan Bator who made the Web such an exciting place to be and who spurred us on with their thanks and suggestions. Turning whatis.com into a book seems like the end of Phase One. I invite the users of this book and the Web site to help us build Phase Two of what we like to hope will become the world's greatest mental construct about information technology.

Lowell Thing

How to Use This Book

You can look up any term by the alphabetical listing.

You can test your knowledge of IT vocabulary by picking out a term and seeing if our definition matches yours.

You may also be able to find the information you need in our "Fast References" section (for example, DSL, transmission speeds, prefix multipliers, fundamental physical units, and so forth).

For a term so new that it may not be in this book, visit the whatis.com Web site. We may have it and, if we don't, you can suggest that we add it.

For a given term, you may also want to visit whatis.com to see the Web sites we recommend for more information about the term.

Some notes about our definitions:

We report which terms are being used in information technology and what they currently mean. We report usage, and, only when it seems helpful, do we recommend a preference.

Because information technology changes rapidly, a definition can become outdated. If in doubt, the best source is always an authority such as the IEEE, the IETF, and similar standards or technology-sponsoring organizations.

We try to describe a term uniquely in the first sentence or two as you would in a dictionary. The rest of the definition is an elaboration that describes the term as you would in an encyclopedia.

We describe pronunciation only for terms we think some users will want to know how to pronounce.

Chat Abbreviations

Chat abbreviations are commonly used in e-mail, online chatting, instant messaging, and conference postings.

Abbreviation	Meaning
ADN	Any day now
AFIK	As far as I know
AFK	Away from keyboard
ARE	Acronym-rich environment
A/S/L?	Age/sex/location?
B4N	Bye for now
BAK	Back at the keyboard
BBIAB	Be back in a bit
BBL	Be back later
BEG	Big evil grin
BFD	Big f***ing deal
BFN	Bye for now
BG	Big grin
BIOYIOP	Blow it out your I/O port
BL	Belly laughing
BOTEC	Back-of-the-envelope calculation
BRB	Be right back
BTA	But then again...
BTW	By the way
BWTHDIK	But what the heck do I know...?
CU	See you
CUL	See you later
CUL8ER	See you later
CYA	Cover your ass
CYO	See you online
DBA	Doing business as
DFLA	Disenhanced four-letter acronym (that is, a TLA)
DL	Dead link
DIKU	Do I know you?
DITYID	Did I tell you I'm distressed?
DQMOT	Don't quote me on this
EG	Evil grin
EMFBI	Excuse me for butting in
EOM	End of message
EOT	End of thread (meaning: end of discussion)
ETLA	Extended three-letter acronym (that is, an FLA)
F2F	Face to face
FAQ	Frequently-ask question(s)
FISH	First in, still here
FLA	Four-letter acronym
FMTYEWTK	Far more than you ever wanted to know
FOMCL	Falling off my chair laughing
FUBAR	F***ed up beyond all repair or recognition
FUD	Fear, Uncertainty, and Doubt
FWIW	For what it's worth

Abbreviation	Meaning
FYI	For your information
G	Grin
GA	Go ahead
GAL	Get a life
GD&R	Grinning, ducking, and running
GIWIST	Gee, I wish I'd said that
GMTA	Great minds think alike
GOL	Giggling out loud
GTRM	Going to read mail
HTH	Hope this helps
IAC	In any case
IANAL	I am not a lawyer (but)
IC	I see
IHA	I hate acronyms
IIRC	If I recall/remember/recollect correctly
ILU or ILY	I love you
IM	Immediate message
IMHO	In my humble opinion
IMing	Chatting with someone online usually while doing other things such as playing trivia or other interactive game
IMNHO	In my not so humble opinion
IMO	In my opinion
IOW	In other words
IPN	I'm posting naked
IRL	In real life (that is, when not chatting)
IYSWIM	If you see what I mean
JBOD	Just a bunch of disks (like redundant array of independent disks, etc.)
JIC	Just in case
JK	Just kidding
KOTC	Kiss on the cheek
KWIM?	Know what I mean?
L8R	Later
LD	Later, dude
LDR	Long-distance relationship
LLTA	Lots and lots of thunderous applause
LOL	Laughing out loud
LRF	Little Rubber Feet (the little pads on the bottom of displays and other equipment)
LTM	Laugh to myself
LTR	Long-term relationship
LULAB	Love you like a brother
LULAS	Love you like a sister
MorF	Male or female
MOSS	Member of the same sex
MOTOS	Member of the opposite sex
MUSM	Miss you so much
NFG	No f*****g good
NFW	No feasible way or no f*****g way
NIFOC	Naked in front of computer
NP or N/P	No problem
NRN	No response necessary
OIC	Oh, I see
OLL	Online love

Abbreviation	Meaning
OTF	Off the floor
OTOH	On the other hand
OTTOMH	Off the top of my head
PANS	Pretty awesome new stuff (as opposed to "POTS")
PCMCIA	People can't master computer industry acronyms
PDA	Public display of affection
PEBCAK	Problem exists between chair and keyboard
PIBKAC	Problem is between keyboard and chair
PITA	Pain in the ass
PMFJIB	Pardon me for jumping in but...
POOF	Goodbye (leaving the room)
POTS	Plain old telephone service
PU	That stinks!
RL	Real life (that is, when not chatting)
ROR	Raffing out roud (Engrish for "laughing out loud")
ROTFL	Rolling on the floor laughing
ROTFLMAO	Rolling on the floor laughing my a** off
ROTFLMAOWPIMP	Rolling on the floor laughing my a** off while peeing in my pants
ROTFLMBO	Rolling on the floor laughing my butt off
RPG	Role-playing games
RSN	Real soon now
RTFM	Read the f***ing manual
RYO	Roll your own (write your own program; derived from cigarettes rolled yourself with tobacco and paper)
S4L	Spam for life (what you may get when you become someone's customer or client)
SHCOON	Shoot hot coffee out of nose
SEG	S***-eating grin
SF	Surfer-friendly (low-graphics Web site)
SNAFU	Situation normal, all f***ed up
SO	Significant other
SOL	Smilling out loud or sh*t out of luck
SOMY	Sick of me yet?
STFW	Search the f*****g Web
STW	Search the Web
SWAG	Stupid wild-a** guess
TAFN	That's all for now
TANSTAAFL	There ain't no such thing as a free lunch
TFH	Thread from hell (a discussion that just won't die and is often irrelevant to the purpose of the forum or group)
TGIF	Thank God it's Friday

Abbreviation	Meaning
THX	Thanks
TIA	Thanks in advance (used if you post a question and are expecting a helpful reply)
TLA	Three-letter acronym
TLK2UL8R	Talk to you later
TMI	Too much information
TOPCA	Til our paths cross again (early Celtic chat term)
TPTB	The powers that be
TTFN	Ta-Ta for now
TTT	Thought that, too (when someone types in what you were about to type)
TTYL	Talk to you later
TU	Thank you
UAPITA	You're a pain in the ass
UW	You're welcome
VBG	Very big grin
VBSEG	Very big s***-eating grin
WDALYIC	Who died and left you in charge?
WFM	Works for me
WIBNI	Wouldn't it be nice if
WT?	What/who the ?
WTFO	What the F***! Over!
WTG	Way to go!
WTGP?	Want to go private?
WU?	What's up?
WUF?	Where are you from?
WYSIWYG	What you see is what you get
YGBSM	You gotta be s***tin' me!
YMMV	Your mileage may vary.

Emoticons (Smileys)

Emoticons (sometimes known as "smileys") are a popular form of expression on the Internet, especially in e-mail. Just type in each character one at a time to create the emoticon.

:-)	Smile
;-)	Smile with a wink
:<})	User with mustache, smiling
:-||	Mad
:-(	Sad
:'-(	Crying
:~	Also crying
:-))	Really happy
:-D	Big grin
:-*	A kiss
:-P~	A lick
:-o	Wow! or I'm surprised
:-|	Grim

:-P	Sticking out your tongue
:-	User happens to be Popeye
:-/	Perplexed
=:O	Frightened (hair standing on end)
=8O	Bug-eyed with fright
:-}	Embarassed smile
:-)<>>>>>	Basic Smiley with a necktie
;-^)	Tongue in cheek
%*@:-(	Hung over
:-~~~	Drooling
>:)	Perplexed look
.)	Keeping an eye out for you
8:-)	Glasses on forehead
8:[	Normal smiling face of a gorilla
0:-)	Angel
]:-|[	Robot
(:V)	Duck 3:-o Cow
:-]	Vampire
(_8-(|)	Homer Simpson
C|:-=	Charlie Chaplin
=|:-)=	Abe Lincoln
*<:-)	Santa Claus
-:-)	User sports a mohawk and admires Mr. T
(:)-)	Scuba diver
:-'|	User has a cold
:-{}	User with heavy lipstick
:-)8	User is well dressed
>:-<	Mad
*#:-)	Scotsman wearing his Scottish tam
%-^	User is another Picasso
#-)	User partied all night
<:I	Dunce
:-| "	Have an ordinary day!" Smiley
:}{:	Kisses (stolen from June bug)
oooo(0) (0)oooo	Toes
(-_-)	Secret smile
#.-o "	Oh, nooooooo Mr. Bill!!!"

The Speed of...

This table shows the stated data rates for the most important end-user and backbone transmission technologies.

Technology	Speed	Physical Medium	Application
GSM mobile telephone service	9.6 to 14.4 **Kbps**	RF in space (**wireless**)	Mobile telephone for business and personal use
High-Speed Circuit-Switched Data service (HSCSD)	Up to 56 Kbps	RF in space (wireless)	Mobile telephone for business and personal use
Regular telephone service (POTS)	Up to 56 Kbps	**Twisted pair**	Home and small business access
Dedicated 56Kbps on Frame Relay	56 Kbps	Various	Business e-mail with fairly large file attachments
DS0	64 Kbps	All	The base signal on a channel in the set of Digital Signal levels
General Packet Radio System (GPRS)	56 to 114 Kbps	RF in space (wireless)	Mobile telephone for business and personal use
ISDN	**BRI**: 64 Kbps to 128 Kbps **PRI**: 23 (T-1) or 30 (E1) assignable 64-Kbps channels plus control channel; up to 1.544 Mbps (T-1) or 2.048 (E1)	**BRI**: Twisted pair **PRI**: T-1 or E1 line	**BRI**: Faster home and small business access **PRI**: Medium and large enter prise access
IDSL	128 Kbps	Twisted-pair	Faster home and small business access
AppleTalk	230.4 Kbps	Twisted pair	Local area network for Apple devices; several networks can be bridged; non-Apple devices can also be connected
Enhanced Data GSM Environment (EDGE)	384 Kbps	RF in space (wireless)	Mobile telephone for business and personal use
Satellite	400 Kbps (DirecPC and others)	RF in space (wireless)	Faster home and small enter prise access
Frame relay	56 Kbps to 1.544 **Mbps**	Twisted-pair or **coaxial cable**	Large company backbone for LANs to **ISP** ISP to Internet infrastructure
DS1/T-1	1.544 Mbps	Twisted-pair, coaxial cable, or **optical fiber**	Large company to ISP ISP to Internet infrastructure
Universal Mobile Telecommunications Service (UMTS)	Up to 2 Mbps	RF in space (wireless)	Mobile telephone for business and personal use (available in 2002 or later)
E-carrier	2.048 Mbps	Twisted-pair, coaxial cable, or **optical fiber**	32-channel European equiva-lent of T-1
T-1C (DS1C)	3.152 Mbps	Twisted-pair, coaxial cable, or optical fiber	Large company to ISP ISP to Internet infrastructure
IBM Token Ring/802.5	4 Mbps (also 16 Mbps)	Twisted-pair, coaxial cable, or optical fiber	Second most commonly used local area network after Ethernet

Technology	Speed	Physical Medium	Application
DS2/T-2	6.312 Mbps	Twisted-pair, coaxial cable, or optical fiber	Large company to ISP ISP to Internet infrastructure
Digital Subscriber Line (DSL)	512 Kbps to 8 Mbps	Twisted-pair (used as a digital, **broadband** medium)	Home, small business, and enterprise access using existing copper lines
E-2	8.448 Mbps	Twisted-pair, coaxial cable, or optical fiber	Carries four multiplexed E-1 signals
Cable modem	512 Kbps to 52 Mbps (see "Key and explanation" below)	Coaxial cable (usually uses Ethernet); in some systems, telephone used for upstream requests	Home, business, school access
Ethernet	10 Mbps	**10BASE-T** (twisted-pair); 10BASE-2 or -5 (**coaxial cable**); 10BASE-F (**optical fiber**)	Most popular business local area network (**LAN**)
IBM Token Ring/802.5	16 Mbps (also 4 Mbps)	Twisted-pair, coaxial cable, or optical fiber	Second most commonly-used local area network after Ethernet
E-3	34.368 Mbps	Twisted-pair or optical fiber	Carries 16 E-l signals
DS3/T-3	44.736 Mbps	Coaxial cable	ISP to Internet infrastructure Smaller links within Internet infrastructure
OC-1	51.84 Mbps	Optical fiber	ISP to Internet infrastructure Smaller links within Internet infrastructure
High-Speed Serial and Interface (HSSI)	Up to 53 Mbps	HSSI cable	Between router hardware WAN lines Short-range (50 feet) interconnection between slower LAN devices and faster WAN lines
Fast Ethernet	100 Mbps	**100BASE-T** (twisted pair); **100BASE-T** (twisted pair); **100BASE-T** (optical fiber)	Workstations with 10 Mbps Ethernet cards can plug into a Fast Ethernet LAN
Fiber Distributed-Data Interface (FDDI)	100 Mbps	Optical fiber	Large, wide-range LAN usually in a large company or a larger ISP
T-3D (DS3D)	135 Mbps	Optical fiber	ISP to Internet infrastructure Smaller links within Internet infrastructure
E-4	139.264 Mbps	Optical fiber	Carries 4 E3 channels Up to 1,920 simultaneous voice conversations
OC-3/SDH	155.52 Mbps	Optical fiber	Large company backbone Internet backbone
E-5	565.148 Mbps	Optical fiber	Carries 4 E4 channels Up to 7,680 simultaneous voice conversations

The Speed of...

Technology	Speed	Physical Medium	Application
OC-12/STM-4	622.08 Mbps	Optical fiber	Internet backbone
Gigabit Ethernet	1 Gbps	Optical fiber (and "copper" up to 100 meters)	Workstations/networks with 10/100 Mbps Ethernet plug into Gigabit Ethernet switches
OC-24	1.244 **Gbps**	Optical fiber	Internet backbone
SciNet	2.325 Gbps (15 OC-3 lines)	Optical fiber	Part of the vBNS backbone
OC-48/STM-16	2.488 Gbps	Optical fiber	Internet backbone
OC-192/STM-64	10 Gbps	Optical fiber	Backbone
OC-256	13.271 Gbps	Optical fiber	Backbone

Kilo, Mega, Giga, Tera, Peta, and All That

Kilo, mega, giga, tera, and peta are among the list of prefixes that are used to denote the quantity of something, such as, in computing and telecommunications, a **byte** or a **bit**. Sometimes called prefix multipliers, these prefixes are also used in electronics and physics. Each multiplier consists of a one-letter abbreviation and the prefix that it stands for.

In communications, electronics, and physics, multipliers are defined in powers of 10 from 10^{-24} to 10^{24}, proceeding in increments of three orders of magnitude (10^3 or 1,000). In IT and data storage, multipliers are defined in powers of 2 from 2^{10} to 2^{80}, proceeding in increments of ten orders of magnitude (2^{10} or 1,024). These multipliers are denoted in the following table.

Prefix	Symbol(s)	Power of 10	Power of 2
yocto-	y	10^{-24} *	—
zepto-	z	10^{-21} *	—
atto-	a	10^{-18} *	—
femto-	f	10^{-15} *	—
pico-	p	10^{-12} *	—
nano-	n	10^{-9} *	—
micro-	m	10^{-6} *	—
milli-	m	10^{-3} *	—
centi-	c	10^{-2} *	—
deci-	d	10^{-1} *	—
(none)	—	10^{0}	2^{0}
deka-	D	10^{1} *	—
hecto-	h	10^{2} *	—
kilo-	k or K **	10^{3}	2^{10}
mega-	M	10^{6}	2^{20}
giga-	G	10^{9}	2^{30}
tera-	T	10^{12}	2^{40}
peta-	P	10^{15}	2^{50}
exa-	E	10^{18} *	2^{60}
zetta-	Z	10^{21} *	2^{70}
yotta-	Y	10^{24} *	2^{80}

* Not generally used to express data speed
** $k = 10^3$ and $K = 2^{10}$

Examples of quantities or phenomena in which power-of-10 prefix multipliers apply include frequency (including computer clock speeds), physical mass, power, energy, electrical voltage, and electrical current. Power-of-10 multipiers are also used to define binary data speeds. Thus, for example, 1 kbps (one kilobit per second) is equal to 10^3, or 1,000, bps (bits per second); 1 Mbps (one megabit per second) is equal to 10^6, or 1,000,000, bps. (The lowercase k is the technically correct symbol for kilo- when it represents 10^3, although the uppercase K is often used instead.)

When binary data is stored in memory or fixed media such as a hard drive, diskette, ZIP disk, tape, or CD-ROM, power-of-2 multipliers are used. Technically, the uppercase K should be used for kilo- when it represents 2^{10}. Therefore 1 KB (one kilobyte) is 2^{10}, or 1,024, bytes; 1 MB (one megabyte) is 2^{20}, or 1,048,576 bytes.

The choice of power-of-10 versus power-of-2 prefix multipliers can appear arbitrary. It helps to remember that in common usage, multiples of bits are almost always expressed in powers of 10, while multiples of bytes are almost always expressed in powers of 2. Rarely is data speed expressed in bytes per second, and rarely is data storage or memory expressed in bits.

International System of Units

The International System of Units (abbreviated "SI" from the French version of the name) is a scientific method of expressing the magnitudes or quantities of seven important natural phenomena. This system was formerly called the meter-kilogram-second (MKS) system.

All SI units can be expressed in terms of standard multiple or fractional quantities, as well as directly. Multiple and fractional SI units are defined by prefix multipliers according to powers of 10 ranging from 10^{-24} to 10^{24}.

The **meter** (abbreviation, m) is the SI unit of displacement or length. One meter is the distance traveled by a ray of electromagnetic (EM) energy through a vacuum in $1/_{299,792,458}$ ($3.33564095 \times 10^{-9}$) second. The meter was originally defined as one ten-millionth (0.0000001 or 10^{-7}) of the distance, as measured over the earth's surface in a great circle passing through Paris, France, from the geographic north pole to the equator.

The **kilogram** (abbreviation, kg) is the SI unit of mass. It is defined as the mass of a particular international prototype made of platinum-iridium and kept at the International Bureau of Weights and Measures. It was originally defined as the mass of one liter (10^{-3} cubic meter) of pure water.

The **second** (abbreviation, s or sec) is the SI unit of time. One second is the time that elapses during 9.192631770×10^9 cycles of the radiation produced by the transition between two levels of Cesium 133. It is also the time required for an EM field to propagate 299,792,458 (2.99792458×10^8) meters through a vacuum.

The **Kelvin** (abbreviation K), also called the degree Kelvin (abbreviation, °K), is the SI unit of temperature. One Kelvin is $1/_{273.16}$ (3.6609×10^{-3}) of the thermodynamic temperature of the triple point of pure water (H_2O).

The **ampere** (abbreviation, A) is the SI unit of electric current. One ampere is the current that would produce a force of 0.0000002 (2×10^{-7}) newton between two straight, parallel, perfectly conducting wires having infinite length and zero diameter, separated by one meter in a vacuum. One ampere represents 6.24×10^{18} unit electric charge carriers, such as electrons, passing a specified fixed point in one second.

The **candela** (abbreviation, cd) is the SI unit of luminous intensity. It is the electromagnetic radiation, in a specified direction, that has an intensity of 1/683 (1.46×10-3) watt per steradian at a frequency of 540 terahertz (5.40×1014 hertz).

The mole (abbreviation, mol) is the SI unit of material quantity. One mole is the number of atoms in 0.012 kilogram of the most common isotope of elemental carbon (C-12). This is approximately 6.022169×1023, and is also called the Avogadro constant.

These units are included in our **Table of Physical Units.**

See the *NIST Reference on Constants, Units, and Uncertainty"* at `http://physics.nist.gov/cuu/Units/current.html`.

Table of Physical Units

This table shows, from the International System of Units, base and derived physical units, their shorthand symbols, and equivalent units in other unit systems. Many of the terms in the table are defined in this encyclopedia.

BASE UNITS

Quantity or phenomenon (and symbol)	Standard International unit (and symbol)	Alternate units (and symbols)
displacement (*d*)	**meter** (m)	**centimeter** (cm) foot (ft)
mass (*m*) **weight** (*w*)	**kilogram** (kg)	**gram** (g) pound (lb)
time (*t*)	**second** (s)	hour (hr) mean solar day (dy) synodic year (yr)
current (*I*)	**ampere** (A)	**statampere** (statA) abampere (abA)
temperature (*T*)	**kelvin** (°K or K)	degree Celsius (°C or C) degree Fahrenheit (°F or F) degree Rankine (°R or R)
amount of substance (*N*)	**mole** (mol)	—
luminous intensity (*B* or *L*)	**candela** (cd)	—

DERIVED UNITS

Quantity or phenomenon (and symbol)	Standard International unit (and symbol)	Alternate units (and symbols)
area (*A*)	**meter squared** (m^2)	centimeter squared (cm^2) circular mil foot squared (ft^2)
volume (*V*)	**meter cubed** (m^3)	centimeter cubed (cm^3) foot cubed (ft^3)
material density (*D*)	**kilogram per meter cubed** ($kg/m3$ or $kg \cdot m{-3}$)	gram per centimeter cubed (g/cm^3 or $g \cdot cm^{-3}$)
specific volume	meter cubed per kilogram (m^3/kg or $m^3 \cdot kg^{-1}$)	centimeter cubed per gram (cm^3/g or $cm^3 \cdot g^{-1}$)
amount of substance concentration	**mole per meter cubed** (mol/m^3 or $mol \cdot m^{-3}$)	—
force (*F* or **F**)	**newton** (N)	dyne (dyn)
pressure stress	**pascal** (Pa)	dyne per centimeter squared (dyn/cm^2 or $dyn \cdot cm^{-2}$)
speed (*s*) velocity (**v** or v)	**meter per second** (m/s or $m \cdot s^{-1}$)	centimeter per second (cm/s or $cm \cdot s{-1}$)
acceleration (*a* or **a**)	**meter per second squared** (m/s^2 or $m \cdot s^{-2}$)	**centimeter per second squared** (cm/s^2 or $cm \cdot s^{-2}$) gravity (g)
current density	**ampere per meter squared** (A/m^2 or $A \cdot m^{-2}$)	ampere per centimeter squared (A/cm^2 or $A \cdot cm^{-2}$)
electromotive force (emf) Voltage (*V* or *E*)	**volt** (V)	**statvolt** (statV) abvolt (abV)
resistance (*R*)	**ohm** (Ω)	**statohm** (statΩ) abohm (abΩ)
conductance (*G*)	**siemens** (S)	**statsiemens** (statS) absiemens (abS)
electric field strength (*E*)	**volt per meter** (V/m or $V \cdot m^{-1}$)	microvolt per meter ($\mu V/m$ or $\mu V \cdot m^{-1}$)

DERIVED UNITS, *Continued...*

Quantity or phenomenon (and symbol)	Standard International unit (and symbol)	Alternate units (and symbols)
electric flux density	coulomb per meter squared (C/m^2 or $C \cdot m^{-2}$)	—
electric charge density	**coulomb per meter cubed** (C/m^3 or $C \cdot m^{-3}$)	—
permittivity(ε)	farad per meter (F/m or $F \cdot m^{-1}$)	picofarad per meter (pF/m or $pF \cdot m^{-1}$)
power (P)	**watt** (W)	horsepower (hp) statwatt (statW) abwatt (abW)
energy (E)	**joule** (J)	erg (erg) watt hour (Wh) kilowatt hour (kWh)
magnetomotive force (M or mmf)	ampere-turn (AT)	gilbert (G)
charge quantity (Q)	**coulomb** (C)	**statcoulomb** (statC) abcoulomb (abC) faraday
capacitance (C)	**farad** (F)	**statfarad** (statF) abfarad (abF)
inductance (L)	**henry** (H)	**stathenry** (statH) abhenry (abH)
magnetic flux (Φ)	weber (Wb)	maxwell (Mx)
magnetic flux density	**tesla** (T)	**gauss** (G)
magnetic field strength (H)	**ampere per meter** (A/m or $A \cdot m^{-1}$)	**oersted** (Oe)
permeability (μ)	**henry per meter** (H/m or $H \cdot m^{-1}$)	microhenry per meter ($\mu H/m$ or $\mu H \cdot m^{-1}$)
electromagnetic field strength	watt per meter squared (W/m^2 or $W \cdot m^{-2}$)	microwatt per meter squared ($\mu W/m^2$ or $\mu W \cdot m^{-2}$)
radiant intensity	**watt per steradian** (W/sr or $W \cdot sr^{-1}$)	**lumen** (lm)
luminance	**candela per meter squared** (cd/m^2 or $cd \cdot m^{-2}$)	candela per centimeter squared (cd/cm^2 or $cd \cdot cm^{-2}$)
luminous flux	**lumen** (lm)	**watt per steradian** (W/sr or $W \cdot sr^{-1}$)
illuminance	**lux** (lx)	watt per meter squared (W/m^2 or $W \cdot m^{-2}$)
plane angular measure	**radian** (rad)	degree (deg or °)
solid angular measure	**steradian** (sr)	—
angular speed (ω) angular velocity (ω)	**radian per second** (rad/s or $rad \cdot s^{-1}$)	degree per second (deg/s or $deg \cdot s^{-1}$)
angular acceleration (α or a)	**radian per second squared** (rad/s^2 or $rad \cdot s^{-2}$)	degree per second squared (deg/s^2 or $deg \cdot s^{-2}$)
ionizing radiation	**becquerel** (Bq)	curie (cu)
absorbed ionizing radiation dose	**gray** (Gy)	**rad** (rad)
frequency (f or ν)	**hertz** (Hz)	kilohertz (kHz) megahertz (MHz) gigahertz (GHz) terahertz (THz)

DERIVED UNITS, *Continued...*

Quantity or phenomenon (and symbol)	Standard International unit (and symbol)	Alternate units (and symbols)
wavelength (λ)	meter (m)	centimeter (cm) millimeter (mm) nanometer (nm) Angström (Å)
wave number	reciprocal meter (m^{-1})	—
data quantity	bit (b) byte (B)	kilobit (kb) megabit (Mb) gigabit (Gb) kilobyte (KB) megabyte (MB) gigabyte (GB)
data speed bandwidth	bit per second (bps)	kilobit per second (kbps) megabit per second (Mbps) gigabit per second (Gbps) character per second (cps)

TYPES OF DSL

This table shows different kinds of Digital Subscriber Line (DSL) service.

DSL Type	Description	Data Rate Downstream; Upstream	Distance Limit	Application
IDSL	ISDN Digital	128 Kbps	18,000 feet on 24 gauge wire	Similar to the ISDN BRI service but data only (no voice on the same line)
CDSL	Consumer DSL from Rockwell	1 Mbps downstream; less upstream	18,000 feet on 24 gauge wire	Splitterless home and small business service; similar to DSL Lite
DSL Lite (same as G. Lite)	"Splitterless" DSL without the "truck roll"	From 256 Kbps to 6 Mbps downstream on the subscribed service	18,000 feet on 24 gauge wire	The standard ADSL; sacrifices speed for not having to install a splitter at the user's home or business
G.Lite (same as	"Splitterless" DSL without the "truck roll"	From 256 kbps to 6 Mbps, depending on the Subscribed service	18,000 feet on 24 gauge wire	The standard ADSL; sacrifices speed for not having to install a splitter at the user's home or business
HDSL	High bit-rate Digital Subscriber	1.544 Mbps duplex on two twisted-pair lines;	12,000 feet on 24 gauge wire	T1/E1 service between server and phone company or within a company; WAN, LAN, server access
SDSL	Symmetric DSL	1.544 Mbps duplex (U.S. and Canada); 2.048 Mbps Europe) on a single duplex line downstream and upstream	12,000 feet on 24 gauge wire	Same as for HDSL but requiring only one line of twisted-pair

TYPES OF DSL, *Continued...*

DSL Type	Description	Data Rate Downstream; Upstream	Distance Limit	Application
ADSL	Asymmetric Digital Subscriber Line	1.544 to 6.1 Mbps downstream; 16 to 640 Kbps upstream	1.544 Mbps at 18,000 feet; 2.048 Mbps at 16,000 feet; 6.312 Mpbs at 12,000 feet; 8.448 Mbps at 9,000 feet	Used for Internet and Web access, motion video, video on demand remote LAN access
RADSL	Rate-Adaptive DSL from Westell	Adapted to the line, 640 Kbps to 2.2 Mbps to 1.088 Mbps upstream	Not provided	Similar to ADSL
UDSL	Unidirectional DSL proposed by a company in Europe	Not known	Not known	Similar to HDSL
VDSL	Very high digital Subscriber Line	12.9 to 52.8 Mbps downstream; 1.5 to 2.3 Mbps upstream; 1.6 Mbps to 2.3 Mbps downstream	4,500 feet at 12.96 Mbps; 3,000 feet at 25.82 Mbps; 1,000 feet at 51.84 Mbps	ATM networks; Fiber to the Neighborhood

TYPES OF RAM

This table summarizes many types of random access memory (RAM).

RAM Technology	Application and Computer Location	Access Speed Range	Ports	Characteristic
Static RAM (SRAM)	Level-1 and level-2 cache memory Also used in RAMDAC	Fast	One	RAM that is continually charged More expensive than DRAM
Burst SRAM (BSRAM)	Level-2 cache memory	Fast	One	SRAM inburst mode
DRAM	Main memory Low-cost video	Slow	One	A generic term for any king dynamic (constantly recharged) RAM
FPM (Fast page Mode) DRAM	Main memory low-cost video memory	slow	One	Prior to EDO DRAM, the most common type of DRAM
EDO (Extended Data Out)	Main memory low-cost video	5-20% faster than FPM DRAM	One	Uses overlapping reads (one can begin while another is finishing). Currently, the most common type of DRAM
BEDO (Burst Extended Data DRAM)	Main memory and low-cost video	Faster than EDO DRAM 4-1-1-1 at 66 MHz	One	Not widely used because not supported by processor chipset makers
EDRAM Enhanced DRAM	Level-2 cache memory	15 ns access to SRAM 35 ns access to DRAM	One	Contains a 256-byte SRAM inside a larger DRAM

RAM Technology	Application and Computer Location	Access Speed Range	Ports	Characteristic
Nonvolatile RAM	Preset phone numbers and profiles in modems	Fast	One	Battery-powered RAM
Synchronous DRAM (SDRAM)	Main memory	See specific forms of SDRAM	One	Generic term for DRAMS with a synchronous interface
JEDEC Synchronous DRAM JEDEC SDRAM)	Main memory	Intended to run at	One	An Intel specification designed to work with their i440 BX
PC100 Synchronous DRAM (PC100 SDRAM)	Main memory	Intended to run at	One	An Intel specification designed to work with their i440BX
Double Data Rate Synchronous DRAM (DDR DRAM)	Main memory	Up to 200 MHz	One	Activates output on both the up and the down part of the clock cycle, doubling the DATA RATE OF PC100 SDRAM
Enhanced Synchronous DRAM	Main memory	Fast (100 MHz +)	Two	Twice as fast as SDRAM
SyncLink DRAM (SLDRAM)	Main memory	Fastest (200 MHz +)	One	Open protocol-based design Uses "packets" for address, data, and control signals
Direct Rambus DRAM (DRDRAM)	Main memory	Up to 800 MHz but with a 16-bit bus width	One	Backed by Intel and Rambus
Ferroelectric RAM	Main memory in			Developed by Ramtron
RAMDAC	Video Card	Fast	One	Uses a small SRAM to store the color **palette** table used to provide data for **digital-to analog** conversion
Rambus DRAM (RDRAM)	Video memory for Nintendos	Up to 600 MHz	One	Intel and Rambus architecture
Synchronous Graphics RAM	Moderate to high-end video memory	Closer to VRAM than DRAM	One	Has special performance enhancing features Example: Matrox Mystique
VRAM (Video RAM)	Higher-cost video memory	Twice the speed of DRAM	Two	Dual-ported, meaning a new image can be stored in RAM while a previous image is being sent to the display
WRAM (Window RAM)	Less expensive video memory	25% faster than VRAM	Two	With **RAMDAC**, can handle **true color** at 1600 by 1200 pixel resolution
Multibank DRAM (MDRAM)	Low-cost high-end video memory	Faster	One	Interleaved memory accesses between banks Memory has multiple 32 kilobyte banks that can be accessed independently Can be manufactured to fit the amount of memory the card requires. No size-related performance penalty

TYPES OF CD AND DVD

Drive Type	"Read" & "Write" Capability
CD (CD player)	Reads audio CD only
CD-ROM (Compact Disc-Read Only Memory)	Reads audio CD, CD-ROM, CD-R, Photo CD
CD-ROM multiread (Compact Disc-Read Only Memory, Multiread)	CD-ROM, CD-R, CD-RW, CD-i, Photo CD
CD-R (Compact Disc-Recordable)	Reads CD-ROM and CD-R, some read CD-RW (Writes once on CD-R discs)
CD-RW (Compact Disc-Rewritable)	Reads CD-ROM, CD-R, and CD-RW (Writes and rewrites on CD-RW discs)
DVD-RAM (Digital Versatile Disc-Random-Access-Memory)	Reads all CD formats. Reads DVD ROM. Reads and writes DVD discs.

CD AND DVD DATA TRANSFER RATES AND RPMS

Optical Media Drive Speed	Maximum Data Transfer Rate	RPMs (revolutions per minute)
1X CD-ROM	150 KB/sec	200–530
2X CD-ROM	300 KB/sec	400–1060
4X CD-ROM	600 KB/sec	800–2120
8X 12X CD-ROM	1.2 MB/sec	1600–4240
24X 50X	1.8–6 MB/sec	2400–6360 approximately
1X DVD-ROM	1.25 MB/sec	No exact data, but much slower than 1X CD-ROM

Favorite Technology Quotations

Where is all the knowledge we lost with information?
—**T.S. Elliot**

The telephone wire, as we know it, has become too slow and too small to handle Internet traffic. It took 75 years for telephones to be used by 50 million customers, but it took only four years for the Internet to reach that many users.
—**Lori Valigra**

640K ought to be enough for anybody.
— **Microsoft Chairman Bill Gates, 1981**

The real problem is not whether machines think but whether men do.
—**B. F. Skinner**

There are three roads to ruin; women, gambling and technicians. The most pleasant is with women, the quickest is with gambling, but the surest is with technicians.
—**George Pompidou**

Technology is dominated by two types of people: those who understand what they do not manage, and those who manage what they do not understand.
—**Anonymous**

Computers make it easier to do a lot of things, but most of the things they make it easier to do don't need to be done.
—**Andy Rooney**

I think there is a world market for maybe five computers.
—**IBM Chairman Thomas Watson, 1943**

If you have any trouble sounding condescending, find a Unix user to show you how it's done.
—**Scott Adams**

In a few minutes a computer can make a mistake so great that it would have taken many men many months to equal it.
—**Anonymous**

If computers get too powerful, we can organize them into a committee. That will do them in.
—**Bradley's Bromide**

The Internet is the Viagra of big business.
—**Jack Welch, Chairman and CEO, General Electric**

There are two major products that came out of Berkeley: LSD and UNIX. We don't believe this to be a coincidence.
—**Jeremy S. Anderson**

One machine can do the work of fifty ordinary men. No machine can do the work of one extraordinary man.
—**Elbert Hubbard**

Any teacher that can be replaced by a computer, deserves to be.
—**David Thornburg**

Those parts of the system that you can hit with a hammer are called hardware; those program instructions that you can only curse at are called software.
—**Anonymous**

We live in a society exquisitely dependent on science and technology, in which hardly anyone knows anything about science and technology.
—**Carl Sagan**

If you tried to read every document on the web, then for each day's effort you would be a year further behind in your goal.
—**Anonymous**

There might be new technology, but technological progress itself was nothing new - and over the years it had not destroyed jobs, but created them.
—**Margaret Thatcher**

The most overlooked advantage to owning a computer is that if they foul up there's no law against whacking them around a little.
—**Porterfield**

Everything that can be invented has been invented.
—**Charles H. Duell, Commissioner, U.S. Office of Patents, 1899**

Computers are magnificent tools for the realization of our dreams, but no machine can replace the human spark of spirit, compassion, love, and understanding.
—**Louis Gerstner, CEO, IBM**

GARBAGE IN—GOSPEL OUT
—**Fairchild Research and Development, 1969**

Any science or technology which is sufficiently advanced is indistinguishable from magic.
—**Arthur C. Clarke**

Never let a computer know you're in a hurry.
—**Anonymous**

A year spent in artificial intelligence is enough to make one believe in God.
—**Alan J. Perlis**

I have not failed. I've just found 10,000 ways that won't work.
—**Thomas Edison**

Get your feet off my desk, get out of here, you stink, and we're not going to buy your product.
—**Joe Keenan, President of Atari, in 1976**

Responding to Steve Jobs' offer to sell him rights to the new personal computer he and Steve Wozniak developed

The Internet is a great way to get on the net.
—**Senator Bob Dole**

Computers in the future may have only 1,000 vacuum tubes and perhaps only weigh 1 1/2 tons.
—**Popular Mechanics, 1949**

From then on, when anything went wrong with a computer, we said it had bugs in it.
—**Rear Admiral Grace Murray Hopper, U.S. Navy**

Technology is like fish. The longer it stays on the shelf, the less desirable it becomes.
—**Andrew Heller, IBM**

AOL is like the cockroach left after the nuclear bomb hits. They know how to survive.
—**Jan Horsfall, VP of marketing for Lycos**

How could this be a problem in a country where we have Intel and Microsoft?
—**Al Gore on Y2K**

The modern computer hovers between the obsolescent and the nonexistent.
—**Sydney Brenner in 1927**

The Linux philosophy is 'Laugh in the face of danger'. Oops. Wrong One. 'Do it yourself'. Yes, that's it.
—**Linus Torvalds**

Windows is just DOS in drag.
—**Anonymous**

There is no reason for any individual to have a computer in their home.
—**Ken Olson (President of Digital Equipment Corporation) at the Convention of the World Future Society in Boston in 1977**

During my service in the United States Congress, I took the initiative in creating the Internet.
—**Al Gore describing his 1986 legislation to interconnect five supercomputer centers (17 years after the first Internet servers hooked up)**

The day I made that statement, I was tired because I'd been up all night inventing the Camcorder.
—**Al Gore attempting damage control**

@

See "at sign"

10BASE- 2

10BASE-2, one of several physical media specified by **IEEE 802.3** for use in an **Ethernet** local area network (**LAN**), consists of **Thinwire coaxial cable** with a maximum segment length of 185 meters. Like other specified media, 10BASE-2 supports Ethernet's 10 **Mbps** data rate.

In addition to 10BASE-2, 10 megabit Ethernet can be implemented with these media types:

- 10BASE-5 (**Thickwire** coaxial cable with a maximum segment length of 500 meters)

- 10BASE-F (**optical fiber** cable)

- 10BASE-T (ordinary telephone **twisted pair** wire)

- 10BASE-36 (broadband multi-channel coaxial cable with a maximum segment length of 3,600 meters)

This designation is an Institute of Electrical and Electronics Engineers (**IEEE**) shorthand identifier. The "10" in the media type designation refers to the transmission speed of 10 Mbps. The "BASE" refers to baseband signalling, which means that only Ethernet signals are carried on the medium (or, with 10BASE-36, on a single channel). The "T" represents twisted-pair; the "F" represents fiber optic cable; and the "2", "5", and "36" refer to the coaxial cable segment length (the 185 meter length has been rounded up to "2" for 200).

Also see **100BASE-T** and **Gigabit Ethernet**.

10BASE-5

10BASE-5, one of several physical media specified by **IEEE 802.3** for use in an **Ethernet** local area network (**LAN**), consists of **Thickwire coaxial cable** with a maximum segment length of 500 meters. Like other specified media, 10BASE-2 supports Ethernet's 10 **Mbps** data rate.

In addition to 10BASE-5, 10 megabit Ethernet can be implemented with these media types:

- 10BASE-2 (**Thinwire** coaxial cable with a maximum segment length of 185 meters)

- 10BASE-F (**optical fiber** cable)

- 10BASE-T (ordinary telephone **twisted pair** wire)

- 10BASE-36 (broadband multi-channel coaxial cable with a maximum segment length of 3,600 meters)

This designation is an Institute of Electrical and Electronics Engineers (**IEEE**) shorthand identifier. The "10" in the media type designation refers to the transmission speed of 10 Mbps. The "BASE" refers to baseband signalling, which means that only Ethernet signals are carried on the medium (or, with 10BASE-36, on a single channel). The "T" represents twisted-pair; the "F" represents fiber optic cable; and the "2", "5", and "36" refer to the coaxial cable segment length (the 185 meter length has been rounded up to "2" for 200).

Also see **100BASE-T** and **Gigabit Ethernet**.

10BASE-36

10BASE-36 is a type of physical cabling defined in the **IEEE** 802.3 (**Ethernet**) standard for **broadband** application. Although Ethernet is inherently a **baseband** system, 10BASE-36 specifies the use of a 10-**megahertz** signal on each channel within a 75-ohm coaxial broadband cable so that bandwidth is effectively expanded. Each channel requires 3 pairs of wires in the **coaxial cable**. Baseband differential phase-shift keying (**PSK**) is used to modulate the signal on each channel. Each channel has a transmission speed of 10 **Mbps**. The cable can extend for up to 3,600 meters.

10BASE-F

10BASE-F, one of several physical media specified by **IEEE 802.3**, is the use of **optical fiber** in an **Ethernet** local area network (**LAN**). Like other specified media, 10BASE-F supports Ethernet's 10 **Mbps** data rate.

In addition to 10BASE-F, 10 megabit Ethernet can be implemented with these media types:

- 10BASE-2 (**Thinwire** coaxial cable with a maximum segment length of 185 meters)

- 10BASE-5 (**Thicknet** coaxial cable with a maximum segment length of 500 meters)

- 10BASE-T (ordinary telephone **twisted pair** wire)

- 10BASE-36 (broadband multi-channel coaxial cable with a maximum segment length of 3,600 meters)

This designation is an Institute of Electrical and Electronics Engineers (**IEEE**) shorthand identifier. The "10" in the media type designation refers to the transmission speed of 10 Mbps. The "BASE" refers to baseband signalling, which means that only Ethernet signals are carried on the medium (or, with 10BASE-36, on a single channel). The "T" represents twisted-pair; the "F" represents fiber optic cable; and the "2", "5", and "36" refer to the coaxial cable segment length (the 185 meter length has been rounded up to "2" for 200).

Also see **100BASE-T** and **Gigabit Ethernet**.

10BASE-T

10BASE-T, one of several physical media specified in the **IEEE 802.3** standard for **Ethernet** local area networks (**LANs**), is ordinary telephone **twisted pair** wire. 10BASE-T supports Ethernet's 10 **Mbps** transmission speed. In addition to 10BASE-T, 10 megabit Ethernet can be implemented with these media types:

- 10BASE-2 (Thinwire **coaxial cable** with a maximum segment length of 185 meters)

- 10BASE-5 (Thickwire coaxial cable with a maximum segment length of 500 meters)

- 10BASE-F (**optical fiber** cable)

- 10BASE-36 (broadband coaxial cable carrying multiple baseband channels for a maximum length of 3,600 meters)

This designation is an Institute of Electrical and Electronics Engineers (**IEEE**) shorthand identifier. The "10" in the media type designation refers to the transmission speed of 10 Mbps. The "BASE" refers to baseband signalling, which means that only Ethernet signals are carried on the medium. The "T" represents twisted-pair; the "F" represents fiber optic cable; and the "2", "5", and "36" refer to the coaxial cable segment length (the 185 meter length has been rounded up to "2" for 200).

Also see **100BASE-T** and **Gigabit Ethernet**.

100BASE-T

In 100 **Mbps** (megabits per second) **Ethernet** (known as **Fast Ethernet**), there are three types of physical wiring that can carry signals:

- 100BASE-T4 (four pairs of telephone **twisted pair** wire)

- 100BASE-TX (two pairs of data grade twisted-pair wire)

- 100BASE-FX (a two-strand **optical fiber** cable)

This designation is an **Institute of Electrical and Electronics Engineers** shorthand identifier. The "100" in the media type designation refers to the transmission speed of 100 Mbps. The "BASE" refers to baseband signalling, which means that only Ethernet signals are carried on the medium. The "T4," "TX," and "FX" refer to the physical medium that carries the signal. (Through repeaters, media segments of different physical types can be used in the same system.)

The TX and FX types together are sometimes referred to as "100BASE-X." (The designation for "100BASE-T" is also sometimes seen as "100BaseT.")

1000BASE-T

1000BASE-T is **Gigabit Ethernet** (1 **gigabit** is 1000 **megabits** per second) on copper cables, using four pairs of **Category 5 unshielded twisted pair** to achieve the gigabit data rate. 1000BASE-T can be used in data centers for server switching, for uplinks from desktop computer switches, or directly to the desktop for **broadband** applications. A big advantage of 1000BASE-T is that existing copper cabling can be used instead of having to rewire with optical fiber.

For Gigabit Ethernet, industry offerings include these types of wiring:

- 1000BASE-SX (a short **laser wavelength** on multimode **fiber optic** cable for a maximum length of 550 meters)

- 1000BASE-LX/LH (a long wavelength for a "long haul" fiber optic cable for a maximum length of 10 kilometers)

- 1000BASE-ZX (an extended wavelength single-mode optical fiber for up to 100 kilometers)

- 1000BASE-CX (two pairs of 150-**ohm shielded twisted pair** cable for a maximum length of 25 meters)

- 1000BASE-T (four pairs of **Category 5 unshielded twisted pair** cable for a maximum length of 100 meters)

The 1000BASE designation is an **IEEE** shorthand identifier. The "1000" in the media type designation refers to the transmission speed of 1000 Mbps. The "BASE" refers to baseband signalling, which means that only Ethernet signals are carried on the medium. (Through repeaters, media segments of different physical types can be sometimes be used in the same system.)

The designation for "1000BASE-T" is also sometimes seen as "1000BaseT."

10-Gigabit Ethernet

10-Gigabit Ethernet, being standardized in **IEEE** 802.3a, is a developing telecommunication technology that offers data speeds up to 10 billion bits per second. Built on the **Ethernet** technology used in most of today's local area networks (**LANs**), 10-Gigabit Ethernet is described as a "disruptive" technology that offers a more efficient and less expensive approach to moving data on **backbone** connections between networks while also providing a consistent technology end-to-end. Using **optical fiber**, 10-Gigabit Ethernet can replace existing networks that use **ATM switch**es and **SONET multiplexer**s on an **OC-48** SONET ring with a simpler network of 10-Gigabit Ethernet switches and at the same time improve the data rate from 2.5 **Gbps** to 10 Gbps.

10-Gigabit Ethernet is expected to be used to interconnect local area networks (LANs), wide area networks (**WANs**), and metropolitan area networks (**MANs**). 10-Gigabit Ethernet uses the familiar IEEE **802.3** Ethernet **media access control** (MAC) protocol and its **frame** format and size. Like **Fast Ethernet** and **Gigabit Ethernet**, 10-Gigabit Ethernet uses **full-duplex** transmission, which makes possible a considerable distance range. On **multimode fiber**, 10-Gigabit Ethernet will support distances up to 300 **meter**s; on **single mode fiber**, it will support distances up to 40 kilometers. Smaller Gigabit Ethernet networks can feed into a 10-Gigabit Ethernet network.

10-high-day busy period

In designing and assessing **network**s, the peak load is sometimes measured using the 10HD (10-high-day) busy period method. The 10HD busy period is the average of the amount of traffic during the busiest hour of the 10 days during the year when the overall traffic is heaviest.

Another index to peak traffic is the average bouncing busy hour (**ABBH**).

121

In Internet **e-commerce**, 121 is short for *one-to-one*, the philosophy that treating each customer as a special individual is a more successful approach than treating customers as a group of similar individuals.

1170

"Spec 1170" was the working name of the standard **UNIX** programming interface specification that is now known as *X/Open Programming Guide 4.2 (XPG 4.2)*. The specification has also been known as the "Single UNIX Specification" and, most recently, as "UNIX 98." In the "Spec 1170" or first version of the Single UNIX Specification, there were 1,170 **C** language functions or individual instructions.

The Single UNIX Specification is maintained by **The Open Group**, which certifies implementations and provides UNIX product branding following conformance assurance and testing.

1284

The IEEE 1284 parallel interface standard is the prevalent standard for connecting a computer to a printer or certain other devices over a **parallel** (eight bits of data at a time) physical and electrical **interface**. The physical connection is similar to the older Centronics interface, which it continues to support. Whereas the Centronics interface only allowed data to flow in one direction, from computer to peripheral, IEEE 1284 also supports bi-directional data flow.

When the Centronics parallel interface was first developed, the main peripheral was the printer. Since then, portable disk drives, **tape** drives, and **CD-ROM** players are among devices that have adopted the parallel interface. These new uses caused manufacturers to look at new ways to make the Centronics parallel interface better. In 1991, Lexmark, IBM, Texas Instruments, and others met to discuss a standard that would offer more speed and bi-directional communication. Their effort and the sponsorship of the Institute of Electrical and Electronics Engineers (**IEEE**) resulted in the IEEE 1284 committee. The IEEE 1284 standard was approved for release in March 1994.

The IEEE 1284 standard specifies five modes of operation, each mode providing data transfer in either the forward direction (computer to peripheral), backward direction (peripheral to computer), or bi-directional (one direction at a time).

- **Compatibility mode** is the original Centronics parallel interface and is intended for use with dot matrix printers and older laser printers. The compatibility mode can be combined with the nibble mode for bi-directional data transfer.

- **Nibble mode** allows data transfer back to the computer. The nibble mode uses the status lines to send 2 **nibble** (4-bit units) of data to the computer in two data transfer cycles. This mode is best used with printers.

- **Byte mode** uses software drivers to disable the drivers that control the data lines in order for data to be sent from the printer to the computer. The data is sent at the same speed as when data is sent from the computer to the printer. One byte of data is transferred instead of the two data cycles required by the nibble mode.

- **ECP mode** (Enhanced Capability Port mode) is an advanced bi-directional mode for use with printers and scanners. It allows data **compression** for images, **FIFO** (first in, first out) for items in a **queue**, and high-speed, bi-directional communication. Data transfer occurs at two to four megabytes per second. An advanced feature is **channel** addressing. This is used for multifunction devices such as printer/fax/modem devices. For example, if a printer/fax/modem device needs to print and send data over the **modem** at the same time, the channel address software driver of the ECP mode assigns a new channel to the modem so that both devices can work simultaneously.

- **EPP mode** (Enhanced Parallel Port mode) was designed by Intel, Xircom, and Zenith Data Systems to provide a high-performance parallel interface that could also be used with the standard interface. EPP mode was adopted as part of the IEEE 1284 standard. The EPP mode uses data cycles that transfer data between the computer and the peripheral and address cycles that assign address, channel, or command information. This allows data transfer speeds of 500 kilobytes to 2 megabytes per second, depending on the speed of the slowest interface. The EPP mode is bi-directional. It is suited for network adapters, data acquisition, portable hard drives, and other devices that need speed.

The computer must determine what the capabilities of the attached peripheral are and which mode to utilize. The concept developed to determine these factors is called negotiation. Negotiation is a sequence of events on the parallel port interface that determines which IEEE 1284 modes the device can handle. An older device will not respond to the negotiation sequence and compatibility mode

is selected to operate that device. A newer device will respond to the negotiation sequence and a more advanced mode can be set.

12X

See "X (compact disc access time)"

1394

See "IEEE 1394"

14000

See "ISO 14000 and 14001"

14001

See "ISO 14000 and 14001"

1GL

See "programming language generations"

1NF

See "normalization"

1X

See "X (compact disc access time)"

2.5G

2.5G describes the state of **wireless** technology and capability usually associated with General Packet Radio Services (**GPRS**)—that is, between the second and third generations of wireless technology. The second generation or 2G-level of wireless is usually identified as Global System for Mobile (**GSM**) service and the third generation or **3G**-level is usually identified as Universal Mobile Telecommunication Service (**UMTS**). Each generation provides a higher data rate and additional capabilities. There is also a fourth generation (**4G**) of technology in the planning and research stages.

GPRS offers data speeds at 28 **Kbps** (and possibly higher) and is expected to be introduced in the 2001 through 2003 timeframe.

2000

The year 2000 (also known as "Y2K") raised questions for anyone who depended on a program in which the year was represented by a two-digit number, such as "97" for 1997. Many programs written years ago (when storage limitations encouraged such information economies) are still being used. The problem was that when the two-digit space allocated for "99" rolled over to 2000, the next number was "00." Frequently, program logic assumes that the year

number gets larger, not smaller—so "00" was anticipated to wreak havoc in a program that hadn't been modified to account for the millennium.

So pervasive was the problem in the world's **legacy application** payroll, billing, and other programs that a new industry sprang up dedicated to helping companies solve the problem. IBM and other major computer manufacturers, software houses, and consultants offered tools and services to address this problem.

2001

Midnight **UTC** on January 1, 2001 marked the beginning of the third **millennium** on the Western world's **Gregorian calendar**. *2001* is also the name of the 1968 movie, written by Arthur C. Clarke and directed by Stanley Kubrick, that shaped views of the future for several decades, especially about what future computers might be like. HAL (officially HAL 9000) is the human-like computer that manages the spaceship in the movie. HAL (the script says that HAL stands for "Heuristically Programmed ALgorithmic computer" but the letters in the name are one letter away from "IBM") is programmed to think and talk like a human being, an **artificial intelligence** combining people skills with ruthless calculation. As the movie became part of history and the real 2001 approached, new views of technology tended toward the envisionment of a globally networked "intelligence" for which William Gibson's **matrix** in his fictional *Neuromancer* and the real **World Wide Web** seemed to be harbingers.

24/7

See "24x7"

24X

See "X (compact disc access time)"

24X7

24x7 means "24 hours a day, 7 days a week" and is used to describe a service, such as computer **server** monitoring, that is continuous, is always available (day or night), or involves products that can run constantly without disruption or *downtime*.

2600

2600 is the frequency in **hertz** (cycles per second) that AT&T formerly put as a steady **signal** on any long-distance telephone line that was not currently in use. Prior to widespread use of *out-of-band signaling*, AT&T used *in-band signaling*, meaning that signals about telephone connections were transmitted on the same line as the voice conversations. Since no signal at all on a line could indicate a pause in a voice conversation, some other way was needed for the phone company to know when a line was free for use. So

AT&T put a steady 2600 hertz signal on all free lines. Knowing this, certain people developed a way to use a whistle or other device to generate a 2600 hertz tone on a line that was already in use, making it possible to call anywhere in the world on the line without anyone being charged. Cracking the phone system became a hobby for some in the mostly under-20 set who came to be known as **phreak**s.

In the 1960s, a breakfast cereal named Captain Crunch included a free premium: a small whistle that generated a 2600 hertz signal. By dialing a number and then blowing the whistle, you could fool the phone company into thinking the line was not being used while, in fact, you were now free to make a call to any destination in the world.

Today, long-distance companies use Signaling System 7, which puts all **channel** signals on a separate signaling channel, making it more difficult to break into the phone system.

2GL

See "programming language generations"

2NF

See "normalization"

2X

See "X (compact disc access time)"

3000

See "HP e3000"

3270

The 3270 Information Display System, a product from IBM, was, prior to the arrival of the PC, the way that almost the entire corporate world interfaced with a computer. In its day (the early 1970s), a 3270 display terminal was considered a vast improvement over its predecessor, the 2260.

The 3277 terminal was a non-graphical (text only) monochrome (black screen with green letters) display that **buffer**ed data so that key strokes could be saved until the ENTER key was pressed. (Previous terminals sent every key stroke immediately to the computer to which the terminal was attached.) The 3277 was also *field-oriented* rather than *line-oriented* which meant that a program could write an output data stream to the terminal based on application-oriented fields rather than having to create the display output line by line. A number of 3277s could be attached to a control unit or cluster controller which in turn was attached to an IBM **mainframe** computer. Terminals could be attached to the computer on a relatively high-bandwidth local link called a **channel** or "remotely" over a telecommunication link that was either dedicated (leased) or dial-up.

After the **personal computer** arrived with its own self-sufficient operating system and applications, it gradually replaced the 3270 system in much of the corporate world (although there are almost certainly are some working 3270s in use as this is being written). A 3270 terminal became the most prominent example of what became known as a "dumb terminal," since it relied entirely on its attachment to a mainframe (and sometimes a **minicomputer**) for its "brains." The PC attached to a mainframe then became known generically as an "intelligent workstation." It could run its own programs independently of the mainframe and it could also interface with mainframe applications. There was one product attempt to blend the two, called the 3270 PC.

The terminals themselves were the 3277 (which attached to a control unit), a 3275 standalone terminal (for locations where only a single terminal was needed), the 3278 (a sleeker version of the 3277), and the 3279 color terminal. The control units were the 3271 (channel attachment), 3272 (telecommunication attachment), and the 3274 (a control unit with a smaller form factor that could handle up to 32 terminals). For about 15 years, the 3270 family, one of IBM's most successful products ever, was a ubiquitous feature of offices the world over. The PC changed all that.

However, many thousands of corporate **legacy application** programs written to interact with users at 3270s are being used from PCs equipped with software known generally as *3270 emulation*. TN3270 is a program that provides PC users remote (**Telnet**) connection to an IBM computer that is running 3270 applications.

3-D

In computers, 3-D (three dimensions or three-dimensional) describes an image that provides the perception of depth. When 3-D images are made interactive so that users feel involved with the scene, the experience is called **virtual reality**. You usually need a special **plug-in** viewer for your Web browser to view and interact with 3-D images. Virtual reality experiences may also require additional equipment.

3-D image creation can be viewed as a three-phase process of tessellation, geometry, and rendering. In the first phase, models are created of individual objects using linked points that are made into a number of individual polygons (tiles). In the next stage, the polygons are transformed in various ways and lighting effects are applied. In the third stage, the transformed images are rendered into objects with very fine detail.

Popular products for creating 3-D effects include Extreme 3D, LightWave 3D, Ray Dream Studio, 3D Studio MAX, Softimage 3D, and Visual Reality. The Virtual Reality Modelling Language (**VRML**) allows the creator to specify images and the rules for their display and interaction using textual language statements.

3-D browser

A 3-D browser is a Web **browser** that allows the viewer to view and interact with six Web pages at a time by creating a virtual room on the viewer's screen. Instead of opening six Web pages, minimizing your screen and toggling back and forth between pages, imagine you are standing inside a six-sided cube and each side of the cube is displaying a Web page. There is a Web page in front of you, a Web page on each side of you, a page above you, a page below you and a page behind you. You can use your cursor to rotate the cube and put any side of the cube directly in front of you. Links on all the pages are active, so you can click from page to page and change the "walls" of your virtual Web room. If you see something that catches your interest, you can use the zoom feature to enlarge the "wall" so that it becomes a traditional page viewed on your flat screen.

The concept of a 3-D Web browser has been promoted by former architect and chief executive officer of 2ce, Mike Rosen. Rosen hopes that the next generation of computer users, who have grown up multi-tasking in virtual reality gaming environments, will embrace a 3-D version of the Web. Besides being fun, Rosen believes that having the ability to view multiple pages will be of practical use to day traders and others whose occupations require them to view multiple Web pages throughout the day.

3G

Also see **UMTS**.

3G is a short term for third-generation wireless, and refers to near-future developments in personal and business **wireless** technology, especially mobile communications. This phase is expected to reach maturity between the years 2003 and 2005.

The third generation, as its name suggests, follows the first generation (1G) and second generation (2G) in wireless communications. The 1G period began in the late 1970s and lasted through the 1980s. These systems featured the first true mobile phone systems, known at first as "cellular mobile radio telephone." These networks used **analog** voice signaling, and were little more sophisticated than repeater networks used by **amateur radio** operators. The 2G phase began in the 1990s, and much of this technology is still in use. The 2G cell phone features **digital** voice encoding. Examples include **CDMA**, **TDMA**, and **GSM**. Since its inception, 2G technology has steadily improved, with increased **bandwidth**, **packet** routing, and the introduction of multimedia. The present state of mobile wireless communications is often called 2.5G.

Ultimately, 3G is expected to include capabilities and features such as

- Enhanced multimedia (voice, data, video, and remote control)
- Usability on all popular modes (cellular telephone, e-mail, paging, fax, videoconferencing, and Web browsing)
- Broad bandwidth and high speed (upwards of 2 Mbps)
- Routing flexibility (repeater, satellite, LAN)
- Operation at approximately 2 GHz transmit and receive frequencies
- Roaming capability throughout Europe, Japan, and North America

While 3G is generally considered applicable mainly to mobile wireless, it is also relevant to **fixed wireless** and portable wireless. The ultimate 3G system might be operational from any location on, or over, the earth's surface, including use in or by

- Homes
- Businesses
- Government offices
- Medical establishments
- The military
- Personal and commercial land vehicles
- Private and commercial watercraft and marine craft
- Private and commercial aircraft (except where passenger use restrictions apply)
- Portable (pedestrians, hikers, cyclists, campers)
- Space stations and spacecraft

Proponents of 3G technology promise that it will "keep people connected at all times and in all places."

3GL

See "programming language generations"

3NF

See "normalization"

3-tier application

A 3-tier application is an **application** program that is organized into three major parts, each of which is **distributed** to a different place or places in a network. The three parts are

- The workstation or presentation interface
- The business logic
- The database and programming related to managing it

In a typical 3-tier application, the application user's workstation contains the programming that provides the graphical user interface (**GUI**) and application-specific entry forms or interactive windows. (Some data that is local or unique for the workstation user is also kept on the local hard disk.)

Business logic is located on a local area network (**LAN**) server or other shared computer. The business logic acts as the server for client requests from workstations. In turn, it determines what data is needed (and where it is located) and acts as a client in relation to a third tier of programming that might be located on a **mainframe** computer.

The third tier includes the **database** and a program to manage read and write access to it. While the organization of an application can be more complicated than this, the 3-tier view is a convenient way to think about the parts in a large-scale program.

A 3-tier application uses the **client/server** computing model. With three tiers or parts, each part can be developed concurrently by different team of programmers coding in different languages from the other tier developers. Because the programming for a tier can be changed or relocated without affecting the other tiers, the 3-tier model makes it easier for an enterprise or software packager to continually evolve an application as new needs and opportunities arise. Existing applications or critical parts can be permanently or temporarily retained and encapsulated within the new tier of which it becomes a component.

42

42 is the number from Douglas Adams' *The Hitchhiker's Guide to the Galaxy* from which all meaning ("the meaning of life, the universe, and everything") could be derived.

A BBC radio script based on Adams' book contains the following lines:

("Cave man" lays out following sentence in Scrabble stones: "What do you get if you multiply six by nine?")
Arthur: Six by nine? Forty-two? You know, I've always felt that there was something fundamentally wrong with the Universe.
(Faint and distant voice:) Base thirteen!

For the literal-minded and those unfamiliar with terms like "base thirteen," this is a number system in which the number 10 is equivalent to our more familiar decimal 13. A base-13 number 42, therefore, is the same as four 13s plus 2, or decimal 54. So "six by nine" (six times nine) or decimal 54 is, in base 13, 42. For the mystically inclined, 42 in base 13 is the same as 110110 in binary (base 2). This could mean almost anything, and many Adams fans have spent untold hours discovering all of the places where the number "42" pops up. For example, there are many mentions of the number in the Book of Revelations. Others have made a game of finding 42s, such as these:

- The angle at which light reflects off of water to create a rainbow is 42 degrees.
- Two physical constants in the universe are the speed of light and the diameter of a proton. It takes light 10 to the minus 42nd power seconds to cross the diameter of a proton.
- A barrel holds 42 gallons.

(It should be noted that all of these 42's are base 10, not base 13.)

404

Also see **errors**.

404 is a frequently-seen status code that tells a Web user that a requested page is "Not found." 404 and other status codes are part of the Web's Hypertext Transfer Protocol (**HTTP**), written in 1992 by the Web's inventor, Tim Berners-Lee. He took many of the status codes from the earlier Internet protocol for transferring files, the File Transfer Protocol (**FTP**).

What to Do If You Get a 404

If the site no longer exists, there's nothing you can do. However, it only takes one mistyped character to result in a 404. See whether the ".htm" should be an ".html" or vice versa. If you're linking from a Web site, you can do a "View source" to make sure it wasn't miscoded. Whether or not it is, you may want to send a note to the Webmaster so that the link can be fixed for the next users.

How to Handle 404s If You Have a Web Site

Here are some things you can do:

- Use a Web site analysis tool such as Web Trends or Weblog to identify links that result in 404s, then fix the links.
- If you change the Uniform Resource Locator (**URL**) for a page on your site, retain the old URL as a redirect file, putting a message on it and inserting a META element with a REFRESH to change to the new URL in a specified number of seconds.

- You can create the page contents for a 404 status code page and substitute it for the 404 page that the browser usually provides. This will allow you to personalize the message and encourage the user to send a note to the Webmaster so that the situation can be fixed.

4G

4G is the short term for fourth-generation **wireless**, the stage of **broadband** mobile communications that will follow the still-burgeoning third generation (**3G**) that is expected to reach maturity between 2003-2005. 4G services are expected to be introduced first in Japan, as early as 2006—four years ahead of the previous target date. The major distinction of 4G over 3G communications is increased data transmission rates, just as it is for 3G over 2G and 2.5G (the present state of wireless services, hovering somewhere between 2G and 3G). According to NTT-DoCoMo, the leading Japanese wireless company, the current download speed for **i-mode** (mobile internet service) data is—theoretically—9.6 **Kbps**, although in practice the rates tend to be slower. 3G rates are expected to reach speeds 200 times that, and 4G to yield further increases, reaching 20-40 **Mbps** (about 10-20 times the current rates of **ADSL** service).

4G is expected to deliver more advanced versions of the same improvements promised by 3G, such as enhanced **multimedia**, smooth **streaming video**, universal access, and portability across all types of devices. Industry insiders are reluctant to predict the direction that less-than-immediate future technology might take, but 4G enhancements are expected to include worldwide **roaming** capability. As was projected for the ultimate 3G system, 4G might actually connect the entire globe and be operable from any location on—or above—the surface of the earth.

4GL

See "programming language generations"

4X

See "X (compact disc access time)"

50X

See "X (compact disc access time)"

5GL

See "programming language generations"

64-bit processor

A 64-bit processor is a **microprocessor** with a **word** size of 64 bits, a requirement for memory and data intensive applications such as computer-aided design (**CAD**) applications, database management systems, technical and scientific applications, and high-performance servers. 64-bit computer **architecture** provides higher performance than 32-bit architecture by handling twice as many bits of information in the same **clock cycle**.

The 64-bit processor is backwards compatible with older applications and operating systems; it detects whether an application or operating system is 16-bit, 32-bit, or 64-bit and computes accordingly. This is essential for enterprise situations where purchasing new software is not feasible.

Intel, IBM, Sun Microsystems, Hewlett Packard, and AMD currently develop or offer 64-bit processors.

80

If you occasionally see a mysterious "80" on the name of a Web **server** that is handling your request for Web pages, this is a bit of technical stuff showing through when perhaps it shouldn't. A Web server sits and waits for requests from a **client** (such as your Web browser). Most Web servers are set up to "awaken" and respond to requests from clients whose Uniform Resource Locator (**URL**) requests include "**port 80**" as part of their information. When you see the "80" showing up in the server address at the bottom of your screen, all it means is that the server uses the usual default port number. (You don't usually see this because some servers can be set up so that this number is not visible to the browser user.)

802.11

In **wireless LAN** (WLAN) technology, 802.11 refers to a family of specifications developed by a working group of the Institute of Electrical and Electronics Engineers (**IEEE**). There are three specifications in the family: 802.11, 802.11a, and 802.11b. All three specify the use of CSMA/CA (carrier sense multiple access with collision avoidance) as the path-sharing protocol.

The 802.11 and 802.11b specifications apply to wireless **Ethernet** LANs, and operate at frequencies in the 2.4-GHz region of the radio spectrum. Data speeds are generally 1 **Mbps** or 2 Mbps for 802.11, and 5.5 Mbps or 11 Mbps for 802.11b, although speeds up to about 20 Mbps are realizable with 802.11b. The 802.11b standard is **backward compatible** with 802.11. The **modulation** used in 802.11 has historically been phase-shift keying (**PSK**). The modulation method selected for 802.11b is known as complementary code keying (CCK), which allows higher data speeds and is less susceptible to multipath-propagation interference.

The 802.11a specification applies to wireless **ATM** systems and operates at radio frequencies between 5 **GHz** and 6 GHz. A modulation scheme known as **OFDM** (orthogonal frequency-division multiplexing) makes possible data speeds as high as 54 Mbps, but most commonly, communications take place at 6 Mbps, 12 Mbps, or 24 Mbps.

Also see **HiperLAN**.

802.3

802.3 is a standard specification for **Ethernet**, a method of physical communication in a local area network (**LAN**), which is maintained by the Institute of Electrical and Electronics Engineers (**IEEE**). In general, 802.3 specifies the physical media and the working characteristics of Ethernet. The original Ethernet supports a data rate of 10 megabits per second (**Mbps**) and specifies these possible physical media:

- 10BASE-2 (**Thinwire coaxial cable** with a maximum segment length of 185 meters)

- 10BASE-5 (**Thickwire** coaxial cable with a maximum segment length of 500 meters)

- 10BASE-F (**optical fiber** cable)

- 10BASE-T (ordinary telephone **twisted pair** wire)

- 10BASE-36 (broadband multi-channel coaxial cable with a maximum segment length of 3,600 meters)

This designation is an IEEE shorthand identifier. The "10" in the media type designation refers to the transmission speed of 10 Mbps. The "BASE" refers to baseband signalling, which means that only Ethernet signals are carried on the medium (or, with 10BASE-36, on a single channel). The "T" represents twisted-pair; the "F" represents fiber optic cable; and the "2", "5", and "36" refer to the coaxial cable segment length (the 185 meter length has been rounded up to "2" for 200).

Also see **100BASE-T** and **Gigabit Ethernet**.

8-VSB

8-VSB (8-level **vestigial sideband**) is a standard radio frequency (**RF**) **modulation** format chosen by the Advanced Television Systems Committee (**ATSC**) for the transmission of digital television (**DTV**) to consumers in the United States and other adopting countries. In the US, the standard is specified by the Federal Communications Commission (**FCC**) for all digital television broadcasting. Countries in Europe and elsewhere have adopted an alternative format called Coded Orthogonal Frequency Division Multiplexing (**COFDM**).

The main ATSC standards for DTV are 8-VSB, which is used in the transmission of video data, MPEG-2 for video signal compression, and **Dolby Digital** for audio coding.

The 8-VSB mode includes eight amplitude levels that support up to 19.28 Mbps of data in a single 6 Mhz **channel**. There is also a 16-VSB mode that has 16 amplitude levels and

supports up to 38.57 Mbps of data on a 6 Mhz channel. 8-VSB is considered effective for the simultaneous transmission of more than one DTV program (multicasting) and the transmission of data along with a television program (datacasting) because it supports large data payloads.

The ATSC adopted the VSB transmission system because of its large **bandwidth**, which is needed to transmit **HDTV** (high definition television) programming. Detractors claim that this larger bandwidth is irrelevant if customers cannot view the transmitted program because of multipath effects. When a signal is transmitted, it is met with obstructions such as canyons, buildings, and even people, which scatter the signal, causing it to take two or more paths to reach its final destination, the television set. The late arrival of the scattered portions of the signal causes ghost images. For this reason, some consumers in metropolitan areas or areas with rugged terrain opt for cable television instead of fighting their antennas for better reception. Because a VSB signal is transmitted on one carrier, it scatters like water blasted on a wall when met with obstacles, which is not a problem with Coded Orthogonal Frequency Division Multiplexing (**COFDM**), the European standard modulation technique, because it transmits a signal on multiple carriers.

VSB advocates state that simply buying an outdoor antenna that rotates solves the multipath interference problem, but critics worry that customers do not want to buy an expensive rotating outdoor antenna to view free television programs. They also worry that the poor reception and the added expense of an outdoor antenna are slowing the transition to DTV in ATSC-compliant countries. The VSB scheme also does not support mobile television viewing. VSB equipment manufacturers are working on solutions to these two problems.

8X

See "X (compact disc access time)"

9000

See "ISO 9000"

A Programming Language

See "APL"

A+

A-Plus (A+) is the name of a process, developed by the Computing Technology Industry Association (CompTIA), a large trade group, that certifies individuals for knowledge about and competency in installing, maintaining, customizing, and operating personal computers. The examination is in two parts, the first covering computer hardware and software in general and the second covering a specific operating system, such as Windows 98. The exam is administered by Drake Parametric and there is a fee. A number of companies provide in-house or self-taught preparation for the exam.

CompTIA also sponsors specialized certification for document imaging and a network certification exam. The A-Plus certification is somewhat more basic and less product-specific than other certifications, such as Microsoft's **Microsoft Certified Systems Engineer** certifications.

An advantage of certification in any industry is that it promotes self-regulation rather than government regulation.

a2b

a2b (for short; the site is actually called "a2b music") is a Web site that lets you **download** and play samples or complete songs from popular music recordings, using a music player developed by AT&T. At the a2b music Web site, after first downloading the player, you can then download and play short samples or complete songs from new CD music recordings. The sound, which is said to be "CD-quality," is made possible through **MPEG** standard Advanced Audio Coding (AAC), a technology that AT&T Labs helped to develop. After sampling a short preview of a song, you can download the entire song from the Web site. Some songs are free and some require an online purchase. You are also invited to purchase the entire CD from the site using secure online ordering. a2b music partners include major recording companies and new releases include those from such artists as Tori Amos, Counting Crows, Willie Nelson, and Bonnie Raitt.

The **compression algorithm** uses a successor to the MP3 (MPEG-1. layer 3) technology that a2b says offers better stereo sound and such advances as *temporal noise shaping* and *pairwise coding*. a2b uses public key cryptography to ensure that only the purchaser can play the music. The player is initially offered for Windows 9x/NT users and is promised for Mac users.

AA

See "modem lights"

AAA server

An AAA server is a **server** program that handles user requests for **access** to computer resources and, for an enterprise, provides **authentication**, **authorization**, and accounting (AAA) services. The AAA server typically interacts with network access and **gateway** servers and with databases and directories containing user information. The current standard by which devices or applications communicate with an AAA server is the Remote Authentication Dial-In User Service (**RADIUS**).

Also see **authentication, authorization, and accounting**.

AARP

AARP (AppleTalk Address Resolution Protocol) is a way to map between the physical hardware addresses of computers, such as those known to an **Ethernet** or **token ring** local area network, and their temporarily assigned **AppleTalk** network addresses.

AAUI

An AAUI (Apple **attachment unit interface**) is the 14- or 15-**pin** port or connection interface on earlier models of **Macintosh** computers that allowed it to be connected by a short interface cable (or "transceiver") to an **Ethernet** cable. Later or more advanced models provide a standard registered jack (10Base-T) connection from an Ethernet-capable Macintosh to the Ethernet cable.

abacus

An abacus is a manual aid to calculating that consists of beads or disks that can be moved up and down on a series of sticks or strings within a usually wooden frame. The abacus itself doesn't calculate; it's simply a device for helping a human being to calculate by remembering what has been counted. The modern Chinese abacus, which is still widely used in China and other countries, dates from about 1200 A.D. It is possible that it derives from the earlier **counting board**s used around the Mediterranean as early as 300 B.C. An Aztec version of an abacus, circa 900-1000 A.D., is made from maize (corn) threaded through strings mounted in a wooden frame.

There are Japanese and Russian versions of the abacus and several modern "improved" versions.

abampere

The abampere (symbolized abA) is the unit of **current** in the **cgs** (centimeter/gram/second) system of electromagnetic units. It is the equivalent of one **abcoulomb** (1 abC) of charge carriers moving past a specific point in one second.

The abampere is a moderately large unit of current, equivalent to 10 **ampere**s (A). In most applications, the ampere, which is the unit of current in the International System of Units (**SI**), is preferred.

Also see **current**, **cgs** or **small-unit metric system**, and International System of Units (**SI**).

abandonware

Abandonware is computer software (such as an **operating system**, word processor, interactive game, or audio file) that is no longer marketed or distributed by the company that created it, but is obtainable from some other source. Some popular products that have been at least temporarily abandoned include NeXTStep, the operating system for the **NEXT** computer; OpenStep, its successor; and many interactive games that were replaced by more sophisticated products. In some cases, a company or Web site gets permission from the creator to distribute the abandoned program; but sometimes they don't. To use abandonware that you download, you often need a *license string* that the software recognizes as entitling the user to install it. In this case, the downloading site provides a license string that is known to work.

Abandonware is often provided as **freeware** or as priced **shareware**.

ABAP

ABAP is a programming language for developing applications for the **SAP R/3** system, a widely-installed business application subsystem. The latest version, ABAP Objects, is **object-oriented programming**. SAP will run applications written using ABAP/4, the earlier ABAP version, as well as applications using ABAP Objects.

SAP's original business model for R/3 was developed before the idea of an object-oriented model was widespread. The transition to the object-oriented model reflects an increased customer demand for it. ABAP Objects uses a single **inheritance** model and full support for object features such as **encapsulation**, **polymorphism**, and persistence.

ABBH

See "average bouncing busy hour"

ABCD data switch

An ABCD data switch is a small box that lets you hook up to four devices from one PC serial or parallel **port** on your computer. For example, if you have both a black-and-white

laser printer for regular printing and a color inkjet printer for when you want color, you may want to attach them both to your computer. Perhaps you also have a tape backup drive that needs to be attached. You can connect all of them to the ABCD box which is in turn connected to your PC's parallel port. By turning a rotary switch on the box to the A, B, C, or D (if you have a fourth device attached) position, you can select the device you want to be active. (You will need to tell your operating system the kind of device that's attached whenever you switch.)

The data switch can also be used to have up to four computers share the same printer or other device.

This handy little switch costs about $20 (U.S.) and can be purchased in local PC stores.

abcoulomb

The abcoulomb (abbreviated abC) is the unit of **charge quantity** in the **cgs** (centimeter/gram/second) system of electromagnetic units. It is approximately equal to the charge contained in 6.24×10^{19} **electron**s.

The force with which two electrically charged bodies attract or repel one another depends on the product of the charges in abcoulombs in both objects, and also on the distance between the objects. If the polarities are the same, the force is repulsive; if the polarities are opposite, the force is attractive. For any two charged bodies, the force decreases in proportion to the square of the distance between their charge centers.

The abcoulomb is a moderately large unit in practical terms, equivalent to 10 coulombs (C). In most applications, the **coulomb**, which is the standard unit of charge quantity in the International System of Units (**SI**), is preferred.

Also see **charge quantity**, **cgs** or **small-unit metric system**, and International System of Units (**SI**).

abend

An abend (a combining of two words, *abnormal end*, when operator messages were as short as possible) is an abnormal, rather than planned, end or termination of a computer program because of some problem with how it is running. For example, the program may have attempted to address some computer memory space that it was not given the right to address. This term is more common in older **mainframe** systems than in PC systems.

When used, abend usually refers to the abnormal end of an application program because of application errors. Failure of the operating system is usually called a **crash**. In smaller systems, the term crash is applied to both application program and operating system failure. A crash also can be caused by hardware failure.

abfarad

The abfarad (abbreviated abF) is the unit of electromagnetic **capacitance** in the **cgs** (centimeter/gram/second) system of units. If a charge of one **abcoulomb** (1 abC) produces a potential difference of one **abvolt** (1 abV) in a capacitance, then that capacitance is 1 abF.

A capacitance as large as 1 abF is unknown. It is equivalent to 10^9 farads. The **farad** (F) is the standard unit of capacitance in the International System of Units (**SI**). Even this unit is large; a 1-F capacitor is almost never found in the real world.

In practical applications, the microfarad (μF) and the picofarad (pF) are most often used to quantify capacitance; the abfarad is rarely seen in literature. For comparison, 1 μF $= 10^{-6}$ F and 1 pF $= 10^{-12}$ F. Thus, 1 abF $= 10^{15}$ μF $= 10^{21}$ pF.

Also see **capacitance**, **farad**, **cgs** or **small-unit metric system**, and International System of Units (**SI**).

abhenry

The abhenry (abbreviated abH) is the unit of electromagnetic **inductance** in the **cgs** (centimeter/gram/second) system of units. It is equivalent to 10^{-9} **henry**. In a 1-abH inductance, a **current** that increases or decreases at one **abampere** per second (1 abA/s) will produce an electromotive force (EMF) of one **abvolt** (1 abV).

It is unusual to see an inductance as large as one henry (1 H) in the real world, but a 1-abH inductance is small, and is not uncommon. In fact, 1 abH is the equivalent of one nanohenry (1 nH), an often-used unit of inductance, especially at ultra-high and microwave radio frequencies. The henry is the standard unit of inductance in the International System of Units (**SI**).

In practical applications, the microhenry (μH) and the nanohenry (nH) are most often used to quantify inductance. For comparison, 1 μH $= 10^{-6}$ H and 1 nH $= 10^{-9}$ H. Thus, 1 abH = 0.001 μH = 1 nH.

Also see **inductance**, **henry**, **cgs** or **small-unit metric system**, and International System of Units (**SI**).

abohm

The abohm (symbolized abΩ) is the unit of electromagnetic **resistance** in the **cgs** (centimeter/gram/second) system of units. It is equivalent to 10^{-9} **ohm**s. When a current of one **abampere** (1 abA) flows through a resistance of 1 abΩ, the resulting potential difference across the component is one **abvolt** (1 abV).

The abohm is an extremely small unit of resistance. In fact, an object with a resistance of 1 abΩ would make an excellent electrical **conductor**. In practical applications, the ohm, the kilohm (kΩ) and the megohm (MΩ or M) are most often used

to quantify resistance. For comparison, 1 abΩ $= 10^{-15}$ MΩ $= 10^{-12}$ kΩ. The ohm (Ω) is the standard unit of resistance in the International System of Units (**SI**).

Also see **resistance**, **ohm**, **cgs** or **small-unit metric system**, and International System of Units (**SI**).

absiemens

The absiemens (symbolized abS) is the unit of **conductance** in the **cgs** (centimeter/gram/second) electromagnetic system of units. It is equivalent to 10^9 siemens (S).

When a **current** of one **abampere** (1 abA) flows through a conductance of 1 abS, the resulting potential difference across the component is one **abvolt** (1 abV). If the conductance is doubled while the current remains the same, the resulting voltage across the component is cut in half. Conversely, if the conductance is cut in half while the current remains the same, the resulting voltage across the component is doubled. The conductance in absiemens is the reciprocal of the resistance in **abohms** (abΩ).

The absiemens is an extremely large unit of conductance. In fact, an object with a conductance of 1 abS would make an excellent electrical conductor. In practical applications, the siemens, the millisiemens (mS) and the microsiemens (μS) are most often used to quantify conductance. For comparison, 1 abS $= 10^{15}$ μS $= 10^{12}$ mS. The siemens is the standard unit of conductance in the International System of Units (**SI**).

Also see **abohm**, **conductance**, **siemens**, **cgs** or **small-unit metric system**, and International System of Units (**SI**).

Abstract Syntax Notation One

Abstract Syntax Notation One (ASN.1) is a standard way to describe a **message** (a unit of **application data**) that can be sent or received in a network. ASN.1 is divided into two parts: (1) the rules of **syntax** for describing the contents of a message in terms of **data type** and content sequence or structure and (2) how you actually encode each data item in a message. ASN.1 is defined in two **ISO** standards for applications intended for the Open Systems Interconnection (**OSI**) framework:

- ISO 8824/ITU X.208 specifies the syntax (for example, which data item comes first in the message and what its data type is)
- ISO 8825/ITU X.209 specifies the basic encoding rules for ASN.1 (for example, how to state how long a data item is)

Here's an example of a message definition specified with ASN.1 notation:

```
Report ::= SEQUENCE {
        author          OCTET STRING,
        title           OCTET STRING,
        body            OCTET STRING,
        biblio          Bibliography  }
```

In this very simple example, "Report" is the name of this type of message. SEQUENCE indicates that the message is a sequence of data items. The first four data items have the data type of OCTET STRING, meaning each is a string of eight-bit **byte** (the term OCTET was used rather than BYTE because it can't be assumed that all computers will have eight bits in a byte). The bibliography data item is another definition named "Bibliography" that is used within this one. It might look like this:

```
Bibliography ::= SEQUENCE {
    author       OCTET STRING
    title        OCTET STRING
    publisher    OCTET STRING
    year         OCTET STRING       }
```

Other data types that can be specified include: INTEGER, BOOLEAN, REAL, and BIT STRING. An ENUMERATED data type is one that takes one of several possible values. Data items can be specified as OPTIONAL (not necessarily present).

Abstract Window Toolkit

Abstract Window Toolkit (AWT) is a set of application program interfaces (**API**s) used by **Java** programmers to create graphical user interface (**GUI**) objects, such as buttons, scroll bars, and windows. AWT is part of the Java Foundation Classes (**JFC**) from Sun Microsystems, the company that originated Java. The JFC are a comprehensive set of GUI **class** libraries that make it easier to develop the user interface part of an application program.

A more recent set of GUI interfaces called **Swing** extends the AWT so that the programmer can create generalized GUI objects that are independent of a specific operating system's **windowing system**.

abstraction

Abstraction (from the Latin *abs*, meaning *away from* and *trahere*, meaning *to draw*) is the process of taking away or removing characteristics from something in order to reduce it to a set of essential characteristics. In **object-oriented programming**, abstraction is one of three central principles (along with **encapsulation** and **inheritance**). Through the process of abstraction, a programmer hides all but the relevant data about an **object** in order to reduce complexity and increase efficiency. In the same way that abstraction sometimes works in art, the object that remains is a representation of the original, with unwanted detail omitted. The resulting object itself can be referred to as an abstraction, meaning *a named entity made up of selected attributes and behavior specific to a particular usage of the originating entity*. Abstraction is related to both **encapsulation** and **data hiding**.

In the process of abstraction, the programmer tries to ensure that the **entity** is named in a manner that will make sense and that it will have all the relevant aspects included and none of the extraneous ones. A real-world analogy of abstraction might work like this: You (the object) are arranging to meet a blind date and are deciding what to tell them so that they can recognize you in the restaurant. You decide to include the information about where you will be located, your height, hair color, and the color of your jacket. This is all data that will help the procedure (your date finding you) work smoothly. You should include all that information. On the other hand, there are a lot of bits of information about you that aren't relevant to this situation: your social security number, your admiration for obscure films, and what you took to "show and tell" in fifth grade are all irrelevant to this particular situation because they won't help your date find you. However, since entities may have any number of abstractions, you may get to use them in another procedure in the future.

abvolt

The abvolt (symbolized abV) is the unit of electromotive force (EMF) or potential difference in the **cgs** (centimeter/gram/second) electromagnetic system of units. When an EMF of 1 abV exists between two points, then one **erg** of energy is needed to move one **abcoulomb** (1 abC) of charge carriers between those two points.

A potential difference of 1 abV will drive a current of one **abampere** (1 abA) through a resistance of one abohm (abΩ). **Ohm's Law** applies for the cgs electromagnetic units, just as it does for the units in the International System of Units (**SI**). That is:

$$E = IR$$

where E is the EMF in abvolts, I is the **current** in abamperes, and R is the **resistance** in abohms.

The abvolt is a tiny unit of EMF, equal to 10^{-8} volts (V). In most practical applications, the **volt**, which is the unit of potential difference in SI, is preferred.

Also see **voltage**, **cgs** or **small-unit metric system**, and International Systems of Units (**SI**).

abwatt

The abwatt (symbolized abW) is the unit of power in the **cgs** (centimeter/gram/second) electromagnetic system of units. In a direct-current (**DC**) circuit, 1 abW is the **power** dissipated, radiated, or expended when one **abvolt** (1 abV) of potential difference drives a **current** of one **abampere** (1 abA) through a component.

In a DC circuit, or in an alternating-current (**AC**) circuit in which there is no **reactance**, the following formula holds:

$$P = EI$$

where P is the power in abwatts, E is the potential difference in abvolts, and I is the current in **abampere**s.

The abwatt is a small unit of power, equivalent to 10^{-7} watt (W) or 0.1 microwatt (μW). The abwatt, by coincidence, is the same size as the **statwatt** (statW), the unit of power in the cgs

electrostatic system of units. But in most applications, the watt, which is the unit of power in the International System of Units (SI), is preferred.

Also see **power**, **watt**, **cgs** or **small-unit metric system**, and International System of Units (**SI**).

AC

See "alternating current"

Accelerated Graphics Port

AGP (Accelerated Graphics Port) is an **interface** specification that enables 3-D graphics to display quickly on ordinary personal computers. AGP is an interface designed to convey 3-D images (for example, from Web sites or CD-ROMs) much more quickly and smoothly than is possible today on any computer other than an expensive graphics workstation. The interface uses your computer's main storage (**RAM**) for refreshing the monitor image and to support the *texture mapping*, *z-buffering*, and *alpha blending* required for 3-D image display. The AGP main memory use is dynamic, meaning that when not being used for accelerated graphics, main memory is restored for use by the **operating system** or other applications.

Intel, which has taken the lead in developing its specifications, introduced AGP into a **chipset** for its **Pentium microprocessor**. The newer, faster microchips in Intel's Pentium line are designed to work with the AGP chipset. Intel says the advanced **floating point unit** and faster **cache** algorithm of the more advanced Pentiums are better adapted for 3-dimensional applications.

Accelerated Hub Architecture

Accelerated Hub Architecture (AHA) (also called Intel Hub Architecture) is an Intel 800-series **chipset** design that uses a dedicated **bus** to transfer data between the two main **processor** chips instead of using the Peripheral Component Interconnect (**PCI**) bus, which was used in previous chipset architectures. The Accelerated Hub Architecture provides twice the **bandwidth** of the traditional PCI bus architecture at 266 **MB** per second. The Accelerated Hub Architecture consists of a **memory** controller **hub** and an input/output (**I/O**) controller hub (a controller directs or manages access to devices). The memory controller hub provides the central processing unit (**CPU**) **interface**, the memory interface, and the accelerated graphics port (**AGP**) interface. The memory controller hub supports single or dual processors with up to 1 **GB** of memory. The memory controller hub also allows for simultaneous processing, which enables more life-like audio and video capabilities.

The I/O controller hub provides a direct connection from the memory to the I/O devices, which includes any built-in modem and audio controllers, hard drives, Universal Serial Bus (**USB**) ports, and PCI add-in cards. The I/O controller

hub also includes the Alert on LAN (**local area network**) feature that sounds an alert when software failures or system intrusion occurs.

acceptable use policy

An acceptable use policy (AUP) is a policy that a network access user must agree to follow in order to be provided with access service. When you sign up with an Internet service provider (**ISP**), you will usually be presented with an AUP, which states that you agree to adhere to stipulations such as:

- Not using the service as part of violating any law
- Not attempting to break the security of any computer network or user
- Not posting commercial messages to **Usenet** groups without prior permission
- Not attempting to send junk e-mail or **spam** to anyone who doesn't want to receive it
- Not attempting to **mail bomb** a site with mass amounts of e-mail in order to flood their server.

Users also typically agree to report any attempt to break into their accounts. A number of spammers have had their access service terminated.

access

Access is simply being able to get to what you need. Data access is being able to get to (usually having permission to use) particular data on a computer. Web access means having a connection to the World Wide Web through an **access provider** or an **online service provider** such as America Online.

For data access, access is usually specified as read-only access and read/write access.

access control list

An access control list (ACL) is a table that tells a computer **operating system** which **access** rights each user has to a particular system object, such as a file **directory** or individual **file**. Each object has a security attribute that identifies its access control list. The list has an entry for each system user with access privileges. The most common privileges include the ability to read a file (or all the files in a directory), to write to the file or files, and to execute the file (if it is an executable file, or program). Microsoft **Windows NT/2000**, Novell's **NetWare**, Digital's **OpenVMS**, and **UNIX**-based systems are among the operating systems that use access control lists. The list is implemented differently by each operating system.

In Windows NT/2000, an access control list (ACL) is associated with each system object. Each ACL has one or more access control entries (ACEs) consisting of the name of a user or group of users. The user can also be a role name, such as "programmer," or "tester." For each of these users, groups, or roles, the access privileges are stated in a string of bits called an *access mask*. Generally, the system administrator or the object owner creates the access control list for an object.

access log

An access log is a list of all the requests for individual files that people have requested from a Web site. These files will include the **HTML** files and their imbedded graphic images and any other associated files that get transmitted. The access log (sometimes referred to as the "raw data") can be analyzed and summarized by another program.

In general, an access log can be analyzed to tell you:

- The number of visitors (unique first-time requests) to a **home page**
- The origin of the visitors in terms of their associated server's **domain name** (for example, visitors from .edu, .com, and .gov sites and from the online services)
- How many requests for each page at the site, which can be presented with the pages with most requests listed first
- Usage patterns in terms of time of day, day of week, and seasonally

Access log keepers and analyzers can be found as **shareware** on the Web or may come with a Web **server**.

access method

1) In computing, an access method is a program or a hardware mechanism that moves data between the computer and an outlying device such as a **hard disk** (or other form of **storage**) or a display terminal. The term is sometimes used to refer to the mechanics of placing or locating specific data at a particular place on a storage medium and then writing the data or reading it. It is also used to describe the way that data is located within a larger unit of data such as a **data set** or **file**.

2) An access method is also an application program interface (**API**) that a programmer uses to create or access data sets or to read from or write to a display terminal or other output device. Examples are the Virtual Sequential Access Method (**VSAM**) and the Virtual Telecommunication Access Method (**VTAM**).

access provider

An access provider is any organization that arranges for an individual or an organization to have access to the Internet. Access providers are generally divided into two classes: Internet access providers (**ISP**s) and online service providers (**OSP**s). ISPs can be local businesses that pay for a high-speed connection to one of the companies (such as AT&T, Sprint, or MCI in the U.S.) that are part of the Internet. They can also be national or international companies that have

their own networks (such as AT&T's WorldNet or IBM's Global Services). OSPs, sometimes just called "online services," also have their own networks but provide additional information services not available to non-subscribers. America Online is the most successful example of an OSP.

A typical charge from an access provider for an individual account is $10−30 U.S. a month, depending on the amount of usage you contract for. Hours of use beyond the arranged number are billed as an extra charge at an hourly rate. Both national and local access providers compete for business in national and local publications.

Microsoft's Windows systems offer personal computer users access to the Microsoft Internet service as well as to America Online, IBM, and several other services.

An access provider may have its own point-of-presence (**POP**) on the Internet, or it may be a company that has a telecommunication connection to someone else with a POP.

An access provider is not the same as a "space provider" (**virtual host**), a company that provides space and management for individual or business Web sites. However, some access providers do provide a certain amount of space for a Web site as part of their service.

access time

Access time is the time from the start of one storage device access to the time when the next access can be started. Access time consists of **latency** (the overhead of getting to the right place on the device and preparing to access it) and transfer time.

The term is applied to both random access memory (**RAM**) access and to **hard disk** and **CD-ROM** access. For RAM access, IBM prefers the term **cycle time**. However, the use of *access time* for RAM access is common. Access time to RAM is usually measured in **nanosecond**s. Access time to a hard disk or CD-ROM is usually measured in **millisecond**s.

ACD

See "Automatic Call Distributor"

ACH

See "Automated Clearing House"

ACID

ACID (atomicity, consistency, isolation, and durability) is an acronym and **mnemonic** device for learning and remembering the four primary attributes ensured to any transaction by a **transaction** manager (which is also called a transaction monitor). These attributes are:

Atomicity. In a transaction involving two or more discrete pieces of information, either all of the pieces are committed or none are.

Consistency. A transaction either creates a new and valid state of data, or, if any failure occurs, returns all data to its state before the transaction was started.

Isolation. A transaction in process and not yet committed must remain isolated from any other transaction.

Durability. Committed data is saved by the system such that, even in the event of a failure and system restart, the data is available in its correct state.

The ACID concept is described in ISO/IEC 10026-1:1992 Section 4. Each of these attributes can be measured against a **benchmark**. In general, however, a transaction manager or monitor is designed to realize the ACID concept. In a **distributed** system, one way to achieve ACID is to use a (2PC), which ensures that all involved sites must commit to transaction completion or none do, and the transaction is **rollback**.

ACL

See "access control list"

ACM

See "Association for Computing Machinery"

acoustic coupler

An acoustic coupler is a hardware device that enables a **modem** (a device that converts signals from **analog** to **digital** and from digital back to analog) to connect to a voice circuit. A handset adapter is used to receive modem tones through the handset's mouthpiece, and the earpiece is used to transmit these tones to the modem.

Acrobat

Acrobat is a program from Adobe that lets you capture a document and then view it in its original format and appearance. Acrobat is ideal for making documents or brochures that were designed for the print medium viewable electronically and capable of being shared with others on the Internet. To view an Acrobat document, which is called a Portable Document Format (**PDF**) file, you need Acrobat Reader. The Reader is free and can be downloaded from Adobe. You can use it as a standalone reader or as a **plug-in** in a Web browser.

Acrobat is actually a set of products. The latest version includes a "toolkit" that lets you scan in or otherwise capture documents created with Word, Pagemaker, and other desktop publishing products. The resulting PDF files can then be available for viewing either directly with the Reader or they can be viewed as embedded files within the browser.

acronym

An acronym (pronounced AK-ruh-nihm, from Greek *acro-* in the sense of *extreme* or *tip* and *onyma* or *name*) is an abbreviation of several words in such a way that the abbreviation itself forms a word. According to Webster's, the word doesn't have to already exist; it can be a new word. Webster's cites "snafu" and "radar", two terms of World War Two vintage, as examples. Implicit is the idea that the new word has to be pronounceable and ideally easy to remember.

Frequently, acronyms are formed that use existing words (and sometimes the acronym is invented first and the phrase name represented is designed to fit the acronym). Here are some examples of acronyms that use existing words:

BASIC....Beginner's All-Purpose Symbolic Instruction Code
NOW.....National Organization for Women
WHO.....World Health Organization

Abbreviations that use the first letter of each word in a phrase are sometimes referred to as initialisms. Initialisms can be but are not always acronyms. AT&T, BT, CBS, CNN, IBM, and NBC are initialisms that are not acronyms. Many acronym lists you'll see are really lists of acronyms and initialisms or just lists of abbreviations. (Note that abbreviations include shortened words like "esp" for "especially" as well as shortened phrases.)

Summing up:

- An abbreviation is a shortening of a word or a phrase.

- An acronym is an abbreviation that forms a word.

- An initialism is an abbreviation that uses the first letter of each word in the phrase (thus, some but not all initialisms are acronyms).

By the way, an acronym so familiar that no one remembers what it stands for is called an **anacronym**.

acronyms used in online chatting

See "chat abbreviations"

ACTA

ACTA (America's Carriers Telecommunications Association) is a lobbying organization for over 165 small long-distance telephone **carrier** companies. It was organized in 1985 to represent the interests of the group before legislative and regulatory bodies. The organization is based in Casselberry, Florida.

Active Directory

Active Directory is Microsoft's trademarked **directory** service, an integral part of the **Windows 2000** architecture. Like other directory services, such as Novell Directory Services (**NDS**), Active Directory is a centralized and standardized system that automates network management of user data, security, and **distributed** resources, and enables interoperation with other directories. Active Directory is designed especially for distributed networking environments.

Active Directory features include:

- Support for the **X.500** standard for global directories

- The capability for secure extension of network operations to the Web

- A hierarchical organization that provides a single point of access for system administration (management of user accounts, clients, servers, and applications, for example) to reduce redundancy and errors

- An object-oriented storage organization, which allows easier access to information

- Support for the Lightweight Directory Access Protocol (**LDAP**) to enable inter-directory operability

- Designed to be both **backward compatible** and **forward compatible**

active matrix display

Active matrix (also known as **thin film transistor**) is a technology used in the flat panel liquid crystal displays of notebook and laptop computers. Active matrix displays provide a more responsive image at a wider range of viewing angle than *dual scan* (passive matrix) displays.

Desktop computer displays or monitors usually have *cathode ray tube* technology.

active network

An active network is a **network** in which the **nodes** are programmed to perform custom operations on the messages that pass through the node. For example, a node could be programmed or customized to handle **packet**s on an individual user basis or to handle **multicast** packets differently than other packets. Active network approaches are expected to be especially important in networks of mobile users. "Smart packets" use a special self-describing language that allows new kinds of information to be carried within a packet and operated on by a node.

A Secure Active Network Environment (SANE) is an architecture for a trusted or secure active network.

Active Server Page

ASP is also an abbreviation for **application service provider**.

An Active Server Page (ASP) is an **HTML** page that includes one or more **script**s (small embedded programs) that are processed on a Microsoft Web **server** before the **page** is sent to the user. An ASP is somewhat similar to a **server-side include** or a common gateway interface (**CGI**) application in that all involve programs that run on the server, usually tailoring a page for the user. Typically, the script in the Web page at the server uses input received as the result of the

user's request for the page to access data from a **database** and then builds or customizes the page **on the fly** before sending it to the requestor.

ASP is a feature of the Microsoft Internet Information Server (**IIS**), but, since the server-side script is just building a regular HTML page, it can be delivered to almost any **browser**. You can create an ASP file by including a script written in **VBScript** or **JScript** in an HTML file or by using ActiveX Data Objects (**ADO**s) program statements in the HTML file. You name the HTML file with the ".asp" file suffix. Microsoft recommends the use of the server-side ASP rather than a client-side script, where there is actually a choice, because the server-side script will result in an easily displayable HTML page. Client-side scripts (for example, with **JavaScript**) may not work as intended on older browsers.

Active Template Library

Active Template Library (ATL), formerly called ActiveX Template Library) is a Microsoft program library (set of prepackaged program routines) for use when creating Active Server Page (**ASP**) code and other **ActiveX** program **component**s with **C++** (including Visual C++). A Web site developer that wants to forward user requests to a program in the Web **server** can write a **common gateway interface** application or, if the server is Microsoft's Internet Information Server (**IIS**), can include a **script** in the **HTML** (Web) page. The page itself is called an Active Server Page (ASP) and has a suffix of .asp. The script in the Active Server Page is interpreted and performed at the server before the page is sent on to the user. Another approach is to have this script (written in Microsoft's VBScript or JScript) in turn call a compiled program, written typically in C++, a sophisticated **object-oriented programming** language. Since a compiled program runs faster than a script, the Web page will be formulated faster and returned more quickly to the user. A C++ program also can interface more closely with the **operating system** than a script can, and there are several other advantages. On the other hand, it is more difficult and time-consuming to write a program in C++ than to write one in a script language.

The Active Template Library lets the programmer build **Component Object Model**s **object** that can be called by the script on an ASP page. These objects are described by Microsoft as being fast and having **industrial strength**. Objects you can build using the ATL include full controls, Internet Explorer controls, property pages, and dialog boxes.

ActiveX

Also see **ActiveX control**.

ActiveX is the name Microsoft has given to a set of "strategic" **object-oriented programming** technologies and tools. The main technology is the **Component Object Model** (COM). Used in a network with a directory and additional

support, COM becomes the **Distributed Component Object Model** (DCOM). The main thing that you create when writing a program to run in the ActiveX environment is a **component**, a self-sufficient program that can be run anywhere in your ActiveX network (currently a network consisting of Windows and Macintosh systems). This component is known as an **ActiveX control**. ActiveX is Microsoft's answer to the **Java** technology from Sun Microsystems. An ActiveX control is roughly equivalent to a Java **applet**.

If you have a Windows operating system on your personal computer, you may notice a number of Windows files with the "**OCX**" file name suffix. OCX stands for "Object Linking and Embedding control." Object Linking and Embedding (**OLE**) was Microsoft's program technology for supporting **compound documents** such as the Windows **desktop**. The Component Object Model now takes in OLE as part of a larger concept. Microsoft now uses the term "ActiveX control" instead of "OCX" for the component object.

One of the main advantages of a component is that it can be re-used by many applications (referred to as component **container**s). A COM component object (ActiveX control) can be created using one of several languages or development tools, including **C++** and **Visual Basic**, or **PowerBuilder**, or with scripting tools such as **VBScript**.

Currently, ActiveX controls run in Windows 95/98/NT/2000 and in Macintosh. Microsoft plans to support ActiveX controls for **UNIX**.

ActiveX control

An ActiveX control is a **component** program **object** that can be re-used by many application programs within a computer or among computers in a network. The technology for creating ActiveX controls is part of Microsoft's overall **ActiveX** set of technologies, chief of which is the **Component Object Model** (COM). ActiveX controls can be downloaded as small programs or animations for Web pages, but they can also be used for any commonly needed task by an application program in the latest Windows and Macintosh environments. In general, ActiveX controls replace the earlier **OCX** (Object Linking and Embedding custom controls). An ActiveX control is roughly equivalent in concept and implementation to the **Java applet**.

An ActiveX control can be created in any programming language that recognizes Microsoft's Component Object Model. The distributed support for COM is called the Distributed Component Object Model (**DCOM**). In implementation, an ActiveX control is a dynamic link library (**DLL**) module. An ActiveX control runs in what is known as a **container**, an application program that uses the Component Object Model program interfaces. This reuseable component approach to application development reduces development time and improves program capability and

quality. Windows application development programs such as **PowerBuilder** and Microsoft Access take advantage of ActiveX controls.

Visual Basic and **C++** are commonly used to write ActiveX controls.

ActiveX Data Objects

ActiveX Data Objects (ADO) is an **application program interface** from Microsoft that lets programmers writing Windows applications get access to a relational or nonrelational **database** from both Microsoft and other database providers. For example, if you wanted to write a program that would provide users of your Web site with data from an IBM **DB2** database or an **Oracle** database, you could include ADO program statements in an **HTML** file that you then identified as an **Active Server Page**. When a user requested the page from the Web site, the page sent back could include appropriate data from a database, obtained using ADO code.

Like Microsoft's other system interfaces, ADO is an **object-oriented programming** interface. It is also part of an overall data access strategy from Microsoft called **Universal Data Access**. Microsoft says that rather than try to build a universal database as IBM and Oracle have suggested, why not provide universal *access* to various kinds of existing and future databases? In order for this to work, Microsoft and other database companies provide a "bridge" program between the database and Microsoft's OLE DB, the low-level interface to databases. OLE DB is the underlying system service that a programmer using ADO is actually using. A feature of ADO, Remote Data Service, supports "data-aware" **ActiveX control**s in Web pages and efficient client-side **cache**s. As part of **ActiveX**, ADO is also part of Microsoft's overall **Component Object Model** (COM), its **component**-oriented framework for putting programs together.

ADO evolved from an earlier Microsoft data interface, **Remote Data Objects** (RDO). RDO works with Microsoft's ODBC to access relational databases, but not nonrelational databases such as IBM's **ISAM** and **VSAM**.

ACTS

ACTS (Automatic Coin Telephone System) is a public coin-operated telephone service that completes a variety of phone calls, times the calls, and collects payment without the aid of an operator.

Ada

Ada (pronounced AY-duh) is a programming language somewhat similar to **Pascal** that was selected in a competition and made a U.S. Defense Department standard. (It is named for Augusta Ada Byron, Countess of Lovelace [1815-1852], who helped **Charles Babbage** conceive how programs might run in his mechanical Analytical Engine.

She is often considered the first computer programmer.) Ada was originally intended for real-time **embedded systems programming**.

By its supporters, Ada is described as a programming language that avoids error-prone notation, is relatively quick to implement, encourages reuse and team coordination, and is relatively easy for other programmers to read. The most recent version, Ada 95, is apparently a significant improvement over earlier versions. Among the sophisticated, according to *The New Hacker's Dictionary*, Ada has a reputation as a committee-written language, with poor exception-handling and **interprocess communication** features. It's not clear that "hackers" still feel this way. The Ada home page says: "The original Ada design was the winner of a language design competition; the winning team was headed by Jean Ichbiah (Ichbiah's language was called "Green"). The 1995 revision of Ada (Ada 95) was developed by a small team led by Tucker Taft. In both cases, the design underwent a public comment period where the designers responded to public comments."

Ada 95 can be used with **object-oriented programming** design methodology and source code can be compiled into **Java** classes by the Ada 95 **compiler**. These classes can be run as Java applets or applications on a Java **virtual machine**.

First standardized by **ANSI** in 1983 and **ISO** in 1987, the latest standard is ANSI/ISO/IEC-8652:1995 Ada 95.

adapter

An adapter is a physical device that allows one hardware or electronic interface to be adapted (accommodated without loss of function) to another hardware or electronic interface. In a computer, an adapter is often built into a **card** that can be inserted into a slot on the computer's motherboard. The card adapts information that is exchanged between the computer's microprocessor and the devices that the card supports.

adaptive differential pulse-code modulation

See "ADPCM"

ADAT

The ADAT (a registered trademark of Alesis) is an eight-track digital tape recorder that caught the recording industry by storm when it was first released in the early 1990s. Today, with over 100,000 ADATs in use in recording facilities around the world, it is the most widely used professional digital recording system. The ADAT was the first product in the category now known as modular digital multitracks (MDMs).

The ADAT system allows up to 16 ADAT units to be used in synchronization, enabling the user to build a very cost-effective multi-track recording environment. The transportability and modularity of the system makes it ideal for mobile recording and wherever space is limited.

Digital transfer between ADATs in a system uses a **optical fiber** digital communication standard pioneered by Alesis which has become known as Lightpipe. The Lightpipe digital interface has been adopted by other manufacturers as a means of transferring digital data from other types of audio devices, such as mixers, synthesizers, and effect processors.

The ADAT uses the S-VHS ½ inch tape format. This tape is similar in design to the tape used in consumer VCRs.

ADC

See "analog-to-digital conversion"

add-in

Add-in is a term used, especially by Microsoft, for a software **utility** or other program that can be added to a primary program. The Microsoft Style Guide says that Microsoft Bookshelf is an add-in for Word and that Analysis Toolpak is an add-in for Microsoft Excel. According to the Style Guide, add-in should not be confused with **add-on**, a term for a hardware expansion unit. (However, some add-on manufacturers do call them "add-ins.")

A similar term is **plug-in**, a term originated by Netscape for application programs that can be activated within a Netscape Web **browser** window.

add-on

An add-on is either a hardware unit that can be added to a computer to increase its capabilities or a program **utility** that enhances a primary program. Less frequently, some manufacturers and software developers use the term **add-in**. Examples of add-ons for a computer include **card**s for sound, graphics acceleration, modem capability, and memory. Software add-ons are common for games, word processors, and accounting programs.

The Microsoft Style Guide suggests using add-ons for hardware only and add-ins for software utilities. Industry-wide, however, this guideline does not seem to be widely followed.

A similar term is **plug-in**, a term originated by Netscape for application programs that can be activated within a Netscape Web **browser** window.

address

People use this word several ways. You can ask someone for the address of their **server**, or for their **home page** on the Web, or where to send **e-mail**. So an "address" can mean the

unique location of either (1) an Internet server, (2) a specific file (for example, a Web page), or (3) an e-mail user. It is also used to specify the location of data within computer **storage**.

1) An **Internet address** or IP address is a unique computer (**host**) location on the Internet (expressed either as a unique string of numbers or as its associated **domain name**).

Example of an IP address expressed in dot notation: 205.245.172.72

Example of the domain name version: whatis.com

For more information, see **IP address**.

2) A **file (or home page) address** is expressed as the defining directory path to the file on a particular server. (A Web page address is also called a Uniform Resource Locator, or **URL**.)

Example: http://www.hitmill.com/computers/computerhx1.html

3) An **e-mail address** is the location of an e-mail user (expressed by the user's e-mail name followed by an "at" sign followed by the user's server domain name.)

Example: missmuffet@tuffet.org

4) In a computer, a **storage address** is the beginning location of a sequence of data that is stored on some electronic storage medium.

Address Resolution Protocol

Address Resolution Protocol (ARP) is a **protocol** for mapping an Internet Protocol address (**IP address**) to a physical machine address that is recognized in the local network. For example, in IP Version 4, the most common level of IP in use today, an address is 32 bits long. In an **Ethernet** local area network, however, addresses for attached devices are 48 bits long. (The physical machine address is also known as a Media Access Control or **MAC address**.) A table, usually called the ARP cache, is used to maintain a correlation between each MAC address and its corresponding IP address. ARP provides the protocol rules for making this correlation and providing address conversion in both directions.

How ARP Works

When an incoming packet destined for a host machine on a particular local area network arrives at a **gateway**, the gateway asks the ARP program to find a physical host or MAC address that matches the IP address. The ARP program looks in the ARP cache and, if it finds the address, provides it so that the packet can be converted to the right packet length and format and sent to the machine. If no entry is found for the IP address, ARP broadcasts a request packet in a special format to all the machines on the LAN to see if one machine knows that it has that IP address associated with it. A machine that recognizes the IP address as its own returns a reply so indicating. ARP updates the ARP cache for future reference and then sends the packet to the MAC address that replied.

Since protocol details differ for each type of local area network, there are separate ARP Requests for Comments (**RFC**) for Ethernet, **ATM**, Fiber Distributed-Data Interface, HIPPI, and other protocols.

There is a Reverse ARP (**RARP**) for host machines that don't know their IP address. RARP enables them to request their IP address from the gateway's ARP cache.

address sign

See "at sign"

ad-hoc network

An ad-hoc (or "spontaneous") network is a **local area network** or other small network, especially one with **wireless** or temporary plug-in connections, in which some of the network devices are part of the network only for the duration of a communications session or, in the case of mobile or portable devices, while in some close proximity to the rest of the network. In Latin, *ad hoc* literally means "for this," further meaning "for this purpose only," and thus usually temporary. The term has been applied to future office or home networks in which new devices can be quickly added, using, for example, the proposed **Bluetooth** technology in which devices communicate with the computer and perhaps other devices using wireless transmission.

One vendor offers an ad-hoc network technology that allows people to come to a conference room and, using **infrared transmission** or radio frequency (**RF**) wireless signals, join their notebook computers with other conferees to a local network with shared data and printing resources. Each user has a unique network address that is immediately recognized as part of the network. The technology would also include remote users and hybrid wireless/wire connections.

Jini is an approach to instant recognition of new devices in a network that would seem to make it easier to have an ad-hoc network.

admittance

Admittance (symbolized *Y*) is an expression of the ease with which alternating current (**AC**) flows through a complex circuit or system. Admittance is a **vector** quantity comprised of two independent **scalar** phenomena: **conductance** and **susceptance**.

Conductance, denoted *G*, is a measure of the ease with which charge carriers can pass through a component or substance. The more easily the charge carriers move in response to a given applied electric potential, the higher the conductance, which is expressed in positive real-number **siemens**. Conductance is observed with AC and also with direct current (**DC**).

Susceptance, denoted *B*, is an expression of the readiness with which an electronic component, circuit, or system releases stored energy as the current and voltage fluctuate. Susceptance is expressed in **imaginary number** siemens. It is observed for AC, but not for DC. When AC passes through a component that contains susceptance, energy might be stored and released in the form of a magnetic field, in which case the susceptance is inductive (denoted $-jB_L$), or energy might be stored and released in the form of an electric field, in which case the susceptance is capacitive (denoted $+jB_C$).

Admittance is the vector sum of conductance and susceptance. Susceptance is conventionally multiplied by the positive square root of -1, the unit imaginary number called symbolized by *j*, to express *Y* as a complex quantity $G - jB_L$ (when the net susceptance is inductive) or $G + jB_C$ (when the net susceptance is capacitive).

In parallel circuits, conductance and susceptance add together independently to yield the composite admittance. In series circuits, conductance and susceptance combine in a more complicated manner. In these situations, it is easier to convert conductance to resistance, susceptance to reactance, and then calculate the composite impedance.

Also see **conductance**, **reactance**, **resistance**, **impedance**, **ohm**, **siemens**, **henry**, and **farad**.

ADO

See "ActiveX Data Objects"

ADPCM

ADPCM (adaptive differential pulse-code modulation) is a technique for converting sound or **analog** information to **binary** information (a string of 0's and 1's) by taking frequent samples of the sound and expressing the value of the sampled sound modulation in binary terms. ADPCM is used to send sound on fiber-optic long-distance lines as well as to store sound along with text, images, and code on a **CD-ROM**.

ADSI

ADSI (Analog Display Services Interface) is the standard **protocol** for enabling alternate voice and data services, such as a visual display at the phone, over the **analog** telephone network. Developed by Bellcore in 1993, ADSI is now built into devices such as special telephones with small display screens, cable TV **set-top box**, personal digital assistants (**PDAs**), pagers, and personal computers with telephone applications.

A popular application enabled by ADSI is Call Waiting Deluxe, an application that displays the name and number of an incoming call while you are on the phone. If you have an ADSI screen phone, several options are displayed on your screen including switching to the new call, forwarding the new call to your voice mail, putting the new caller on hold, playing a recorded message, or dropping the current call and switching to the new call.

Other ADSI applications include:

- Visual voice mail, the display of telephone voice mail menu options and a list of your voice mail messages
- Visual directory, a service that allows you to locate the telephone number of an individual or business and, possibly at extra charge, to download the address of that individual to your screen phone
- E-mail browsing, allowing you to send and receive e-mail messages via an ADSI-enabled device.
- Schedule-based services, faxing abilities, notification of incoming e-mail messages, home banking, ticket purchasing, and access to train and plane schedules

ADSL Terminal Unit—Remote

See "ATU-R"

ADSL

Also see **Fast Guide to DSL**.

ADSL (Asymmetric Digital Subscriber Line) is a technology for transmitting **digital** information at a high **bandwidth** on existing phone lines to homes and businesses. Unlike regular dialup phone service, ADSL provides continously available, "always on" connection. ADSL is asymmetric in that it uses most of the channel to transmit downstream to the user and only a small part to receive information from the user. ADSL simultaneously accommodates **analog** (voice) information on the same line. ADSL is generally offered at downstream data rates from 512 **Kbps** to about 6 **Mbps**. A form of ADSL, known as Universal ADSL or **G.lite**, has been approved as a standard by the **ITU-TS**.

ADSL was specifically designed to exploit the one-way nature of most multimedia communication in which large amounts of information flow toward the user and only a small amount of interactive control information is returned. Several experiments with ADSL to real users began in 1996. In 1998, wide-scale installations began in several parts of the U.S. In 2000 and beyond, ADSL and other forms of DSL are expected to become generally available in urban areas. With ADSL (and other forms of DSL), telephone companies are competing with cable companies and their **cable modem** services.

ADSM

See "ADSTAR Distributed Storage Management"

ADSTAR Distributed Storage Management

ADSTAR Distributed Storage Management (ADSM) is a collective term for IBM's family of high-end software that helps a customer manage the storage devices (such as **mainframe** storage, PC disk drives, and Zip drives) that are scattered around the company.

ADSM helps medium and large companies automatically **back up** the business information in all of the storage devices throughout the enterprise. ADSM software works with a variety of database formats, including those made by IBM competitors.

The basic premise behind ADSM is to allow customers to view and manage storage as a single comprehensive endeavor. The idea is to let customers back up on an enterprise level, instead of having to save all the data residing in all the PCs, networks and other machines throughout a company at each individual location.

IBM is no longer actively selling ADSM software. Instead, IBM and its **Tivoli** subsidiary are selling Tivoli Storage Manager software as the ADSM successor.

Advanced Configuration and Power Interface

ACPI (Advanced Configuration and Power Interface) is an industry specification for the efficient handling of power consumption in desktop and mobile computers. ACPI specifies how a computer's **basic input/output system**, **operating system**, and **peripheral** devices communicate with each other about power usage.

With ACPI, the following capabilities are possible (assuming the operating system supports them):

- The user can specify at what time a device, such as a display monitor, is to turn off or on.

- The user of a notebook computer can specify a lower-level of power consumption when the battery starts running low so that essential applications can still be used while other, less important applications are allowed to become inactive.

- The operating system can lower the **clock speed** during times when applications don't require the full processor clock speed.

- The operating system can reduce motherboard and peripheral device power needs by not activating devices until they are needed.

- The computer can enter a *stand-by mode* when no one is using it, but with modem power left on to receive incoming faxes.

- Devices can be **plug and play**. As soon as plugged in, they can be controlled by ACPI.

ACPI must be supported by the computer **motherboard**, **basic input/output system** (BIOS), and the **operating system**. One of several *power schemes* can be chosen. Within a power scheme, the user can control the power to individual devices. In order for ACPI to work on your computer, your BIOS must include the ACPI software and the operating system must be ACPI-compatible. ACPI is designed to work with Windows 98 and with Windows 2000. If you have **Windows 98**, you'll find a description of ACPI in the help files. Click Start->Help->Index-> and type in: ACPI.

ACPI is in part a response to global concerns about energy conservation and environmental control. ACPI replaces Intel's SL technology and the more recent APM (Advanced Power Management) technology. Based on the collaborative effort of Intel, Toshiba, and Microsoft, ACPI moves away from power management that simply times out during inactivity to a more sophisticated demand-based power management. ACPI components collect information about power consumption from the computer and gives that information to the operating system. The operating system then distributes power to the different computer components on an as-needed basis. With ACPI, the computer can power itself down to a deep sleep state but still be capable of responding to an incoming phone call or a timed backup procedure. Another feature of ACPI is the "hibernation" mode. Before the computer goes into a deep sleep or hibernation, the contents of RAM are written to an image file and saved on the hard drive. When the computer is turned back on, the image file is reloaded, eliminating the need to reboot the system and open applications.

Advanced Encryption Standard

Also see **cryptography**.

The Advanced Encryption Standard (AES) is an **encryption algorithm** for securing sensitive but unclassified material by US Government agencies and, as a likely consequence, may eventually become the de facto encryption standard for commercial transactions in the private sector. (Encryption for the US military and other classified communications is handled by separate, secret algorithms.)

In January 1997, a process was initiated by the National Institute of Standards and Technology (**NIST**), a unit of the US Commerce Department, to find a more robust replacement for the Data Encryption Standard (**DES**) and to a lesser degree Triple DES. The specification called for a symmetric algorithm (same **key** for encryption and decryption) using block encryption (see **block cipher**) of 128 bits in size, supporting key sizes of 128, 192 and 256 bits, as a minimum. The algorithm was required to be royalty-free for use worldwide and offer security of a sufficient level to protect data for the next 20 to 30 years. It was to be easy to implement in hardware and software, as well as in restricted environments (for example, in a **smart card**) and offer good defenses against various attack techniques.

The entire selection process was fully open to public scrutiny and comment, it being decided that full visibility would ensure the best possible analysis of the designs. In 1998, the NIST selected 15 candidates for the AES, which were then subject to preliminary analysis by the world cryptographic community, including the National Security Agency. On the basis of this, in August 1999, NIST selected five algorithms for more extensive analysis. These were:

- MARS, submitted by a large team from IBM Research

- RC6, submitted by **RSA** Security

- Rijndael, submitted by two Belgian cryptographers, Joan Daemen and Vincent Rijmen

- Serpent, submitted by Ross Andersen, Eli Biham and Lars Knudsen

- Twofish, submitted by a large team of researchers including Counterpane's respected cryptographer, Bruce Schneier

Implementations of all of the above were tested extensively in **ANSI C** and **Java** languages for speed and reliability in such measures as encryption and decryption speeds, key and algorithm set-up time and resistance to various attacks, both in hardware- and software-centric systems. Once again, detailed analysis was provided by the global cryptographic community (including some teams trying to break their own submissions). The end result was that on October 2, 2000, NIST announced that Rijndael had been selected as the proposed candidate as the AES. After a 90 day period of public comment when the algorithm is presented as a Federal Information Processing Standard (**FIPS**), the Secretary of Commerce will approve it after final, detailed analysis. Final, official acceptance is expected some time in June 2001.

Advanced Function Printing

Advanced Function Printing (AFP) is an IBM architecture and family of associated printer software and hardware that provides document and information presentation control independent of specific applications and devices. Using AFP, users can control formatting, the form of paper output, whether a document is to be printed or viewed online, and manage document storage and access in a distributed network across multiple **operating system** platforms. AFP is primarily used in large **enterprise**s with printer rooms and expensive high-speed printers. AFP applications allow users or print room operators to distributed print jobs among a group of printers and to designate backup printers when one fails. IBM considers AFP to be a "cornerstone" of **EDM** applications such as print-and-view, **archive** and retrieval, and Computer Output to Laser Disk (COLD).

AFP printer and software support is provided in all of IBM's major operating systems: **OS/390**, **virtual machine**, VSE, **OS/400**, **AIX**, and **OS/2**, as well as in **DOS** and **Windows**.

The AFP architecture is primarily designed to work with the Intelligent Printer Datastream (IPDS), but also can print using Hewlett-Packard's Printer Control Language (**PCL**) and the Page Printer Datastream(PPDS). Other supported data streams include **ASCII**, Metafiles, **Postscript**, TeX, and Ditroff.

An application program interface (**API**) is provided so that **COBOL** application programmers can use AFP functions without having to specify them using AFP **syntax** or semantics.

Advanced Intelligent Network

The Advanced Intelligent Network (AIN) is a telephone network architecture that separates service logic from switching equipment, allowing new services to be added without having to redesign switches to support new services. It encourages competition among service providers since it makes it easier for a provider to add services and it offers customers more service choices.

Developed by Bell Communications Research, AIN is recognized as an industry standard in North America. Its initial version, AIN Release 1, is considered a model toward which services will evolve. Meanwhile, evolutionary subsets of AIN Release 1 have been developed. These are shown in the (#ainrels) AIN Release Table below. Elsewhere, the International Telecommunications Union (see **ITU-TS**), endorsing the concepts of AIN, developed an equivalent version of AIN called Capability Set 1 (CS-1). It comes in evolutionary subsets called the Core INAP capabilities.

How It Works

Briefly, here's how AIN Release 1 works:

- A telephone caller dials a number that is received by a **switch** at the telephone company central office.

- The switch—known as the Service Switching Point (SSP)—forwards the call over a Signaling System 7 (**SS7**) network to a Service Control Point (SCP) where the service logic is located.

- The Service Control Point identifies the service requested from part of the number that was dialed and returns information about how to handle the call to the Service Switching Point. Examples of services that the SCP might provide include area number calling service, disaster recovery service, do not disturb service, and 5-digit extension dialing service.

- In some cases, the call can be handled more quickly by an Intelligent Peripheral (IP) that is attached to the Service Switching Point over a high-speed connection. For example, a customized voice announcement can be delivered in response to the dialed number or a voice call can be analyzed and recognized.

- In addition, an "adjunct" facility can be added directly to the Service Switching Point for high-speed connection to additional, undefined services.

One of the services that AIN makes possible is Local Number Portability (**Local Number Portability**).

The AIN Release Table

AIN Release	Capabilities
Release 0	Trigger checkpoints at off-hook, digit collection and analysis, and routing points of call Code gapping to check for overload conditions at SCP 75 announcements at the switching system Based on ANSI TCAP issue 1
Release 0.1	Adds a formal call model that distinguishes the originating half of the call from the terminating half Additional triggers 254 announcements at the switching system Based on ANSI TCAP issue 2
Release 0.2	Adds Phase 2 Personal Communication Service (PCS) support Voice Activated Dialing (VAD) ISDN-based SSP-IP interface Busy and no-answer triggers Next events list processing at SCP Default routing
Release 1	A full set of capabilities

Advanced Mobile Phone Service

Advanced Mobile Phone Service (AMPS) is a standard system for **analog** signal **cellular telephone** service in the United States and is also used in other countries. It is based on the initial **electromagnetic radiation spectrum** allocation for cellular service by the Federal Communications Commission (FCC) in 1970. Introduced by AT&T in 1983, AMPS became and currently still is the most widely deployed cellular system in the United States.

AMPS allocates frequency ranges within the 800 and 900 megahertz (**MHz**) spectrum to cellular telephone. Each service provider can use half of the 824-849 MHz range for receiving signals from cellular phones and half the 869-894 MHz range for transmitting to cellular phones. The bands are divided into 30 **kHz** sub-bands, called *channels*. The receiving channels are called *reverse channels* and the sending channels are called *forward channels*. The division of the spectrum into sub-band channels is achieved by using frequency division multiple access (**FDMA**).

The signals received from a transmitter cover an area called a **cell**. As a user moves out of the cell's area into an adjacent cell, the user begins to pick up the new cell's signals without any noticeable transition. The signals in the adjacent cell are sent and received on different channels than the previous cell's signals to so that the signals don't interfere with each other.

The analog service of AMPS has been updated with **digital** cellular service by adding to FDMA a further subdivision of each channel using time division multiple access (**TDMA**). This service is known as digital AMPS (**D-AMPS**). Although AMPS and D-AMPS originated for the North American cellular telephone market, they are now used worldwide with over 74 million subscribers, according to Ericsson, one of the major cellular phone manufacturers.

Advanced Peer-to-Peer Networking (APPN)

Advanced Peer-to-Peer Networking (APPN), part of IBM's Systems Network Architecture (**SNA**), is a group of protocols for setting up or configuring program-to-program communication within an IBM SNA network. Using APPN, a group of computers can be automatically configured by one of the computers acting as a network controller so that peer programs in various computers will be able to communicate with other using specified network routing.

APPN features include:

- Better **distributed** network control; because the organization is peer-to-peer rather than solely hierarchical, terminal failures can be isolated

- Dynamic peer-to-peer exchange of information about network **topology**, which enables easier connections, reconfigurations, and routing

- Dynamic definition of available network resources

- Automation of resouce registration and directory lookup

- Flexibility, which allows APPN to be used in any type of network topology

How Dynamic Configuration Works

APPN works with Advanced Program-to-Program Communication (APPC) software that defines how programs will communicate with each other through two interfaces: one that responds to requests from **application** programs that want to communicate and one that exchanges information with communications hardware. When one program wants to communicate with another, it sends out a request (called an *allocate call*) that includes the destination's **logical unit** (LU) name—the APPC program on each computer that uniquely identifies it. APPC sets up a session between the originating and destination LUs.

APPN network **nodes** are differentiated as *low entry networking* (LEN) nodes, *end nodes* (ENs), and *network nodes* (NNs). When the network computers are powered on and the software activated, links are established throughout the specified topology. The linked nodes exchange information automatically. If we consider a simplified APPN network, with one end node connected to a network node, the following would describe the sequence of events:

- Each node indicates APPN capability and defines its node type.

- The network node asks the end node if it requires a network node server, which handles requests for LU locations.

- If it responds that it does, the two nodes establish APPC sessions to exchange program-to-program information.

- The end node registers any other LUs defined at its node by sending the networked node formatted information gathered from the APPC session.

- After this sequence is completed, the network node knows the location of the EN and what LUs are located there. This information, multiplied across the network, enables LU location and routing.

Advanced Program-to-Program Communication

See "APPC"

Advanced Television

See "ATV"

Advanced Television Enhancement Forum

The Advanced Television Enhancement Forum (ATVEF) is an alliance of leaders in the broadcast and cable industry, the consumer electronics industry, and the computer industry that developed the ATVEF enhanced content specification. The ATVEF specification delivers Web content to television viewers using current Internet technologies over both **analog** and digital television (**DTV**) systems. ATVEF uses existing terrestrial, cable, satellite, and Internet networks to deliver Web content. ATVEF content is broadcast over one-way or two-way television systems. Supported files include Hypertext Markup Language (**HTML**), Virtual Reality Modeling Language (**VRML**), **Java**, and private data files. Consumers can receive Web content using a personal computer, cable or satellite **set-top box**, or **WebTV** device.

The ATVEF specification consists of three parts: the announcement, trigger, and content:

- The announcement notifies the television viewer of any current Web content available and expires after a set time period. The announcement also includes information that helps the set-top box to decide whether to accept the Web content or to determine whether the Web content is designed to automatically begin without authorization.

- The trigger contains the URL that points to the Web content.

- The content delivered is a collection of Web pages that is displayed along with the television program. It can include text, pictures, and audio files. If the television system is a two-way system, the viewer can browse Web pages and even purchase advertised items using his television.

The ATVEF specification also defines a degree of forward error correction. The data to be transmitted is processed through an **algorithm** that adds extra bits for error correction. If the Web content is damaged during transmission, the extra bits are used to correct the damage. It also allows the data to be reconstructed if received out of order. The forward error correction defined by the ATVEF specification also allows a viewer to receive Web content even if the viewer has tuned into the middle of a broadcast.

Advanced Television Systems Committee

The Advanced Television Systems Committee (ATSC) is a standards organization that was created in 1982 as part of the Advanced Television Committee (ATV) to promote the establishment of technical standards for all aspects of advanced television systems. Based in Washington, D.C., ATSC has grown from 25 original organizational members to an international membership of over 200, including broadcasters, motion picture companies, telecommunications carriers, cable TV programmers, consumer electronics manufacturers, and computer hardware and software companies.

The ATSC developed standards for digital television (**DTV**) that specify technologies for the transport, format, compression, and transmission of DTV in the U.S. ATSC DTV Standards developed, or in development currently, include digital high definition television (term>>HDTV), standard definition television (**SDTV**), datacasting (the transmission of separate information streams that might allow, for example, someone watching a baseball game to choose a different camera angle, or someone watching a cooking show to view and download particular recipes), multichannel surround-sound audio, **conditional access** (methods, such as encryption or electronic locking systems, used to restrict service access to authorized users), and interactive services. For SDTV and HDTV, ATSC chose **MPEG-2** for video and **Dolby Digital** for audio.

ATSC standards are expected to revolutionize the television industry as defined by the National Television Standards Committee (**NTSC**) standards set in 1953. ATSC standards for DTV are being adopted internationally.

AES

See "Advanced Encryption Standard"

AES/EBU

AES/EBU (Audio Engineering Society/European Broadcasting Union) is the name of a **digital audio** transfer standard. The AES and EBU developed the specifications for the standard.

The AES/EBU digital interface is usually implemented using 3-**pin** XLR connectors, the same type connector used in a professional microphone. One cable carries both left- and right-channel audio data to the receiving device. AES/EBU is an alternative to the **S/PDIF** standard.

AF

See also **RF** (radio frequency).

AF (audio frequency) (also abbreviated af or a.f.) refers to alternating current (**AC**) having a frequency such that, if applied to a transducer such as a loudspeaker or headset, it will produce acoustic waves within the range of human hearing. The AF range is generally considered to be from 20 **Hz** to 20,000 Hz.

All telephone circuits operate with AF signals in a restricted range of approximately 200 Hz to 3000 Hz. A telephone-line **modem** is an AF device that converts binary **digital** data into **analog** signals that can be transmitted over the telephone circuit, and also converts incoming AF signals into binary digital data.

AFC

See "pixie dust"

AFM

See "atomic force microscopy"

AFS

See "Andrew file system"

agent

On the Internet, an agent (also called an **intelligent agent**) is a program that gathers information or performs some other service without your immediate presence and on some regular schedule. Typically, an agent program, using parameters you have provided, searches all or some part of the Internet, gathers information you're interested in, and presents it to you on a daily or other periodic basis.

An example of an agent is Infogate, which alerts you about news on specified topics of interest. A number of similar agents compare shopping prices and bring the news back to the user. Other types of agents include specific site watchers that tell you when the site has been updated or look for other events and analyst agents that not only gather but organize and interpret information for you.

An agent is sometimes called a **bot** (short for robot). The practice or technology of having information brought to you by an agent is sometimes referred to as **push** technology.

aggregate

In general, to aggregate (verb, from Latin *aggregare* meaning to add to) is to collect things together. An aggregate (adjective) thing is a collection of other things. An aggregation is a collection.

In information technology, individual items of data are sometimes aggregated into a database. Unlike **marshalling**, aggregation doesn't require giving one thing precedence over another thing.

aggregator

Like its synonym **concentrator**, an aggregator is any **device** that serves multiple other devices or users either with its own capabilities or by forwarding transmissions in a more concentrated and economical way. A remote access **hub** is sometimes referred to as an aggregator. A typical aggregator or remote access hub is a device that handles incoming dial-up calls for an Internet (or other network) **POP** and performs other services. An aggregator may be able to handle up to 100 dial-up modem calls, support a certain number of **Integrated Services Digital Network** connections, and support **leased line** and **frame relay** traffic while also functioning as a **router**.

aglet

1) In computer technology, an aglet (or "agile applet") is a small application program or **applet** with the capability to serve as a mobile **agent** of services in a computer network. An aglet has these characteristics:

- **Object-passing capability**. It is a complete program **object** with its own methods, data states, and travel itinerary that can send other aglets or pass itself along in a network as an entity.

- **Autonomous**. An aglet has the ability to decide on its own what actions to take and where and when to go elsewhere.

- **Interaction with other program objects**. It can interact locally with other aglets or stationary objects. When necessary, it can dispatch itself or other aglets to remote locations to interact with other objects there.

- **Disconnected operation**. If a computer is currently disconnected from the network, the aglet can schedule itself to move when the computer is reconnected.

- **Parallel execution**. Multiple aglets can be dispatched to run concurrently in different computers.

An aglet is a **class** or template in the **Java object-oriented programming** language and the mobile agent instances of its use are also called aglets.

Relatively simple examples of aglets are applications in which one aglet can dispatch another to a remote computer to display a note or to search for information and send it back or to notify a user on another computer that a page had changed. Much more complicated applications are envisioned (or are waiting to be envisioned).

The term apparently originated at IBM's research laboratory in Japan. IBM offers a free Aglets Workbench, which is a visual programming environment for creating aglets. IBM has also created an application program interface, the Agent Transfer Protocol (ATP), for transferring agents between networked computers. Both the Agent Transfer Protocol and the Workbench framework protocol have been offered to the Object Management Group (OMG), an industry standards body, as a proposal for a standard Mobile Agent Facility. IBM is offering the Workbench free to developers.

2) An aglet is also the small plastic or fiber tube that binds the end of a shoelace (or similar cord) to prevent fraying and to allow the lace to be passed through an eyelet or other opening.

AGP

See "Accelerated Graphics Port"

Ah

See "ampere hour"

AHA

See "Accelerated Hub Architecture"

AI

AI (pronounced AYE-EYE) or artificial intelligence is the simulation of human intelligence processes by machines, especially computer systems. These processes include learning (the acquisition of information and rules for using the information), reasoning (using the rules to reach approximate or definite conclusions), and self-correction. Particular applications of AI include expert systems, **speech recognition**, and **machine vision**.

AIBO

AIBO (pronounced eye-bow) is an entertainment **robot** designed by Sony. AIBO means "companion" in Japanese. It is also an abbreviation for "artificial intelligence bot" ("**bot**" is short for "robot") in English. Sony created AIBO to be a robotic pet and promotes AIBO as having the capability to interact with its human owner in many of the same ways a living pet would—without the high maintenance.

Sony classifies AIBO as an **autonomous robot**, meaning that it has the ability to learn, mature, and act on its own in response to external stimuli. AIBO has a brain (**CPU**), the ability to move (20 points of articulation), and sensory

organs (sensors). AIBO's developmental stages are controlled by a "memory stick" application software. Human interaction with AIBO determines its ability to express its needs and emotions, as well as its ability to learn and mature. AIBO is capable of expressing happiness, sadness, anger, surprise, fear and dislike. Just like a pet that's alive, the more interaction AIBO has with humans, the faster it learns.

AIBO's head has a touch sensor for non-verbal communication, stereo microphones for hearing, a color video camera for vision, and a distance detector to allow AIBO to avoid obstacles. AIBO has **voice recognition** components that allow AIBO to be programmed to recognize its own name and understand over 50 verbal commands (depending on where AIBO is in its growth cycle). At present, AIBO is bi-lingual and understands Japanese and English; Sony plans to add German and French to increase the robot's worldwide appeal. AIBO is able to communicate with humans by emitting musical tones and changing the color and shape of its eyes. AIBO can be "taught" to play games, but unlike a game, AIBO cannot be reset.

AIBO uses Sony's OPEN-R platform to operate. OPEN-R is modular, so the robot's hardware and software components can be easily changed. Sony plans to initiate a licensing program that will allow developers to use OPEN-R technology to create new applications for AIBO. They hope that opening up development will encourage the public's acceptance of personal robots and help create a broad base of consumers interested in purchasing entertainment or household-helper robots. SONY has released two models of AIBO. The first version of AIBO resembled a dog. The second version of AIBO is said to be modeled after a lion cub. The basic AIBO model sells in the United States for $1,500. The deluxe version, which comes with a charging station, carrying bag, extra battery and additional software package sells for $2,800.

AIFF

AIFF (Audio Interchange File Format) is one of the two most-used **audio file** formats used in the Apple **Macintosh operating system**. The other is Sound Designer II (SDII). Most CD writers can accept AIFF or SDII files interchangeably when writing a Red Book audio CD. AIFF is sometimes referred to as "Apple Interchange File Format."

The extension for this file type is ".aif" when it is used on a PC. On a Mac, the file extension is not needed. A Mac file uses a Type and Creator resource to identify itself to the operating system and the applications that can open it.

An AIFF file contains the raw audio data, channel information (monophonic or stereophonic), bit depth, **sample rate**, and application-specific data areas. The application-specific data areas let different applications add information to the file header that remains there even if the file is opened and processed by another application. For

example, a file could retain information about selected regions of the audio data used for recalling zoom levels not used by other applications.

AIM

See "instant messaging"

AIN

See "Advanced Intelligent Network"

air interface

In **cellular telephone** communications, the air interface is the radio-frequency portion of the circuit between the cellular phone set or wireless modem (usually portable or mobile) and the active base station. As a subscriber moves from one cell to another in the system, the active base station changes periodically. Each changeover is known as a **handoff**.

A cellular connection is only as good as its weakest link, which is almost always the air interface. Radio-frequency (**RF**) circuits are subject to many variables that affect signal quality. Factors that can cause problems include:

- Use of the handheld phone set or portable wireless modem inside buildings, cars, buses, trucks, or trains

- Proximity to human-made, steel-frame obstructions, especially large buildings and freeway overpasses

- Abundance of utility wires that can reflect radio signals and/or generate noise that interferes with reception

- Irregular terrain, particularly canyons and ravines

- Inadequate transmitter power in phone set or wireless modem

- Poorly designed antenna in phone set or wireless modem

In addition to these variables, some cellular networks have inadequate coverage in certain geographic areas. Usually this is because there are not enough base stations to ensure continuous communications for subscribers using portable (handheld) phone sets. As a network evolves, more base stations may be installed in a given region, and in that case, this problem will diminish with time. Conversion of a network from analog to digital can result in dramatic improvement.

AIX

AIX is an **open** operating system from IBM that is based on a version of **UNIX**. AIX/ESA was designed for IBM's System/390 or large server hardware platform. AIX/6000 is an operating system that runs on IBM's workstation platform, the RISC System/6000.

algebraic number

An algebraic number is any **real number** that is a solution of some single-variable **polynomial** equation whose **coefficient**s are all **integer**s. While this is an abstract notion, theoretical mathematics has potentially far-reaching applications in communications and computer science, especially in data **encryption** and security.

The general form of a single-variable polynomial equation is:

$$a_0 + a_1x + a_2x^2 + a_3x^3 + ... + a_nx^n = 0$$

where a_0, a_1, a_2, ..., a_n are the coefficients, and x is the unknown for which the equation is to be solved. A number x is algebraic if and only if there exists some equation of the above form such that a_0, a_1, a_2, ..., a_n are all integers.

All **rational number**s are algebraic. Examples include 25, $^7/_9$, and -0.245245245. Some **irrational number**s are also algebraic. Examples are $2^{1/2}$ (the square root of 2) and $3^{1/3}$ (the cube root of 3). There are irrational numbers x for which no single-variable, integer-coefficient polynomial equation exists with x as a solution. Examples are **pi** (the ratio of a circle's circumference to its diameter in a plane) and e (the natural **logarithm** base). Numbers of this type are known as **transcendental number**s.

algorithm

The term algorithm (pronounced AL-go-rith-um) is a procedure or formula for solving a problem. The word derives from the name of the mathematician, Mohammed ibn-Musa Al-Khowarizmi, who was part of the royal court in Baghdad and who lived from about 780 to 850. Al-Khowarizmi's work is the likely source for the word *algebra* as well.

A computer **program** can be viewed as an elaborate algorithm. In mathematics and computer science, an algorithm usually means a small procedure that solves a recurrent problem.

alias

In general, as a noun, an alias (pronounced AY-lee-uhs) is an alternate name for someone or something. In literature, a "pen name" is an alias for the author's real name. The noun is derived from the Latin adverb *alias*, meaning "otherwise" and by extension "otherwise known as" and the latter meaning is still used in English, as in: Clark Kent, alias Superman. In information technology, the noun has at least two different usages.

1) In some computer **operating system**s and programming languages, an alias is an alternative and usually easier-to-understand or more significant name for a defined data object. The data object can be defined once and later a programmer can define one or more equivalent aliases that will also refer to the data object. In some languages, this is known as an "equate" instruction.

2) In **Macintosh** operating systems, an alias is a **desktop icon** for a particular program or data object.

aliasing

In sound and image generation, aliasing is the generation of a false (alias) frequency along with the correct one when doing frequency sampling. For images, this produces a jagged edge, or stair-step effect. For sound, it produces a buzz.

See **antialiasing**.

Aloha

Aloha, also called the *Aloha method*, refers to a simple communications scheme in which each source (transmitter) in a network sends data whenever there is a **frame** to send. If the frame successfully reaches the destination (receiver), the next frame is sent. If the frame fails to be received at the destination, it is sent again. This protocol was originally developed at the University of Hawaii for use with **satellite** communication systems in the Pacific.

In a **wireless** broadcast system or a half-duplex two-way link, Aloha works perfectly. But as networks become more complex, for example in an **Ethernet** system involving multiple sources and destinations that share a common data path, trouble occurs because data frames collide (conflict). The heavier the communications volume, the worse the collision problems become. The result is degradation of system efficiency, because when two frames collide, the data contained in both frames is lost.

To minimize the number of collisions, thereby optimizing network efficiency and increasing the number of subscribers that can use a given network, a scheme called *slotted Aloha* was developed. This system employs signals called beacons that are sent at precise intervals and tell each source when the channel is clear to send a frame. Further improvement can be realized by a more sophisticated protocol called Carrier Sense Multiple Access with Collision Detection (**CSMA/CD**).

Alpha

Alpha is both a **microprocessor** and the name of a computer system from the Digital Equipment Corporation (DEC), which is now part of Compaq. The Alpha processor uses a newer and more advanced architecture than DEC's flagship computer line, the **VAX**. The Alpha is based on **reduced instruction set computer** (reduced instruction set computing) architecture and handles 64 bits at a time. DEC has added its own refinements to the RISC architecture to further increase performance.

The latest models of DEC's Alpha computer systems are offered with either DEC's **UNIX** operating system or with **Windows NT**. (DECUS states that DEC's **OpenVMS** also runs on Alpha computers.) DEC offers its AlphaServer

together with a packaged solution with Digital's **AltaVista** search engine for indexing and searching data within an enterprise's **intranet**. Its AlphaStation line offers personal workstations in the $4-8,000 range.

alt.

See "alternate newsgroup"

AltaVista

AltaVista is a popular **search engine** on the Web. In addition to full-text searches, AltaVista can also search graphic images and tell you who is linked to your own Web pages. AltaVista's search robot, known as **Scooter**, can look at and collect data from three million Web pages per day. Its indexer, **Ni2**, indexes one gigabyte of data per hour.

alternate newsgroup

"alt." is the prefix for any of the hundreds of "alternate" user-originated **newsgroup**s that are part of **Usenet**. Like other newsgroups, each "alt." newsgroup is arranged in a hierarchy of topical discussion boards that you may read or post to. "alt" is one of many major newsgroups; others include: news, rec (recreation), comp (computers), and soc (social). The "alt" newsgroups are known (and used most frequently) for their alt.sex and related categories, but are also known for including a wide and inventive range of discussion topics.

The easiest way to get access to newsgroups is through the Google Web site.

alternating current

Also see **current**, **voltage**, and **direct current**.

In electricity, alternating current (AC) occurs when charge carriers in a conductor or **semiconductor** periodically reverse their direction of movement. Household utility current in most countries is AC with a **frequency** of 60 **hertz** (60 complete cycles per second), although in some countries it is 50 Hz. The radio-frequency (**RF**) current in antennas and transmission lines is another example of AC.

An AC **waveform** can be sinusoidal, square, or sawtooth-shaped. Some AC waveforms are irregular or complicated. An example of sine-wave AC is common household utility current (in the ideal case). Square or sawtooth waves are produced by certain types of electronic oscillators, and by a low-end uninterruptible power supply (**UPS**) when it is operating from its battery. Irregular AC waves are produced by audio amplifiers that deal with analog voice signals and/or music.

The **voltage** of an AC power source can be easily changed by means of a power transformer. This allows the voltage to be stepped up (increased) for transmission and distribution.

High-voltage transmission is more efficient than low-voltage transmission over long distances, because the loss caused by conductor **resistance** decreases as the voltage increases.

The voltage of an AC power source changes from instant to instant in time. The *effective voltage* of an AC utility power source is usually considered to be the DC voltage that would produce the same power dissipation as heat assuming a pure resistance. The effective voltage for a sine wave is not the same as the *peak voltage*. To obtain effective voltage from peak voltage, multiply by 0.707. To obtain peak voltage from effective voltage, multiply by 1.414. For example, if an AC power source has an effective voltage of 117 V, typical of a household in the United States, the peak voltage is 165 V.

AM

See "amplitude modulation"

amateur radio

Amateur radio, also known as ham radio, is a hobby enjoyed by several hundred thousand people in the United States and by over a million people worldwide. Amateur radio operators call themselves "radio hams" or simply "hams."

To become a radio ham, you must pass an examination. Wireless amateur communication is done on numerous bands (relatively narrow frequency segments) extending from 1.8 **MHz** (a **wavelength** of about 160 meters) upwards through several hundred gigahertz (wavelengths in the millimeter range). There are several license classes. The more privileges a class of license conveys, the more difficult is the examination that one must pass to obtain it.

Amateur radio operation is fun, and that is one of the main reasons hams do it. But ham radio can provide communication during states of emergency. Ham radio works when all other services fail. After Hurricane Andrew struck South Florida in 1992, the utility grid was destroyed over hundreds of square miles. All cellular towers and antennas were blown down. Only amateur radio, the Citizens Radio Service ("Citizens Band"), and a few isolated pay phones with underground lines provided communication between the outside world and the public in the affected area.

Amateur radio operators are known as technical innovators, and have been responsible for important discoveries. For example, in the early part of the 20th century, government officials believed that all the frequencies having wavelengths shorter than 200 meters (1.5 MHz) were useless for radio communications, so they restricted radio amateurs to these frequencies. It was not long before ham radio operators discovered the truth, and were communicating on a worldwide scale using low-power transmitters. Thus the shortwave radio era began.

Amaya

Amaya is the Web **browser** that was developed by members of the World Wide Web Consortium (**W3C**) as a practical tool as well as a testing ground for W3C ideas. Amaya includes an **HTML** editor as well as a viewer and can be downloaded freely from the W3C Web site for use in either Linux or Windows 95/NT/2000 **operating system**. Amaya is distributed as **open source software**, meaning that software developers are free to add to or modify its code and extend its capabilities.

According to Web inventor and W3C Director Tim Berners-Lee, Amaya was developed because at the time no commercially available browser included editing capabilities. The idea was to develop the browser as a way to see why such capabilities hadn't been provided and perhaps help solve any problems that were in the way. Amaya also offers a testing platform for other W3C developments such as MathML, a user interface for creating complex mathematical expressions. Berners-Lee and staff members use Amaya as their primary browser.

Here are some interesting features of Amaya:

- A what-you-see-is-what-you-get (**WYSIWYG**) authoring interface similar to that of commercial products such as Microsoft's FrontPage and the ability to upload the pages to a server

- Support for the latest level of HTML, **XHTML**

- The ability to work on either the coded HTML view or the WYSIWYG source view of the page

- Special support for people with disabilities

- Assurance that the Web page you create will be properly constructed so that other tools will know what to expect when they work with your page

- Assistance in creating and viewing hypertext links

- The ability to display images in the **Portable Network Graphics** format, a more capable graphic format than the **Graphics Interchange Format** format that is also free from licensing requirements

- The ability to print the table of contents or the table of links in a document

- An application program interface (**API**) in **C** for adding new functions or modifying existing ones. Amaya is also used within the W3C to experiment with the **Java** API used in the Document Object Model (**DOM**)

Amaya is the **client** counterpart to the W3C's experimental Web **server**, *Jigsaw* (but you don't need Jigsaw to use Amaya).

AMD

AMD is the second largest maker of personal computer **microprocessor**s after Intel. They also make **flash memory**, integrated circuits for networking devices, and programmable logic devices. AMD reports that it has sold over 100 million x86 (Windows-compatible) microprocessors. Its **Athlon** (formerly called the "K7") microprocessor, delivered in mid-1999, was the the first to support a 200 **MHz bus**. In March 2000, AMD announced the first 1 **gigahertz** PC microprocessor in a new version of the Athlon.

Founded in 1969, AMD along with **Cyrix** has often offered computer manufacturers a lower-cost alternative to the microprocessors from Intel. AMD develops and manufactures its processors and other products in facilities in Sunnyvale, California, and Austin, Texas. A new fabrication facility was opened in Dresden, Germany, in 1999.

The lower cost of AMD's microprocessors was a contributor to lower PC prices in the 1998-2000 period. Reviewers generally rated the K6 and Athlon equivalent to or slightly better than comparable Pentium microprocessors from Intel. In addition to "the first mainstream 200 MHz system bus," Athlon includes a superscalar **pipelining floating point unit**, and a programmable **L1 and L2**. The Athlon uses AMD's aluminum 0.18 **micron** technology.

Amdahl's law

In computer programming, Amdahl's law is that, in a program with **parallel processing**, a relatively few **instruction**s that have to be performed in sequence will have a limiting factor on program speedup such that adding more **processor**s may not make the program run faster. This is generally an argument against parallel processing for certain applications and, in general, against overstated claims for parallel computing. Others argue that the kinds of applications for which parallel processing is best suited tend to be larger problems in which scaling up the number of processors does indeed bring a corresponding improvement in throughput and performance.

AMD-K6

See "K6"

American National Standards Institute

See "ANSI"

American Registry of Internet Numbers

The American Registry of Internet Numbers (ARIN) is the organization in the U.S. that manages **IP address** numbers for the U.S. and assigned territories. Because Internet addresses must be unique and because address space on the Internet is limited, there is a need for some organization to control and allocate address number blocks. IP number management was formerly a responsibility of the Internet Assigned Numbers Authority (**IANA**), which contracted with Network Solutions Inc. for the actual services. In December 1997, IANA turned this responsibility over to

ARIN, which, along with Reseaux IP Europeens (RIPE) and Asia Pacific Network Information Center (APNIC), now manages the world's Internet address assignment and allocation. **Domain name** management is still the separate responsibility of Network Solutions and a number of other registrars accredited by the Internet Corporation for Assigned Names and Numbers (**ICANN**).

For Internet Protocol Version 6 (**IPv6**), which extends the length of an Internet address from 32 bits to 128 bits, ARIN will have many more addresses to manage and allocate.

American Wire Gauge

American Wire Gauge (AWG) is a U.S. standard set of non-ferrous wire conductor sizes. The "gauge" means the diameter. Non-ferrous includes copper and also aluminum and other materials, but is most frequently applied to copper household electrical wiring and telephone wiring. Typical household wiring is AWG number 12 or 14. Telephone wire is usually 22, 24, or 26. The higher the gauge number, the smaller the diameter and the thinner the wire. Since thicker wire carries more current because it has less electrical resistance over a given length, thicker wire is better for longer distances. For this reason, where extended distance is critical, a company installing a network might prefer telephone wire with the lower-gauge, thicker wire of AWG 24 to AWG 26.

AWG is sometimes known as Brown and Sharpe (B&S) Wire Gauge.

Amiga

Amiga is a personal computer designed especially for high-resolution, fast response graphics and multimedia applications. Its **microprocessor** is based on Motorola's 680x0 line of processors. It was one of the first computers to offer **true color**. It comes with its own **operating system**, AmigaOS. Since its first appearance from Commodore Business Machines in 1985, Amiga has become a synonym for fast, high-resolution graphics and best known for its quickly responsive user interface and suitability for playing action games. AmigaOS handles 32-bit instructions and uses **preemptive multitasking**. Its design favors user input to the extent that it is sometimes described as a realtime operating system (**RTOS**).

Since Amiga was designed as a special-purpose system, AmigaOS, which is written in **C** and **assembler** language, is especially compact. All versions of the operating system will run on 512 **kilobyte**s of **RAM**. All versions of the Amiga can run at 50 **MHz** or faster, using an accelerator card. A G4 processor can be used through adding an accelerator card. The Amiga supports **plug and play** and can be adapted with software to emulate Windows and Mac OS.

The Amiga has the ability to become a video monitor by locking into a video signal from an external source such as a video camera. As a result, Amigas are used by television stations and sports arenas to display video clips on large screens.

Amiga is working on a "Next Generation" system that will use **Linux** as its basic core. (Earlier plans favored another operating system, QNX.)

amp hour

See "ampere hour"

ampere

An ampere is a unit of measure of the rate of **electron** flow or **current** in an electrical conductor. One ampere of current represents one coulomb of electrical charge (6.24×10^{18} charge carriers) moving past a specific point in one second. Physicists consider current to flow from relatively positive points to relatively negative points; this is called conventional current or Franklin current.

The ampere is named after Andre Marie Ampere, French physicist (1775-1836).

ampere hour

An ampere hour (abbreviated Ah, or sometimes amp hour) is the amount of energy charge in a **battery** that will allow one **ampere** of **current** to flow for one hour.

A milliampere hour (mAh) is 1,000th of an Ah, and is commonly used as a measure of charge in portable computer batteries. The mAh provides an indication of how long the PC will operate on its battery without having to recharge it.

ampere per meter

The **ampere** per **meter** (symbolized A/m) is the International Unit of **magnetic field** strength. It is derived from basic standard units, but is expressed directly in base units and cannot be further reduced.

Consider the interior of a long, cylindrical coil with a single winding and an air core. Suppose that the linear **current** density in this coil is 1 ampere per meter of displacement as measured along the coil axis. (This expression differs from current density per unit area, which is expressed in **amperes per meter squared**.) Then the magnetic field strength in the interior of the coil is defined as 1 A/m.

For a given coil, the magnetic field strength is directly proportional to the linear current density. Thus, if the linear current density doubles, so does the magnetic field strength; if the linear current density becomes $^{1}/_{10}$ as great, the magnetic field strength also diminishes by a factor of 10.

Sometimes, magnetic field strength is expressed in units called oersteds (symbolized Oe). The oersted is a larger unit than the ampere per meter. Approximate conversions are:

1 Oe = 79.578 A/m
1 A/m = 0.012566 Oe

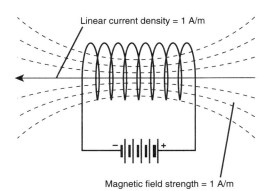

Also see **ampere**, **current**, **magnetic field**, **meter**, and International System of Units (**SI**).

ampere per meter squared

The ampere per meter squared, symbolized A/m^2, is the International Unit of electric **current density**. A current density of 1 A/m^2 represents one **ampere** of electric **current** flowing through a material with a cross-sectional area of one square meter.

The ampere per meter squared is a small unit of current density. Suppose a wire has a cross-sectional area of one millimeter squared (1 mm^2). This is 0.000001 meter squared (10^{-6} m^2). If the current density in this wire is 1 A/m^2, then the wire carries 10^{-6} A, or one microampere (1 µA), a tiny current. Suppose this same wire carries a current of one ampere (1 A), which is an entirely plausible scenario. Then the current density in the wire is 1,000,000 amperes per meter squared (10^6 A/m^2).

Sometimes, larger units of current density are specified. For example, one ampere per millimeter squared (A/mm^2) represents a current of 1 A flowing through a conductor with a cross-sectional area of 1 mm. This unit is equal to 1,000,000 (10^6) A/m^2. One milliampere per millimeter squared (mA/mm^2) represents a current of 1 mA flowing through a conductor with a cross-sectional area of 1 mm. This unit is equal to 1,000 (10^3) A/m^2.

Determination of current density is straightforward in direct-current (**DC**) and low-frequency alternating-current (**AC**) circuits, because the current is distributed uniformly throughout the cross section of a solid conductor. But at radio frequencies (**RF**), more current flows near the outer surface of a solid conductor than near its center. This is known as **skin effect**, and it dramatically reduces the conductivity of wires in RF applications as compared with DC and low-frequency AC circuits. At RF, current density is sometimes near zero near the center of a solid conductor, and quite high near the outer periphery. The average current density can nevertheless be calculated according to the following formula:

$$D = I/X$$

where D is the current density in amperes per meter squared, I is the current in amperes, and X is the cross-sectional area of the conductor in meters squared.

Also see **ampere**, **meter squared**, **skin effect**, and International System of Units (**SI**).

amplification factor

The amplification factor, also called *gain*, is the extent to which an **analog amplifier** boosts the strength of a **signal**. Amplification factors are usually expressed in terms of **power**.

The **decibel** (dB), a **logarithmic** unit, is the most common way of quantifying the gain of an amplifier. For power, doubling the signal strength (an output-to-input power ratio of 2:1) translates into a gain of 3 dB; a tenfold increase in power (output-to-input ratio of 10:1) equals a gain of 10 dB; a hundredfold increase in power (output-to-input ratio of 100:1) represents 20 dB gain. If the output power is less than the input power, the amplification factor in decibels is negative. If the output-to-input signal power ratio is 1:1, then the amplification factor is 0 dB.

Power amplifiers typically have gain figures from a few decibels up to about 20 dB. Sensitive amplifiers used in **wireless** communications equipment can show gain of up to about 30 dB. If higher gain is needed, amplifiers can be cascaded, that is, hooked up one after another. But there is a limit to the amplification that can be attained this way. When amplifiers are cascaded, the later circuits receive noise at their inputs along with the signals. This noise can cause distortion. Also, if the amplification factor is too high, the slightest feedback can trigger oscillation, rendering an amplifier system inoperative.

amplifier

An amplifier is an electronic device that increases the **voltage**, **current**, or **power** of a **signal**. Amplifiers are used in **wireless** communications and broadcasting, and in **audio** equipment of all kinds. They can be categorized as either *weak-signal amplifiers* or *power amplifiers*.

Weak-signal amplifiers are used primarily in wireless receivers. They are also employed in acoustic pickups, audio tape players, and compact disc players. A weak-signal amplifier is designed to deal with exceedingly small input signals, in some cases measuring only a few nanovolts (units of 10^{-9} volt). Such amplifiers must generate minimal internal noise while increasing the signal voltage by a large factor. The most effective device for this application is the **field-effect transistor**. The specification that denotes the effectiveness of a weak-signal amplifier is *sensitivity*, defined

as the number of microvolts (units of 10^{-6} volt) of signal input that produce a certain ratio of signal output to noise output (usually 10 to 1).

Power amplifiers are used in wireless transmitters, broadcast transmitters, and hi-fi audio equipment. The most frequently-used device for power amplification is the **bipolar transistor**. However, vacuum tubes, once considered obsolete, are becoming increasingly popular, especially among musicians. Many professional musicians believe that the **vacuum tube** (known as a "valve" in England) provides superior fidelity.

Two important considerations in power amplification are *power output* and *efficiency*. Power output is measured in watts or kilowatts. Efficiency is the ratio of signal power output to total power input (wattage demanded of the power supply or battery). This value is always less than 1. It is typically expressed as a percentage. In audio applications, power amplifiers are 30 to 50 percent efficient. In wireless communications and broadcasting transmitters, efficiency ranges from about 50 to 70 percent. In hi-fi audio power amplifiers, *distortion* is also an important factor. This is a measure of the extent to which the output waveform is a faithful replication of the input **waveform**. The lower the distortion, in general, the better the fidelity of the output sound.

amplitude modulation

Also see **modulation**.

Amplitude modulation (AM) is a method of impressing data onto an alternating-current (**AC**) **carrier waveform**. The highest **frequency** of the modulating data is normally less than 10 percent of the carrier frequency. The instantanous amplitude (overall signal power) varies depending on the instantaneous amplitude of the modulating data.

In AM, the carrier itself does not fluctuate in amplitude. Instead, the modulating data appears in the form of signal components at frequencies slightly higher and lower than that of the carrier. These components are called *sidebands*. The lower **sideband** (LSB) appears at frequencies below the carrier frequency; the upper sideband (USB) appears at frequencies above the carrier frequency. The LSB and USB are essentially "mirror images" of each other in a graph of signal amplitude versus frequency, as shown in the illustration. The sideband power accounts for the variations in the overall amplitude of the signal.

When a carrier is amplitude-modulated with a pure sine wave, up to $1/3$ (33 percent) of the overall signal power is contained in the sidebands. The other $2/3$ of the signal power is contained in the carrier, which does not contribute to the transfer of data. With a complex modulating signal such as voice, video, or music, the sidebands generally contain 20 to 25 percent of the overall signal power; thus the carrier consumes 75 to 80 percent of the power. This makes AM an inefficient mode. If an attempt is made to increase the

modulating data input amplitude beyond these limits, the signal will become distorted, and will occupy a much greater **bandwidth** than it should. This is called *overmodulation*, and can result in interference to signals on nearby frequencies.

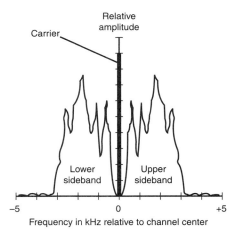

AMPS

See "Advanced Mobile Phone Service"

AMR

AMR (Audio/Modem Riser) is a specification developed by Intel for packaging the **analog I/O audio** functions of **modem** circuitry together with a **codec** chip (which converts back and forth from analog to digital) on a small board that plugs directly into a computer's **motherboard**. The small board is called a *riser* because it rises above the motherboard rather than laying flatly on it. Having this circuitry on a riser means that it doesn't have to be part of the motherboard itself. Because getting certification for the manufacture of a new motherboard design is a lengthy process, removing this function from the motherboard provides more flexibility for manufacturers and allows advances in audio modem design to be implemented more easily. Another specification, MDC (Mobile Daughter Card) is the equivalent of AMR but for use in mobile computers.

In the past, an internal modem was installed in one of several **slot**s inside the computer **chassis** and an external modem was plugged into a serial port at the rear of the computer. With AMR design, the slot can now be used for other purposes. The AMR card can also provide the foundation for higher-quality audio solutions such as 3D positional audio and better **MIDI** music production.

AMR slot

See "AMR"

anacronym

An anacronym is an **acronym** or an abbreviation so old or familiar that no one remembers what its letters stand for. By the way, an "acronym" is not just any abbreviation. It's a word that is short for other words, usually using their initial letters. An abbreviation formed of letters that don't form a word is sometimes known as an "initialism." Our Webster's cites "snafu" and "radar" as examples of acronyms. (Good examples of anacronyms, too!) But "snafu" and "**radar**" seem like acronyms that have passed into general usage (notice the all lowercase). Most of today's acronyms are still all uppercase; only a few will ever become generic. An example of an acronym that probably won't become lower-cased is **WINS** (Windows Internet Naming Service). "IBM" is an initialism, not an acronym. So are "**MPEG**" (Moving Picture Experts Group) and "**EPROM**" (erasable programmable read-only memory).

The Webster's definition does raise a question (and begs one, too). Is the "word" an acronym forms a real, already existing word, or intended to be accepted as a new "word," or just something easily pronounceable? If the first case, then "snafu" and "radar" really aren't acronyms. If the second or third case, they are. However, since any initialism can be thought of as a word and certainly has to be pronounceable so you can say it out loud, one could argue that any initialism is an acronym. We don't think anyone has looked at this issue squarely (and we're not planning to ourselves, but just wanted to demonstrate the ambiguous kind of world we live in...which is why most people frankly don't care whether an acronym is a word or not).

But getting back to anacronyms, they seem to be forming at an alarming rate. Do you remember what this mixture of acronyms and initialisms stand for?

- **ASCII**
- **OSI**
- **BASIC**
- **ISO**
- **I18N**
- **MOO**
- **SCSI**
- **URL**
- **VSAT**
- **WORM**

analog

Analog technology refers to electronic transmission accomplished by adding signals of varying frequency or amplitude to carrier waves of a given frequency of alternating electromagnetic current. Broadcast and phone transmission have conventionally used analog technology.

Analog also connotes any fluctuating, evolving, or continually changing process. Analog is usually represented as a series of sine waves. The term originated because the modulation of the carrier wave is analogous to the fluctuations of the voice itself.

A **modem** is used to convert the digital information in your computer to analog signals for your phone line and to convert analog phone signals to digital information for your computer.

analog computing

Analog computing is a term used by Paul Saffo of the Institute for the Future in Palo Alto, California, to describe silicon-based microsensors that sense and react to external (natural) stimuli in something that approximates the rhythm of reality rather than the "artificial" binary behavior of digital computing. Saffo foresees that, by implanting tiny machines including sensors and actuators in the same materials used to manufacture digital memory and processors (and by using some of the same manufacturing techniques), the next decade will increasingly find uses for "intelligent" material that responds to its environment in **analog** or dynamically responding fashion. Examples include packages that can "talk back" to their handlers; airplane wings that can reshape themselves as they meet turbulence; chairs that can mold themselves into the best supporting shape for each person.

Saffo's analog computers also go by the names of **MEMS** (micro-electromechanical systems) and **smart matter**.

Analog Display Services Interface

See "ADSI"

analog-to-digital conversion

Analog-to-digital conversion is an electronic process in which a continuously variable (**analog**) signal is changed, without altering its essential content, into a multi-level (**digital**) signal.

The input to an *analog-to-digital converter (ADC)* consists of a **voltage** that varies among a theoretically infinite number of values. Examples are sine waves, the waveforms representing human speech, and the signals from a conventional television camera. The output of the ADC, in contrast, has defined levels or states. The number of states is almost always a power of two—that is, 2, 4, 8, 16, etc. The simplest digital signals have only two states, and are called **binary**. All whole numbers can be represented in binary form as strings of ones and zeros.

Digital signals propagate more efficiently than analog signals, largely because digital impulses, which are well-defined and orderly, are easier for electronic circuits to distinguish from noise, which is chaotic. This is the chief advantage of digital modes in communications. Computers

"talk" and "think" in terms of binary digital data; while a **microprocessor** can analyze analog data, it must be converted into digital form for the computer to make sense of it.

A typical telephone **modem** makes use of an ADC to convert the incoming audio from a twisted-pair line into signals the computer can understand. In a **digital signal processing** system, an ADC is required if the signal input is analog.

analytical CRM

See "CRM analytics"

Analytical Engine

The Analytical Engine was, or would have been, the world's first general-purpose computer. Designed in the 1830s by the English mathematician and inventor **Charles Babbage**, the Analytical Engine introduced a number of computing concepts still in use today. Features included a store and mill, analogous to today's **memory** and **processor**. Input and output was provided using punched cards, based on the invention by Jacquard in the early 1800s.

Babbage began his work on the Analytical Engine in 1834. He envisaged the computer to be constructed with brass fittings and powered by steam. It was never built, since the government of the day was unwilling to fund its construction, having already sunk 17,000 English pounds into Babbage's fruitless project to build an earlier invention, the **Difference Engine**.

Babbage was assisted in his endeavours by Ada Augusta, Countess of Lovelace (and daughter of the poet Byron) who is regarded as the world's first computer programmer for her work with Babbage. She developed a punched card program to calculate the Bernoulli numbers.

While Babbage's earlier Difference Engine was finally contructed in 1991, his Analytical Engine remains unrealized. As the originator of several important concepts in computing, however, Babbage's place in history is secure.

analytics

See "CRM analytics"

anchor

In Hypertext Markup Language (**HTML**), an anchor is the establishing of a term, phrase, image, or other information object as being either:

- The target of a **hypertext link** within a document, or
- A reference (a link you can select) to such a target

Note that any HTML file name is automatically an anchor or target that can be linked to. An anchor WITHIN a file to which you can link directly is identified by the # sign followed by the name.

AND

See "logic gate"

Andrew

Andrew was a joint project between Carnegie-Mellon University and IBM to set up a distributed computing environment on the CMU campus. It was designed to serve 4,000 UNIX workstations. The project was named for Andrew Carnegie and Andrew Mellon. One result of Andrew was the **Andrew file system**.

Andrew file system

An **Andrew** file system (AFS) is a location-independent file system that uses a local cache to reduce the workload and increase the performance of a distributed computing environment. A first request for data to a server from a workstation is satisfied by the server and placed in a local cache. A second request for the same data is satisfied from the local cache.

The Andrew file system was developed at Carnegie-Mellon University.

ANI

ANI (Automatic Number Identification) is a service that provides the receiver of a telephone call with the number of the calling phone. The method of providing this information is determined by the service provider (such as AT&T, MCI, Sprint, and so forth). The service is often provided by sending the digital tone multi frequency (**DTMF**) tones along with the call. Home users of ANI can screen callers. **Call centers** can use the information to forward calls to different people for different geographic areas. It is commonly used by emergency center dispatchers to save the caller having to report the information and, when necessary, to help locate callers. A telephone company's 9-1-1 service to a public safety point usually includes the ANI feature.

animated GIF

An animated GIF (**Graphics Interchange Format**) file is a graphic image on a Web page that moves—for example, a twirling icon or a banner with a hand that waves or letters that magically get larger. In particular, an animated GIF is a file in the Graphics Interchange Format specified as **GIF89a** that contains within the single file a set of images that are presented in a specified order. An animated GIF can loop endlessly (and it appears as though your document never finishes arriving) or it can present one or a few sequences and then stop the animation. Animated GIFs are frequently used in Web ad **banner**s.

Java, **Flash**, and other tools can be used to achieve the same effects as an animated GIF. However, animated GIFs are generally easier to create than comparable images with Java or Flash and usually smaller in size and thus faster to display.

anime

Anime (pronounced AH-nee-may) is a term for a style of Japanese comic book and video cartoon animation in which the main characters have large doe-like eyes. Many Web sites are devoted to anime. Anime is the prevalent style in Japanese comic books or *manga*. In Japan, the comic book is a popular form of entertainment for adults as well as for younger audiences. Story lines are often very sophisticated and complex and extend into episodic series. Typical anime themes or genres include Ninja and other martial arts; the supernatural or horror story; the romance; and science fiction including robots and space ships. Foils for the main characters, including robots, monsters, or just plain bad people, often lack the doe-eyed quality.

Variations of anime called *hentai* and *ecchai* are sexually-oriented. *Doujinshi* is the term for "autonomous comics," or comics written and distributed by independent and often amateur devotees of anime.

anonymous e-mail

Anonymous e-mail is e-mail that has been directed to a recipient through a third-party server that does not identify the originator of the message.

anonymous FTP

Using the Internet's File Transfer Protocol (FTP), anonymous FTP is a method for giving users access to files so that they don't need to identify themselves to the server. Using an FTP program or the FTP command interface, the user enters "anonymous" as a user ID. Usually, the password is defaulted or furnished by the FTP server. Anonymous FTP is a common way to get access to a server in order to view or download files that are publicly available.

If someone tells you to use anonymous FTP and gives you the server name, just remember to use the word "anonymous" for your user ID. Usually, you can enter anything as a password.

ANSI

ANSI (American National Standards Institute) is the primary organization for fostering the development of technology standards in the United States. ANSI works with industry groups and is the U.S. member of the International Organization for Standardization (**ISO**) and the International Electrotechnical Commission (**IEC**).

Long-established computer standards from ANSI include the American Standard Code for Information Interchange (**ASCII**) and the Small Computer System Interface (**SCSI**).

antenna

An antenna is a specialized **transducer** that converts **RF** (radio-frequency) fields into **AC** (alternating current) or vice-versa. There are two basic types: the receiving antenna, which intercepts RF energy and delivers AC to electronic equipment, and the transmitting antenna, which is fed with AC from electronic equipment and generates an RF field.

In computer and Internet **wireless** applications, the most common type of antenna is the *dish*, used for **satellite** communications. Dish antennas are generally practical only at microwave frequencies (above approximately 3 **GHz**). The dish consists of a paraboloidal or spherical reflector with an active element at its focus. When used for receiving, the dish collects RF from a distant source and focuses it at the active element. When used for transmitting, the active element radiates RF that is collimated by the reflector for delivery in a specific direction.

At frequencies below 3 GHz, many different types of antennas are used. The simplest is a length of wire, connected at one end to a transmitter or receiver. More often, the radiating/receiving element is placed at a distance from the transmitter or receiver, and AC is delivered to or from the antenna by means of an RF transmission line, also called a *feed line* or *feeder*.

anthropomorphism

Anthropomorphism is the tendency for people to think of inanimate objects as having human-like characteristics. If you have ever named your car, talked to your computer or begged your printer to work, you are guilty of assigning anthropomorphic characteristics to a machine. In recent years, artificial intelligence (**AI**) has progressed to the point that computers can learn from their mistakes so that they do not make a specific error more than once. The ability to self-correct, combined with the ability programmers have to enable speech synthesizers to produce responses that seem emotional, makes **robot**s and other interactive devices seem more human-like than ever.

antialiasing

Antialiasing is the smoothing of the image or sound roughness caused by **aliasing**. With images, approaches include adjusting pixel positions or setting pixel intensities so that there is a more gradual transition between the color of a line and the background color. With sound, aliases are removed by eliminating frequencies above half the sampling frequencies.

antidisintermediation

In commerce, antidisintermediation is a term used to describe the preservation of intermediary positions. Today's consumer can access goods or information on the Internet that traditionally required the assistance of an intermediary such as a retailer, travel agent, or banker. By cutting out the middleman (**disintermediation**), e-businesses are able to sell goods and services more quickly and efficiently, and for lower prices.

Antidisintermediation measures are carried out through business incentives (or disincentives) and legal actions to ensure that intermediary positions are not eliminated. Since a good deal of profit is made by individuals or businesses serving as intermediaries between the primary source of a good or service and the consumer, intermediaries are using antidisintermediation measures to re-establish their niche in the changing economy.

In one example of antidisintermediation (cited in ''The death of ''e'' and the Birth of the Real New Economy: Business Models, Technologies and Strategies for the 21st Century'' by Peter Fingar and Ronald Aronica), Home Depot sent a letter to 1,000 of its suppliers (including Black & Decker and General Electric, for example) warning them that the company would be less likely to do business with those among them who also marketed their goods online.

antiferromagnetically-coupled media

See ''pixie dust''

Antigen

1) Sybari's Antigen is **antivirus software** for Lotus Domino and Microsoft Exchange.

2) AntiGen (with a capital G) is freeware developed by Fresh Software to detect the presence of **Back Orifice** on a machine running Microsoft Windows. AntiGen removes Back Orifice and cleans up system changes that have been made, using a wizard interface. According to Fresh Software, AntiGen was the first application to offer protection from Back Orifice in 1998.

These product names are apparently derived from the biological term, antigen, which is a foreign substance in the body that stimulates the production of an antibody (which fights disease).

anti-replay protocol

The anti-replay protocol is part of the Internet Engineering Task Force (**IETF**) Internet Protocol Security (**IPSec**) standard. Anti-replay ensures IP **packet**-level security by making it impossible for a hacker to intercept message packets and insert changed packets into the data stream between a source computer and a destination computer. By detecting packets that match the sequence numbers of those

that have already arrived, the anti-replay mechanism helps to ensure that invalid packets are discarded. Both of the main protocols in the IPSec standard, the Encapsulating Security Payload (**ESP**) and the Authentication Header (AH), use anti-replay protection.

The anti-replay mechanism works by keeping track of the sequence numbers in packets as they arrive. Whether the mechanism is used at the receiving end depends upon a security level setting set by the receiver. When a security association has been established between a sender and a receiver, their counters are initialized at zero. The first packet sent will have a sequence number of 1, the second 2, and so on. Each time a packet is sent, the receiver verifies that the number is not that of a previously sent packet. When detection of a replayed packet occurs, the program sends an error message, discards the replayed packet, and logs the event—including in the log entry identifiers such as the date/time received, source address, destination address, and the sequence number.

antivirus software

Antivirus (or "anti-virus") software is a class of program that searches your hard drive and floppy disks for any known or potential **virus**es. The market for this kind of program has expanded because of Internet growth and the increasing use of the Internet by businesses concerned about protecting their computer assets.

any key

The phrase "any key," which frequently appears in the direction to computer users to "Press any key," is reportedly a source of confusion to many. At least one **help desk** person reports that users sometimes examine that direction more carefully than intended and call to find out whether "any key" includes such keys as the tilde, the Break key, and the key on many keyboards that shows the Microsoft Windows logo.

"Any key" does indeed include those keys.

anycast

In Internet Protocol Version 6 (**IPv6**), anycast is communication between a single sender and the nearest of several receivers in a group. The term exists in contradistinction to **multicast**, communication between a single sender and multiple receivers, and **unicast**, communication between a single sender and a single receiver in a network.

Anycasting is designed to let one host initiate the efficient updating of **router** tables for a group of hosts. IPv6 can determine which gateway host is closest and sends the packets to that host as though it were a **unicast** communication. In turn, that host can anycast to another host in the group until all routing tables are updated.

AOP

See "aspect-oriented programming"

Apache

Apache is a freely available Web **server** that is distributed under an "open source" license. Version 2.0 runs on most **UNIX**-based operating systems (such as **Linux**, **Solaris**, Digital UNIX, and **AIX**), on other UNIX/**POSIX**-derived systems (such as Rhapsody, **BeOS**, and BS2000/OSD), on AmigaOS, and on **Windows 2000**. According to the Netcraft (www.netcraft.com) Web server survey in February, 2001, 60% of all Web sites on the Internet are using Apache (62% including Apache derivatives), making Apache more widely used than all other Web servers combined.

Apache complies with the newest level of the Hypertext Transport Protocol, **HTTP 1.1**. Free support is provided through a bug reporting system and several **Usenet** newsgroups. Several companies offer priced support.

APAR

See "authorized program analysis report"

API

See "application program interface"

APL

APL (A Programming Language) is a general-purpose, third-generation (**3GL**) programming language that allows certain data manipulations to be expressed with a special non-**ASCII** set of symbols, resulting in programs that are shorter than would be possible using most other languages. APL's notation allows **matrix** manipulation as well as **recursion** functions to be built into simple expressions rather than requiring multiple language statements. APL is more frequently thought of as a language for scientific computation, but it can be used for other purposes as well. Programs can be developed interactively and are usually **interpreted** rather than compiled. The special symbols require keyboard support and specific editors so that the symbols can be displayed and printed.

A-Plus

See "A+"

apogee

When a satellite follows a non-circular orbit around the earth, the satellite's path is an ellipse with the center of the earth at one focus. Such a satellite has variable altitude and variable orbital speed. The point of highest altitude is called apogee. The term also applies to the maximum distance in kilometers or miles between the satellite and the center of the earth. (Apogee can be measured between the satellite and the earth's surface, although this is a less precise specification because the earth is not a perfect sphere. The difference is approximately 4,000 miles or 6,400 kilometers.)

At apogee, a satellite travels more slowly than at any other point in its orbit. When viewed from the earth's surface, a satellite at or near apogee takes a long time to traverse the sky. In communications, apogee is the best time to access a satellite. Although its distance means that the signal path is long, the fact that the satellite is slowly moving means that it is accessible for a comparatively long time. In addition, if a directional antenna is used at a ground-based station, it is relatively easy to track the satellite because the position of the antenna (azimuth and elevation) need not be adjusted very often or rapidly.

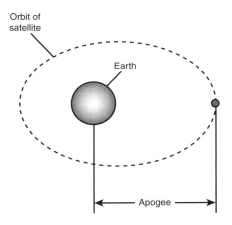

One of the principal advantages of a geostationary satellite is the fact that it follows a circular orbit, so the orbital speed is constant. In addition, the satellite's synchronization with the earth's orbit means that the antenna of an earth-based station can be pointed at a fixed spot in the sky, and no further adjustment of antenna orientation is needed.

Compare **perigee**.

apparent power

Apparent power is a measure of alternating current (**AC**) power that is computed by multiplying the root-mean-square (**rms**) current by the root-mean-square voltage. In a direct current (**DC**) circuit, or in an AC circuit whose **impedance** is a pure **resistance**, the voltage and current are in phase, and the following formula holds:

$P = E_{rms}I_{rms}$

where P is the power in watts, E_{rms} is the **root-mean-square** (rms) voltage in volts, and I_{rms} is the rms current in amperes. But in an AC circuit whose impedance consists of reactance as well as resistance, the voltage and current are not in phase. This complicates the determination of **power**.

In an AC circuit, the product of the rms voltage and the rms current is called *apparent power*. When the impedance is a pure resistance, the apparent power is the same as the **true power**. But when reactance exists, the apparent power is greater than the true power. The vector difference between the apparent and true power is called **reactive power**.

If P_a represents the apparent power in a complex AC circuit, P_t represents the true power, and P_r represents the reactive power, then the following equation holds:

$P_a{}^2 = P_t{}^2 + P_r{}^2$

APPC

APPC (Advanced Program-to-Program Communication, sometimes called LU 6.2) is a communication **protocol** and programming interface standard that operates in the **presentation layer** (the layer that ensures that messages are in the proper format for the recipient) and the **session layer** (the layer responsible for setting up and taking down the association of the two end points in a connection) of the Open Systems Interconnection (**OSI**) communications model. Originally developed by IBM as a remote **transaction** processing tool, APPC is now used to provide **distributed** services within a **heterogeneous** computing environment.

APPC software enables high-speed communication to take place between programs residing on different computers, and between workstations and **midrange** and **mainframe** computer servers. APPC is an **open** standard that is supported on most platforms.

APPC is based on IBM's Systems Network Architecture (**SNA**).

Apple attachment unit interface

See "AAUI"

Appleshare

The AppleShare protocol is a communications **protocol** from Apple Computer that allows **client** applications in a computer to exchange **files** with and request services from **server** programs in a computer network. AppleShare can be used over the Internet on top of the **TCP/IP** protocol, or on top of other network protocols such as **Internetwork Packet Exchange** and **AppleTalk**. Using the AppleShare protocol, a user can access files, applications, printers, and other resources on a remote server. It can communicate with any server program that is set up to receive an AppleShare client request.

All Macintosh and **Mac OS** clones include client and server AppleShare protocol support. Microsoft **Windows NT** Server and Novell **NetWare** both provide AppleShare server protocol support, although they currently only support AppleShare over AppleTalk. Third-party AppleShare client/

server support is available for Microsoft Windows for Workgroups, Windows 95, and Windows NT, as well as for **UNIX** systems.

A given client and server may implement different sets of AppleShare protocol variations. The set of protocols to be used is negotiated before starting a session.

applet

An applet is a little **application**. Prior to the World Wide Web, the built-in writing and drawing programs that came with Windows were sometimes called "applets." On the Web, using **Java**, the **object-oriented programming** language, an applet is a small program that can be sent along with a Web page to a user. Java applets can perform interactive animations, immediate calculations, or other simple tasks without having to send a user request back to the server.

AppleTalk

AppleTalk is a set of local area network communication **protocols** originally created for Apple computers. An AppleTalk network can support up to 32 devices and data can be exchanged at a speed of 230.4 kilobits per second (**Kbps**). Devices can be as much as 1,000 feet apart. AppleTalk's Datagram Delivery Protocol corresponds closely to the **Network layer** of the Open Systems Interconnection (**OSI**) communication model.

AppleTalk Address Resolution Protocol

See "AARP"

appliance

An appliance or "network appliance" is a term used to denote a relatively low-cost PC designed for Internet access and specialized business use, but without the capabilities of a fully-equipped PC.

application

1) In information technology, an application is the use of a technology, system, or product.

2) The term *application* is a shorter form of **application program**. An application program is a **program** designed to perform a specific function directly for the user or, in some cases, for another application program. Examples of applications include word processors, database programs, Web browsers, development tools, drawing, paint, image editing programs, and communication programs. Applications use the services of the computer's **operating system** and other supporting applications. The formal requests and means of communicating with other programs that an application program uses is called the application program interface (**API**).

application integration

Application integration is the process of bringing **data** or a function from one **application** program together with that of another application program. **Object-oriented programming** technology makes application integration easier to achieve. With traditional procedural programming, "bridge" programs had to be written so that one program could work with data or the output from functions in another program. The introduction of program "objects" such as Windows **OCX** and **ActiveX controls** provide standard interfaces so that objects designed for use in one application can be reused in other applications. Some software houses have developed programs that exploit this object technology so that you can have data or functions (object components or "controls") from one application (such as a word processor) be recognized by another application (such as a spreadsheet program).

The result of integration may be a new application with its own user interface or the capability of a desktop or mainframe application to handle data and include capabilities borrowed from other applications.

Application layer

In the Open Systems Interconnection (**OSI**) communications model, the Application layer provides services for **application programs** that ensure that communication is possible. The Application layer is NOT the application itself that is doing the communication. It is a service layer that provides these services:

- Makes sure that the other party is identified and can be reached

- If appropriate, authenticates either the message sender or receiver or both

- Makes sure that necessary communication resources exist (for example, is there a modem in the sender's computer?)

- Ensures agreement at both ends about error recovery procedures, data integrity, and privacy

- Determines protocol and data syntax rules at the application level. It may be convenient to think of the Application layer as the high-level set-up services for the application program or an interactive user.

application program

An application program (sometimes shortened to **application**) is any **program** designed to perform a specific function directly for the user or, in some cases, for another application program. Examples of application programs include word processors; database programs; Web browsers; development tools; drawing, paint, and image editing programs; and communication programs. Application programs use the services of the computer's **operating** system and other supporting programs. The formal requests for services and means of communicating with other programs that a programmer uses in writing an application program is called the application program interface (**API**).

application program interface

An application program interface (API—and sometimes spelled *application programming interface*) is the specific method prescribed by a computer **operating system** or by an **application program** by which a programmer writing an application program can make requests of the operating system or another application.

An API can be contrasted with a **graphical user interface** or a *command interface* (both of which are direct *user interfaces*) as interfaces to an operating system or a program.

application server

An application server is a **server** program in a computer in a **distributed network** that provides the business logic for an application program. The application server is frequently viewed as part of a **three-tier application**, consisting of a graphical user interface (**GUI**) server, an application (business logic) server, and a **database** and **transaction** server. More descriptively, it can be viewed as dividing an application into:

1. A first-tier, **front-end**, Web browser-based graphical user interface, usually at a personal computer or workstation

2. A middle-tier business logic application or set of applications, possibly on a local area network or intranet server

3. A third-tier, **back-end**, database and transaction server, sometimes on a mainframe or large server

Older, **legacy application** databases and transaction management applications are part of the back end or third tier. The application server is the middleman between browser-based front-ends and back-end databases and legacy systems.

In many usages, the application server combines or works with a Web (**Hypertext Transfer Protocol**) server and is called a *Web application server*. The Web browser supports an easy-to-create HTML-based front-end for the user. The Web server provides several different ways to forward a request to an application server and to forward back a modified or new Web page to the user. These approaches include the Common Gateway Interface (**CGI**), **FastCGI**, Microsoft's **Active Server Page**, and the **Java Server Page**. In some cases, the Web application servers also support request "brokering" interfaces such as **CORBA** Internet Inter-ORB Protocol (**IIOP**).

application service provider

ASP is also an abbreviation for **Active Server Page**.

An application service provider (ASP) is a company that offers individuals or enterprises access over the Internet to applications and related services that would otherwise have to be located in their own personal or enterprise computers. Sometimes referred to as "apps-on-tap," ASP services are expected to become an important alternative, not only for smaller companies with low budgets for information technology, but also for larger companies as a form of **outsourcing** and for many services for individuals as well. Early applications include:

- **Remote access** serving for the users of an enterprise

- An off-premises local area network to which mobile users can be connected, with a common file server

- Specialized applications that would be expensive to install and maintain within your own company or on your own computer

Hewlett-Packard, **SAP**, and **Qwest** have formed one of the first major alliances for providing ASP services. They plan to make SAP's popular **R/3** applications available at "cybercenters" that will serve the applications to other companies. Microsoft is allowing some companies to offer its BackOffice products, including SQL Server, Exchange and Windows NT Server on a rental, pay-as-you-use basis.

While ASPs are forecast to provide applications and services to small enterprises and individuals on a pay-per-use or yearly license basis, larger corporations are essentially providing their own ASP service in-house, moving applications off personal computers and putting them on a special kind of **application server** that is designed to handle the stripped-down kind of **thin client** workstation. This allows an enterprise to reassert the central control over application cost and usage that corporations formerly had in the period prior to the advent of the PC. Microsoft's **Terminal Server** product and Citrix's **WinFrame** products are leading thin-client application server products.

Application Service Provider Industry Consortium

See "ASPIC"

application-specific integrated circuit

See "ASIC"

apps-on-tap

Apps-on-tap (short for "applications on tap") is computer industry jargon for **application program**s or other services (Hewlett-Packard calls them **e-services**) that are available online for businesses or consumers. ("On tap" is an

idiomatic expression for "available.") The businesses that furnish apps-on-tap are called **application service providers**. The use of apps-on-tap is a form of **outsourcing**.

aptent

Aptent (pronounced AP-tehnt, compounded from 'application' and 'content') is the combination of computer program applications with textual and graphic content on the Internet. The term was used by Tim Miller in an article on the subject in *The Industry Standard* magazine. Aptent, Miller observes, is increasingly what makes Web enterprises successful since it blends the capabilities of the computer and networking with the Web's amazing capacity to amass content. Aptent is sometimes mostly programming, sometimes mostly content. Content is made available in new ways, arriving with programs that can interact with users, interpret and react to user behavior, send agents in search of content to be provided later, explode into more detailed content, allow users to develop their own content, and so forth. Advertisers and marketers, interested in ads and ideas that engage and involve, are also embracing aptent. Miller identifies some classes of aptent as:

Search engines and directories. The original aptent providers, Yahoo, Excite, Lycos, Infoseek, and others scour the Web's content and digest and index it so that users can access its millions of pages.

Communications aptent. E-mail and chat and discussion group sites and programming provide new ways for content to be created and exchanged. Important companies in communications aptent are Hotmail, WebChat Broadcasting, Parachat, Mirabilis, Silicon Investor, and Go2Net.

"Squirrel" aptent. Providing space where users can create their own personal home pages, address books, and special-event calendars, companies like GeoCities have brought users actively to the Web as full-time participants or at least allowed them to view the Web as a place to store their own content. Tripod and WhoWhere are other sites that let users create their own content.

Agent or "bot" aptent. These sites or applications allow users to gather information tailored to individual needs, compare prices at different online stores, and even discover or "mine" information that matches a user's profile. Junglee, C2B, Quando, and Computer ESP are product examples.

Companies or Web sites that provide aptent rather than mere content tend to "scale" in terms of potential revenue and are attractive to angels, venture capitalists, and investors. Some aptent is able to self-proliferate, users spreading it to other users, a kind of **viral marketing**.

Aptent, Miller concludes, is still in its infancy. The message, he says, is "about doing things, not reading things."

arachniography

An arachniography (pronounced uh-RAK-nee-AH-gruf-ee) is a bibliography of Web pages. The term was coined by Andrew J. Butrica of NASA who first considered "webography" but didn't like the mixing of word origins. He asked his brother, James, who teaches Classics at Memorial University, for a classical language equivalent of "web." In Greek, *arachne* means both the spider and its web. So, for his history of NASA's X-33 project, Andrew called his annotated list of Web pages an annotated arachniography. Since the Web is not a "biblio," this particular **neologism** would seem to be useful.

The term has not yet been widely used, but it's still early in the history of the Web. Meanwhile, if you are including Web sites in a bibliography for an academic or other formal paper or printed work, the Style Guide of the Modern Language Association (MLA) tells how to write a citation. The MLA guideline includes a number of examples of citations for use as models. For a Web site that is a scholarly project, they offer this model:

Victorian Women Writers Project. Ed. Perry Willett.
    Apr. 1997. Indiana U. 26 Apr. 1997
    <http://www.indiana.edu/~letrs/vwwp/>.

A drawback in the MLA's Web citation style is that, if the **Uniform Resource Locator** and its angular brackets are transferred to a Web page, the URL will no longer be visible when viewed on a browser. This is because Web browsers view the information within a matched pair of angular brackets as an HTML tag and therefore not to be displayed. When creating the URL part of a citation, we recommend enclosing it within parentheses instead of angular brackets.

arachnotaxis

Arachnotaxis is the use of a table or structured list of URLs for Web sites (or words that hyperlink to Web sites) in order to help locate them. A structured **bookmark** list or a **portal directory** (such as the ones at Yahoo.com or SearchITServices.com) exemplify arachnotaxis, a term derived from Arachne, the weaver who in Greek legend was turned into a spider, and thence *arachnion*, a variation that meant the spider's web, and *taxis*, a Greek word for an orderly or systematic arrangement of items or terms, especially by classification.

As a term, arachnotaxis could be considered a "serious" **sniglet** (a meaning in search of a term) until such time as its use is more widely adopted. Its inventor, Steve Gruenwald, first used the term in mid-1998, when he was searching for something to describe a taxonomy used to guide users to Web sites. (TechTarget.com sites use the term *taxonomy* to describe our catogorized lists of Web sites.)

Also see **arachniography**, an independently-coined synonym.

Archie

Archie is a program that allows you to search the files of all the Internet **FTP server**s that offer **anonymous FTP**. Archie is actually an indexing **spider** that visits each anonymous FTP site, reads all the **directory** and **file** names, and then indexes them in one large index. A user can then query Archie, which checks the query against its index. To use Archie, you can **Telnet** to a server that you know has Archie on it and then enter Archie search commands. However, it's easier to use a forms interface on the Web called ArchiePlex.

Archie has become less important with the growth of the World Wide Web. It is perhaps of most use for serious researchers who have already tried the Web's main search engines first or who already know that the topic of their search is likely to be found on FTP servers.

architecture

In information technology, especially computers and more recently networks, architecture is a term applied to both the process and the outcome of thinking out and specifying the overall structure, logical components, and the logical interrelationships of a **computer**, its **operating system**, a **network**, or other conception. An architecture can be a *reference model*, such as the Open Systems Interconnection (**OSI**) reference model, intended as a model for specific product architectures or it can be a specific product architecture, such as that for an Intel **Pentium microprocessor** or for IBM's OS/390 operating system.

Computer architecture can be divided into five fundamental components: input/output, storage, communication, control, and processing. In practice, each of these components (sometimes called *subsystems*) is sometimes said to have an architecture, so, as usual, context contributes to usage and meaning.

By comparison, the term *design* connotes thinking that has less scope than architecture. An architecture is a design, but most designs are not architectures. A single **component** or a new **function** has a design that has to fit within the overall architecture.

A similar term, *framework*, can be thought of as the structural part of an architecture.

archive

1) An archive is a collection of computer **file**s that have been packaged together for backup, to transport to some other location, for saving away from the computer so that more hard disk storage can be made available, or for some other purpose. An archive can include a simple list of files or files organized under a directory or catalog structure (depending on how a particular program supports archiving).

On personal computers with the Windows operating system, WinZip is a popular program that lets you create an archive (a single file that holds a number of files that you plan to save to another medium or send someone electronically) or extract its files. WinZip also compresses the files that are archived, but compression is not required to create an archive. A WinZip archive has the file name suffix ".zip".

In **UNIX**-based operating systems, the **tar** (tape archive) utility can be used to create an archive or extract files from one. On **mainframe** operating systems such as IBM's MVS and OS/390, procedures for archiving or backing up files are often automated as a daily operation.

2) On Web sites as well as in libraries, an archive is a collection of individual publications that are often cataloged or listed and made accessible in some way. Magazines, journals, and newspapers with Web sites sometimes refer to their back issues as an archive.

3) Web and **File Transfer Protocol** sites that provide software programs that can be downloaded sometimes refer to the list of downloadable files as an archive or as archives.

ARCNET

ARCNET is a widely-installed local area network (**LAN**) technology that uses a *token-bus* scheme for managing line sharing among the workstations and other devices connected on the LAN. The LAN server continuously circulates empty message frames on a **bus** (a line in which every message goes through every device on the line and a device uses only those with its address). When a device wants to send a message, it inserts a "token" (this can be as simple as setting a token bit to 1) in an empty frame in which it also inserts the message. When the destination device or LAN server reads the message, it resets the token to 0 so that the frame can be reused by any other device. The scheme is very efficient when traffic increases since all devices are afforded the same opportunity to use the shared network.

ARCNET can use **coaxial cable** or **fiber optic** lines. ARCNET is one of four major LAN technologies, which also include **Ethernet**, **token ring**, and **FDDI**.

area

Area (symbolized *A*) is a two-dimensional quantity representing amount or extent of surface. The standard unit of area in the International System of Units (**SI**) is the **meter squared** (m^2).

Area is usually measured or defined on a flat surface, also called a Euclidean plane, or on a spherical surface. For example, we might speak of the area of a parcel of land, the cross-sectional area of a **fiber optic** cable, or the surface area of the earth. However, surface area is occasionally determined for irregular or complex objects. In the case of certain extremely complex or esoteric surfaces, the area might be impossible to define or measure. One example is a mathematical object having a fractional number of dimensions. Another example is an object without a well-defined surface.

When expressing large or small areas, **prefix multipliers** are attached to the meter squared. The table below shows the most common alternative displacement units and their relationship to the meter squared.

Unit (and symbol)	To convert to meters squared, multiply by:	Conversely, multiply by:
kilometer squared (km²)	10^6	10^{-6}
centimeter (cm²)	10^{-4}	10^4
millimeter (mm²)	10^{-6}	10^6
circular mil	5.06×10^{-10}	1.97×10^9
foot squared (ft²)	0.0929	10.76
micrometer squared or micron squared (μ²)	10^{-12}	10^{12}
nanometer squared (nm²)	10^{-18}	10^{18}
Angström squared (Ä²)	10^{-20}	10^{20}

Compare **displacement**, and **volume**.

Also see **centimeter**, **meter**, **meter squared**, **meter cubed**, and International System of Units (**SI**).

area code

In the North American telephone system, an area code is a three-digit code delineating a "toll" area in the United States, Canada, and Mexico. Area codes are distributed according to the North American Number Plan (NANP). The area code is also referred to as a Number Plan Area or NPA.

ARIN

See "American Registry of Internet Numbers"

arithmetic-logic unit

An arithmetic-logic unit (ALU) is the part of a computer **processor** (**CPU**) that carries out arithmetic and logic operations on the **operand**s in computer **instruction word**s. In some processors, the ALU is divided into two units, an arithmetic unit (AU) and a logic unit (LU). Some processors contain more than one AU—for example, one for *fixed-point* operations and another for *floating-point* operations. (In personal computers floating point operations are sometimes done by a **floating point unit** on a separate chip called a numeric coprocessor.)

Typically, the ALU has direct input and output access to the processor controller, main memory (random access memory or **RAM** in a personal computer), and input/output devices. Inputs and outputs flow along an electronic path that is called a **bus**. The input consists of an instruction word (sometimes called a machine instruction word) that contains an operation code (sometimes called an "op code"), one or more operands, and sometimes a format code. The operation code tells the ALU what operation to perform and the operands are used in the operation. (For example, two operands might be added together or compared logically.) The format may be combined with the op code and tells, for example, whether this is a fixed-point or a floating-point instruction. The output consists of a result that is placed in a storage *register* and settings that indicate whether the operation was performed successfully. (If it isn't, some sort of status will be stored in a permanent place that is sometimes called the machine status word.)

In general, the ALU includes storage places for input operands, operands that are being added, the accumulated result (stored in an *accumulator*), and shifted results. The flow of bits and the operations performed on them in the subunits of the ALU is controlled by gated circuits. The gates in these circuits are controlled by a sequence logic unit that uses a particular **algorithm** or sequence for each operation code. In the arithmetic unit, multiplication and division are done by a series of adding or subtracting and shifting operations. There are several ways to represent negative numbers. In the logic unit, one of 16 possible logic operations can be performed—such as comparing two operands and identifying where bits don't match.

The design of the ALU is obviously a critical part of the processor and new approaches to speeding up instruction handling are continually being developed.

ARJ

ARJ is an **archiving** program created by Robert Jung for IBM-compatible computers. The letters stand for "Archive Robert Jung."

ARJ compresses files to save storage space and speed transmission when moved from one computer to another. The program has long filename support, file version management, archive merging, **password** protection, data damage protection, a **digital signature** option, recurse directory support, ANSI escape sequence display handler, configurable command options, handling of up to 99 volumes, ability to store up to 250 **backup**s per archive, ability to work with duplicate filenames within archives, and archives that span diskettes.

There are two versions of ARJ currently available, called ARJ and ARJ32. ARJ runs in **DOS** (Disk Operating System) 2.11 and above, and requires only 512K of random-access memory (**RAM**). ARJ32 runs in 32-bit Windows 95 and later systems. Either version can work with files of up to 1 **gigabyte**, and can process a drive larger than 2 gigabytes with its multiple volume feature as long as any individual file is not larger than 1 GB. Both ARJ and ARJ32 are available in English, Portuguese, German, Polish, French, and Czech.

ARP

See "Address Resolution Protocol"

ARPA

An agency of the United States Department of Defense, ARPA (Advanced Research Projects Agency) underwrote the development of the Internet beginning in 1969. Known as **ARPANET**, it was designed so that, in case of war and the loss of any group of sites, remaining sites would still be able to communicate along alternate routes. No site would be critical to the operation of the network.

Eventually, ARPANET was divided into Milnet, which connected military sites, and a new ARPANET that connected other sites, mainly universities. A new communication protocol was developed, **TCP/IP**, so that all sites on either of the networks could communicate.

Additional networks came into being, all using the new protocol, TCP/IP, making possible the enormous number of interconnections that we have today.

ARPANET

ARPANET was the network that became the basis for the **Internet**. It was funded mainly by U.S. military sources and consisted of a number of individual computers connected by leased lines and using a packet-switching scheme.

ARPANET was replaced over time in the 1980's by a separate new military network, the Defense Data Network, and NSFNet, a network of scientific and academic computers funded by the National Science Foundation. In 1995, NSFNet in turn began a phased withdrawal to turn what has become the *backbone* of the Internet (called vBNS) over to a consortium of commercial backbone providers (PSINet, UUNET, ANS/AOL, Sprint, MCI, and AGIS-Net99).

array

1) In general, an array is a number of items arranged in some specified way—for example, in a list or in a three-dimensional table.

2) In computer programming languages, an array is a group of objects with the same attributes that can be addressed individually, using such techniques as subscripting.

3) In random access memory (**RAM**), an array is the arrangement of memory cells.

artificial intellect

An artificial intellect (or "artilect"), according to Dr. Hugo de Garis, is a computer intelligence superior to that of humans in one or more spheres of knowledge together with an implicit will to use the intelligence. Artilects are the concern of artificial intelligence specialists (or "intelligists") like de Garis, who speculates that human society may soon have to face the question of whether and how we can restrain artificial intelligence from making decisions inimical to humans.

Dr. de Garis assumes that within one or two generations, we will have computers that are more sophisticated than human brains with the ability to experimentally evolve their intelligence into something much beyond what humans might contemplate or understand. de Garis wonders whether such machines would consider human beings important enough to preserve. He speculates that society will soon need to face the question of whether we should permit artilects to be built. He foresees two factions arising: the Cosmists, who argue that they should be built, and the Terras, believing that they should not. The Cosmists might believe that artilects would probably want to leave our planet to seek intelligences elsewhere in the universe. The Terras believe that it would be too dangerous for the human race to allow artilects to be developed.

artificial intelligence

See "AI"

AS/400

The AS/400—formally renamed the "eServer iSeries/400," but still commonly known as AS/400—is a middle-size **server** designed for small businesses and departments in large enterprises and now redesigned so that it will work well in **distributed network**s with Web **application**s. The AS/400 uses the **PowerPC** microprocessor with its **reduced instruction set computer** technology. Its **operating system** is called the OS/400. With multi-**terabyte**s of disk storage and a **Java virtual memory** closely tied into the operating system, IBM hopes to make the AS/400 a kind of versatile all-purpose server that can replace PC servers and Web servers in the world's businesses, competing with both **Wintel** and **UNIX** servers, while giving its present enormous customer base an immediate leap into the Internet.

The AS/400, one of IBM's greatest success stories, is widely installed in large enterprises at the department level, in small corporations, in government agencies, and in almost every industry segment. It succeeded another highly popular product, the System/36 and was itself based on a later, more sophisticated product, the System/38. AS/400 customers can choose from thousands of applications that have already been written and many have been "Web-enabled." IBM points to the AS/400's "uptime" of 99.9%.

The AS/400 comes with a **database** built-in. One widely-installed option is **Domino** (**Notes** with a Web browser).

According to IBM, these are some important new uses for the AS/400:

- **Data warehousing:** With multi-**gigabyte**s of RAM and multi-terabytes of hard disk space, the AS/400 can be a repository for large amounts of company data to which **data mining** could be applied.

- **Java application development:** With its closely integrated Java virtual machine and new tools designed by IBM for building commercial applications with Java, the AS/400 can be used as a development system.

- **Web and e-commerce serving:** Equipped with a Web server and applications designed to support **e-commerce** (taking orders, tracking orders, providing service to customers, working with partners and suppliers) and with **firewall** capabilities, the AS/400 can handle Internet serving for a moderate-size company.

- **Corporate groupware services:** Assuming that Domino and Notes have been included with the system, it's designed to quickly provide a corporation with sophisticated e-mail, project file sharing, whiteboards, and electronic collaboration.

ASCII

ASCII (American Standard Code for Information Interchange) is the most common **format** for **text files** in computers and on the Internet. In an ASCII file, each alphabetic, numeric, or special character is represented with a 7-**bit binary** number (a string of seven 0s or 1s). 128 possible characters are defined.

UNIX and **DOS**-based operating systems use ASCII for text files. Windows NT and 2000 uses a newer code, **Unicode**. IBM's **S/390** systems use a proprietary 8-bit code called **EBCDIC**. Conversion programs allow different operating systems to change a file from one code to another.

ASCII was developed by the American National Standards Institute (**ANSI**).

Asia Cellular Satellite System

Asia Cellular Satellite System (ACeS) is a combined **cellular telephone** and **satellite wireless** system from Ericsson that provides digital communication service to mobile phone and computer users in the Asia Pacific Region. Adding satellite communication to the terrestrial Global System for Mobile (**GSM**) communication system, ACeS is billed as the first integrated satellite-GSM system in the world. Users with Ericsson dual-mode terminals will be able to roam within the region switching as necessary between cellular (local) service and satellite service.

ACeS is expected to be available in an area from Indonesia in the South; Papua, New Guinea in the East; Japan in the North; and Pakistan in the West, an area with a combined population of three billion. ACeS will make it possible for many people to have telecommunication services for the first time. ACeS has signed over 19 **roaming service** agreements with GSM operators.

ACeS subscribers are provided with a GSM subscriber identify module (SIM) and a network access code (which is a telephone number) that can be used outside the region or within the region when blockage of satellite signals occur

(typically, by nearby buildings). GSM subscribers visiting the region can also reach other GSM services via satellite if they have an ACeS SIM and an ACeS terminal.

ASIC

An ASIC (application-specific integrated circuit) is a **microchip** designed for a special application, such as a particular kind of transmission protocol or a hand-held computer. You might contrast it with general integrated circuits, such as the microprocessor and the random access memory chips in your PC. ASICs are used in a wide-range of applications, including auto emission control, environmental monitoring, and personal digital assistants (**PDAs**).

An ASIC can be pre-manufactured for a special application or it can be custom manufactured (typically using components from a "building block" library of components) for a particular customer application.

Asimov's Three Laws of Robotics

Science-fiction author Isaac Asimov is often given credit for being the first person to use the term **robotics** in a short story composed in the 1940s. In the story, Asimov suggested three principles to guide the behavior of robots and smart machines. Asimov's Three Laws of Robotics, as they are called, have survived to the present:

1. Robots must never harm human beings.

2. Robots must follow instructions from humans without violating rule 1.

3. Robots must protect themselves without violating the other rules.

Also see **artificial intelligence**, mechatronics, **nanorobot**, and **robot**.

ASN.1

See "Abstract Syntax Notation One"

ASP

See "application service provider"

ASP.NET

See "ASP+"

ASP+

ASP+ (also called ASP.NET), is the next generation of Microsoft's Active Server Page (**ASP**), a feature of their Internet Information Server (**IIS**). Both ASP and ASP+ allow a Web site builder to dynamically build Web pages **on the fly** by inserting queries to a **relational database** in the Web page. ASP+ is different than its predecessor in two major ways: It supports code written in compiled languages such as **Visual Basic**, **C++**, **C#**, and **Perl**, and it features server controls that can separate the code from the content, allowing **WYSIWYG** editing of pages. Although ASP+ is not **backwards compatible** with ASP, it is able to run side by side with ASP applications. ASP+ files can be recognized by their .aspx extension.

aspect-oriented programming

Aspect-oriented programming (AOP) is an approach to programming that allows global properties of a program to determine how it is compiled into an executable program. AOP can be used with object-oriented programming (**OOP**).

An *aspect* is a subprogram that is associated with a specific property of a program. As that property varies, the effect "ripples" through the entire program. The aspect subprogram is used as part of a new kind of **compiler** called an *aspect weaver*.

The conceptualizers of AOP compare aspect programming to the manufacturing of cloth in which threads are automatically interwoven. Without AOP, programmers must stitch the threads by hand.

ASPI

ASPI (Advanced SCSI Programming Interface) specifies how an application program can communicate with a **SCSI** (Small Computer System Interface) device through a common SCSI **device driver**. ASPI provides a set of functions that are common to any SCSI device.

Developed by Adaptec, ASPI has become the industry standard for controlling SCSI devices. The ASPI device driver is the program that actually interacts with the SCSI device. The layering looks something like this: application/utility, ASPI, ASPI driver, SCSI card.

ASPI driver

In a personal computer, an ASPI driver is a software **driver** or program that uses the Advanced SCSI Programming Interface (ASPI) **protocol** to interface with the Small Computer System Interface (**SCSI**) **bus**. The ASPI interface specification was developed by Adaptec as a means of sending commands to a SCSI **host** adapter. ASPI provides an **abstraction** layer that hides irrelevant details about the host adapter from the programmer and standardizes the interface to simplify application development.

Common Access Method (CAM), the main alternative to ASPI, performs the same basic tasks, but in a different and slightly more complicated way. CAM is not as widely used. ASPI is compatible with most operating systems, and has become the standard for enabling the development of **applications** and drivers that will work with all compatible SCSI adapters.

ASPIC

ASPIC (Application Service Provider Industry Consortium) is a non-profit, international advocacy group comprised of some 700 companies in nearly 30 countries. The ASPIC was formed in May, 1999 to promote and help create an understanding of the application service provider (**ASP**) industry by sponsoring research, establishing guidelines to promote best practices, and conveying the benefits of the ASP computing model.

assembler

An assembler is a **program** that takes basic computer **instruction**s and converts them into a pattern of **bit**s that the computer's **processor** can use to perform its basic operations. Some people call these instructions assembler language and others use the term assembly language.

Here's how it works:

- Most computers come with a specified set of very basic instructions that correspond to the basic machine operations that the computer can perform. For example, a "Load" instruction causes the processor to move a string of bits from a location in the processor's **memory** to a special holding place called a **register**. Assuming the processor has at least eight registers, each numbered, the following instruction would move the value (string of bits of a certain length) at memory location 3000 into the holding place called register 8:
  L   8,3000

- The programmer can write a program using a sequence of these assembler instructions.

- This sequence of assembler instructions, known as the **source code** or source program, is then specified to the assembler program when that program is started.

- The assembler program takes each program statement in the source program and generates a corresponding bit stream or pattern (a series of 0's and 1's of a given length).

- The output of the assembler program is called the **source code** or object program relative to the input source program. The sequence of 0's and 1's that constitute the object program is sometimes called **machine code**.

- The object program can then be run (or **executed**) whenever desired.

In the earliest computers, programmers actually wrote programs in machine code, but assembler languages or instruction sets were soon developed to speed up programming. Today, assembler programming is used only where very efficient control over processor operations is needed. It requires knowledge of a particular computer's instruction set, however. Historically, most programs have been written in "higher-level" languages such as COBOL, FORTRAN, PL/I, and C. These languages are easier to learn and faster to write programs with than assembler language.

The program that processes the source code written in these languages is called a **compiler**. Like the assembler, a compiler takes higher-level language statements and reduces them to machine code.

A newer idea in program preparation and portability is the concept of a **virtual machine**. For example, using the **Java** programming language, language statements are compiled into a generic form of machine language known as **bytecode** that can be run by a virtual machine, a kind of theoretical machine that approximates most computer operations. The bytecode can then be sent to any computer platform that has previously downloaded or built in the Java virtual machine. The virtual machine is aware of the specific instruction lengths and other particularities of the platform and ensures that the Java bytecode can run.

Association for Computing Machinery

The Association for Computing Machinery (ACM), founded in 1947, is the largest and oldest international scientific and industrial computer society. Through its many Special Interest Groups, the ACM fosters research and communication in a broad range of computing areas.

Many of the Special Interest Groups publish their own journals or proceedings. There is a Usenet group at comp.org.acm.

ASSP

In computers, an ASSP (application-specific standard product) is a **semiconductor** device integrated circuit (**IC**) product that is dedicated to a specific **application** market and sold to more than one user (and thus, "standard"). The ASSP is marketed to multiple customers just as a general-purpose product is, but to a smaller number of customers since it is for a specific application. Like an **ASIC** (application-specific integrated circuit), the ASSP is for a special application, but it is sold to any number of companies. (An ASIC is designed and built to order for a specific company.)

An ASSP generally offers the same performance characteristics and has the same die size as an ASIC. According to a Dataquest study, 17% of all semiconductor products sold in 1999 were ASSPs; 83% were general-purpose. According to Dataquest's Jim Walker, the trend is toward more application-specific products.

asymmetric communications

For an example of asymmetric communications, see Asymmetric Digital Subscriber Line (**ADSL**).

In telecommunications, the term asymmetric (also asymmetrical or non-symmetrical) refers to any system in which the data speed or quantity differs in one direction as compared with the other direction, averaged over time. Asymmetrical data flow can, in some instances, make more efficient use of the available infrastructure than symmetrical data flow, in which the speed or quantity of data is the same in both directions, averaged over time.

Consider an Internet connection in which downstream data (from an Internet server to the subscriber) flows over a **broadband satellite downlink**, while upstream data (from the end user to the server) is sent over a **twisted-pair** telephone line. This is an example of asymmetric communications. The hardware for reception of satellite signals is simple, consisting of a small dish **antenna**, an amplifier/converter, and a modem. While the downstream data might flow at 1 **MBps** or more, upstream data is limited to 56 kpbs (often much less). In most Web browsing applications, this is a major improvement over a connection in which the upstream and downstream data both must flow through the twisted pair. This is because most of the bytes come downstream as relatively large graphics, sound, multimedia, and HTML files, while upstream data consists mainly of new content requests by the subscriber, which, in comparison, contain few bytes. In this environment, it would not make sense to supply the subscriber with the sophisticated hardware necessary for a broadband satellite uplink.

In some situations, asymmetric communications is not satisfactory. An example is two-way, full-motion video-conferencing, in which broadband data must flow in two directions between two end users. Another example is File Trasfer Protocol (**FTP**) applications in which the volume of upstream data is considerable. For communications of this type, broadband cable modem, optical fiber, or broadband wireless Internet access is available in some locations. At the time of this writing, symmetric broadband is not generally available outside of metropolitan areas.

Asymmetric Digital Subscriber Line

See "ADSL"

asynchronous transfer mode

See "ATM"

asynchronous

In general, asynchronous (pronounced ay-SIHN-kro-nuhs, from Greek *asyn-*, meaning "not with," and *chronos*, meaning "time") is an adjective describing objects or events that are not coordinated in time. In information technology, the term has several different usages.

1) In telecommunication signaling within a network or between networks, an asynchronous signal is one that is transmitted at a different clock rate than another signal. (**Plesiochronous** signals are almost but not quite in synchronization—and a method is used to adjust them—and **synchronous** signals are those that run at the same clock rate.

2) In computer programs, asynchronous operation means that a process operates independently of other processes, whereas synchronous operation means that the process runs only as a result of some other process being completed or handing off operation. A typical activity that might use a synchronous protocol would be a transmission of files from one point to another. As each transmission is received, a response is returned indicating success or the need to resend. Each successive transmission of data requires a response to the previous transmission before a new one can be initiated.

Synchronous program communication is contrasted with **asynchronous** program communication.

AT Attachment Packet Interface

See "ATAPI"

at sign

On the Internet, @ (pronounced "at" or "at sign" or "address sign") is the symbol in an **e-mail** address that separates the name of the user from the user's Internet address, as in this hypothetical e-mail address example: msmuffet@tuffet.org.

In business, @ is a symbol meaning "at" or "each." For example, it means "each" in "4 apples @ $.35 = $1.40." Perhaps because it was one of the standard characters designed into typewriters (usually with the upper shift key pressed), the @ was chosen for inclusion as one of the special characters in the **ASCII** set of characters that became standard for computer keyboards, programs, and online message transmission. In July 1972, as the specifications for the File Transfer Protocol (**FTP**) were being written, someone suggested including some e-mail programs written by Ray Tomlinson, an engineer at Bolt Beranek and Newman, chief contractor on **ARPANet** (Advanced Research Projects Agency Network), the precursor of the Internet. In their book, *Where Wizards Stay Up Late*, Katie Hafner and Matthew Lyon describe how the @ sign got there:

> Tomlinson...became better known for a brilliant (he called it obvious) decision he made while writing [the e-mail] programs. He needed a way to separate, in the e-mail address, the name of the user from the machine the user was on. How should that be denoted? He wanted a character that would not, under any circumstances, be found in the user's name. He looked down at the keyboard he was using, a Model 33 Teletype, which almost everyone else on the Net used, too. In addition to the letters and numerals there were about a dozen punctuation marks. "I got there first, so I got to choose any punctuation I wanted," Tomlinson said. "I chose the @ sign." The character also had the advantage of meaning "at" the designated institution. He had no idea he was creating an icon for the wired world.

ATA

ATA (Advanced Technology Attachment) is the official name that **American National Standards Institute** group X3T10 uses for what the computer industry calls **Integrated Drive Electronics** (IDE).

ATAPI

ATAPI (AT Attachment Packet Interface) is an interface between your computer and attached **CD-ROM** drives and tape backup drives. Most of today's PC computers use the standard **Integrated Drive Electronics** (IDE) interface to address hard disk drives. ATAPI provides the additional commands needed for controlling a CD-ROM player or tape backup so that your computer can use the IDE interface and controllers to control these relatively newer device types.

ATAPI is part of the Enhanced IDE (**EIDE**) interface (also known as *ATA*-2).

Athlon

Athlon, a popular **microprocessor** from AMD that is used in many personal computers, was the first processor to be shipped in a 1 **gigahertz** (one billion **clock speed**) version. Compaq and Gateway are among companies that will manufacture computers that include the 1 GHz Athlon. Athlon also comes in versions that have clock speeds somewhat below 1 GHz.

The second largest maker of microprocessors after Intel, AMD has gained on its rival in recent years. The Athlon achieved favorable press reviews for its speed and cost when compared to Intel's **Pentium 3**. Athlon has an **x86**-compatible processor architecture that comes with a fully **pipelining**, superscalar **floating point unit**, a 128 **kilobyte L1 and L2** that is built into the microprocessor chip, and a programmable **backside bus** to a **L1 and L2**. A notable feature is the system's 200 **MHz bus**. The Athlon chip uses AMD's aluminum 0.18-**micron** technology.

As the successor to AMD's K6 microprocessor, Athlon was previously called the K7.

ATL

See "Active Template Library"

ATM

ATM (asynchronous transfer mode) is a dedicated-connection switching technology that organizes digital data into 53-**byte cell** units and transmits them over a physical medium using digital signal technology. Individually, a cell is processed **asynchronously** relative to other related cells and is queued before being **multiplexed** over the transmission path.

Because ATM is designed to be easily implemented by hardware (rather than software), faster processing and **switch** speeds are possible. The prespecified bit rates are either 155.520 **Mbps** or 622.080 Mbps. Speeds on ATM networks can reach 10 **Gbps**. Along with Synchronous Optical Network (**SONET**) and several other technologies, ATM is a key component of broadband ISDN (**BISDN**).

ATM also stands for *automated teller machine*, a machine that bank customers use to make transactions without a human teller.

atom

An atom is a particle of matter that uniquely defines a chemical element. An atom consists of a central nucleus that is usually surrounded by one or more electrons. Each **electron** is negatively charged. The nucleus is positively charged, and contains one or more relatively heavy particles known as *protons* and *neutrons*.

A proton is positively charged. The number of protons in the nucleus of an atom is the *atomic number* for the chemical element. A proton has a rest mass, denoted m_p, of approximately 1.673 x 10^{-27} kilogram (kg). A neutron is electrically neutral and has a rest mass, denoted m_n, of approximately 1.675 x 10^{-27} kg. The mass of a proton or neutron increases when the particle attains extreme speed, for example in a cyclotron or linear accelerator.

An early model of the atom was developed by the physicist Ernest Rutherford in 1912. He was the first to suggest that atoms are like miniature solar systems, except that the attractive force is not caused by gravity, but by opposing electrical charges. In the so-called *Rutherford atom*, electrons orbit the nucleus in circular paths. Niels Bohr revised Rutherford's theory in 1913. In the *Bohr atom*, the negatively charged electrons orbit the nucleus at specific median distances. These distances are represented by spheres, called *shells*, surrounding the nucleus. Electrons can move from shell to shell. When an electron absorbs enough energy, it moves to a larger, or higher, shell. When it loses a certain amount of energy, it falls to a smaller, or lower, shell.

The total mass of an atom, including the protons, neutrons and electrons, is the *atomic mass* or *atomic weight*. Electrons contribute only a tiny part of this mass. For most practical purposes, the atomic weight can be thought of as the number of protons plus the number of neutrons. Because the number of neutrons in an atom can vary, there can be several different atomic weights for most elements.

Atoms having the same number of protons, but different numbers of neutrons, represent the same element, but are known as different *isotopes* of that element. The isotope for an element is specified by the sum of the number of protons and neutrons. Examples of different isotopes of an element are carbon 12 (the most common, non-radioactive isotope of carbon) and carbon 14 (a less common, radioactive isotope of carbon).

Protons and electrons have equal and opposite charge, and normally an atom has equal numbers of both. Thus, atoms are usually neutral. An *ion* is an atom with extra electrons or with a deficiency of electrons, resulting in its being electrically charged. An ion with extra electrons is negatively charged and is called an *anion*; an ion deficient in electrons is positively charged and is called a *cation*.

atomic

In ancient philosophy, an atom was the ultimate unit of matter on which more complex views of material reality were based. In computer programming, atomic describes a unitary action or object that is essentially indivisible, unchangeable, whole, and irreducible. Here are some usages:

1) In **Structured Query Language**, an atomic function is one that will either complete or return to its original state if a power interruption or an abnormal end occurs.

2) In some **UNIX**-base operating systems, an atomic operation is one in which no change can take place in the time between the setting of a mask and the receiving of a signal to change the mask.

3) In some programming languages, including Lisp, an *atom* is the basic unit of executable code or data.

atomic force microscopy

Atomic force microscopy (AFM) is a technique for analyzing the surface of a rigid material all the way down to the level of the **atom**. AFM uses a mechanical probe to magnify surface features up to 100,000,000 times, and it produces 3-D images of the surface.

The technique is derived from a related technology, called scanning tunneling microscopy (STM). The difference is that AFM does not require the sample to conduct electricity, whereas STM does. AFM also works in regular room temperatures, while STM requires special temperature and other conditions.

AFM is being used to understand materials problems in many areas, including data storage, telecommunications, biomedicine, chemistry, and aerospace. In data storage, it is helping researchers to "force" a disk to have a higher capacity. Today's magnetic storage devices typically have a capacity limit of between 20 and 50 gigabits (billions of bits) per square inch of storage medium. Researchers are looking into AFM to help raise read and write densities to between 40 gigabits and 300 gigabits per square inch. No one has yet commercialized AFM technology for this purpose, but IBM and others are actively pursuing it.

atomicity, consistency, isolation, and durability

See "ACID"

ATSC

See "Advanced Television Systems Committee"

attachment unit interface

See "AUI"

attempt

In a telecommunications system, an attempt is a user request to get connected to the system or to initiate a call, whether or not the connection is made or the call is initiated.

attenuation

Attenuation is a general term that refers to any reduction in the strength of a **signal**. Attenuation occurs with any type of signal, whether **digital** or **analog**. Sometimes called *loss*, attenuation is a natural consequence of signal transmission over long distances. The extent of attenuation is usually expressed in units called *decibels*.

If P_s is the signal power at the transmitting end (source) of a communications circuit and P_d is the signal power at the receiving end (destination), then $P_s > P_d$. The power attenuation A_p in decibels is given by the formula:

$A_p = 10 \log_{10}(P_s/P_d)$

Attenuation can also be expressed in terms of voltage. If A_v is the voltage attenuation in decibels, V_s is the source signal voltage, and V_d is the destination signal voltage, then:

$A_v = 20 \log_{10}(V_s/V_d)$

In conventional and fiberoptic cables, attenuation is specified in terms of the number of decibels per foot, 1,000 feet, kilometer, or mile. The less the attenuation per unit distance, the more efficient the cable. When it is necessary to transmit signals over long distances via cable, one or more **repeaters** can be inserted along the length of the cable. The repeaters boost the signal strength to overcome attenuation. This greatly increases the maximum attainable range of communication.

attosecond

(This definition follows U.S. usage in which a billion is a thousand million and a trillion is a 1 followed by 12 zeros.)

An attosecond is one quintillionth (10^{-18}) of a **second** and is a term used in **photon** research.

For comparison, a millisecond (ms or msec) is one thousandth of a second and is commonly used in measuring the time to read to or write from a **hard disk** or a **CD-ROM** player or to measure **packet** travel time on the Internet.

A microsecond (μs or Greek letter mu plus s) is one millionth (10^{-6}) of a second.

A nanosecond (ns or nsec) is one billionth (10^{-9}) of a second and is a common measurement of read or write access time to random access memory (**RAM**).

A picosecond is one trillionth (10^{-12}) of a second, or one millionth of a microsecond.

A femtosecond is one millionth of a nanosecond or 10^{-15} of a second and is a measurement sometimes used in **laser** technology.

attribute

In general, an attribute is a property or characteristic. Color, for example, is an attribute of your hair. In using or programming computers, an attribute is a changeable property or characteristic of some component of a program that can be set to different values.

In the Hypertext Markup Language (**HTML**), an attribute is a characteristic of a page element, such as a font. An HTML user can set font attributes, such as size and color, to different values. In some programming languages, such as **PowerBuilder** PowerScript, an attribute is a property of an **object** or may be considered a container for the property of the object. For example, color might be an attribute of a text object, containing the value of "red."

In a database management system (**DBMS**), an attribute may describe a component of the database, such as a table or a **field**, or may be used itself as another term for a field.

In the **DOS** operating system, file properties, such as "read-only" or "visible," are called file attributes.

ATU-R

An ATU-R (ADSL Terminal Unit—Remote), sometimes called an "ADSL modem," is a hardware unit that is installed in any computer that uses a telephone company connection with Asymmetric Digital Subscriber Line (**ADSL**) service. The ATU-R connects to an **Ethernet** network interface card (**NIC**) in the computer and, on the other side, to a telephone jack in the home or business. Ideally (for less interference), the telephone jack hooks up to a new wire that goes to a signal **splitter** that the telephone company installs at the telephone company demarcation point (the place where the outside phone company wire or wires connect to the network of phone lines within the customer's building). The splitter divides the signal into low frequencies for voice and high frequencies for data.

ATV

ATV (Advanced Television) is the name given by the U.S. Federal Communications Commission to digital TV (**DTV**), the use of digital transmission of video and audio information on broadcast channels and **cable TV**. ATV includes both high-definition television (**HDTV**), a format

for digital video compression, transmission, and presentation and also the creation of additional channels on the current **analog** 6 **MHz** channel.

For additional information, see **HDTV**.

ATX

ATX is an industry-wide **open** specification for a desktop computer's **motherboard**. The most current version (December, 1996) is Specification 2.0.

ATX improves the motherboard design by taking the small AT motherboard that has been an industry standard and rotating by 90 degrees the layout of the **microprocessor** and expansion **slot**s. This allows space for more full-length add-in **card**s. A double-height aperture is specified for the rear of the chassis, allowing more possible I/O arrangements for a variety of devices such as TV input and output, LAN connection, and so forth. The new layout is also intended to be less costly to manufacture. Fewer cables will be needed. The power supply has a side-mounted fan, allowing direct cooling of the processor and cards, making a secondary fan unnecessary. Version 2.0 incorporates improvements suggested by chassis and power supply vendors.

Almost all major computer manufacturers, including IBM, Compaq, and Apple build desktops with ATX motherboards. IBM is using ATX in both Intel and PowerPC platforms.

audible ring

In a telephone system, an audible ring is the tone that is returned from the called party's switching device and heard by the caller. This tone indicates to the caller that the desired party is being rung.

audio

Audio is sound within the acoustic range available to humans. An audio frequency (**AF**) is an electrical alternating current within the 20 to 20,000 **hertz** (cycles per second) range that can be used to produce acoustic sound. In computers, audio is the sound system that comes with or can be added to a computer. An audio **card** contains a special built-in processor and memory for processing audio files and sending them to *speakers* in the computer. An audio file is a record of captured sound that can be played back. Sound is a sequence of natural **analog** signals that are converted to **digital** signals by the audio card, using a microchip called an analog-to-digital converter (**ADC**). When sound is played, the digital signals are sent to the speakers where they are converted back to analog signals that generate varied sound.

Audio files are usually **compressed** for storage or faster transmission. Audio files can be sent in short stand-alone segments—for example, as files in the **Wave file** format. In order for users to receive sound in real-time for a multimedia effect, listening to music, or in order to take part

in an audio or video conference, sound must be delivered as **streaming sound**. More advanced audio cards support **wavetable**, or precaptured tables of sound. The most popular audio file format today is **MP3** (MPEG-1 Audio Layer-3).

Audio Engineers Society/European Broadcasting Union

AES/EBU (Audio Engineering Society/European Broadcasting Union) is the name of a **digital audio** transfer standard. The AES and EBU developed the specifications for the standard.

The AES/EBU digital interface is usually implemented using 3-**pin** XLR connectors, the same type connector used in a professional microphone. One cable carries both left- and right-channel audio data to the receiving device. AES/EBU is an alternative to the **S/PDIF** standard.

audio frequency

See "AF"

audio noise

Also see **noise**.

In **audio**, noise is generally any unpleasant sound and, more technically, any unwanted sound that is unintentionally added to a desired sound. Ambient sound itself is a series of changes in air pressure transmitted in waves from the sound source to anyone with the sensory apparatus to detect the waves (human beings and other animals with ears, for example). Sound waves are expressed as a series of **analog** sine waves. The combination and blend of these waves gives sounds their individual characteristics, making them pleasant or unpleasant to listen to. Some sounds are combination of waves that are related to each other, as in the case of a pitched instrument that transmits one dominant frequency of sound wave and additional frequencies that enhance the fundamental or dominant frequency. An oboe is an example of a pitched instrument. Other sounds are made from a grouping of tightly spaced waves that do not have a specific fundamental frequency that is dominant over the others. A snare drum is an example.

In recording sound, noise is often present on analog tape or low-fidelity digital recordings. The standard audio cassette includes a layer of hiss on every recording. When doing digital recording, the conversion of a sound file from 16-bit to 8-bit adds a layer of noise.

White noise is a sound that contains every frequency within the range of human hearing (generally from 20 **hertz** to 20 **kHz**) in equal amounts. Most people perceive this sound as having more high-frequency content than low, but this is not the case. This perception occurs because each successive octave has twice as many frequencies as the one preceding it.

For example, from 100 Hz to 200 Hz, there are one hundred discrete frequencies. In the next octave (from 200 Hz to 400 Hz), there are two hundred frequencies.

White noise can be generated on a sound synthesizer. Sound designers can use this sound, with some processing and filtering, to create a multitude of effects such as wind, surf, space whooshes, and rumbles.

Pink noise is a variant of white noise. Pink noise is white noise that has been filtered to reduce the volume at each octave. This is done to compensate for the increase in the number of frequencies per octave. Each octave is reduced by 6 **decibel**s, resulting in a noise sound wave that has equal energy at every octave.

Audio Visual Interleaved file

See "AVI file"

Audio/Modem Riser

See "AMR"

audio/video

See "AV"

audit trail

In accounting, an audit trail is the sequence of paperwork that validates or invalidates accounting entries. In computing, the term is also used for an electronic or paper log used to track computer activity. For example, a corporate employee might have access to a section of a network in a corporation such as billing but be unauthorized to access all other sections. If that employee attempts to access an unauthorized section by typing in passwords, this improper activity is recorded in the audit trail.

Audit trails are used to record customer activity in e-commerce. The customer's initial contact is recorded in an audit trail as well as each subsequent action such as payment and delivery of the product or service. The customer's audit trail is then used to respond properly to any inquiries or complaints. A company might also use an audit trail to provide a basis for account reconciliation, to provide a historical report to plan and support budgets, and to provide a record of sales in case of a tax audit.

Audit trails are also used to investigate cybercrimes. In order for investigators to expose a hacker's identity, they can follow the trail the hacker left in cyberspace. Sometimes hackers unknowingly provide audit trails through their Internet service providers' activity logs or through chat room logs.

auditor

In Web advertising, this usually means a third-party company that audits the number of visitors to or **impression** sent from a Web site during some time period. When you try to sell advertising, having a third-party auditor gives the prospect more confidence in your audience numbers.

AUI

The AUI (attachment unit interface) is the 15-**pin** physical connector interface between a computer's network interface card (**NIC**) and an **Ethernet** cable. On **10Base-5** ("thicknet") Ethernet, a short cable is used to connect the AUI on the computer with a transceiver on the main cable. In **10Base-2** or "thinnet" Ethernet networks, the NIC connects directly to the Ethernet coaxial cable at the back of the computer.

IEEE 802.3, the Ethernet standard, defines the AUI 15-pin physical layer interface. This interface is also called a DB-15 interface or a DIX interface (DIX refers to the three major companies who helped standardize Ethernet: Digital Equipment Corporation, Intel, and Xerox).

AUP

See "acceptable use policy"

authentication

Authentication is the process of determining whether someone or something is, in fact, who or what it is declared to be. In private and public computer networks (including the Internet), authentication is commonly done through the use of **logon** passwords. Knowledge of the password is assumed to guarantee that the user is authentic. Each user registers initially (or is registered by someone else), using an assigned or self-declared password. On each subsequent use, the user must know and use the previously declared password. The weakness in this system for transactions that are significant (such as the exchange of money) is that passwords can often be stolen, accidentally revealed, or forgotten.

For this reason, Internet business and many other transactions require a more stringent authentication process. The use of **digital certificate**s issued and verified by a Certificate Authority (**CA**) as part of a **public key infrastructure** is considered likely to become the standard way to perform authentication on the Internet.

Logically, authentication precedes **authorization** (although they may often seem to be combined).

authentication, authorization, and accounting

Authentication, authorization, and accounting (AAA) is a term for a framework for intelligently controlling **access** to computer resources, enforcing policies, auditing usage, and providing the information necessary to bill for services. These combined processes are considered important for effective network management and security.

Authentication provides a way of identifying a user, typically by having the user enter a valid user name and valid password before access is granted. The process of authentication is based on each user having a unique set of criteria for gaining access. The AAA server compares a user's authentication credentials with other user credentials stored in a database. If the credentials match, the user is granted access to the network. If the credentials are at variance, authentication fails and network access is denied.

Following authentication, a user must gain **authorization** for doing certain tasks. After logging into a system, for instance, the user may try to issue commands. The authorization process determines whether the user has the authority to issue such commands. Simply put, authorization is the process of enforcing policies: determining what types or qualities of activities, resources, or services a user is permitted. Usually, authorization occurs within the context of authentication. Once you have authenticated a user, they may be authorized for different types of access or activity.

The final plank in the AAA framework is accounting, which measures the resources a user consumes during access. This can include the amount of system time or the amount of data a user has sent and/or received during a session. Accounting is carried out by logging of session statistics and usage information and is used for authorization control, billing, trend analysis, resource utilization, and capacity planning activities.

Authentication, authorization, and accounting services are often provided by a dedicated **AAA server**, a program that performs these functions. A current standard by which network access servers interface with the AAA server is the Remote Authentication Dial-In User Service (**RADIUS**).

authorization

Authorization is the process of giving someone permission to do or have something. In multi-user computer systems, a system administrator defines for the system which users are allowed **access** to the system and what privileges of use (such as access to which file directories, hours of access, amount of allocated storage space, and so forth). Assuming that someone has logged in to a computer **operating system** or **application**, the system or application may want to identify what resources the user can be given during this session. Thus, authorization is sometimes seen as both the

preliminary setting up of permissions by a system adminstrator and the actual checking of the permission values that have been set up when a user is getting access.

Logically, authorization is preceded by **authentication**.

authorized program analysis report

An APAR (authorized program analysis report) is a term used in IBM for a description of a problem with an IBM program that is formally tracked until a solution is provided. An APAR is created or "opened" after a customer (or sometimes IBM itself) discovers a problem that IBM determines is due to a bug in its code. The APAR is given a unique number for tracking and a target date for solution. When the support group that maintains the code solves the problem, it develops a *program temporary fix (PTF)* that, when applied, possibly with a **SuperZap**, will temporarily solve the problem for the customers that may be affected. The PTF will "close" the APAR. PTFs can be applied individually but are usually made available as part of a *fix package* that includes a number of PTFs. Meanwhile, the PTFs are provided to the development group that is working on the next product release. The developers may or may not use the PTFs (since these are temporary fixes), but will determine and design the correct problem solution to incorporate in the next product release.

autoexec.bat

AUTOEXEC.BAT is a file containing **Disk Operating System command**s that are **executable** when the computer is **boot**ed (started). The commands in AUTOEXEC.BAT tell the **operating system** which application programs are to be automatically started, how memory is to be managed, and initialize other settings. Each command in AUTOEXEC.BAT could be typed in manually after the computer is started, but that would take too long. The AUTOEXEC.BAT file is, in fact, a command **script** that is written beforehand so that it can be automatically executed when the operating system is started. The BAT suffix stands for **batch**, indicating that this is a file containing a sequence of commands entered from a file rather than interactively by a user.

automagically

Automagically is a term used when the user either doesn't want to go into the technical details of something or doesn't know the details but does know what the end result has to be. The term is sometimes used in planning and design discussions and trade show demonstrations. For example, one might say:

> "Our new CD-ROM will put a handy button on your computer desktop automagically. You won't even have to think about it."

The term is a playful variation of *automatically*.

Automated Clearing House

Automated Clearing House (ACH) is a secure payment transfer system that connects all U.S. financial institutions. The ACH network acts as the central clearing facility for all Electronic Fund Transfer (**EFT**) transactions that occur nationwide, representing a crucial link in the national banking system. It is here that payments linger in something akin to a holding pattern while awaiting clearance for their final banking destination. Scores of financial institutions transmit or receive ACH entries through ACH operators such as the American Clearing House Association, the Federal Reserve, the Electronic Payments Network, and Visa.

In 1998, the network processed nearly 5.3 billion ACH transactions with a total value of more than $16 trillion.

Automatic Call Distributor

An Automatic Call Distributor (ACD) is a telephone facility that manages incoming calls and handles them based on the number called and an associated **database** of handling instructions. Many companies offering sales and service support use ACDs to validate callers, make outgoing responses or calls, forward calls to the right party, allow callers to record messages, gather usage statistics, balance the use of phone lines, and provide other services.

ACDs often provide some form of Automatic Customer/Caller Identification (**ACIS**) such as that provided by Direct Inward Dialing (**DID**), Dialed Number Identification Service (**DNIS**), or Automatic Number Identification (**ANI**).

Automatic Coin Telephone System

Automatic Coin Telephone System (ACTS) is a public coin-operated telephone service that completes a variety of phone calls, times the calls, and collects payment without the aid of an operator.

automatic language translation

Automatic language translation is the use of a computer program to translate input text from one national language to another while maintaining the original document format. Yahoo and some other sites offer what is sometimes called **instant translation** using such a tool. Since language is heavily dependent on context and connoted as well as denoted meaning, a program needs to have access to such context as well as the ability to use it. Since providing enough context is difficult, automatic language translation thus far seems to be successful only in limited and well-understood situations and as a first time-saving step toward translation (or "post-editing") by a human being.

Automatic Number Identification

See "ANI"

automatic vehicle locator

An automatic vehicle locator (AVL) is a device that makes use of the Global Positioning System (**GPS**) to enable a business or agency to remotely track the location of its vehicle fleet by using the Internet. These devices combine GPS technology, cellular communications, street-level mapping, and an intuitive user interface, with the ostensible goal of improving fleet management and customer service. For example, a company using an AVL system is able to pinpoint the longitude, latitude, ground speed, and course direction of a given vehicle. The vehicle's location can be quickly found and it could be rerouted to provide timely delivery to a nearby customer. AVL systems also enable companies to structure delivery routes more efficiently by compiling a database of vehicle information, including location of customers in relation to established delivery routes.

AVL systems generally include a network of vehicles that are equipped with a mobile radio receiver, a GPS receiver, a GPS modem, and a GPS antenna. This network connects with a base radio consisting of a PC computer station as well as a GPS receiver and interface. GPS uses interactive maps rather than static map images on the Web. This means users can perform conventional GPS functions such as zoom, pan, identify and queries.

AVL systems can be used to increase the accountability of field personnel and boost the efficiency of a company's dispatching procedure. Dispatchers can get a real-time snapshot of driver adherence to a route, provide customers with an estimated time of arrival, and communicate directly with drivers. Public safety agencies, such as police departments or fire departments, can use AVL technology to improve response times by being able to dispatch the closest vehicles for emergencies.

Most AVL suppliers have created products that don't require dedicated servers and require minimal training of dispatchers. AVL systems use mouse clicks instead of keystrokes to page a single vehicle, a designated group of vehicles or an entire fleet. The Aertrax system, for example, operates without expensive receivers or other equipment. It can be operated with a PC or desktop that connects to the Internet. Aertrax includes a completely self-contained unit that uses a minimal amount of power from the vehicle in which it is installed. This unit transmits GPS location data, either on a regularly timed basis or in response to a command. This data is then converted into mapping that is instantly available via the Internet.

In Corpus Christi, Texas, a regional transit authority is collaborating with Texas AM University-Corpus Christi to develop an AVL system that not only would enable it to track bus locations but also enable automated ridership data collection and dynamic routing. Until recently, the availability of GPS to the commercial and civil sectors had been controlled by the U.S. Department of Defense through

an internationally imposed degradation standard known as Selective Availability. This standard degraded the accuracy of civilian GPS so that the highest degree of accuracy was reserved for the military. SA restrictions have since been lifted, enabling GPS to be dispersed for commercial application.

autonomous robot

See "robot"

autonomous system

On the Internet, an autonomous system (AS) is the unit of **router** policy, either a single network or a group of **network** that is controlled by a common network administrator (or group of administrators) on behalf of a single administrative entity (such as a university, a business enterprise, or a business division). An autonomous system is also sometimes referred to as a routing **domain**. An autonomous system is assigned a globally unique number, sometimes called an Autonomous System Number (ASN).

Networks within an autonomous system communicate routing information to each other using an **Interior Gateway Protocol** (IGP). An autonomous system shares routing information with other autonomous systems using the **Border Gateway Protocol** (BGP). Previously, the **Exterior Gateway Protocol** (EGP) was used. In the future, the BGP is expected to be replaced with the **OSI** Inter-Domain Routing Protocol (IDRP).

The Internet's protocol guideline for autonomous systems, after offering a definition similar to the one above, provides a more technical definition as follows:

> An AS is a connected group of one or more **Internet Protocol** prefixes run by one or more network operators which has a SINGLE and CLEARLY DEFINED routing policy.

autoresponder

An autoresponder is a computer program that automatically returns a prewritten message to anyone who submits **e-mail** to a particular Internet address, whether an individual or a Web site. Autoresponders are widely used by Web sites for the purpose of responding to visitor comments and suggestions in a preliminary way and, in cases where traffic is heavy, as the sole way to communicate with user inquiries.

Publishers of **ezine** and other online e-mail newsletters typically use an autoresponder to respond to people who subscribe or cancel their subscriptions.

auxiliary storage

Auxiliary storage is all addressable data **storage** that is not currently in a computer's **main storage** or **memory**. Synonyms are **external storage** and **secondary storage**.

AV

AV, an abbreviation for audio/video, is frequently used as a generic term for the audio and video components and capabilities in home entertainment system and related product descriptions and reviews.

availability

1) In a telephone **circuit**, availability is the ratio between the time during which the circuit is operational and elapsed time.

2) In a network switching system, availability is the accessibility of input and output **port**s.

avatar

In **3D** or **virtual reality** games and in some **chat** forums on the Web, your avatar is the visual "handle" or display appearance you use to represent yourself. On Worlds Chat and similar sites, you can be a unicorn, a bluebird, or any kind of creature or object that seems right.

In the Hindu religion, an avatar is an incarnation of a deity; hence, an embodiment or manifestation of an idea or greater reality.

average bouncing busy hour

In designing and assessing **networks**, one approach is to measure the average bouncing busy hour (ABBH) traffic in various network **trunks** or trunk groups of the network. The ABBH is the traffic load on a switching system during the peak (most busy) hour of each day, over a certain period, typically one week, then averaged for the time period.

Another traditional index to peak traffic is the **10-high-day busy period**.

AVI file

An AVI (Audio Video Interleaved) file is a sound and motion picture file that conforms to the Microsoft Windows Resource Interchange File Format (RIFF) specification. AVI files (which end with an .avi extension) require a special player that may be included with your Web browser or may require downloading.

Avogadro Constant

See "mole per meter cubed"

AWG

See "American Wire Gauge"

awk

awk (also written as Awk and AWK) is a utility that enables a programmer to write tiny but effective programs in the form of statements that define text patterns that are to be searched for in each line of a document and the action that is to be taken when a match is found within a line. awk comes with most **UNIX**-based operating systems such as **Linux**, and also with some other operating systems, such as Windows 95/98/NT.

An awk program is made up of patterns and actions to be performed when a pattern match is found. awk scans input lines sequentially and examines each one to determine whether it contains a pattern matching one specified by the user. When the matching pattern is found, awk carries out the instructions in the program. For example, awk could scan text for a critical portion and reformat the text contained in it according to the user's command. If no pattern is specified, the program will carry out the command on all of the input data.

awk breaks each line into fields, which are groups of characters with spaces acting as separators so that a word, for example, would be a field. A string is encased in backslashes and actions to be performed are encased in curly brackets. The lines are numbered in order of their appearance, with "0" referring to the entire line. "$" is the symbol for field. So, for example, to search for a line containing the word "nutmeg," and to print each line in which the word occurs, the awk program would consist of:

/nutmeg/ { print $0 }.

The name "awk" is derived from the names of its three developers: Alfred Aho, Peter Weinberger, and Brian Kernighan. It was developed from **grep**, **C**, and sed syntax, a combination that allows complex programs to be developed quickly. awk is frequently used for prototyping. Versions of awk include **Portable Operating System Interface** awk, New awk (Nawk) and **GNU** awk (Gawk). The **Practical Extraction and Reporting Language** language was developed as an improved version of awk, with which Perl is **backward compatible**.

AWT

See "Abstract Window Toolkit"

B

See "susceptance"

B channel

See "B-channel"

B2B

On the Internet, B2B (business-to-business), also known as e-biz, is the exchange of products, services, or information between businesses rather than between businesses and consumers. Although early interest centered on the growth of retailing on the Internet (sometimes called **e-tailing**), forecasts are that B2B revenue will far exceed business-to-consumers (B2C) revenue in the near future. According to studies published in early 2000, the money volume of B2B exceeds that of e-tailing by 10 to 1. Over the next five years, B2B is expected to have a compound annual growth of 41%. The Gartner Group estimates B2B revenue worldwide to be $7.29 trillion dollars by 2004. In early 2000, the volume of investment in B2B by venture capitalists was reported to be accelerating sharply although profitable B2B sites were not yet easy to find.

B2B Web sites can be sorted into:

- **Company Web sites**, since the target audience for many company Web sites is other companies and their employees. Company sites can be thought of as round-the-clock mini-trade exhibits. Sometimes a company Web site serves as the entrance to an exclusive **extranet** available only to customers or registered site users. Some company Web sites sell directly from the site, effectively e-tailing to other businesses.

- **Product supply and procurement exchanges**, where a company purchasing agent can shop for supplies from vendors, request proposals, and, in some cases, bid to make a purchase at a desired price. Sometimes referred to as **e-procurement** sites, some serve a range of industries and others focus on a niche market.

- **Specialized or vertical industry portals** which provide a "subWeb" of information, product listings, discussion groups, and other features. These vertical **portal** sites have a broader purpose than the procurement sites (although they may also support buying and selling).

- **Brokering sites** that act as an intermediary between someone wanting a product or service and potential providers. Equipment leasing is an example.

- **Information sites** (sometimes known as **infomediary**), which provide information about a particular industry for its companies and their employees. These include specialized search sites and trade and industry standards organization sites. Many B2B sites may seem to fall into more than one of these groups. Models for B2B sites are still evolving.

Another type of B2B enterprise is software for building B2B Web sites, including site building tools and templates, **database**, and methodologies as well as transaction software.

B2B is **e-commerce** between businesses. An earlier and much more limited kind of online B2B prior to the Internet was Electronic Data Interchange (**EDI**), which is still widely used.

B2C

B2C is short for *business-to-consumer*, or the retailing part of e-commerce on the Internet. It is often contrasted to **B2B** or *business-to-business*.

B2E

B2E is business-to-employee, an approach in which the focus is the employee, rather than the consumer (as it is in business-to-consumer, or **B2C**) or other businesses (as it is in business-to-business, or **B2B**). The B2E approach grew out of the ongoing shortage of information technology (**IT**) workers. In a broad sense, B2E encompasses everything that businesses do to attract and retain well-qualified staff in a competitive market, such as aggressive recruiting tactics, benefits, education opportunities, flexible hours, bonuses, and employee empowerment strategies.

More specifically, the term "B2E" is frequently used to refer to the B2E portal (sometimes called a *people portal*), which is a customized **home page** or **desktop** for everyone within an organization. The B2E portal is sometimes considered to be synonymous with an **intranet**, but it differs in its focus on the employee's desires. The intranet's focus is the organization; the B2E portal focus is the individual. The B2E portal is designed to include not only everything that an employee might hope to find on an intranet (such as a corporate directory, or customer support information), but also any personal information and links that the employee might want (such as stocks information, or even games). The intention is to increase not only efficiency, but also employee satisfaction and a sense of community within the organization.

A B2E portal has three distinguishing characteristics:

- A single point of entry: one **URL** for everyone within an organization.

- A mixture of organization-specific and employee-defined components.

- The potential to be highly customized and easily altered to suit the particular employee.

Corporations may develop their own portals or they may rely on the services of any of the large and growing number of B2E portal developers.

B2G

On the Internet, B2G is business-to-government (a variation of the term **B2B** or business-to-business), the concept that businesses and government agencies can use central Web sites to exchange information and do business with each other more efficiently than they usually can off the Web. For example, a Web site offering B2G services could provide businesses with a single place to locate applications and tax forms for one or more levels of governent (city, state or province, country, and so forth); provide the ability to send in filled-out forms and payments; update corporate information; request answers to specific questions; and so forth. B2G may also include **e-procurement** services, in which businesses learn about the purchasing needs of agencies and agencies request proposal responses. B2G may also support the idea of a **virtual workplace** in which a business and an agency could coordinate the work on a contracted project by sharing a common site to coordinate online meetings, review plans, and manage progress. B2G may also include the rental of online applications and databases designed especially for use by government agencies.

According to the Gartner Group, B2G revenue is expected to grow from $1.5 billion in 2000 to $6.2 billion in 2005. B2G is sometimes called *e-government*.

B8ZS

B8ZS (bipolar 8-zero substitution, also called *binary 8-zero substitution*, *clear channel*, and *clear 64*) is an encoding method used on **T1** circuits that inserts two successive ones of the same **voltage**—referred to as a **bipolar** *violation*—into a signal whenever eight consecutive zeros are transmitted. The device receiving the signal interprets the bipolar violation as a timing mark, which keeps the transmitting and receiving devices synchronized. Ordinarily, when successive ones are transmitted, one has a positive voltage and the other has a negative voltage.

B8ZS is based on an older encoding method called alternate mark inversion (**AMI**). AMI is used with Dataphone Digital Service, the oldest data service still in use that uses 64 **Kbps channel**s. AMI, however, requires the use of 8 Kbps of the 64 Kbps of each channel to maintain synchronization. In a T1

circuit, there are 24 channels. This loss adds up to 192 Kbps, which means that in reality only 56 Kbps is available for data transmission. B8ZS uses bipolar violations to synchronize devices, a solution that does not require the use of extra bits, which means a T1 circuit using B8ZS can use the full 64 Kbps for each channel for data. B8ZS is not compatible with older AMI equipment.

T1 technology is used in the United States and Japan. In Europe, a comparable technology called **E1** provides 32 channels instead of 24 and uses an encoding scheme called high-density bipolar 3 (HDB3) instead of B8ZS.

Babbage

See "Charles Babbage"

Back Orifice

Back Orifice is a **rootkit** program designed for the purpose of exposing the security deficiencies of Microsoft's Windows **operating system**s. The program's name is inspired by the name of Microsoft's BackOffice product. Created by a group of **hacker**s called the Cult of the Dead Cow, Back Orifice allows someone at one computer to control everything on another, remote computer running Windows 95 or later. Back Orifice can **sniff** passwords, record keystrokes, access a desktop's file system and more, while remaining undetected.

Back Orifice is provided free as an **open source** program. It can then be delivered to unsuspecting users as a **Trojan horse** for hacking purposes, or used as a networked remote administration tool.

Back Orifice 2000 (BO2K) allows access to Windows NT and 2000, in addition to 95 and 98. BO2K has the same capabilities as Back Orifice, plus it uses cryptography for secure network administration and features extended plugin architecture for flexibility.

backbone

A backbone is a larger transmission line that carries data gathered from smaller lines that interconnect with it.

1) At the local level, a backbone is a line or set of lines that local area networks connect to for a wide area network connection or within a local area network to span distances efficiently (for example, between buildings).

2) On the Internet or other wide area network, a backbone is a set of paths that local or regional networks connect to for long-distance interconnection. The connection points are known as network *nodes* or telecommunication data switching exchanges (DSEs).

back-end

Front-end and back-end are terms used to characterize program interfaces and services relative to the initial user of these interfaces and services. (The "user" may be a human

being or a program.) A "front-end" **application** is one that application users interact with directly. A "back-end" application or program serves indirectly in support of the front-end services, usually by being closer to the required resource or having the capability to communicate with the required resource. The back-end application may interact directly with the front-end or, perhaps more typically, is a program called from an intermediate program that mediates front-end and back-end activities.

For example, the Telephone Application Program Interface (**TAPI**) is sometimes referred to as a front-end interface for telephone services. A program's TAPI requests are mapped by Microsoft's TAPI Dynamic Link Library programs (an intermediate set of programs) to a "back-end" program or **driver** that makes the more detailed series of requests to the telephone hardware in the computer.

As another example, a front-end application might interface directly with users and forward requests to a remotely-located back-end program in another computer to get requested data or perform a requested service. Relative to the **client/server** computing model, a front-end is likely to be a client and a back-end to be a server.

backhaul

Backhaul, a term probably derived from the trucking industry, has several usages in information technology.

1) In **satellite** communication, backhaul is used to mean getting data to a point from which it can be distributed over a network. For example, to deliver a live television program from Chicago to authorized DirecPC satellite terminals around the country, the video signals would have to be backhauled by some means (by **optical fiber** cable or by another satellite system) to the Hughes DirecPC facility in Germantown, Maryland. From there, it would be *uplinked* to the Galaxy IV satellite from which DirecPC users could view the broadcast (receive it in a downlink from the satellite at their individual terminals). Backhauling is also used to get non-live audio and video material to distribution points at the major broadcast news organizations for broadcast in the evening or ongoing news.

2) Manufacturers of network switching equipment use the term to mean "getting data to the network **backbone**" (which is similar to its use in the satellite communication industry). For example, Ascend uses the term to describe how its MAX 2000 switch can be used to interconnect data from a backhaul T-1 line on which mobile and remote office users are connected to an Internet service provider and the backbone of the Internet.

3) Backhauling is sending network data over an out-of-the-way route (including taking it farther than its destination) in order to get the data there sooner or because it costs less. This kind of backhauling involves understanding changing network conditions and economics.

4) Backhauling may sometimes be used to mean the use of the *back channel* on a bidirectional communications line.

backlink

In **Hyper-G** and possibly other **hypertext** systems, a backlink is a link back to the page or one of the pages that currently link to the page you're using. Backlinks are already supported to some extent in the present Web system. Using JavaScript or a similar technique, you can add a button to your page that, when clicked, results in a request to the Alta Vista search engine to locate all the Web sites that link to your page (that is, to your home page backlinks).

Incidentally, you don't have to create a button or put this information on a page. You may just want to find out how many people on the Web have linked to your home page. To do this, go to Alta Vista and enter a search for: link:http://whatis.com
Substitute your own home page address for "whatis.com". Alta Vista will tell you how many sites link to you and return the list so that you can find out which sites link to you. (Note that the Alta Vista list provides only those links to your site that they have currently indexed.)

backplane

A backplane is an electronic circuit board containing circuitry and sockets into which additional electronic devices on other circuit boards or **card**s can be plugged; in a computer, generally synonymous with or part of the **motherboard**.

back-pressure sensor

A back-pressure sensor is a **transducer** that detects and measures the instantaneous torque that a **robot** motor applies. The sensor produces a variable signal, usually a **voltage**, that changes in a linear manner as the torque varies.

When a robot motor operates, it encounters mechanical resistance. This resistance might depend on lifted mass, mechanical friction against a surface or within a system, or the opposition to applied force caused by electromagnetic interaction (as in an electric generator). Torque is the turning force that a robot motor delivers. It is important that a robot motor provide enough torque to overcome the resistance in external systems, but excessive torque can be destructive.

A robot motor produces a measurable back pressure that depends on the applied torque. The greater the torque, the greater the back pressure, and the greater the output of the back-pressure sensor. This output, called the back signal or back voltage, can be used in a feedback loop to reduce the torque applied by the motor. The loop configuration acts as a force limiter that minimizes the possibility of damage to objects handled by a robotic end effector. The force limiter can also reduce the chance of injury to personnel working around the robot.

Also see **end effector** and **robotics**.

backside bus

In a personal computer with an Intel **processor chipset** that includes a Dual Independent Bus (DIB), the frontside **bus** is the data path and physical interface between the processor and the main memory (**RAM**). The backside bus is the data path and physical interface between the processor and the **L1 and L2** memory. Both the frontside bus and the backside bus can be in use at the same time, meaning that the processor gets more done in a given number of pulses per second (see **clock speed**).

Prior to Intel's **Pentium** Pro processor, both the L2 cache and RAM were accessed using the same bus, creating an occasional bottleneck and reducing the overall **throughput** of the computer. Beginning with the Pentium Pro, the level-2 (**L2**) is packaged on the same module or **chipset** as the processor. Intel's Dual Independent Bus (DIB) design separates and coordinates accesses between the processor and RAM and accesses between the processor and the L2 cache. The frontside bus operates at 66 or 100 **MHz**, depending on the chipset. In the Pentium Pro, the backside bus (to the L2 cache) operates at the same clock speed as the processor. In the Pentium II, the backside bus operates at one-half the processor clock speed.

backup

Backup is the activity of copying **files** or **database**s so that they will be preserved in case of equipment failure or other catastrophe. Backup is usually a routine part of the operation of large businesses with **mainframe**s as well as the administrators of smaller business computers. For personal computer users, backup is also necessary but often neglected. The retrieval of files you backed up is called *restoring* them.

Personal computer users can consider both local backup and Internet backup.

Local Backup

These are some options, with the least expensive approach listed first.

- Backing up critical files to diskettes. This approach is commonly used by people who keep their checkbooks and personal finance data on the computer. Programs like Quicken and Managing Your Money always remind users when they quit the program to backup their data. If your **hard disk** crashes, you'll be able to reconstruct your checkbook balances. If you have other files (for example, chapters of a book you're working on), you'll want to backup every single day's work. Copying it to a diskette is quick and economical.

- Backing up to a **Zip drive**, Jaz, Syquest, or similar hard disks. Once a week or so, you should back up your files (at least your own data files and perhaps the entire contents of your hard drive) to an alternative storage device, such as a Zip drive. These devices hold at least one million bytes on a special hard disk. Backing up usually takes a while (about 45 minutes for the contents of a 500 megabyte hard disk).

- There are also easily removable drives that you can back up to, especially if you have other reasons to use these (for example, for large graphic images that you store offline).

Internet Backup

You can also consider sending your files to another site for safekeeping. In case your hard disk crashes, you'll be able to download them from the safekeeping site. These are some products and services that are offered:

- Atrieva provides the user with a client program that allows the user to send files being backed up to an Atrieva-designated backup site. One monthly charge entitles you to back up up to 25 megabytes.

- BackupNet sells both a server and a client and is aimed at helping you set up your own **intranet**.

- QuickBackup is a client program from McAfee Associates. They have a modest charge for the client and a relatively low monthly charge for storing 30 MB. QuickBackup lets you save by folder or file types.

backward compatible

Backward compatible (or sometimes backward-compatible or backwards compatible) refers to a hardware or software system that can successfully use interfaces and data from earlier versions of the system or with other systems. For example, **Perl**, the scripting language, was designed to be backward compatible with **awk**, an earlier language that Perl was designed to replace.

Backward compatibility is more easily accomplished if the previous versions have been designed to be **forward compatible**, or **extensible**, with built-in features such as **Hooks**, **plug-in**, or an application program interface (**API**) that allows the addition of new features.

The term *backward combatible* (notice the "b") is sometimes used to describe hardware or software that is designed without regard for compatibility with earlier versions, causing the two versions to fight (or combat) each other. In this case, the two versions cannot share data easily and may have features that cause errors or crashes when they are installed on the same computer, often because the computer does not understand which version is being referred to. Even if the earlier version is removed, remaining vestiges of it may cause problems in running the newer version.

BAL

1) BAL (Basic Assembler Language) is a version of IBM's **assembler** language (sometimes called *assembly language*) for its System/360 and System/370 **mainframe operating systems**. An assembler language consists of computer **instructions** to the **processor**, each specifying a specific processor operation and input or output registers or data addresses. Most programs are written in higher-level languages. However, assembler language may be needed for programs that must run using little memory or that must execute very quickly.

2) BAL (branch-and-link) is the name of a System/360/370 assembler language instruction.

balanced scorecard methodology

Balanced scorecard methodology is an analysis technique designed to translate an organization's mission statement and overall business strategy into specific, quantifiable goals and to monitor the organization's performance in terms of achieving these goals. Developed by Robert Kaplan and David Norton in 1992, the balanced scorecard methodology is a comprehensive approach that analyzes an organization's overall performance in four ways, based on the idea that assessing performance through financial returns only provides information about how well the organization did prior to the assessment, so that future performance can be predicted and proper actions taken to create the desired future.

The methodology examines performance in four areas: financial analysis, the most traditionally used performance indicator, includes assessments of measures such as operating costs and return-on-investment; customer analysis looks at customer satisfaction and retention; internal analysis looks at production and innovation, measuring performance in terms of maximizing profit from current products and following indicators for future productivity; and finally, learning and growth analysis explores the effectiveness of management in terms of measures of employee satisfaction and retention and information system performance.

As a structure, balanced scorecard methodology breaks broad goals down successively into vision, strategies, tactical activities, and **metrics**. As an example of how the methodology might work, an organization might include in its mission statement a goal of maintaining employee satisfaction. This would be the organization's vision. Strategies for achieving that vision might include approaches such as increasing employee-management communication. Tactical activities undertaken to implement the strategy could include, for example, regularly scheduled meetings with employees. Finally, metrics could include quantifications of employee suggestions or employee surveys.

The balanced scorecard approach to management has gained popularity worldwide since the 1996 release of Norton and Kaplan's text, *The Balanced Scorecard: Translating Strategy into Action*. Kaplan has subsequently published another book on the subject, called *The Balanced Scorecard: You Can't Drive a Car Solely Relying on a Rearview Mirror*. The Gartner Group estimates that at least forty percent of all Fortune 1000 companies are now using the methodology.

balun

A balun is a device that joins a balanced line (one that has two conductors, with equal currents in opposite directions, such as a **twisted pair** cable) to an unbalanced line (one that has just one conductor and a ground, such as a **coaxial cable**). A balun is a type of transformer: it's used to convert an unbalanced signal to a balanced one or vice versa. Baluns isolate a transmission line and provide a balanced output. A typical use for a balun is in a television **antenna**. The term is derived by combining *balanced* and *unbalanced*.

In a balun, one pair of terminals is balanced, that is, the currents are equal in magnitude and opposite in phase. The other pair of terminals is unbalanced; one side is connected to electrical ground and the other carries the signal.

Balun transformers can be used between various parts of a **wireless** or cable communications system. The following table denotes some common applications.

Balanced	Unbalanced
Television receiver	**Coaxial cable** network
Television receiver	Coaxial antenna system
FM broadcast receiver	Coaxial antenna system
Dipole antenna	Coaxial transmission line
Parallel-wire	Coaxial transmitter output transmission line
Parallel-wire	Coaxial receiver input transmission line
Parallel-wire	Coaxial transmission line transmission line

Some baluns provide **impedance** transformation in addition to conversion between balanced and unbalanced signal modes; others provide no impedance transformation. For 1:1 baluns (no impedance transformation), the input and output are usually both 50 ohms or 75 ohms. The most common impedance-transformation ratio is 1:4 (alternatively 4:1). Some baluns provide other impedance-transformation ratios, such as 1:9 (and 9:1), 1:10 (and 10:1), or 1:16 (and 16:1). Impedance-transformer baluns having a 1:4 ratio are used between systems with impedances of 50 or 75 ohms (unbalanced) and 200 or 300 ohms (balanced). Most television and FM broadcast receivers are designed for 300-ohm balanced systems, while coaxial cables have characteristic impedances of 50 or 75 ohms. Impedance-transformer baluns with larger ratios are used to match high-impedance balanced antennas to low-impedance unbalanced wireless receivers, transmitters, or transceivers.

In order to function at optimum efficiency, a balun must be used with loads whose impedances present little or no **reactance**. Such impedances are called "purely resistive." As a general rule, well-designed communications antennas present purely resistive loads of 50, 75, or 300 ohms, although a few antennas have higher resistive impedances.

The "balanced" terminals of some baluns can be connected to an unbalanced system. One terminal of the balanced pair (input or output) is connected to ground, while the other is connected to the active system element. When this is done, the device does not operate as a true balun, because both the input and the output are unbalanced. A balun used in this way has been called an "un-un" (for "unbalanced-to-unbalanced"). Some baluns can work as an impedance transformer between two unbalanced systems if there is little or no reactance. But certain types of baluns do not work properly when connected in this manner. It is best to check the documentation provided with the device, or contact the manufacturer, if "un-un" balun operation is contemplated.

band

In telecommunication, a band—sometimes called a **frequency** band—is a specific range of frequencies in the radio frequency (**RF**) spectrum, which is divided among ranges from *very low frequencies* (vlf) to *extremely high frequencies* (ehf). Each band has a defined upper and lower frequency limit.

Because two radio transmitters sharing the same frequency band cause mutual interference, band usage is regulated. International use of the radio spectrum is regulated by the International Telecommunication Union (**ITU**). Domestic use of the radio spectrum is regulated by national agencies such as the Federal Communications Commission (**FCC**) in the U.S. Regulatory organizations assign each transmission source a band of operation, a transmitter radiation pattern, and a maximum transmitter power.

Bands, Frequency Ranges, and Allocations:

- Very low frequencies (vlf) range from 3 to 30 kilohertz (**kHz**). Time signals and standard frequencies are among the users of this band.

- Low frequencies (lf) range from 30 to 300 kHz. Fixed, maritime mobile and navigational systems and radio broadcasting are among the users of this band.

- Medium frequencies (mf) range from 300 to 3000 kHz. Land, maritime mobile and radio broadcasting are among the users of this band.

- High frequencies (hf)—also called *shortwaves*—range from 3 to 30 megahertz (MHz). Fixed, mobile, aeronautical and marine mobile, amateur radio, and radio broadcasting are among the users of this band.

- Very high frequencies (vlf) range from 30 to 300 MHz. Fixed, mobile, aeronautical and marine mobile, amateur radio, television and radio broadcasting, and radio navigation are among the users of this band.

- Ultra high frequencies (uhf) range from 300 to 3000 MHz. Fixed, mobile, aeronautical and marine mobile, amateur radio, television, radio navigation and location, meteorological, and space communication are among the users of this band.

- Super high frequencies (shf) range from 3 to 30 gigahertz (GHz). Fixed, mobile, radio navigation and location, and space and satellite communication are among the users of this band.

- Extremely high frequencies (ehf) range from 30 to 300 GHz. Amateur radio, satellite, and earth and space exploration are among the users of this band.

bandpass filter

A bandpass filter is an electronic device or circuit that allows signals between two specific frequencies to pass, but that discriminates against signals at other frequencies. Some bandpass filters have amplifiers that boost the levels of signals in the accepted frequency range; these require an external source of power and are known as active bandpass filters. Other devices do not amplify and consume no power in doing their task; these are passive bandpass filters.

The illustration is an amplitude-vs-frequency graph, also called a spectral plot, of the characteristic curve of a hypothetical bandpass filter. The cutoff frequencies, f_1 and f_2, are the frequencies at which the output signal power falls to half of its level at f_0, the center frequency of the filter. The value $f_2 - f_1$, expressed in **hertz** (Hz), **kilohertz** (kHz), **megahertz** (MHz), or **gigahertz** (GHz), is called the filter bandwidth. The range of frequencies between f_1 and f_2 is called the filter passband.

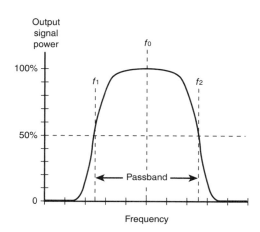

Bandpass filters are used primarily in wireless transmitters and receivers. The main function of such a filter in a transmitter is to limit the bandwidth of the output signal to the minimum necessary to convey data at the desired speed and in the desired form. In a receiver, a bandpass filter allows signals within a selected range of frequencies to be heard or decoded, while preventing signals at unwanted frequencies from getting through. A bandpass filter also optimizes the **signal-to-noise ratio** (sensitivity) of a receiver.

In both transmitting and receiving applications, well-designed bandpass filters, having the optimum bandwidth for the mode and speed of communication being used, maximize the number of signals that can be transferred in a system, while minimizing the interference or competition among signals.

bandwidth

Bandwidth (the width of a **band** of electromagnetic frequencies) is used to mean (1) how fast **data** flows on a given transmission path, and (2), somewhat more technically, the width of the range of frequencies that an electronic **signal** occupies on a given transmission medium. Any **digital** or **analog** signal has a bandwidth.

Generally speaking, bandwidth is directly proportional to the amount of data transmitted or received per unit time. In a qualitative sense, bandwidth is proportional to the complexity of the data for a given level of system performance. For example, it takes more bandwidth to download a photograph in one second than it takes to download a page of text in one second. Large sound files, computer programs, and animated videos require still more bandwidth for acceptable system performance. Virtual reality (VR) and full-length three-dimensional audio/visual presentations require the most bandwidth of all.

In digital systems, bandwidth is expressed as data speed in bits per second (**bps**). Thus, a **modem** that works at 57,600 bps has twice the bandwidth of a modem that works at 28,800 bps. In analog systems, bandwidth is expressed in terms of the difference between the highest-frequency signal component and the lowest-frequency signal component. **Frequency** is measured in the number of cycles of change per second, or **hertz**. A typical voice signal has a bandwidth of approximately three kilohertz (3 kHz); an analog television (TV) broadcast video signal has a bandwidth of six megahertz (6 MHz)—some 2,000 times as wide as the voice signal.

Communications engineers once strove to minimize the bandwidths of all signals, while maintaining a minimum acceptable level of system performance. This was done for at least two reasons: (1) low-bandwidth signals are less susceptible to noise interference than high-bandwidth signals; and (2) low-bandwidth signals allow for a greater number of communications exchanges to take place within a specified band of frequencies. However, this simple rule no longer applies in general. For example, in **spread spectrum** communications, the bandwidths of signals are deliberately expanded. In digital cable and fiber optic systems, the demand for ever-increasing data speeds outweighs the need for bandwidth conservation. In the **electromagnetic radiation spectrum**, there is only so much available bandwidth to go around, but in hard-wired systems, available bandwidth can literally be constructed without limit by installing more and more cables.

bandwidth test

A bandwidth test is a program that sends one or more files of known size over a network to a distant computer (for example, your own computer), measures the time required for the file(s) to successfully download at the destination, and thereby obtains a theoretical figure for the data speed between two or more points, usually in kilobits per second (**Kbps**) or megabits per second (**Mbps**).

Bandwidth test results vary greatly, even from moment to moment, and occasionally produce absurd or improbable figures. Factors that affect test results include:

- Internet traffic (speed generally decreases as volume increases)
- Variable propagation delays (can artificially inflate or degrade the result)
- Noise on data lines (has a real detrimental effect)
- The size(s) of file(s) used for the test
- The number of files used for the test
- The demand load on the test server at time of test
- Geomagnetic and/or thunderstorm activity

In order to get a reasonable estimate of **bandwidth** (sometimes referred to as **throughput**), experts suggest that three or more different test sites be used, and that each test be conducted six times at each site. Then the top and bottom $1/3$ of the figures should be disregarded. Finally, the middle $1/3$ of the results should be averaged.

banner

Depending on how it's used, a banner is either a graphic image that announces the name or identity of a site (and often is spread across the width of the Web page) or is an advertising image. Advertisers sometimes count banner "views," or the number of times a banner graphic image was downloaded over a period of time.

bar code

A bar code (often seen as a single word, *barcode*) is the small image of lines (bars) and spaces that is affixed to retail store items, identification cards, and postal mail to identify a particular product number, person, or location. The code uses a sequence of vertical bars and spaces to represent numbers and other symbols. A bar code reader is used to read the code. The reader uses a laser beam that is sensitive to the reflections from the line and space thickness and variation. The reader translates the reflected light into digital data that is transferred to a computer for immediate action or storage. Bar codes and readers are most often seen in supermarkets and retail stores, but a large number of different uses have been found for them. They are also used to take inventory in retail stores; to check out books from a library; to track manufacturing and shipping movement; to sign in on a job; to identify hospital patients; and to tabulate the results of direct mail marketing returns. Very small bar codes have been used to tag honey bees used in research. Readers may be attached to a computer (as they often are in retail store settings) or separate and portable, in which case they store the data they read until it can be fed into a computer.

There is no one standard bar code; instead, there are several different bar code standards that serve different uses, industries, or geographic needs. Since 1973, the Uniform Product Code (UPC), regulated by the Uniform Code Council, an industry organization, has provided a standard bar code used by most retail stores. The European Article Numbering system (EAN), developed by Joe Woodland, the inventor of the first bar code system, allows for an extra pair of digits and is becoming widely used. POSTNET is the standard bar code used in the United States for ZIP codes in bulk mailing. The following table summarizes the most common bar code standards.

Bar Code Standard	Uses
Uniform Product Code (UPC)	Retail stores for sales checkout; inventory, etc.
Code 39 (Code 3 of 9)	Identification, inventory, and tracking shipments
POSTNET	Encoding **zip codes** on U.S. mail
European Article Number (EAN)	A superset of the UPC that allows extra digits for country identification

Bar Code Standard	Uses
Japanese Article Number (JAN)	Similar to the EAN, used in Japan
Bookland	Based on ISBN numbers and used on book covers
ISSN bar code	Based on ISSN numbers, used on periodicals outside the U.S.
Code 128	Used in preference to Code 39 because it is more compact
Interleaved 2 of 5	Used in the shipping and warehouse industries
Codabar	Used by Federal Express, in libraries, and blood banks
MICR (Magnetic Ink Character Recognition)	A special font used for the numbers on the bottom of bank checks
OCR-A	The optical character recognition format used on book covers for the human readable version of the ISBN number
OCR-B	Used for the human readable version of the UPC, EAN, JAN, Bookland, and ISSN bar codes and for optional human-readable digits with Code 39 and Interleaved 2 of 5 symbols
Maxicode	Used by the United Parcel Service
PDF417	A new 2-D type of bar code that can encode up to 1108 bytes of information; can become a compressed, portable data file (which is what the "PDF" stands for)

bar

In programming, bar is a **metasyntactic variable** that is used to temporarily represent a **function**. Other examples include (but are by no means limited to) ack, baz, blarg, wibble, **foo**, fum, and qux. Metasyntactic variables are sometimes used in developing a conceptual version of a program or examples of programming code written for illustrative purposes.

Any filename beginning with a metasyntactic variable denotes a scratch file. This means the file can be deleted at any time without affecting the program.

When two or more metasyntactic variables are needed, *bar* is often paired with *foo* as a result of the fact that foo is phonetically the first part of the otherwise unrelated acronym, **FUBAR**. In other words, foo (which has its own history; see Smokey Stover) gave rise to the later use of bar as a metasyntactic variable because of its phonetic association with the well-known acronym.

Sometimes the terms Base Address Register and Buffer Address Register are shortened to the acronym bar or BAR.

In physics, the bar is a unit of pressure equal to one million (10^6) dynes, equivalent to 10 newtons, per square centimeter. This is approximately the pressure exerted by Earth's atmosphere at sea level.

Also see **foo** and **FUBAR**.

baseband

Also see **band**, **bandwidth**, **broadband**, and **narrowband**.

Baseband has several usages:

1) Describing a telecommunication system in which information is carried in digital form on a single unmultiplexed signal channel on the transmission medium. This usage pertains to a **baseband network** such as **Ethernet** and **token ring local area network**s.

2) Same as the above, but allowing that the information could also be carried in analog form.

3) Any frequency **band** on which information is super-imposed, whether or not the band is multiplexed and information is sent on subbands. In this usage, there is sometimes the meaning that the frequency band is not shifted to some other frequency band but remains at its original place in the electromagnetic spectrum.

BASIC

BASIC was an early programming language that is still among the most popular programming languages. Originally designed as an interactive **mainframe** timesharing language by John Kemeney and Thomas Kurtz in 1963, it became widely used on personal computers everywhere. On IBM's first "family" computer, the PCJr, a BASIC cartridge was a popular add-on. Because of its simplicity, BASIC has frequently been used in teaching the introductory concepts of programming with a working language.

BASIC continues to be widely used because it can be learned quickly, its statements are easy to read by other programmers, and support is available on most operating systems. BASIC's documentation has been translated into many national languages. It often comes with sound and graphics support. A popular version of BASIC today is QBASIC.

BASIC is used in many business applications and is still considered a valid choice as a programming language for some purposes. Microsoft's **Visual Basic** adds object-oriented features and a graphical user interface to the standard BASIC.

The following example of BASIC gets a number from a user, multiplies the number by 10, and prints or displays the result:

```
10 PRINT 'Enter a number'
20 INPUT NUM
30 PRINT 'Your number * 10 is ';NUM*10;
```

basic input/output system

See "BIOS"

Basic Rate Interface

In the Integrated Services Digital Network (**ISDN**), there are two levels of service: the Basic Rate Interface (BRI), intended for the home and small enterprise, and the Primary Rate Interface (**PRI**), for larger users. Both rates include a number of B-channels and a D-channel. Each **B-channel** carries data, voice, and other services. The **D-channel** carries control and signaling information.

The Basic Rate Interface consists of two 64 **Kbps** B-channels and one 16 Kbps D-channel. Thus, a Basic Rate Interface user can have up to 128 Kbps service. The Primary Rate Interface consists of 23 B-channels and one 64 Kpbs D-channel in the United States or 30 B-channels and 1 D-channel in Europe.

For more information, see **ISDN**.

bastion host

On the Internet, a bastion host is the only **host** computer that a company allows to be addressed directly from the public network and that is designed to screen the rest of its network from security exposure.

batch

In a computer, a batch job is a program that is assigned to the computer to run without further user interaction. Examples of batch jobs in a PC are a printing request or an analysis of a Web site log. In larger commercial computers or servers, batch jobs are usually initiated by a system user. Some are defined to run automatically at a certain time.

In some computer systems, batch jobs are said to run in the background and interactive programs run in the foreground. In general, interactive programs are given priority over batch programs, which run during the time intervals when the interactive programs are waiting for user requests.

The term originated when punched cards were the usual form of computer input and you put a batch of cards (one batch per program) in a box in the sequence that they were to be fed into the computer by the computer operator. (Hopefully, you got the output back the next morning.)

batch file

A batch file is a text **file** that contains a sequence of commands for a computer **operating system**. It's called a batch file because it batches (bundles or packages) into a single file a set of commands that would otherwise have to be presented to the system interactively from a keyboard one at a time. A batch file is usually created for command sequences for which a user has a repeated need. Commonly needed batch files are often delivered as part of an operating system. You initiate the sequence of commands in the batch file by simply entering the name of the batch file on a command line.

In the **Disk Operating System** (DOS), a batch file has the file name extension ".BAT". (The best known DOS batch file is the AUTOEXEC.BAT file that initializes DOS when you start the system.) In **UNIX**-based operating systems, a batch file is called a **shell script**. In IBM's mainframe VM operating systems, it's called an EXEC.

battery

A battery is an electrochemical cell (or enclosed and protected material) that can be charged electrically to provide a static potential for power or released electrical charge when needed.

A battery generally consists of an *anode*, a *cathode*, and an *electrolyte*.

Common types of commercial batteries and some of their characteristics and advantages are summarized in the following table. Battery types not shown include the Zinc-Air, Flooded Lead Acid, and Alkaline batteries.

baud

Baud was the prevalent measure for data transmission speed until replaced by a more accurate term, **bps** (bits per second). One baud is one electronic state change per second. Since a single state change can involve more than a single bit of data, the bps unit of measurement has replaced it as a better expression of data transmission speed.

The measure was named after a French engineer, Jean-Maurice-Emile Baudot. It was first used to measure the speed of telegraph transmissions.

Bayesian logic

Named for Thomas Bayes, an English clergyman and mathematician, Bayesian logic is a branch of logic applied to decision making and inferential statistics that deals with **probability** inference: using the knowledge of prior events to predict future events. Bayes first proposed his theorem in his 1763 work (published two years after his death in 1761), *An Essay Towards Solving a Problem in the Doctrine of Chances*. Bayes' theorem provided, for the first time, a mathematical method that could be used to calculate, given occurrences in prior trials, the likelihood of a target occurrence in future trials. According to Bayesian logic, the only way to quantify a situation with an uncertain outcome is through determining its probability.Bayes' Theorem is a means of quantifying uncertainty.

Battery Type	Characteristics	Typical Uses	Advantages
Sealed Lead Acid (SLA) battery	Can hold a charge for up to 3 years	Backup emergency power source	Inexpensive
Nickel-Cadmium (Ni-Cd) battery	Fast, even energy discharge	Appliances, audio and video equipment, toys; most popular battery	Relatively inexpensive; widely available
Nickel-Metal Hydride (Ni-MH) battery	Typical power capacity i1.2 V—1200 to 1500 mAh; extended life 2300 mAh; 2.5 to 4 hours battery life	Portable computers; cellular phones; same as for Ni-Cd batteries	No memory effect; unused capacity remains usable
Lithium Ion (Li-Ion) battery	Stable and safe; highest energy capacity	Portable computers; cellular phones; same as for Ni-Cd batteries	Twice the charge capacity of Ni-Cd; slow self-discharge

Based on probability theory, the theorem defines a rule for refining an hypothesis by factoring in additional evidence and background information, and leads to a number representing the degree of probability that the hypothesis is true. To demonstrate an application of Bayes' Theorem, suppose that we have a covered basket that contains three balls, each of which may be green or red. In a blind test, we reach in and pull out a red ball. We return the ball to the basket and try again, again pulling out a red ball. Once more, we return the ball to the basket and pull a ball out—red again. We form a hypothesis that all the balls are all, in fact, red. Bayes' Theorem can be used to calculate the probability (p) that all the balls are red (an event labeled as "A") given (symbolized as " | ") that all the selections have been red (an event labeled as "B"):

$$p(A \mid B) = p\{A + B\}/p\{B\}$$

Of all the possible combinations (RRR, RRG, RGG, GGG), the chance that all the balls are red is $^1/_4$; in $^1/_8$ of all possible outcomes, all the balls are red AND all the selections are red. Bayes' Theorem calculates the probability that all the balls in the basket are red, given that all the selections have been red as .5 (probabilities are expressed as numbers between 0. and 1., with "1." indicating 100% probability and "0." indicating zero probability).

The International Society for Bayesian Analysis (ISBA) was founded in 1992 with the purpose of promoting the application of Bayesian methods to problems in diverse industries and government, as well as throughout the Sciences. The modern incarnation of Bayesian logic has evolved beyond Bayes' initial theorem, developed further by the 18th century French theorist Pierre-Simon de Laplace, and 20th and 21st century practitioners such as Edwin Jaynes, Larry Bretthorst, and Tom Loredo. Current and possible applications of Bayesian logic include an almost infinite range of research areas, including genetics, astrophysics, psychology, sociology, artificial intelligence (**AI**), **data mining**, and computer **programming**.

BBS

See "bulletin board system"

Bcc

In Eudora and perhaps other e-mail facilities, you'll see the abbreviations "Fcc" and "Bcc". "Fcc" is the same as "cc" or **carbon copy**—that is: Send a copy of the message to the address you fill in. "Bcc" stands for "Blind carbon copy" which says: Send a copy to another address...but in this case, don't indicate to the Fcc recipient that you also sent this copy.

B-channel

In the Integrated Services Digital Network (**ISDN**), the B-channel is the channel that carries the main data. (The "B" stands for "bearer" channel.)

In ISDN, there are two levels of service: the Basic Rate Interface, intended for the home and small enterprise, and the Primary Rate Interface, for larger users. Both rates include a number of B- (bearer) channels and a **D-channel**. The B-channels carry data, voice, and other services. The D-channel carries control and signaling information.

The Basic Rate Interface consists of two 64 Kbps B-channels and one 16 Kbps D-channel. Thus, a Basic Rate Interface user can have up to 128 Kbps service. The Primary Rate Interface consists of 23 B-channels and one 64 Kpbs D-channel in the United States or 30 B-channels and 1 D-channel in Europe.

Bean

In its **JavaBeans** application program interface for writing a component, Sun Microsystems calls a component a "Bean" (thus continuing their coffee analogy). A Bean is simply the Sun Microsystems variation on the idea of a component.

In **object-oriented programming** and **distributed** object technology, a component is a reusable program building block that can be combined with other components in the same or other computers in a distributed network to form an application. Examples of a component include: a single button in a graphical user interface, a small interest calculator, an interface to a database manager. Components can be deployed on different servers in a network and communicate with each other for needed services. A component runs within a context called a **container**. Examples of containers include pages on a Web site, Web browsers, and word processors.

becquerel

The becquerel is the derived unit of radioactivity in the International System of Units (**SI**), symbolized Bq and equal to one disintegration or nuclear transformation per second. Reduced to base SI units, $1\ Bq = 1\ s^{-1}$. The becquerel is named after Antoine Henri Becquerel, the French physicist credited with the discovery of radioactivity. In the 1970s, the becquerel replaced the curie as the standard unit of radioactivity.

The becquerel is a small unit. In practical situations, radioactivity is often quantified in kilobecqerels (kBq) or megabecquerels (MBq), where:

$1\ kBq = 1000\ Bq = 10^3\ Bq$
$1\ MBq = 1000\ kBq = 1,000,000\ Bq = 10^6\ Bq$

Thus, 1 kBq is the equivalent of 1000 disintegrations per second ($10^3\ s^{-1}$), or an average of one disintegration per millisecond, and 1 MBq is the equivalent of 1,000,000 disintegrations per second ($10^6\ s^{-1}$), or an average of one disintegration per microsecond.

Also see International System of Units (**SI**).

BEDO DRAM

BEDO DRAM (Burst Extended Data Output DRAM) is a type of dynamic random access memory (**DRAM**) that can send data back to the computer from one read operation at the same time it is reading in the address of the next data to be sent. In addition, after reading the address, it is able to send the data back in three successive clock cycles without clock coordination (that is, the three successive outputs seem to be sent from the RAM in a sudden **burst**). It works well with microprocessors that operate up to 66 MHz.

BEDO DRAM and various types of **SDRAM** are two recent RAM technologies that are being incorporated in newer computers.

beep code

A beep code is the audio signal given out by a computer to announce the result of a short diagnostic testing sequence the computer performs when first powering up (called the Power-On-Self-Test or **POST**). The POST is a small program contained in the computer's basic input/output operating system (**BIOS**) that checks to make sure necessary hardware is present and required memory is accessible. If everything tests out correctly, the computer will typically emit a single beep and continue the starting-up process. If something is wrong, the computer will display an error message on the monitor screen and announce the errors audibly with a series of beeps that vary in pitch, number and duration (this is especially useful when the error exists with the monitor or graphic components). The beeping sequence is really a coded message (beep code) designed to tell the user what is wrong with the computer.

There is no official standard for beep codes; audio patterns vary according to the manufacturer of the computer's BIOS program. If an error message is beeped on startup, the user must first determine what kind of BIOS the computer is running (Phoenix or AMI are the most popular) and use that information to look up the particular beep code sequence that is being sent. BIOS information and beep code interpretations can be found in the manual that comes with the computer and on the manufacturer's Web site.

Beginners All-Purpose Symbolic Instruction Code

See "BASIC"

Bell Communications Research

See "Bellcore"

Bell operating company

See "BOC"

Bellcore

Bellcore (Bell Communications Research) provides certain centralized research and standards coordination for the regional Bell operating companies (**RBOC**)s. It also coordinates security and emergency preparedness for the U.S. government. Bellcore was formed in 1984 when AT&T was broken up into the seven RBOCs. Bellcore's budget comes from the RBOCs. Bellcore coordinated the design for the Advanced Intelligent Network (**AIN**).

benchmark

A benchmark is a point of reference by which something can be measured. In surveying, a "bench mark" (two words) is a post or other permanent mark established at a known elevation that is used as the basis for measuring the elevation of other topographical points.

In computer and Internet technology, the term may have any of these meanings:

1) A set of conditions against which a product or system is measured. PC magazine laboratories frequently test and compare several new computers or computer devices against the same set of application programs, user interactions, and contextual situations. The total context against which all products are measured and compared is referred to as the benchmark.

2) A program that is specially designed to provide measurements for a particular operating system or application.

3) A known product with which users are familiar or accustomed to that other newer products can be compared to.

4) A set of performance criteria which a product is expected to meet.

Laboratory benchmarks sometimes fail to reflect real-world product use. For this reason, Eric Raymond defines a benchmark as "an inaccurate measure of computer performance" and cites the "old hacker's saying" that "In the computer industry, there are three kinds of lies: lies, damn lies, and benchmarks."

Still, benchmarks can be useful. If you'd like to try one out yourself on your own operating system, browser, file server, or notebook battery life, the ZDNet Testing Labs site offers downloads of popular benchmark programs.

BeOS

BeOS is a personal computer **operating system** that its makers describe as designed for the multimedia applications of the future. Be founder Jean-Louis Gasse left Apple Computer in 1990 to create an operating system that could exploit new architectural ideas and be free of the baggage that older operating systems invariably bring with them. The first BeOS was used in a computer called the BeBox, since

abandoned so the company could concentrate on the software. In 1996, BeOS had Apple's **Macintosh** users in mind when it ported the system to the **PowerPC microprocessor**. More recently, BeOS has been ported to Intel's **Pentium** computers. It can be installed in the same computer with another operating system such as Windows or Mac OS and used as an alternative operating system for applications requiring fast handling of streaming video, games, and other multimedia applications.

BeOS can run on multiple microprocessors at the same time (using **symmetric multiprocessing**) and is able to coordinate work threads across the processors. Anticipating the arrival of **digital versatile disk** and very large files such as feature-length movies, BeOS provides a 64-bit file system that can handle files of **terabyte** size. The operating system, say the BeOS makers, no longer has to be a bottleneck between the Internet, applications, and the user.

BeOS comes with a **desktop** user interface that improves in some ways on both Windows and the Mac and a built-in Web browser, audio, **MIDI**, and its own 3D interface as well as support for **OpenGL**. Other features include **antialiasing** fonts, **Unicode**, and support for **POSIX** utilities and shell commands.

BeOS is also sold as a good system to develop programs for. Programmers are given a relatively simple **object-oriented programming application program interface**. Metrowerks provides **C++** and **Java** development environments. Because BeOS has little legacy baggage to carry, its system is seen as simpler, easier to maintain and evolve, and less prone to failure. The industry assessment, however, is that without a **killer app**, BeOS faces an uphill battle. Meanwhile, a number of games are in development and Beatware has developed an office suite (Writer, Sum-It, and Get-It) for it.

Beowulf

Beowulf is an approach to building a **supercomputer** as a *cluster* of commodity off-the-shelf personal computers, interconnected with a   technology like **Ethernet**, and running programs written for **parallel processing**. The Beowulf idea is said to enable the average university computer science department or small research company to build its own small supercomputer that can operate in the **gigaflop** (billions of operations per second) range. In addition to possible cost savings, building your own supercomputer is said to be a learning investment and make you less dependent in the future on particular hardware and software vendors. As off-the-shelf technology evolves, a Beowulf can be upgraded to take advantage of it.

The original Beowulf cluster was developed in 1994 at the Center of Excellence in Space Data and Information Sciences (CESDIS), a contractor to the US National Aeronautics and Space Administration (NASA) at the Goddard Space Flight Center in Greenbelt, Maryland. Thomas Sterling and Don Becker built a cluster computer that consisted of 16 Intel DX4 **processor**s connected by channel-bonded 10 **Mbps Ethernet**.

Their success led to the Beowulf Project, which fosters the development of similar commodity off-the-shelf (COTS) clusters. A number have been developed in universities and research groups, ranging from the original 16-processor Beowulf to Avalon, a cluster of 140 **Alpha** processors built by the Los Alamos National Laboratory. A more typical smaller cluster might have 16 200-**MHz** (or faster) Intel P6 processors connected by **Fast Ethernet** and a Fast Ethernet switch.

As a way to lower cost and increase vendor independency, Beowulf developers often choose the **Linux** operating system and use standard message passing **protocol**s between the computers within the cluster. A Beowulf cluster is placed in the taxonomy of parallel computing as somewhere below a massively parallel processor (**MPP**) and a network of workstations (NOW) that is clustered for the purpose of load-balancing.

BER

See "bit error rate"

bespoke

Bespoke (pronounced bee-SPOHK) is a term used in the United Kingdom and elsewhere for an individually- or custom-made product or service. Traditionally applied to custom-tailored clothing, the term has been extended to information technology, especially for software consulting services. Typically, software consulting companies offer packaged (already invented and generally applicable) software and bespoke software for client needs that can't be satisfied by packaged software. In the U.S., bespoke software is often called custom or custom-designed software.

Bespoke is a form derived from *bespeak*, which was used as early as 1583 to refer to the ordering of goods.

best practice

A best practice is a technique or methodology that, through experience and research, has proven to reliably lead to a desired result. A commitment to using the best practices in any field is a commitment to using all the knowledge and technology at one's disposal to ensure success. The term is used frequently in the fields of health care, government administration, the education system, project management, hardware and software product development, and elsewhere.

In software development, a best practice is a well-defined method that contributes to a successful step in product development. Throughout the software industry, several best practices are widely followed. Some of the more commonly used are: an iterative development process, requirement management, quality control, and change control.

An iterative (meaning repetitive) development process, which progresses in incremental stages, helps to maintain a focus on manageable tasks and ensures that earlier stages are successful before the later stages are attempted. Requirement management addresses the problem of creeping requirements, which is a situation in which the client requests additional changes to the product that are beyond the scope of what was originally planned. To guard against this common phenomenon, requirement management employs strategies such as documentation of requirements, sign-offs, and methodologies such as the **use case**. Quality control is a strategy that defines objective measures for assessing quality throughout the development process in terms of the product's **functionality**, reliability, and performance. Change control is a strategy that seeks to closely monitor changes throughout the iterative process to ensure that records are intact for changes that have been made and that unacceptable changes are not undertaken.

A best practice tends to spread throughout a field or industry after a success has been demonstrated. However, it is often noted that demonstrated best practices can be slow to spread, even within an organization. According to the American Productivity & Quality Center, the three main barriers to adoption of a best practice are a lack of knowledge about current best practices, a lack of motivation to make changes involved in their adoption, and a lack of knowledge and skills required to do so.

beta test

In software development, a beta test is the second phase of software testing in which a sampling of the intended audience tries the product out. (Beta is the second letter of the Greek alphabet.) Originally, the term *alpha test* meant the first phase of testing in a software development process. The first phase includes unit testing, component testing, and system testing. Beta testing can be considered "pre-release testing." Beta test versions of software are now distributed to a wide audience on the Web partly to give the program a "real-world" test and partly to provide a preview of the next release.

BetterWhois

BetterWhois, named after the original **whois**, lets you look up registration information from all Internet **domain name** registrars at the same time. BetterWhois is located at the BetterWhois.com Web site.

In the past, the whois facility provided the way for anyone to find out whether a domain name had been taken and, if so, the name of the company who had reserved or paid for it. whois is maintained by Network Solutions, the original .com, .org, and .net registrar on the Internet. Network Solutions has a contract with the U.S. Commerce Department and, until recently, has been the sole registrar in these domains. Recently, however, the newly-formed Internet Corporation for Assigned Names and Numbers

(ICANN) has opened the service of domain name registration in these domains to other companies. While Network Solutions continues to be the largest registrar, at least six new companies are now offering similar services, and scores of companies are expected to be offering registration services in the near future.

BetterWhois lets you search the registration databases of all the accredited registrars in a single search. They also provide a linked list of all the registrars and allow a user to receive the detailed domain report by e-mail.

BGP

BGP (Border Gateway Protocol) is a **protocol** for exchanging routing information between **gateway host**s (each with its own **router**) in a network of **autonomous system**s. BGP is often the protocol used between gateway hosts on the Internet. The routing table contains a list of known routers, the addresses they can reach, and a cost **metric** associated with the path to each router so that the best available route is chosen.

Hosts using BGP communicate using the Transmission Control Protocol (**TCP**) and send updated router table information only when one host has detected a change. Only the affected part of the routing table is sent. BGP-4, the latest version, lets adminstrators configure cost metrics based on policy statements. (BGP-4 is sometimes called BGP4, without the hyphen.)

BGP communicates with autonomous (local) networks using Internal BGP (IBGP) since it doesn't work well with IGP. The routers inside the autonomous network thus maintain two routing tables: one for the interior gateway protocol and one for IBGP.

BGP-4 makes it easy to use Classless Inter-Domain Routing (**CIDR**), which is a way to have more addresses within the network than with the current **IP address** assignment scheme.

BGP is a more recent protocol than the Exterior Gateway Protocol (**EGP**).

Also see the Interior Gateway Protocol (**IGP**) and the Open Shortest Path First (**OSPF**) interior gateway protocol.

Big Blue

Big Blue refers to IBM, which has used blue as a branding color in its logo and elsewhere.

Big Chief tablet

The Big Chief tablet was for many years the most popular brand of paper writing tablet among school children and hopeful novelists in the U.S. and exemplified the lined writing tablet as a communications medium. The tablet featured a native American with full headdress on the cover. The Big Chief Writing Tablet copyright was originally held by William Albrecht at the Western Tablet Company in St.

Joseph, Missouri, and was later sold to the Mead Corporation, which also manufactured a Son of Big Chief tablet.

On January 5, 2001, the Everett Pad and Paper purchased the latest makers of the tablet, Springfield Tablet, and closed the plant after 80 years. At present, the Big Chief tablet is no longer being made. However, the lined writing tablet is likely to remain a useful artifact of information technology for many years to come even as its electronic counterpart (see Microsoft's **Tablet PC**) gains popularity.

big-endian and little-endian

Big-endian and little-endian are terms that describe the order in which a sequence of **byte**s are stored in computer memory. Big-endian is an order in which the "big end" (most significant value in the sequence) is stored first (at the lowest storage address). Little-endian is an order in which the "little end" (least significant value in the sequence) is stored first. For example, in a big-endian computer, the two bytes required for the **hexadecimal** number 4F52 would be stored as 4F52 in storage (if 4F is stored at storage address 1000, for example, 52 will be at address 1001). In a little-endian system, it would be stored as 524F (52 at address 1000, 4F at 1001).

IBM's 370 computers, most **RISC**-based computers, and Motorola microprocessors use the big-endian approach. For people who use languages that read left-to-right, this seems like the natural way to think of a storing a string of characters or numbers—in the same order you expect to see it presented to you. Many of us would thus think of big-endian as storing something in *forward* fashion, just as we read.

On the other hand, Intel **processor**s (CPUs) and DEC Alphas and at least some programs that run on them are little-endian. An argument for little-endian order is that as you increase a numeric value, you may need to add digits to the left (a higher non-exponential number has more digits). Thus, an addition of two numbers often requires moving all the digits of a big-endian ordered number in storage, moving everything to the right. In a number stored in little-endian fashion, the least significant bytes can stay where they are and new digits can be added to the right at a higher address. This means that some computer operations may be simpler and faster to perform.

Language **compiler**s such as that of **Java** or **FORTRAN** have to know which way the object code they develop is going to be stored. Converters can be used to change one kind of endian to the other when necessary.

Note that within both big-endian and little-endian byte orders, the bits within each byte are big-endian. That is, there is no attempt to be big- or little-endian about the entire bit stream represented by a given number of stored bytes. For example, whether hexadecimal 4F is put in storage first or last with other bytes in a given storage address range, the bit order within the byte will be:
01001111

It is *possible* to be big-endian or little-endian about the bit order, but CPUs and programs are almost always designed for a big-endian bit order. In data transmission, however, it is possible to have either bit order.

Eric Raymond observes that Internet **domain name** addresses and e-mail addresses are little-endian. For example, a big-endian version of our domain name address would be:
com.whatis.www

Big-endian and little-endian derive from Jonathan Swift's *Gulliver's Travels* in which the Big Endians were a political faction that broke their eggs at the large end ("the primitive way") and rebelled against the Lilliputian King who required his subjects (the Little Endians) to break their eggs at the small end.

binary

Binary describes a numbering scheme in which there are only two possible values for each digit: 0 and 1. The term also refers to any **digital** encoding/decoding system in which there are exactly two possible states. In digital data memory, storage, processing, and communications, the 0 and 1 values are sometimes called "low" and "high," respectively.

Binary numbers look strange when they are written out directly. This is because the digits' weight increases by powers of 2, rather than by powers of 10. In a digital numeral, the digit furthest to the right is the "ones" digit; the next digit to the left is the "twos" digit; next comes the "fours" digit, then the "eights" digit, then the "16s" digit, then the "32s" digit, and so on. The decimal equivalent of a binary number can be found by summing all the digits. For example, the binary 10101 is equivalent to the decimal 1 + 4 + 16 = 21:

DECIMAL = 21	64	32	**16**	8	**4**	2	**1**
BINARY = 10101	0	0	1	0	1	0	1

The numbers from decimal 0 through 15 in decimal, binary, **octal**, and **hexadecimal** form are listed below.

DECIMAL	BINARY	OCTAL	HEXA-DECIMAL
0	0	0	0
1	1	1	1
2	10	2	2
3	11	3	3
4	100	4	4
5	101	5	5
6	110	6	6
7	111	7	7
8	1000	10	8
9	1001	11	9
10	1010	12	A
11	1011	13	B

DECIMAL	BINARY	OCTAL	HEXA-DECIMAL
12	1100	14	C
13	1101	15	D
14	1110	16	E
15	1111	17	F

binary 8-zero substitution

See "B8ZS"

binary digit

See "bit"

binary file

A binary file is a **file** whose content must be interpreted by a program or a hardware processor that understands in advance exactly how it is formatted. That is, the file is not in any externally identifiable format so that any program that wanted to could look for certain data at a certain place within the file. A progam (or hardware processor) has to know exactly how the data inside the file is laid out to make use of the file.

In general, **executable** (ready-to-run) programs are often identified as binary files and given a file name extension of ".bin". Programmers often talk about an executable program as a "binary" and will ask another programmer to "send me the binaries." (A synonym for this usage is **object code**.) A binary file could also contain data ready to be used by a program.

In terms of transmitting files from one place to another, a file can be transmitted as a "binary," meaning that the programs handling it don't attempt to look within it or change it, but just pass it along as a "chunk of 0s and 1s," the meaning of which is unknown to any network device.

binary large object

See "BLOB"

Binary Runtime Environment for Wireless

See "BREW"

binary search

A binary search, also called a dichotomizing search, is a digital scheme for locating a specific object in a large set. Each object in the set is given a key. The number of keys is always a power of 2. If there are 32 items in a list, for example, they might be numbered 0 through 31 (binary 00000 through 11111). If there are, say, only 29 items, they can be numbered 0 through 28 (binary 00000 through 11100), with the numbers 29 through 31 (binary 11101, 11110, and 11111) as dummy keys.

To conduct the search, the keys are listed in tabular form. The position of the desired object is compared with the halfway point in the list (which lies between the two keys in the center of the list). If the key of the desired object is smaller than the halfway point value, then the first half of the list is accepted and the second half is rejected. If the key of the desired object is larger than the halfway point value, then the second half of the list is accepted and the first half is rejected. The process is repeated, each time selecting half of the list and rejecting the other half, until only one object remains. This is the desired object.

The following list shows an example of a binary search to choose the fifth object in a set of 13 objects. Keys are denoted X; the desired key is denoted by +. Dummy keys are denoted O.

XXXX+XXXXXXXXOOO	(initial list)
XXXX+XXX	(first half accepted)
+XXX	(second half accepted)
+X	(first half accepted)
+	(first half accepted)

binary tree

A binary tree is a method of placing and locating files (called records or keys) in a **database**, especially when all the data is known to be in random access memory (**RAM**). The **algorithm** finds data by repeatedly dividing the number of ultimately accessible records in half until only one remains.

In a tree, records are stored in locations called leaves. This name derives from the fact that records always exist at end points; there is nothing beyond them. Branch points are called nodes. The order of a tree is the number of branches (called children) per node. In a binary tree, there are always two children per node, so the order is 2. The number of leaves in a binary tree is always a power of 2. The number of access operations required to reach the desired record is called the depth of the tree. The image below shows a binary tree for locating a particular record among seven records in a set of eight leaves. The depth of this tree is 4.

In a practical tree, there can be thousands, millions, or billions of records. Not all leaves necessarily contain a record, but more than half do. A leaf that does not contain a record is called a null. In the example shown here, the eighth leaf is a null, indicated by an open circle.

Binary trees are used when all the data is in random-access memory (RAM). The search algorithm is simple, but it does not minimize the number of database accesses required to reach a desired record. When the entire tree is contained in RAM, which is a fast-read, fast-write medium, the number of required accesses is of little concern. But when some or all of the data is on disk, which is slow-read, slow-write, it is advantageous to minimize the number of accesses (the tree depth). Alternative algorithms such as the **B-tree** accomplish this.

Also see **binary search** and **tree structure**. Compare B-tree, **M-tree**, **splay tree**, and **X-tree**.

bind

In computer programming, to bind is to make an association between two or more programming objects or value items for some scope of time and place. Here are some usages:

1) In general, when a program is compiled, to bind is to substitute a real for a variable value in the program or to ensure that additional programming will be loaded into storage along with the compiled program.

2) When a server application is started, it issues a bind request to **TCP/IP** to indicate that it is ready to listen to (receive) client application requests from the Internet that are associated with a specified **IP address**. (Using the **C** programming language, the request is specified in a *bind( )* function request.)

3) In IBM's Systems Network Architecture (**SNA**), to bind is to set up a session between two *logical units (LUs)* or network end points prior to communicating.

4) In using Remote Procedure Call (**RPC**), to bind is to locate the remote server application to which a client application can make requests. This is often done by accessing a centrally-maintained directory of the names of accessible network server applications.

5) An earlier program that did "binding" so that different programs that called each other knew each other's addresses in memory was called a *linkage editor*.

BinHex

BinHex is a utility for converting (encoding) Macintosh files into files that will travel well on networks either as files or e-mail attachments. Like **Uuencode**, BinHex encodes a file from its 8-bit binary or bit-stream representation into a 7-bit **ASCII** set of text characters. The recipient must decode it at the other end. Older e-mail utilities sometimes can't handle binary transmissions so text encoding ensures that a tranmission will get to an older system. BinHex specifically handles both resource and data forks in Macintosh files (which Uuencode doesn't). BinHex files have a suffix of ".hqx". (Earlier versions have the suffix ".hex".)

Netscape and possibly other Web browsers as well as some popular e-mail applications (including Eudora) include BinHex encoding and decoding capability. Otherwise, you can download a BinHex utility for use either the Macintosh, Windows, or other systems. (In Eudora, when writing a note you want to be transmitted in BinHex, look for the little box set to a default of "MIME" and change it to "BinHex.")

biochip

A biochip is a glass or silicon wafer that is designed for the purpose of accelerating genetic research. It may also be able to rapidly detect chemical agents used in biological warfare so that defensive measures can be taken. A biochip is designed to "freeze" into place the structures of many short strands of DNA (deoxyribonucleic acid), the basic chemical instruction that determines the characteristics of an organism. Effectively, it is used as a kind of "test tube" for real chemical samples. A specially designed microscope can determine where the sample hybridized with DNA strands in the biochip.

Biochips helped to dramatically accelerate the identification of the estimated 80,000 genes in human DNA, an ongoing world-wide research collaboration known as the **Human Genome Project**. The microchip is described as a sort of word search function that can quickly sequence DNA.

Researchers believe another important use for the biochip would be to quickly identify chemical warfare agents. Known chemical agents could be immobilized on the biochips so that real agents could be compared and identified. Biochips may also be useful in hospitals for detecting specific causes of local infection and in agriculture for testing for pesticides in the soil.

A biochip called the MAGIChip is being developed jointly by the Argonne National Laboratory and the Russian Academy of Sciences' W. A. Engelhardt Institute of Molecular Biology. Commercial use of biochips is seen as about five years away.

bioinformatics

Bioinformatics is the science of developing computer **database**s and **algorithm**s for the purpose of speeding up and enhancing biological research. Bioinformatics is being used most noticeably in the Human Genome Project, the effort to identify the 80,000 genes in human DNA. New academic programs are training students in bioinformatics by providing them with backgrounds in molecular biology and in computer science, including database design and analytical approaches. Rensselaer Polytechnic Institute in Troy, New York, is offering both a bachelor of science and a master's degree in bioinformatics and molecular biology.

Much information that has been captured is not yet available in the databases. The databases themselves are expected to be publicly online and Internet-accessible by the end of 2003. Database information will be analyzed for new information as new algorithms are developed. Motorola is working on a **biochip**, a processor expressly designed to speed up experiments with different combinations of protein-DNA reactions.

biomechatronics

Biomechatronics is the interdisciplinary study of biology, mechanics, and electronics. Biomechatronics focuses on the interactivity of biological organs (including the brain) with **electromechanical** devices and systems. Universities and research centers worldwide have taken notice of biomechatronics in light of its potential for development of advanced medical devices and life-support systems. Primitive biomechatronic devices have existed for some time; the heart pacemaker and the defibrillator are examples. More exciting biometchatronic possibilities that scientists foresee in the near future include pancreas pacemakers for diabetics, mentally controlled electronic muscle stimulators for stroke and accident survivors, cameras that can be wired into the brain allowing blind people to see, and microphones that can be wired into the brain allowing deaf people to hear.

biometrics

Biometrics is the science and technology of measuring and statistically analyzing biological data. In information technology, biometrics usually refers to technologies for measuring and analyzing human body characteristics such as fingerprints, eye retinas and irises, voice patterns, facial patterns, and hand measurements, especially for the **authentication** of someone. Often seen in science-fiction action adventure movies, face pattern matchers and body scanners seem about to emerge as replacements for computer passwords. A fingerprint reader is now sold by Compaq Computer. It plugs into a **parallel port** on back of the computer. Compaq believes that help desk centers will appreciate systems with fingerprint rather than password authentication since up to 50% of calls are from users having trouble with their passwords.

Fingerprint and other biometric devices consist of a reader or scanning device, software that converts the scanned information into digital form, and, wherever the data is to be analyzed, a **database** that stores the biometric data for comparison with entered biometric data. In converting the biometric input, the software identifies specific points of data as *match points*. The match points are processed using an **algorithm** into a value that can be compared with biometric data scanned when a user tries to gain access.

Besides fingerprints, voice patterns, face measurement, and retina and iris measurements are considered viable approaches. Miros makes a product called TrueFace that analyzes patterns using a **neural network** approach.

Fingerprint, facial, or other biometric data can be placed on a **smart card** and users can present both the smartcard and their fingerprints or faces to merchants, banks, or telephones for an extra degree of authentication. Some analysts feel that biometric data is likely to be used instead of a password to authorize sales and other transactions.

IBM, Microsoft, Novell, and others are developing a standard, called BioAPI, that will allow different manufacturers' software to interact. There are privacy concerns about the gathering and proliferation of biometric data. One suggestion is to **encrypt** the biometric data and discard the original data.

biomimetic

Biomimetic refers to human-made processes, substances, devices, or systems that imitate nature. The art and science of designing and building biomimetic apparatus is called biomimetics, and is of special interest to researchers in nanotechnology, robotics, artificial intelligence (AI), the medical industry, and the military.

Some biomimetic processes have been in use for years. An example is the artificial synthesis of certain vitamins and antibiotics. More recently, biomimetics have been suggested as applicable in the design of **machine vision** systems, machine hearing systems, signal amplifiers, navigational systems, and data converters. The neural network (which has suffered through on-again, off-again status in the opinions of prominent researchers) is a hypothetical biomimetic computer that works by making associations and educated guesses, and that can learn from its own mistakes.

Other possible applications of biomimetics include nanorobot antibodies that seek and destroy disease-causing bacteria, artificial organs, artificial arms, legs, hands, and feet, and various electronic devices. One of the more intriguing ideas is the so-called **biochip**, a microprocessor that grows from a starter crystal in much the same way that a seed grows into a tree, or a fertilized egg grows into an embryo.

Also see **nanotechnology** and **self-assembly**.

BIOS

BIOS is the program a personal computer's **microprocessor** uses to get the computer system started after you turn it on. It also manages data flow between the computer's **operating system** and attached devices such as the **hard disk**, **video adapter**, **keyboard**, **mouse**, and **printer**.

BIOS is an integral part of your computer and comes with it when you bring it home. (In contrast, the operating system can either be preinstalled by the manufacturer or vendor or installed by the user.) BIOS is a program that is made accessible to the microprocessor on an eraseable programmable read-only memory (**EPROM**) chip. When

you turn on your computer, the microprocessor passes control to the BIOS program, which is always located at the same place on EPROM.

When BIOS boots up (starts up) your computer, it first determines whether all of the attachments are in place and operational and then it loads the operating system (or key parts of it) into your computer's random access memory (**RAM**) from your hard disk or diskette drive.

With BIOS, your operating system and its applications are freed from having to understand exact details (such as hardware addresses) about the attached input/output devices. When device details change, only the BIOS program needs to be changed. Sometimes this change can be made during your system setup. In any case, neither your operating system or any applications you use need to be changed.

Although BIOS is theoretically always the intermediary between the microprocessor and I/O device control information and data flow, in some cases, BIOS can arrange for data to flow directly to memory from devices (such as video cards) that require faster data flow to be effective.

bipolar 8-zero substitution

See "B8ZS"

bipolar signaling

See also **unipolar signaling**.

Bipolar signaling, also called *bipolar transmission*, is a **baseband** method of sending **binary** data over wire or cable. There are two logic states, low and high, represented by the digits 0 and 1 respectively.

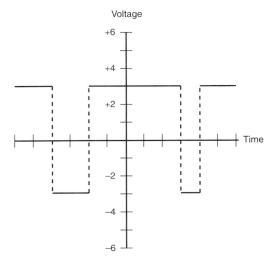

The illustration shows a bipolar signal as it might appear on the screen of an oscilloscope. Each horizontal division represents one **bit** (binary digit). The logic 0 state is -3 volts and logic 1 is $+3$ volts. This is *positive logic*. Alternatively, logic 0 might be $+3$ volts, and logic 1 might be -3 volts; this would be *negative logic*. Whether positive or negative logic is used, the voltages representing the low and high states are equal and opposite; over time, the average voltage is approximately equal to 0.

A bipolar signal resembles an **alternating current** (AC) rectangular wave, except that the **frequency** is not constant. The **bandwidth** of the signal is inversely proportional to the duration of each data bit. Typical data speeds in baseband are several megabits per second (Mbps); hence the duration of each bit is a fraction of a microsecond.

bipolar transistor

See also field-effect transistor (**FET**) and **transistor**.

A bipolar transistor is a semiconductor device commonly used for amplification. The device can amplify **analog** or **digital** signals. It can also switch DC or function as an oscillator. Physically, a bipolar transistor amplifies **current**, but it can be connected in circuits designed to amplify voltage or power.

There are two major types of bipolar transistors, called *PNP* and *NPN*. A PNP transistor has a layer of N-type semiconductor between two layers of P-type material. An NPN transistor has a layer of P-type material between two layers of N-type material. In P-type material, electric charges are carried mainly in the form of **electron** deficiencies called *holes*. In N-type material, the charge carriers are primarily electrons.

The bipolar transistor has advantages and disadvantages relative to the **field-effect transistor** (field-effect transistor). Bipolar devices can switch signals at high speeds, and can be manufactured to handle large currents so that they can serve as high-power amplifiers in audio equipment and in **wireless** transmitters. Bipolar devices are not especially effective for weak-signal amplification, or for applications requiring high circuit **impedance**.

Bipolar transistors are fabricated onto silicon integrated circuit (IC) **chips**. A single IC can contain many thousands of bipolar transistors, along with other components such as resistors, capacitors, and diodes.

bipolar transmission

See "bipolar signaling"

birdie

A birdie is a false, or phantom, signal that appears in a superheterodyne **wireless** receiver. Birdies are internally generated, resulting from the outputs of the oscillators that form part of the receiver circuit. They usually sound like unmodulated carriers—signals with "dead air." Occasionally they are modulated by clicks, humming sounds, or audible tones.

Birdies can occur as a result of the receiver being tuned to a **frequency** that is a multiple of the output frequency of one of the internal oscillators. These signals are known as harmonics. A birdie might also be heard at a frequency corresponding to the sum or the difference of the internal **oscillator** frequencies. These signals are called mixing products. Birdies are inevitable in any superheterodyne wireless receiver. However, in a well-engineered receiver, most or all of the birdies occur at frequencies outside the normal range of operation, so they have little or no detrimental effect on receiver performance.

A birdie is not the same thing as a spurious response. If a receiver picks up a signal whose transmitter is operating at a frequency other than that to which the receiver is tuned, the **modulation** of the unwanted signal will be heard or decoded. In some cases, two or more strong external signals can combine in a receiver's radio-frequency amplifier, causing numerous spurious responses. This phenomenon, called intermodulation ("intermod"), can be a problem in downtown metropolitan areas where many wireless transmitters operate simultaneously.

bis

The word (also used as a prefix or suffix) *bis*, applied to some **modem protocol** standards, is Old Latin for "repeat" (akin to Old High German "twice"). When a protocol ends with "bis," it means that it's the second version of that protocol.

Similarly, *ter* is from Old Latin meaning "three times." The suffix *terbo* in the **V.xx** modem protocol is an invented word based on the Old Latin *ter* and the word *turbo* (Latin for "whirling top" or "whirlwind") meaning "speed." V.32terbo is the third version developed of the V.32 modem protocol.

BISDN

See "Broadband Integrated Services Digital Network"

bit

A bit (short for *binary digit*) is the smallest unit of **data** in a computer. A bit has a single **binary** value, either 0 or 1. Although computers usually provide **instructions** that can test and manipulate bits, they generally are designed to store data and execute instructions in bit multiples called bytes. In most computer systems, there are eight bits in a **byte**. The value of a bit is usually stored as either above or below a designated level of electrical charge in a single capacitor within a memory device.

Half a byte (four bits) is called a **nibble**. In some systems, the term **octet** is used for an eight-bit unit instead of byte. In many systems, four eight-bit bytes or octets form a 32-bit

word. In such systems, instruction lengths are sometimes expressed as full-word (32 bits in length) or half-word (16 bits in length).

In telecommunication, the **bit rate** is the number of bits that are transmitted in a given time period, usually a second.

bit bucket

Computer jargon users say that data which has been lost or thrown away has gone in the bit bucket. (A **bit**, short for *binary digit*, is the smallest unit of **data** in a computer.)

For example, once you read an e-mail note and then delete it, it goes into the bit bucket (which sometimes is represented by a trash can icon). Of course, you can always look at deleted data as being recycled to make way for more new data.

In data that is truncated, the data after the truncation point gets put in the bit bucket. Actually, it doesn't get put anywhere; it just isn't considered at all by the program that does the truncation.

bit depth

In **digital audio**, bit depth describes the potential accuracy of a particular piece of hardware or software that processes audio data. In general, the more bits that are available, the more accurate the resulting output from the data being processed.

Bit depth is frequently encountered in specifications for analog-to-digital converters (**ADCs**) and digital-to-analog converters (**DACs**), when reading about software **plug-ins**, and when recording audio using a professional medium such as a **digital audio workstation** or a **Digital Audio Tape** machine.

Bit depth is the number of **bit**s you have in which to describe something. Each additional bit in a binary number doubles the number of possibilities. By the time you have a 16-bit sequence, there are 65,536 possible levels. Add one more bit, and you double the possible accuracy (to 131,072 levels). When you have a 24-bit process or piece of 24-bit hardware, there are 16,777,216 available levels of audio.

bit error rate

In telecommunication transmission, the bit error rate (BER) is the percentage of bits that have errors relative to the total number of bits received in a transmission, usually expressed as ten to a negative power. For example, a transmission might have a BER of 10 to the minus 6, meaning that, out of 1,000,000 bits transmitted, one bit was in error. The BER is an indication of how often a **packet** or other data unit has to be retransmitted because of an error. Too high a BER may indicate that a slower data rate would actually improve overall transmission time for a given amount of transmitted data since the BER might be reduced, lowering the number of packets that had to be resent.

A BERT (bit error rate test or tester) is a procedure or device that measures the BER for a given transmission.

bit map

A bit map (often spelled "bitmap") defines a display space and the color for each **pixel** or "bit" in the display space. A **Graphics Interchange Format** and a **JPEG** are examples of graphic image file types that contain bit maps.

A bit map does not need to contain a bit of color-coded information for each pixel on every row. It only needs to contain information indicating a new color as the display scans along a row. Thus, an image with much solid color will tend to require a small bit map.

Because a bit map uses a fixed or **raster graphics** method of specifying an image, the image cannot be immediately rescaled by a user without losing definition. A **vector graphics** graphic image, however, is designed to be quickly rescaled. Typically, an image is created using vector graphics and then, when the artist is satisfied with the image, it is converted to (or saved as) a raster graphic file or bit map.

bit rate

In **digital** telecommunication, the bit rate is the number of **bit**s that pass a given point in a telecommunication network in a given amount of time, usually a second. Thus, a bit rate is usually measured in some multiple of bits per second—for example, kilobits, or thousands of bits per second (**Kbps**). The term *bit rate* is a synonym for **data transfer rate** (or simply *data rate*). *Bit rate* seems to be used more often when discussing transmission technology details and *data transfer rate* (or *data rate*) when comparing transmission technologies for the end user.

bit robbing

Bit robbing is a technique used in **signaling** on the **T-carrier system**, the widely-used system for transmitting both voice and data in **digital** form in the public switched telephone network (**PSTN**) and in private networks. In the basic T-1 system, a 193 bit frame, serving 24 **channel**s, is transmitted in a sequence of 12 frames that are referred to as a *superframe*. Special signaling information, such as whether a voice channel is on-hook or off-hook, is included within the superframe by using a bit (called the *a bit*) that is "robbed" from the sixth frame as a signaling bit and another bit (the *b bit*) that is robbed from the 12th frame.

Bit robbing is acceptable for voice conversations or data transmissions that are received by a modem but not for "pure" data transmission (where every bit is significant). Bit robbing is the reason that a 64 **Kbps** channel only carries 56 Kbps of usable data. Bit robbing is a form of in-band signaling.

bit stream

A bit stream is a contiguous sequence of **bit**s, representing a stream of **data**, transmitted continuously over a communications path, serially (one at a time).

bit stuffing

In telecommunication, bit stuffing is the addition of a small number of **binary** digits to a transmission unit in order to fill it up to a standard size or to help synchronize signaling rates between points in a network. The receiver knows how to detect and remove or disregard the stuffed bits.

For example, the timing or bit rate of **T-carrier system** signals is constantly synchronized between any terminal device and an adjacent **repeater** or between any two repeaters. The synchronization is achieved by detecting the transition in polarity for 1 bits in the data stream. (T-1 signaling uses *bipolar* signaling, where each successive bit with a value of 1 is represented by **voltage** with a reverse polarity from the previous bit. Bits with a value of 0 are represented by a no-voltage time slot.) If more than 15 bits in a row are sent with a 0 value, this "lull" in 1 bits that the system depends on for synchronization may be long enough for two end points to become out of synchronization. To handle this situation (the sequence of more than 15 0 bits), the signal is "stuffed" with a short, unique bit pattern (which includes some 1 bits) that is recognized as a synchronization pattern. The receiving end removes the stuffed bits and restores the bit stream to its original sequence.

bitmap

See "bit map"

BITNET

BITNET is a network of academic sites comparable to but separate from the Internet. BITNET originated the utility known as the **list server** and Internet users can get access to BITNET list servers (or subscription lists). E-mail can be exchanged between users on BITNET and the Internet. As the Internet grows, BITNET is becoming less important.

bits per second

In data communications, bits per second (abbreviated bps) is a common measure of data speed for computer **modem** and transmission carriers. As the term implies, the speed in bps is equal to the number of bits transmitted or received each second. The duration d of a data bit, in seconds, is inversely proportional to the **digital** transmission speed s in bps:

$$d = 1/s$$

Larger units are sometimes used to denote high data speeds. One kilobit per second (abbreviated Kbps in the U.S.; kbps elsewhere) is equal to 1,000 bps. One megabit per second (Mbps) is equal to 1,000,000 bps or 1,000 Kbps.

Computer modems for **twisted pair** telephone lines usually operate at speeds between 14.4 and 57.6 Kbps. The most common speeds are 28.8 and 33.6 Kbps. So-called "cable modems," designed for use with TV cable networks, can operate at more than 100 Kbps. Fiberoptic modems are the fastest of all; they can send and receive data at many Mbps.

The **bandwidth** of a signal depends on the speed in bps. With some exceptions, the higher the bps number, the greater is the nominal signal bandwidth. (Speed and bandwidth are, however, not the same thing.) Bandwidth is measured in standard frequency units of **kHz** or **MHz**.

Data speed was formerly specified in terms of **baud**, which is a measure of the number of times a digital signal changes state in one second. Baud, sometimes called the "baud rate," is almost always a lower figure than bps for a given digital signal. The terms are often used interchangeably, even though they do not refer to the same thing. If you hear that a computer modem can function at "33,600 baud" or "33.6 kilobaud," you can be reasonably sure that the term is being misused, and the figures actually indicate bps.

BizTalk

BizTalk is an industry initiative headed by Microsoft to promote Extensible Markup Language (**XML**) as the common data exchange language for e-commerce and application integration on the Internet. While not a standards body per se, the group is fostering a common XML message-passing architecture to tie systems together. BizTalk says that the growth of e-commerce requires businesses using different computer technologies to have a means to share data. Accepting XML as a platform-neutral way to represent data transmitted between computers, the BizTalk group provides guidelines, referred to as the BizTalk Framework, for how to publish **schema** (standard data structures) in XML and how to use XML messages to integrate software programs.

In addition to Microsoft, other vendors such as **SAP** and CommerceOne are supporting BizTalk. Microsoft offers BizTalk Server 2000, which can implement XML-based data integration. The server software includes tools to create and design XML definitions, map data from one definition to another, and manage process flow, document verification, and data exchange and processing.

black hat

Black hat is used to describe a **hacker** (or, if you prefer, **cracker**) who breaks into a computer system or network with malicious intent. Unlike a **white hat** hacker, the black hat hacker takes advantage of the break-in, perhaps destroying files or stealing data for some future purpose. The black hat hacker may also make the exploit known to other hackers and/or the public without notifying the victim. This gives others the opportunity to exploit the vulnerability before the organization is able to secure it.

The term comes from old Western movies, where heros often wore white hats and the "bad guys" wore black hats.

Blackberry

BlackBerry is a **handheld** device made by RIM (Research In Motion) that competes with another popular handheld, the **Palm**, and is marketed primarily for its **wireless e-mail** handling capability. Through partners, BlackBerry also provides access to other Internet services. Like the Palm, BlackBerry is also a personal digital assistant (**PDA**) that can include software for maintaining a built-in address book and personal schedule. In addition, it can also be configured for use as a **pager**.

Exploiting the trends toward worker mobility and the growth in e-mail traffic, BlackBerry's makers provide software that forwards a user's incoming mail from the user's individual e-mail account or to a user's corporate e-mail address through a customer-selected wireless network to the BlackBerry where it is stored for reading. Outgoing e-mail goes directly to the addressee from the BlackBerry but a copy of the e-mail also goes to the user's home e-mail box. Software is also provided for synchronizing address books and schedules with the desktop system.

Compared to the Palm, the BlackBerry is somewhat simpler and offers fewer options and applications. Its unnamed **operating system** apparently takes up a relatively small space on its 4 megabyte flash memory, which is also used to store user data. Unlike the Palm, whose users write text using a stylus, BlackBerry offers a tiny keyboard that some users say is faster to use in spite of its size. BlackBerry comes in two configurations, one with a slightly larger **LCD** display.

blind carbon copy

See "Bcc"

BLOB

1) In computers, a BLOB (binary large object), pronounced BLAHB and sometimes spelled in all lower case, is a large **file**, typically an **image** or sound file, that must be handled (for example, uploaded, downloaded, or stored in a **database**) in a special way because of its size. According to Eric Raymond, the main idea about a BLOB is that the handler of the file (for example, the database manager) has no way of understanding the file in order to figure out how to deal with it—it might as well be a large piece of coal, but there it is and now what? Other sources emphasize that the term was coined to refer to big data objects and to connote the problems they sometimes present in handling them. One application that deals with BLOBs is the database storage of large multimedia objects, such as films and television programs.

2) In computer graphics, a blob (lowercase) is a visual object that, according to one user of the Persistence of Vision ray tracer, a freeware image creation tool, has "an interesting shape type" that is flexible and amenable to animation.

3) In general, a blob is an amorphous and undefinable object. There are blobs in astronomy as well as in unidentified flying object studies. There was a science-fiction movie called "The Blob."

block cipher

A block **cipher** is a method of **encrypting text** (to produce **ciphertext**) in which a cryptographic key and **algorithm** are applied to a block of data (for example, 64 contiguous **bit**s) at once as a group rather than to one bit at a time. The main alternative method, used much less frequently, is called the **stream cipher**.

So that identical blocks of text do not get encrypted the same way in a message (which might make it easier to decipher the ciphertext), it is common to apply the ciphertext from the previous encrypted block to the next block in a sequence. So that identical messages encrypted on the same day do not produce identical ciphertext, an *initialization vector* derived from a *random number generator* is combined with the text in the first block and the key. This ensures that all subsequent blocks result in ciphertext that doesn't match that of the first encrypting.

blog

On a Web site, a blog, a short form of *Web log* or *weblog*, is a personal journal that is frequently updated and intended for general public consumption. Blogs generally represent the personality of the author or the Web site and its purpose. Topics sometimes include brief philosophical musings, commentary on Internet and other social issues, and links to other sites the author favors. The essential characteristics of the blog are its journal form, typically a new entry each day, and its informal style.

The author of a blog is often referred to as a blogger. People who post new journal entries to their blog may often say they blogged today, they blogged it to their site, or that they still have to blog.

blogging

See "blog"

Blowfish

Blowfish is an **encryption algorithm** that can be used as a replacement for the **DES** or **IDEA** algorithms. It is a symmetric (that is, a secret or **private key**) **block cipher** that uses a variable-length **key**, from 32 bits to 448 bits, making it useful for both domestic and exportable use. (The U.S. government forbids the exportation of encryption software using keys larger than 40 bits except in special cases.)

Blowfish was designed in 1993 by Bruce Schneier as an alternative to existing encryption algorithms. Designed with 32-bit instruction processors in mind, it is significantly faster than DES. Since its origin, it has been analyzed considerably. Blowfish is unpatented, license-free, and available free for all uses.

blue bomb

A "blue bomb" (also known as "WinNuke") is a technique for causing the Windows **operating system** of someone you're communicating with to crash or suddenly terminate. The "blue bomb" is actually an out-of-band network **packet** containing information that the operating system can't process. This condition causes the operating system to "crash" or terminate prematurely. The operating system can usually be restarted without any permanent damage other than possible loss of unsaved data when you crashed.

The blue bomb derives its name from the effect it sometimes causes on the display as the operating system is terminating—a white-on-blue error screen that is commonly known as **blue screen of death**. Blue bombs are sometimes sent by multi-player game participants who are about to lose or users of Internet Relay Chat (**IRC**) who are making a final comment. This is known as "nuking" someone. A commonly-used program for causing the blue bomb is WinNuke. Many Internet service providers are filtering out the packets so they don't reach users.

Blue Book

The Blue Book is the informal name for the standard specification document for *stamped multisession* (also known as the **enhanced CD** or **E-CD**) disk format, developed in 1995 from a supplement to Philips and Sony's 1988 **Orange Book**. The Blue Book defines a format for enhanced CDs for inclusion of multimedia data (such as video clips, text, and images) on a standard audio **CD**. The disks play normally on a CD-player, and display the extra data when they are played on a device with multimedia capabilities, such as a computer's **CD-ROM** drive, or a **CD-i** player.

Like all CD formats, the Blue Book specifications are built on the details of the **Red Book**, which defined the format for audio CDs. The Blue Book specifies two sessions: up to 99 Red Book audio tracks in the first session (closest to the center of the disk), and a **Yellow Book**-based data track in the second session (closest to the outside edge of the disk). Other Blue Book details include the Red Book disk specification, file formats (including CD Plus information files), and an **ISO 9660**-compatible directory structure to organize the various types of data. The Blue Book is supported as a licensed standard definition by Philips, Sony, Microsoft, and Apple.

A B C D E F G H I J K L M N O P Q R S T U V,W X,Y,Z

blue laser

A blue laser is a **laser** (pronounced LAY-zer) with a shorter **wavelength** than the red laser used in today's **compact disk** and **laser printer** technologies and the ability to store and read two to four times the amount of data. When available in the marketplace, personal computer users may be able to buy a laser printer with a resolution up to 2400 pixels or dots per inch at an affordable price. The same technology in compact disk and CD-ROM devices may provide a dramatic breakthrough in storage capability without an increase in device size.

A laser (an acronym for "light amplification by stimulated emission of radiation") is a *coherent* (meaning all one wavelength, unlike ordinary light which showers on us in many wavelengths) and focused beam of *photons* or particles of light. The photons are produced as the result of a chemical reaction between special materials and then focused into a concentrated beam in a tube containing reflective mirrors. In the blue laser technology, the special material is **gallium nitride**. Even a small shortening of wavelength of light can have a dramatic effect in the ability to store and access data. A shorter wavelength allows a single item of data (0 or 1) to be stored in a smaller space.

Red lasers used in today's technologies have wavelengths of over 630 nanometers (or 630 billionths of a meter). The blue laser has a wavelength of 414 nanometers.

Shuji Nakamura, a Japanese researcher working in a small chemical company, Nichia Chemical Industries, built the first blue laser diode. However, Fujitsu and Xerox have also announced progress in the ability to manufacture blue laser diodes. Several companies, including Sony, have developed a blue-green laser. However, the shorter wavelength of the blue laser is much more of a breakthrough.

Cree Research and Hewlett-Packard are other companies making advances in this technology, some of which has been underwritten by the U.S. Defense Advanced Research Projects Agency (DARPA).

blue screen of death

The blue screen of death is a rather terrifying display image containing white text on a blue background that is generated by Windows operating systems when the system has suddenly terminated with an error. The system is locked up and must be restarted. The blue screen may include some **hexadecimal** values from a **core dump** that may help determine what caused the crash.

The blue screen of death can strike anywhere. At the Comdex trade show, Microsoft Chairman Bill Gates encountered the blue screen during a demonstration of Windows 98. (He had a spare computer standing by.)

Bluetooth

Bluetooth is a computing and telecommunications industry specification that describes how mobile phones, computers, and personal digital assistants (**PDA**s) can easily interconnect with each other and with home and business phones and computers using a short-range **wireless** connection. Using this technology, users of cellular phones, pagers, and personal digital assistants such as the PalmPilot will be able to buy a three-in-one phone that can double as a portable phone at home or in the office, get quickly synchronized with information in a desktop or notebook computer, initiate the sending or receiving of a fax, initiate a print-out, and, in general, have all mobile and fixed computer devices be totally coordinated. The technology requires that a low-cost transceiver chip be included in each device. Products with Bluetooth technology are expected to appear in large numbers beginning in 2001.

How It Works

Each device is equipped with a microchip tranceiver that transmits and receives in a previously unused frequency band of 2.45 GHz that is available globally (with some variation of bandwidth in different countries). In addition to data, up to three voice channels are available. Each device has a unique 48-bit address from the **IEEE** 802 standard. Connections can be point-to-point or multipoint. The maximum range is 10 meters. Data can be exchanged at a rate of 1 **megabit** per second (up to 2 Mbps in the second generation of the technology). A frequency hop scheme allows devices to communicate even in areas with a great deal of electromagnetic interference. Built-in encryption and verification is provided.

BMAN

BMAN (Broadband Metropolitan Area Network) is a telecommunications service from Sprint in the U.S. that provides corporate users in a metropolitan area with **broadband** access to the Internet on **optical fiber** lines in a system that preserves a connection even when one line is cut or fails. Using existing and supplemented infrastructure, BMAN uses a series of interlocking **ring**s so that a connection can be restored within 60 milliseconds if a single line goes down. The system uses **Synchronous Optical Network multiplexing**. BMAN is the metropolitan part of Sprint's overall national network, which it calls ION (Integrated On-Demand Network).

BNC

A BNC (Bayonet Neil-Concelman, or sometimes British Naval Connector) connector is used to connect a computer to a **coaxial cable** in a **10BASE-2 Ethernet** network. 10BASE-2 is a 10 MHz **baseband** network on a cable extending up to 185 meters—the 2 is a rounding up to 200 meters—without a repeater cable. 10BASE-2 Ethernets are also known as

"**Thinnet**," "thin Ethernet," or "cheapernets." The wiring in this type of Ethernet is thin, 50 ohm, baseband coaxial cable. The BNC connector in particular is generally easier to install and less expensive than other coaxial connectors.

A BNC male connector has a pin that connects to the primary conducting wire and then is locked in place with an outer ring that turns into locked position.

Different sources offer different meanings for the letters BNC. However, our most knowledgeable source indicates that the B stands for a bayonet-type connection (as in the way a bayonet attaches to a rifle) and the NC for the inventors of the connector, Neil and Concelman.

BO2K

See "Back Orifice"

board

In computers, a board, depending on usage, can be short for **motherboard**, the physical arrangement of a computer's basic components and circuitry, or it can refer to an expansion board (or *card* or *adapter*), which fits into one of the computer's expansion **slot**s and provides expanded capability.

BOC

BOC (Bell operating company) is a term for any of the 22 original companies (or their successors) that were created when AT&T was broken up in 1983 and given the right to provide local telephone service in a given geographic area. The companies had previously existed as subsidiaries of AT&T and were called the "Bell System." The purpose of the breakup was to create competition at both the local and long-distance service levels. BOCs compete with other, independent companies to sell local phone service. In certain areas, long-distance companies, including AT&T, can now compete for local service. Collectively, companies offering local phone service are referred to legally as local exchange carriers (**local exchange carrier**).

BOCs are not allowed to manufacture equipment and were initially not allowed to provide long-distance service. The **Telecommunications Act of 1996** now permits them to engage in long-distance business under certain circumstances. As of 1996, the BOCs consisted of original and successor companies to:

> Bell Telephone Company of Nevada, Illinois Bell, Indiana Bell, Michigan Bell, New England Telephone and Telegraph Company, New Jersey Bell, New York Telephone Company, U S West Communications Company, South Central Bell, Southern Bell, Southwestern Bell, Bell Telephone of Pennsylvania, The Chesapeake and Potomac Telephone Company, The Chesapeake and Potomac Telephone Company of Maryland, The Chesapeake and Potomac Telephone

Company of Virginia, The Diamond State Telephone Company, The Ohio Bell Telephone Company, The Pacific Telephone and Telegraph Company, and the Wisconsin Telephone Company.

bogie

The term bogie, also spelled bogey, refers to a false blip on a radar display. The term is also used to describe radar echoes that occur for unknown reasons, especially in the military, where such a signal might indicate hostile aircraft. There are two types of bogies: those that occur because of some real but unidentified or irrelevant object (called "real bogies" for the purpose of this discussion), and those that occur as a result of no concrete external object ("imaginary bogies").

A "real bogie" can be caused by an aircraft, a missile, a flock of birds, a tall ground-based metal structure, a balloon with a large payload or a radar-reflective coating, or (perhaps) an extraterrestrial spacecraft. Thunderstorms produce radar echoes, as do concentrated weather phenomena such as tornadoes. Meteors passing through the atmosphere create trails of ionized gas that can return radar signals. In the military, "real bogies" are sometimes produced by dropping myriad scraps of metal foil from high-flying aircraft, producing diffuse echoes that blind enemy radar over large regions.

An "imaginary bogie" can occur because of an external signal having a frequency and pulse rate near, or identical to, that of the radar's internal transmitter. When the radar receiver picks up the offending signal, it cannot differentiate between that signal and a true echo, so a blip appears on the display. This is how radar jamming works. The blip might exhibit fantastic velocity or acceleration as viewed on the radar display.

In computerized radar, bogie signals might conceivably arise from a specialized **virus** or **Trojan horse**, or from the activities of a brilliant but malicious hacker. This is an example of how, as systems get increasingly sophisticated, they often become more vulnerable to electronic attack.

bogomips

Bogomips is a measurement provided in the **Linux operating system** that indicates in a relative way how fast the computer **processor** runs. The program that provides the measurement is called BogoMips. Written by Linus Torvalds, the main developer of **Linux**, BogoMips can indicate when you **boot** a computer whether the system options have been specified for optimum performance. You compare the bogomips for your computer with what they ought to be for your computer's particular type of processor. Torvalds named the program BogoMips (for "bogus (or fake) MIPs") to suggest that performance measurements between two computers can be misleading because not all contributing factors are stated or even understood. Although **MIPS** (millions of instructions per second) has been frequently used in computer benchmarks, it's agreed that the variation of context tends to make the measurement misleading. Bogomips measures how many times the processor goes through a particular programming **loop** in a second.

BogoMIPS is built into some versions of Linux. It also exists as a stand-alone application program that you can download from certain Web sites. Currently, the record of 2182.35 bogomips was measured on a computer with an **AMD Athlon** microprocessor operating at 1,100 **MHz**.

boilerplate

In information technology, a boilerplate is a unit of writing that can be reused over and over without change. By extension, the idea is sometimes applied to reusable programming as in "boilerplate code." The term derives from steel manufacturing, where boilerplate is steel rolled into large plates for use in steam boilers. The implication is either that boilerplate writing has been time-tested and strong as "steel," or possibly that it has been rolled out into something strong enough for repeated reuse. Legal agreements, including software and hardware terms and conditions, make abundant use of boilerplates. The term is also used as an adjective as in "a boilerplate paragraph" and also as in "The entire document was boilerplate."

A boilerplate can be compared to a certain kind of **template**, which can be thought of as a fill-in-the-blanks boilerplate. Some typical boilerplates include: mission statements, safety warnings, commonly used installation procedures, copyright statements, and responsibility disclaimers.

In the 1890s, boilerplate was actually cast or stamped in metal ready for the printing press and distributed to newspapers around the United States. Until the 1950s, thousands of newspapers received and used this kind of boilerplate from the nation's largest supplier, the Western Newspaper Union. Some companies also sent out press releases as boilerplate so that they had to be printed as written.

bolt-on

On the Internet, bolt-on, perhaps inspired by **add-on**, is used to describe products and systems that can be quickly but securely attached to an existing **Web site**. The term most often describes some **e-commerce** solution for adding an online store to a Web site. A "bolt-on e-commerce solution" typically allows a Web site owner to create customized Web catalog pages, using a furnished template that includes a shopping cart approach for multiple item orders, and to have these pages hosted at the solution provider's server, where orders can be taken and reported to the Web site. Solution packages typically include the handling of credit-card applications and credit checking.

bookmark

Using a World Wide Web **browser**, a bookmark is a saved link to a Web **page** that has been added to a list of saved links. When you are looking at a particular Web site or **home page** and want to be able to quickly get back to it later, you can create a bookmark for it. You can think of your browser as a book full of (millions of) Web pages and a few well-placed bookmarks that you have chosen. The list that contains your bookmarks is the "bookmark list" (and sometimes it's called a "hotlist.")

Netscape and some other browsers use the bookmark idea. Microsoft's Internet Explorer uses the term "favorite."

bookmark portal

A bookmark portal is a free application service provider (**ASP**) Web site that allows registered users to save "bookmark" (Netscape) or "favorite" (Internet Explorer) Web links so that they can be accessed at any time from any Internet-connected device. With a bookmark portal, it is not necessary to transfer bookmarks from browser to browser or from machine to machine; instead, the user simply logs on to the ASP's Web site to access their bookmarks.

Many bookmark sites give users the option of creating a "personal web portal" where it is possible to manage multiple e-mail accounts and calendars, share files as well as bookmarks, and synchronize personal digital assistant (**PDA**) devices remotely.

Boole, George

See "George Boole"

Boolean

The term "Boolean," often encountered when doing searches on the Web (and sometimes spelled "boolean"), refers to a system of logical thought developed by the English mathematician and computer pioneer, George Boole (1815-64). In Boolean searching, an "and" operator between two words or other values (for example, "pear AND apple") means one is searching for documents containing both of the words or values, not just one of them. An "or" operator between two words or other values (for example, "pear OR apple") means one is searching for documents containing either of the words.

In computer operation with binary values, Boolean logic can be used to describe electromagnetically charged memory locations or circuit states that are either charged (1 or true) or not charged (0 or false). The computer can use an AND gate or an OR gate operation to obtain a result that can be used for further processing. The following table shows the results from applying AND and OR operations to two compared states:

0 AND 0 = 0   1 AND 0 = 0   1 AND 1 = 1
0 OR 0 = 0   0 OR 1 = 1   1 OR 1 = 1

For a summary of logic operations in computers, see **logic gate**.

boot

Tip: Make sure you have a **bootable floppy** diskette so you can restore your hard disk in the event it gets infected with a boot **virus**.

To boot (as a verb; also "to boot up") a computer is to load an **operating system** into the computer's main memory or random access memory (**RAM**). Once the operating system is loaded (and, for example, on a PC, you see the initial Windows or Mac desktop screen), it's ready for users to run **applications**. Sometimes you'll see an instruction to "reboot" the operating system. This simply means to reload the operating system (the most familiar way to do this on PCs is pressing the Ctrl, Alt, and Delete keys at the same time).

On larger computers (including **mainframe**), the equivalent term for "boot" is "Initial Program Load" (**IPL**) and for "reboot" is "re-IPL." Boot is also used as a noun for the act of booting, as in "a system boot." The term apparently derives from "bootstrap" which is a small strap or loop at the back of a leather boot that enables you to pull the entire boot on. There is also an expression, "pulling yourself up by your own bootstraps," meaning to leverage yourself to success from a small beginning. The booting of an operating system works by loading a very small program into the computer and then giving that program control so that it in turn loads the entire operating system.

Booting or loading an operating system is different from installing it, which is generally an initial one-time activity. (Those who buy a computer with an operating system already installed don't have to worry about that.) When you install the operating system, you may be asked to identify certain options or configuration choices. At the end of installation, your operating system is on your hard disk ready to be booted (loaded) into random access memory, the computer storage that is closer to the microprocessor and faster to work with than the hard disk. Typically, when an operating system is installed, it is set up so that when you turn the computer on, the system is automatically booted as well. If you run out of storage (memory) or the operating system or an application program encounters an error, you may get an error message or your screen may "freeze" (you can't do anything). In these events, you may have to reboot the operating system.

How Booting Works

Note: This procedure may differ slightly for Mac, UNIX, OS/2, or other operating systems.

When you turn on your computer, chances are that the operating system has been set up to boot (load into RAM) automatically in this sequence:

1. As soon as the computer is turned on, the Basic Input-Output System (**BIOS**) on your system's read-only memory (**ROM**) chip is "woken up" and takes charge. BIOS is already loaded because it's built-in to the ROM chip and, unlike random access memory (**RAM**), ROM contents don't get erased when the computer is turned off.

2. BIOS first does a "power-on self test" (POST) to make sure all the computer's components are operational. Then the BIOS's boot program looks for the special boot programs that will actually load the operating system onto the hard disk.

3. First, it looks on drive A (unless you've set it up some other way or there is no diskette drive) at a specific place where operating system boot files are located. (If the operating system is MS-DOS, for example, it will find two files named IO.SYS and MSDOS.SYS.) If there is a diskette in drive A but it's not a system disk, BIOS will send you a message that drive A doesn't contain a system disk. If there is no diskette in drive A (which is the most common case), BIOS looks for the system files at a specific place on your hard drive.

4. Having identified the drive where boot files are located, BIOS next looks at the first *sector* (a 512-byte area) and copies information from it into specific locations in RAM. This information is known as the *boot record* or **Master Boot Record**.

5. It then loads the boot record into a specific place (**hexadecimal** address 7C00) in RAM.

6. The boot record contains a program that BIOS now branches to, giving the boot record control of the computer.

7. The boot record loads the initial system file (for example, for DOS systems, IO.SYS) into RAM from the diskette or hard disk.

8. The initial file (for example, IO.SYS, which includes a program called SYSINIT) then loads the rest of the operating system into RAM. (At this point, the boot record is no longer needed and can be overlaid by other data.)

9. The initial file (for example, SYSINIT) loads a system file (for example, MSDOS.SYS) that knows how to work with the BIOS.

10. One of the first operating system files that is loaded is a system configuration file (for DOS, it's called CONFIG.SYS). Information in the configuration file tells the loading program which specific operating system files need to be loaded (for example, specific device **driver**).

11. Another special file that is loaded is one that tells which specific applications or commands the user wants to have included or performed as part of the boot process. In DOS, this file is named AUTOEXEC.BAT. In Windows, it's called WIN.INI.

12. After all operating system files have been loaded, the operating system is given control of the computer and performs requested initial commands and then waits for the first interactive user input.

bootable floppy

A bootable floppy is a diskette containing a back-up copy of your **hard disk** master boot record (MBR). In the event that the master boot record becomes "infected" by a **boot virus**, having a bootable floppy will allow you to load it back onto your hard disk. (Otherwise, you may have to reformat your hard disk which first erases everything on the disk including files you may not have a backup copy of. Even if you do, reformatting your hard disk will mean you have to reinstall everything you've backed up, a time-consuming procedure at the very least.)

BOOTP

BOOTP (Bootstrap Protocol) is a **protocol** that lets a network user be automatically configured (receive an **IP address**) and have an **operating system boot** or initiated without user involvement. The BOOTP **server**, managed by a network administrator, automatically assigns the IP address from a pool of addresses for a certain duration of time.

BOOTP is the basis for a more advanced network manager protocol, the Dynamic Host Configuration Protocol (**DHCP**).

Bootstrap Protocol

See "BOOTP"

bootstrapping

Bootstrapping is the leveraging of a small initial effort into something larger and more significant. A bootstrap is a small strap or loop at the back of a leather boot that enables you to pull the entire boot on. There is also a common expression, "pulling yourself up by your own bootstraps," meaning to leverage yourself to success from a small beginning.

The term **boot** is derived from *bootstrapping*. The booting of an **operating system** works by loading a very small program into the computer and then giving that program control so that it in turn loads the entire operating system.

Border Gateway Protocol

See "BGP"

bot

A bot (short for "robot") is a program that operates as an **agent** for a user or another program or simulates a human activity. On the Internet, the most ubiquitous bots are the programs, also called **spiders** or **crawlers**, that access Web sites and gather their content for **search engine** indexes.

A **chatterbot** is a program that can simulate talk with a human being. One of the first and most famous chatterbots (prior to the Web) was Eliza, a program that pretended to be a psychotherapist and answered questions with other questions.

Red and Andrette are two examples of programs that can be customized to answer questions from users seeking service for a product. Such a program is sometimes called a *virtual representative* or a *virtual service agent*.

Shopbots are programs that shop around the Web on your behalf and locate the best price for a product you're looking for. There are also bots such as OpenSesame that observe a user's patterns in navigating a Web site and customize the site for that user.

Knowbots are programs that collect knowledge for their users by automatically visiting Internet sites and gathering information that meets certain specified criteria.

bottleneck

A bottleneck is a stage in a process that causes the entire process to slow down or stop. For instance, if your dial-up Internet service provider (**ISP**) promises you Internet access at 56 **Kbps**, but your **modem** can only handle 14.4 Kbps, your modem's slow performance would be a bottleneck. The term bottleneck is derived from the narrow part of a bottle used to slow down the flow of liquid so that it doesn't flow too fast. However, in information technology, the bottleneck metaphor describes a link in a process that tends to slow down the entire process.

In "The Goal," a best-selling book about business development, author Eliyahu M. Goldratt's fictional character, factory manager Alex Rogo, struggles with bottlenecks in manufacturing and distribution in what Goldratt calls the "theory of constraints." Business Week credits Goldratt with inspiring businesses across America to look closely at how bottlenecks affect their ability to make money. A distribution center that receives goods faster than they can ship them out, for example, is forced to stockpile goods (often inefficiently) and becomes a bottleneck. Goldratt urges managers to step back and examine where the bottlenecks occur, determine why they are occurring, and find the most **elegant solution** to resolve them—which may or may not involve technology.

bounce e-mail

Bounce e-mail (sometimes referred to as *bounce mail*) is electronic mail that is returned to the sender because it cannot be delivered for some reason. Unless otherwise arranged, bounce e-mail usually appears as a new note in your inbox. E-mail users can encounter bounce e-mail because an addressee has changed his or her address, because their mail box is full, because the note is misaddressed, or for some other reason.

Bounce e-mail can be handled by a program when sending e-mail to a distribution list and most e-mail distribution list vendors include this capability. Such a bounce handler can retry later, unsubscribe the addressee from the list, or take some other action.

Some products and individuals have developed bounce e-mail handlers that recognize **spam** messages and return a bounce message so that the recipient will be taken off the list.

Some products and users use the term *bounce* to mean "forward a received note to someone else."

bouncing

See "debouncing"

Bourne shell

The Bourne shell is the original **UNIX shell** (command execution program, often called a *command interpreter*) that was developed at AT&T. Named for its developer, Stephen Bourne, the Bourne shell is also known by its program name, *sh*. The shell prompt (character displayed to indicate readiness for input) used is the $ symbol. The Bourne shell family includes the Bourne, **Korn shell**, bash, and zsh shells.

Bourne Again Shell (*bash*) is the free version of the Bourne shell distributed with **Linux** systems. Bash is similar to the original, but has added features such as command-line editing. Its name is sometimes spelled as Bourne Again SHell, the capitalized *Hell* referring to the difficulty some people have with it.

Zsh was developed by Paul Falstad as a replacement for both the Bourne and **C shell**. It incorporates features of all the other shells (such as file name completion and a history mechanism) as well as new capabilities. Zsh is considered similar to the Korn shell. Falstad intended to create in zsh a shell that would do whatever a programmer might reasonably hope it would do. Zsh is popular with advanced users.

Along with the Korn shell and the C shell, the Bourne shell remains among the three most widely used and is included with all UNIX systems. The Bourne shell is often considered the best shell for developing **script**s.

boustrophedon

Boustrophedon (from Greek for *ox-turning*) is writing that proceeds in one direction in one line (such as from left to right) and then in the reverse direction in the next line (such as from right to left). Some ancient languages, including one form of ancient Greek (650 BC), were written this way. The term derives from the way one would plow land with an ox, turning the ox back in the other direction at the end of a row. (It could be argued that boustrophedon is a more efficient way to both write and read, especially if your lines are very long.)

Some types of printers and their software print in this fashion (although the results, of course, are lines that are read in only one direction). The term is also used in describing a method used by a **raster** to scan (put the horizontal lines on) a display monitor.

BPCS

See "Business Planning and Control System"

BPML

See "Business Process Modeling Language"

BPR

See "business process reengineering"

bps

See "bits per second"

brain-machine interface

In artificial intelligence (**AI**), brain-machine interface is the potential ability of the human brain to accept a mechanical device as a natural part of its representation of the body. The immediate goal of brain-machine interface study is to provide a way for people with damaged sensory/motor functions to use their brain to control artificial devices and restore lost capabilities. By combining the latest developments in computer technology and hi-tech engineering, a person suffering from paralysis might be able to control a motorized wheelchair or a prosthetic limb by just thinking about it.

Before humans can use brain-interface techniques to control artificial devices, scientists feel they must first understand how the brain gives commands. They are gaining a better understanding of how brain-interface might work by recording neurological activity over long periods of time. For instance, Duke University Medical Center researchers have tested a neural system that allows scientists to record individual neuron responses from multiple electrodes implanted in a monkey's brain. The research team was able to combine the individual neuron responses outside the monkey by running the data through a computer using an algorithmic program. The monkey was encouraged to control its **robot** arm and reach for food. The monkey was able to successfully complete the task. Scientists were then able to use the neuron data they gathered to transmit the monkey's brain signals over the Internet in real time and control a robot arm 600 miles away. This is considered to be a major breakthrough in brain-machine interface study.

One of the biggest challenges in developing true brain-machine interface involves the development of electrode devices and surgical methods that are minimally invasive to allow safe, long-term recording of neurological activity. Duke's biomedical engineering department is now working on developing a telemetry **chip** to collect and transmit **data** through the skull without any external sockets or cables. This is expected to provide the necessary information needed to make brain-interface devices, which require deliberate conscious thought, as common as pacemakers for the heart, which work involuntarily.

brand

A brand is a product, service, or concept that is publicly distinguished from other products, services, or concepts so that it can be easily communicated and usually marketed. A brand name is the name of the distinctive product, service, or concept. Branding is the process of creating and disseminating the brand name. Branding can be applied to the entire corporate identity as well as to individual product and service names.

Brands are usually protected from use by others by securing a trademark or service mark from an authorized agency, usually a government agency. Before applying for a trademark or service mark, you need to establish that someone else hasn't already obtained one for your name. Although you can do the searching yourself, it is common to hire a law firm that specializes in doing trademark searches and managing the application process, which, in the U.S., takes about a year. Once you've learned that no one else is using it, you can begin to use your brand name as a trademark simply by stating it is a trademark (using the "TM" where it first appears in a publication or Web site). After you receive the trademark, you can use the registered ® symbol after your trademark.

Brands are often expressed in the form of *logos*, graphic representations of the brand. In computers, a recent example of widespread brand application was the "Intel Inside" label provided to manufacturers that use Intel's microchips.

A company's brands and the public's awareness of them is often used as a factor in evaluating a company. Corporations sometimes hire market reseach firms to study public recognition of brand names as well as attitudes toward the brands.

Here is the famous advertising copywriter and ad agency founder David Ogilvy's definition of a brand:

The intangible sum of a product's attributes: its name, packaging, and price, its history, its reputation, and the way it's advertised.

BREW

BREW (Binary Runtime Environment for Wireless) is Qualcomm's **open source** application development **platform** for **wireless** devices equipped for code division multiple access (**CDMA**) technology. BREW makes it possible for developers to create portable applications that will work on any handsets equipped with CDMA **chipset**s. Because BREW runs in between the application and the chip operating system software, the application can use the device's functionality without the developer needing to code to the system interface or even having to understand wireless applications. Users can download applications—such as text chat, enhanced e-mail, location positioning, games (both online and offline), and Internet radio—from carrier networks to any BREW-enabled phone.

BREW is competing for wireless software market share with **J2ME** (Java 2 Micro Edition), a similar platform from Sun Microsystems. The initial version of BREW is solely for CDMA networks; later versions could be enabled for time division multiple access (**TDMA**) and Global System for Mobile Communication (**GSM**) networks.

bricks and mortar

Bricks and mortar refers to businesses that have physical (rather than virtual or online) presences—in other words, stores (built of physical material such as bricks and mortar) that you can drive to and enter physically to see, touch, and purchase merchandise. This term is used as the basis for the term **clicks and mortar**, a business that sells products and services on the Web as well as from physical locations.

In an ongoing trend, large businesses that existed before the invention of the Web (and were therefore bricks and mortar businesses) are becoming clicks and mortar businesses. Companies like Amazon.com and others that have never owned a bricks and mortar storefront are generally known as **dotcom** companies.

bridge

In telecommunication networks, a bridge is a product that connects a local area network (**LAN**) to another local area network that uses the same **protocol** (for example, **Ethernet** or **token ring**). You can envision a bridge as being a device that decides whether a message from you to someone else is going to the local area network in your building or to someone on the local area network in the building across the street. A bridge examines each message on a LAN, "passing" those known to be within the same LAN, and forwarding those known to be on the other interconnected LAN (or LANs).

In bridging networks, computer or **node** addresses have no specific relationship to location. For this reason, messages are sent out to every address on the network and accepted only by the intended destination node. Bridges learn which addresses are on which network and develop a *learning table* so that subsequent messages can be forwarded to the right network.

Bridging networks are generally always interconnected local area networks since broadcasting every message to all possible destinations would flood a larger network with unnecessary traffic. For this reason, **router** networks such as the Internet use a scheme that assigns addresses to nodes so that a message or packet can be forwarded only in one general direction rather than forwarded in all directions.

A bridge works at the data-link (physical network) level of a network, copying a data **frame** from one network to the next network along the communications path.

A bridge is sometimes combined with a router in a product called a **brouter**.

bridge disc

See "CD-Bridge Disc"

bridge disk

See "CD-Bridge Disc"

bridge tap

A bridge tap is an extraneous length of dangling, unterminated cable on a communications line, usually left over from an earlier configuration, that can cause **impedance** mismatches and other undesired effects in transmissions. In a given cabling arrangement, allowance is usually made for a certain length of bridge taps.

ISDN uses the standard line code, 2B1Q, because it has the ability to handle the incidence of bridge taps well.

brightness

Hue, saturation, and brightness are aspects of color in the red, green, and blue (**RGB**) scheme. These terms are most often used in reference to the color of each **pixel** in a cathode ray tube (**cathode ray tube**) display. All possible colors can be specified according to hue, saturation, and brightness (also called *brilliance*), just as colors can be represented in terms of the R, G, and B components.

Most sources of visible light contain energy over a band of **wavelength**. Hue is the wavelength within the visible-light spectrum at which the energy output from a source is greatest. This is shown as the peak of the curves in the accompanying graph of intensity versus wavelength. In this example, all three colors have the same hue, with a wavelength slightly longer than 500 nanometers, in the yellow-green portion of the spectrum.

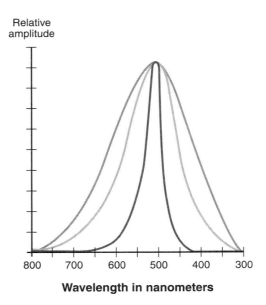

Wavelength in nanometers

Saturation is an expression for the relative **bandwidth** of the visible output from a light source. In the diagram, the saturation is represented by the steepness of the slopes of the curves. Here, the outer curve represents a color having low saturation, the middle curve represents a color having greater saturation, and the inner curve represents a color with fairly high saturation. As saturation increases, colors appear more "pure." As saturation decreases, colors appear more "washed-out."

Brightness is a relative expression of the intensity of the energy output of a visible light source. It can be expressed as a total energy value (different for each of the curves in the diagram), or as the amplitude at the wavelength where the intensity is greatest (identical for all three curves). In the RGB color model, the amplitudes of red, green, and blue for a particular color can each range from 0 to 100 percent of full brilliance. These levels are represented by the range of decimal numbers from 0 to 255, or hexadecimal numbers from 00 to FF.

British thermal unit (Btu)

A British thermal unit (Btu) is an English standard unit of **energy**. One Btu is the amount of thermal energy necessary to raise the temperature of one pound of pure liquid water by one degree Fahrenheit at the temperature at which water has its greatest density (39 degrees Fahrenheit). This is equivalent to approximately 1055 **joule** (or 1055 watt-seconds).

The Btu is often used as a quantitative specification for the energy-producing or energy-transferring capability of heating and cooling systems such as furnaces, ovens, refrigerators, and air conditioners. The heat output of computer equipment is often specified so that it can be considered when planning the size of climate control systems in buildings. Computer device heat output is expressed in Btus per hour. 3.7 Btus per hour is equivalent to 1 watt of heat dissipation.

broadband

Also see **bandwidth**.

In general, broadband refers to telecommunication in which a wide **band** of frequencies is available to transmit information. Because a wide band of frequencies is available, information can be multiplexed and sent on many different frequencies or channels within the band concurrently, allowing more information to be transmitted in a given amount of time (much as more lanes on a highway allow more cars to travel on it at the same time). Related terms are *wideband* (a synonym), **baseband** (a one-channel band), and **narrowband** (sometimes meaning just wide enough to carry voice, or simply "not broadband," and sometimes meaning specifically between 50 **cps** and 64 **Kpbs**).

Various definers of *broadband* have assigned a minimum data rate to the term. Here are a few:

- Newton's Telecom Dictionary: "...greater than a voice grade line of 3 KHz...some say [it should be at least] 20 KHz."

- Jupiter Communications: at least 256 Kbps.

- IBM Dictionary of Computing: A broadband channel is "6 MHz wide."

It is generally agreed that Digital Subscriber Line (**DSL**) and **cable TV** are broadband services in the downstream direction.

Broadband Integrated Services Digital Network

BISDN is both a concept and a set of services and developing standards for integrating digital transmission services in a **broadband** network of fiber optic and radio media. BISDN will encompass *frame relay* service for high-speed data that can be sent in large bursts, the Fiber Distributed-Data Interface (**FDDI**), and the Synchronous Optical Network (**SON**). BISDN will support transmission from 2 Mbps up to much higher, but as yet unspecified, rates.

BISDN is the broadband counterpart to **Integrated Services Digital Network**, which provides digital transmission over ordinary telephone company copper wires on the narrowband **local loop**.

broadcast

Also see **unicast**, **multicast**, and **anycast**.

In general, to broadcast (verb) is to cast or throw forth something in all directions at the same time. A radio or television broadcast (noun) is a program that is transmitted over airwaves for public reception by anyone with a receiver tuned to the right signal **channel**.

The term is sometimes used in e-mail or other message distribution for a message sent to all members, rather than specific members, of a group such as a department or enterprise.

On the Internet, certain **Web site**s deliver original or redistributed broadcasts from existing radio and television stations, using **streaming sound** or **streaming video** techniques, to Web users who visit the Web site or "tune it in" using a special program such as RealPlayer. Like publicly available radio and television broadcasts, Web broadcasts are available to anyone. The Web now offers live as well as prepackaged broadcasts and also plays back audio and video tapes. Some programming is scheduled and other prepackaged programs can be delivered on demand. Many Web users listen to music from a particular broacasting site as they **surf** other sites on the Web.

Broadcast should not be confused with **unicast**, a transmission to a specific receiver (like most e-mail messages); **multicast**, a transmission to multiple specific receivers (as in e-mail to a distribution list or a Web transmission over the **MBone** network to a specific group of receiving addresses); or **anycast**, a transmission to the nearest of a group of routers, used in Internet Protocol Version 6 (**IPv6**) as a technique for chain-updating a group of routers with new routing information.

brochureware

Brochureware refers to Web sites or pages that are produced by taking an organization's printed brochure and translating it directly to the Web without regard for the possibilities of the new medium. In extreme cases, all the copy in the brochure will be used as-is and visual images will be copied as well. The result will almost always be static and uninteresting.

Web designers usually suggest making a fresh start, using existing printed material as possible source material. While a Web site can be thought of as an "online brochure," most designers suggest taking advantage of the Web's interactive and dynamic capabilities, including **hypertext**, built-in programming, and **streaming video**.

brouter

A brouter (pronounced BRAU-tuhr or sometimes BEE-rau-tuhr) is a network **bridge** and a **router** combined in a single product. A bridge is a device that connects one local area network (**LAN**) to another local area network that uses the same **protocol** (for example, **Ethernet** or **token ring**). If a data unit on one LAN is intended for a destination on an interconnected LAN, the bridge forwards the data unit to that LAN; otherwise, it passes it along on the same LAN. A bridge usually offers only one path to a given interconnected LAN. A router connects a network to one or more other networks that are usually part of a wide area network (**WAN**) and may offer a number of paths to destinations on those networks. A router therefore needs to have more information than a bridge about the interconnected networks. It consults a routing table for this information. Since a given outgoing data unit or **packet** from a computer may be intended for an address on the local network, on an interconnected LAN, or the wide area network, it makes sense to have a single unit that examines all data units and forwards them appropriately.

browser

A browser is an application program that provides a way to look at and interact with all the information on the World Wide Web. The word "browser" seems to have originated prior to the Web as a generic term for user interfaces that let you browse (navigate through and read) **text** files online. By the time the first Web browser with a **graphical user interface** was available (**Mosaic**, in 1993), the term seemed to apply to Web content, too. Technically, a Web browser is a **client** program that uses the Hypertext Transfer Protocol (**HTTP**) to make requests of Web **server**s throughout the Internet on behalf of the browser user. A commercial version of the original browser, **Mosaic**, is in use. Many of the user interface features in Mosaic, however, went into the first widely-used browser, **Netscape** Navigator. Microsoft followed with its **Microsoft Internet Explorer**. Today, these two browsers are the only two browsers that the vast majority of Internet users are aware of. Although the online services, such as America Online, originally had their own browsers, virtually all now offer the Netscape or Microsoft browser. **Lynx** is a text-only browser for UNIX shell and VMS users. Another recently offered and well-regarded browser is **Opera**.

While some browsers also support e-mail (indirectly through e-mail Web sites) and the File Transfer Protocol (**FTP**), a Web browser is not required for those Internet protocols and more specialized client programs are more popular.

browserless Web

The browserless Web describes communication over the World Wide Web between programs rather than between people (with their Web **browser**s) and the server programs at Web sites. Some people believe that, within five years, program-to-program communication will generate more Internet traffic than browser-to-Web site communication. Although technically browser-to-Web site communication is program-to-program—the browser is a client program and the Web server is a server program on behalf of a Web site—the new program-to-program communication will not involve an interactive user. Such applications as ordering and order fulfillment are likely candidates for the browserless Web.

Program-to-program communication between businesses has been conducted for many years, most notably using Electronic Data Interchange (**EDI**). However, the arrival of a new data exchange technology—Extensible Markup Language (**XML**)—makes it possible for industries to develop standard names for data and for a company to easily tell other companies how its data is organized and can be accessed.

brute force cracking

Brute force (also known as brute force cracking) is a trial-and-error method used by application programs to decode encrypted data such as passwords or Data Encryption Standard (**DES**) keys, through exhaustive effort (using brute force) rather than employing intellectual strategies. Just as a criminal might break into, or "crack" a safe by trying many possible combinations, a brute force cracking application proceeds through all possible combinations of legal characters in sequence. Brute force is considered to be an infallible, although time-consuming, approach.

Crackers are sometimes used in an organization to test network security, although their more common use is for malicious attacks. Some variations, such as L0phtcrack from L0pht Heavy Industries, start by making assumptions, based on knowledge of common or organization-centered practices and then apply brute force to crack the rest of the data. L0phtcrack uses brute force to crack Windows NT passwords from a workstation. PC Magazine reported that a system administrator who used the program from a Windows 95 terminal with no administrative privileges, was able to uncover 85 percent of office passwords within twenty minutes.

BSB

See "backside bus"

BSD

BSD (originally: Berkeley Software Distribution) refers to the particular version of the **UNIX operating system** that was developed at and distributed from the University of California at Berkeley. "BSD" is customarily preceded by a number indicating the particular distribution level of the BSD system (for example, "4.3 BSD"). BSD UNIX has been popular and many commercial implementations of UNIX systems are based on or include some BSD code.

BSM

See "balanced scorecard methodology"

BSOD

See "blue screen of death"

BSP

See "business service provider"

BSRAM

See "burst SRAM"

B-tree

A B-tree is a method of placing and locating files (called records or keys) in a **database**. (The meaning of the letter B has not been explicitly defined.) The B-tree **algorithm** minimizes the number of times a medium must be accessed to locate a desired record, thereby speeding up the process.

B-trees are preferred when decision points, called nodes, are on **hard disk** rather than in random-access memory (**RAM**). It takes thousands of times longer to access a data element from hard disk as compared with accessing it from RAM, because a **disk drive** has mechanical parts, which read and write data far more slowly than purely electronic media. B-trees save time by using nodes with many branches (called children), compared with binary trees, in which each node has only two children. When there are many children per node, a record can be found by passing through fewer nodes than if there are two children per node. A simplified example of this principle is shown below.

In a tree, records are stored in locations called leaves. This name derives from the fact that records always exist at end points; there is nothing beyond them. The maximum number of children per node is the order of the tree. The number of required disk accesses is the depth. The image at left shows a binary tree for locating a particular record in a set of eight leaves. The image at right shows a B-tree of order three for locating a particular record in a set of eight leaves (the ninth leaf is unoccupied, and is called a null). The binary tree at left has a depth of four; the B-tree at right has a depth of three. Clearly, the B-tree allows a desired record to be located faster, assuming all other system parameters are

identical. The tradeoff is that the decision process at each node is more complicated in a B-tree as compared with a binary tree. A sophisticated program is required to execute the operations in a B-tree. But this program is stored in RAM, so it runs fast.

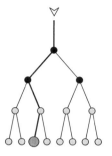
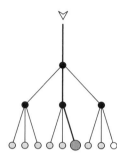

In a practical B-tree, there can be thousands, millions, or billions of records. Not all leaves necessarily contain a record, but at least half of them do. The difference in depth between binary-tree and B-tree schemes is greater in a practical database than in the example illustrated here, because real-world B-trees are of higher order (32, 64, 128, or more). Depending on the number of records in the database, the depth of a B-tree can and often does change. Adding a large enough number of records will increase the depth; deleting a large enough number of records will decrease the depth. This ensures that the B-tree functions optimally for the number of records it contains.

Also see **tree structure**. Compare **binary tree**, **M-tree**, **splay tree**, and **X-tree**.

Btu

See "British thermal unit (Btu)"

BTW

See "chat abbreviations"

bubble help

In a computer user interface, bubble help is text information that is displayed in a small balloon or box when a computer user moves the mouse cursor over a selected user interface element, such as the iconic items in a task bar. The box (or "bubble") is usually timed to disappear after a few seconds.

When developing a user interface with bubble help, a programmer writes code that tells the size and background color of the box, the text message to display, and when it should be removed. Bubble help is provided in most Microsoft applications, including Access and Word.

bucket brigade

A bucket brigade attack is one in which the attacker intercepts messages in a **public key exchange** and then retransmits them, substituting their own **public key** for the requested one, so that the two original parties still appear to be communicating with each other directly. The attacker uses a program that appears to be the **server** to the **client** and appears to be the client to the server. The attack may be used simply to gain access to the messages, or enable the attacker to modify them before retransmitting them. The term derives from the bucket brigade method of putting out a fire by handing buckets of water from one person to another between a water source and the fire. Another name for the bucket brigade attack is the more accurately descriptive name, man-in-the-middle, based on the ball game where a number of people try to throw a ball directly to each other while one person in between them attempts to catch it.

buckytube

See "nanotube"

buffer

A buffer is a data area shared by hardware devices or program processes that operate at different speeds or with different sets of priorities. The buffer allows each device or process to operate without being held up by the other. In order for a buffer to be effective, the size of the buffer and the algorithms for moving data into and out of the buffer need to be considered by the buffer designer. Like a **cache**, a buffer is a "midpoint holding place" but exists not so much to accelerate the speed of an activity as to support the coordination of separate activities.

This term is used both in programming and in hardware. In programming, buffering sometimes implies the need to screen data from its final intended place so that it can be edited or otherwise processed before being moved to a regular file or database.

buffer overflow

A buffer overflow occurs when a program or process tries to store more data in a **buffer** (temporary data storage area) than it was intended to hold. Since buffers are created to contain a finite amount of data, the extra information—which has to go somewhere—can overflow into adjacent buffers, corrupting or overwriting the valid data held in them. Although it may occur accidentally through programming error, buffer overflow is an increasingly common type of security attack on **data integrity**. In buffer overflow attacks, the extra data may contain codes designed to trigger specific actions, in effect sending new **instructions** to the attacked computer that could, for example, damage the user's files, change data, or disclose confidential information. Buffer overflow attacks are said to have arisen because the **C** programming language supplied the framework, and poor programming practices supplied the vulnerability.

In July 2000, a vulnerability to buffer overflow attack was discovered in Microsoft Outlook and Outlook Express. A programming flaw made it possible for an attacker to compromise the integrity of the target computer by simply sending an e-mail message. Unlike the typical **e-mail virus**, users could not protect themselves by not opening attached files; in fact, the user did not even have to open the message to enable the attack. The programs' message header mechanisms had a defect that made it possible for senders to overflow the area with extraneous data, which allowed them to execute whatever type of code they desired on the recipient's computers. Because the process was activated as soon as the recipient downloaded the message from the server, this type of buffer overflow attack was very difficult to defend. Microsoft has since created a **patch** to eliminate the vulnerability.

bug

In computer technology, a bug is a coding error in a computer **program**. (Here we consider a program to also include the *microcode* that is manufactured into a **microprocessor**.) The process of finding bugs before program users do is called **debugging**. Debugging starts after the code is first written and continues in successive stages as code is combined with other units of programming to form a software product, such as an **operating system** or an **application**. After a product is released or during public **beta test**ing, bugs are still apt to be discovered. When this occurs, users have to either find a way to avoid using the "buggy" code or get a **patch** from the originators of the code.

A bug is not the only kind of problem a program can have. It can run bug-free and still be difficult to use or fail in some major objective. This kind of flaw is more difficult to test for (and often simply isn't). It is generally agreed that a well-designed program developed using a well-controlled process will result in fewer bugs per thousands of lines of code.

The term's origin has been wrongly attributed to the pioneer programmer, **Grace Hopper**. In 1944, Hopper, a young Naval Reserve officer, went to work on the Mark I computer at Harvard, becoming one of the first people to write programs for it. As Admiral Hopper, she later described an incident in which a technician is said to have pulled an actual bug (a moth, in fact) from between two electrical relays in the Mark II computer. In his book, *The New Hacker's Dictionary*, Eric Raymond reports that the moth was displayed for many years by the Navy and is now the property of the Smithsonian. Raymond also notes that Admiral Hopper was already aware of the term when she told the moth story. The term was used prior to modern computers to mean an industrial or electrical defect.

Less frequently, the term is applied to a computer hardware problem.

bulletin board system

A bulletin board system (BBS), is a computer that can be reached by computer **modem** dialing (and, in some cases, by **Telnet**) for the purpose of sharing or exchanging messages or other files. Some BBS's are devoted to specific interests; others offer a more general service. The definitive *BBS List* says that there are 40,000 BBS's world-wide.

Among special interests represented on BBS's are dentistry, law, guns, multi-player games, Druidic practices, and information for the disabled. A significant number of BBS sites offer "adult-oriented" chat and images that can be downloaded. Many BBS's are free; some charge a membership or use fee.

Essentially, a bulletin board system is a **host** computer that is accessible by dial-up phone (you need to know the phone number) or, at some sites, via Telnet. Since calling a bulletin board system can involve long-distance charges, you may want to try starting with some in your area.

Bulletin board systems originated and generally operate independently of the Internet. However, many BBS's have Web sites. And many Internet **access provider**s have bulletin board systems from which new Internet users can download the necessary software to get connected.

BBS's have their own culture and jargon. A **sysop** is the person who runs the site (many BBS's are on small home computers that have simply added the necessary software to keep track of files and users). Many BBS users chat online (see **chat abbreviations**).

burn

To burn (verb) a CD-ROM is a colloquial term meaning to write to the CD-ROM all the content that is to be put on it for a given purpose. After you've burned or burnt (either is correct) the CD-ROM, copies can be made one at a time or in multiples (the latter process is usually called duplication or replication).

burn rate

In venture investing and new company development, the burn rate is the rate at which a new company is spending its capital while waiting for profitable operation. Typically, a new company, especially in new, fast-growing fields such as Internet commerce or publishing, expects in its early stages to spend money faster than it can take in revenue. The term is often seen in financial reviews and discussions about new Internet companies, public or private, where the question is whether revenue will begin to flow in sufficient amounts before the invested capital plus revenue is "burnt up." When the burn rate begins to exceed plan or revenue fails to meet expectations, the usual recourse is to reduce the burn rate

(which, in most companies, means reducing the staff). When it is burnt up (or before), a company has to find additional capital through loans, private equity investors, or a public stock offering; merge with or sell itself to another company; go non-profit; or terminate its operation.

Michael Wolff's book, *Burn Rate* (subtitled "How I Survived the Gold Rush Years on the Internet"), describes the emotional peaks and valleys associated with the term.

BURN-Proof

BURN-Proof (Buffer Under Run Error Proof) is a technology developed by Sanyo that allows compact disc (**CD**) recording to automatically stop in the event of an unplanned interruption and then to resume recording. BURN-Proof is a registered trademark of Sanyo.

When a CD is burned (recorded), the data must usually be written onto the CD without any interruption. If an interruption, such as the opening of a new application, does occur, a Buffer Under Run error occurs and the burn is unsuccessful. BURN-Proof technology located on **firmware** inside the **CD-R** or **CD-RW** drive monitors the recording process. If the drive detects a Buffer Under Run error, it suspends recording. When the problem is resolved, the CD-R or CD-RW drive restarts recording data from where it stopped.

BURN-Proof technology is used with CD drive speeds **12x** and higher because Buffer Under Run errors occur more often with faster drives. Many CD recording application vendors provide BURN-Proof support with their software.

burst

Burst is a term used in a number of information technology contexts to mean a specific amount of data sent or received in one intermittent operation. It can be contrasted with *streamed*, *paced*, or *continuous*. Generally, a burst operation implies that some threshold has been reached that triggers the burst. Depending on the particular technology, a burst operation can be intermittent at a regular or an irregular rate.

Burst Extended Data Output DRAM

See "BEDO DRAM"

burst SRAM

Burst SRAM is used as the external **L1 and L2** memory for the **Pentium** microprocessor chipset. Burst SRAM (also known as SynchBurst **SRAM**) is synchronized with the system clock or, in some cases, the cache bus clock. This allows it be more easily synchronized with any device that accesses it and reduces access waiting time.

bus

In a computer or on a network, a bus is a transmission path on which **signal**s are dropped off or picked up at every device attached to the line. Only devices addressed by the signals pay attention to them; the others discard the signals. According to Winn L. Rosch, the term derives from its similarity to autobuses that stop at every town or block to drop off or take on riders

In general, the term is used in two somewhat different contexts:

1) A bus is a network topology or circuit arrangement in which all devices are attached to a line directly and all signals pass through each of the devices. Each device has a unique identity and can recognize those signals intended for it.

2) In a computer, a bus is the data path on the computer's **motherboard** that interconnects the microprocessor with attachments to the motherboard in expansion slots (such as hard disk drives, CD-ROM drives, and graphics adapters).

bus master

A bus master is the program, either in a microprocessor or more usually in a separate I/O controller, that directs traffic on the computer **bus** or input/output paths. The bus master is the "master" and the I/O devices on the bus are the "slaves." The bus master actually controls the bus paths on which the address and control signals flow. Once these are set up, the flow of data bits goes directly between the I/O device and the microprocessor.

Bush, Vannevar

See "Vannevar Bush"

business intelligence

Business intelligence (BI) is a broad category of **application**s and technologies for gathering, storing, analyzing, and providing access to **data** to help **enterprise** users make better business decisions. BI applications include the activities of **decision support system**s, query and reporting, online analytical processing (**OLAP**), statistical analysis, forecasting, and **data mining**.

Business intelligence applications can be:

- Mission-critical and integral to an enterprise's operations or occasional to meet a special requirement

- Enterprise-wide or local to one division, department, or project

- Centrally initiated or driven by user demand

This term was used as early as September, 1996, when a Gartner Group report said:

By 2000, Information Democracy will emerge in forward-thinking enterprises, with Business Intelligence information and applications available broadly to employees, consultants, customers, suppliers, and the public. The key to thriving in a competitive marketplace is staying ahead of the competition. Making sound business decisions based on accurate and current information takes more than intuition. Data analysis, reporting, and query tools can help business users wade through a sea of data to synthesize valuable information from it—today these tools collectively fall into a category called "Business Intelligence."

Business Planning and Control System

Business Planning and Control System (BPCS) is a popular system of **application program**s for manufacturing and other industries that is developed and sold by Systems Software Associates (SSA). SSA reports that BPCS is installed at over 8,000 business sites worldwide. The BPCS applications are divided into:

- Configurable enterprise financials (including accounts receivable and payable, cost accounting, remittance processing, and budgeting and analysis)

- Supply chain management applications (including sale performance management, purchasing, promotion, inventory management, and forecasting)

- Multi-mode manufacturing applications (including planning, production scheduling, capacity planning, shop floor control, and plant maintenance)

The key ideas in BPCS include:

- A general adherence to programming standards for distributed object computing (including **Common Object Request Broker Architecture**) and other standards

- A sophisticated use of **client/server** computing and **object** data repositories

- Adoption of the Microsoft Windows Desktop user interface for all end users site-wide

- A guided workstation-based system of installation

SSA augments its own sales and support force with a system of independent business associates. It has a widely-distributed customer base, with 34% of its customers in Europe, 22% in the Asia Pacific region, and 10% in Latin America.

Business Process Management Initiative

Established in August 2000, the Business Process Management Initiative (BPMI) is a non-profit organization that exists to promote the standardization of common business processes, as a means of furthering **e-business** and **B2B** development. BPMI was founded by a group of 16 e-business industry leaders: Aventail, Black Pearl, Blaze

Software, Bowstreet, Cap Gemini Ernst & Young, Computer Sciences Corporation, Cyclone Commerce, DataChannel, Entricom, Intalio, Ontology.Org, S1 Corporation, Versata, VerticalNet, Verve, and XMLFund. Since its inception, the group has grown to include more than 80 companies. BPMI's stated **mission** is "to promote and develop the use of Business Process Management (BPM) through the establishment of standards for process design, deployment, execution, maintenance, and optimization." By so doing, BPMI intends to make it much easier for enterprises to interact and to further develop the global marketplace. Currently, e-business reflects the idiosyncratic ways that business processes work within an organization. There are, for example, different names for the same item, and incompatible processes across organizations. The goal of BPMI is to overcome these problems and make it possible for organizations to communicate more effectively and share not only data, but applications.

The BPMI model of any two-way e-business process involves three main components, the *public interface* and two *private implementations*. The public interface, which is the area of interaction between two business partners, is supported by various protocols such as those associated with **BizTalk**, **ebXML**, and **RosettaNet**. The model further defines two private implementations, which are specific to the individual partners involved and can be described in any executable language. The Initiative has specified such a language, Business Process Modeling Language (**BPML**), which is an **XML**-based **metalanguage** that can be used to model components of business processes in the same way that XML can be used to model components of business data. An associated **query** language, BPQL (Business Process Query Language) has been developed by Initiative members as a standard management interface that can be used to deploy and execute defined business processes. Both BPML and BPQL are open specifications; BPML is available for download from the BPMI Web site. The organization intends to continue to develop and promote open standards specific to particular e-business needs.

Business Process Modeling Language

Business Process Modeling Language (BPML) is an Extensible Markup Language (**XML**)-based **metalanguage** developed by the Business Process Management Initiative (**BPMI**) as a means of modeling business processes, much as XML is, itself, a metalanguage with the ability to model enterprise data. BPML 0.4 is BPMI's first release, and includes specifications for **transaction**s and compensating transactions, dataflow, **message**s and scheduled events, business rules, security roles, and exceptions. BPMI has identified three crucial aspects of BPML capability: Because it will be used for **mission critical** applications, it must support both **synchronous** and **asynchronous distributed** transactions; because it will model business processes deployed over the Internet, it must offer reliable security

mechanisms; and because it will be used throughout integrated development environments, it must encompass project management capabilities.

An associated **query** language, Business Process Query Language (**BPQL**) has been developed by Initiative members as a standard management interface that can be used to deploy and execute defined business processes. According to BPMI, BPML and BPQL will be used to establish a standardized means of managing e-business processes through *Business Process Management Systems*, similarly to the way that **SQL** established a standardized means of managing business data through packaged database management systems (**DBMS**s). Both BPML and BPQL are open specifications. The first draft of the BPML specification was submitted to BPMI members in August 2000, and subsequently made publicly available in March 2001; the first BPQL draft is to be be made available by the end of 2001. The organization intends to continue to develop and promote open standards specific to particular **e-business** needs.

business process reengineering

Business process reengineering (BPR) is the analysis and redesign of **workflow** within and between enterprises. BPR reached its heyday in the early 1990's when Michael Hammer and James Champy published their best-selling book, "Reengineering the Corporation." The authors promoted the idea that sometimes radical redesign and reorganization of an **enterprise** (wiping the slate clean) was necessary to lower costs and increase quality of service and that **information technology** was the key enabler for that radical change. Hammer and Champy felt that the design of workflow in most large corporations was based on assumptions about technology, people, and organizational goals that were no longer valid. They suggested seven principles of reengineering to streamline the work process and thereby achieve significant levels of improvement in quality, time management, and cost:

1. Organize around outcomes, not tasks.

2. Identify all the processes in an organization and prioritize them in order of redesign urgency.

3. Integrate information processing work into the real work that produces the information.

4. Treat geographically dispersed resources as though they were centralized.

5. Link parallel activities in the workflow instead of just integrating their results.

6. Put the decision point where the work is performed, and build control into the process.

7. Capture information once and at the source.

By the mid-1990's, BPR gained the reputation of being a nice way of saying "**downsizing**." According to Hammer, lack of sustained management commitment and leadership,

unrealistic scope and expectations, and resistance to change prompted management to abandon the concept of BPR and embrace the next new methodology, enterprise resource planning (**ERP**).

business service provider

A business service provider (BSP) is a company that rents third-party software **application** packages to their customers. A BSP is similar to an an application service provider (**ASP**) in that it provides a cost-effective way to procure applications via networks. A BSP differs from an ASP in that it tailors a software package to its customer's needs and offers back-office solutions by **outsourcing** most (if not all) business processes, such as payroll and bookkeeping. Small and mid-sized firms are attracted to BSPs because they have low start-up costs and low monthly fees, whereas ASPs are more capital intensive. Agillon, eAlity, Employease and EConvergent are examples of succesful BSP companies.

business-to-business

See "B2B"

bypass

Bypass, in general, means either *to go around something by an external route rather than going through it*, or the means of accomplishing that feat. In network security, a bypass is a flaw in a security system that allows an attacker to circumvent security mechanisms to get system or network access. The actual point of entry is through a mechanism (either a hardware device or program, even just a piece of code) that enables the user to access the system without going through the security clearance procedures (such as **authentication**) that were set up by the system administrator. A bypass may be a mechanism put in place by an attacker, a flaw in the design, or an alternate access route left in place by developers. A bypass that is purposefully put in place as a means of access for authorized users is called a *back door* or a *trap door*. A *crypto bypass* is a flaw that allows data to circumvent the **encryption** process and escape, unencrypted, as **plaintext**.

byte

In most computer systems, a byte is a unit of data that is eight **binary** digits long. A byte is the unit most computers use to represent a character such as a letter, number, or typographic symbol (for example, "g", "5", or "?"). A byte can also hold a string of bits that need to be used in some larger unit for application purposes (for example, the stream of bits that constitute a visual image for a program that displays images or the string of bits that constitutes the machine code of a computer program).

In some computer systems, four bytes constitute a **word**, a unit that a computer processor can be designed to handle efficiently as it reads and processes each instruction. Some computer processors can handle two-byte or single-byte instructions.

A byte is abbreviated with a "B". (A bit is abbreviated with a small "b".) Computer storage is usually measured in byte multiples. For example, an 820 MB hard drive holds a nominal 820 million bytes—or megabytes—of data. Byte multiples are based on powers of 2 and commonly expressed as a "rounded off" decimal number. For example, one megabyte ("one million bytes") is actually 1,048,576 (decimal) bytes. (Confusingly, however, some hard disk manufacturers and dictionary sources state that bytes for computer storage should be calculated as powers of 10 so that a megabyte really would be one million decimal bytes.)

Some language scripts require two bytes to represent a character. These are called double-byte character sets (DBCS).

According to Fred Brooks, an early hardware architect for IBM, project manager for the OS/360 operating system, and author of *The Mythical Man-Month*, Dr. Werner Buchholz originated the term *byte* in 1956 when working on IBM's STRETCH computer.

Also see **megabyte**, **gigabyte**, **terabyte**, **petabyte**, and **exabyte**.

byte code

See "bytecode"

bytecode

Bytecode is computer **object code** that is processed by a program, usually referred to as a **virtual machine**, rather than by the "real" computer machine, the hardware **processor**. The virtual machine converts each generalized machine **instruction** into a specific machine instruction or instructions that this computer's processor will understand. Bytecode is the result of compiling source code written in a language that supports this approach. Most computer languages, such as **C** and **C++**, require a separate **compiler** for each computer **platform**—that is, for each computer **operating system** and the hardware set of instructions that it is built on. Windows and the Intel line of microprocessor architectures are one platform; Apple and the PowerPC processors are another. Using a language that comes with a virtual machine for each platform, your source language statements need to be compiled only once and will then run on any platform.

The best-known language today that uses the bytecode and virtual machine approach is **Java**. The **LISP** language, used in artificial intelligence applications, is an earlier language that compiled bytecode. Other languages that use bytecode or a similar approach include Icon and Prolog.

Rather than being interpreted one instruction at a time, Java bytecode can be recompiled at each particular system platform by a **just-in-time compiler**. Usually, this will enable the Java program to run faster. In Java, bytecode is contained in a **binary file** with a .CLASS suffix.

C

C is a structured, procedural programming language that has been widely used both for operating systems and applications and that has had a wide following in the academic community. Many versions of **UNIX**-based operating systems are written in C. C has been standardized as part of the Portable Operating System Interface (**POSIX**).

With the increasing popularity of **object-oriented programming**, C is being rapidly replaced as "the" programming language by **C++**, a superset of the C language that uses an entirely different set of programming concepts, and by **Java**, a language similar to but simpler than C++, that was designed for use in distributed networks.

C sharp

See "C#"

C shell

C shell is the **UNIX shell** (command execution program, often called a *command interpreter*) created by Bill Joy at the University of California at Berkeley as an alternative to UNIX's original shell, the **Bourne shell**. These two UNIX shells, along with the **Korn shell**, are the three most commonly used shells. The C shell program name is *csh*, and the shell prompt (the character displayed to indicate readiness for user input) is the % symbol. The C shell was invented for programmers who prefer a **syntax** similar to that of the **C** programming language.

The other popular member of the C shell family is called *tcsh* (for Tab C shell) and is an extended version of C shell. Some of tcsh's added features are: enhanced *history substitution* (which allows you to reuse commands you have already typed), spelling correction, and *word completion* (which allows you to type the first couple of letters in a word and hit the tab key to have the program complete it).

Once considered "bug**gy**", the C shell has had a number of different versions developed to overcome the flaws in the original program. Most often, only experienced users prefer to use the C shell. C is frequently the default shell at universities and research organizations and is the default on many systems, especially those derived from Berkeley UNIX.

C#

C# (pronounced "C-sharp") is a new **object-oriented programming** language from Microsoft, which aims to combine the computing power of **C++** with the programming ease of **Visual Basic**. C# is based on C++ and contains features similar to those of **Java**.

C# is designed to work with Microsoft's **.Net** platform. Microsoft's aim is to facilitate the exchange of information and services over the Web, and to enable developers to build highly **portable** applications. C# simplifies programming through its use of Extensible Markup Language (**XML**) and Simple Object Access Protocol (**SOAP**) which allow access to a programming **object** or **method** without requiring the programmer to write additional code for each step. Because programmers can build on existing code, rather than repeatedly duplicating it, C# is expected to make it faster and less expensive to get new products and services to market.

Microsoft is collaborating with ECMA, the international standards body, to create a standard for C#. International Standards Organization (**ISO**) recognition for C# would encourage other companies to develop their own versions of the language. Companies that are already using C# include Apex Software, Bunka Orient, Component Source, devSoft, FarPoint Technologies, LEAD Technologies, ProtoView, and Seagate Software.

C++

C++ is an object-oriented programming (**OOP**) language that is viewed by many as the best language for creating large-scale applications. C++ is a superset of the **C** language.

A related programming language, **Java**, is based on C++ but optimized for the distribution of program objects in a network such as the Internet. Java is somewhat simpler and easier to learn than C++ and has characteristics that give it other advantages over C++. However, both languages require a considerable amount of learning time.

C2

See "Class C2"

C3D

C3D (pronounced SEE-THREE-DEE) is a combined hardware/software process that captures a pair of two-dimensional images, objects, or scenes and automatically reconstructs them into a digital three-dimensional (**3-D**) model. In turn, this model can be used to create a **virtual** representation of the image, object, or scene. The C3D process uses a standard PC and camera to produce a realistic photographic model for viewing on a PC at a reconstruction accuracy of 50 **microns**. C3D can be used with other tools, such as the Virtual Reality Modelling Language (**VRML**).

C3D exploits the stereoptic function of the human brain, which is able to combine an image perceived by each eye into a 3-D perception. Capturing images using the C3D process allows the image to be manipulated horizontally, vertically, or spatially (that is, by distance) using one of three modelling representations: a polygon wire frame, shaded, or naturally rendering. Once you create the modeling representation, a photographic rendering from the image pairing is placed on the modelling representation to create the shaped model.

Current C3D application uses include: tire footprints, health care studies, police mugshots, virtual studio applications for TV, microscopic modelling objects, aerial road surveys, and museum artifact archiving.

C6

See "WinChip"

CA

See "certificate authority"

CAB

See "cabinet file"

cabinet file

In Microsoft program development, a cabinet is a single file created to hold a number of compressed files. A related set of cabinet files can be contained in a folder. During installation of a program, the compressed files in a cabinet are decompressed and copied to an appropriate directory for the user. A cabinet file usually has the file name **suffix** of ".cab".

Microsoft uses cabinet files in distributing its own products, such as PowerPoint, Microsoft Office for Windows, and Microsoft Money. Cabinet files save space and time during software distribution. They are decompressed during installation. Large files can be compressed and included in more than one cabinet file, each of which logically points to the next file, with all contained in a logical folder.

Development accountability for cabinet files is ensured by providing a signed digital certificate with the cabinet file. One "signature" covers all the files in a cabinet file. Cabinet files are created using Lempel-Ziv compression.

cable

See "coaxial cable"

cable head-end

A cable head-end is the facility at a local cable TV office that originates and communicates **cable TV** services and **cable modem** services to subscribers. In distributing cable television services, the head-end includes a satellite dish **antenna** for receiving incoming programming. This programming is then passed on to the subscriber. (Cable TV companies may also play videotapes and originate live programming.) Normally, all signals are those that are sent

downstream to the subscriber, but some are received upstream such as when a customer requests a **pay-per-view** program.

When a cable company provides Internet access to subscribers, the head-end includes the computer system and databases needed to provide Internet access. The most important component located at the head-end is the cable modem termination system (**CMTS**), which sends and receives digital cable modem signals on a cable network and is necessary for providing Internet services to cable subscribers.

cable modem

A cable modem is a device that enables you to hook up your PC to a local **cable TV** line and receive data at about 1.5 **Mbps**. This data rate far exceeds that of the prevalent 28.8 and 56 Kbps telephone modems and the up to 128 Kbps of Integrated Services Digital Network (**ISDN**) and is about the data rate available to subscribers of Digital Subscriber Line (**DSL**) telephone service. A cable modem can be added to or integrated with a **set-top box** that provides your TV set with channels for Internet access. In most cases, cable modems are furnished as part of the cable access service and are not purchased directly and installed by the subscriber.

A cable modem has two connections: one to the cable wall outlet and the other to a PC or to a set-top box for a TV set. Although a cable modem does **modulate** between **analog** and **digital** signals, it is a much more complex device than a telephone **modem**. It can be an external device or it can be integrated within a computer or set-top box. Typically, the cable modem attaches to a standard **10BASE-T Ethernet card** in the computer.

All of the cable modems attached to a cable TV company **coaxial cable** line communicate with a cable modem termination system (CMTS) at the local cable TV company office. All cable modems can receive from and send signals only to the CMTS, but not to other cable modems on the line. Some services have the upstream signals returned by telephone rather than cable, in which case the cable modem is known as a *telco-return* cable modem.

The actual **bandwidth** for Internet service over a cable TV line is up to 27 Mbps on the download path to the subscriber with about 2.5 Mbps of bandwidth for interactive responses in the other direction. However, since the local provider may not be connected to the Internet on a line faster than a **T-carrier system** at 1.5 Mpbs, a more likely data rate will be close to 1.5 Mpbs.

Leading companies using cable TV to bring the Internet to homes and businesses are @Home and Time-Warner.

In addition to the faster data rate, an advantage of cable over telephone Internet access is that it is a continuous connection.

cable modem termination system

A cable modem termination system (CMTS) is a component that exchanges digital signals with **cable modem**s on a cable network. A cable modem termination system is located at the local office of a cable television company.

A data service is delivered to a subscriber through **channel**s in a **coaxial cable** or **optical fiber** cable to a cable modem installed externally or internally to a subscriber's **computer** or television set. One television channel is used for upstream signals from the cable modem to the CMTS, and another channel is used for downstream signals from the CMTS to the cable modem. When a CMTS receives signals from a cable modem, it converts these signals into Internet Protocol (**IP**) **packets**, which are then sent to an IP **router** for transmission across the Internet. When a CMTS sends signals to a cable modem, it **modulates** the downstream signals for tranmission across the cable to the cable modem. All cable modems can receive from and send signals to the CMTS but not to other cable modems on the line.

cable TV

Cable TV is also known as "**CATV**" (community antenna television). In addition to bringing television programs to those millions of people throughout the world who are connected to a community antenna, cable TV will likely become a popular way to interact with the World Wide Web and other new forms of multimedia information and entertainment services.

Also see **cable modem**, **interactive TV**, and **WebTV**.

CableLabs Certified Cable Modems

See "DOCSIS"

cache

A cache (pronounced CASH) is a place to store something more or less temporarily. Web pages you request are stored in your browser's cache directory on your hard disk. That way, when you return to a page you've recently looked at, the browser can get it from the cache rather than the original server, saving you time and the network the burden of some additional traffic. You can usually vary the size of your cache, depending on your particular browser.

Computers include caches at several levels of operation, including **cache memory** and a **disk cache**. Caching can also be implemented for Internet content by distributing it to multiple servers that are periodically refreshed. (The use of the term in this context is closely related to the general concept of a distributed information base.)

Altogether, we are aware of these types of caches:

- International, national, regional, organizational and other "macro" caches to which highly popular information can be distributed and periodically updated and from which most users would obtain information.

- Local server caches (for example, corporate LAN servers or access provider servers that cache frequently accessed files). This is similar to the previous idea, except that the decision of what data to cache may be entirely local.

- Your Web **browser**'s cache, which contains the most recent Web files that you have downloaded and which is phyically located on your hard disk (and possibly some of the following caches at any moment in time).

- A **disk cache** (either a reserved area of RAM or a special hard disk cache) where a copy of the most recently accessed data and adjacent (most likely to be accessed) data is stored for fast access.

- RAM itself, which can be viewed as a cache for data that is initially loaded in from the hard disk (or other I/O storage systems).

- L2 **cache memory**, which is on a separate chip from the microprocessor but faster to access than regular RAM.

- L1 cache memory on the same chip as the microprocessor.

Also see: **buffer**, which, like a cache, is a temporary place for data, but with the primary purpose of coordinating communication between programs or hardware rather than improving process speed.

cache coherence

In a shared memory **multiprocessor** with a separate **cache memory** for each **processor**, it is possible to have many copies of any one instruction **operand**: one copy in the main memory and one in each cache memory. When one copy of an operand is changed, the other copies of the operand must be changed also. Cache coherence is the discipline that ensures that changes in the values of shared operands are propagated throughout the system in a timely fashion.

There are three distinct levels of cache coherence:

1. Every write operation appears to occur instantaneously.

2. All processes see exactly the same sequence of changes of values for each separate operand.

3. Different processes may see an operand assume different sequences of values. (This is considered noncoherent behavior.) In both level 2 behavior and level 3 behavior, a program can observe **stale data**. Recently, computer designers have come to realize that the programming discipline required to deal with level 2 behavior is sufficient to deal also with level 3 behavior. Therefore, at some point only level 1 and level 3 behavior will be seen in machines.

cache engine

See "cache server"

cache memory

Cache memory is random access memory (**RAM**) that a computer **microprocessor** can access more quickly than it can access regular RAM. As the microprocessor processes data, it looks first in the **cache** memory and if it finds the data there (from a previous reading of data), it does not have to do the more time-consuming reading of data from larger **memory**.

Cache memory is sometimes described in levels of closeness and accessibility to the microprocessor. An **L1** cache is on the same chip as the microprocessor. (For example, the **PowerPC** 601 processor has a 32 kilobyte level-1 cache built into its chip.) **L2** is usually a separate static RAM (**SRAM**) chip. The main RAM is usually a dynamic RAM (**DRAM**) chip.

In addition to cache memory, one can think of RAM itself as a cache of memory for **hard disk** storage since all of RAM's contents come from the hard disk initially when you turn your computer on and load the operating system (you are loading it into RAM) and later as you start new applications and access new data. RAM can also contain a special area called a **disk cache** that contains the data most recently read in from the hard disk.

cache server

A cache server (sometimes called a cache engine) is a **server** relatively close to Internet users and typically within a business enterprise that saves (**caches**) Web pages and possibly FTP and other files that all server users have requested so that successive requests for these pages or files can be satisfied by the cache server rather than requiring the user of the Internet. A cache server not only serves its users by getting information more quickly but also reduces Internet traffic.

A cache server is almost always also a **proxy server**, which is a server that "represents" users by intercepting their Internet requests and managing them for users. Typically, this is because enterprise resources are being protected by a **firewall** server that allows outgoing requests to go out but needs to screen all incoming traffic. A proxy server helps match incoming messages with outgoing requests and is in a position to also cache the files that are received for later recall by any user. To the user, the proxy and cache servers are invisible; all Internet requests and returned responses appear to be coming from the addressed place on the Internet. (The proxy is not quite invisible; its IP address has to be specified as a configuration option to the browser or other protocol program.)

CAD

CAD (computer-aided design) software is used by architects, engineers, drafters, artists, and others to create precision drawings or technical illustrations. CAD software can be used to create two-dimensional (2-D) drawings or three-dimensional (3-D) models.

CAD/CAM (computer-aided design/computer-aided manufacturing) is software used to design products such as electronic circuit boards in computers and other devices.

CAD/CAM

CAD/CAM (computer-aided design/computer-aided manufacturing) is software used to design products such as electronic circuit boards in computers and other devices.

call center

A call center is a central place where customer and other telephone calls are handled by an organization, usually with some amount of computer automation. Typically, a call center has the ability to handle a considerable volume of calls at the same time, to screen calls and forward them to someone qualified to handle them, and to log calls. Call centers are used by mail-order catalog organizations, telemarketing companies, computer product help desks, and any large organization that uses the telephone to sell or service products and services.

call failure rate

Call failure rate (CFR) is a statistical measure commonly used in assessing Internet Service Providers (**ISPs**) or any network provider. The call failure rate is the percentage of calls to an ISP or network provider that fail to get through. Companies can measure the CFR for their own employees who dial in for access to the company's network. Rating companies report on the CFRs for major ISPs like AOL, Ameritech, and Mindspring. Visual Networks, formerly Inverse Network Technology, is probably the best known benchmarking company of ISPs.

callback

Callback, also known as *international callback*, is a system for avoiding regular phone company long-distance charges by having a call initiated from within the U.S. with the orginating caller joining in a conference call. Here's how the procedure works:

- A call originator (for example, someone in South America) calls a predesignated number in the U.S., waits until it rings once, and then hangs up.

- A machine in the office where the phone rang recognizes that the phone number was called and knows the phone number of the party that called it (because it was the only party that knew the number).

- The machine places a call (which may be a local or a long-distance call) that originates from the U.S. location and also calls the party who initiated this procedure, thus arranging a conference call but at the U.S. long-distance rate.

- In another variation, the automatically-generated call from the U.S. may call the originator and ask the originator to dial their desired number or provide a U.S. dial tone.

- The originator (who subscribes to this callback service) is billed by the U.S.-based service at its own rates.

In localities where portable phone (cellphone) companies do not charge for incoming calls, callback is also sometimes used to avoid airtime charges for outgoing calls.

CallXML

CallXML is a language based on the Extensible Markup Language (**XML**) that lets a company describe a phone-to-**Web site** application in terms of how the call would be handled at the Web site and how it would interact with the caller based on keyed-in or voice responses. CallXML is similar to other voice markup languages such as VoiceXML and Microsoft's WTE.

Basically, CallXML is used to describe the user interface of a telephone, VoIP, or multimedia application to a CallXML browser. A CallXML browser then uses that description to control and react to the call itself. According to a Voxeo, a vendor that supports CallXML, the markup language includes:

- Media action elements such as "playAudio" and "recordAudio" to describe what to be presented to the user during a call

- Call action elements such as "answer," "call" and "hangup" to describe how to control and route the call

- Logic action elements such as "assign," "clear," and "goto" to describe how to modify variables and interact with traditional server-side Web logic such as Perl, other CGI languages, PHP or ASP

- Event elements such as "onTermDigit," "onHangup" to describe how to react to things the user can do during the call, such as pressing digits or hanging up

- Block elements that logically group actions & events together, so that one set of event handling elements can be used for several sequential actions

Whereas VoiceXML, another computer telephony language, is used with voice-based applications that provide access to Web content and information, CallXML aims to make it easy for Web developers to create applications that can interact with and control any number or type of calls. VoiceXML 1.0 was created through a collaboration of AT&T, IBM, Lucent Technologies, and Motorola.

calm technology

In computing, calm technology aims to reduce the "excitement" of information overload by letting the user select what information is at the center of their attention and what information is peripheral. The term was coined by Mark Weiser, chief technologist, and John Seeley Brown, director of the Xerox Palo Alto Research Lab. In the coming age of *ubiquitous computing* in which technology will become at once pervasive yet invisible, Weiser and Brown foresee the need for design principles and methods that enable users to sense and control what immediately interests them while retaining peripheral awareness of other information possibilities that they can at any time choose to focus on. Calm technology, they envision, will not only relax the user but, by moving unneeded information to the edge of an interface, allow more information to exist there, ready for selection when needed. An example: A video conference may be a calmer interface than a phone conference because the explicit visual knowledge of details that are peripheral gives participants more confidence in what can be focused on and what can be left at the edge. (Think of phone conferences in which participants are never quite sure who has entered or left the room at the other end. This lack of information is not necessarily calming!) Knowledge of the periphery gives us "locatedness" without unduly distracting us.

As another example of calm technology, Weiser and Brown cite inner office windows. An office occupant can choose to focus on work within the office while maintaining some low level of awareness of the larger environment as people are seen moving in the office aisles. From the aisle, a worker has a sense of who is or isn't at work in their office. Weiser and Brown see this example as a metaphor for the Internet in which people can locate and be located by others in cyberspace while maintaining various degrees of control over their privacy and the timing in which they are willing to communicate.

As devices with embedded programming become an all-pervasive part of our environment (see **micro-electromechanical systems**), the ability to design encalming devices and environments is apt to become much more important.

cam

A cam, homecam, or Webcam is a video camera, usually attached directly to a computer, whose current or latest image is requestable from a Web site. A live cam is one that is continually providing new images that are transmitted in rapid succession or, in some cases, in streaming video. Sites with live cams sometimes embed them as **Java applet**s in Web pages. Cams have caught on; there are now (we estimate) several thousand sites with cams. The first cams were positioned mainly on fish tanks and coffee machines. Many of today's live cams are on sex-oriented sites. For travel promotion, traffic information, and the remote visualization of any ongoing event that's interesting, webcams seem like an exciting possibility that will become more common as users get access to more **bandwidth**.

camcorder

A camcorder is a portable electronic recording device that is capable of recording live-motion video and audio for later replay through VCRs, TVs, and, in some models, a personal computer. Compounded from "camera" and "recorder," the term originated in the early 1980s. Camcorders are also called *video recorders*. Ordinary consumers use camcorders to film home movies of special events or vacations. Professionals such as professional videographers and filmmakers use camcorders along with other editing and film studio equipment to produce video segments or films for commercial sale.

Camcorders come in an assortment of formats, features, and price ranges. When they first arrived, camcorders recorded in one of two analog formats, VHS and Betamax formats, onto video casettes for replay from the most popular VCRs. These camcorders often produce less than ideal quality images and earlier models can be large and cumbersome to use.

As technology improved, other formats became available, such as S-VHS, 8mm, Hi-8, and DV (digital video). Many of these formats offer a clearer, sharper picture over the original formats, and, in some cases, allow more hours of recording on a single tape than previously. These types often require an adapter for playback from a TV or VCR.

With the latest digital camcorders, many now are capable of being connected directly to a personal computer, using an i.LINK (IEEE 1394) or **FireWire** digital interface, so that the video can be edited directly on the computer for more professional results. The personal computer must be equipped with the right video editing software, a digital video capture board, and with i.Link/FireWire ports.

Camcorder features for a prospective buyer to consider include: horizontal image resolution, the size and quality of the **liquid crystal display** monitor for quick viewing as you record, the types of zooms and lenses available, and the actual size and comfort of the equipment. Leading camcorder manufacturers include Canon, Sony, JVC, Panasonic, and Sharp.

campus

In telecommunications, a campus is a physically contiguous association of locations such as several adjacent office buildings. Typically, such areas require one or more local area networks and bridging, routing, and aggregation equipment based on situational needs.

cancelbot

A cancelbot is a program or **bot** (robot) that sends a message to one or more **Usenet** newsgroups to cancel (remove from posting) a certain type of message. It searches for messages matching a certain pattern, whether it be a duplicate message or offensive material, and sends out cancels for them. When a message has been canceled, its status is changed to "cancel," and the Usenet servers will no longer post them.

Some Usenet users consider cancelbots a form of censorship. Many Usenet newsgroup administrators, however, believe that they have a right to cancel material they consider to be offensive or unwanted, such as **spam** (bulk mail). Anyone with authority to send a cancelbot has to be careful to make sure that they don't cancel more messages than they intended to.

candela

The candela (abbreviation, cd) is the standard unit of luminous intensity in the International System of Units (**SI**). It is formally defined as the magnitude of an **electromagnetic field**, in a specified direction, that has a power level of $^1/_{683}$ watt (1.46×10^{-3} W) per steradian at a frequency of 540 terahertz (540 THz or 5.40×10^{14} **Hz**).

Originally, luminous intensity was measured in terms of units called candles. This expression arose from the fact that one candle represented approximately the amount of visible radiation emitted by a candle flame. This was an inexact specification because burning candles vary in brilliance. So, for a time, a specified amount of radiation from elemental platinum at its freezing temperature was used as the standard. Late in the 20th century, the current definition and terminology were adopted.

The quantities comprising the specification of the candela are obscure to some non-scientists. An **EM-field** power level of 1.46×10^{-3} W is small; the radio-frequency (RF) output of a children's toy two-way radio is several times that much. A frequency of 540 THz corresponds to a wavelength of about 556 nanometers (nm), which is in the middle of the visible-light spectrum. A steradian is the standard unit solid angle in three dimensions; a sphere encloses 4 pi (approximately 12.57) steradians.

candela per meter squared

The candela per meter squared (cd/m^2) is the standard unit of luminance. It represents a luminous intensity of one candela radiating from a surface whose area is one square meter.

Formally, the candela is defined as the magnitude of an electromagnetic field (**EM field**), in a specified direction, that has a power level of $^1/_{683}$ **watt** (1.46×10^{-3} W) per **steradian** at a frequency of 540 **terahertz** (540 THz or 5.40×10^{14} Hz). This is in the middle of the visible-light spectrum.

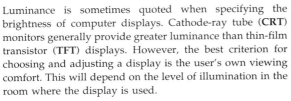

Luminance is sometimes quoted when specifying the brightness of computer displays. Cathode-ray tube (**CRT**) monitors generally provide greater luminance than thin-film transistor (**TFT**) displays. However, the best criterion for choosing and adjusting a display is the user's own viewing comfort. This will depend on the level of illumination in the room where the display is used.

Also see **candela**, **meter squared**, **steradian**, and **SI** (International System of Units).

canonical

In programming, canonical means "according to the rules." And non-canonical means "not according to the rules." In the early Christian church, the "canon" was the officially chosen text. In *The New Hacker's Dictionary*, Eric Raymond tells us that the word meant "reed" in its Greek and Latin origin, and a certain length of reed came to be used as a standard measure. In some knowledge areas, such as music and literature, the "canon" is the body of work that everyone studies.

The terms are sometimes used to distinguish whether a programming interface follows a particular standard or precedent or whether it departs from it.

CAP

CAP (carrierless amplitude/phase) modulation was the original approach for **modulation** of a Digital Subscriber Line (**DSL**) **signal**. Discrete multitone (**DMT**) is now the preferred modulation alternative over CAP.

CAP is closely related to quadrature amplitude modulation (**QAM**).

capacitance

See "capacitor"

capacitor

A capacitor is a passive electronic component that stores energy in the form of an electrostatic field. In its simplest form, a capacitor consists of two conducting plates separated by an insulating material called the **dielectric**. The capacitance is directly proportional to the surface areas of the plates, and is inversely proportional to the separation between the plates. Capacitance also depends on the dielectric constant of the substance separating the plates.

The standard unit of capacitance is the **farad**, abbreviated F. This is a large unit; more common units are the microfarad, abbreviated μF ($1 \mu F = 10^{-6}$ F) and the picofarad, abbreviated pF (1 pF $= 10^{-12}$ F).

Capacitors can be fabricated onto integrated circuit (**IC**) chips. They are commonly used in conjunction with **transistor**s in dynamic random access memory (**DRAM**). The capacitors help maintain the contents of memory.

Because of their tiny physical size, these components have low capacitance. They must be recharged thousands of times per second or the DRAM will lose its data.

Large capacitors are used in the power supplies of electronic equipment of all types, including computers and their peripherals. In these systems, the capacitors smooth out the rectified utility **AC**, providing pure, battery-like **DC**.

capacity on demand

Capacity on demand (COD) is a purchasing option that allows companies to receive equipment with more computer processing, storage, or other **capacity** than the company needs at the time of purchase, and have that extra capacity remain unused and unpaid for until the company actually requires it. Vendors are promoting capacity on demand as a cost-effective and time-saving alternative to more traditional methods of upgrading. With COD, a vendor might provide a company with a fully-configured 24-**processor** computer **server** but only charge the company for the number of processors they actually use. The vendor provides the additional capacity hoping that when the company expands and needs more capacity, they will not look around elsewhere but will simply take advantage of the extra capacity the vendor had already provided. In this scenario, the company would contact the vendor to have the extra processors activated, and the vendor would bill them accordingly.

Critics of COD compare the service with that of a hotel mini-bar, pointing out that the convenience of "instant gratification" can lead to poor capacity planning and ultimately, higher costs. The Meta Group has estimated that 80% of the world's 2,000 largest companies will provide customers with some kind of COD model by 2006. Leading COD vendors include IBM, Sun Microsystems, and Hewlett-Packard. Storage is currently the leading COD commodity.

CAPI

CAPI (Common Application Programming Interface) is an international standard **interface** that **application**s can use to communicate directly with **ISDN** equipment. Using CAPI, an application program can be written to initiate and terminate phone calls in computers equipped for ISDN. Computer telephony (**ICTI**) applications can be written for ISDN users. Officially, CAPI is referred to as Common-ISDN-API and is embodied in ETS 300 838 ("Integrated Service Digital Network (ISDN); Harmonized Programmable Communication Interface (HPCI) for ISDN." ETS refers to standards from the European Telecommunication Standards Institute (ETSI). The standard is internationalized by recommendation T.200 "Programmable communication interface for terminal equipment connected to ISDN" from the International Telecommunications Union (ITU).

CAPI can be compared with the Intel-Microsoft "standard" programming interface, the Telephony Application Program Interface (**TAPI**). CAPI includes signaling and data exchange **protocol**s not included in TAPI. TAPI services are also provided by CAPI and a TAPI application can be mapped to CAPI functions.

Because ISDN is widely used in Germany, the Netherlands, and Scandinavia, users there are accustomed to receiving a CAPI software program or **driver** along with their ISDN computer **card**. Not all CAPI driver versions support all functions. CAPI provides functions that are independent from physical signaling protocols that vary among different countries. CAPI supports these protocols: **HDLC**, HDLC inverted, **SDLC**, LAPD, X.75, Voice (PCM), Fax group 3 (T.30), V.110/V.120, and compression (**V.xx**).

carbon copy

In **e-mail**, a carbon copy (abbreviated "cc," and sometimes "fcc" for "first carbon copy") is a copy of a note sent to an addressee other than the main addressee. A blind carbon copy is a copy sent to an addressee that is not visible to the main and carbon copy addressees. For example, you may have a work colleague that acts as a back-up when you're on vacation or not at work. You don't necessarily want the people you correspond with to know that you have a back-up. So, to keep your back-up informed, you always send the back-up a blind carbon copy. The fact that a blind carbon copy was sent is not apparent to the main and carbon copy recipients.

The term is borrowed from the days of the mechanical and later the electronic typewriter (circa 1879-1979) when copies of typed sheets of paper were made by inserting a special sheet of inked paper called carbon paper into the typewriter. For two copies, you would insert carbon paper (sometimes just called a "carbon") between the original being typed and each of the two sheets that would become the carbon copies.

card

A card (or *expansion card*, **board**, or **adapter**) is circuitry designed to provide expanded capability to a computer. It is provided on the surface of a standard-size rigid material (fiberboard or something similar) and then plugged into one of the computer's expansion **slot**s in its **motherboard** (or **backplane**). Cards may come in one of two sizes designed to match standard slot dimensions. A card can actually contain the capability within its circuitry (as a video card does) or it can control (through an extended connection) a device (such as a hard disk drive).

CardBus

CardBus is the trade name for an advanced **PC Card** (also known as PCMCIA card) specification. The technology is used primarily in notebook and portable computers. The CardBus card fits in a slot like a conventional PC card.

CardBus allows for all the functions that are possible with PC cards, but with these improvements:

- Direct Memory Access (**DMA**) is supported.
- A 32-bit path is used for data transfer.
- The operating speed is several times greater.
- CardBus works at lower battery voltage.

A CardBus slot, and the associated software, interrogates a card when the card is first inserted in the slot. If a PC card has been inserted, the computer uses it as if the slot were a conventional PCMCIA slot. If a CardBus card has been inserted, the computer reconfigures the slot to take advantage of the enhanced operating features. For CardBus to work, the **operating system** must support 32-bit data paths.

cardinal

Cardinal refers to a basic or primary value. Examples of cardinal numbers are 1, 7, 9, and 123. A cardinal rule is a rule that is basic or essential. Cardinal numbers can be contrasted with **ordinal** numbers.

cardinality

See also **integer**, **natural number**, **rational number**, and **real number**.

The term cardinality refers to the number of **cardinal** (basic) members in a **set**. Cardinality can be finite (a non-negative integer) or infinite. For example, the cardinality of the set of people in the United States is approximately 270,000,000; the cardinality of the set of integers is denumerably infinite.

In tables, the number of rows (or tuples) is called the cardinality. In practice, tables always have positive-integer cardinality. The reason for this is simple: tables with no rows, or with a negative number of rows, cannot exist. In theory, however, tables with denumerably infinite cardinality can exist. An example is a multiplication table of non-negative integers in which entries are implied for all possible values:

0	1	2	3	..
1	1	2	3	..
2	2	4	6	..
3	3	6	9	..
:	:	:	:	

The concept of cardinality is of interest to set theoreticians because it has been used to demonstrate that some infinite sets are larger than others. The cardinality of the set of real numbers is greater than the cardinality of the set of integers, even though both sets are infinite. The cardinality of the set of integers is called aleph-null or aleph-nought; the cardinality of the set of real numbers is called aleph-one.

One of the great mysteries of mathematics is contained in the question, "What is the cardinality of the set of points on a geometric line?" Generally it is presumed to be aleph-one;

the set of points on a line is thought to correspond one-to-one with the set of real numbers. This is by no means a trivial supposition, and has become known as the Continuum Hypothesis.

Carnivore

Carnivore is the Internet surveillance system developed by the U.S. Federal Bureau of Investigation (FBI), who developed it to monitor the electronic transmissions of criminal suspects. Critics, however, charge that Carnivore does not include appropriate safeguards to prevent misuse and might violate the constitutional rights of the individual.

Carnivore, a PC- or laptop-based application, is installed with an Internet service provider (**ISP**) to keep court-ordered tabs on a criminal suspect's e-mail and instant messages. The FBI says it cannot be enabled without help from the ISP. It works much like a commercial **sniffer** and other network diagnostic tools. The FBI says Carnivore has a unique ability to distinguish between communications that have been authorized for interception and those it does not have the right to search. For instance, Carnivore could be configured to intercept e-mail but not online shopping records.

Documents suggest that the FBI may have been working on a predecessor to Carnivore as early as 1996. But the FBI officially began the Carnivore project, under the name "Omnivore," in February 1997. It was proposed originally for a **Solaris** X86 computer. In June 1999, Omnivore was replaced by Carnivore running on a **Windows NT**-based system.

Carnivore's chief critic is the Electronic Privacy Information Center (EPIC), a public interest group dedicated to emerging civil liberties issues. The group sued and got the FBI to release background information on the system, although the Bureau refused to turn over Carnivore's source code. A private study conducted by the Illinois Institute of Technology Research Institute, which was commissioned by the U.S. Justice Department, found several shortcomings in Carnivore. For example, the system does not keep track of individual users, so any operator defaults to "administrator," leaving no audit trail. Also, the system lacks a feature that would require users to confirm that a court order was granted. The U.S. Congress is currently considering bills that would restrict the FBI's use of Carnivore.

Some security software vendors now claim to have developed alternatives to Carnivore. Carnivore could also lead to a rise in **encryption** software for Internet transactions, which would make such "sniffer" tools less effective.

carrier

1) In information technology, a carrier (or carrier signal) is a transmitted electromagnetic pulse or wave at a steady base frequency of alternation on which information can be imposed by increasing signal strength, varying the base frequency, varying the wave phase, or other means. This variation is called **modulation**. With the advent of laser transmission over **optical fiber** media, a carrier can also be a laser-generated light beam on which information is imposed.

Types of **analog** modulation of a carrier include amplitude modulation (AM), frequency modulation (FM), and phase modulation. Types of **digital** modulation include varieties of pulse code modulation (PCM), including pulse amplitude modulation (PAM), pulse duration modulation (PDM), and pulse position modulation (PPM).

Carrier detect (see **modem lights**) is a control signal between a **modem** and a computer that indicates that the modem detects a "live" carrier that can be used for sending and receiving information.

2) In the telecommunications industry, a carrier is a telephone or other company that sells or rents tele-communication transmission services. A local exchange carrier (LEC) is a local phone company and an inter-exchange carrier (IEC or IXC) carries long-distance calls.

Carrier Sense Multiple Access/Collision Detect

Carrier Sense Multiple Access/Collision Detect (CSMA/CD) is the **protocol** for carrier transmission access in **Ethernet** networks. On Ethernet, any device can try to send a **frame** at any time. Each device senses whether the line is idle and therefore available to be used. If it is, the device begins to transmit its first frame. If another device has tried to send at the same time, a **collision** is said to occur and the frames are discarded. Each device then waits a random amount of time and retries until successful in getting its transmission sent.

CSMA/CD is specified in the IEEE 802.3 standard.

carrierless amplitude/phase modulation

See "CAP"

cartridge

See "tape"

CAS

1) In computer **memory** technology, CAS (column address strobe) is a signal sent to a dynamic random access memory (**DRAM**) that tells it that an associated address is a column address. A data bit in DRAM is stored in a cell located by the intersection of a column address and a row address. A **RAS** (row address strobe) signal is used to validate the row address.

2) In telecommunications, CAS (channel associated signaling) is signaling (for example, in a **T-carrier system** line) in which control **signals**, such as those for synchronizing and bounding **frame**s, are carried in the same **channel**s along with voice and **data** signals. This arrangement is an alternative to CCS (common channel signaling) in which a group of voice-and-data channels share a separate channel that is used only for control signals.

cascading style sheet

A cascading style sheet (CSS) is a Web page derived from multiple sources with a defined order of precedence where the definitions of any style element conflict. The Cascading Style Sheet, level 1 (**CSS1**) recommendation from the World Wide Web Consortium (**W3C**), which is implemented in the latest versions of the Netscape and Microsoft Web browsers, specifies the possible style sheets or statements that may determine how a given element is presented in a Web page.

CSS gives more control over the appearance of a Web page to the page creator than to the browser designer or the viewer. With CSS, the sources of style definition for a given document element are in this order of precedence:

1. The STYLE attribute on an individual element tag.

2. The STYLE element that defines a specific style sheet containing style declarations or a LINK element that links to a separate document containing the STYLE element. In a Web page, the STYLE element is placed between the TITLE statement and the BODY statement.

3. An imported style sheet, using the CSS @import notation to automatically import and merge an external style sheet with the current style sheet.

4. Style attributes specified by the viewer to the browser.

5. The default style sheet assumed by the browser.

In general, the Web page creator's style sheet takes precedence, but it's recommended that browsers provide ways for the viewer to override the style attributes in some respects. Since it's likely that different browsers will choose to implement CSS1 somewhat differently, the Web page creator must test the page with different browsers.

Cascading Style Sheet, level 1

CSS1 (Cascading Style Sheet, level 1) is the recommendation from the World Wide Web Consortium (**W3C**) for a standard **cascading style sheet** specification.

A cascading style sheet (CSS) is a **style sheet** derived from multiple sources with a defined order of precedence where the definitions of a style element conflict. CSS1 describes the recommended approach for Web page designers and browser developers to adhere to.

CASE

CASE (computer-aided software engineering) is the use of a computer-assisted method to organize and control the development of software, especially on large, complex projects involving many software components and people. Using CASE allows designers, code writers, testers, planners, and managers to share a common view of where a project stands at each stage of development. CASE helps ensure a disciplined, check-pointed process. A CASE tool may portray progress (or lack of it) graphically. It may also serve as a repository for or be linked to document and program libraries containing the project's business plans, design requirements, design specifications, detailed code specifications, the code units, test cases and results, and marketing and service plans.

CASE originated in the 1970s when computer companies were beginning to borrow ideas from the hardware manufacturing process and apply them to software development (which generally has been viewed as an insufficiently disciplined process). Some CASE tools supported the concepts of *structured programming* and similar organized development methods. More recently, CASE tools have had to encompass or accommodate visual programming tools and **object-oriented programming**. In corporations, a CASE tool may be part of a spectrum of processes designed to ensure quality in what is developed. (Many companies have their processes audited and certified as being in conformance with the ISO 9000 standard.)

Some of the benefits of CASE and similar approaches are that, by making the customer part of the process (through market analysis and focus groups, for example), a product is more likely to meet real-world requirements. Because the development process emphasizes testing and redesign, the cost of servicing a product over its lifetime can be reduced considerably. An organized approach to development encourages code and design reuse, reducing costs and improving quality. Finally, quality products tend to improve a corporation's image, providing a competitive advantage in the marketplace.

CAT 1 – CAT 2 – CAT 3 – CAT 4 – CAT 5 – CAT 5E – CAT 6 – CAT 7

See "Categories of twisted pair cabling systems"

catalog

In computing, a catalog is a directory of information about data sets, files, or a **database**. A catalog usually describes where a data set, file or database entity is located and may also include other information, such as the type of device on which each data set or file is stored.

categories of twisted pair cabling systems

ANSI/EIA (American National Standards Institute/ Electronic Industries Association) Standard 568 is one of several standards that specify "categories" (the singular is commonly referred to as "CAT") of **twisted pair** cabling systems (wires, junctions, and connectors) in terms of the data rates that they can sustain. The specifications describe the cable material as well as the types of connectors and junction blocks to be used in order to conform to a category. These categories are:

Category	Maximum data rate	Usual application
CAT 1	Less than 1 **Mbps**	**Analog** voice **(POTS)** **Integrated** Services Digital Network **Basic Rate** Interface in ISDN Doorbell wiring
CAT 2	4 Mbps	Mainly used in the IBM Cabling System for **Token Ring** networks
CAT 3	16 Mbps	Voice and data on **10BASE-T Ethernet**
CAT 4	20 Mbps	Used in 16 Mbps Token Ring Otherwise not used much
CAT 5	100 Mbps	100 Mbps TPDDI 155 Mbps **ATM**
CAT 5E	100 Mbps	100 Mbps TPDDI 155 Mbps **ATM**
CAT 6	200-250 **MHz**	Super-fast broadband applications

CAT 5 is currently under consideration to be incorporated into the **Gigabit Ethernet** specification for short distance wiring. While longer connections using Gigabit Ethernet use **optical fiber**, the goal is to leverage the CAT 5 twisted-pair wiring most organizations already have in place for connections out to the desktop.

The two most popular specifications are CAT 3 and CAT 5. While the two cables may look identical, CAT 3 is tested to a lower set of specifications and can cause transmission errors if pushed to faster speeds. CAT 3 cabling is **near-end crosstalk**-certified for only a 16 MHz signal, while CAT 5 cable must pass a 100 MHz test.

The CAT 6 specification was not yet formally approved by the EIA as of March 2001, although products are being offered that conform to a proposed specification. A CAT 7 specification is reportedly being considered.

cathode ray tube

A cathode ray tube (CRT) is a specialized **vacuum tube** in which images are produced when an electron beam strikes a phosphorescent surface. Most desktop computer displays make use of CRTs. The CRT in a computer display is similar to the "picture tube" in a television receiver.

A cathode ray tube consists of several basic components, as illustrated below. The electron gun generates a narrow beam of electrons. The anodes accelerate the electrons. Deflecting coils produce an **extremely low frequency** electromagnetic field that allows for constant adjustment of the direction of the electron beam. There are two sets of deflecting coils: horizontal and vertical. (In the illustration, only one set of coils is shown for simplicity.) The intensity of the beam can be varied. The electron beam produces a tiny, bright visible spot when it strikes the phosphor-coated screen.

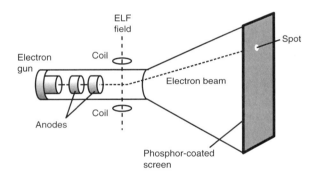

To produce an image on the screen, complex signals are applied to the deflecting coils, and also to the apparatus that controls the intensity of the electron beam. This causes the spot to race across the screen from right to left, and from top to bottom, in a sequence of horizontal lines called the raster. As viewed from the front of the CRT, the spot moves in a pattern similar to the way your eyes move when you read a single-column page of text. But the scanning takes place at such a rapid rate that your eye sees a constant image over the entire screen.

The illustration shows only one electron gun. This is typical of a monochrome, or single-color, CRT. However, virtually all CRTs today render color images. These devices have three electron guns, one for the primary color red, one for the primary color green, and one for the primary color blue. The CRT thus produces three overlapping images: one in red (R), one in green (G), and one in blue (B). This is the so-called **RGB** color model.

In computer systems, there are several **display modes**, or sets of specifications according to which the CRT operates. The most common specification for CRT displays is known as SVGA (Super Video Graphics Array). Notebook computers typically use **liquid crystal displays**. The technology for these displays is much different than that for CRTs.

CATV

CATV (originally "community antenna television," now often "community access television") is more commonly known as "cable TV." In addition to bringing television programs to those millions of people throughout the world who are connected to a community antenna, **cable TV** is an increasingly popular way to interact with the World Wide Web and other new forms of multimedia information and entertainment services.

CB

See "Citizen's Band Radio"

CBC

See "cipher block chaining"

CBR

See "Citizen's Band Radio"

CCD

See "charge-coupled device"

CCITT

The CCITT, now known as the ITU-T (for Telecommunication Standardization Sector of the International Telecommunications Union), is the primary international body for fostering cooperative standards for telecommunications equipment and systems. It is located in Geneva, Switzerland.

CCTV

CCTV (closed circuit television) is a television system in which signals are not publicly distributed; cameras are connected to television **monitor**s in a limited area such as a store, an office building, or on a college campus. CCTV is commonly used in surveillance systems.

CD

See "compact disc"

CD burner

A CD burner is the informal name for a CD recorder, a device that can record data to a compact disc. CD-Recordable (**CD-R**) and CD-Rewritable (**CD-RW**) are the two most common types of drives that can write CDs, either once (in the case of CD-R) or repeatedly (in the case of CD-RW). In the recording process, the data is actually etched into the disc (burned) with a **laser**, as compared with non-recordable CDs. Audio CDs and **CD-ROMs** are pressed from copies of the original recordings (which are burned by lasers). Since the non-recordable CDs are manufactured in this manner, they can not be written, or rewritten in a desktop environment.

CD-Rs and CD-RWs, like all CDs, are made up of a polycarbonate substrate, a thin metal coating, and a protective outer layer. In a CD-R, a layer of organic polymer dye between the polycarbonate and metal layers serves as the recording medium. The composition of the dye is permanently transformed by exposure to a specific frequency of light. Some CD-Rs have an additional protective layer to make them less vulnerable to damage from scratches, since the data—unlike that on a regular CD—is closer to the label side of the disc. A pregrooved spiral track helps to guide the laser for recording data, which is encoded from the inside to the outside of the disc in a single continuous spiral. The laser creates marks in the dye layer that mimic the reflective properties of the *pits* and *lands* (lower and higher areas) of the traditional CD. The distinct differences in the way the areas reflect light register as **digital** data that is then unencoded for playback. With **packet writing** software and a compatible CD-R or CD-RW drive, it is possible to save data to a CD-R in the same way as one can save it to a floppy disk, although—since each part of the disk can only be written once—it is not possible to delete files and then reuse the space. The composition of the dye is permanently transformed by exposure to the laser.

In a CD-RW, the dye is replaced with an alloy that can change back and forth from a crystalline form when exposed to a particular light, through a technology called *optical phase change*. The patterns created are less distinct than those of other CD formats, requiring a more sensitive device for playback. Only drives designated as "MultiRead" are able to read CD-RW reliably. Similar to CD-R, the CD-RW's polycarbonate substrate is preformed with a spiral groove to guide the laser. The alloy phase-change recording layer, which is commonly a mix of silver, indium, antimony and tellurium, is sandwiched between two dielectric layers that draw excess heat from the recording layer. After heating to one particular temperature, the alloy will become crystalline when it is cooled; after heating to a higher temperature it will become amorphous (won't hold its shape) when it is cooled. By controlling the temperature of the laser, crystalline areas and non-crystalline areas are formed. The crystalline areas will reflect the laser, while the other areas will absorb it. The differences will register as binary data

that can be unencoded for playback. To erase or write over recorded data, the higher temperature laser is used, which results in the non-crystalline form, which can then be reformed by the lower temperature laser.

The first CD recorders were made available in 1988, but were not an option for the average home recorder because, with the requisite hardware and software, they cost upwards of $100,000. At a weight of 600 pounds, the Meridian Data CD Professional was the first CD recorder. Today's CD recorders typically weigh a few pounds and can be bought for less than $300.

CD Plus

See "enhanced CD"

CD recorder

See "CD burner"

CD-Bridge Disc

A CD-Bridge Disc (sometimes just called a *bridge disc*) is a compact disc (**CD**) format that includes extra information on a **CD-ROM XA** (extended architecture) track, so that the disc can be played on either a **CD-i** (interactive) player attached to a television, or a CD-ROM XA drive attached to a computer. A bridge disc with appropriate application software may also play on other XA-compatible devices, such as a **Photo CD** or Karaoke CD player. Video CD (**VCD**), Photo CD, and Karaoke CD are three bridge disc formats.

CD-Bridge Disc specifications are built on those from the **Yellow Book** extension, which defined CD-ROM XA, and the **Green Book**, which defined CD-i, and must conform to the complete requirements of both formats. The complete CD-Bridge Disc definition is described in the **White Book**, which was released by Sony, Philips, Matsushita, and JVC in 1993.

CD-Bridge Disk

See "CD-Bridge Disc"

CDF

See "Channel Definition Format"

CD-i

CD-i (Compact Disc—interactive) is the multimedia **CD** format specified in 1986 (in the **Green Book**). CD-i was specified as an entire system, comprising not just a disc and data format, but a hardware and software system, a variety of special **compression** methods for audio and visual data, and a method of interleaving audio, video, and text data. Developed as a user-friendly alternative to a PC, CD-I

players are easier to use, and have TV video output as well. Full screen motion video capabilities were added to the original specification later.

A CD-i player is a stand-alone system that includes a **CPU**, **memory**, and an integrated **operating system**. It can be connected to a TV set for displaying pictures and sound, or to a stereo system. The user interacts by positioning a cursor and selecting options, with a device such as a specialized remote control.

Although CD-i never realized broad commercial success, it is now used in education, training, and other professional applications.

CDMA

Also see **CDMA One**, **CDMA2000**, and **WCDMA**. Compare time-division multiplex (**TDM**) and frequency-division multiplex (**FDM**).

CDMA (code-division multiple access) refers to any of several protocols used in so-called second-generation (**2G**) and third-generation (**3G**) **wireless** communications. As the term implies, CDMA is a form of **multiplexing**, which allows numerous signals to occupy a single transmission **channel**, optimizing the use of available **bandwidth**. The technology is used in ultra-high-frequency (UHF) **cellular telephone** systems in the 800-**MHz** and 1.9-**GHz** bands.

CDMA employs analog-to-digital conversion (**ADC**) in combination with **spread spectrum** technology. Audio input is first digitized into binary elements. The frequency of the transmitted signal is then made to vary according to a defined pattern (code), so it can be intercepted only by a receiver whose frequency response is programmed with the same code, so it follows exactly along with the transmitter frequency. There are trillions of possible frequency-sequencing codes; this enhances privacy and makes cloning difficult.

The CDMA channel is nominally 1.23 MHz wide. CDMA networks use a scheme called **soft handoff**, which minimizes signal breakup as a handset passes from one cell to another. The combination of digital and spread-spectrum modes supports several times as many signals per unit bandwidth as analog modes. CDMA is compatible with other cellular technologies; this allows for nationwide **roaming**.

The original CDMA standard, also known as **CDMA One** and still common in cellular telephones in the U.S., offers a transmission speed of only up to 14.4 **Kbps** in its single channel form and up to 115 Kbps in an eight-channel form. **CDMA2000** and **wideband CDMA** deliver data many times faster.

CDMA One

Also see **CDMA**, **WCDMA**, and **CDMA2000**.

CDMA One, also written cdmaOne, refers to the original **ITU** IS-95 (**CDMA**) **wireless** interface protocol that was first standardized in 1993. It is considered a second-generation (2G) mobile wireless technology.

Today, there are two versions of IS-95, called IS-95A and IS-95B. The IS-95A protocol employs a 1.25-**MHz** carrier, operates in radio-frequency bands at either 800 MHz or 1.9 **GHz**, and supports data speeds of up to 14.4 **Kbps**. IS-95B can support data speeds of up to 115 kbps by bundling up to eight channels.

CDMA2000

Also see **CDMA**, **WCDMA**, and **CDMA One**.

CDMA2000, also known as IMT-CDMA Multi-Carrier or IS-136, is a code-division multiple access (**CDMA**) version of the IMT-2000 standard developed by the International Telecommunication Union (**ITU**). The CDMA2000 standard is third-generation (**3-G**) mobile **wireless** technology.

CDMA2000 can support mobile data communications at speeds ranging from 144 **Kbps** to 2 **Mbps**. Deployment is in the planning stages. Versions have been developed by Ericsson and Qualcomm.

CD-Magneto Optical

CD-Magneto Optical (CD-MO) is a **compact disc** format that uses magnetic fields for data storage. Defined by Philips and Sony in their 1990 *Recordable CD Standard*, informally known as the **Orange Book**), CD-MO discs can, at least theoretically, be rewritten an unlimited number of times.

CD-MO discs are constructed of an alloy of terbium ferrite and cobalt. The reading of an MO disc is based on the Kerr effect. In the Kerr effect, linear, polarized light is deflected when it is influenced by a magnetic field, and the plane of polarization is twisted. The MO method changes the magnetic characteristics of tiny areas on the disk's surface so that the reading **laser** beam is reflected differently on altered areas than on unaltered areas.

When writing to the disc, a laser beam is focused on an extremely small spot, and the alloy is heated to a specific temperature (called the *Curie point*) sufficient to cause the ferromagnetic properties of the aligned elementary particles to be lost. An electromagnet is positioned on the other side of the disc, changing the polarity of the particles, whose differences will be encoded as **binary** data for storage. Like other **optical media**, such as DVD and other CD formats, CD-MO is read by a laser beam, which makes it more reliable than a hard disk or a floppy disk. However, a strong magnetic field can corrupt the stored data.

CD-MO

See "CD-Magneto Optical"

CDO

See "Collaboration Data Objects"

CDPD

CDPD (Cellular Digital Packet Data) is a specification for supporting **wireless** access to the Internet and other public **packet-switched** networks. **Cellular telephone** and **modem** providers that offer CDPD support make it possible for mobile users to get access to the Internet at up to 19.2 **Kbps**. Because CDPD is an **open** specification that adheres to the layered structure of the Open Systems Interconnection (**OSI**) model, it has the ability to be extended in the future. CDPD supports both the Internet's **Internet Protocol** and the ISO Connectionless Network Protocol (**CLNP**).

CDPD also supports IP **multicast** (one-to-many) service. With multicast, a company can periodically broadcast company updates to sales and service people on the road or a news subscription service can transmit its issues as they are published. It will also support the next level of IP, **IPv6**.

For the mobile user, CDPD's support for packet-switching means that a persistent link isn't needed. The same broadcast channel can be shared among a number of users at the same time. The user's modem recognizes the packets intended for its user. As data such as e-mail arrives, it is forwarded immediately to the user without a circuit connection having to be established.

There is a **circuit-switched** version, called CS CDPD, that can be used where traffic is expected to be heavy enough to warrant a dedicated connection.

CD-R

CD-R (for *compact disc, recordable*) is a type of *write once, read many* (**WORM**) compact disc (**CD**) format that allows one-time recording on a disc. The CD-R (as well as the **CD-RW**) format was introduced by Philips and Sony in their 1988 specification document, the **Orange Book**. Prior to the release of the Orange Book, CDs had been read-only audio (CD-Digital Audio, described in the **Red Book**), to be played in CD players, and multimedia (**CD-ROM**), to be played in computers' CD-ROM drives. After the Orange Book, any user with a CD recorder drive could create their own CDs from their desktop computers.

Like regular CDs (all the various formats are based on the original Red Book CD-DA), CD-Rs are composed of a polycarbonate plastic substrate, a thin reflective metal coating, and a protective outer coating. However, in a CD-R, a layer of organic polymer dye between the polycarbonate and metal layers serves as the recording medium. The composition of the dye is permanently transformed by

exposure to a specific frequency of light. Some CD-Rs have an additional protective layer to make them less vulnerable to damage from scratches, since the data—unlike that on a regular CD—is closer to the label side of the disc. A pregrooved spiral track helps to guide the **laser** for recording data, which is encoded from the inside to the outside of the disk in a single continuous spiral. The laser creates marks in the dye layer that mimic the reflective properties of the *pits* and *lands* (lower and higher areas) of the traditional CD. The distinct differences in the way the areas reflect light register as **digital** data that is then unencoded for playback.

CD-R discs usually hold 74 minutes (650 **MB**) of data, although some can hold up to 80 minutes (700 MB). With **packet writing** software and a compatible CD-R or CD-RW drive, it is possible to save data to a CD-R in the same way that one can save it to a floppy disk, although—since each part of the disc can only be written once—it is not possible to delete files and then reuse the space. The rewriteable CDs, CD-RWs, use an alloy layer (instead of the dye layer) which can be transformed to and from a crystalline state repeatedly.

CD recorders (usually referred to as **CD burners**), were once much too expensive for the home user, but now are similar in price to CD-ROM drives. CD-Rs can be created in any CD-R or CD-RW drive.

CD-ROM

CD-ROM (Compact Disc – read-only-memory) is an adaptation of the **CD** that is designed to store computer data in the form of text and graphics, as well as hi-fi stereo sound. The original data format standard was defined by Philips and Sony in the 1983 **Yellow Book.** Other standards are used in conjunction with it to define directory and file structures, including **ISO 9660**, HFS (Hierarchal File System, for Macintosh computers), and Hybrid HFS-ISO. Format of the CD-ROM is the same as for audio CDs: A standard CD is 120 mm (4.75 inches) in diameter and 1.2 mm (0.05 inches) thick and is composed of a polycarbonate plastic substrate (underlayer—this is the main body of the disc), one or more thin reflective metal (usually aluminum) layers, and a lacquer coating.

The Yellow Book specifications were so general that there was some fear in the industry that multiple incompatible and proprietary formats would be created. In order to prevent such an occurrence, representatives from industry leaders met at the High Sierra Hotel in Lake Tahoe to collaborate on a common standard. Nicknamed the *High Sierra Format*, this version was later modified to become ISO 9660. Today, CD-ROMs are standardized and will work in any standard CD-ROM drive. CD-ROM drives can also read audio compact discs for music, although CD players cannot read CD-ROM discs.

CD-ROM Data Storage

Although the disc media and the drives of the CD and CD-ROM are, in principle, the same, there is a difference in the way data storage is organized. Two new sectors were defined, Mode 1 for storing computer data and Mode 2 for compressed audio or video/graphic data.

CD-ROM Mode 1

CD-ROM Mode 1 is the mode used for CD-ROMs that carry data and applications only. In order to access the thousands of data files that may be present on this type of CD, precise addressing is necessary. Data is laid out in nearly the same way as it is on audio disks: Data is stored in sectors (the smallest separately addressable block of information), which each hold 2,352 bytes of data, with an additional number of bytes used for error detection and correction, as well as control structures. For mode 1 CD-ROM data storage, the sectors are further broken down, and 2,048 used for the expected data, while the other 304 bytes are devoted to extra error detection and correction code, because CD-ROMs are not as fault tolerant as audio CDs. There are 75 sectors per second on the disk, which yields a disc capacity of 681,984,000 bytes (650MB) and a single speed transfer rate of 150 KBps, with higher rates for faster CD-ROM drives. Drive speed is expressed as multiples of the single speed transfer rate, as 2X, 4X, 6X, and so on. Most drives support **CD-ROM XA** (Extended Architecture) and Photo-CD (including multiple session discs).

CD-ROM Mode 2

CD-ROM Mode 2 is used for compressed audio/video information and uses only two layers of error detection and correction, the same as the CD-DA. Therefore, all 2,336 bytes of data behind the sync and header bytes are for user data. Although the sectors of CD-DA, CD-ROM Mode 1 and Mode 2 are the same size, the amount of data that can be stored varies considerably because of the use of sync and header bytes, error correction and detection. The Mode 2 format offers a flexible method for storing graphics and video. It allows different kinds of data to be mixed together, and became the basis for CD-ROM XA. Mode 2 can be read by normal CD-ROM drives, in conjunction with the appropriate drivers.

Data Encoding and Reading

The CD-ROM, like other CD adaptations, has data encoded in a spiral track beginning at the center and ending at the outermost edge of the disc. The spiral track holds approximately 650 MB of data. That's about 5.5 billion bits. The distance between two rows of pits, measured from the center of one track to the center of the next track is referred to as track pitch. The track pitch can range from 1.5 to 1.7 microns, but in most cases is 1.6 microns.

Constant Linear Velocity (CLV) is the principle by which data is read from a CD-ROM. This principal states that the read head must interact with the data track at a constant rate, whether it is accessing data from the inner or outermost portions of the disc. This is affected by varying the rotation speed of the disc, from 500 rpm at the center, to 200 rpm at the outside. In a music CD, data is read sequentially, so rotation speed is not an issue. The CD-ROM, on the other hand, must read in random patterns, which necessitates constantly shifting rotation speeds. Pauses in the read function are audible, and some of the faster drives can be quite noisy because of it.

CD-ROM XA

CD-ROM XA (Compact Disc—read-only-memory, extended architecture) is a modification of **CD-ROM** that defines two new types of sectors that enable it to read and display data, graphics, video, and audio at the same time. CD-ROM XA was developed jointly by Sony, Philips, and Microsoft, and its specifications were published in an extension to the **Yellow Book**.

CD-ROM XA (for eXtended Architecture) discs contain Mode 2 sectors (areas left free for extra data by the omission of error detection and correction code) and were designed to allow audio and other data to be interleaved and read simultaneously. Formerly, images had to be loaded before the audio tracks could be played. The CD-ROM XA specifications include 256 color modes, which are compatible with PC formats and **CD-I**, and Adaptive Differential Pulse Code Modulation (**ADPCM**) audio, which is also defined for CD-I. Photo CD, Video CD and **CD-EXTRA** have all subsequently been based on CD-ROM XA, although it has not survived as a separate technology.

CD-RW

CD-RW (for *compact disc, rewriteable*) is a compact disc (**CD**) format that allows repeated recording on a disc. The CD-RW format was introduced by Hewlett-Packard, Mitsubishi, Philips, Ricoh, and Sony, in a 1997 supplement to Philips and Sony's **Orange Book**. CD-RW is Orange Book III (**CD-MO** was I, while **CD-R** was II). Prior to the release of the Orange Book, CDs had been read-only audio (CD-Digital Audio, described fully in the **Red Book**), to be played in CD players, and multimedia (**CD-ROM**), to be played in computers' CD-ROM drives. After the Orange Book, any user with a CD Recorder drive could create their own CDs from their desktop computers. CD-RW drives can write both CD-R and CD-RW discs and can read any type of CD.

Like regular CDs (all the various formats are based on the original Red Book CD-DA), CD-Rs and CD-RWs are composed of a polycarbonate plastic substrate, a thin reflective metal coating, and a protective outer coating. CD-R is a *write once, read many* (**WORM**) format, in which a layer of organic polymer dye between the polycarbonate and metal layers serves as the recording medium. The

composition of the dye is permanently transformed by exposure to a specific frequency of light. In a CD-RW, the dye is replaced with an alloy that can change back and forth from a crystalline form when exposed to a particular light, through a technology called *optical phase change*. The patterns created are less distinct than those of other CD formats, requiring a more sensitive device for playback. Only drives designated as "MultiRead" are able to read CD-RW reliably.

Similar to CD-R, the CD-RW's polycarbonate substrate is preformed with a spiral groove to guide the **laser**. The alloy phase-change recording layer, which is commonly a mix of silver, indium, antimony, and tellurium, is sandwiched between two layers of **dielectric material** that draw excess heat from the recording layer. After heating to one particular temperature, the alloy will become crystalline when it is cooled; after heating to a higher temperature it will become amorphous (won't hold its shape) when it is cooled. By controlling the temperature of the laser, crystalline areas and non-crystalline areas are formed. The crystalline areas will reflect the laser, while the other areas will absorb it. The differences will register as **digital** data that can be unencoded for playback. To erase or write over recorded data, the higher temperature laser is used, which results in the non-crystalline form, which can then be reformed by the lower temperature laser.

CD-RW discs usually hold 74 minutes (650 **MB**) of data, although some can hold up to 80 minutes (700 MB) and, according to some reports, can be rewritten as many as 1000 times. With **packet writing** software and a compatible CD-RW drive, it is possible to save data to a CD-RW in the same way as one can save it to a floppy disk. CD recorders (usually referred to as **CD burners**), were once much too expensive for the home user, but now are similar in price to CD-ROM drives.

Celeron

Also see **Pentium**, **Xeon**, and **Pentium 3**.

Celeron is the low-end (and low cost) member of the family of **microprocessor**s from Intel that is based on its P6 **architecture**. Although it is based on the same architecture as the Pentium II, it lacks some high-**performance** features of the Pentium II line. Celeron models later than the 300A include an **L1 and L2 cache** on the microchip, meaning that the cache is accessed at the same **clock speed** that the processor operates with. The Celeron L2 cache is smaller (128 **kilobyte**s) than the Pentium II's (512 KB). However, because the Celeron L2 cache is on the processor chip and the Pentium II's is not, their effective L2 speeds are closely comparable. With clock speeds up to 466 **MHz**, Celeron processors are attractive to power users at first glance, but they should be compared to the Pentium II's computing power in order to get an idea of their useful application.

In ZDNet's CPUmark 99 **benchmark** tests, the Celeron processors compared favorably with Pentium II processors. Intel is marketing the processor as a chip for the basic PC.

They view it as providing performance good enough for home and business users doing word processing and Internet surfing. Power users and serious gamers may want to think about spending more for the Pentium II's top performance.

Celeron can be mounted in a **Slot 1 motherboard** or in a Socket 370 motherboard. Like Intel's other P6 microprocessors, the Celeron can be used for symmetric multiprocessing (**SMP**).

cell

1) In wireless telephony, a cell is the geographical area covered by a cellular telephone transmitter. The transmitter facility itself is called the *cell site*. The cell provided by a cell site can be from one mile to twenty miles in diameter, depending on terrain and transmission power. Several coordinated cell sites are called a cell system. When you sign up with a cellular telephone service provider, you generally are given access to their cell system, which is essentially local. When travelling out of the range of this cell system, the cell system can enable you to be transferred to a neighboring company's cell system without your being aware of it. This is called **roaming service**.

The cell sites in a system connect to a Mobile Telephone Switching Office (MTSO), which in turn connects to the standard landline telephone system.

2) In a battery power source, a cell is a single energy or charge-storing unit within a *pack* of cells that form the battery. Each cell has a voltage rating that is combined with the other cells' voltages to form the overall battery voltage rating.

Cell of Origin

Cell of Origin (COO) is a **mobile** positioning technique for finding a caller's **cell** (the basic geographical coverage unit of a **cellular telephone** system) location. It may be used by emergency services or commercial use. COO is the only positioning technique that is widely used in **wireless** networks and is used for Phase 1 of 911 service in the United States.

For COO positioning, the location of the base station is ascertained and considered to be the location of the caller. COO is a variable and not a very precise locator; depending on the number of base stations in the search area, accuracy may be as close as within one hundred meters of the target (in an urban area) or as far off as thirty kilometers away from the target where base stations are less densely concentrated. For this reason, when precision is important COO is often used in conjunction with some other technology, such as the Global Positioning System (**GPS**) or Time of Arrival (TOA).

Although COO positioning is not as precise as other methods, it offers unique advantages: It can very quickly identify the location (generally in about three seconds) and does not require equipment or network upgrades, which

makes it easily deployed to existing customer bases. The American National Standards Institute (**ANSI**), and the European Telecommunications Standards Institute (ETSI) recently formed the T1P1 subcommittee dedicated to creating standardization for positioning systems using TOA, Assisted GPS, and Enhanced Observed Time Difference in addition to COO.

cellspace

According to writer David S. Bennahum, cellspace is the kind of **cyberspace** you experience when equipped with a **cellular telephone** that can be connected to the Internet. Bennahum describes being able to receive e-mail through an air shaft in a subway tunnel, reading the mail on the subway, and sending the replies back after ascending to the street. Bennahum envisions new services that could be provided for mobile users, especially one that combined all the map, restaurant, airline reservation and timetable, rental car, and hotel information into a single site. Already, he notes, there are special services for travellers providing remote access to corporate **intranets**. Apart from services, Bennahum notes one characteristic common to many cellspace travellers: Because packet delivery is relatively slow with today's technology, services or users tend to dispense with the graphic images.

Bennahum's concept of cellspace is based on experience with his 3Com Palm Pilot, a Novatel Minstrel modem, and connection to a Cellular Digital Packet Data (**CDPD**) packet-switched network at 19 **kilobit**s per second.

Cellular Digital Packet Data

See "CDPD"

cellular telephone

Cellular telephone is a type of short-wave **analog** or **digital** transmission in which a subscriber has a **wireless** connection from a mobile telephone to a relatively nearby transmitter. The transmitter's span of coverage is called a **cell**. Generally, cellular telephone service is available in urban areas and along major highways. As the cellular telephone user moves from one cell or area of coverage to another, the telephone is effectively passed on to the local cell transmitter.

A cellular telephone is not to be confused with a *cordless telephone* (which is simply a phone with a very short wireless connection to a local phone outlet). A newer service similar to cellular is **personal communications services** (PCS).

centimeter

The centimeter (abbreviation, cm) is a unit of displacement or length in the **cgs** (centimeter/gram/second) system of units. One centimeter is the distance traveled by a ray of electromagnetic (EM) energy through a vacuum in $3.33564095 \times 10^{-11}$ of a second. It is equivalent to 0.01 **meter**. There are about 2.54 centimeters in one linear inch.

Power-of-10 **prefix multiplier**s facilitate the derivation of other, often more convenient, distance units from the centimeter. One meter (m) is equal to 100 cm, one millimeter (mm) is equal to 0.1 cm, and one kilometer (km) is equal to 100,000 (10^5) cm. These units are found in nonscientific as well as scientific literature. Smaller units are the realm of the scientist and engineer. One micrometer (symbolized μm or μ), also called a micron, is equal to 0.0001 (10^{-4}) cm. One nanometer (nm) is equal to 10^{-7} cm. One Angström unit (symbolized Å) is equal to 10^{-8} cm, or 0.1 nm.

The centimeter and its kin are used to specify the **wavelength**s of EM fields, particularly at ultra-high and microwave radio frequencies. The so-called radio spectrum occupies an informally defined range of wavelengths from roughly 1 mm to several tens of kilometers. A 300-cm radio wave falls near the middle of the standard **FM** (frequency-modulation) broadcast band; a 1-cm radio wave corresponds to a frequency of approximately 30 gigahertz (**GHz**). The range of visible light wavelengths is from approximately 390 nm (violet) to 770 nm (red). The speed of **EM-field** propagation in a vacuum, to nine significant figures, is $2.99792458 \times 10^{10}$ centimeters per second.

Also see **displacement**, **meter**, **prefix multiplier**s, and International System of Units (**SI**).

central office

In telephone communication in the U.S., a central office (CO) is an office in a locality to which subscriber home and business lines are connected on what is called a **local loop**. The central office has switching equipment that can switch calls locally or to long-distance carrier phone offices.

In other countries, the term *public exchange* is used.

Centronics parallel interface

The Centronics **parallel interface** is an older and still widely-used standard **I/O** interface for connecting **printer**s and certain other devices to computers. The interface typically includes a somewhat cumbersome cable and a 36-**pin** male and female connector at the printer or other device. The cable plugs into a 25-pin parallel **port** on the computer. Data flows in one direction only, from the computer to the printer or other device. In addition to eight parallel data lines, other lines are used to read status information and send control signals. Centronics Corporation designed the original Centronics parallel interface for dot matrix printers. In 1981, IBM used this interface as an alternative to the slower one-bit-at-a-time **serial** interface.

When the Centronics parallel interface was first developed, the main peripheral was the printer. Since then, portable disk drives, **tape backup** drives, and **CD-ROM** players are among devices that have adopted the parallel interface.

These new uses caused manufacturers to look at new ways to make the Centronics parallel interface better. In 1991, Lexmark, IBM, Texas instruments, and others met to discuss a standard that would offer more speed and bi-directional communication. Their effort and the sponsorship of the **IEEE** resulted in the IEEE 1284 committee. The IEEE 1284 standard was approved for release in March 1994.

The IEEE 1284 standard specifies five modes of operation, each mode providing data transfer in either the forward direction (computer to peripheral), backward direction (peripheral to computer), or bi-directional (one direction at a time).

- **Compatibility mode** is the original Centronics parallel interface and intended for use with dot matrix printers and older laser printers. The compatibility mode can be combined with the nibble mode for bi-directional data transfer.

- **Nibble mode** allows data transfer back to the computer. The nibble mode uses the status lines to send 2 **nibbles** (4-bit units) of data to the computer in two data transfer cycles. This mode is best used with printers.

- **Byte mode** uses software **drivers** to disable the drivers that control the data lines in order for data to be sent from the printer to the computer. The data is sent at the same speed as when data is sent from the computer to the printer. One byte of data is transferred instead of the two data cycles required by the nibble mode.

- **ECP mode** (Enhanced Capability Port mode) is an advanced bi-directional mode for use with printers and **scanner**s. It allows data **compression** for **images**, **FIFO** (first in, first out) for items in **queue**s, and high-speed, bi-directional communication. Data transfer occurs at two to four megabytes per second. An advanced feature of **ECP** is **channel addressing**. This is used for multifunction devices such as printer/fax/modem devices. For example, if a printer/fax/modem device needs to print and send data over the modem at the same time, the channel address software driver of the ECP mode assigns a new channel to the modem so that both devices can work simultaneously.

- **EPP mode** (Enhanced Parallel Port mode) was designed by Intel, Xircom, and Zenith Data Systems to provide a high-performance parallel interface that could also be used with the standard interface. EPP mode was adopted as part of the IEEE 1284 standard. The EPP mode uses data cycles that transfer data between the computer and the peripheral and address cycles that assign address, channel, or command information. This allows data transfer speeds of 500 kilobytes to 2 megabytes per second, depending on the speed of the slowest interface. The EPP mode is bi-directional. It is suited for network adapters, data acquisition, portable hard drives, and other devices that need speed.

The computer must determine what the capabilities of the attached peripheral are and which mode to utilize. The concept developed to determine these factors is called negotiation. Negotiation is a sequence of events on the parallel port interface that determines which IEEE 1284 modes the device can handle. An older device will not respond to the negotiation sequence and compatibility mode is selected to operate that device. A newer device will respond to the negotiation sequence and a more advanced mode can be set.

CEO and others

CEO, CFO, CIO, and CTO are abbreviations that stand for: Chief Executive Officer, Chief Financial Officer, Chief Information Officer, and Chief Technology Officer. Modern corporations commonly use these terms to describe their top executives.

The CEO (Chief Executive Officer) is often but not always also the President of a company. The CEO reports to the Chairman of the Board and board members. The CEO is usually the most important spokesperson for the company, the person who is responsible for quarterly results, and the best paid member of the company.

The CFO (Chief Financial Officer) is sometimes also the company Treasurer and, in many companies, is seen as the second most important person in the company (since managing the quarterly results often depends on an understanding of how to keep the books).

The CIO (Chief Information Officer), a relative newcomer to the ranks of the top executives in a corporation, is responsible for a company's internal information systems, and, especially with the arrival of the Internet, sometimes in charge of the company's **e-business** infrastructure.

The CTO (Chief Technology Officer), an even newer arrival to the top executive ranks in many companies, is likely to be seen as the second or third most important person in any technology company. The CTO is responsible for research and development and possibly for new product plans.

CERN

CERN, the high-energy particle physics laboratory in Geneva, Switzerland, is where, in 1991, a researcher, Dr. Tim Berners-Lee, essentially invented the World Wide Web. Berners-Lee is credited with developing the idea of combining **hypertext** with the speed of today's electronic networks. Working with a small team, he developed the Hypertext Transfer Protocol (**HTTP**) on which the Web is based.

CERT

CERT (pronounced SUHRT), officially called the CERT Coordination Center, is the Internet's official emergency team. CERT (originally called the "Computer Emergency Response Team") was formed by the Defense Advanced Research Projects Agency (**DARPA**) in November 1988 after the Internet was assaulted in the Internet worm incident. Today, CERT focuses on security breach and **denial-of-service** incidents, providing alerts and incident-handling and avoidance guidelines. CERT also conducts an ongoing public awareness campaign and engages in research aimed at improving security systems.

CERT is located at Carnegie-Mellon University in Pittsburgh where it is part of the Networked Systems Survivability program in the Software Engineering Institute, a federally funded research and development center.

certificate authority

A certificate authority (CA) is an authority in a network that issues and manages security credentials and **public key**s for message **encryption**. As part of a public key infrastructure (**PKI**), a CA checks with a registration authority (**RA**) to verify information provided by the requestor of a **digital certificate**. If the RA verifies the requestor's information, the CA can then issue a certificate.

Depending on the public key infrastructure implementation, the certificate includes the owner's public key, the expiration date of the certificate, the owner's name, and other information about the public key owner.

Certified Internet Webmaster

Certified Internet Webmaster (CIW) is a set of courses and exams that, when completed successfully, certifies an individual as capable in Web site development and server administration, including security and e-commerce. The CIW curriculum provides hands-on training for real-world Internet technologies that is independent of particular product vendors. A student may train at an instructor-led training site or train at home or at the office using conference calls, e-mail, and Web-based support. Examinations are administered by Sylvan Prometric, an independent testing body, at one of their testing centers. The Internet Certification Institute International (ICII) offers CIW certification worldwide and ProsoftTraining.Com offers the CIW certification program in the U.S. CIW certification is accredited by the Association of Internet Professionals and endorsed by the World Organization of Webmasters.

The first step toward certification is the CIW Foundations course. It provides basic knowledge of Internet technologies, network infrastructure, and Web page creation with the Hypertext Markup Language (**HTML**). All students must pass the exam at this level before taking other courses. Thereafter, the student may choose from one or more of the following courses:

- **CIW Site Designer:** This level teaches the student how to design, implement, and maintain a Web site with HTML, other authoring tools, and **script** languages, and how to use Web management and new media tools. This is a five-day course.

- **CIW Application Developer:** The student learns to build client and server-side Web applications. This course is divided into four sections totaling 10 days: **JavaScript** Fundamentals (2 days); Visual Java Using Visual Café or Visual Age (3 days); Fundamentals of **CGI** Programming Using **Perl** (2 days); and Server-Side Scripting and Security (3 days).

- **CIW Enterprise Developer:** An Enterprise Developer builds n-**tier** database and **legacy** solutions for Web applications. This course takes 10 days and is divided into four sections: Java Programming Fundamentals (5 days); Enterprise Development with JFC (Java Foundation Classes) and Swing, which is used to create **GUI** (graphical user interface) (2 days); Enterprise Development with **JDBC** (Java Database Connectivity) (1 day); and Enterprise Development with **CORBA** (Common Object Request Broker Architecture) and Java (2 days). A student needs a familiarity with Windows NT and web server administration concepts and a working knowledge of C, Pascal or C++. A student must complete the Foundations and Application Developer courses before taking this course.

- **CIW Server Administrator:** This course teaches a student how to manage and tune corporate Internet and intranet infrastructures, monitor Web server systems, news and mail servers, and configure and deploy e-business servers. A student needs a working knowledge of Windows NT including installation and configuration. The course takes five days to complete and is divided into two sections: Internet System Management (2 days) and Advanced Internet System Management (3 days).

- **CIW Internetworking Professional:** An Internetworking Professional defines network architecture, identifies infrastructure components, and monitors and analyzes network performance. Basically, the Internetworking Professional is responsible for the design and management of enterprise **TCP/IP** networks, including troubleshooting when necessary. This course is divided into three parts totaling seven days: TCP/IP Internetworking (2 days); Advanced TCP/IP Concepts and Practices (3 days); and Simple Network Management Protocol (**SNMP**) Network Management (2 days).

- **CIW Security Professional:** The Security Professional implements security policies, identifies security threats, develops and provides countermeasures using firewall systems and attack-recognition technologies, and manages the **deployment** of security solutions. The course is divided into four sections each two days long:

Network Security and Firewalls; Windows NT Network Security; UNIX and TCP/IP Network Security; and Security Auditing, Attacks, and Threat Analysis. A student must successfully complete both the Foundations and Internetworking Professional courses before taking this course.

- **CIW E-Commerce Professional:** The student learns how to design and implement **e-commerce** Web sites, identify customer needs, monitor customer usage patterns, determine order processes and service after the sale and how to determine what e-business solutions increase sales. The student examines the relationships between cardholders, issuers, merchants, acquirers, payment gateways, and third parties using Secure Electronic Transactions (**SET**), cryptography standards, **certificate authority**, and services including VeriSign and **CyberCash**. This course is five days long divided into two parts: E-commerce Concepts and Practices (2 days) and E-commerce Strategy and Solutions (3 days).

CFB

See "ciphertext feedback"

CFML

CFML (ColdFusion Markup Language) is a Web **page markup** language that allows a **Web site** developer to create **page**s with variable information (text or graphics) that is filled in dynamically (**on the fly**) in response to variables such as user input. Along with the usual Hypertext Markup Language (**HTML**) tags that determine page layout and appearance, the page creator uses CFML **tag**s to bring in content based on the results of a database **query** or user input. CMFL is a proprietary language developed for use with **ColdFusion**, a product from Allaire.

CFML tags perform all server-side tasks (such as **database** queries) by condensing complex processes, that would normally require knowledge of programming languages such as Java or C++, into four basic tags: CFQUERY, which is used to submit a structured query language (**SQL**) request to the database; CFOUTPUT, which is used to display the result of a query; and CFTABLE or CFCOL, which are used to display a preformatted table containing the results of a set of queries. Files created with CFML are saved as ColdFusion **template**s and use a ".cfm" extension.

CFR

See "call failure rate"

CGA

See "display modes"

CGI

See "common gateway interface"

cgs system of units

See "small-unit metric system"

Challenge-Handshake Authentication Procedure

See "CHAP"

change mode

See "chmod"

channel

1) In telecommunications in general, a channel is a separate path through which signals can flow.

2) In the public switched telephone network (**PSTN**), a channel is one of multiple transmission paths within a single link between network points. For example, the commonly used (in North America) **T-carrier system** line service provides 24 64 **Kbps** channels for digital data transmission.

3) In radio and television, a channel is a separate incoming signal or program source that a user can select.

4) In optical fiber transmission using dense wavelength-division multiplexing (**DWDM**), a channel is a separate wavelength of light within a combined, multiplexed light stream.

5) On the World Wide Web, a channel is a preselected Web site that can automatically send updated information for immediate display or viewing on request. See **push technology**.

6) In computer and Internet marketing, a channel is a "middleman" between a product creator and the marketplace. Value-added resellers (**VAR**) and retail store chains are examples of channels in this context.

7) Using **Internet Relay Chat**, a channel is a specific chat group.

8) In IBM **mainframe** systems, a channel is a high bandwidth connection between a processor and other processors, workstations, printers, and storage devices within a relatively close proximity. It's also called a *local connection* as opposed to a *remote* (or telecommunication) *connection*.

channel 64

See "B8ZS"

channel associated signaling

See "CAS"

channel bank

A channel bank is a device at a telephone company **central office** (public exchange) that converts **analog** signals from home and business users into digital signals to be carried over higher-speed lines between the central office and other exchanges. The analog signal is converted into a digital signal that transmits at a rate of 64 thousand bits per second (**Kbps**). This 64 Kbps signal is a standard known as a **digital signal X** signal. The signal is **time-division multiplexed** with other DS0 signals on the same line. Usually, the digital information is put on each DS0 signal using pulse code modulation (**PCM**).

Channel Definition Format

The Channel Definition Format (CDF) is a **file format** from Microsoft that lets you create a file that defines a Web "**channel**," which is a preselected Web site or group of related Web sites. To use the channel, a user needs to have the Microsoft Internet Explorer 4 or later **browser**. The CDF file identifies the Web page and subpages that the user sees after selecting a channel on the browser. The file may also identify subpages that may be selected from the main channel page. A channel developer for a Web site puts the CDF file on the Web server. A user who clicks on a channel (for example, from the Internet Explorer channel menu bar) is actually specifying the **Uniform Resource Locator** or Internet file name of the Channel Definition File that defines the channel.

The Channel Definition Format is an application of Extensible Markup Language (**XML**) that Microsoft is proposing as a standard way to describe a Web site channel. In Internet Explorer 5, the channel user implementation has been changed. The *Channel Bar* that formerly appeared automatically when Windows was started has been removed. Channels are now accessed as a special folder in the Favorites menu.

channel extender

A channel extender is a device used with IBM's **S/390** line of computers to increase the maximum communication distances between the S/390 **channel**-connected **mainframe** computers, or between an S/390 and **peripheral** devices such as workstations, printers, and storage devices. As a rule, optical fiber channel connections transmit over **multimode fiber**, which sends data over multiple paths within the fiber for distances less than two miles. Channel extenders transmit over **single mode fiber**, which sends data over a single path for distances of up to—and sometimes greater than—eighteen miles. Because the channel extender increases the distance of possible connections, a channel-connected network may be able to operate with fewer S/390 computers.

CHAP

See "CHAP"

character

1) In information technology, a character is a printable symbol having phonetic or pictographic meaning and usually forming part of a word of **text**, depicting a numeral, or expressing grammatical punctuation. In information technology today, a character is generally one of a limited number of symbols, including the letters of a particular language's alphabet, the numerals in the decimal number system, and certain special symbols such as the ampersand (&) and "**at sign**" (@).

Several standards of computer encoding have been developed for characters. The most commonly used in personal computers is **ASCII**. IBM mainframe systems use **EBCDIC**. A new standard, **Unicode**, is supported by later Windows systems.

2) A distinction is sometimes made between a character and a **glyph**. In this distinction, a character can be distinguished from other characters in terms of meaning and sound—a glyph is the graphic image used to portray the character. In different implementations, a character can have more than one possible glyph, and a glyph can represent more than one possible character.

characters per inch

See "CPI"

charge quantity

Charge quantity is an expression of the extent to which an object is electrically charged. It is also an expression of the relative number of charge carriers in a given region or volume.

The force with which two electrically charged bodies attract or repel depends on the product of the charge quantities in both objects, and also on the distance between the charge centers of the objects. If the polarities are the same, the force is repulsive; if the polarities are opposite, the force is attractive. For any two charged bodies, the force decreases in proportion to the square of the distance between their charge centers, assuming the charges on the objects do not change.

The most common unit of charge quantity is the **coulomb** (symbolized C). This is the charge unit in the International System of Units (**SI**) and represents approximately 6.24×10^{18} unit electric charges. The statcoulomb (statC) is the **cgs** (centimeter/gram/second) unit of charge quantity, and represents approximately 2.082×10^9 unit electric charges. A unit electric charge is the charge quantity contained in a single **electron** or **proton**. By convention, electrons are assigned negative charge, and protons are assigned positive charge.

The tables below facilitate conversion among coulombs, statcoulombs, and unit electric charges.

Unit (and symbol)	To convert to coulombs, multiply by:	Conversely, multiply by:
statcoulomb (statC)	3.3356×10^{-10}	2.9980×10^9
unit charge	1.60×10^{-19}	6.24×10^{18}

Unit (and symbol)	To convert to statcoulombs, multiply by:	Conversely, multiply by:
coulomb (C)	2.9980×10^9	3.3356×10^{-10}
unit charge	4.803×10^{-10}	2.082×10^9

Also see **coulomb**, **statcoulomb**, **small-unit metric system**, and International System of Units (**SI**).

charge-coupled device

A charge-coupled device (CCD) is a light-sensitive **integrated circuit** that stores and displays the data for an image in such a way that each **pixel** (picture element) in the image is converted into an electical charge the intensity of which is related to a color in the color spectrum. For a system supporting 65,535 colors, there will be a separate value for each color that can be stored and recovered. CCDs are now commonly included in digital still and video cameras. They are also used in astronomical telescopes, scanners, and **bar code** readers. The devices have also found use in **machine vision** for robots, in **optical character recognition** (OCR), in the processing of **satellite** photographs, and in the enhancement of **radar** images, especially in meteorology.

A CCD in a digital camera improves **resolution** compared with older technologies. Some digital cameras produce images having more than one million pixels, yet sell for under $1,000. The term *megapixel* has been coined in reference to such cameras. Sometimes a camera with an image of 1,024 by 768 pixels is given the label "megapixel," even though it technically falls short of the mark. Another asset of the CCD is its high degree of sensitivity. A good CCD can produce an image in extremely dim light, and its resolution does not deteriorate when the illumination intensity is low, as is the case with conventional cameras.

The CCD was invented in 1969 at Bell Labs, now part of Lucent Technologies, by George Smith and Willard Boyle.

Charles Babbage

If John von Neumann is the father of modern computing, then the English mathematician and inventor Charles Babbage can be considered its grandfather. Babbage designed, though never built, a **Difference Engine** and an **Analytical Engine**, the world's first computing machines.

Babbage worked as a mathematician in Cambridge University where he received his MA in 1817 and later, like Newton, whose mathematical principles he espoused, occupied the Lucasian chair in mathematics. As a scientist, Babbage was obsessed with facts and statistics and lived in a rationalistic world where it was assumed that if all facts, past and present, could be known then all future events were determinable. His statistical publications include "Table of the Relative Frequency of the Causes of Breaking of Plate Glass Windows" and "Table of Constants of the Class Mammalia," the minutiae of which included the heart rate of the pig. Babbage founded the Statistical Society in 1834.

A prolific disseminator of ideas and an eclectic inventor, Babbage's varied range of inventions reflected the diversity of his interests. Fascinated by the railroad, which was invented in his native England in 1823, Babbage devised a standard rail gauge width as well as a cowcatcher (for the front of trains). He also recorded inventions related to lighthouse signalling, code breaking, and the postal system. He founded the British Association for the Advancement of Science and the (Royal) Astronomical Society.

Although remembered today primarily for his calculating engines, Babbage left a legacy in the fields of political theory (he was an ardent industrialist) and operations research (where his 1832 publication, "On the Economy of Manufactures," cataloged the manufacturing processes of the day).

Charles Babbage died in London on October 18, 1871.

chassis

A chassis (pronounced TCHA-see or SHA-see) is the physical frame or structure of an automobile, an airplane, a desktop computer, or other multi-component device. *Case* is very similar in meaning, but tends to connote the protective aspect of the frame rather than its structure. People tend to choose one term or the other. The rest of this definition uses *chassis* but applies as well to the term *case*. Both terms (and *casing*) are derived from the Vulgate Latin for *box*. The plural form is also *chassis*.

In a computer, the chassis houses the main electronic components, including the **motherboard** (with places to insert or replace microchips for the main and possibly specialized processors and random access memory (**RAM**) and places for adding optional adapters (for example, for audio or video capabilities). Typically, room is provided for a **hard disk** drive and a **CD-ROM** drive.

The IBM PC chassis for its XT computers set an early de facto standard for a chassis configuration (sometimes referred to as the **form factor**). The desktop computer has since evolved through the AT model, the mini-AT, and the small-footprint PC. A later development was the vertical or tower chassis configuration, designed to be placed under a desk. The outer dimensions of a chassis are said to form its **footprint**.

The term is not usually applied to mobile and notebook computers perhaps because the hardware components have to be more tightly integrated. Some communications devices such as terminal servers have a chassis especially designed to handle many combinations of hardware add-ons. Such a chassis is described as *modular*.

chat abbreviations

For the funny little faces made with keyboard characters, see **emoticon**.

Usage note: Chat abbreviations that describe emotions are typically typed within less-than and greater-than symbols (for example, <BG> for "big grin"). Chat abbreviations that represent shorthand for sentences or phrases, such as "BBL" for "Be back later" are not usually typed within these symbols. Since some of these phrases happen to denote emotions, this usage rule can easily be violated.

Abbreviation	Meaning
ADN	Any day now
AFAIK	As far as I know
AFK	Away from keyboard
ARE	Acronym-rich environment
A/S/L?	Age/sex/location?
B4N	Bye for now
BAK	Back at the keyboard
BBIAB	Be back in a bit
BBL	Be back later
BEG	Big evil grin
BFD	Big f***ing deal
BFN	Bye for now
BG	Big grin
BIOYIOP	Blow it out your I/O port
BL	Belly laughing
BOTEC	Back-of-the-envelope calculation
BRB	Be right back
BTA	But then again...
BTW	By the way
BWTHDIK	But what the heck do I know...?
CU	See you
CUL	See you later
CUL8ER	See you later
CYA	Cover your ass
CYO	See you online
DBA	Doing business as
DFLA	Disenhanced four-letter acronym (that is, a TLA)
DL	Dead link
DIKU	Do I know you?
DITYID	Did I tell you I'm distressed?
DQMOT	Don't quote me on this
EG	Evil grin

Abbreviation	Meaning
EMFBI	Excuse me for butting in
EOM	End of message
EOT	End of thread (meaning: end of discussion)
ETLA	Extended three-letter acronym (that is, an FLA)
F2F	Face to face
FAQ	Frequently-ask question(s)
FISH	First in, still here
FLA	Four-letter acronym
FMTYEWTK	Far more than you ever wanted to know
FOMCL	Falling off my chair laughing
FUBAR	F***ed up beyond all repair or recognition
FUD	Fear, Uncertainty, and Doubt
FWIW	For what it's worth
FYI	For your information
G	Grin
GA	Go ahead
GAL	Get a life
GDR	Grinning, ducking, and running
GIWIST	Gee, I wish I'd said that
GMTA	Great minds think alike
GOL	Giggling out loud
GTRM	Going to read mail
HTH	Hope this helps
IAC	In any case
IANAL	I am not a lawyer (but)
IC	I see
IHA	I hate acronyms
IIRC	If I recall/remember/recollect correctly
ILU or ILY	I love you
IM	Immediate message
IMHO	In my humble opinion
IMing	Chatting with someone online usually while doing other things such as playing trivia or other interactive game
IMNSHO	In my not so humble opinion
IMO	In my opinion
IOW	In other words
IPN	I'm posting naked
IRL	In real life (that is, when not chatting)
IYSWIM	If you see what I mean
JBOD	Just a bunch of disks (like redundant array of independent disks, etc.)
JIC	Just in case
JK	Just kidding
KOTC	Kiss on the cheek

Abbreviation	Meaning
KWIM?	Know what I mean?
L8R	Later
LD	Later, dude
LDR	Long-distance relationship
LLTA	Lots and lots of thunderous applause
LOL	Laughing out loud
LRF	Little Rubber Feet (the little pads on the bottom of displays and other equipment)
LTM	Laugh to myself
LTR	Long-term relationship
LULAB	Love you like a brother
LULAS	Love you like a sister
MorF	Male or female
MOSS	Member of the same sex
MOTOS	Member of the opposite sex
MUSM	Miss you so much
NFG	No f*****g good
NFW	No feasible way or no f*****g way
NIFOC	Naked in front of computer
NP or N/P	No problem
NRN	No response necessary
OIC	Oh, I see
OLL	Online love
OTF	Off the floor
OTOH	On the other hand
OTTOMH	Off the top of my head
PANS	Pretty awesome new stuff (as opposed to "POTS")
PCMCIA	People can't master computer industry acronyms
PDA	Public display of affection
PEBCAK	Problem exists between chair and keyboard
PIBKAC	Problem is between keyboard and chair
PITA	Pain in the ass
PMFJIB	Pardon me for jumping in but...
::POOF::	Goodbye (leaving the room)
POTS	Plain old telephone service
PU	That stinks!
RL	Real life (that is, when not chatting)
ROR	Raffing out roud (Engrish for "laughing out loud")
ROTFL	Rolling on the floor laughing

Abbreviation	Meaning
ROTFLMAO	Rolling on the floor laughing my a** off
ROTFLMAOWPIMP	Rolling on the floor laughing my a** off while peeing in my pants
ROTFLMBO	Rolling on the floor laughing my butt off
RPG	Role-playing games
RSN	Real soon now
RTFM	Read the f***ing manual
RYO	Roll your own (write your own program; derived from cigarettes rolled yourself with tobacco and paper)
S4L	Spam for life (what you may get when you become someone's customer or client)
SHCOON	Shoot hot coffee out of nose
SEG	S***-eating grin
SF	Surfer-friendly (low-graphics Web site)
SNAFU	Situation normal, all f***ed up
SO	Significant other
SOL	Smiling out loud or sh*t out of luck
SOMY	Sick of me yet?
STFW	Search the f*****g Web
STW	Search the Web
SWAG	Stupid wild-a** guess
TAFN	That's all for now
TANSTAAFL	There ain't no such thing as a free lunch
TFH	Thread from hell (a discussion that just won't die and is often irrelevant to the purpose of the forum or group)
TGIF	Thank God it's Friday
TIA	Thanks in advance (used if you post a question and are expecting a helpful reply)
TLA	Three-letter acronym
TLK2UL8R	Talk to you later
TMI	Too much information
TOPCA	Til our paths cross again (early Celtic chat term)
TPTB	The powers that be
TTFN	Ta-Ta for now
TTT	Thought that, too (when someone types in what you were about to type)
TTYL	Talk to you later
TU	Thank you
UAPITA	You're a pain in the ass

Abbreviation	Meaning
UW	You're welcome
VBG	Very big grin
VBSEG	Very big s***-eating grin
WDALYIC	Who died and left you in charge?
WFM	Works for me
WIBNI	Wouldn't it be nice if
WT?	What/who the ?
WTFO	What the F***! Over!
WTG	Way to go!
WTGP?	Want to go private?
WU?	What's up?
WUF?	Where are you from?
WYSIWYG	What you see is what you get
YGBSM	You gotta be s***tin' me!
YMMV	Your mileage may vary

chat room

A chat room is a Web site, part of a Web site, or part of an online service such as America Online, that provides a venue for communities of users with a common interest to communicate in real time. Forums and discussion groups, in comparison, allow users to post messages but don't have the capacity for interactive messaging. Most chat rooms don't require users to have any special software; those that do, such as Internet Relay Chat (**IRC**) allow users to download it from the Internet.

Chat room users register for the chat room of their choice, choose a user name and password, and log into a particular room (most sites have multiple chat rooms). Inside the chat room, generally there is a list of the people currently online, who also are alerted that another person has entered the chat room. To chat, users type a message into a text box. The message is almost immediately visible in the larger communal message area and other users respond. Users can enter chat rooms and read messages without sending any, a practice known as **lurking**.

Because chat room messages are spontaneous and instantly visible, there is a potential for abuse, which may or may not be intentional. Site hosts typically post a frequently asked questions (**FAQ**) list to guide users to appropriate chat room behavior, such as introducing yourself when you enter a room, making it clear when you are directing a question or response to a specific user, and reporting disruptive users, for example. Disruptive users may verbally abuse other chatters, monopolize the conversation, or even just disable it by repeatedly typing the same word or phrase into the conversation, a practice (much frowned upon) known as *scrolling*.

Chat rooms can be found that focus on virtually any aspect of human endeavor or interest: There are current communities based on classic movies, Irish ancestry, baton twirling, and psychic readings, for example. Various sites, such as Yahoo, provide a directory of chat sites. Others, such as MSN Web Communities, guide users through the steps required to create their own chat room.

chatterbot

A chatterbot is a program that attempts to simulate the conversation or "chatter" of a human being. Chatterbots such as "Eliza" and "Parry" were well-known early attempts at creating programs that could at least temporarily fool a real human being into thinking they were talking to another person. A chatterbot can be thought of as the spokesperson for an artificial intelligence (**AI**).

Chatterbots have been used in the online interactive games called Tinymuds. A single player may be able to interact with a chatterbot while awaiting other "live" players. At least one company is making a product that lets you build a chatterbot to handle sales-related or other questions on your Web site. And it is not difficult to imagine two chatterbots talking to each other and perhaps even exchanging information about each other so that their conversation could become more sophisticated. (To see how scary this could become, see **artificial intellect**.) And, of course, they would use some of the more common **chat abbreviations**.

chatting

For terms frequently used in online keyboard chatting, see **chat abbreviations**.

On the Internet, chatting is talking to other people who are using the Internet at the same time you are. Usually, this "talking" is the exchange of typed-in messages requiring one site as the repository for the messages (or "chat site") and a group of users who take part from anywhere on the Internet. In some cases, a private chat can be arranged between two parties who meet initially in a group chat. Chats can be ongoing or scheduled for a particular time and duration. Most chats are focused on a particular topic of interest and some involve guest experts or famous people who "talk" to anyone joining the chat. (Transcripts of a chat can be archived for later reference.)

Chats are conducted on online services (especially America Online), by bulletin board services, and by Web sites. Several Web sites, notably Talk City, exist solely for the purpose of conducting chats. Some chat sites such as Worlds Chat allow participants to assume the role or appearance of an **avatar** in a simulated or *virtual reality* environment.

Talk City and many other chat sites use a protocol called **Internet Relay Chat**.

A chat can also be conducted using sound or sound and video, assuming you have the bandwidth access and the appropriate programming.

Cheapernet

See "Thinnet"

checksum

A checksum is a count of the number of bits in a transmission unit that is included with the unit so that the receiver can check to see whether the same number of bits arrived. If the counts match, it's assumed that the complete transmission was received. Both **TCP** and **UDP** communication layers provide a checksum count and verification as one of their services.

Chief Information Officer

CIO (Chief Information Officer) is a job title commonly given to the person in an **enterprise** responsible for the information technology and computer systems that support enterprise goals. As information technology and systems have become more important, the CIO has come to be viewed in many organizations as a key contributor in formulating strategic goals. In many companies, the CIO reports directly to the Chief Executive Officer (CEO). In some companies, the CIO sits on the executive board. Typically, the CIO in a large enterprise delegates technical decisions to employees more familiar with details. Usually, a CIO proposes the information technology an enterprise will need to achieve its goals and then works within a budget to implement as much as possible of the plan.

Typically, a CIO is involved with analyzing and reworking existing business processes, with identifying and developing the capability to use new tools, with reshaping the enterprise's physical infrastructure and network access, and with identifying and exploiting the enterprise's knowledge resources. Many CIOs head the enterprise's efforts to integrate the Internet and the World Wide Web into both its long-term strategy and its immediate business plans.

Chief Visionary Officer

Chief Visionary Officer (CVO) is a new title being used in corporations to differentiate the holder from other corporate executives including the Chief Executive Officer (CEO), the Chief Financial Officer (CFO), the Chief Information Officer (CIO), and the Chief Technology Officer (CTO). The CVO is expected to have a broad and comprehensive knowledge of all matters related to the business of the organization, as well as the vision required to steer its course into the future. The title is sometimes used to define a higher ranking position than that held by the CEO, and sometimes used to formalize a high-level advisory position. In some cases, the CVO is added to the CEO title (for CEO/CVO status), much in the same way that people with multiple university degrees list them after their names.

The first CVO was Tim Roberts, the young entrepreneurial founder of Broadband Investment Group. Roberts said he invented the title as a rank, superior to CEO, that served to recognize the visionary attributes needed to integrate a complex business with many diverse aspects. Roberts chose the title solely as definitive of his role in the organization, and didn't intend the designation to proliferate across the corporate world in the way that it has.

Corporations continue to invent new titles at an increasing rate—Chief Zoom Officer (CZO), Chief Smart Officer (CSO), and Chief Techie (CT) are a few of the more recent creations. Quinn Mills, a professor of business administration at Harvard Business School, claims that the proliferation of new titles is being used to attract and retain employees by offering them status—which is free—rather than money.

chip

"Chip" is short for microchip, the incredibly complex yet tiny modules that store computer **memory** or provide logic circuitry for microprocessors. Perhaps the best known chips are the **Pentium** microprocessors from Intel. The **PowerPC** microprocessor, developed by Apple, Motorola, and IBM, is used in Macintosh personal computers and some workstations. AMD and Cyrix also make popular microprocessor chips.

There are quite a few manufacturers of memory chips. Many special-purpose chips, known as application-specific integrated circuits, are being made today for automobiles, home appliances, telephones, and other devices.

A chip is manufactured from a **silicon** (or, in some special cases, a sapphire) wafer, which is first cut to size and then etched with circuits and electronic devices. The electronic devices use **complementary metal-oxide semiconductor** technology. The current stage of micro-integration is known as Very Large-Scale Integration (**VLSI**). A chip is also sometimes called an **IC** or *integrated circuit*.

chip art

See "microchip art"

chipset

A chipset is a group of **microchip**s designed to work and sold as a unit in performing one or more related functions. A typical chipset is the Intel 430HX PCIset for the **Pentium** microprocessor, a two-chip set that provides a **Peripheral Component Interconnect bus** controller and is designed for a business computer that "optimizes CPU, PCI and ISA transactions for faster, smoother multimedia performance in video conferencing, playback, and capture applications." This chipset includes support for the Universal Serial Bus (**USB**).

chmod

In a **UNIX**-based **operating system**, chmod (change mode) is a command used by a file owner or administrator to change the definition of access permissions to a file or set of files.

chorus

In audio production, chorus is one of the two standard audio effects defined by the Musical Instrument Digital Interface (**MIDI**). The other effect is **reverb** (reverberation). Chorus adds a swirling property to a sound that it is applied to, thickening the sound. Chorus is commonly used with instruments like the electric piano and guitar and with synthesizers. Most sound cards that have an onboard MIDI sound set contain both chorus and reverb.

A digital signal processing (**DSP**) **algorithm** that combines digital delays and at least one low-frequency **oscillator** (LFO) produces the chorus effect. The delays add a time offset and the LFOs vary the pitch. Varying the number of delays used in the design of the chorus DSP algorithm changes the quality of the chorusing effect. In addition, the number and speed of the LFOs used in the algorithm design also contribute to the overall effect. In general, the more individual delay lines and LFOs that are part of the DSP algorithm, the thicker and more complex the effect can be.

Here's how it works: An audio signal that is to be processed with chorus is first delayed by a small amount. (Typical delay times are small, in the range of 5 to 40 milliseconds.) This produces a doubling effect. Each delayed signal is then sent to the LFO. The LFO takes the delayed signal and moves its pitch up and down, changing the tuning from sharp to flat. The LFO usually runs at a slow speed; 1 to 5 oscillations per second are typical. The output of the delayed and pitch-altered signal is then mixed in with the original audio. This blending completes the chorusing effect.

CICS

CICS (Customer Information Control System) is an online transaction processing (**OLTP**) program from IBM that, together with the **COBOL** programming language, has formed over the past several decades the most common set of tools for building customer transaction applications in the world of large **enterprise mainframe** computing. A great number of the **legacy application**s still in use are COBOL/CICS applications. Using the application programming interface (**API**) provided by CICS, a programmer can write programs that communicate with online users and read from or write to customer and other records (orders, inventory figures, customer data, and so forth) in a database (usually referred to as "data sets") using CICS facilities rather than IBM's access methods directly. Like other transaction managers, CICS can ensure that transactions are completed and, if not, undo partly completed transactions so that the integrity of data records is maintained.

IBM markets or supports a CICS product for **OS/390**, **UNIX**, and Intel PC operating systems. Some of IBM's customers use IBM's Transaction Server to handle **e-business** transactions from Internet users and forward these to a mainframe server that accesses an existing CICS order and inventory database.

CIDR

CIDR (Classless Inter-Domain Routing) is a way to allocate and specify the Internet addresses used in inter-**domain router** more flexibly than with the original system of Internet Protocol (**IP**) address classes. As a result, the number of available Internet addresses has been greatly increased. CIDR is now the routing system used by virtually all gateway hosts on the Internet's **backbone** network. The Internet's regulating authorities now expect every Internet service provider (**ISP**) to use it for routing.

The original Internet Protocol defines **IP address**es in four major classes of address structure, Classes A through D. Each of these classes allocates one portion of the 32-bit Internet address format to a network address and the remaining portion to the specific host machines within the network specified by the address. One of the most commonly used classes is (or was) Class B, which allocates space for up to 65,533 host addresses. A company who needed more than 254 host machines but far fewer than the 65,533 host addresses possible would essentially be "wasting" most of the block of addresses allocated. For this reason, the Internet was, until the arrival of CIDR, running out of address space much more quickly than necessary. CIDR effectively solved the problem by providing a new and more flexible way to specify network addresses in routers. (With a new version of the Internet Protocol—**IPv6**—a 128-bit address is possible, greatly expanding the number of possible addresses on the Internet. However, it will be some time before IPv6 is in widespread use.)

Using CIDR, each IP address has a *network prefix* that identifies either an aggregation of network gateways or an individual gateway. The length of the network prefix is also specified as part of the IP address and varies depending on the number of bits that are needed (rather than any arbitrary class assignment structure). A destination IP address or route that describes many possible destinations has a shorter prefix and is said to be less specific. A longer prefix describes a destination gateway more specifically. Routers are required to use the most specific or longest network prefix in the routing table when forwarding packets.

A CIDR network address looks like this:
192.30.250.00/18

The "192.30.250.00" is the network address itself and the "18" says that the first 18 bits are the network part of the address, leaving the last 14 bits for specific host addresses. CIDR lets one routing table entry represent an aggregation of networks that exist in the forward path that don't need to be specified on that particular gateway, much as the public telephone system uses area codes to channel calls toward a certain part of the network. This aggregation of networks in a single address is sometimes referred to as a *supernet*.

CIDR is supported by The **Border Gateway Protocol**, the prevailing exterior (interdomain) gateway protocol. (The older exterior or interdomain gateway protocols, **Exterior Gateway Protocol** and **Routing Information Protocol**, do not support CIDR.) CIDR is also supported by the **OSPF** interior or intradomain gateway protocol.

CIFS

See "Common Internet File System"

cipher

A cipher (pronounced SAI-fuhr) is any method of encrypting text (concealing its readability and meaning). It is also sometimes used to refer to the encrypted text message itself although here the term **ciphertext** is preferred. Its origin is the Arabic *sifr*, meaning *empty* or *zero*. In addition to the cryptographic meaning, cipher also means (1) someone insignificant, and (2) a combination of symbolic letters as in an entwined weaving of letters for a monogram.

Some ciphers work by simply realigning the alphabet (for example, A is represented by F, B is represented by G, and so forth) or otherwise manipulating the text in some consistent pattern. However, almost all serious ciphers use both a **key** (a variable that is combined in some way with the unencrypted text) and an **algorithm** (a formula for combining the key with the text). A **block cipher** is one that breaks a message up into chunks and combines a key with each chunk (for example, 64-bits of text). A **stream cipher** is one that applies a key to each bit, one at a time. Most modern ciphers are block ciphers.

cipher block chaining

Also see **cryptography**.

Cipher block chaining (CBC) is a mode of operation for a **block cipher** (one in which a sequence of bits are encrypted as a single unit or block with a **cipher key** applied to the entire block). Cipher block chaining uses what is known as an initialization vector (IV) of a certain length. One of its key characteristics is that it uses a chaining mechanism that causes the **decryption** of a block of **ciphertext** to depend on all the preceding ciphertext blocks. As a result, the entire validity of all preceding blocks is contained in the immediately previous ciphertext block. A single bit error in a ciphertext block affects the decryption of all subsequent blocks. Rearrangement of the order of the ciphertext blocks causes decryption to become corrupted. Basically, in cipher block chaining, each plaintext block is XORed (see **XOR**) with the immediately previous ciphertext block, and then encrypted.

Identical ciphertext blocks can only result if the same plaintext block is encrypted using both the same key and the initialization vector, and if the ciphertext block order is not changed. It has the advantage over the **Electronic Code Book** mode in that the XOR'ing process hides plaintext patterns.

Ideally, the initialization vector should be different for any two messages encrypted with the same key. Though the initialization vector need not be secret, some applications may find this desirable.

ciphertext feedback

Also see **cryptography**.

Ciphertext feedback (CFB) is a mode of operation for a **block cipher**. In contrast to the **cipher block chaining** (CBC) mode, which encrypts a set number of bits of **plaintext** at a time, it is at times desirable to encrypt and transfer some plaintext values instantly one at a time, for which ciphertext feedback is a method. Like cipher block chaining, ciphertext feedback also makes use of an initialization vector (IV). CFB uses a block cipher as a component of a random number generator. In CFB mode, the previous ciphertext block is encrypted and the output is XORed (see **XOR**) with the current plaintext block to create the current ciphertext block. The XOR operation conceals plaintext patterns. Plaintext cannot be directly worked on unless there is retrieval of blocks from either the beginning or end of the ciphertext.

The **entropy** that results can be implemented as a **stream cipher**. In fact, CFB is primarily a mode to derive some characteristics of a stream cipher from a block cipher. In common with CBC mode, changing the IV to the same plaintext block results in different output. Though the IV need not be secret, some applications would see this desirable. Chaining dependencies are similar to CBC, in that reordering ciphertext block sequences alters decryption output, as decryption of one block depends on the decryption of the preceding blocks.

ciphertext

Ciphertext is encrypted **text**. **Plaintext** is what you have before **encryption**, and ciphertext is the encrypted result. The term **cipher** is sometimes used as a synonym for ciphertext, but it more properly means the method of encryption rather than the result.

CIR

See "committed information rate"

circuit

1) In electronics, a circuit is a path between two or more points along which an electrical current can be carried. (A *circuit breaker* is a device that interrupts the path when necessary to protect other devices attached to the circuit—for example, in case of a power surge.)

2) In telecommunications, a circuit is a discrete (specific) path between two or more points along which **signals** can be carried. Unless otherwise qualified, a circuit is a physical path, consisting of one or more wires and possibly intermediate switching points. A **network** is an arrangement of circuits. In a **dial-up** (switched) connection, a circuit is reserved for use by one user for the duration of the calling session. In a dedicated or leased line arrangement, a circuit is reserved in advance and can only be used the owner or renter of the circuit.

A **virtual circuit**, sometimes called a *logical circuit*, is a path between two or more points that seems like a fixed physical path, but actually is one path out of many possible physical paths that can be arranged. A permanent virtual circuit (**PVC**) is a virtual circuit that provides a guaranteed connection between two or more points when needed without having to reserve or commit to a specific physical path in advance. This allows many companies to share a common pool of circuits. This approach is used in a **frame relay** network and offers a committed set of resources to a telephone company customer at a lower price than if the customer leases their own circuits. A switched virtual circuit (**SVC**) is similar to a permanent virtual circuit, but allows users to dial in to the network of virtual circuits.

circuit-switched

Circuit-switched is a type of network in which a physical path is obtained for and dedicated to a single connection between two end-points in the network for the duration of the connection. Ordinary voice phone service is circuit-switched. The telephone company reserves a specific physical path to the number you are calling for the duration of your call. During that time, no one else can use the physical lines involved.

Circuit-switched is often contrasted with **packet-switched**. Some packet-switched networks such as the **X.25** network are able to have virtual circuit-switching. A virtual circuit-switched connection is a dedicated logical connection that allows sharing of the physical path among multiple virtual circuit connections.

CISC

The term "CISC" (complex instruction set computer or computing) refers to computers designed with a full set of computer instructions that were intended to provide needed capabilities in the most efficient way. Later, it was discovered that, by reducing the full set to only the most frequently used instructions, the computer would get more work done in a shorter amount of time for most applications. Since this was called reduced instruction set computing (**RISC**), there was now a need to have something to call full-set instruction computers—thus, the term CISC.

The **PowerPC** microprocessor, used in IBM's RISC System/6000 workstation and Macintosh computers, is a RISC microprocessor. Intel's **Pentium** microprocessors are CISC microprocessors. RISC takes each of the longer, more complex instructions from a CISC design and reduces it to multiple instructions that are shorter and faster to process.

Citizen's Band Radio

Compare with **amateur radio**.

The Citizen's Band (CB) Radio Service, also known simply as CB, is a public, two-way personal radio service. There are several classifications of CB operation. The best-known form of CB is voice communications that became a fad in the 1970s. Mobile CB operation, especially in cars and trucks, remains popular. To a lesser extent, "CB'ers" engage in fixed operation from homes, and in portable communications using handheld transceivers.

Most CB operation takes place within a narrow band of frequencies near 27 MHz. There are 40 channels in this band. These channels are overcrowded. Congestion is worst during peaks in the 11-year sunspot cycle when the 27-MHz band supports worldwide communication known as "skip." Sunspot cycle peaks occurred in 1967-69, 1978-80, 1989-91, and 2000-2002. During the long intervals between these peaks, the normal range of operation on the 27-MHz band is rarely more than 20 miles.

Some CB operators illegally modify their equipment, or obtain illegally modified equipment, capable of higher transmitter output power and greater frequency coverage than is allowed by Federal Communications Commission (FCC) regulations. These operators use their equipment in an attempt to communicate over long distances, and/or to compete with other users of the service. This is called freebanding or bootlegging.

The CB Radio Service has proven useful in disaster situations, both small-scale (for example, for a stranded motorist) and large-scale (such as after a hurricane or during a flash flood). An organization of expert communicators known as the Radio Emergency Associated Communications Teams (REACT) provides communications support in emergency situations. Channel 9 (at 27.065 MHz) is monitored by members of REACT, and is recognized as the CB emergency channel in the U.S.

CIW

See "Certified Internet Webmaster"

class

In **object-oriented programming**, a class is a template definition of the **method**s and **variable**s in a particular kind of **object**. Thus, an object is a specific instance of a class; it contains real values instead of variables.

The class is one of the defining ideas of object-oriented programming. Among the important ideas about classes are:

- A class can have subclasses that can inherit all or some of the characteristics of the class. In relation to each subclass, the class becomes the superclass.

- Subclasses can also define their own methods and variables that are not part of their superclass.

- The structure of a class and its subclasses is called the class hierarchy.

Class C2

Class C2 is a security rating established by the U.S. National Computer Security Center (**NCSC**) and granted to products that pass Department of Defense (DoD) Trusted Computer System Evaluation Criteria (TCSEC) tests. A C2 rating ensures the minimum allowable levels of confidence demanded for government agencies and offices and other organizations that process classified or secure information. TCSEC standards were established in the 1985 DoD document, *Department of Defense Trusted Computer System Evaluation Criteria*, known unofficially as the "Orange Book" (evaluation criteria for networks, the *Trusted Network Interpretation* is known as the "Red Book"). NCSC's objectives in publishing the document were: to provide DoD users with a means of ensuring the security of sensitive information; to provide manufacturers with guidelines to be followed; and to provide those involved in acquisitions with criteria for specifications.

According to TCSEC, system security is evaluated at one of four broad levels, ranging from class D to class A1, each level building on the previous one, with added security measures at each level and partial level. Class D is defined as *Minimum Security*; systems evaluated at this level have failed to meet higher level criteria. Class C1 is defined as *Discretionary Security Protection*; systems evaluated at this level meet security requirements by controlling user access to data. Class C2, defined as *Controlled Access Protection* adds to C1 requirements additional user accountability features, such as login procedures. Class B1 is defined as *Labeled Security Protection*; systems evaluated at this level also have a stated policy model, and specifically labeled data. Class B2, defined as *Structured Protection*, adds to B1 requirements a more explicit and formal security policy. Class B3, defined as *Security Domains*, adds stringent engineering and monitoring requirements and is highly secure. Class A1 is defined as *Verified Design*; systems evaluated at this level are functionally equivalent to B3 systems, but include more formal analysis of function to assure security.

Class of Service

Class of Service (CoS) is a way of managing traffic in a **network** by grouping similar types of traffic (for example, e-mail, streaming video, voice, large document file transfer) together and treating each type as a class with its own level of service priority. Unlike Quality of Service (**QoS**) traffic management, Class of Service technologies do not guarantee a level of service in terms of **bandwidth** and delivery time; they offer a "best-effort." On the other hand, CoS technology is simpler to manage and more scalable as a network grows in structure and traffic volume. One can think of CoS as "coarsely-grained" traffic control and QoS as "finely-grained" traffic control.

There are three main CoS technologies:

- 802.1p Layer 2 Tagging
- Type of Service (ToS)
- Differentiated Services (**DiffServ**)

802.1p Layer 2 Tagging and ToS make use of three bits in the **Layer 2 packet header** that can be used to specify priority. Since three bits does not allow for much sophistication in managing traffic, a new protocol, Differentiated Services (DS or DiffServ), has been developed in draft form by an **IETF** Working Group. Differentiated Services uses a different approach to managing packets than simple priority labeling. It uses an indication of how a given packet is to be forwarded, known as the Per Hop Behavior (PHB). The PHB describes a particular service level in terms of bandwidth, **queueing theory**, and dropping (discarding the packet) decisions.

The Differentiated Services protocol exists as a set of related working documents from the Internet Engineering Task Force (**IETF**).

Classless Inter-Domain Routing

See "CIDR"

Claude Shannon

Claude Elwood Shannon, a mathematician born in Gaylord, Michigan (U.S.) in 1916, is credited with two important contributions to information technology: the application of **Boolean** theory to electronic switching, thus laying the groundwork for the digital computer, and developing the new field called *information theory*. It is difficult to overstate the impact which Claude Shannon has had on the 20th century and the way we live and work in it, yet he remains practically unknown to the general public. Shannon spent the bulk of his career, a span of over 30 years from 1941 to 1972, at Bell Labs where he worked as a mathematician dedicated to research.

While a graduate student at MIT in the late 1930s, Shannon worked for **Vannevar Bush** who was at that time building a mechanical computer, the Differential Analyser. Shannon

had the insight to apply the two-valued Boolean logic to electrical circuits (which could be in either of two states—on or off). This syncretism of two hitherto distinct fields earned Shannon his MS in 1937 and his doctorate in 1940.

Not content with laying the logical foundations of both the modern telephone switch and the digital computer, Shannon went on to invent the discipline of information theory and revolutionize the field of communications. He developed the concept of entropy in communication systems, the idea that information is based on uncertainty. This concept says that the more uncertainty in a communication channel, the more information that can be transmitted and vice versa. Shannon used mathematics to define the capacity of any communications channel to optimize the **signal-to-noise ratio**. He envisioned the possibility of error-free communications for telecommunications, the Internet, and satellite systems.

A Mathematical Theory Of Communication, published in the Bell Systems Technical Journal in 1948, outlines the principles of his information theory. Information Theory also has important ramifications for the field of **cryptography** as explained in his 1949 paper *Communication Theory of Secrecy Systems*—in a nutshell, the more entropy a cryptographic system has, the harder the resulting **encryption** is to break.

Shannon's varied retirement interests included inventing unicycles, motorized pogo sticks, and chess-playing robots as well as juggling—he developed an equation describing the relationship between the position of the balls and the action of the hands. Claude Shannon died on February 24, 2001.

CLC

See "customer life cycle"

clear channel

See "B8ZS"

CLEC

In the U.S., a CLEC (competitive local exchange carrier) is a company that competes with the already established local telephone business by providing its own network and switching. The term distinguishes new or potential competitors from established local exchange carriers (**LEC**) and arises from the **Telecommunications Act of 1996**, which was intended to promote competition among both long-distance and local phone service providers.

North American Telecom and Winstar Communications are examples of CLECs (which generally are listed as simply "local exchange carriers").

click rate

In Web advertising, the click rate is the number of **click**s on an ad on an HTML page as a percentage of the number of times that the ad was downloaded with a page. Thus, the click rate on a particular page with an ad would be 10% if one in ten people who downloaded the page clicked on the ad.

click stream

In Web advertising, a click stream is the sequence of clicks or pages requested as a visitor explores a Web site.

click

In Web advertising, a click is an instance of a user pressing down (clicking) on a mouse button in an ad space. The term *clickthrough* is also sometimes used. The **click rate** is the number of clicks on an ad as a percentage of the number of times that the ad was downloaded with a page.

clicks and mortar

Clicks and mortar (sometimes seen as *clicks-and-mortar*) is a term describing traditional *old economy* companies that are taking advantage of the Internet and the *new economy* it has introduced. The term derives from *bricks and mortar*, used in the context of the Web to describe traditional companies with physical (rather than Web site) locations. In the news media, the success of Internet companies like Amazon.com, the online bookstore, led to a comparison with traditional bricks and mortar businesses such as Barnes and Noble (which at some point added a competitive Web site and became an example of clicks and mortar).

As typically used in the media, a clicks and mortar company is one that has begun to exploit the Internet, not only in marketing and sales, but also in terms of its total business process. A clicks and mortar firm would be likely to take part in business-to-business (**B2B**) exchanges.

The term's origin is attributed to David Pottruck, CEO of Charles Schwab Corp, in a July 1999 speech at a conference sponsored by the Industry Standard. Pottruck is quoted as saying:

> Schwab's vision has always been designed around customer needs and the company is engaged in constant reinvention to stay ahead of these powerful investors. Schwab believes that it is the combination of people and technology that investors want—a "high-tech and high-touch" approach. As such, Schwab is redefining the full-service business around the integration of "clicks and mortar."

clickthrough rate

In banner advertising on a Web site, the clickthrough rate (CTR) is the percentage of times that viewers of a Web page click on a given banner ad, causing a request for the advertiser's Web site to be transmitted to the viewer. For example, if two out of every 100 visitors to a Web page clicked on a given ad, that ad would be said to have a 2% clickthrough rate. (In most cases, a 2% clickthrough rate would be considered very successful, by the way. In many campaigns, especially as ads become familiar to users, the clickthrough rate is well below 1%.)

Many advertisers rate the success of a given ad placement on clickthrough rate alone. Other advertisers also place a value on the visitor's viewing of the ad, which is believed to create a desired company or product brand impression over time.

client

A client is the requesting program or user in a **client/server** relationship. For example, the user of a Web browser is effectively making client requests for pages from servers all over the Web. The browser itself is a client in its relationship with the computer that is getting and returning the requested HTML file. The computer handling the request and sending back the HTML file is a **server**.

client/server

Client/server describes the relationship between two computer programs in which one program, the client, makes a service request from another program, the server, which fulfills the request. Although the client/server idea can be used by programs within a single computer, it is a more important idea in a network. In a network, the client/server model provides a convenient way to interconnect programs that are distributed efficiently across different locations. Computer transactions using the client/server model are very common. For example, to check your bank account from your computer, a client program in your computer forwards your request to a server program at the bank. That program may in turn forward the request to its own client program that sends a request to a **database** server at another bank computer to retrieve your account balance. The balance is returned back to the bank data client, which in turn serves it back to the client in your personal computer, which displays the information for you.

The client/server model has become one of the central ideas of network computing. Most business applications being written today use the client/server model. So does the Internet's main program, **TCP/IP**. In marketing, the term has been used to distinguish distributed computing by smaller dispersed computers from the "monolithic" centralized computing of **mainframe** computers. But this distinction has largely disappeared as mainframes and their applications have also turned to the client/server model and become part of network computing.

In the usual client/server model, one server, sometimes called a **daemon**, is activated and awaits client requests. Typically, multiple client programs share the services of a common server program. Both client programs and server programs are often part of a larger program or application. Relative to the Internet, your Web **browser** is a client program that requests services (the sending of Web pages or files) from a Web server (which technically is called a Hypertext Transport Protocol or **HTTP** server) in another computer somewhere on the Internet. Similarly, your computer with TCP/IP installed allows you to make client requests for files from File Transfer Protocol (**FTP**) servers in other computers on the Internet.

Other program relationship models included *master/slave*, with one program being in charge of all other programs, and **peer-to-peer**, with either of two programs able to initiate a transaction.

clip art

Clip art, frequently used in desktop publishing before the arrival of the Web, is "canned" artwork designed for use in publications or Web pages by artists or non-artists . The use of clip art can save artists time and make art both possible and economical for non-artists. Clip art includes both subject-related illustrations and visual elements such as horizontal lines, bullets, and text separators.

You can purchase clip art on specialized subjects from Adobe, Corel, and many smaller companies. You can purchase clip art and stock photography at Photodisc. You can also find much useful clip art for free personal use at many Web sites. For use on a commercial page, make sure you understand any restrictions. Some artwork requires written permission for use or the payment of a fee.

Many clip art sites now include **animated GIF**s.

cloaking

Also see **anonymous e-mail** and **remailer**.

Cloaking is the masking of the sender's name and address in an e-mail note or distribution. An individual or company that sends **spam** or, as they prefer to call it, "bulk e-mail" usually conceals their own e-mail address for various reasons, including the possibility that someone will swamp the originator's own e-mail server with retributional spam.

clock cycle

In a computer, the clock cycle is the time between two adjacent pulses of the **oscillator** that sets the tempo of the computer processor. The number of these pulses per second is known as the **clock speed**, which is generally measured in **Mhz** (megahertz, or millions of pulses per second) and lately even in **Ghz** (gigahertz, or billions of pulses per second). The clock speed is determined by a quartz-crystal circuit, similar to those used in radio communications equipment.

Some processors execute only one **instruction** per clock cycle. More advanced processors, described as **superscalar**, can perform more than one instruction per clock cycle. The latter type of processor gets more work done at a given clock speed than the former type. Similarly, a computer with a 32-bit bus will work faster at a given clock speed than a computer with a 16-bit bus. For these reasons, there is no simple, universal relation among clock speed, "bus speed," and millions of instructions per second (**MIPS**).

clock speed

In a computer, clock speed refers to the number of pulses per second generated by an **oscillator** that sets the tempo for the **processor**. Clock speed is usually measured in **MHz** (megahertz, or millions of pulses per second) or **GHz** (gigahertz, or billions of pulses per second). Today's personal computers run at a clock speed in the hundreds of megahertz and some exceed one gigahertz. The clock speed is determined by a quartz-crystal circuit, similar to those used in radio communications equipment.

Computer clock speed has been roughly doubling every year. The Intel 8088, common in computers around the year 1990, ran at 4.77 MHz. The 1 GHz mark was passed in the year 2000.

Clock speed is one measure of computer "power," but it is not always directly proportional to the performance level. If you double the speed of the clock, leaving all other hardware unchanged, you will not necessarily double the processing speed. The type of microprocessor, the **bus** architecture, and the nature of the instruction set all make a difference. In some applications, the amount of random access memory (**RAM**) is important, too.

Some processors execute only one **instruction** per clock pulse. More advanced processors can perform more than one instruction per clock pulse. The latter type of processor will work faster at a given clock speed than the former type. Similarly, a computer with a 32-bit bus will work faster at a given clock speed than a computer with a 16-bit bus. For these reasons, there is no simplistic, universal relation among clock speed, "bus speed," and millions of instructions per second (MIPS).

Excessive clock speed can be detrimental to the operation of a computer. As the clock speed in a computer rises without upgrades in any of the other components, a point will be reached beyond which a further increase in frequency will render the processor unstable. Some computer users deliberately increase the clock speed, hoping this alone will result in a proportional improvement in performance, and are disappointed when things don't work out that way.

clocks or cycles per instruction

See "CPI"

clone

A clone is an identical copy of something and is a term that first became familiar to the public from the biosciences. In the computer industry, the term became widely used in referring to imitations of the IBM PC by Compaq, Dell, and others. Clones of the PC allowed users to purchase a comparable personal computer at a much lower price than that offered by IBM and helped make PCs affordable for more people.

closed circuit television

Closed circuit television (CCTV) is a television system in which signals are not publicly distributed; cameras are connected to television **monitor**s in a limited area such as a store, an office building, or on a college campus. CCTV is commonly used in surveillance systems.

cloud

In telecommunications, a cloud is the unpredictable part of any **network** through which data passes between two end points. Possibly the term originated from the clouds used in blackboard drawings or more formal illustrations to describe the nonspecifiable or uninteresting part of a network. Clouds exist because between any two points in a **packet-switched** network, the physical path on which a packet travels can vary from one packet to the next and, in a **circuit-switched** network, the specific circuit that is set up can vary from one connection to the next.

cluster

1) In personal computer storage technology, a cluster is the logical unit of file storage on a **hard disk**; it's managed by the computer's **operating system**. Any file stored on a hard disk takes up one or more clusters of storage. A file's clusters can be scattered among different locations on the hard disk. The clusters associated with a file are kept track of in the hard disk's file allocation table (**FAT**). When you read a file, the entire file is obtained for you and you aren't aware of the clusters it is stored in.

Since a cluster is a logical rather than a physical unit (it's not built into the hard disk itself), the size of a cluster can be varied. The maximum number of clusters on a hard disk depends on the size of a FAT table entry. Beginning with DOS 4.0, the FAT entries were 16 **bits** in length, allowing for a maximum of 65,536 clusters. Beginnning with the Windows 95 **OSR2** service release, a 32-bit FAT entry is supported, allowing an entry to address enough clusters to support up to two **terabyte**s of data (assuming the hard disk is that large!).

The tradeoff in cluster size is that even the smallest file (and even a directory itself) takes up the entire cluster. Thus, a 10-byte file will take up 2,048 bytes if that's the cluster size. In fact, many operating systems set the cluster size default at 4,096 or 8,192 bytes. Until the **file allocation table** support in Windows 95 OSR2, the largest size hard disk that could be supported in a single **partition** was 512 **megabyte**s. Larger hard disks could be divided into up to four partitions, each with a FAT capable of supporting 512 megabytes of clusters.

2) In information technology marketing and infrastructure terminology, a cluster is a group of terminals or workstations attached to a common control unit or server or a group of several servers that share work and may be able to back each other up if one server fails.

CM

See "configuration management"

CMIP

See "Common Management Information Protocol"

CMS

See "Conversational Monitor System"

CMTS

See "cable modem termination system"

CMYK

Also see **hue, saturation, and brightness**.

CMYK is a scheme for combining primary pigments. The C stands for cyan (aqua), M stands for magenta (pink), Y is yellow, and K stands for black. The CMYK pigment model works like an "upside-down" version of the **RGB** (red, green, and blue) color model. Many paint and draw programs can make use of either the RGB or the CMYK model. The RGB scheme is used mainly for computer displays, while the CMYK model is used for printed color illustrations (hard copy).

There is a fundamental difference between color and pigment. Color represents energy *radiated* by a luminous object such as a cathode ray tube (**CRT**) or a light-emitting diode (**LED**). The *primary colors* are red (R), green (G), and blue (B). When you see a red area on a CRT, it looks red because it radiates a large amount of light in the red portion of the **electromagnetic radiation spectrum** (around 750 nanometers), and much less at other wavelength. Pigments, as opposed to colors, represent energy that is *not absorbed* by a substance such as ink or paint. The primary pigments are cyan (C), magenta (M), and yellow (Y). Sometimes black (K) is also considered a primary pigment, although black can be obtained by combining pure cyan, magenta, and yellow in equal and large amounts. When you see yellow ink on a

page, it looks yellow because it absorbs most energy at all visible wavelengths except in the yellow portion of the spectrum (around 600 nanometers), where most of the energy is reflected.

The primary pigments and the primary colors are mathematically related. Any two pure radiant primary colors (R, G, or B), when combined, produce radiation having the appearance of one of the pure non-black primary pigments (C, M, or Y). Any two pure non-black primary pigments, when mixed, produce a substance having the appearance of one of the pure primary colors.

The primary colors RGB, combined at 100-percent brilliance, produce white. The primary pigments CMY, combined at maximum concentration, produce black. Shades of gray result from equal (but not maximum) brilliances of R, G, and B, or from equal (but not maximum) concentrations of C, M, and Y. If you have a paint or draw program such as CorelDRAW! that employs both the RGB and the CMYK schemes, you can investigate these relationships by filling in regions with solid colors using one mode, and examining the equivalent in the other mode. After a while you will develop an intuitive sense of how these schemes work, how they resemble each other, and how they differ.

In general, the RGB mode should be used when preparing graphics intended mainly for viewing on computer displays. The CMYK mode should be used when creating illustrations for print media.

CNR

See "Communication and Networking Riser"

CO

See "central office"

coaxial antenna

A coaxial antennna is a variant of the **dipole antenna**, designed for use with an unbalanced **feed line**. One side of the antenna element consists of a hollow conducting tube through which a **coaxial cable** passes. The shield of the cable is connected to the end of the tube at the center of the radiating element. The center conductor of the cable is connected to the other half of the radiating element. The element can be oriented in any fashion, although it is usually vertical.

Coaxial antennas are used at frequencies above approximately 10 MHz, where the size is manageable. The design is especially popular among Class-D Citizens Band radio enthusiasts, who operate in a narrow band of frequencies near 27 **MHz**. Coaxial antennas are also used in short-range communications installations at VHF (very high frequencies) between 30 and 300 MHz.

If f is the frequency of operation in MHz, the overall length or height h of a coaxial antenna element in feet is given approximately by:

$h = 460/f$

For example, at 27 MHz:

$h = 460/27 = 17$ feet

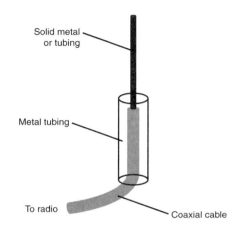

This is a manageable size for a self-supporting vertical antenna. The tubing, through which the feed line passes, forms the lower half of the antenna. It must be insulated from ground and from metallic supporting structures.

coaxial cable

Coaxial cable is the kind of copper cable used by **cable TV** companies between the community antenna and user homes and businesses. Coaxial cable is sometimes used by telephone companies from their central office to the telephone poles near users. It is also widely installed for use in business and corporation **Ethernet** and other types of **local area network**.

Coaxial cable is called "coaxial" because it includes one physical **channel** that carries the signal surrounded (after a layer of insulation) by another concentric physical channel, both running along the same axis. The outer channel serves as a ground. Many of these cables or pairs of coaxial tubes can be placed in a single outer sheathing and, with repeaters, can carry information for a great distance.

Coaxial cable was invented in 1929 and first used commercially in 1941. AT&T established its first cross-continental coaxial transmission system in 1940. Depending on the carrier technology used and other factors, **twisted pair** copper wire and **optical fiber** are alternatives to coaxial cable.

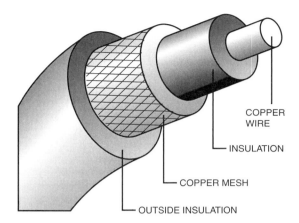

COPPER WIRE

INSULATION

COPPER MESH

OUTSIDE INSULATION

COBOL

COBOL (Common Business Oriented Language) was the first widely-used high-level programming language for business applications. Many payroll, accounting, and other business application programs written in COBOL over the past 35 years are still in use and it is possible that there are more existing lines of programming code in COBOL than in any other programming language. While the language has been updated over the years, it is generally perceived as out-of-date and COBOL programs are generally viewed as **legacy** applications.

COBOL was an effort to make a programming language that was like natural English, easy to write and easier to read the code after you'd written it. The earliest versions of the language, COBOL-60 and -61, evolved to the COBOL-85 standard sponsored by the Conference on Data Systems Languages (CODASYL).

In years immediately preceding the year **2000**, many COBOL programs required change to accommodate the new century. Programmers with COBOL skills were in demand by major corporations and contractors. A number of companies have updated COBOL and sell development tools that combine COBOL programming with relational databases and the Internet.

cobot

See "collaborative robot"

COD

See "capacity on demand"

code

1) In programming, code (noun) is a term used for both the statements written in a particular programming language—the **source code**, and a term for the source code after it has been processed by a **compiler** and made ready to run in the computer—the **object code**.

To code (verb) is to write programming statements—that is, to write the source code for a program.

2) In cryptography, code has both a specific technical meaning and a general meaning. In the technical sense, code is the substitution of one word or phrase by another word, number, or symbol for the purpose of concealing the original word or phrase. Basically, it's substitution at the word or phrase level. In industry, a developing product is sometimes given a code name to conceal its probable marketing name. Historically, military operations have often had a code name while in the preparation stage. In World War II, Germany's invasion of the Soviet Union was given the code name of Barbarossa. Code in this sense is sometimes confused with a **cipher**, which is substitution of symbols at the letter level. Modern cryptography is much more concerned with ciphers than with code in its limited technical meaning.

Code is often used generally to mean any kind of concealed writing, including ciphers. "Breaking the code" usually means the discovery of a way to read one or a series of encrypted messages without being given the key to decrypt them.

codec

1) In communications engineering, the term *codec* is used in reference to integrated circuits, or **chips** that perform data conversion. In this context, the term is an acronym for "**co**der/**dec**oder." This type of codec combines **analog-to-digital conversion** and **digital-to-analog conversion** functions in a single chip. In personal and business computing applications, the most common use for such a device is in a **modem**.

2) The term *codec* is also an acronym that stands for "**co**mpression/**dec**ompression." A codec is an **algorithm**, or specialized computer program, that reduces the number of bytes consumed by large files and programs.

In order to minimize the amount of storage space required for a complicated file, such as a video, **compression** is used. Compression works by eliminating redundancies in data. Compression can be done for any kind of file, including text, programs, images, audio, video, and virtual reality (VR). Compression can reduce the size of a file by a factor of 100 or more in some cases. For example, a 15-megabyte video might be reduced to 150 kilobytes. The uncompressed file would be far too large to download from the Web in a reasonable length of time, but the compressed file could usually be downloaded in a few seconds. For viewing, a *decompression* algorithm, which "undoes" the compression, would have to be used.

There are numerous standard codec schemes. Some are used mainly to minimize file transfer time, and are employed on the Internet. Others are intended to maximize the data that can be stored in a given amount of disk space, or on a CD-ROM.

Codecs are used in many popular Internet products, including QuickTime, Netmeeting, Cu-Seeme, and VDOphone.

coded orthogonal frequency division multiplexing

See "COFDM"

code-division multiple access

See "CDMA"

COFDM

COFDM is a **modulation** scheme that divides a single digital signal across 1,000 or more signal carriers simultaneously. The signals are sent at right angles to each other (hence, **orthogonal**) so they do not interfere with each other. COFDM is used predominately in Europe and is supported by the Digital Video Broadcasting (**DVB**) set of standards. In the U.S., the Advanced Television Standards Committee (**ATSC**) has chosen **8-VSB** (8-level Vestigial Sideband) as its equivalent modulation standard.

The main reason for Europe's decision to use COFDM is its ability to completely overcome multipath effects. When a signal is transmitted, it is met with obstructions such as canyons, buildings, and even people, which scatter the signal causing it to take two or more paths to reach its final destination, the television. The late arrival of the scattered portions of the signal cause ghost images. Multipath effects can occur simply by an individual walking into the room. For this very reason, some consumers in metropolitan areas or areas with rugged terrain opt for cable or satellite television instead of fighting their antennas for better reception. COFDM is resistant to multipath effects because it uses multiple carriers to transmit the same signal. Instead of the signal scattering when met with an obstacle, it flows around the obstacle like a river flows around a rock making it perfect for free DTV programming and for mobile television viewing. Problems with multipath effects were often cited in early evaluations of 8-VSB, although it is expected that devices such as internal antennas will overcome them.

In Europe, stations transmit the same signal 100 percent of the time across many borders using single frequency networks. A single frequency network is a network of several stations that broadcast the same signal simultaneously using multiple transmitters. This allows television viewers to watch the same broadcast anywhere in Europe without interference. COFDM is ideal for single frequency networks.

COLD

COLD (Computer Output to Laser Disk) is a system for archiving data such as business records and reports to one or more optical disks in a compressed but easily retrievable format. COLD systems make it unnecessary to archive reports in printed form and are easier to work with than microfiche, an earlier solution. Vendors of COLD systems point out that more than one million paper pages can be stored on a single 5 $^1/_4$ inch optical disk. A COLD system consists of software and hardware. The software allows a user to send a document to the COLD system (much like sending it to be printed), organizes the documents for access, and compresses them for storage. The hardware consists of optical disk drives, which typically are mounted in a unit called a *jukebox*.

COLD software may offer the ability to do archiving automatically at scheduled times of day, to index documents in a variety of ways, and to periodically distribute the archive indexes.

COLD systems are used to archive accounting reports, credit reports, loan records, inventories, shipping and receiving documents, customer bills, lab reports, and many other kinds of records and reports. A COLD system is a form of **EDM** and is often used together with an **imaging** system.

cold site

See "hot site and cold site"

ColdFusion Markup Language

See "CFML"

ColdFusion

ColdFusion, developed by Allaire which has recently merged with Macromedia, is a popular and sophisticated set of products for building **Web site**s and serving **page**s to users. With ColdFusion, a company can build a content **database** using input **template**s and combine these with application programs to create a Web site in which pages are developed dynamically as they are served. ColdFusion consists of ColdFusion Studio, which is used to build a site, and ColdFusion Server, which serves the pages to users. ColdFusion Studio is described as "a complete integrated development environment (IDE)" and ColdFusion Server as "a **deployment** platform."

The most valuable feature for many companies that use ColdFusion is the ability to build Web sites as "piece parts" that can be stored in a **database** and then reassembled for Web pages, e-mail newsletters, and other uses. ColdFusion provides a visual interface for building Web pages directly or for building the "piece parts." For example, a newspaper with a Web site can have a reporter enter a story, dateline, author, and other information, using a text entry form free of all Web page formatting and structure details or language **tag**s. (The newspaper uses ColdFusion to design the forms and to define the database.) The content entered by the reporter is later gathered and formatted into a Web page when it is requested. The reporter is free from having to understand **HTML** and other details. ColdFusion is also a popular tool for building **e-commerce** sites.

ColdFusion has its own page **markup** language, called ColdFusion Markup Language (**CFML**). CFML encompasses the Web's Hypertext Markup Language (**HTML**) and Extensible Markup Language (**XML**). A just-in-time (**JIT**) compiler turns the CFML into the pages that get served. Allaire emphasizes that their product set is **open** and "extensible." Applications can access databases using Microsoft's OLE DB, Open Database Connectivity (**ODBC**), or **driver**s that access Oracle and Sybase databases. ColdFusion can be coordinated with distributed applications that use Common Object Request Broker Architecture (**CORBA**) or Microsoft's Distributed Component Object Model (**DCOM**) to interact with other network applications.

Allaire also says that ColdFusion is **scalable**, allowing both the size of a database and the number of users that can be served to grow. For large Web sites, multiple ColdFusion servers can be run together as a cluster.

Collaboration Data Objects

Collaboration Data Objects (CDO) is Microsoft's technology for building **messaging** or collaboration **application**s or adding these capabilities to existing applications. Part of the Microsoft Exchange Server product, CDO has evolved from what Microsoft formerly called **Object Linking and Embedding** Messaging and, more recently, Active Messaging. Using **Active Server Page** (ASP) technology with CDO, a Web site builder can, for example, write a **script** that will exchange e-mail with users or with other Web sites, collaborate in discussions on other Web sites, or allow employees to schedule meetings with multiple recipients, review existing appointments, schedule new events, and so forth.

CDO is really an additional scripting interface to an existing Microsoft messaging model, the Messaging Application Programming Interface (**MAPI**). Collaborative Data Objects are made available through two CDO libraries. These libraries let you address programmable messaging objects (including folders, messages, recipient addresses, attachments, and other messaging components). These objects are extensions to the programmable objects, such as forms and controls, that are offered as part of Microsoft's **Visual Basic** program development environment.

collaborative authoring

See "WebDAV"

collaborative robot

A cobot or "collaborative robot" is a robot designed to assist human beings as a guide or assistor in a specific task. A regular robot is designed to be programmed to work more or less autonomously. In one approach to cobot design, the cobot allows a human to perform certain operations successfully if they fit within the scope of the task and to steer the human on a correct path when the human begins to stray from or exceed the scope of the task.

collision

In an **Ethernet** network, a collision is the result of two devices on the same Ethernet network attempting to transmit data at exactly the same time. The network detects the "collision" of the two transmitted packets and discards them both. Collisions are a natural occurrence on Ethernets. Ethernet uses Carrier Sense Multiple Access/Collision Detect (**CSMA/CD**) as its method of allowing devices to "take turns" using the signal carrier line. When a device wants to transmit, it checks the signal level of the line to determine whether someone else is already using it. If it is already in use, the device waits and retries, perhaps in a few seconds. If it isn't in use, the device transmits. However, two devices can transmit at the same time in which case a collision occurs and both devices detect it. Each device then waits a random amount of time and retries until successful in getting the transmission sent.

colocation

Colocation (sometimes spelled "co-location" or "collocation") is the provision of space for a customer's telecommunications equipment on the service provider's premises. For example, a **Web site** owner could place the site's own computer **server**s on the premises of the Internet service provider (**ISP**). Or an ISP could place its network **router**s on the premises of the company offering switching services with other ISPs. The alternative to colocation is to have the equipment and the **demarc** located at the customer's premises.

Colocation is sometimes provided by companies that specialize in **Web site hosting**.

color thin film transistor

Color thin film transistor (CTFT) displays are **Thin Film Transistor** displays with color.

column address strobe

See "CAS"

com

On the Internet, "com" is one of the top-level **domain name**s that can be used when choosing a domain name. It generally describes the entity owning the domain name as a commercial organization. Along with the second-level domain name (for example: "whatis" in whatis.com), the top-level domain name is required in Web and e-mail addresses.

The Internet Corporation for Assigned Names and Numbers (**ICANN**) has overall responsibility for domain names (as well as for **Internet Protocol** addresses and many other Internet parameters). Day-to-day responsibility is delegated to specific registrars, such as Network Solutions and a number of competing companies for .com, .org, .net, and .edu top-level domains.

Specific criteria are set forth for the use of the top-level domain name in RFC 1591—Domain Name System Structure and Delegation.

The top-level domain names administered by ICANN and its delegate agencies are: **com**, **edu**, **gov**, **int**, **mil**, **net**, and **org**. In addition to these, domain name applicants within the U.S. may also be able to register a name under a U.S. top-level domain name based on geography. See RFC 1480—The U.S. Domain and visit the U.S. Domain Registry for registration procedures.

Top-level domain names for countries other than the United States are administered by each country and are based on the ISO-3166 list of country codes.

COM+

COM+ is an extension of **Component Object Model** (COM), Microsoft's strategic building block approach for developing application programs. COM+ is both an **object-oriented programming architecture** and a set of operating system services. It adds to COM a new set of system services for application **components** while they are running, such as notifying them of significant events or ensuring they are authorized to run. COM+ is intended to provide a model that makes it relatively easy to create business applications that work well with the Microsoft Microsoft Transaction Server (**MTS**) in a **Windows NT** or subsequent system. It is viewed as Microsoft's answer to the Sun Microsystems-IBM-Oracle approach known as Enterprise JavaBeans (**EJB**).

Among the services provided by COM+ are:

- An event registry that allows components to publish the possibility of an event and other components to subscribe to be notified when the event takes place. For example, when a sales transaction is completed, it could trigger an event that would allow other programs to be notified for subsequent processing.

- The interception of designated system requests for the purpose of ensuring security

- The **queues** of asynchronously received requests for a service

How COM+ Works Briefly

A "component" is a building block program that is self-describing. This means that it can be run with a mix of other components and each will be able to understand the capabilities and characteristics of the other components. Practically, this means that a new application can be built by reusing components already known to exist and without having to **compile** the application. It also makes it relatively easy to distribute different components of an application among different computers in a network. Microsoft's Distributed Component Object Model (**DCOM**) adds interfaces to do this.

In addition to its self-description, a component consists of one or more **classes** that describe objects and the methods or actions that can be performed on an **object**. A class (or *coclass* in COM+ terminology) has properties described in an *interface* (or *cointerface*). The class and its interface are language-neutral.

Associated with the class are one or more **methods** and fields that are implemented in a specific language such as **C++** or **Java** or a visual programming environment. When you **instantiate** a class, you create an object (something real that can be executed in the computer). Sometimes the term "class" is also used for the instantiated object (which can be confusing).

Using COM, objects (or classes) and their methods and associated data are compiled into binary executable **modules**, that are, in fact, files with a dynamic link library (**DLL**) or EXE file name suffix. A module can contain more than one class.

command interpreter

A command interpreter is the part of a computer **operating system** that understands and executes commands that are entered interactively by a human being or from a program. In some operating systems, the command interpreter is called the **shell**.

command line interface

A CLI (command line interface) is a user interface to a computer's **operating system** or an **application** in which the user responds to a visual prompt by typing in a command on a specified line, receives a response back from the system, and then enters another command, and so forth. The MS-DOS Prompt application in a Windows operating system is an example of the provision of a command line interface. Today, most users prefer the graphical user interface (**GUI**) offered by Windows, **Mac OS**, **BeOS**, and others. Typically, most of today's **UNIX**-based systems offer both a command line interface and a graphical user interface.

command

In computers, a command is a specific order from a user to the computer's **operating system** or to an **application** to perform a service, such as "Show me all my files" or "Run this program for me." Operating systems such as **DOS** that do not have a graphical user interface (**GUI**) offer a simple *command line interface* in which you type the command on a designated line in a **display panel**. In a system such as Windows, a graphical user interface lets you implicitly enter commands by selecting objects or word selections and clicking your **mouse** button on them. (Windows does offer a command line interface for certain facilities if you select the "MS-DOS Prompt" under "Programs.")

The part of the operating system that handles commands is usually called a **command interpreter** or a **shell**. Some application programs, especially in DOS, provide a command mode for interfacing with the application from the display. In some operating systems, commands can be included in a list and presented to the system as a package to be **executed** in sequence, either immediately or at some specified time. Such a list is usually known as a **script**. One in which a time of execution is specified for each command is called a **CRON script**. In some systems, commands can be initiated from application programs as well as from a user interface.

Other approaches to giving commands to computers include **voice recognition**, **gesture recognition**, and even **thought recognition**.

comma-separated values file

In computers, a CSV (comma-separated values) file contains the values in a table as a series of **ASCII** text lines organized so that each column value is separated by a comma from the next column's value and each row starts a new line. Here's an example:

Doe,John,944-7077
Johnson,Mary,370-3920
Smith,Abigail,299-3958 (etc.)

A CSV file is a way to collect the data from any table so that it can be conveyed as input to another table-oriented application such as a application. Microsoft Excel, a leading spreadsheet or relational database application, can read CSV files. A CSV file is sometimes referred to as a **flat file**.

Commerce XML

Commerce XML (cXML) is a standard for the online exchange of business transaction information in common formats. It defines the structure of purchase orders, order acknowledgements, and other core e-business documents. cXML is a document type definition (DTD) based on XML

tags that defines fields for a specific type of document, like a purchase order. The XML structure enables an application program to easily extract data and deliver it to another application program.

Online catalog company Ariba Technologies led the cXML effort, but more than 40 companies collaborated on cXML, including Hewlett-Packard and Microsoft. The organizations hoped a common standard would reduce the cost of doing business online. The first version of cXML (version 0.91) appeared in May 1999.

commercial off-the-shelf

COTS (commercial off-the-shelf) describes ready-made products that can easily be obtained. The term is sometimes used in military procurement specifications.

commit

A commit is the final step in the successful completion of a previously started **database** change as part of handling a **transaction** in a computing system.

committed information rate

In **frame relay** networks, a committed information rate (CIR) is a **bandwidth** (expressed in bits per second) associated with a logical connection in a permanent virtual circuit (**PVC**). Frame relay networks are **digital** networks in which different logical connections share the same physical path and some logical connections are given higher bandwidths than others. For example, a connection conveying a high proportion of video signals (which require a high bandwidth) could be set up for certain workstations in a company (or on a larger network) and other connections requiring less bandwidth could be set up for all other workstations. Using statistical multiplexing, frame relay assemblers and dissemblers (**FRADs**), the devices that interconnect to the frame relay network, manage the logical connections so that, for example, those with the video signals (and higher CIRs) get more use of the paths. Because the CIR is defined in software, the network's mix of traffic bandwidths can be redefined in a relatively short amount of time.

Common Application Programming Interface

See "CAPI"

Common Business Oriented Language

See "COBOL"

common gateway interface

Also see **FastCGI**.

The common gateway interface (CGI) is a standard way for a Web **server** to pass a Web user's request to an application program and to receive data back to forward to the user. When the user requests a Web page (for example, by clicking on a highlighted word or entering a Web site address), the server sends back the requested page. However, when a user fills out a form on a Web page and sends it in, it usually needs to be processed by an application program. The Web server typically passes the form information to a small application program that processes the data and may send back a confirmation message. This method or convention for passing data back and forth between the server and the application is called the common gateway interface (CGI). It is part of the Web's Hypertext Transfer Protocol (**HTTP**).

If you are creating a Web site and want a CGI application to get control, you specify the name of the application in the uniform resource locator (**URL**) that you code in an HTML file. This URL can be specified as part of the FORMS tags if you are creating a form. For example, you might code:

<FORM METHOD=POST ACTION=http://www.mybiz.-com/cgi-bin/formprog.pl>

and the server at "mybiz.com" would pass control to the CGI application called "formprog.pl" to record the entered data and return a confirmation message. (The ".pl" indicates a program written in **PERL** but other languages could have been used.)

The common gateway interface provides a consistent way for data to be passed from the user's request to the application program and back to the user. This means that the person who writes the application program can makes sure it gets used no matter which operating system the server uses (PC, Macintosh, UNIX, OS/390, or others). It's simply a basic way for information to be passed from the Web server about your request to the application program and back again.

Because the interface is consistent, a programmer can write a CGI application in a number of different languages. The most popular languages for CGI applications are: **C**, **C++**, **Java**, and **PERL**.

An alternative to a CGI application is Microsoft's **Active Server Page** (ASP), in which a **script** embedded in a Web page is executed at the server before the page is sent.

Common Internet File System

Common Internet File System (CIFS) is a proposed standard **protocol** that lets programs make requests for files and services on remote computers on the Internet. CIFS uses the **client/server** programming model. A **client** program makes a request of a **server** program (usually in another computer) for access to a file or to pass a message to a program that runs in the server computer. The server takes the requested

action and returns a response. CIFS is a public or **open** variation of the **Server Message Block Protocol** developed and used by Microsoft. The SMB Protocol is widely used in today's local area networks for server file access and printing. Like the SMB protocol, CIFS runs at a higher level than and uses the Internet's **TCP/IP** protocol. CIFS is viewed as a complement to the existing Internet application protocols such as the File Transfer Protocol (**FTP**) and the Hypertext Transfer Protocol (**HTTP**).

CIFS lets you:

- Get access to files that are local to the server and read and write to them.
- Share files with other clients using special locks.
- Restore connections automatically in case of network failure.
- Use **Unicode** file names In general, CIFS gives the client user better control of files than the File Transfer Protocol. It provides a potentially more direct interface to server programs than currently available through the Web browser and its use of the HTTP protocol.

CIFS is an Open Group standard, X/Open CAE Specification C209, and has been proposed to the Internet Engineering Task Force (**IETF**) as an Internet application standard.

Common Management Information Protocol

Common Management Information Protocol (CMIP) is a network management protocol built on the Open Systems Interconnection (**OSI**) communication model. The related Common Management Information Services (CMIS) defines services for accessing information about network objects or devices, controlling them, and receiving status reports from them.

Common Object Request Broker Architecture

See "CORBA"

Common Programming Interface

See "CPI"

Communication and Networking Riser

Communication and Networking Riser (CNR), which was developed by Intel, is an open industry standard for a **scalable riser card**, which is a hardware device that plugs into a **motherboard** and holds chips for functions like modems and audio devices. The CNR architecture, and electrical, mechanical, and thermal requirements of the riser interface are defined in the specification.

The specification was developed for products used to implement low-cost local area network (**LAN**), modem, and audio subsystems and supports broadband, multichannel audio, **V.90** analog modem, Home PNA, and Ethernet-based networking, and can be expanded upon to meet the requirements of developing technologies, such as **DSL**. In addition to cost benefits, CNR has the capacity to minimize electrical noise interference, through physical separation of noise-sensitive elements from the motherboard's own communication systems.

competitive local exchange carrier

See "CLEC"

compiler

A compiler is a special program that processes statements written in a particular programming language and turns them into machine language or "code" that a computer's **processor** uses. Typically, a programmer writes language statements in a language such as **Pascal** or **C** one line at a time using an *editor*. The file that is created contains what are called the *source statements*. The programmer then runs the appropriate language compiler, specifying the name of the file that contains the source statements.

When executing (running), the compiler first parses (or analyzes) all of the language statements syntactically one after the other and then, in one or more successive stages or "passes," builds the output code, making sure that statements that refer to other statements are referred to correctly in the final code. Traditionally, the output of the compilation has been called *object code* or sometimes an *object module*. (Note that the term "object" here is not related to **object-oriented programming**.) The object code is **machine code** that the processor can process or "execute" one instruction at a time.

More recently, the **Java** programming language, a language used in **object-oriented programming**, has introduced the possibility of compiling output (called **bytecode**) that can run on any computer system platform for which a Java **virtual machine** or bytecode interpreter is provided to convert the bytecode into instructions that can be executed by the actual hardware processor. Using this virtual machine, the bytecode can optionally be recompiled at the execution platform by a **just-in-time compiler**.

Traditionally in some operating systems, an additional step was required after compilation—that of resolving the relative location of instructions and data when more than one object module was to be run at the same time and they cross-refered to each other's instruction sequences or data. This process was sometimes called *linkage editing* and the output known as a *load module*.

A compiler works with what are sometimes called **3GL** and higher-level languages. An **assembler** works on programs written using a processor's assembler language.

complementary metal-oxide semiconductor

See "CMOS"

complex instruction set computer

See "CISC"

complex number

A complex number is a quantity of the form $v + iw$, where v and w are **real numbers**, and i represents the unit **imaginary numbers** equal to the positive square root of -1. The **set C** of all complex numbers corresponds one-to-one with the set R R of all ordered pairs of real numbers. The set **C** also corresponds one-to-one with the points on a geometric plane.

The set of complex numbers is two-dimensional, and a coordinate plane is required to illustrate them graphically. This is in contrast to the real numbers, which are one-dimensional, and can be illustrated by a simple number line. The rectangular complex number plane is constructed by arranging the real numbers along the horizontal axis, and the imaginary numbers along the vertical axis. Each point in this plane can be assigned to a unique complex number, and each complex number can be assigned to a unique point in the plane.

Complex numbers are used in engineering, particularly in electronics. Real numbers are used to denote electrical **resistance**, imaginary numbers are used to denote **reactance**, and complex numbers are used to represent **impedance**.

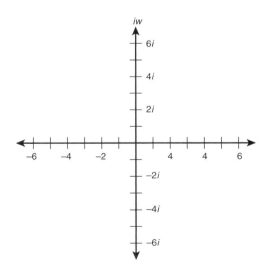

component

1) In programming and engineering disciplines, a component is an identifiable part of a larger program or construction. Usually, a component provides a particular function or group of related functions. In programming design, a *system* is divided into *components* that in turn are made up of *modules*. *Component test* means testing all related modules that form a component as a group to make sure they work together.

2) In **object-oriented programming** and **distributed** object technology, a component is a reusable program building block that can be combined with other components in the same or other computers in a distributed network to form an application. Examples of a component include: a single button in a graphical user interface, a small interest calculator, an interface to a database manager. Components can be deployed on different servers in a network and communicate with each other for needed services. A component runs within a context called a **container**. Examples of containers include pages on a Web site, Web browsers, and word processors.

Sun Microsystems, whose **JavaBeans** application program interface defines how to create component, defines "a component model" as typically providing these major types of services:

- Component interface exposure and discovery. Thus, during application use, one component can interrogate another one to discover its characteristics and how to communicate with it. This allows different companies (possibly independent service providers) to create components that can interoperate with the components of other companies without either having to know in advance exactly which components it will be working with.

- Component properties. This allows a component to make its characteristics publicly visible to other components.

- Event handling. This allows one component to identify to one or more other components that an event (such as a user pressing a button) has occurred so that the component can respond to it. In Sun's example, a component that provided a button user interface for a finance application would "raise" an event when the button was pressed, resulting in a graph-calculating component gaining control, formulating a graph, and displaying it to the user.

- Persistence. This allows the state of components to be preserved for later user sessions.

- Application builder support. A central idea of components is that they will not only be easy and flexible for deploying in a distributed network, but that developers can easily create new components and see the properties of existing ones.

- Component packaging. Since a component may comprise several files, such as icons and other graphical files, Sun's component model includes a facility for packaging the files in a single file format that can be easily administered and distributed. (Sun calls their component package a JAR [Java Archive] file format.)

Component Object Model

Component Object Model (COM) is Microsoft's framework for developing and supporting program **component object**s. It is aimed at providing similar capabilities to those defined in the Common Object Request Broker Architecture (**CORBA**), a framework for the interoperation of distributed objects in a network that is supported by other major companies in the computer industry. Whereas Microsoft's **Object Linking and Embedding** provides services for the **compound document** that users see on their display, COM provides the underlying services of interface negotiation, life cycle management (determining when an object can be removed from a system), licensing, and event services (putting one object into service as the result of an event that has happened to another object).

COM includes **COM+**, Distributed Component Object Model (**DCOM**), and **ActiveX** interfaces and programming tools.

Component Object Model +

See "COM+"

compound document

In information technology, a compound document is an organized collection of user interfaces that form a single integrated perceptual environment. A compound document includes a data structure that contains different data types, such as text, audio files, and motion video files. A compound document is also an application environment containing program **object**s that can be interlinked and interacted with by a user.

Compound documents can be formed of information parts that originate from different sources and that are assembled **on the fly**. Microsoft's Internet Explorer **desktop** uses the compound document concept. Microsoft's **Object Linking and Embedding** is a framework for assembling and managing compound documents. *OpenDoc* is an alternative standard.

compression

Compression is the reduction in size of data in order to save space or transmission time. For data transmission, compression can be performed on just the data content or on the entire transmission unit (including *header* data) depending on a number of factors.

Content compression can be as simple as removing all extra space characters, inserting a single repeat character to indicate a string of repeated characters, and substituting smaller bit strings for frequently occurring characters. This kind of compression can reduce a text file to 50% of its original size. Compression is performed by a program that uses a formula or **algorithm** to determine how to compress or decompress data.

Graphic image file formats are usually designed to compress information as much as possible (since these can tend to become very large files).

When you send or receive information on the Internet, larger text files, either singly or with others as part of an **archive** file, may be transmitted in a zip, gzip, or other compressed format. **WinZip** is a popular Windows program that compresses files when it packages them in an archive.

compression artifact

A compression artifact is the fuzz or distortion in a **compressed** image or sequence of video images. When a photo is compressed into a **JPEG** format, some data is lost, which is why this type of compression is called **lossy compression**. The data that is lost is considered to be not necessary for the viewer to perceive or perhaps not perceivable in any case. In creating a JPEG, if you wish to have a smaller file size regardless of quality, then the result may introduce perceivable compression artifacts. However, if you wish to maintain the quality of the photo and have a larger file size, then the viewer may not notice any artifacts. Artifacts are more evident on a computer image than in a printed photograph.

A digital video file is also compressed and, depending on the amount of compression, may present artifacts. A digital video file has the same fuzzy edges and distortion of images as a still image (JPEG) file may have. The break up of the video into large digital **pixel**s and jerkiness in the video stream are examples of compression artifacts.

computational reflection

Computational reflection (sometimes just called *reflection*) is a computer process involving self-awareness. Just as with humans, reflection depends on the capacity for independent reason, and particularly, reason about one's own processes. A reflective **program** has the ability to *metaprogram*: It can, itself, write programs. The capacity for reflection is one of the most important components of artificial intelligence (**AI**), and can be related to other aspects of AI such as **fuzzy logic** and **neural networks**.

When a reflective program operates, it does so in the same manner as a person. It takes variables, such as its own conditions, and contextual information into account. As an analogy, think of the operations involved in getting from your car to your house. If you see an obstacle in your path, you take in that information and adapt to it by either stepping around or over the object, or picking it up. When you get to your door, if you find it locked, usually you don't stop and stand there, continue to turn the knob, or turn around and walk away; usually you take out your key and unlock the door. In the same way, a reflective program has the ability to think about what is happening and to alter itself to address the circumstances.

computer

A computer is a device that accepts **information** (in the form of **digital data**) and manipulates it for some result based on a **program** or sequence of instructions on how data is to be processed. Complex computers also include the means for storing data (including the program, which is also a form of data) for some necessary duration. A program may be invariable and built into the computer (and called *logic circuitry* as it is on **microprocessor**s) or different programs may be provided to the computer (loaded into its storage and then started by an administrator or user). Today's computers have both kinds of programming.

Most histories of the modern computer begin with the **Analytical Engine** envisioned by **Charles Babbage** following the mathematical ideas of **George Boole**, the mathematician who first stated the principles of logic inherent in today's digital computer. Babbage's assistant and collaborator, **Ada Lovelace**, is said to have introduced the ideas of program loops and subroutines and is sometimes considered the first programmer. Apart from mechanical calculators, the first really useable computers began with the **vacuum tube**, accelerated with the invention of the **transistor**, which then became embedded in large numbers in integrated circuits, ultimately making possible the relatively low-cost personal computer.

Modern computers inherently follow the ideas of the stored program laid out by **John von Neumann** in 1945. Essentially, the program is read by the computer one instruction at a time, an operation is performed, and the computer then reads in the next instruction, and so on. Recently, computers and programs have been devised that allow multiple programs (and computers) to work on the same problem at the same time in parallel. With the advent of the Internet and higher **bandwidth** data transmission, programs and data that are part of the same overall project can be distributed over a network and embody the Sun Microsystems slogan: "The network is the computer."

Also see **analog computing**.

Computer Emergency Response Team

See "CERT"

computer operator

A computer operator is the person responsible for monitoring and controlling computer systems especially **mainframe** computer systems in a company or organization.

Responsibilities include troubleshooting software and hardware problems, monitoring **batch** processing, maintaining and improving system performance and online availability, maintaining all system and **application** documentation, and assisting personnel with computer problems. Other responsibilities depend on the employer but might include system backups, maintaining computer room equipment including printers and tape storage devices, and providing customer support.

A computer operator may often be asked to know or learn the main computers' operating systems, such as IBM's **OS/ 390** and its Job Entry Subsystem (**JES**), local area network operation, and applications used by an employer. A high school diploma is usually required. Most employers also require formal technical training or one to three years' experience. A computer operator must effectively interact and communicate with others, be able to work independently, have strong analytical skills, and be able to recognize and respond to problem situations.

Computer Output to Laser Disk

See "COLD"

computer-assisted software engineering

See "CASE"

computer-telephony integration

See "CTI"

concatenation

Concatenation (from Latin *concatenare*, to link together) is taking two or more separately located things and placing them side-by-side next to each other so that they can now be treated as one thing. In computer programming and data processing, two or more **character string**s are sometimes concatenated for the purpose of saving space or so that they can be addressed as a single item. (Of course, some way may be needed to know how to unconcatenate them later.)

A simple way to remember concatenation is to think of any word. What makes a word separate from other words is that all the letters are lined up together with no intervening spaces. That is, in a word, all letters are concatenated. Sometimes new words can be made by concatenating two existing words—for example, "airline" is a concatenation of the words "air" and "line" into a new word.

concentrator

As generally used, a concentrator is a device that acts as an efficient forwarder of data transmission signals. A remote access **hub** is sometimes referred to as a concentrator. The term **aggregator** is also frequently used with approximately the same meaning. A typical concentrator or remote access hub is a device that handles incoming dial-up calls for an Internet (or other network) **point-of-presence** and performs other services. A concentrator or hub may be able to handle up to 100 dial-up modem calls, support a certain number of **ISDN** connections, and support **leased line** and **frame relay** traffic while also functioning as a **router**.

Concurrent Versions System

CVS also is an abbreviation for *Computer Vision Syndrome*.

Concurrent Versions System (CVS) is a program that lets a code developer save and retrieve different development versions of **source code**. It also lets a team of developers share control of different versions of files in a common repository of files. This kind of program is sometimes known as a *version control system*. CVS was created in the **UNIX operating system** environment and is available in both **Free Software Foundation** and commercial versions. It is a popular tool for programmers working on **Linux** and other UNIX-based systems.

CVS works not by keeping track of multiple copies of source code files, but by maintaining a single copy and a record of all the changes. When a developer specifies a particular version, CVS can reconstruct that version from the recorded changes. CVS is typically used to keep track of each developer's work individually in a separate working directory. When desired, the work of a team of developers can be merged in a common repository. Changes from individual team members can be added to the repository through a "commit" command.

CVS uses another program, Revision Control System (RCS), to do the actual revision management—that is, keeping the record of changes that goes with each source code file. The writers of the most popular CVS Frequently Asked Questions document are careful to emphasize that CVS is not a *build system*, a code configuration management system, or a substitute for other good development practices, but simply a way to control the versions of the pieces of a program as they are developed.

conditional access

Conditional access (CA) is a technology used to control access to digital television (**DTV**) services to authorized users by encrypting the transmitted programming. CA has been used for years for pay-TV services. There are numerous **ATSC** and **DVB**-compliant CA systems available for a broadcaster to choose from. The CA system provider provides the equipment and software to the broadcaster who then integrates the CA system into his equipment. CA is not designed solely for DTV. It can be used for digital radio broadcasts, digital data broadcasts, and non-broadcast information and interactive services. A CA system consists of several basic components:

- **Subscriber Management System (SMS):** The SMS is a subsystem of the CA system that manages the subscriber's information and requests entitlement management messages (EMM) from the Subscriber Authorization System (SAS). An EMM provides general information about the subscriber and the status of the subscription. The EMM is sent with the ECM. The ECM is a data unit that contains the **key** for decrypting the transmitted programs.

- **Subscriber Authorization System (SAS):** The SAS is a subsystem of the CA system that translates the information about the subscriber into an EMM at the request of the SMS. The SAS also ensures that the subscriber's security module receives the authorization needed to view the programs, and the SAS acts as a backup system in case of failure.

- **Security module:** The security module, usually in the form of a **smart card**, extracts the EMM and ECM necessary for decrypting the transmitted programs. The security module is either embedded within the **set-top box** or in a **PC card** that plugs into the set-top box.

- **Set-top box:** The set-top box houses the security module that gives authorization for decrypting the transmitted programs. The set-top box also converts the digital signal to an analogue signal so an older television can display the programs. There are two DVB protocols used by CA systems: SimulCrypt and MultiCrypt. SimulCrypt uses multiple set-top boxes, each using a different CA system, to authorize the programs for display. The different ECMs and EMMs required by each CA system are transmitted simultaneously. Each set-top box recognizes and uses the appropriate ECM and EMM needed for authorization. The ATSC standard uses SimulCrypt. MultiCrypt allows multiple CA systems to be used with one set-top box by using a PC card with an embedded smart card for each CA system used. Each card is then plugged into a slot in the set-top box. Each card recognizes the ECM and EMM needed for authorization.

A typical CA process involves three basic elements: the broadcast equipment, the set-top box, and the security module. The broadcast equipment generates the encrypted programs that are transmitted to the subscriber. When these are transmitted, the set-top box filters out the signals and passes them to the security module. The security module then authorizes these programs for decryption. The programs are then descrypted in **real time** and sent back to the set-top box for display.

conductance

Conductance is an expression of the ease with which electric **current** flows through a substance. In equations, conductance is symbolized by the uppercase letter *G*. The standard unit of conductance is the *siemens* (abbreviated S), formerly known as the *mho*.

When a current of one ampere (1 A) passes through a component across which a **voltage** of one volt (1 V) exists, then the conductance of that component is 1 S. The siemens is, in fact, equivalent to one ampere per volt. If G is the conductance of a component (in siemens), I is the current through the component (in amperes), and E is the voltage across the component (in volts), then:

$$G = I/E$$

In general, when the applied voltage is held constant, the current in a direct-current (**DC**) circuit is directly proportional to the conductance. If the conductance is doubled, the current is also doubled; if the conductance is cut to $1/10$ its initial value, the current also becomes $1/10$ as great. This rule also holds for most low-frequency alternating-current (**AC**) systems, such as household utility circuits. In some AC circuits, especially at high frequencies, the situation is more complex, because some components in these systems store and release energy, as well as dissipating or converting it.

Conductance is inversely related to **resistance**. If R is the resistance of a component or device (in ohms), then the conductance G (in siemens) is given by:

$$G = 1/R$$

CONFIG.SYS

CONFIG.SYS is a text file containing **DOS** (Disk Operating System) **command**s that tell the **operating system** how the computer is initially set up. More specifically, CONFIG.SYS commands specify memory device **driver**s and programs that control hardware devices; enable or disable system features; and set limits on system resources. CONFIG.SYS loads at startup before the **autoexec.bat** (automatic execute.batch program) file. Because CONFIG.SYS is a text file, it is editable in any text-editing program.

configuration management

Configuration management (CM) is the detailed recording and updating of information that describes an enterprise's computer systems and networks, including all hardware and software components. Such information typically includes the versions and updates that have been applied to installed software packages and the locations and network addresses of hardware devices. Special configuration management software is available. When a system needs a hardware or software upgrade, a computer technician can accesses the configuration management program and database to see what is currently installed. The technician can then make a more informed decision about the upgrade needed.

An advantage of a configuration management application is that the entire collection of systems can be reviewed to make sure any changes made to one system do not adversely affect any of the other systems

Configuration management is also used in software development, where it is called Unified Configuration Management (UCM). Using UCM, developers can keep track of the **source code**, documentation, problems, changes requested, and changes made.

connection

1) In telecommunication and computing in general, a connection is the successful completion of necessary arrangements so that two or more parties (for example, people or programs) can communicate at a long distance. In this usage, the term has a strong physical (hardware) connotation although logical (software) elements are usually involved as well.

A **dialup** (sometimes called a **switched**) connection is a telephonic arrangement that is set up only when needed, using shared, **circuit-switched** communication lines (as in "**plain old telephone service**"). A **dedicated** (sometimes called a **nonswitched**) connection is a continuous, always available connection (familiar to users of Digital Subscriber Line or **DSL** service). A **leased line** is a line rented from a telephone company that provides dedicated connection between two points (such as a headquarters office and a manufacturing plant).

2) In computer programming, a connection is the setting up of resources (such as computer memory and buffers) so that a particular object such as a **database** or **file** can be read or written to. Typically, a programmer encodes an OPEN or similar request to the operating system that ensures that system resources such as memory are set up, encodes READs and WRITES or similar requests, and then encodes a CLOSE when a connection is no longer needed so that the resources are returned to the system for other users.

A closely related term is **session**, which is sometime used to distinguish the ability to communicate for some duration in a logical sense. In this usage, the connection is regarded as the physical setup and the session is regarded as the logical setup. A session could be terminated and the connection maintained with the expectation of a new session later.

connectoid

A connectoid is a dial-up connection profile using the Microsoft Windows 95 or the **Windows 98 operating system**. The connection profiles allow a user to dial out (or really have the computer dial out) to a number of different Internet connection points such as Compuserve or a local Internet service provider (**ISP**).

Any user that connects to an Internet provider can decrease logon time by specifying only those services and **protocol** that are necessary in the Server Type settings for your connectoid.

contact port numbers

See "well-known port numbers"

container

1) In Sun Microsystems' **JavaBeans** component architecture and in Microsoft's **Component Object Model** (COM), a container is an application program or subsystem in which the program building block known as a **component** is run. For example, a component—such as a button or other graphical user interface or a small calculator or database requestor—can be developed using JavaBeans that can run in Netscape containers such as browsers and in Microsoft containers such as Internet Explorer, Visual Basic, and Word.

2) In the Common Object Request Broker Architecture (**CORBA**) Interface Repository, a hierarchy for *metadata*, a Container is one of three *abstract superclasses* (along with IRObject, and Contained).

content caching

See "content delivery"

content delivery

On the Internet, content delivery (sometimes called *content distribution, content distribution delivery,* or *content caching*) is the service of copying the pages of a Web site to geographically dispersed **servers** and, when a page is requested, dynamically identifying and serving page content from the closest server to the user, enabling faster delivery. Typically, high-traffic Web site owners and Internet service providers (**ISP**s) hire the services of the company that provides content delivery.

A common content delivery approach involves the placement of **cache** servers at major Internet access points around the world and the use of a special routing code that redirects a Web page request (technically, a Hypertext Transfer Protocol—**HTTP**—request) to the closest server. When the Web user clicks on a **URL** that is content-delivery enabled, the content delivery network re-routes that user's request away from the site's originating server to a cache server closer to the user. The cache server determines what content in the request exists in the cache, serves that content, and retrieves any non-cached content from the originating server. Any new content is also cached locally. Other than faster loading times, the process is generally transparent to the user, except that the URL served may be different than the one requested.

The three main techniques for content delivery are: HTTP redirection, Internet Protocol (IP) redirection, and domain name system (**DNS**) redirection. In general, DNS redirection is the most effective technique.

Content delivery can also be used for specific high-traffic events such as live Web broadcasts by continually dispersing content from the originating server to other servers via **satellite** links.

Content delivery is similar to but more selective and dynamic than the simple copying or **mirror site** of a Web site to one or several geographically dispersed servers.

content distribution

See "content delivery"

content management system

A content management system (CMS) is a system used to manage the content of a **Web site**. Typically, a CMS consists of two elements: the content management application (CMA) and the content delivery application (CDA). The CMA element allows the content manager or author, who may not know Hypertext Markup Language (**HTML**), to manage the creation, modification, and removal of content from a Web site without needing the expertise of a **Webmaster**. The CDA element uses and compiles that information to update the Web site. The features of a CMS system vary, but most include Web-based publishing, format management, revision control, and indexing, search, and retrieval.

The Web-based publishing feature allows individuals to use a **template** or a set of templates approved by the organization, as well as wizards and other tools to create or modify Web content. The format management feature allows documents including **legacy** electronic documents and scanned paper documents to be formatted into HTML or Portable Document Format (**PDF**) for the Web site. The revision control feature allows content to be updated to a newer version or restored to a previous version. Revision control also tracks any changes made to files by individuals. An additional feature is indexing, search, and retrieval. A CMS system indexes all data within an organization. Individuals can then search for data using keywords, which the CMS system retrieves.

A CMS system may also provide tools for one-to-one marketing. One-to-one marketing is the ability of a Web site to tailor its content and advertising to a user's specific characteristics using information provided by the user or gathered by the site (for example, a particular user's page sequence pattern). For example, if you visit a **search engine** and search for "**digital camera**," the advertising banners will advertise businesses that sell digital cameras instead of businesses that sell garden products.

Two factors must be considered before an organization decides to invest in a CMS. First, an organization's size and geographic dispersion must be considered especially if an organization is spread out over several countries. For these organizations, the transition to CMS is more difficult. Secondly, the diversity of the electronic data forms used within an organization must be considered. If an organization uses text documents, graphics, video, audio, and diagrams to convey information, the content will be more difficult to manage.

Content Protection for Removable Media

Content Protection for Removable Media (CPRM) is a hardware-based technology designed to enforce copy protection restrictions through built-in mechanisms in **storage media** that would prevent unauthorized **file** copying.

Based on a technology called *broadcast encryption* that was developed by Amos Fiat and Moni Naar in 1993, the CPRM system would be used to incorporate digital tags into storage media, such as recordable CDs (**CD-R**, **CD-RW**) and **flash memory** cards for **MP3** players.

CPRM was developed by 4C Entity, an industry consortium originally made up of Intel, IBM, Matsushita, and Toshiba. The system has been highly controversial, because it could be used not only with removable media, but as a part of every new hard drive produced as well. Technical Committee T13 (a coalition of companies that produce both flash memory and hard drives) considered adopting CPRM as an industry standard, but has since given approval to an alternative plan in development at Phoenix Technologies that would be used for other purposes—such as security mechanisms on removable media—in addition to copy protection.

Content Scrambling System

Content Scrambling System (CSS) is a data **encryption** and **authentication** method used to protect digital versatile disk (**DVD**) movies from being illegally copied, distributed, and viewed from other devices, such as computer hard drives. CSS is one of several copy-protection methods currently used in today's DVDs.

The CSS method was developed by members of the DVD Copy Control Association (DVDCCA). This association includes companies in the U.S. motion picture industry (members of the MPAA) and the consumer electronics industry. The Matsushita and Toshiba companies are largely credited with the first main development efforts of the CSS method for encryption and decryption of DVD movies.

In general, the CSS method encrypts (scrambles) the video files on a DVD to prevent illegal viewing or copying. In order to view any video files found on the DVD, the user must use a hardware device that is CSS-licensed to decrypt, or decode, the data in the video file. One such hardware device is a DVD-ROM (DVD-read only memory) device that can be installed with a computer or a specially designed TV in order to view DVD movies. Another possible device could be the hard disk of a personal computer.

DVD disc manufacturers or DVD-ROM manufacturers must first be licensed to use CSS before they can produce discs or DVD-ROMs that will successfully encrypt or decrypt CSS-protected video files. Once a DVD-ROM manufacturer is licensed to use CSS, the manufacturer receives one of 400 keys which are stored in a locked section on every CSS-supported disc.

The DVD-ROM then uses this key information to decode the video file on the DVD and display the related movie. The actual operation of CSS involves the use of a decryption algorithm that mixes the key information exchanged between the disc and the hardware device in order to produce a unique key that will successfully decrypt the movie or video file for viewing.

As with many encryption methods of the past, CSS came under intense scrutiny in October 1999 when it was reported that a 16-year-old Norwegian programmer cracked the CSS code and posted the decryption method (quickly coined *DeCSS*) on the Internet. This action, and the subsequent postings of DeCSS code elsewhere on the Internet, heralded a series of lawsuits from the DVDCCA. In response, some pro-DeCSS organizations also sprouted up to protest what they perceived of as a lack of rights to freely distribute the reverse-engineered, CSS code for other programming uses.

Lawsuits over the future rights to access the CSS/deCSS code are still being waged today. The DVDCCA maintains that CSS can be licensed for free to any manufacturer who agrees to follow the terms of its CSS license.

contiguity

Contiguity (from Latin *contiguus* and *contingere*, to have contact with) is the state of being in close proximity with or even touching another object. In data processing, a group of data fields that are contiguous (rather than dispersed among other groups or locations) consists of fields that can be processed one after the other in sequence.

control network

A control network is a **network** of **node**s that collectively monitor, sense, and control or enable control of an environment for a particular purpose. A home appliance network is a good example of a control network. In fact, thousands of control networks already exist in everyday life in automobiles, refrigerators, traffic light controls, city lighting systems, and on factory floors. Control networks vary enormously in the number of nodes (from three to thousands) in the network and in their complexity. Unlike networks that people use to communicate with each other, control networks tend to be invisible. In the future, control networks are expected to become an important aspect of what is sometimes called *ubiquitous computing*.

Communication between nodes in a control network may be peer-to-peer or master-slave. The nodes in some control networks contain three processors in one: two dedicated to

moving data within the network and one for the specialized program associated with that node. This modularity makes it cheaper and faster to build new processors for control networks. Increasingly, control networks are being made from off-the-shelf hardware and software components.

One future role for control networks will be as the controllers of microelectromechanical sytems (**MEMS**), sometimes referred to as *smart matter*. Because it greatly expands the number of items in the world that can be uniquely addressed in a network, **IPv6**, a new version of the Internet Protocol (**IP**), is expected to make remote access and control of all kinds of devices possible, including every networked appliance at your office or at home. Sun Microsystem's **Jini**, will make it easy to plug new devices into a control network and have their characteristics immediately recognized by the system.

conventional memory

DOS memory, sometimes referred to as conventional memory, refers to the **memory**-addressing scheme used in the original IBM and compatible PCs. These came with only one **operating system**, **Disk Operating System**, and this operating system had to be designed to work with the PC's **microprocessor**, the Intel 8088. Because of 8088 engineering limitations, storage or memory addresses were limited to a maximum of one **megabyte**. (Later, of course, PC's came with 2, 4, 8, and today's common 16 and 32 megabytes of RAM.) At the time, however, one megabyte was considered a rather large amount of memory to be able to access.

A certain amount of the random access memory was reserved as a place to load in the **basic input/output system** or initializing program, another space was reserved for **buffer** areas for display data, and another space for **interrupt** data, and so forth. The remaining 640 **kilobyte**s of memory could be used by the DOS operating system (which was relatively small) and **application** programs.

The reason that all of this is not academic is that, as new microprocessors and operating systems have been developed, many older programs written with the original memory addressing limitations need to continue running in the newer systems. This means that the newer systems have had to accommodate the older programs so that they can run in the original limited 640 kilobye contiguous address range. A program that is run with this constraint is described as running in **protected mode**. (Programs running without this constraint are described as running in **protected mode**.)

With the successors to the 8088, the 80286 and 80386 microprocessors, available memory increased considerably, with up to 15 megabytes possible in a 286 and up to almost 4 **gigabyte** of RAM possible in a 386. This extra memory above the orginal one megabyte that DOS was designed to address is called *extended memory*. Being able to address extended memory means running in protected mode.

In general, DOS applications can only run in real mode since DOS itself requires the memory constraint. However, some programs have been developed called *DOS extenders* that can be compiled with the application and provide a built-in memory management capability. In order for multiple DOS programs with memory extenders to run concurrently, some common approach was required so that programs could share the extended memory effectively. Several standards developed to manage this sharing: XMS (Extended Memory Specification), VCPI (Virtual Control Program Interface), and **DOS Protected Mode Interface** (DOS protected mode interface).

convergence

In information technology, convergence is a term for the combining of personal computers, telecommunication, and television into a user experience that is accessible to everyone. In the U.S., an estimated 30% of homes have computers with modems. Virtually, 100% of homes have a TV set. Studies show a large populace of TV users who would embrace the Internet, video-on-demand, and greater interaction with content, but who are diffident about buying and using a personal computer. For these reasons, both the computer and the television industries are embarked on bringing digital TV and the Internet to a larger market.

Convergence is not simply an issue of technology, but also of culture and life style. In general, TV is visual, not very interactive (except for changing channels), oriented primarily toward entertainment and news. Displays are large and TVs are easy to operate, requiring almost no education to use. Personal computers, in spite of their graphical user interfaces (**GUI**) tend to be more text-oriented, highly interactive, oriented in terms of purpose and content toward business and education uses. Displays are smaller. Computers can be very challenging to use and usually require formal education or a certain personal learning curve.

Convergence is already underway with **WebTV**, which pipes the World Wide Web to a slightly-modified TV set with a set-top box from an ordinary phone line and provides a degree of interactivity. A number of interactive games designed for the TV environment can also be played over the Internet. Broadcasting companies such as NBC have partnered with computer companies such as Microsoft for TV program content.

A major barrier to more rapid convergence is the large investment required to bring **cable TV** to households, both by cable access providers and individual households. **Satellite wireless** service is another approach that is only beginning to bring its subscribers access to the Internet. Digital Subscriber Line (**DSL**) technologies offer the possibility of sufficient **bandwidth** connections over ordinary phone wires for streaming video to TV sets.

A consortium of leading computer and telecommunication companies including Compaq, IBM, and Microsoft are working toward common standards that will help speed up convergence and hope to sponsor a standard for a relatively low-cost **digital TV**. They have endorsed a subset of the recommendations of the Advanced Television System Committee (ATSC) that would speed up a transition to digital TV and so that personal computers could have the ability to receive digital video and data.

Conversational Monitor System

CMS (Conversational Monitor System) is a product that comes with IBM's **VM/ESA operating system** and allows each of many simultaneous interactive users to appear to have an entire mainframe computer at their personal disposal. Almost as old as IBM's **MVS** operating sysem, VM/ESA (generally known as "VM") and CMS originated at IBM's Cambridge Scientific Center in 1964. VM provides an extra layer of programming below an operating system, called the *control program* that handles the actual machine operation of the computer. The control program lets each operating system, such as MVS and CMS, appear to be in sole charge of the computer—effectively, creating a *virtual machine*. CMS goes a step further and lets each CMS user appear to have their own personal operating system.

Users of a VM system typically log on to VM first and then (virtually) start their own personal CMS (by entering the command: i cms). Thereafter, the user can communicate with other active users, send mail, develop and run applications, and use many standard applications and tools that have been developed over VM and CMS's evolution.

COO

See "Cell of Origin"

cookie

A cookie is information that a **Web site** puts on your **hard disk** so that it can remember something about you at a later time. (More technically, it is information for future use that is stored by the **server** on the **client** side of a **client/server** communication.) Typically, a cookie records your preferences when using a particular site. Using the Web's Hypertext Transfer Protocol (**HTTP**), each request for a Web page is independent of all other requests. For this reason, the Web page server has no memory of what pages it has sent to a user previously or anything about your previous visits. A cookie is a mechanism that allows the **server** to store its own information about a user on the user's own computer. You can view the cookies that have been stored on your hard disk (although the content stored in each cookie may not make much sense to you). The location of the cookies depends on the browser. Internet Explorer stores each cookie as a

separate file under a Windows subdirectory. Netscape stores all cookies in a single cookies.txt fle. **Opera** stores them in a single cookies.dat file.

Cookies are commonly used to rotate the banner ads that a site sends so that it doesn't keep sending the same ad as it sends you a succession of requested pages. They can also be used to customize pages for you based on your browser type or other information you may have provided the Web site. Web users must agree to let cookies be saved for them, but, in general, it helps Web sites to serve users better.

cool

On the World Wide Web, cool has a number of meanings, including:

- Engaging
- Laid-back, understated
- In tune with the latest thinking, even a little ahead of it
- Technically or graphically impressive

The term "cool" seems to have originated among jazz musicians in the 1940s. In *Understanding Media*, Marshall MacLuhan described television as a "cool" medium (unlike the "hot" media of radio and print) because it is sensorily more complex and involving. "A cool medium," said Professor MacLuhan, "whether the spoken word or the manuscript or TV, leaves much more for the listener or user to do than a hot medium." A composite of several media (photographs, print, animated images, movies, sound, telephone conversations, posted notes...) and also in itself a new medium of over 100 million potential "publishers" and interactors, the Web itself seems much closer to MacLuhan's "cool."

co-opetition

Co-opetition is a business strategy based on a combination of cooperation and competition, derived from an understanding that business competitors can benefit when they work together. The co-opetition business model is based on *games theory*, a scientific approach (developed during World War II) to understanding various strategies and outcomes through specifically designed games. Traditional business philosophy translates to games theory's *zero-sum game* in which the winner takes all, and the loser is left empty-handed; proponents of co-opetition claim that it can lead to a *plus-sum game*, in which the sum of what is gained by all players is greater than the combined sum of what the players entered the game with.

The co-opetition model starts out with a diagramming process called the *value net*, which is represented as a diamond shape, with four defined player designations at the corners: customers, suppliers, competitors and *complementors*. Complementors are defined as players whose product adds value to yours, the way, for example, that software products gain value because hardware products coexist with

them, and vice-versa. In comparison, a competitor is defined as someone whose product makes your product less valued, the way, for example, a second brand of toothpaste would make one that had previously been the only one less valued.

The game of business is then broken down into its PARTS (players, added values, rules, tactics, and scope) as a means of viewing practices and strategies. *Added value* focuses on ways to improve products and services to find ways of making more money from an existing customer base. *Rules* specify ways of attracting customers with strategies such as price-matching. *Tactics* are the practices sometimes used to take away a competitor's likely market share, for example, announcing an upcoming (and possibly non-existent) new and improved product when a competitor's product is released. Scope is the final part, used to take a broader prospective and create links between competitor's games and interests and see how co-opetition can benefit the players.

Although several people have been credited with inventing the term *co-opetition*, including Sam Albert, Microsoft's John Lauer, and Ray Noorda, Novell's founder, its principles and practices were fully articulated originally in the 1996 book, *Co-opetition*, by Harvard and Yale business professors, Adam M. Brandenburger and Barry J. Nalebuff.

Coordinated Universal Time

Coordinated Universal Time (abbreviated as UTC, and therefore often spelled out as Universal Time Coordinated and sometimes as Universal Coordinated Time) is the standard time common to every place in the world. Formerly and still widely called Greenwich Mean Time (GMT) and also World Time, UTC nominally reflects the mean solar time along the Earth's prime meridian. (The prime meridian is $\bar{0}$ longitude in the 360 lines of longitude on Earth. There are 179 meridians toward the East and 179 toward the West. The 180th meridian is also called the International Date Line.) The prime meridian is arbitrarily based on the meridian that runs through the Greenwich Observatory outside of London, where the present system originated. The UTC is based on an atomic clock to which adjustments of a second (called a *leap second*) are sometimes made to allow for variations in the solar cycle.

Coordinated Universal Time is expressed using a 24-hour clock but can be converted into a 12-hour clock (AM and PM). UTC is used in plane and ship navigation, where it also sometimes known as **Zulu**. UTC uses the **Gregorian calendar** calendar.

UTC was defined by the International Radio Consultative Committee (CCIR), a predecessor organization of the **ITU-TS**, and is maintained by the Bureau International des Poids et Mesures (BIPM).

COPS

COPS (Common Open Policy Service Protocol) is a proposed standard **protocol** for exchanging network **policy** information between a policy decision point (PDP) in a network and policy enforcement points (PEPs) as part of overall Quality of Service (**QoS**)—the allocation of network traffic resources according to desired priorities of service. The policy decision point might be a network server controlled directly by the network administrator who enters policy statements about which kinds of traffic (voice, bulk data, video, teleconferencing, and so forth) should get the highest priority. The policy enforcement points might be **router**s or layer 3 switches that implement the policy choices as traffic moves through the network. Currently, COPS is designed for use with the Resource Reservation Protocol (**RSVP**), which lets you allocate traffic priorities in advance for temporary high-bandwidth requirements (for example, video broadcasts or multicasts). It is possible that COPS will be extended to be a general policy communications protocol.

In operation, RSVP makes two determinations when an RSVP request arrives at a router or **layer 3** switch. First, it determines whether there are enough resources to satisfy the **bandwidth** reservation request. If there are, RSVP determines whether the user is authorized to make the reservation. The first determination is known as the *admission control* decision; the second is known as the *policy control* decision. COPS allows the router or layer 3 switch to communicate with the policy decision point about whether the request for the bandwidth reservation should be permitted. Without COPS, all resources would be reserved on a first come-first served basis only, and one or more requesters could easily take all the bandwidth.

The current COPS protocol is specified in an Internet-Draft working document of the Internet Engineering Task Force (**IETF**).

copyleft

Copyleft is the idea and the specific stipulation when distributing software that the user will be able to copy it freely, examine and modify the source code, and redistribute the software to others (free or priced) as long as the redistributed software is also passed along with the copyleft stipulation. The term was originated by Richard Stallman and the **Free Software Foundation**. Copyleft favors the software user's rights and convenience over the commercial interests of the software makers. It also reflects the belief that freer redistribution and modification of software would encourage users to make improvements to it. ("Free software" is not the same as **freeware**, which is usually distributed with copyright restrictions.)

Stallman and his adherents do not object to the price or profit aspects of creation and redistribution of software—only to the current restrictions placed on who can use how many copies of the software and how and whether the software can be modified and redistributed.

The de facto collaboration that developed and refined **UNIX** and other collegially-developed programs led the FSF to the idea of "free" software and copyleft. In 1983, the FSF began developing a "free software" project that would both demonstrate the concept while providing value to users. The project was called **GNU**, an operating system similar to a UNIX system. GNU and its various components are currently available and are distributed with copyleft stipulations. New software is being developed.

CORBA

Common Object Request Broker Architecture (CORBA) is an architecture and specification for creating, distributing, and managing **distributed** program **object**s in a network. It allows programs at different locations and developed by different vendors to communicate in a network through an "interface broker." CORBA was developed by a consortium of vendors through the Object Management Group (**OMG**), which currently includes over 500 member companies. Both International Organization for Standardization (**ISO**) and X/Open have sanctioned CORBA as the standard architecture for distributed objects (which are also known as **component**s). CORBA 3 is the latest level.

The essential concept in CORBA is the Object Request Broker (**ORB**). ORB support in a network of clients and servers on different computers means that a client program (which may itself be an **object**) can request services from a server program or object without having to understand where the server is in a distributed network or what the interface to the server program looks like. To make requests or return replies between the ORBs, programs use the General Inter-ORB Protocol (**GIOP**) and, for the Internet, its Internet Inter-ORB Protocol (**IIOP**). IIOP maps GIOP requests and replies to the Internet's Transmission Control Protocol (**TCP**) layer in each computer.

A notable hold-out from CORBA is Microsoft, which has its own distributed object architecture, the Distributed Component Object Model (**DCOM**). However, CORBA and Microsoft have agreed on a gateway approach so that a client object developed with the Component Object Model will be able to communicate with a CORBA server (and vice versa).

Distributed Computing Environment (**DCE**), a distributed programming architecture that preceded the trend toward object-oriented programming and CORBA, is currently used by a number of large companies. DCE will perhaps continue to exist along with CORBA and there will be "bridges" between the two.

More information is available in our definitions of **Internet Inter-ORB Protocol** and **Object Request Broker**.

cordless mouse

A cordless **mouse** frees you from cord problems. It connects to your computer with a radio (rather than an infrared) signal, powered by two AAA batteries. One manufacturer, Logitech, offers two versions of a three-button mouse; one includes a button positioned for the thumb (for right-handed users). The buttons can be assigned different uses during system setup.

core competency

A core competency is fundamental knowledge, ability, or expertise in a specific subject area or skill set. For example, an individual who becomes certified as a Microsoft Certified Software Engineer (**MCSE**) is said to have a core competency in certain Microsoft systems and networks. Companies with specific strengths in the marketplace, such as data storage or the development of accounting applications, can be said to have a core competency in that area. The *core* part of the term indicates that the individual has a strong basis from which to gain the additional competence to do a specific job or that a company has a strong basis from which to develop additional products.

core dump

A core dump is the printing or the copying to a more permanent medium (such as a **hard disk**) the contents of random access memory (**RAM**) at one moment in time. One can think of it as a full-length "snapshot" of RAM. A core dump is taken mainly for the purpose of debugging a program. With the arrival of higher-level languages and interactive debugging, few problems require a core dump these days. It's more likely to be used by specialized programmers who maintain and occasionally have to debug problems in **operating system**.

The "core" refers to the ferrite cores of earlier memory technology. In some earlier operating systems, certain system errors would automatically result in the performing of a core dump. Typically, a core dump or actually the report that results from the core dump presents the RAM contents as a formatted series of lines that indicate memory locations and the **hexadecimal** values recorded at each location. Additional information tells exactly which instruction was executing at the time the core dump was initiated.

IBM's dictionary does not include the term and Microsoft mentions it as an antiquated term. *The New Hacker's Dictionary* says the term is from the "Iron Age."

A *dump* is a more general term that includes the copying of a large portion of one storage medium to another storage medium or to a printer, display, or other output device. A dump report is formatted for readability.

The term is sometimes applied to human beings as a variation of *brain dump*.

corporate portal

See "corportal"

corportal

Corportal is short for "corporate portal." Many corporations are building and, in some cases, rebuilding their **Web site**s along the model of the **enterprise information portal**, a model that emphasizes the exploitation of a company's information resources. A corportal can be internal (an intranet), a public site, or, with appropriate safeguards, both combined.

CoS

See "Class of Service"

COTS

See "commercial off-the-shelf"

coulomb

The coulomb (symbolized C) is the standard unit of electric charge in the International System of Units (**SI**). It is a dimensionless quantity, sharing this aspect with the **mole**. A quantity of 1 C is equal to approximately 6.24×10^{18}, or 6.24 quintillion.

In terms of SI base units, the coulomb is the equivalent of one **ampere**-second. Conversely, an electric **current** of A represents 1 C of unit electric charge carriers flowing past a specific point in 1 s. The unit electric charge is the amount of charge contained in a single **electron**. Thus, 6.24×10^{18} electrons have 1 C of charge. This is also true of 6.24×10^{18} positrons or 6.24×10^{18} protons, although these two types of particle carry charge of opposite **polarity** to that of the electron.

The force with which two electrically charged bodies attract or repel one another depends on the product of the charges (in coulombs) in both objects, and also on the distance between the objects. If the polarities are the same (negative/negative or positive/positive), the so-called coulomb force is repulsive; if the polarities are opposite (negative/positive or positive/negative), the force is attractive. For any two charged bodies, the coulomb force decreases in proportion to the square of the distance between their charge centers.

coulomb per meter cubed

The coulomb per meter cubed (symbolized $C \cdot m^{-3}$) is the unit of electric charge density. Reduced to base units in the International System of Units (**SI**), $1 \ C \cdot m^{-3}$ is equivalent to one **ampere second** per **meter cubed** ($1 \ A \cdot s \cdot m^{-3}$).

Suppose there is a globe having volume of one **meter** cubed, and it is supplied with one **coulomb** of charge with respect to electrical ground. Then the average charge density in the globe is $1 \ C \cdot m^{-3}$. The local charge density might not be uniform throughout the globe, but might instead be concentrated near the surface, especially if the charge is comprised of an excess of **electron**s (that is, a negative charge). This is because particles of like charge tend to repel each other. In that case, the local charge density near the center of the globe will be less than $1 \ C \cdot m^{-3}$, and the local charge density near the surface will be greater than $1 \ C \cdot m^{-3}$.

If the charge on the globe is doubled, then the average charge density will become $2 \ C \cdot m^{-3}$. If the diameter of the globe is cut in half while the charge remains the same, then the average charge density will increase by a factor of 8, because the volume will become $1/8$ $(1/2^3)$ as great as before.

Also see **electric field**, **coulomb**, **meter cubed**, **coulomb per meter squared**, and International System of Units (**SI**).

counter

On the Web, a counter is a program that counts and typically displays how many people have visited an **HTML** page (usually the **home page**). Many sites include a counter, either as a matter of interest or to show that the site is popular. The counter can be part of the **common gateway interface** application that logs and analyzes requests.

At least one company provides the service of monitoring sites that request it, counting home page requests, and updating the number of visitors each time the home page is sent. A third-party who monitors the counting of site visitors is called an **auditor**.

counting board

Historically, a counting board was a portable flat surface, usually of wood or stone, on which a user placed objects such as pebbles or beads for the purpose of maintaining a count of something. The counting board is thought to have originated so that you didn't have to draw lines on the ground or in sand as points of reference for counters every time you needed to add figures up. The oldest surviving counting board was discovered on the island of Salamis in 1899 and was used in Babylonia, circa 300 B.C.

The counting board led to the **abacus**.

courseware

Courseware, a term that combines the words *course* with *software*, is educational material intended as kits for teachers or trainers or as tutorials for students, usually packaged for use with a computer. Courseware can encompass any knowledge area, but information technology subjects are most common. Courseware is frequently used for delivering education about the personal computer and its most popular business applications, such as word processing and spreadsheet programs. Courseware is also widely used in information technology industry certification programs, such as the Microsoft Certified Systems Engineer (**MCSE**) and the Computing Technology Industry Associaton's **A+** examination.

Courseware can include:

● Material for instructor-led classes

● Material for self-directed computer-based training (CBT)

● Web sites that offer interactive tutorials

● Material that is coordinated with distance learning, such as live classes conducted over the Internet

● Videos for use individually or as part of classes

The **CD-ROM** is the most common means of delivering courseware that is not offered online. For teachers and trainers, courseware content may include set-up information, a course plan, teaching notes, and exercises.

CPI

1) For a given **font**, cpi (characters per inch) is the number of typographic **character** that will fit on each inch of a printed line. The measurement applies mainly to *monospace (fixed-width)* fonts. Fonts with characters of proportional (varying) widths have an average cpi.

2) cpi (cyles per instruction, or clocks per instruction) is the number of computer **clock speed** cycles (alternating current pulses) that occur while a computer **instruction** is being executed (performed by the computer processor). The number of cycles per instruction can be reduced by using **pipelining**. In some *superscalar* processors, more than one instruction can be performed during a single clock cycle.

3) CPI (Common Programming Interface) is the application program interface (**API**) specified as part of IBM's proprietary software architecture, the Systems Application Architecture (**SNA**).

CPNI

In the U.S., CPNI (Customer Proprietary Network Information) is information that telecommunications services such as local, long distance, and **wireless** telephone companies acquire about their subscribers. It includes not only what services they use but their amount and type of usage. The **Telecommunications Act of 1996** together with clarifications from the Federal Communications Commission (FCC) generally prohibits the use of that information without customer permission, even for the purpose of marketing the customers other services. In the case of customers who switch to other service providers, the original service provider is prohibited from using the information to try to get the customer back. CPNI includes such information as optional services subscribed to, current charges, directory assistance charges, usage data, and calling patterns.

The CPNI rules do not prohibit the gathering and publishing of aggregate customer information nor the use of customer information for the purpose of creating directories.

CPRM

See "Content Protection for Removable Media"

CRA

See "customer relationship analysis"

cracker

A cracker is someone who breaks into someone else's computer system, often on a network; bypasses passwords or licenses in computer programs; or in other ways intentionally breaches computer security. A cracker can be doing this for profit, maliciously, for some altruistic purpose or cause, or because the challenge is there. Some breaking-and-entering has been done ostensibly to point out weaknesses in a site's security system.

The term "cracker" is not to be confused with "**hacker**." Hackers generally deplore cracking. However, as Eric Raymond, compiler of *The New Hacker's Dictionary* notes, some journalists ascribe break-ins to "hackers."

A classic story of the tracking down of a cracker on the Internet who was breaking into U.S. military and other computers is told in Clifford Stoll's *The Cuckoo's Egg*.

cracking

See "brute force cracking"

crash

A crash is the sudden failure of a software application or **operating system** or of a hardware device such as a **hard disk**.

crawler

A crawler is a program that visits Web sites and reads their pages and other information in order to create entries for a **search engine** index. The major search engines on the Web all have such a program, which is also known as a "spider" or a "bot." Crawlers are typically programmed to visit sites that have been submitted by their owners as new or updated. Entire sites or specific pages can be selectively visited and indexed. Crawlers apparently gained the name because they crawl through a site a page at a time, following the links to other pages on the site until all pages have been read.

The crawler for the **AltaVista** search engine and its Web site is called **Scooter**. Scooter adheres to the rules of politeness for Web crawlers that are specified in the Standard for Robot Exclusion (SRE). It asks each server which files should be excluded from being indexed. It does not (or can not) go

through **firewall**s. And it uses a special **algorithm** for waiting between successive server requests so that it doesn't affect response time for other users.

CRC

See "cyclic redundancy checking"

critical section routine

In computers, a critical section routine is an approach to the problem of two or more programs competing for the same resource at the same time. Imagine that two programs want to increment a counter. If both do it at the same time: fetch the **operand**, increment it, and store back the incremented value, then one of the increments will be lost. On today's processors, the programs can use an **atomic** read-modify-write instruction, such as fetch-and-op, compare-and-swap, or exchange. On early processors, these instructions did not exist; the problem was to accomplish the incrementing atomically, using only ordinary **assembler** instructions. The problem was defined and first solved by Edsgar Dijkstra. "Critical section routine" was his name for the code that solved the problem.

CRM

See "customer relationship management"

CRM analytics

CRM (**customer relationship management**) analytics comprises all programming that analyzes data about an enterprise's customers and presents it so that better and quicker business decisions can be made. CRM analytics can be considered a form of online analytical processing (**OLAP**) and may employ **data mining**. As Web sites have added a new and often faster way to interact with customers, the opportunity and the need to turn data collected about customers into useful information has become generally apparent. As a result, a number of software companies have developed products that do customer data analysis.

According to an article in *InfoWorld*, CRM analytics can provide customer segmentation groupings (for example, at its simplest, dividing customers into those most and least likely to repurchase a product); profitability analysis (which customers lead to the most profit over time); personalization (the ability to market to individual customers based on the data collected about them); event monitoring (for example, when a customer reaches a certain dollar volume of purchases); what-if scenarios (how likely is a customer or customer category that bought one product to buy a similar one); and predictive modeling (for example, comparing various product development plans in terms of likely future success given the customer knowledge base). Data collection and analysis are viewed as a continuing and iterative process and ideally over time business decisions are refined based on feedback from earlier analysis and consequent decisions.

Benefits of CRM analytics are said to lead not only to better and more productive customer relations in terms of sales and service but also to improvement in **supply chain management** (lower inventory and speedier delivery) and thus lower costs and more competitive pricing.

One of the major challenges implicit in CRM analytics is how to integrate the analytical software with existing **legacy** systems as well as with other new systems.

A new area of application and data collection has to do with Web site customer usage.

CRON script

A CRON **script** is a list of one or more **command**s to a computer **operating system** or application server that are to be executed at a specified time. Each command is executed when its triggering time arrives. In **UNIX**-based **operating system**s, the **crontab** command is a user interface command that creates or changes a file (called a *crontab file*). This file contains a list of UNIX shell commands, each with a specified time of execution. A CRON script is similar.

crontab

crontab is a **UNIX command** that creates a table or list of commands, each of which is to be executed by the operating system at a specified time. *crontab* is used to create the *crontab file* (the list) and later used to change the previously created crontab file.

Also see **CRON script**.

cross section

1) A cross section is a cut through something (such as a **coaxial cable**) at an angle perpendicular to its axis in order to view its interior structure. A well-known example is a cross section of a tree that shows its growth rings and tells its age.

2) Somewhat less precisely, a cross section can be any view of something that shows a representative portion of each of its parts. For example, a cross section of a **Web site** might show a representative **page** of content at each of its hierarchical levels. A cross section of a Web site audience would indicate its demographics (types of people who used the site in terms of gender, age, occupation, and so forth).

cross-bar switch

In a network, a cross-bar switch is a device that is capable of channeling data between any two devices that are attached to it up to its maximum number of **ports**. The paths set up

between devices can be fixed for some duration or changed when desired and each device-to-device path (going through the **switch**) is usually fixed for some period.

Cross-bar **topology** can be contrasted with **bus** topology, an arrangement in which there is only one path that all devices share. Traditionally, computers have been connected to storage devices with a large bus. A major advantage of cross-bar switching is that, as the traffic between any two devices increases, it does not affect traffic between other devices. In addition to offering more flexibility, a cross-bar switch environment offers greater **scalability** than a bus environment.

In an IBM **mainframe** environment, the **ESCON** director is an example of a cross-bar switch.

crossfade

In digital audio production, a crossfade is editing that makes a smooth transition between two audio files. In **analog** days, crossfades required dubbing the inputs of two source tapes onto a new tape while manually turning down the volume of one source tape while turning up the other, a relatively cumbersome procedure. Crossfading became easier to achieve with the invention of the computer-based digital audio editor. A digital editor allows two or more files to be crossfaded with the fade length limited only by the amount of audio contained in the source files. The edit consists of fading out one source file while fading in the other. This method creates a smooth transition because for a short period of time the listener hears both files playing simultaneously.

A crossfade is the opposite of a butt splice. In a butt splice, the end of the first file is joined to the beginning of the second file.

crossover cable

A crossover cable is a cable that is used to interconnect two computers by "crossing over" (reversing) their respective **pin** contacts. Either an **RS-232C** or an **registered jack** connection is possible. A crossover cable is sometimes known as a **null modem**. Possible reasons to connect two computers directly to each other include:

- Playing a game competitively (one person at each computer) with fast response time
- Testing one computer by examining its behavior at the other computer
- Saving the cost of a **hub** when you want to interconnect two devices in the same home or office

cross-post

On a Web or bulletin board discussion list or a **Usenet newsgroup**, a cross-post is the posting (submission) of an article to more than one discussion list or newsgroup at a time. On Usenet, the cross-post can be done in such a way

that all newsgroup users can link to, read, and, if desired, respond to one copy of the posting on one of the newsgroups. Each of the other posted newsgroups contains a reference to it.

Cross-post is also used to mean simply copying the posting to each of a number of discussion groups. Most discussion groups and newsgroups provide rules about how and whether to submit articles as cross-posts.

crosstalk

Crosstalk is a disturbance caused by the electric or magnetic fields of one telecommunication **signal** affecting a signal in an adjacent **circuit**. In an telephone circuit, crosstalk can result in your hearing part of a voice conversation from another circuit. The phenomenon that causes crosstalk is called electromagnetic interference (**EMI**). It can occur in microcircuits within computers and audio equipment as well as within network circuits. The term is also applied to optical signals that interfere with each other.

CRT

See "cathode ray tube"

crumb

In computers, crumb is jargon for two **bit**s (that is, two **binary digit**s).

According to the *Jargon File*, synonyms are: quad, taste, and tastye. The term is rarely used.

Crusoe

Crusoe is a family of "smart" microprocessors from **Transmeta** that combines a relatively simple, low-powered hardware **processor** with software that makes the hardware processor look like an **x86** Intel processor (such as a **Pentium III**). Because Crusoe requires only one-fourth of the usual number of **transistors**, the processor has a small power requirement. As a result, Crusoe is expected to introduce a new era of mobile devices that can run all day without requiring a **battery** recharge.

The hardware processor operates with very long instruction word (**VLIW**) **instructions**. The VLIW instructions are developed by the software, which is on **flash memory** and which Transmeta calls its Code Morphing Software. The software takes the x86 instructions from the **operating system** or applications and develops them into optimized VLIW instructions for the hardware processor.

Initially, the Crusoe family consists of two processors:

- **The TM3120—for mobile devices weighing two pounds or less**. The speed is 333-400 **MHz** and the power requirement is low enough to allow a full day of Web browsing without a battery recharge.

- **The TM5400—for mobile PCs weighing four pounds or less**. Performance is up to 700 MHz, providing up to eight hours of "everyday office use" and up to four hours of playing DVD movies without needing a recharge.

Crusoe processors are expected to appear in mobile devices, including the *Web pad*, the notebook computer, and the **wearable computer**.

cryptanalysis

Cryptanalysis refers to the study of ciphers, **ciphertext**, or cryptosystems (that is, to secret code systems) with a view to finding weaknesses in them that will permit retrieval of the **plaintext** from the ciphertext, without necessarily knowing the **key** or the **algorithm**. This is known as *breaking* the cipher, ciphertext, or cryptosystem.

Breaking is sometimes used interchangeably with *weakening*. This refers to finding a property (fault) in the design or implementation of the **cipher** that reduces the number of keys required in a brute force attack (that is, simply trying every possible key until the correct one is found). For example, assume that a symmetric cipher implementation uses a key length of 2^{128} bits (2 to the power of 128): this means that a brute force attack would need to try up to all 2^{128} possible combinations (rounds) to be certain of finding the correct key (or, on average, 2^{127} possible combinations) to convert the ciphertext into plaintext, which is not possible given present and near future computing abilities. However, a cryptanalysis of the cipher reveals a technique that would allow the plaintext to be found in 2^{40} rounds. While not completely broken, the cipher is now much weaker and the plaintext can be found with moderate computing resources.

There are numerous techniques for performing cryptanalysis, depending on what access the cryptanalyst has to the plaintext, ciphertext, or other aspects of the cryptosystem. Below are some of the most common types of attacks:

1) **Known-plaintext analysis:** With this procedure, the cryptanalyst has knowledge of a portion of the plaintext from the ciphertext. Using this information, the cryptanalyst attempts to deduce the key used to produce the ciphertext.

2) **Chosen-plaintext analysis (also known as differential cryptanalysis):** The cryptanalyst is able to have any plaintext encrypted with a key and obtain the resulting ciphertext, but the key itself cannot be analyzed. The cryptanalyst attempts to deduce the key by comparing the entire ciphertext with the original plaintext. The **Rivest-Shamir-Adleman** encryption technique has been shown to be somewhat vulnerable to this type of analysis.

3) **Ciphertext-only analysis:** The cryptanalyst has no knowledge of the plaintext and must work only from the ciphertext. This requires accurate guesswork as to how a

message could be worded. It helps to have some knowledge of the literary style of the ciphertext writer and/or the general subject matter.

4) **Man-in-the-middle attack:** This differs from the above in that it involves tricking individuals into surrendering their keys. The cryptanalyst/attacker places him or herself in the communication channel between two parties who wish to exchange their keys for secure communication (via asymmetric or **public key infrastructure** cryptography). The cryptanalyst/attacker then performs a key exchange with each party, with the original parties believing they are exchanging keys with each other. The two parties then end up using keys that are known to the cryptanalyst/attacker. This type of attack can be defeated by the use of a **hash function**.

5) **Timing/differential power analysis:** This is a new technique made public in June 1998, particularly useful against the **smart card**, that measures differences in electrical consumption over a period of time when a microchip performs a function to secure information. This technique can be used to gain information about key computations used in the encryption algorithm and other functions pertaining to security. The technique can be rendered less effective by introducing random noise into the computations, or altering the sequence of the executables to make it harder to monitor the power fluctuations. This type of analysis was first developed by Paul Kocher of Cryptography Research, though Bull Systems claims it knew about this type of attack over four years before.

In addition to the above, other techniques are available, such as convincing individuals to reveal passwords/keys, developing **Trojan horse** programs that steal a victim's secret key from their computer and send it back to the cryptanalyst, or tricking a victim into using a weakened cryptosystem. All of these are valid techniques in cryptanalysis, even though they may be considered unorthodox.

Successful cryptanalysis is a combination of mathematics, inquisitiveness, intuition, persistence, powerful computing resources—and more often than many would like to admit—luck. However, successful cryptanalysis has made the enormous resources often devoted to it more than worthwhile: the breaking of the German Enigma code during WWII, for example, was one of the key factors in an early Allied victory.

Today, cryptanalysis is practiced by a broad range of organizations: governments try to break other governments' diplomatic and military transmissions; companies developing security products send them to cryptanalysts to test their security features and to a **hacker** or **cracker** to try to break the security of Web sites by finding weaknesses in the securing protocols. It is this constant battle between cryptographers trying to secure information and cryptanalysts trying to break cryptosystems that moves the entire body of cryptology knowledge forward.

crypto

Depending on its usage, crypto can be a short form for **cryptography** or for **encryption**. The term is sometimes used to broadly encompass the major aspects and issues of developing and using cryptography technologies.

cryptography

Cryptography is the science of information security. The word is derived from the Greek *kryptos*, meaning hidden. Cryptography is closely related to the disciplines of **cryptology** and **cryptanalysis**. Cryptography includes techniques such as microdots, merging words with images, and other ways to hide information in storage or transit. However, in today's computer-centric world, cryptography is most often associated with scrambling **plaintext** (ordinary text, sometimes referred to as cleartext) into **ciphertext** (a process called **encryption**), then back again (known as **decryption**). Individuals who practice this field are known as cryptographers.

Modern cryptography concerns itself with the following four objectives:

1) **Confidentiality** (the information cannot be understood by anyone for whom it was unintended)

2) **Integrity** (the information cannot be altered in storage or transit between sender and intended receiver without the alteration being detected)

3) **Non-repudiation** (the creator/sender of the information cannot deny at a later stage his or her intentions in the creation or transmission of the information)

4) **Authentication** (the sender and receiver can confirm each other's identity and the origin/destination of the information)

Procedures and **protocol**s that meet some or all of the above criteria are known as cryptosystems. Cryptosystems are often thought to refer only to mathematical procedures and computer programs; however, they also include the regulation of human behavior, such as choosing hard-to-guess passwords, logging off unused systems, and not discussing sensitive procedures with outsiders.

The origin of cryptography is usually dated from about 2000 BC, with the Egyptian practice of hieroglyphics. These consisted of complex pictograms, the full meaning of which was only known to an elite few. The first known use of a modern **cipher** was by Julius Caesar (100 BC to 44 BC), who did not trust his messengers when communicating with his governors and officers. For this reason, he created a system in which each character in his messages was replaced by a character three positions ahead of it in the Roman alphabet.

In recent times, cryptography has turned into a battleground of some of the world's best mathematicians and computer scientists. The ability to securely store and transfer sensitive information has proved a critical factor in success in war and business.

Because governments do not wish certain entities in and out of their countries to have access to ways to receive and send hidden information that may be a threat to national interests, cryptography has been subject to various restrictions in many countries, ranging from limitations of the usage and export of software to the public dissemination of mathematical concepts that could be used to develop cryptosystems. However, the Internet has allowed the spread of powerful programs and, more importantly, the underlying techniques of cryptography, so that today many of the most advanced cryptosystems and ideas are now in the public domain.

cryptology

Cryptology is the mathematics, such as number theory, and the application of formulas and **algorithm**s, that underpin **cryptography** and **cryptanalysis**. Since the cryptanalysis concepts are highly specialized and complex, we concentrate here only on some of the key mathematical concepts behind cryptography.

In order for data to be secured for storage or transmission, it must be transformed in such a manner that it would be difficult for an unauthorized individual to be able to discover its true meaning. To do this, certain mathematical equations are used, which are very difficult to solve unless certain strict criteria are met. The level of difficulty of solving a given equation is known as its *intractability*. These types of equations form the basis of cryptography.

Some of the most important are:

The Discrete Logarithm Problem: The best way to describe this problem is first to show how its inverse concept works. The following applies to Galois fields (groups). Assume we have a **prime number** P (a number that is not divisible except by 1 and itself, P). This P is a large prime number of over 300 digits. Let us now assume we have two other **integer**s, a and b. Now say we want to find the value of N, so that value is found by the following formula:

$N = a^b \bmod P$, where $0 <= N <= (P \cdot 1)$

This is known as *discrete exponentiation* and is quite simple to compute. However, the opposite is true when we invert it. If we are given P, a, and N and are required to find b so that the equation is valid, then we face a tremendous level of difficulty.

This problem forms the basis for a number of **public key infrastructure** algorithms, such as **Diffie-Hellman** and ElGamal. This problem has been studied for many years and cryptography based on it has withstood many forms of attacks.

The Integer Factorization Problem: This is simple in concept. Say that one takes two prime numbers, P2 and P1, which are both "large" (a relative term, the definition of which continues to move forward as computing power increases). We then multiply these two primes to produce the product, N. The difficulty arises when, being given

N, we try and find the original P1 and P2. The **Rivest-Shamir-Adleman** public key infrastructure encryption protocol is one of many based on this problem. To simplify matters to a great degree, the N product is the **public key** and the P1 and P2 numbers are, together, the **private key**.

This problem is one of the most fundamental of all mathematical concepts. It has been studied intensely for the past 20 years and the consensus seems to be that there is some unproven or undiscovered law of mathematics that forbids any shortcuts. That said, the mere fact that it is being studied intensely leads many others to worry that, somehow, a breakthrough may be discovered.

The Elliptic Curve Discrete Logarithm Problem: This is a new cryptographic protocol based upon a reasonably well-known mathematical problem. The properties of elliptic curves have been well known for centuries, but it is only recently that their application to the field of cryptography has been undertaken.

First, imagine a huge piece of paper on which is printed a series of vertical and horizontal lines. Each line represents an integer with the vertical lines forming x class components and horizontal lines forming the y class components. The intersection of a horizontal and vertical line gives a set of coordinates (x,y). In the highly simplified example below, we have an elliptic curve that is defined by the equation:

$y^2 + y = x^3 \cdot x^2$ (this is way too small for use in a real life application, but it will illustrate the general idea)

For the above, given a definable operator, we can determine any third point on the curve given any two other points. This definable operator forms a "group" of finite length. To add two points on an elliptic curve, we first need to understand that any straight line that passes through this curve intersects it at precisely three points. Now, say we define two of these points as u and v: we can then draw a straight line through two of these points to find another intersecting point, at w. We can then draw a vertical line through w to find the final intersecting point at x. Now, we can see that u + v = x. This rule works, when we define another imaginary point, the Origin, or O, which exists at (theoretically) extreme points on the curve. As strange as this problem may seem, it does permit for an effective encryption system, but it does have its detractors.

On the positive side, the problem appears to be quite intractable, requiring a shorter key length (thus allowing for quicker processing time) for equivalent security levels as compared to the Integer Factorization Problem and the Discrete Logarithm Problem. On the negative side, critics contend that this problem, since it has only recently begun to be implemented in cryptography, has not had the intense scrutiny of many years that is required to give it a sufficient level of trust as being secure.

This leads us to more general problem of cryptology than of the intractability of the various mathematical concepts, which is that the more time, effort, and resources that can be devoted to studying a problem, then the greater the possibility that a solution, or at least a weakness, will be found.

cryptoperiod

A cryptoperiod (sometimes called a *key lifetime* or a *validity period*) is a specific time span during which a cryptographic **key** is authorized, or for which a key setting remains in effect. A key uses an **algorithm** to create **ciphertext** from **plaintext** (ordinary unencrypted text). The cryptoperiod is decided by weighing factors such as the sensitivity of the encrypted data, the risk of key compromise, and the cost of **rekeying** (encrypting the same material with a new key). Throughout the cryptoperiod, a key can be used to verify or decrypt data. The effective use of cryptoperiods is an important part of key management.

A cryptoperiod is usually expressed as a span of calendar or clock time, but may also be expressed as a maximum volume of data to be encrypted by an algorithm for a particular key. The span of some cryptoperiods can be a number of decades since keys may sometimes be archived for a very long time.

Crystal Reports

Crystal Reports is a popular Windows-based report writer (report generation program) that allows a programmer to create reports from a variety of data sources with a minimum of written code. Developed by Seagate Software, Crystal Reports can access data from most widely-used databases and can integrate data from multiple databases within one report using Open Database Connectivity (**ODBC**).

Crystal Reports uses an **ActiveX control** called CrystalReport to establish a connection with another program. A programmer can set properties of the CrystalReport control during design time or at run time.

The programmer can use automation tools called Experts to be guided through common tasks, such as linking and embedding reports. Crystal Reports treats all text, graphics, and database fields as **object**s that a programmer can place, arrange, and format on forms. The program also generates a recordset object and code needed to perform programming tasks such as **loop**s or mathematical calculations.

Crystal Reports can create a report **on the fly** from user-defined variables and can convert it to HTML and publish it to the Web automatically.

C-sharp

See "C#"

CSS

See "cascading style sheet"

CSS1

See "Cascading Style Sheet, level 1"

CSSL1

See "Cascading Style Sheet, level 1"

CSU/DSU

A CSU/DSU (Channel Service Unit/Data Service Unit) is a hardware device about the size of an external **modem** that converts a digital data **frame** from the communications technology used on a local area network (**LAN**) into a frame appropriate to a wide-area network (WAN) and vice versa. For example, if you have a Web business from your own home and have leased a digital line (perhaps a **T-1** or fractional T-1 line) to a phone company or a **gateway** at an Internet service provider, you have a CSU/DSU at your end and the phone company or **gateway** host has a CSU/DSU at its end.

The Channel Service Unit (CSU) receives and transmits signals from and to the WAN line and provides a barrier for electrical interference from either side of the unit. The CSU can also echo **loopback** signals from the phone company for testing purposes. The Data Service Unit (DSU) manages line control, and converts input and output between **RS-232C**, RS-449, or **V.xx** frames from the LAN and the time-division multiplexed (**TDM**) DSX frames on the T-1 line. The DSU manages timing errors and signal regeneration. The DSU provides a modem-like interface between the computer as Data Terminal Equipment (**DTE**) and the CSU.

CSU/DSUs are made as separate products or are sometimes part of a T-1 WAN card. A CSU/DSU's Data Terminal Equipment interface is usually compatible with the **V.xx** and **RS-232C** or similar serial interface. Manufacturers of separate unit or integrated CSU/DSUs include Adtran, Cisco, and Memotec.

The CSU originated at AT&T as an interface to their nonswitched digital data system. The DSU provides an interface to the data terminal equipment (DTE) using a standard (EIA/CCITT) interface. It also provides testing capabilities.

CSV

See "comma-separated values file"

CTD

See "cumulative trauma disorder"

CTI

CTI (computer-telephony integration), or sometimes simply "computer telephony," is the use of computers to manage telephone calls. The term is used in describing the

computerized services of **call center**s, such as those that direct your phone call to the right department at a business you're calling. It's also sometimes used to describe the ability to use your personal computer to initiate and manage phone calls (in which case you can think of your computer as your personal call center).

CTI applications provide the ability to do one or more of the following:

- Authenticate callers. Using one of several standard methods, the telephone number of the caller can be screened against a database.

- Recognize a voice, either for authentication or for message forwarding

- Using live, recorded voice, or touch-tone entered input, determine how to process a call (for example, by forwarding it to the appropriate person or department)

- Provide interactive voice response (IVR) to callers

- Match the number of a caller with a customer record and display it for reference when talking to the caller

- Manage voice or video conferences

- Collect and display pending live calls or messages that have been left by callers

- Receive fax messages and route them to appropriate fax machines

- For outbound calling such as telemarketing, predial callers

- Based on call input, initiate a smart agent application to provide help with the caller's request

The Advanced Intelligent Network (**AIN**) is a telephone service **architecture** that separates CTI services from call switching and will make it easier to add new services. The Windows Telephony Application Program Interface (**TAPI**) and Novell's TSAPI are programming interfaces intended to make it easier to create applications that enable telephone services on a personal computer or in a local area network.

CTR

See "clickthrough rate"

cubic meter

The cubic meter, also called the meter cubed, is the unit of **volume** in the International System of Units. The symbol for cubic meters is m³. Less formally, cubic meter is sometimes abbreviated cu m.

When calculating volume, it is important to realize that volume is proportional to the cube of the linear dimension. Thus, if all linear dimensions are doubled, the volume becomes eight times (2^3) as great; if all linear dimensions are cut to $1/3$, the volume becomes $1/27$ ($(1/3)^3$) as great. A volume of 1 m³ is equal to 1,000,000 centimeters cubed (10^6 cm³)

or 1,000,000,000 millimeters cubed (10^9 mm²). In the opposite sense, 1 m³ is equal to 0.000000001 kilometer cubed (10^{-9} km³).

When converting between cubic meters and non-SI units of volume such as cubic inches (cu in) or cubic miles (cu mi), the linear-unit conversion factor must be cubed. For example, one meter is approximately 39.37 inches (39.37 in); therefore 1 m³ = 39.37^3 = 6.102×10^4 cu in (approximately). As another example, 1 meter is about 0.0006215 mile (6.215×10^{-4} mi); therefore 1 m³ = $(6.215 \times 10^{-4})^3$ = 2.401×10^{-10} cu mi (approximately).

Also see **meter**, **square meter**, and International System of Units (**SI**).

cuckoo egg

A cuckoo egg is an **MP3** file that typically contains 30 seconds of the original song with the remainder of the song overwritten with cuckoo clock noises, **white noise**, and/or voice messages such as, "Congratulations, you must've goofed up somewhere." Ideally, a cuckoo egg should have the same playing length as the music it pretends to be. The purpose of cuckoo eggs is to deter the **downloading** and sharing of MP3 files using **Napster** and similar approaches.

Typically, a Napster user downloads an MP3 file and sometimes share it with others before listening to it. Recognizing this, a cuckoo egg creator creates the cuckoo egg to look exactly like a real MP3 file. The user then unknowingly shares the cuckoo egg with other unsuspecting users spreading the cuckoo egg like a virus. Unlike a virus, cuckoo eggs do not damage computers, but simply annoy and waste the time of those who download the files.

The Cuckoo Egg Project began with Michael and Stephanie Fix. Stephanie Fix is a musician who is concerned about the illegal availability of copyrighted music through Napster. The concept centers on the idea of how a real cuckoo bird lays its eggs in another bird's nest. To the Fixes, the Napster system is like a huge nest of MP3 files, a perfect environment in which to lay cuckoo eggs

The first cuckoo egg was laid on June 10, 2000. Since then, Napster users have posted hundreds of angry messages at the Cuckoo Egg Project's Web site. Whether it's deterring them from downloading other songs has not been determined.

There is an ironic twist to the Cuckoo Egg Project. According to the official Web site's **FAQ**, cuckoo eggs are also not legal, because they also use unauthorized portions of copyrighted songs. But they claim that only a sample portion is used compared to the entire song being used with Napster, which is more defendable according to fair use laws. Anyone who creates and distributes MP3 files can create cuckoo eggs.

CUL

See "chat abbreviations"

cumulative trauma disorder

In information technology, cumulative trauma disorder (CTD) refers to any of several physical problems that can result from improper or excessive use of a computer display or terminal. Other terms for repetitive stress disorders are *repetitive stress injury (RSI)* and *repetitive motion disorder (RMD)*.

Perhaps the most well-known CTD is *carpal tunnel syndrome*. In occupations involving long hours of keyboard use over a period of years, the tissue in the wrist can become chronically inflamed and swollen. In severe cases, scarring occurs. The main nerve leading from the arm into the hand becomes pinched. The result is arthritis-like pain and stiffness in the hand and fingers. If not treated, the condition can progress until keyboard use becomes impossible. Proper hand positioning, and the use of wrist supports, can minimize the risk that a computer user will develop this syndrome.

Poor posture, caused by improper chair height, a desk that is too high or low, or a display too far below eye level, can bring about back pain and spasms. In severe cases, the condition can be disabling, and its cause can be mistaken for an organic illness such as kidney disease. Pain and stiffness may also occur in the legs, neck, and shoulders. The problem can usually be corrected by paying careful attention to **ergonomic** aspects of the computer or workstation.

Any type of close-range work over a period of years can cause nearsightedness. Poor lighting, improper display adjustment, or the use of excessively small fonts and/or graphics can result in eye strain, often attended by chronic headaches that can be mistaken for migraines.

current

Also see **voltage**, **resistance**, and **Ohm's Law**.

Current is a flow of electrical charge carriers, usually electrons or electron-deficient atoms. The common symbol for current is the uppercase letter I. The standard unit is the **ampere**, symbolized by A. One ampere of current represents one coulomb of electrical charge (6.24×10^{18} charge carriers) moving past a specific point in one second. Physicists consider current to flow from relatively positive points to relatively negative points; this is called conventional current or Franklin current. Electrons, the most common charge carriers, are negatively charged. They flow from relatively negative points to relatively positive points.

Electric current can be either direct or alternating. Direct current (**DC**) flows in the same direction at all points in time, although the instantaneous magnitude of the current might vary. In an alternating current (**AC**), the flow of charge carriers reverses direction periodically. The number of complete AC cycles per second is the **frequency**, which is measured in **hertz**. An example of pure DC is the current

produced by an electrochemical cell. The output of a power-supply rectifier, prior to filtering, is an example of pulsating DC. The output of common utility outlets is AC.

Current per unit cross-sectional area is known as *current density*. It is expressed in amperes per square meter, amperes per square centimeter, or amperes per square millimeter. Current density can also be expressed in amperes per circular mil. In general, the greater the current in a conductor, the higher the current density. However, in some situations, current density varies in different parts of an electrical conductor. A classic example is the so-called *skin effect*, in which current density is high near the outer surface of a conductor, and low near the center. This effect occurs with alternating currents at high frequencies. Another example is the current inside an active electronic component such as a field-effect transistor (**FET**).

An electric current always produces a **magnetic field**. The stronger the current, the more intense the magnetic field. A pulsating DC, or an AC, characteristically produces an **electromagnetic field**. This is the principle by which **wireless** signal propagation occurs.

curses

In C programming, curses is a collection of precompiled **routine**s stored as **object**s for text-based terminals that is used to create similarity of function. Curses probably gets its name from its purpose of providing a common user interface for terminal-specific initiation of cursor movement.

Terminals frequently use different ways to initiate particular cursor movements. For example, to make the cursor move up a line, a VT100 terminal has to send the characters "Esc," "]" and "A," while a Televideo 920C terminal has to send "CTRL-K." This could get terribly complicated if programmers had to write separate versions for every terminal. Another problem is that the same tasks would have to be redone every time a program that depended on cursor action was written. The curses library contains **function**s that a program calls to send the desired cursor action characters. The program doesn't have to contain information about the proper characters but just uses a simple-to-understand syntax (e.g.: "clear()" will clear the screen).

Curses hides the particular screen details of different terminals, who sees a display containing multiple non-overlapping windows. Window contents can be changed in a fairly straight-forward manner and the curses library will be behind the scenes, working away doing whatever is necessary to get the desired message through—with the least possible stress to the programmer.

cursor

A cursor is the position indicator on a computer **display screen** where a user can enter **text**. In an **operating system** with a graphical user interface (**GUI**), the cursor is also a visible and moving pointer that the user controls with a **mouse**, **touch pad**, or similar input device. The user uses the pointing cursor and special input buttons to establish where the position indicator cursor will be or to select a particular program to run or file to view. Typically, the pointing cursor is an arrow and the text entry position cursor is a blinking underscore or vertical bar. Most operating systems allow the user to choose another appearance for the cursor.

In the Windows operating system, the pointing cursor turns into a pointing hand when it is pointed to a specific object and into an hourglass while the system is starting a requested program.

CUSeeMe

CUseeMe is a low-cost product for Internet videoconferencing. Each user installs the CUseeMe software and, assuming they have an Internet connection, can then have person-to-person or group discussions. A "whiteboard" allows users to exchange messages and collaborate. Users can also chat online. Users with a small attached video camera (optional) can transmit their picture to other users in a conference.

Customer Information Control System

See "CICS"

customer life cycle

In customer relationship management (**CRM**), customer life cycle is a term used to describe the progression of steps a customer goes through when considering, purchasing, using, and maintaining loyalty to a product or service. Marketing analysts Jim Sterne and Matt Cutler have developed a matrix that breaks the customer life cycle into five distinct steps: reach, acquisition, conversion, retention, and loyalty. In layman's terms, this means getting a potential customer's attention, teaching them what you have to offer, turning them into a paying customer, and then keeping them as a loyal customer whose satisfaction with the product or service urges other customers to join the cycle. The customer life cycle is often depicted by an ellipse, representing the fact that customer retention truly is a cycle and the goal of effective CRM is to get the customer to move through the cycle again and again.

customer premises equipment

Customer premises equipment (CPE) is telephone or other service provider equipment that is located on the customer's premises (physical location) rather than on the provider's premises or in between. Telephone handsets, cable TV set-top boxes, and **Digital Subscriber Line** routers are examples. Historically, this term referred to equipment placed at the customer's end of the telephone line and usually owned by the telephone company. Today, almost any end-user equipment can be called customer premise equipment and it can be owned by the customer or by the provider.

Customer Proprietary Network Information

See "CPNI"

customer relationship analysis

Customer relationship analysis (CRA), sometimes termed *customer relationship analytics*, is the processing of data about customers and their relationship with the enterprise in order to improve the enterprise's future sales and service and lower cost. This term is generally a synonym for **CRM analytics**.

Customer relationship analysis can be considered a form of online analytical processing (**OLAP**) and may employ **data mining**. As Web sites have added a new and often faster way to interact with customers, the opportunity and the need to turn data collected about customers into useful information has become generally apparent. As a result, a number of software companies have developed products that do customer data analysis.

According to an article in *InfoWorld*, customer relationship analysis can provide customer segmentation groupings (for example, at its simplest, dividing customers into those most and least likely to repurchase a product); profitability analysis (which customers lead to the most profit over time); personalization (the ability to market to individual customers based on the data collected about them); event monitoring (for example, when a customer reaches a certain dollar volume of purchases); what-if scenarios (how likely is a customer or customer category that bought one product to buy a similar one); and predictive modeling (for example, comparing various product development plans in terms of likely future success given the customer knowledge base). Data collection and analysis are viewed as a continuing and iterative process and ideally over time business decisions are refined based on feedback from earlier analysis and consequent decisions.

Benefits of customer relationship analysis are said to lead not only to better and more productive customer relations in terms of sales and service but also to improvement in **supply chain management** (lower inventory and speedier delivery) and thus lower costs and more competitive pricing.

One of the major challenges implicit in customer relationship analysis is how to integrate the analytical software with existing **legacy** systems as well as with other new systems.

A new area of application and data collection has to do with Web site customer usage.

customer relationship management

CRM (customer relationship management) is an information industry term for methodologies, software, and usually Internet capabilities that help an **enterprise** manage customer relationships in an organized way. For example, an enterprise might build a **database** about its customers that described relationships in sufficient detail so that management, salespeople, people providing service, and perhaps the customer directly could access information, match customer needs with product plans and offerings, remind customers of service requirements, know what other products a customer had purchased, and so forth.

According to one industry view, CRM consists of:

- Helping an enterprise to enable its marketing departments to identify and target their best customers, manage marketing campaigns with clear goals and objectives, and generate quality leads for the sales team.

- Assisting the organization to improve telesales, account, and sales management by optimizing information shared by multiple employees, and streamlining existing processes (for example, taking orders using mobile devices).

- Allowing the formation of individualized relationships with customers, with the aim of improving customer satisfaction and maximizing profits; identifying the most profitable customers and providing them the highest level of service.

- Providing employees with the information and processes necessary to know their customers, understand their needs, and effectively build relationships between the company, its customer base, and distribution partners.

customer valuation

In customer relationship management (**CRM**), customer valuation is a scoring process used to help a company determine which customers the company should target in order to maximize profit. Customer valuation requires that the company evaluate past data to learn which customers purchased recently, which customers purchased frequently, and which customers spent the most money, in hopes that the company can forecast future purchase potential and make sure time and resources are spent only on its best customers.

To understand how customer valuation works, let's imagine there is a company that manufactures skateboards called CoolSkate. CoolSkate's sales are made primarily through Internet and print catalog sales. Through surveys and questionnaires on their Web site, CoolSkate has accumulated quite a bit of data about the buying habits, preferences, and age range of their customers. With this data, CoolSkate will devise a customer valuation scoring system that awards points based on total purchasing dollars, repeat purchases, and customer loyalty. CoolSkate can then use the information gained from the customer valuation scores to predict repeat-purchase probability as well as the probability of attrition, and target their promotions to customers who are likely to make new purchases.

Customer valuation is based upon the 80/20 rule in marketing, whereby a company spends the majority of its time working with its best customers. There are many software applications on the market to help companies determine a point system relevant to their products or services and combine aggregated data to determine customer valuation.

customer-facing

Customer-facing is an adjective used to describe a hardware or software product, technology, or anything that the customer of a business deals with directly. This can include the **user interface** of a software application, the **help desk** that a customer can phone into, any mailing or other contact that a customer receives, or policies that describe how to interact with customers (since the customer will experience the effect of these policies).

Since both customers and companies perceive value in a company's keeping track of and anticipating customer needs, customer-facing software is now sold for the purpose of **customer relationship management**.

CUT

See "Coordinated Universal Time"

cut-and-paste attack

A cut-and-paste attack is an assault on the **integrity** of a security system in which the attacker substitutes a section of **ciphertext** (encrypted text) with a different section that looks like (but is not the same as) the one removed. The substituted section appears to decrypt normally, along with the authentic sections, but results in **plaintext** (unencrypted text) that serves a particular purpose for the attacker. Essentially, the attacker cuts one or more sections from the ciphertext and reassembles these sections so that the decrypted data will result in coherent but invalid information. Cut-and-paste is a type of *message modification* attack: the attacker removes a message from network traffic, alters it, and reinserts it. This is called an *active attack*, because it involves an attempts to change information; in comparison, a *passive attack*, such as **password sniffing**, seeks information but does not itself modify the valid information, although it may be used in conjunction with an active form of attack for various purposes.

When the data modified in the attack involves critical enterprise or personal information, the cut-and-paste attack can pose a serious threat to security. A typical use for a

cut-and-paste attack is the modification of information on a customer order form for the purchase of goods or services over the Web. The attacker modifies the form so that the victim's credit card number is sent to the vendor but other information—such as the attacker's chosen delivery address and the type or quantity of goods ordered—is "pasted" into the form which the customer's valid information has been "cut." The apparently unaltered form, assembled from a "cut-and-pasted" combination of valid and invalid data, is submitted to the vendor.

CVO

See "Chief Visionary Officer"

CVS

See "Concurrent Versions System"

cyber

"Cyber" is a prefix used to describe a person, thing, or idea as part of the computer and information age. Taken from *kybernetes*, Greek for "steersman" or "governor," it was first used in **cybernetics**, a word coined by Norbert Wiener and his colleagues. Common usages include cyberculture, **cyberpunk**, and **cyberspace**.

cybercafe

A cybercafe is a cafe, coffee or espresso shop, or similar food and/or beverage-serving place that has a number of personal computers connected to the Internet and available for use by customers. Some cybercafes allow customers to use the computers at no charge; others charge by the hour or fraction of an hour. In September, 1997, there were estimated to be more than 1,000 cybercafes internationally. By 2001, there were perhaps tens of thousands, with at least one in almost every small community in many countries. In cities such as Beijing, China; Kathmandu, Nepal; and Florence, Italy, there are now chains of cybercafes.

If you travel and need access to the Internet, a cybercafe might be one solution. Call ahead and find out location and hours. If possible, reserve a computer at a certain time.

cybercitizen

The term "cybercitizen" denotes a "citizen of the Internet" or a member of the "cybercommunity."

Netizen has the same meaning.

cybercommuting

See "telecommuting"

cybernetics

Cybernetics is a word coined by group of scientists led by Norbert Wiener and made popular by Wiener's book of 1948, *Cybernetics or Control and Communication in the Animal and the Machine*. Based on the Greek "kybernetes," meaning steersman or governor, cybernetics is the science or study of control or regulation mechanisms in human and machine systems, including computers.

cyberpicketing

Cyberpicketing is the use of the Internet to protest a corporation or other institution's wages, work conditions, products, environmental policy, or other issues. The most common type of cyberpicketing is **e-mail** directed to CEOs or other influential parties. Cyberpicketing can also involve setting up and maintaining a **Web site** as a way to publicize and organize action. In some cases, cyberpicketing sites have been designed to look like and have **domain name**s similar to the Web site of the institution that is being picketed against.

cyberprise

A cyberprise is a Web-enabled enterprise. The word combines the ideas of **cyberspace** and **enterprise** so well that a company named Wall Data has trademarked it. Wall Data's Cyberprise (™) products, which include a Web server, a **database** manager for Web pages, and a Web page publisher, are aimed at allowing an enterprise to quickly get new and existing information on their public Web **site** or on an **intranet** or **extranet**.

cyberpunk

Cyberpunk is a sensibility or belief that a few outsiders, armed with their own individuality and technological capability, can fend off the tendencies of traditional institutions to use technology to control society. The term, combining "**cyber**" and punk, possibly originated in 1980 with Bruce Bethke's short story, "Cyberpunk." An editor of Isaac Asimov's Science Fiction Magazine, Gardner Dozois, is credited with associating the word with a literary movement that includes the science fiction of William Gibson and Neal Stephenson.

The alt.cyberpunk.FAQ lists several categories of groups associated with cyberpunk:

- **hacker**, who represent the best kind of cyberpunk
- **cracker**, who attempt to break into computer systems
- **phreak**, who attempt to break into telephone systems
- Cypher-punks, who attempt to break codes and foil security systems

Additional groups include "transhumans," who attempt to exploit technology to increase life expectancy and human potential and "extropians," a kind of libertarian group that believes in something called "spontaneous order." The writer of the alt.cyberpunk.FAQ indicates that some people believe cyberpunk to be (intrinsically) undefinable and that anyone claiming to be a "cyberpunk" will likely be laughed off their Usenet newsgroup.

cyberspace

Cyberspace has been defined as "the total interconnectedness of human beings through computers and telecommunication without regard to physical geography."

William Gibson is sometimes credited with inventing or popularizing the term by using it in his novel of 1984, *Neuromancer.*

cybersquatting

Cybersquatting is reserving an Internet **domain name** (often referred to as a "dot com" name) for the purpose of selling it later to a company that wants to use it. Commercial domain names (technically, you reserve a **second-level domain** name) are obtained from one of several registries, companies authorized to ensure that a domain name you want is unique (no one else already has it) and issue it to you if it is. However, these registries make no attempt to determine whether the domain name is one that rightfully ought to go to someone else. The principle is "First come, first served." For this reason, a number of enterprising individuals and companies have applied for and reserved domain names that they think someone else will want, either now or in the future. Well-known companies or their products, sports figures and other celebrities, political candidates, and others often discover that someone else has already reserved the domain name (for example, "sammysosa.com") they would most likely want to use. Although trademark laws may offer some protection, it is often cheaper to buy the domain name from the cybersquatter than it is to sue for its use.

Many cybersquatters reserve common English words, reasoning that sooner or later someone will want to use one for their Web site. Examples of words sold by cybersquatters to companies developing significant Web sites include drugstore.com, furniture.com, gardening.com, and Internet.com. eBay, the auction site, sometimes lists domain names for sale. Several cybersquatter companies offer their wares at their own Web sites.

Since there is an initial and yearly fee for owning a domain name, some cybersquatters reserve a long list of names and defer paying for them until forced to—preempting their use by others at no cost to themselves. The registry companies are working on this problem. Meanwhile, the Internet Corporation for Assigned Names and Numbers (**ICANN**),

which licenses the domain name registrars, is working on a process for resolving domain name disagreements outside of the regular court system.

The term derives from *squatting,* the practice of building some kind of home or dwelling or in some way using someone else's landed property without their permission.

cyborg

Cyborg, a compound word derived from **cybernetics** and organism, is a term coined by Manfred Clynes in 1960 to describe the need for mankind to artificially enhance biological functions in order to survive in the hostile environment of Space. Originally, a cyborg referred to a human being with bodily functions aided or controlled by technological devices, such as an oxygen tank, artificial heart valve or insulin pump. Over the years, the term has acquired a more general meaning, describing the dependence of human beings on technology. In this sense, cyborg can be used to characterize anyone who relies on a computer to complete their daily work.

cybrarian

A cybrarian (pronounced sai-BREHR-i-uhn, a compound of **cyber** and librarian) is a library and information science professional that specializes in using the Internet as a resource tool. The term has gained currency among many librarians who use the Internet. The American Library Association hosts a section called Cyberlib.net, written by Pat Sensor, author of *The Cybrarian's Manual.*

cycle time

Cycle time is the time, usually measured in **nanosecond**s, between the start of one random access memory (**RAM**) access to the time when the next access can be started. **Access time** is sometimes used as a synonym (although IBM deprecates it). Cycle time consists of **latency** (the overhead of finding the right place for the memory access and preparing to access it) and transfer time.

Cycle time should not be confused with processor *clock cycles* or **clock speed**, which have to do with the number of cycles per second (in megahertz or **MHz**) to which a processor is paced.

cycles per second

Cps (cycles per second) is the measure of how frequently an **alternating current** changes direction. This term has been replaced by the term **hertz** (Hz).

cyclic redundancy checking

Cyclic redundancy checking is a method of checking for errors in data that has been transmitted on a communications link. A sending device applies a 16- or 32-bit **polynomial** to a block of data that is to be transmitted

and appends the resulting cyclic redundancy code (CRC) to the block. The receiving end applies the same polynomial to the data and compares its result with the result appended by the sender. If they agree, the data has been received successfully. If not, the sender can be notified to resend the block of data.

The **ITU-TS** (CCITT) has a standard for a 16-bit polynomial to be used to obtain the cyclic redundancy code (CRC) that is appended. IBM's **Synchronous Data Link Control** and other protocols use CRC-16, another 16-bit polynomial. A 16-bit cyclic redundancy code detects all single and double-bit errors and ensures detection of 99.998% of all possible errors. This level of detection assurance is considered sufficient for data transmission blocks of 4 kilobytes or less. For larger transmissions, a 32-bit CRC is used. The **Ethernet** and **token ring** local area network protocols both used a 32-bit CRC.

A less complicated but less capable error detection method is the **checksum** method. See **modem error-correcting protocols** for a list of protocols that use either of these methods.

Cyrix

Cyrix (pronounced SYE-rihks) was a line of low-cost microprocessors intended for personal computers and information appliances that competed, along with **AMD** and **Intel**, for the low-cost **microprocessor** market. Acquired by VIA Technologies, a Taiwan supplier of chipsets and processors, the Cyrix technology continues to be offered in the VIA Cyrix MII processor. VIA also offers is own VIA C3 processor.

DAC

See "digital-to-analog conversion"

daemon

A daemon (pronounced DEE-muhn) is a program that runs continuously and exists for the purpose of handling periodic service requests that a computer system expects to receive. The daemon program forwards the requests to other programs (or processes) as appropriate. Each server of pages on the Web has an *HTTPD* or **Hypertext Transfer Protocol** daemon that continually waits for requests to come in from Web clients and their users.

In mythology, a daemon, according to Webster's, was "an attendant power or spirit."

Daemon can be confused with **demon**, which has a different but similar meaning. *The New Hacker's Dictionary* says that a daemon is a program that runs by itself directly under the operating system whereas a demon is part of a larger application program.

DAML

DAML (DARPA Agent Markup Language) is a **markup** language for the U.S. Defense Advanced Research Project Agency (**DARPA**) that is based on the Extensible Markup Language (**XML**). DAML is designed to have a greater capacity than XML for describing objects and the relationships between objects, to express **semantics**, and to create a higher level of **interoperability** among Web sites. As the central research and development agency for the U. S. Department of Defense, DARPA was instrumental in the creation of the **Internet** and many of its technologies. DARPA is developing DAML as a technology with intelligence built into the language through the behaviors of **agent**s, programs that can dynamically identify and comprehend sources of information, and interact with other agents in an autonomous fashion.

DAML agents can be embedded in code and maintain awareness of their environment, are user-directed, but have the capacity to behave autonomously. They also have the capacity to "learn" from experience, so that they improve their behavior over time. DAML uses a number of different types of agents (such as *information agents*, *event monitoring agents*, and *secure agents*) for different purposes. DAML's semantic knowledge and autonomous behavior is expected to make it capable of processing large volumes of data much as a human being would process it. DAML includes a type of **query** language with a specialized ability to find and process relevant information—for example, finding related information on separate Web sites and processing it into a comprehensive report.

D-AMPS

D-AMPS is now called **Time Division Multiple Access/ IS-136**.

D-AMPS (Digital-Advanced Mobile Phone Service), sometimes spelled DAMPS, is a **digital** version of AMPS (**Advanced Mobile Phone Service**), the original **analog** standard for **cellular telephone** phone service in the U.S. Both D-AMPS and AMPS are now used in many countries. D-AMPS adds time division multiple access (**TDMA**) to AMPS to get three channels for each AMPS channel, tripling the number of calls that can be handled on a channel. D-AMPS is Interim Standard-136 from the Electronics Industries Assocation/Telecommunication Industries Assocation (EIA/TIA).

Like AMPS, D-AMPS uses frequency ranges within the 800 and 900 megahertz (**MHz**) **electromagnetic radiation spectrum**. Each service provider can use half of the 824-849 MHz range for receiving signals from cellular phones and half the 869-894 MHz range for transmitting to cellular phones. The bands are divided into 30 **kHz** sub-bands, called *channels*. The receiving channels are called *reverse channels* and the sending channels are called *forward channels*. The division of the spectrum into sub-band channels is achieved by using frequency division multiple access (**FDMA**). The time division multiple access processing (TDMA) is added to each sub-band channel created with FDMA to triple the number of channels available.

Although AMPS and D-AMPS originated for the North American cellular telephone market, they are now used worldwide with over 74 million subscribers, according to Ericsson, one of the major cellular phone manufacturers. D-AMPS is one of three digital wireless technologies that use TDMA. The other two are **GSM** and *PDC*. Each of these technologies interprets TDMA differently so they are not compatible. An advantage of D-AMPS is that it is easier to upgrade to from an existing analog AMPS network. An alternative to D-AMPS and the other two TDMA technologies is direct sequence code division multiple access (**CDMA**).

DAO

DAO (Data Access Objects) is an application program interface (**API**) available with Microsoft's Visual Basic that lets a programmer request access to a Microsoft Access **database**. DAO was Microsoft's first object-oriented interface with databases. DAO objects **encapsulate** Access's Jet functions. Through Jet functions, it can also access other Structured Query Language (**SQL**) databases.

To conform with Microsoft's vision of a Universal Data Access (**UDA**) model, programmers are being encouraged to move from DAO , although still widely used, to ActiveX Data Objects (**ADO**) and its low-level interface with databases, **OLE DB**. ADO and OLE DB offer a faster interface that is also easier to program.

dark fiber

Dark fiber is **optical fiber** infrastructure (cabling and **repeater**s) that is currently in place but is not being used. Optical fiber conveys information in the form of light pulses so the "dark" means no light pulses are being sent. For example, some electric utilities have installed optical fiber cable where they already have power lines installed in the expectation that they can lease the infrastructure to telephone or cable TV companies or use it to interconnect their own offices. To the extent that these installations are unused, they are described as dark.

"Dark fiber service" is service provided by local exchange carriers (**LECs**) for the maintenance of optical fiber transmission capacity between customer locations in which the light for the fiber is provided by the customer rather than the LEC.

DARPA Agent Markup Language

See "DAML"

DARPA

DARPA (Defense Advanced Research Projects Agency) is the independent research branch of the U.S. Department of Defense that, among its other accomplishments, was the funder of a project that in time was to lead to the creation of the **Internet**. Originally called ARPA (the "D" was added to its name later), DARPA came into being in 1958 as a reaction to the success of Sputnik, Russia's first manned satellite. DARPA's explicit mission was (and still is) to think independently of the rest of the military and to respond quickly and innovatively to national defense challenges.

In the late 1960s, DARPA provided funds and oversight for a project aimed at interconnecting computers at four university research sites. By 1972, this initial network, now called the ARPAnet, had grown to 37 computers. ARPANet and the technologies that went into it, including the evolving Internet Protocol (**IP**) and the Transmission Control Protocol (**TCP**), led to the Internet that we know today.

DARPANet

DARPANet originated in 1969 when the Defense Advanced Research Projects Agency, a part of the U.S. Defense Department, recognized a need for an efficient way to exchange military information between scientists and researchers based in different geographic locations.

DARPANet originally consisted of a four-computer network. By 1972, it had grown to a network of 37 computers and was renamed **ARPANet**. ARPANet led to today's **Internet**.

DASD

DASD, pronounced DAZ-dee (direct access storage device), is a general term for magnetic disk **storage** devices that have historically been used in the **mainframe** and **minicomputer** (mid-range computer) environments. When used, it may also include **hard disk** drives for personal computers. A recent form of DASD is the *redundant array of independent disks* (**RAID**).

The "direct access" means that all data can be accessed directly in about the same amount of time rather than having to progress sequentially through the data.

DAT

DAT (Digital Audio Tape) is a standard medium and technology for the **digital** recording of **audio** on tape at a professional level of quality. A DAT drive is a digital tape recorder with rotating heads similar to those found in a video deck. Most DAT drives can record at **sample rate**s of 44.1 **KHz**, the CD audio standard, and 48 KHz. DAT has become the standard archiving technology in professional and semi-professional recording environments for master recordings. Digital inputs and outputs on professional DAT decks allow the user to transfer recordings from the DAT tape to an audio workstation for precise editing. The compact size and low cost of the DAT medium makes it an excellent way to compile the recordings that are going to be used to create a CD master.

As an archiving medium, DAT is an alternative to consider along with:

- Digital Data Storage (DDS1 through DDS3)
- Optical disk
- VHS tape

data

1) In computing, data is **information** that has been translated into a form that is more convenient to move or process. Relative to today's **computer**s and transmission media, data is information converted into **binary digital** form.

2) In computer component interconnection and network communication, data is often distinguished from "control information," "control bits," and similar terms to identify the main content of a transmission unit.

3) In telecommunications, data sometimes means **digital**-encoded information to distinguish it from **analog**-encoded information such as conventional telephone voice calls. In general, "analog" or voice transmission requires a dedicated continual connection for the duration of a related series of

transmissions. Data transmission can often be sent with intermittent connections in **packet**s that arrive in piecemeal fashion.

4) Generally and in science, data is a gathered body of facts.

Some authorities and publishers, cognizant of the word's Latin origin and as the plural form of "datum," use plural verb forms with "data." Others take the view that since "datum" is rarely used, it is more natural to treat "data" as a singular form.

Data Access Arrangement

A Data Access Arrangement (DAA) is an electronic interface within a computer and its **modem** to a public telephone line. A DAA is also sometimes called a Telephone Line Interface Circuit (or Module). DAAs are required in any device that attaches to the public switched telephone network (**PSTN**), including **fax** machines, **private branch exchange**, **set-top box**, and alarm systems. Among other things, the DAA isolates the electronic device from the higher voltage on the telephone line. DAA circuitry requires registration with the telephone system governing authority (such as the Federal Communications Commission in the U. S.). However, most manufacturers of modems and other devices build an already-approved DAA design into the modem.

A Data Access Arrangement can be built into a computer's motherboard but is more commonly built into the modem.

Data Access Objects

See "DAO"

data aggregation

Data aggregation is any process in which information is gathered and expressed in a summary form, for purposes such as statistical analysis. For example, the Web site of a music club might collect aggregate data about music searches, and analyze the resultant data to inform the music club owners about the most frequently requested artists and CDs. A common aggregation purpose is to get more information about particular groups, based on any specific variables, such as age, profession, or income. The information about such groups can then be used for Web site **personalization**, to choose content and advertising likely to appeal to an individual belonging to one or more groups for which data has been collected. For example, a music club might advertise certain music based on the age of the user and the data aggregate for their age group. Online analytic processing (**OLAP**) is a simple type of data aggregation in which the marketer uses an online reporting mechanism to process the information.

Data aggregation can be user-based: Personal data aggregation services offer the user a single point for collection of their personal information from other Web sites. The customer uses a single master personal identification

number (PIN) to give them access to their various accounts (such as those for financial institutions, airlines, book and music clubs, and so on). Performing this type of data aggregation is sometimes referred to as "screen scraping."

data analysis

See "data mining"

data availability

Data availability is a term used by some computer **storage** manufacturers and storage service providers (**SSP**s) to describe products and services that ensure that data continues to be available at a required level of performance in situations ranging from normal through "disastrous." In general, data availability is achieved through **redundancy** involving where the data is stored and how it can be reached. Some vendors describe the need to have a **data center** and a *storage-centric* rather than a *server-centric* philosophy and environment.

In large **enterprise** computer systems, computers typically access data over high-speed **optical fiber** connection to storage devices. Among the best-known systems for access are **ESCON** and **Fibre Channel**. Storage devices often are controlled as a redundant array of independent disks (**RAID**). Flexibility for adding and reconfiguring a storage system as well as automatically switching to a backup or failover environment is provided by a programmable or manually-controlled switch generally known as a *director*.

Two increasingly popular approaches to providing data availability are the storage area network (**SAN**) and network-attached storage (**NAS**). Data availability can be measured in terms of how often the data is available (one vendor promises 99.999% availability) and how much data can flow at a time (the same vendor promises 3200 megabytes per second).

data center

1) A data center is a centralized repository for the storage, management, and dissemination of data and information organized around a particular area or body of knowledge. For example, the National Climatic Data Center (NCDC) maintains the world's largest archive of weather information. Web site visitors can link to information about weather-related research or the forecast for a specific area. The NCDC responds to requests for weather data from all over the world.

2) A data center (sometimes spelled *datacenter*)—see also **hosting** and **application service provider**—is a specialized facility that houses Web sites and provides data serving and other services for other companies.

This kind of data center may contain a network operations center (NOC), which is a restricted access area containing automated systems that constantly monitor server activity,

Web traffic, and network performance and report even very slight irregularities to engineers so that they can spot potential problems before they happen.

3) In a company, data center is a term sometimes used to describe the central data processing facility and/or the group of people who manage the companies' data processing and networks.

Data Communication Equipment

See "DCE"

data dictionary

A data dictionary is a collection of descriptions of the **data** objects or items in a **data model** for the benefit of programmers and others who need to refer to them. A first step in analyzing a system of **object**s with which users interact is to identify each object and its relationship to other objects. This process is called data modeling and results in a picture of object relationships. After each data object or item is given a descriptive name, its relationship is described (or it becomes part of some structure that implicitly describes relationship), the type of data (such as text or image or binary value) is described, possible predefined values are listed, and a brief textual description is provided. This collection can be organized for reference into a book called a data dictionary.

When developing programs that use the data model, a data dictionary can be consulted to understand where a data item fits in the structure, what values it may contain, and basically what the data item means in real-world terms. For example, a bank or group of banks could model the data objects involved in consumer banking. They could then provide a data dictionary for a bank's programmers. The data dictionary would describe each of the data items in its data model for consumer banking (for example, "Account holder" and "Available credit").

Data Encryption Standard

Data Encryption Standard (DES) is a widely-used method of data **encryption** using a private (secret) key that was judged so difficult to break by the U.S. government that it was restricted for exportation to other countries. There are 72,000,000,000,000,000 (72 quadrillion) or more possible encryption keys that can be used. For each given message, the **key** is chosen at random from among this enormous number of keys. Like other private key cryptographic methods, both the sender and the receiver must know and use the same **private key**.

DES applies a 56-bit key to each 64-bit block of data. The process can run in several modes and involves 16 rounds or operations. Although this is considered "strong" encryption, many companies use "triple DES", which applies three keys in succession. This is not to say that a DES-encrypted message cannot be "broken." Early in 1997,

Rivest-Shamir-Adleman, owners of another encryption approach, offered a $10,000 reward for breaking a DES message. A cooperative effort on the Internet of over 14,000 computer users trying out various keys finally deciphered the message, discovering the key after running through only 18 quadrillion of the 72 quadrillion possible keys! Few messages sent today with DES encryption are likely to be subject to this kind of code-breaking effort.

DES originated at IBM in 1977 and was adopted by the U.S. Department of Defense. It is specified in the **ANSI** X3.92 and X3.106 standards and in the Federal **FIPS** 46 and 81 standards. Concerned that the encryption algorithm could be used by unfriendly governments, the U.S. government has prevented export of the encryption software. However, free versions of the software are widely available on bulletin board services and Web sites. Since there is some concern that the encryption algorithm will remain relatively unbreakable, **NIST** has indicated DES will not be recertified as a standard and a replacement has been selected. The new standard, known as the Advanced Encryption Standard (AES), uses the **Rijndael** algorithm.

data hiding

Data hiding is a characteristic of **object-oriented programming**. Because an **object** can only be associated with data in predefined classes or templates, the object can only "know" about the data it needs to know about. There is no possibility that someone maintaining the code may inadvertently point to or otherwise access the wrong data unintentionally. Thus, all data not required by an object can be said to be "hidden."

data integrity

See "integrity"

data key

In **cryptography**, a data key is a **key** (a variable value that is applied to a string or block of text to encrypt or decrypt it) that is used to encrypt or decrypt **data** only and is not used to encrypt or decrypt other keys, as some encryption formulas call for.

Another type of data key is an actual physical object, capable of storing digital information, that is used to store information and required to gain access to the data. An associated program and a mechanism called a *key analyser* enable the data to be processed by a computer. Some crypto systems require the combined use of a number of data keys belonging to separate individuals, so that **data integrity** is not reliant upon the trustworthiness of a single person.

data link control

DLC also is an abbreviation for **digital loop carrier**.

DLC (data link control) is the service provided by the **Data Link layer** of function defined in the Open Systems Interconnection (**OSI**) model for network communication. The Data Link layer is responsible for providing reliable data transfer across one physical link (or telecommunications path) within the network. Some of its primary functions include defining **frame**s, performing error detection or **ECC** on those frames, and performing **flow control** (to prevent a fast sender from overwhelming a slow receiver).

Many point-to-point protocols exist at the Data Link layer including High-level Data Link Control (**HDLC**), Synchronous Data Link Control (**SDLC**), Link Access Procedure Balanced (LAPB), and Advanced Data Communications Control Procedure (ADCCP). All of these protocols are very similar in nature and are found in older networks (such as **X.25** networks). In the Internet, one of two point-to-point protocols are used at this layer: Serial Line Internet Protocol (**SLIP**) or Point-to-Point Protocol (**PPP**) with PPP being the newer, approved standard. All of these protocols are used in point-to-point connections such as those on metropolitan area network (**MAN**) or wide area network (**WAN**) **backbone**s or when we dial our Internet service provider (**ISP**) from home using a modem.

In local area networks (**LAN**s) where connections are multipoint rather than point-to-point and require more line-sharing management, the Data Link layer is divided into two sublayers: the **Logical Link Control layer** and the **Media Access Control layer**. The Logical Link Control layer protocol performs many of the same functions as the point-to-point data link control protocols described above. The Media Access Control (MAC) layer protocols support methods of sharing the line among a number of computers. Among the most widely used MAC protocols are **Ethernet** (IEEE 802.3), Token Bus (IEEE 802.4), and **Token Ring** (IEEE 802.5) and their derivatives.

data mart

A data mart is a repository of data gathered from operational data and other sources that is designed to serve a particular community of knowledge workers. In scope, the data may derive from an **enterprise**-wide database or **data warehouse** or be more specialized. The emphasis of a data mart is on meeting the specific demands of a particular group of knowledge users in terms of analysis, content, presentation, and ease-of-use. Users of a data mart can expect to have data presented in terms that are familiar.

In practice, the terms *data mart* and *data warehouse* each tend to imply the presence of the other in some form. However, most writers using the term seem to agree that the design of a data mart tends to start from an analysis of user needs and that a data warehouse tends to start from an analysis of what data already exists and how it can be collected in such a way

that the data can later be used. A data warehouse is a central aggregation of data (which can be distributed physically); a data mart is a data repository that may derive from a data warehouse or not and that emphasizes ease of access and usability for a particular designed purpose. In general, a data warehouse tends to be a strategic but somewhat unfinished concept; a data mart tends to be tactical and aimed at meeting an immediate need.

One writer, Marc Demerest, suggests combining the ideas into a Universal Data Architecture (UDA). In practice, many products and companies offering data warehouse services also tend to offer data mart capabilities or services.

data mining

Data mining is the analysis of data for relationships that have not previously been discovered. For example, the sales records for a particular brand of tennis racket might, if sufficiently analyzed and related to other market data, reveal a seasonal correlation with the purchase by the same parties of golf equipment.

Data mining results include:

- Associations, or when one event can be correlated to another event (beer purchasers buy peanuts a certain percentage of the time)

- Sequences, or one event leading to another later event (a rug purchase followed by a purchase of curtains)

- Classification, or the recognition of patterns and a resulting new organization of data (for example, profiles of customers who make purchases)

- Clustering, or finding and visualizing groups of facts not previously known

- Forecasting, or simply discovering patterns in the data that can lead to predictions about the future

The **data warehouse** concept is gaining acceptance in part because of the possibility of fruitful data mining.

data modeling

Also see: Unified Modeling Language (**UML**).

Data modeling is the analysis of data objects that are used in a business or other context and the identification of the relationships among these data objects. Data modeling is a first step in doing **object-oriented programming**. As a result of data modeling, you can then define the **class**es that provide the templates for program **object**s.

A simple approach to creating a data model that allows you to visualize the model is to draw a square (or any other symbol) to represent each individual data item that you know about (for example, a product or a product price) and then to express relationships between each of these data items with words such as "is part of" or "is used by" or "uses" and so forth. From such a total description, you can create a set of **class**es and subclasses that define all the

general relationships. These then become the templates for objects that, when executed as a program, handle the variables of new transactions and other activities in a way that effectively represents the real world.

Several differing approaches or methodologies to data modeling and its notation have recently been combined into the Unified Modeling Language (**UML**), which is expected to become a standard modeling language.

Data Over Cable Systems Interface

See "DOCSIS"

data set

In an IBM mainframe **operating system**, a data set is a named collection of data that contains individual data units organized (formatted) in a specific, IBM-prescribed way and accessed by a specific **access method** that is based on the data set organization. Types of data set organization include sequential, relative sequential, indexed sequential, and partitioned. Access methods include the Virtual Sequential Access Method (**VSAM**) and the Indexed Sequential Access Method (**ISAM**).

A data set corresponds to the concept of a **file** in other operating systems such as Linux and Windows 2000. *Data set organization* and *file format* are terms that have a close correspondence. A data set generally contains a collection of business data (names, salaries, sale figures, and so forth) whereas a file can contain many types of data (graphic images, audio data, video data, and so forth). For business data, the **database** is a newer alternative to the data set and the file.

A data set is also an older and now **deprecated** term for **modem**.

Data Space Transfer Protocol

See "DSTP"

Data Terminal Equipment

See "DTE"

data transfer rate

A data transfer rate (or often just *data rate*) is the amount of **digital data** that is moved from one place to another in a given time, usually in a second's time. The data transfer rate can be viewed as **the speed of** travel of a given amount of data from one place to another. In general, the greater the **bandwidth** of a given path, the higher the data transfer rate.

In telecommunications, data transfer is usually measured in bits per second. For example, a typical low-speed connection to the Internet may be 33.6 **kilobit**s per second (Kbps). On **Ethernet** local area networks, data transfer can be as fast as 10 **megabit**s per second. Network **switch**es are planned that

will transfer data in the **terabit** range. In earlier telecommunication systems, data transfer was sometimes measured in characters or blocks (of a certain size) per second.

In computers, data transfer is often measured in **byte**s per second.

data type

A data type in a programming language is a set of **data** with values having predefined characteristics. Examples of data types are: integer, **floating point unit** number, **character**, string, and pointer. Usually, a limited number of such data types come built into a language. The language usually specifies the range of values for a given data type, how the values are processed by the computer, and how they are stored.

With **object-oriented programming**, a programmer can create new data types to meet application needs. Such an exercise as known as "data abstraction" and the result is a new **class** of data. Such a class can draw upon the "built-in" data types such as number integers and characters. For example, a class could be created that would abstract the characteristics of a purchase order. The purchase order data type would contain the more basic data types of numbers and characters and could also include other **objects** defined by another class. The purchase order data type would have all of the inherent services that a programming language provided to its built-in data types.

Languages that leave little room for programmers to define their own data types are said to be **strongly-typed** languages.

data warehouse

A data warehouse is a central repository for all or significant parts of the data that an enterprise's various business systems collect. The term was coined by W. H. Inmon. IBM sometimes uses the term "information warehouse." Typically, a data warehouse is housed on an enterprise **mainframe** server. Data from various online transaction processing (**OLTP**) applications and other sources is selectively extracted and organized on the data warehouse **database** for use by analytical applications and user queries. Data warehousing emphasizes the capture of data from diverse sources for useful analysis and access, but does not generally start from the point-of-view of the end user or knowledge worker who may need access to specialized, sometimes local databases. The latter idea is known as the **data mart**.

Data mining and a **decision support system** (DSS) are two of the kinds of applications that can make use of a data warehouse.

database

A database is a collection of **data** that is organized so that its contents can easily be accessed, managed, and updated. The most prevalent type of database is the **relational database**, a tabular database in which data is defined so that it can be reorganized and accessed in a number of different ways. A distributed database is one that can be dispersed or replicated among different points in a network. An **object-oriented programming** database is one that is congruent with the data defined in object classes and subclasses.

Databases contain aggregations of data records or files, such as sales transactions, product catalogs and inventories, and customer profiles. Typically, a database manager provides users the capabilities of controlling read/write access, specifying report generation, and analyzing usage. Databases and database managers are prevalent in large **mainframe** systems, but are also present in smaller distributed **workstation** and mid-range systems such as the AS/400 and on personal computers. **Structured Query Language** is a standard language for making interactive queries from and updating a database such as IBM's DB2, Microsoft's Access, and database products from Oracle, Sybase, and Computer Associates.

database administrator

DBA is also an abbreviation for *doing business as*—a term sometimes used in business and legal writing.

A database administrator (DBA) directs or performs all activities related to maintaining a successful **database** environment. Responsibilities include designing, implementing, and maintaining the database system; establishing policies and procedures pertaining to the management, security, maintenance, and use of the **database management system**; and training employees in database management and use. A DBA is expected to stay abreast of emerging technologies and new design approaches. Typically, a DBA has either a degree in Computer Science and some on-the-job training with a particular database product or more extensive experience with a range of database products. A DBA is usually expected to have experience with one or more of the major database management products, such as **DB2**, **SAP**, or Oracle-based database management software.

database management system

A database management system (DBMS), sometimes just called a *database manager*, is a program that lets one or more computer users create and access **data** in a **database**. The DBMS manages user requests (and requests from other programs) so that users and other programs are free from having to understand where the data is physically located on storage media and, in a multi-user system, who else may also be accessing the data. In handling user requests, the DBMS ensures the *integrity* of the data (that is, making sure it continues to be accessible and is consistently organized as

intended) and *security* (making sure only those with access privileges can access the data). The most typical DBMS is a relational database management system (**RDBMS**). A standard user and program interface is the Structured Query Language (**SQL**). A newer kind of DBMS is the object-oriented database management system (**ODBMS**).

A DBMS can be thought of as a *file manager* that manages data in databases rather than **files** in **file systems**. In IBM's **mainframe operating system**s, the nonrelational data managers were (and are, because these **legacy application** systems are still used) known as *access methods*.

A DBMS is usually an inherent part of a database product. On PCs, Microsoft Access is a popular example of a single- or small-group user DBMS. Microsoft's **SQL Server** is an example of a DBMS that serves database requests from multiple (**client**) users. Other popular DBMSs (these are all RDBMSs, by the way) are IBM's **DB2**, **Oracle**'s line of database management products, and **Sybase**'s products.

IBM's Information Management System (IMS) was one of the first DBMSs. A DBMS may be used by or combined with **transaction** managers, such as IBM's Customer Information Control System (**CICS**).

datagram

A datagram is, to quote the Internet's Request for Comments 1594, "a self-contained, independent entity of data carrying sufficient information to be routed from the source to the destination computer without reliance on earlier exchanges between this source and destination computer and the transporting network."

The term has been generally replaced by the term **packet**. Datagrams or packets are the message units that the **Internet Protocol** deals with and that the Internet transports. A datagram or packet needs to be self-contained without reliance on earlier exchanges because there is no connection of fixed duration between the two communicating points as there is, for example, in most voice telephone conversations. (This kind of protocol is referred to as *connectionless*.)

Data-Link layer

The Data-Link layer is the **protocol layer** in a program that handles the moving of data in and out across a physical link in a network. The Data-Link layer is layer 2 in the Open Systems Interconnection (**OSI**) model for a set of telecommunication protocols.

The Data-Link layer contains two sublayers that are described in the IEEE-802 LAN standards:

- Media Access Control (MAC)
- Logical Link Control (LLC)

The Data-Link layer ensures that an initial connection has been set up, divides output data into data frames, and handles the acknowledgements from a receiver that the data arrived successfully. It also ensures that incoming data has been received successfully by analyzing bit patterns at special places in the frames.

daughterboard

A daughterboard (or *daughter board*, *daughter card*, or *daughtercard*) is a circuit board that plugs into and extends the circuitry of another circuit board. The other circuit board may be the computer's main board (its **motherboard**) or it may be another board or card that is already in the computer, often a sound card. The term is commonly used by manufacturers of **wavetable** daughterboards that attach to existing sound cards.

A **mezzanine** card is a kind of daughterboard that is installed in the same plane as but on a second level above the motherboard.

DAW

See "digital audio workstation"

dB

See "decibel"

DB2

IBM's DB2 is a relational database management system (**RDBMS**) for large business computers that, according to IBM, leads in terms of database market share and performance. Although DB2 products are offered for **UNIX**-based systems and personal computer operating systems, DB2 trails **Oracle**'s database products in UNIX-based systems and Microsoft's Access in Windows systems.

In addition to its offerings for the **mainframe OS/390** and **VM** operating systems and its mid-range **AS/400** systems, IBM offers DB2 products for a cross-**platform** spectrum that includes UNIX-based **Linux**, **HP-UX**, Sun **Solaris**, and SCO UnixWare; and for its personal computer **OS/2** operating system as well as for Microsoft's **Windows 2000** and earlier systems. DB2 databases can be accessed from any application program by using Microsoft's Open Database Connectivity (**ODBC**) interface, the Java Database Connectivity (**JDBC**) interface, or a **CORBA** interface broker.

DBA

See "database administrator"

DBMS

See "database management system"

DC

See also **Ohm's Law**.

DC (direct current) is the unidirectional flow or movement of electric charge carriers, usually **electrons**. The intensity of the **current** can vary with time, but the general direction of movement stays the same at all times. As an adjective, the term DC is used in reference to **voltage** whose polarity never reverses.

In a DC circuit, electrons emerge from the negative, or minus, pole and move towards the positive, or plus, pole. Nevertheless, physicists define DC as traveling from plus to minus.

Direct current is produced by electrochemical and photovoltaic cells and batteries. In contrast, the electricity available from utility mains in most countries is **AC** (alternating current). Utility AC can be converted to DC by means of a power supply consisting of a transformer, a rectifier (which prevents the flow of current from reversing), and a filter (which eliminates current pulsations in the output of the rectifier).

Virtually all electronic and computer hardware needs DC to function. Most solid-state equipment requires between 1.5 and 13.5 volts. Current demands can range from practically zero for an electronic wristwatch to more than 100 amperes for a radio communications power amplifier. Equipment using vacuum tubes, such as a high-power radio or television broadcast transmitter or a **CRT** (cathode-ray tube) display, require from about 150 volts to several thousand volts DC.

DCE

1) In network computing, DCE (Distributed Computing Environment) is an industry-standard software technology for setting up and managing computing and data exchange in a system of distributed computers. DCE is typically used in a larger network of computing systems that include different size servers scattered geographically. DCE uses the **client/server** model. Using DCE, application users can use applications and data at remote servers. Application programmers need not be aware of where their programs will run or where the data will be located.

Much of DCE setup requires the preparation of distributed directories so that DCE applications and related data can be located when they are being used. DCE includes security support and some implementations provide support for access to popular databases such as IBM's CICS, IMS, and DB2 databases.

DCE was developed by the Open Software Foundation (**OSF**) using software technologies contributed by some of its member companies.

2) In computer data transmission, DCE (Data Communication Equipment) is the **RS-232C** interface that a **modem** or other **serial** device uses in exchanging data with the

computer. For further information about the DCE interface and its relationship to the Data Terminal Equipment (DTE) interface, see **RS-232C**.

D-channel

In the Integrated Services Digital Network (**ISDN**), the D-channel is the channel that carries control and signalling information. (The "D" stands for "delta" channel.) The **B-channel** ("B" for "bearer") carries the main data.

In ISDN, there are two levels of service: the Basic Rate Interface, intended for the home and small enterprise, and the Primary Rate Interface, for larger users. Both rates include a number of B- (bearer) channels and a D- (delta) channel. The B-channels carry data, voice, and other services. The D-channel carries control and signaling information.

The Basic Rate Interface consists of two 64 **Kbps** B-channels and one 16 Kbps D-channel. Thus, a Basic Rate Interface user can have up to 128 Kbps service. The Primary Rate Interface consists of 23 B-channels and one 64 Kpbs D channel in the United States or 30 B-channels and 1 D-channel in Europe.

DCIT

DCIT (Digital Compression of Increased Transmission) is an approach to compressing information that compresses the entire transmission rather than just all or some part of the content. It can be applied on both wire and wireless media. It uses novel coding and modulation techniques devised at the Stevens Institute of Technology in Hoboken, New Jersey.

According to *IEEE Spectrum*, if equipment at home and the phone company's central office used DCIT, existing copper wiring could deliver 3.2 **Mbps** in one direction and 8 to 16 Mbps in the other with a small amount of **bandwidth** available for **analog** voice transmission.

DCOM

DCOM (Distributed Component Object Model) is a set of Microsoft concepts and program interfaces in which **client** program **object**s can request services from **server** program objects on other computers in a network. DCOM is based on the **Component Object Model** (COM), which provides a set of interfaces allowing clients and servers to communicate within the same computer (that is running Windows 95 or a later version).

For example, you can create a page for a Web site that contains a script or program that can be processed (before being sent to a requesting user) not on the Web site server but on another, more specialized server in the network. Using DCOM interfaces, the Web server site program (now acting as a client **object**) can forward a Remote Procedure Call (**RPC**) to the specialized server object, which provides the necessary processing and returns the result to the Web server site. It passes the result on to the Web page viewer.

DCOM can also work on a network within an enterprise or on other networks besides the public Internet. It uses **TCP/IP** and **Hypertext Transfer Protocol**. DCOM comes as part of the Windows operating systems. DCOM is or soon will be available on all major UNIX platforms and on IBM's large server products. DCOM replaces OLE Remote Automation.

DCOM is generally equivalent to the Common Object Request Broker Architecture (**CORBA**) in terms of providing a set of distributed services. DCOM is Microsoft's approach to a network-wide environment for program and data objects. CORBA is sponsored by the rest of the information technology industry under the auspices of the Object Management Group (**OMG**).

DDCD

See "Double-Density Compact Disk"

DDE

See "Dynamic Data Exchange"

DDK

See "driver development kit"

DDoS attack

See "distributed denial-of-service attack"

DDR SDRAM

DDR SDRAM (double data rate SDRAM) is synchronous dynamic RAM (**SDRAM**) that can theoretically improve **memory** clock speed to at least 200 **MHz***. It activates output on both the rising and falling edge of the system clock rather than on just the rising edge, potentially doubling output. It's expected that a number of **Socket 7 chipset** makers will support this form of **SDRAM**.

*Synchronous DRAM speed is measured in MHz rather than **nanosecond**s. You can convert the RAM clock speed to nanoseconds by dividing the chip speed into 1 billion ns (which is one second). For example, an 83 MHz RAM would be equivalent to 12 ns.

DDS

See "Digital Data Storage"

DDS-1 – DDS-2 – DDS-3 – DDS-4

See "Digital Data Storage"

dead media

In 1995, science-fiction writer Bruce Sterling challenged a conference of computer artists and the world at large to help identify the extinct species in the new media taxonomy and face the fact that, for each new medium or technology that

survives, dozens fall by the wayside. Sterling insisted that it's important to recognize, pay homage to, and ponder the "dead media" that seem, once fallen, to pass so quickly from the scene. As a result of Sterling's challenge, fellow enthusiasts have begun to chronicle artifacts of information technology going back to earliest times. Among the inventions cataloged as part of the Dead Media Project are:

- "Primitive" (but not considered so at the time) stone-carvings, bead and knitted mnemonic and historical recordings, stone formations, drum signals, shouting networks, alpenhorns, whistling networks, and town criers

- Early postal systems such as Thurn and Taxis and the U.S. Pony Express

- Many systems of optical telegraphy

- Giovanni Caselli's fascimile pantelegraph

- The chronophotographoscope, Cinerama, and Cinemascope

- Early digital networks, such as Teletext, Viewtron, Viewdata, Prestel, The Source, Qube, Alex (Quebec), Telidon (Canada), Viatel and Discovery 40 (Australia).

deadlock

A deadlock is a situation in which two computer programs sharing the same resource are effectively preventing each other from accessing the resource, resulting in both programs ceasing to function.

The earliest computer **operating system**s ran only one program at a time. All of the resources of the system were available to this one program. Later, operating systems ran multiple programs at once, interleaving them. Programs were required to specify in advance what resources they needed so that they could avoid conflicts with other programs running at the same time. Eventually some operating systems offered dynamic allocation of resources. Programs could request further allocations of resources after they had begun running. This led to the problem of the deadlock. Here is the simplest example:

Program 1 requests resource A and receives it.

Program 2 requests resource B and receives it.

Program 1 requests resource B and is queued up, pending the release of B.

Program 2 requests resource A and is queued up, pending the release of A.

Now neither program can proceed until the other program releases a resource. The operating system cannot know what action to take. At this point the only alternative is to abort (stop) one of the programs.

Learning to deal with deadlocks had a major impact on the development of operating systems and the structure of databases. Data was structured and the order of requests was constrained in order to avoid creating deadlocks.

Debian Linux

See "Debian"

Debian

Debian is a popular and freely-available computer **operating system** that uses the **Linux kernel** and other program components obtained from the **GNU** project. Debian can be downloaded over the Internet or, for a small charge, obtained on CD. As **Open Source** software, Debian is developed by over 500 contributing programmers who collectively form the Debian Project. New releases are provided from time to time. Ongoing service is available through subscription to a mailing list.

Debian supports over 3,950 free, downloadable applications. Although some widely-used applications such as Microsoft Word and Excel are not included, Corel's WordPerfect and similar desktop applications are available.

Debian was one of the first free software projects, begun in 1993 by Ian Murdock. Debian is pronounced deb-EE-uhn since it derives from the names of Ian Murdock and his wife, Debra.

debouncing

Bouncing is the tendency of any two metal contacts in an electronic device to generate multiple signals as the contacts close or open; debouncing is any kind of hardware device or software that ensures that only a single signal will be acted upon for a single opening or closing of a contact.

When you press a key on your computer **keyboard**, you expect a single contact to be recorded by your computer. In fact, however, there is an initial contact, a slight bounce or lightening up of the contact, then another contact as the bounce ends, yet another bounce back, and so forth. A similar effect takes place when a switch made using a metal contact is opened. The usual solution is a debouncing device or software that ensures that only one digital signal can be registered within the space of a given time (usually milliseconds).

debugging

In computers, debugging is the process of locating and fixing or bypassing **bugs** (errors) in computer program code or the engineering of a hardware device. To debug a program or hardware device is to start with a problem, isolate the source of the problem, and then fix it. A user of a program that does not know how to fix the problem may learn enough about the problem to be able to avoid it until it is permanently fixed. When someone says they've debugged a program or "worked the bugs out" of a program, they imply that they fixed it so that the bugs no longer exist.

Debugging is a necessary process in almost any new software or hardware development process, whether a commercial product or an enterprise or personal application program. For complex products, debugging is done as the result of the unit test for the smallest unit of a system, again at component test when parts are brought together, again at system test when the product is used with other existing products, and again during customer **beta test**, when users try the product out in a real world situation. Because most computer programs and many programmed hardware devices contain thousands of lines of code, almost any new product is likely to contain a few bugs. Invariably, the bugs in the functions that get most use are found and fixed first. An early version of a program that has lots of bugs is referred to as "buggy."

Debugging tools help identify coding errors at various development stages. Some programming language packages include a facility for checking the code for errors as it is being written.

DEC

Now part of Compaq, DEC (Digital Equipment Corporation) has long occupied a leading position in the mid-range computer, traditionally known as the **minicomputer**, the business computer platform that fits between the mainframe and the personal computer and serves small and medium-sized businesses with its **VMS** operating system. In recent years, DEC has been addressing IBM's **AS/400** platform, the advent of the **workstation** platforms of Sun Microsystems and others, and the **client/server** concept of computing. Today, DEC is focusing strongly on Internet systems and software.

decibel

In electronics and communications, the decibel (abbreviated as dB, and also as db and DB) is a **logarithmic** expression of the ratio between two signal power, **voltage**, or **current** levels. In acoustics, the decibel is used as an absolute indicator of sound power per unit area. A decibel is one-tenth of a Bel, a seldom-used unit named for Alexander Graham Bell, inventor of the telephone.

Suppose a signal has a power of P_1 watts, and a second signal has a power of P_2 watts. Then the power amplitude difference in decibels, symbolized S_{dBP}, is:

$S_{dBP} = 10 \log_{10} (P_2/P_1)$

Decibels can be calculated in terms of the effective voltage if the load **impedance** remains constant. Suppose a signal has an rms (**root-mean-square**) voltage of V_1 across a load, and a second signal has an rms voltage of V_2 across another load having the same impedance. Then the voltage amplitude difference in decibels, symbolized S_{dBV}, is:

$S_{dBV} = 20 \log_{10} (V_2/V_1)$

Decibels can also be calculated in terms of the effective current (amperage) if the impedance remains constant. Suppose a signal delivers an rms (root-mean-square) amperage of A_1 through a load, and a second signal delivers an rms amperage of A_2 through another load having the same impedance. Then the current amplitude difference in decibels, symbolized S_{dBA}, is:

$S_{dBA} = 20 \log_{10} (A_2/A_1)$

When a decibel figure is positive, then the second signal is stronger than the first signal. When a decibel figure is negative, then the second signal is weaker than the first signal. In amplifiers, the gain, also called the amplification factor, is often expressed in decibels. A circuit amplifies only if the decibel figure for the output-to-input power ratio (S_{dBP}) is positive.

In sound, decibels are defined in terms of power per unit surface area on a scale from the threshold of human hearing, 0 dB, upward towards the threshold of pain, about $120 - 140$ dB. As examples: the sound level in the average residential home is about 40 dB, average conversation is about 60 dB, typical home music listening levels are about 85 dB, a loud rock band about 110 dB, and a jet engine close up is 150dB.

Decibel units are commonly used in audio equalizers, both the hardware kind and the software kind, as a convenient reference point while editing. Boosting an equalizer band whose center point is 1000 by 3 dB means that you have raised the volume level of that frequency band by 3 dB as it relates to the other frequencies in the sound. A typical equalizer has a range for boosting or diminishing a sound level of $+/-18$ dB.

decipher

All three terms—decipher, decrypt, and decode—mean to convert **ciphertext** into the original, unencrypted **plaintext**. *Decrypt* is actually a generic term, covering both the other terms, that simply means to unscramble a message. The root prefix *crypto* is from the Greek *kryptos*, meaning *hidden or secret*.

Although *decipher* and *decode* are frequently used interchangeably, in the strictest sense, a distinction can be made between the two. Both terms refer to a system of encryption in which message data is replaced with other data to make it unreadable. The crucial difference between *decipher* and *decode* lies in the level of substitution used: In some security contexts, a message encrypted through the use of a **cipher** works with substitution at the level of letters; to *decipher* means to unscramble a message that uses substitution at the letter level. According to some accounts, Julius Caesar developed a cipher to encrypt messages so that they could be sent without fear that the messenger would betray him. Caesar replaced each letter in his message with the one three positions ahead of it in the alphabet, so that, for example, "A" became "D," "C" became "F" and so on. Only someone in possession of Caesar's encryption rule (or **key**)

could read the message, by performing the opposite operation: substitute each letter with the one three positions *before* it in the alphabet. Caesar's encrypted message is an example of **ciphertext** and the unencrypted message an example of **plaintext**; the mathematical formula (shift by 3) used for encryption and decryption is a simple example of an **algorithm**.

In contexts where a distinction is made between decipher and decode, to *decode* means to unscramble a message in which text is transformed through the substitution of words or phrases, since, in this context, encoded messages are encrypted at the level of words or phrases.

decision support system

A decision support system (DSS) is a computer program application that analyzes business data and presents it so that users can make business decisions more easily. It is an "informational application" (in distinction to an "operational application" that collects the data in the course of normal business operation). Typical information that a decision support application might gather and present would be:

- Comparative sales figures between one week and the next
- Projected revenue figures based on new product sales assumptions
- The consequences of different decision alternatives, given past experience in a context that is described

A decision support system may present information graphically and may include an expert system or artificial intelligence (**AI**). It may be aimed at business executives or some other group of knowledge workers.

decode

See "decipher"

decompressing

See "uncompressing"

decrypt

See "decipher"

decryption

See "encryption"

DECT

Unlike the **analog** cordless phones you may have in your home, DECT (Digital Enhanced Cordless Telecommunications) is a **digital wireless** telephone technology that is expected to make cordless phones much more common in both businesses and homes in the future. Formerly called the Digital European Cordless Telecommunications standard because it was developed by European companies, DECT's new name reflects its global acceptance. Like another important wireless standard, **Global System for Mobile communication**, DECT uses time division multiple access (**TDMA**) to transmit radio signals to phones. Whereas GSM is optimized for mobile travel over large areas, DECT is designed especially for a smaller area with a large number of users, such as in cities and corporate complexes. A user can have a telephone equipped for both GSM and DECT (this is known as a *dual-mode* phone) and they can operate seamlessly.

DECT has five major applications:

1) **The "cordless private branch exchange."** A company can connect to a wired telephone company and redistribute signals by radio antenna to a large number of telephone users within the company, each with their own number. A cordless PBX would be especially useful and save costs in a company with a number of mobile employees such as those in a large warehouse.

2) **Wireless Local Loop (WLL)**. Users in a neighborhood typically served by a telephone company wired **local loop** can be connected instead by a cordless phone that exchanges signals with a neighborhood antenna. A standard telephone (or any device containing a telephone such as a computer **modem** or **fax** machine) is simply plugged into a fixed access unit (FAU), which contains a transceiver. The Wireless Local Loop would typically be installed in an urban area where many users could share the same antenna.

3) **Cordless Terminal Mobility**. The arrangement used by businesses for a cordless PBX could also be used by a service that provided cordless phone numbers for individual subscribers. In general, the mobility would be less than that available for GSM users.

4) **Home cordless phones**. A homeowner could install a single-**cell** antenna within the home and use it for a number of cordless phones throughout the home and garden.

5) **GSM/DECT internetworking**. Part of the DECT standard describes how it can interact with the GSM standard so that users can be free to move with a telephone from the outdoors (and GSM signals) into an indoor environment (and a DECT system). It's expected that many GSM service providers may want to extend their service to support DECT signals inside buildings. A dual-mode phone would automatically search first for a DECT connection, then for a GSM connection if DECT is not available.

dedicated hosting

See "dedicated server"

dedicated line

A dedicated line is a telecommunications path between two points that is available 24 hours a day for use by a designated user (individual or company). It is not shared in common among multiple users as **dial-up** lines are. A dedicated line can be a physical path owned by the user or rented from a telephone company, in which case it is called a **leased line**. A synonym is *nonswitched line* (as opposed to a *switched* or dial-up line).

dedicated server

In the Web **hosting** business, a dedicated server refers to the rental and exclusive use of a computer that includes a **Web server**, related software, and connection to the Internet, housed in the Web hosting company's premises. A dedicated server is usually needed for a **Web site** (or set of related company sites) that may develop a considerable amount of traffic—for example, a site that must handle up to 35 million **hit**s a day. The server can usually be configured and operated remotely from the client company. Web hosting companies claim that the use of a dedicated server on their premises saves router, Internet connection, security system, and network administration costs.

In renting a dedicated server, the client company may be required to use a specified computer system or may be offered a choice of several systems. Some host providers allow a client company to purchase and install its own computer server at the host provider's location, a service known as **colocation**.

Typically, a dedicated server is rented that provides a stated amount of **memory**, hard disk space, and bandwidth (here meaning the number of **gigabyte**s of data that can be delivered each month). Some hosting companies allow the renter of a dedicated server to do **virtual hosting**, in turn renting services on the server to third parties for their Web sites. **Domain name system**, e-mail, and File Transfer Protocol (**FTP**) capabilities are typically included and some companies provide an easy-to-use control interface.

deep link

A deep link is a **hypertext link** to a **page** on a **Web site** other than its **home page**. The "deep" refers to the depth of the page in a site's hierarchical structure of pages. Any page below the top page in the hierarchy (the home page) can thus be considered deep. The term has been given prominence in the legal suit of the Ticketmaster Corporation against Microsoft. A Microsoft-owned site (one of its Sidewalk sites) linked to a page of useful information within the Ticketmaster site, avoiding the Ticketmaster home page. Ticketmaster sued Microsoft for linking without permission, claiming that they were thus being deprived of advertising viewers for the ads on their home page. In fact, their content was appearing within a Microsoft page containing their advertising.

In his TBTF Newsletter, Keith Dawson refers to deep links as "rifle shots," suggesting that they get the Web surfer immediately to the information they want. Although no one has quantified the number of deep links between Web sites, it would certainly seem to be a very large number. Most major search engine and directory sites like Yahoo invite Web sites to request inclusion with the assumption that all pages will be indexed unless explicitly excluded. And, undoubtedly, most sites welcome links from anywhere to any of their pages.

Although the issue is still to be fully resolved, some observers think it likely that the prevalence of deep links on the Web will continue as an essential characteristic. Brad Templeton, writing at one Web site, suggests that most Web sites implicitly encourage both home page and deep links simply by being part of the Web. He suggests that those sites that want to inhibit deep links to their site could state it clearly as a way to discourage such links. Many feel that the practice of "framing" another site within a **frame** on your site poses some liability for the framing site, unless permission to frame is received first.

Deep Space Network

The Deep Space Network (DSN) is a sophisticated data communications system used by NASA (the U.S. National Aeronautics and Space Administration) in conjunction with manned and unmanned space missions. The DSN is also used by radio astronomers.

The main terminal of the DSN is located at JPL (Jet Propulsion Laboratory) headquarters in Pasadena, California. There are three primary antennas, spaced equally on a great circle that slants around the world. All three are large paraboloid (dish) antennas that can be used for transmitting and receiving signals over a wide range of radio frequencies. One antenna is located in California, another is in Spain, and another is in Australia. The antennas are located in such a way that all existing operational spacecraft can be monitored and controlled, and communications maintained with them, almost 100 percent of the time. This is true of both earth-orbiting **satellite**s and interplanetary space vehicles.

Signals transmitted and received by DSN equipment include satellite control and telemetry, e-mail (including text, graphics, video, programs, and sound attachments), communications with the Space Shuttles, and radio-frequency emanations from distant celestial objects.

deep Web

The deep Web is the hidden part of the Web, containing a huge volume of content that is inaccessible to conventional **search engine**s, and consequently, to most users. According to a recent study by BrightPlanet, a search technology company, the deep web may contain 550 billion documents, perhaps 500 times the content of the surface Web that most

of us are familiar with. In comparison, Google—which claims to index the most comprehensive collection of documents on the Internet—has identified 1.2 billion documents and is actually capable of searching a mere 600 million of those. An article in *Nature* reported that even a large search engine such as Northern Light only indexes 16% of even the surface Web's content. These figures indicate that an Internet search typically searches .03% ($^1/_{3000}$) of available content.

In addition to the surprising quantity of deep Web content in existence, BrightPlanet found that the deep Web was growing much more quickly than the surface Web, and that the quality of the content within it—95% of which is publicly accessible—was significantly higher than the vast majority of surface Web content. According to *The Standard*, among the myriad offerings of the deep Web are: Securities and Exchange Commission filings, telephone yellow pages, IBM's patent database, the Merriam-Webster Dictionary, and Kelly Blue Book information on automobiles. In order to access these and other deep Web content, however, a user must know the exact **URL** of the target Web page. A number of companies are now offering search tools with the capacity to simultaneously search through multiple deep Web databases, including IntelliSeek's Bulls Eye software and BrightPlanet's own **LexiBot**.

default

In computer technology, a default (noun, pronounced dee-FAWLT) is a predesigned value or setting that is used by a computer program when a value or setting is not specified by the program user. The program user can be either an interactive user of a **graphical user interface** or command line interface, or a programmer using an **application program interface**. When the program receives a request from an interactive user or another program, it looks at the information that has been passed to it. If a particular item of information is not specified in the information that is passed, the program uses the default value that was defined for that item when the program was written. In designing a program, each default is usually preestablished as the value or setting that most users would probably choose. This keeps the interface simpler for the interface user and means that less information has to be passed and examined during each program request.

To the program requestor, to default (verb) is to intentionally or accidentally allow the preestablished value or setting for an item to be used by the program. The program is said to default when it uses a default value or setting.

Default (adjective) pertains to something that is used when something else is not supplied or specified. For example, a default printer is a type of printer that is assumed to be connected to a computer unless the computer user specifies another type that is actually connected.

Defense Advanced Research Projects Agency Network

See "DARPANet"

Defense Advanced Research Projects Agency

See "DARPA"

Defense Message System

The Defense Message System (DMS) is a secure **X.400**-based e-mail system developed by the United States government in conjunction with industry partners to ensure safety for critical operations. Essentially an enhanced version of various commercial e-mail products, DMS was developed for the United States Department of Defense (DoD). DMS has replaced AUTODIN (*automated digital network*), the previous official DoD e-mail system as well as 45 separate e-mail systems that functioned within the DoD.

At the **client** level, DMS looks like a typical e-mail application and is designed to feature familiar user-friendly functionality, such as global **X.500** Directory Service, and transmission support for digital files of any type and size. Security and delivery assurance mechanisms are approved by the National Security Agency (**NSA**) for information classified at all levels, up to and including those designated as top secret. Because sending message attachments between the unclassified and secret domains (known, respectively, as *NIPRNET* and *SIPRNET*) requires protection against leakage of classified information, DMS policies require that all organizational messages be signed and encrypted with Class IV Public Key Infrastructure (**PKI**) protection through **Fortezza**, NSA's trademarked security products suite. Originally policies permitted organizational message attachments to be sent only from a low security domain to a high security domain, but security mechanisms (both technological and policy-based) are now in place to allow the information to flow in either direction.

DMS was designed to incorporate components from a variety of leading hardware and software vendors and to leverage the best current and emerging messaging technologies within the Defense Information Infrastructure (DII, a worldwide connectivity transport infrastructure). The DMS development program began in response to Joint Staff requirements for an integrated messaging service that could be accessed from any DoD location in the world, as well as by designated government users or contractors. DMS has been recommended to become the standard messaging system throughout the U.S. government.

defragmenter

When a file is too large to store in a single location on a **hard disk**, it is stored on the disk in discontiguous (not adjacent) parts or fragments. This fragmentation is "invisible" to the user; however. The locations of the fragments are kept track of by the system. Over time, disk access time can be slowed by fragmentation since each fragmented file is likely to require multiple drive head repositionings and accesses. (There's nothing you can do to prevent fragmentation, by the way.)

A disk defragmenter is a utility that rearranges your fragmented files and the free space on your computer so that files are stored in contiguous units and free space is consolidated in one contiguous block. This also improves access time to files that are now contiguous.

A defragmenter utility comes with the DOS 6.0 and with Windows operating systems. In DOS, you can defragment a drive using the DEFRAG command. In Windows operating systems, you'll find "Defragmenter" by going from the Start Menu to Programs, to Accessories, to System Tools, and to Defragmenter. Separate products, sometimes called disk optimizers, will also defragment your disk.

degauss

To degauss (pronounced dee-GOWS) is to demagnetize. Degaussing a computer display removes any undesirable magnetic field that may have built up within the display, causing distortion of the image or color. Display **monitors** with cathode ray tube (**CRT**) technology are subject to the buildup of magnetic fields. Many display manufacturers include an internal coil that will degauss the display when it is turned on. Some displays also include an external control that a user can operate to degauss the display at any time.

Degaussing a magnetic storage medium removes all the data stored on it. A *degausser* is a device used for this purpose.

delimiter

In computer programming, a delimiter is a **character** that identifies the beginning or the end of a character string (a contiguous sequence of characters). The delimiting character is not part of the character string. In command syntax, a space or a backslash () or a forward slash (/) is often a delimiter, depending on the rules of the command language. The program interpreting the character string knows what the delimiters are.

Delimiters can also be used to separate the data items in a **database** (the columns in the database table) when transporting the database to another application. For example, a comma-separated values file (**CSV** file) is one in which each value in the cells of a table row is delimited by and separated from the next value by a comma. The beginning of a row is indicated by a new line character.

demarc

A demarc (an abbreviation for *demarcation point*) marks the point where communications facilities owned by one organization **interface** with that of another organization. In

telephone terminology, this is the interface between *customer-premises equipment* and network service provider equipment.

A synonym is *network terminating interface (NTI)*.

demilitarized zone

See "DMZ"

demo

See "demo and demoscene"

demo and demoscene

In Internet terminology, a demo (sometimes called a *PC demo*, although generally the PC is considered to be implicit) is a non-interactive **multimedia** presentation, the computer world's equivalent of a music video. Demos are usually made to showcase some or all of the following: computer hardware and/or software capabilities (such as multi-channel sound or **3-D** effects); the subject of the demo (such as a product or a musician); and the abilities of the programmer (such as complex motion). Demos are frequently played in competitions, which classify them as belonging to one of three subsets: the *intro 4k*, which is fairly basic and generally has no music; the *intro 64k*, no restrictions other than size; and the full-fledged *demo*, which may contain any possible media. Demos are the work of computer enthusiasts who often spend many days (or even weeks or months) creating a demo that may not have any external motivation (such as money, or acclaim in the broader world).

The typical demo creator (known as a *demomaker*) is a male between the ages of 15 and 30, typically a student who is identified by a pseudonym. Demomakers are part of a subculture called the demoscene, an underground community that is reported to number among its members the elite from the worlds of programming and computer-assisted composing and art. Because each demo may showcase several talents, demomakers with complementary skills often collaborate to form *demogroups* that, like demomakers themselves, are identified by a special name and create their own mystique and reputation. Demomakers gather frequently for *demoparties*, which are arranged around competitions. Some of the largest demoparties have assembled over 4,300 demomakers. The demoscene originated in Europe and is most active in Scandinavia, Denmark, Germany, The Netherlands, Switzerland, Poland and France, although it is gradually making its presence felt in the rest of the world.

demographics

Demographics is the study of the behaviors and other characteristics of groups of human beings in terms of statistics.

demogroup

See "demo and demoscene"

demomaker

See "demo and demoscene"

demon

A demon (also see **daemon** which has a somewhat similar meaning) is a program or process, part of a larger program or process, that is dormant until a certain condition occurs and then is initiated to do its processing. Eric Raymond cites an artificial intelligence (**artificial intelligence**) application as an example. An AI program might include a number of demons, one or more of which might become active when a new piece of knowledge was acquired by the AI program. If the new knowledge affected a particular demon's own sphere of knowledge, it would spring into action and create new pieces of knowledge based on its particular inference rules. Each of these new pieces of knowledge might in turn activate additional demons that would continue to filter through and refine the entire AI knowledge base.

A second example of a demon may be found in personal computer help systems, games, or any application where, when a program so determines by the state of the user interactions with the program, a "popup" window and program is introduced to the user for help, a clue, or a small calculation.

demoparty

See "demo and demoscene"

demoscene

See "demo and demoscene"

DEN

Directory-Enabled Networking (DEN) is an industry-standard initiative and specification for how to construct and store information about a network's users, applications, and data in a central directory. A standard way of describing the network's elements in a central repository can enable applications to be developed that will automatically learn of user access privileges, bandwidth assignments, and the company's resource policies, and provide services accordingly. The result should reduce the cost of running the network and enable new services.

DEN defines an **object-oriented** information model that is based on another recent standard initiative, the Common Information Model (CIM). Both models are being mapped into the directory defined as part of the Lightweight Directory Access Protocol (**LDAP**). DEN and CIM are an

advance over and can be used with the Simple Network Management Protocol (**Simple Network Management Protocol**).

With DEN, a client/server application on the network can be designed to automatically provide the user with the proper level of access to its resources without needing manual assistance from a network administrator when the user changes locations or positions within the company. In the past, the proper level of access has required significant manual assistance to implement and maintain. Information that may affect access can include not only the user's own access privileges but also network resource availability in terms of bandwidth and services.

By entering specific information about the network in the central directory using the DEN model and syntax, network information then becomes available to any DEN-enabled application in the network. When a user attempts to open one of these types of applications on the network, the application checks dynamically in the LDAP global directory in order to see what the user's access privileges should be. The application can then automatically open and configure itself to provide the correct level of access to its features, based on the usage policy information it has located in the LDAP directory.

An example of a "DEN-enabled application" is the Microsoft **Windows NT** operating system, Version 5.0 or higher, which includes the Active Directory Service, an implementation of DEN. DEN was developed by 70 companies, including Microsoft and Cisco. In late 1998, the Desktop Management Task Force (DMTF) took over the DEN work on network data models and began integrating it into its own Common Information Model (CIM).

dendrimer

A dendrimer (from Greek *dendra* for tree) is an artificially manufactured or synthesized molecule built up from branched units called monomers. Such processes involve working on the scale of nanometers (a nanometer is 10^{-9} meter or a millionth of a millimeter). Technically, a dendrimer is a polymer, which is a large molecule comprised of many smaller ones linked together.

Dendrimers have some proven applications, and numerous potential applications. They have been used in the production of industrial adhesives. They are expected to serve as components in a variety of nanomachines. Dendrimers are of interest to researchers in medical technology, where they might help carry and deliver drugs in the body, or serve as replacements for plasma components. Dendrimers might also prove useful in the manufacture of nanoscale batteries and lubricants, catalysts, and herbicides.

Also see **nanomachine** and **nanotechnology**.

deniable encryption

Deniable **encryption** is a type of **cryptography** that allows an encrypted text to be decrypted in two or more ways, depending on which decryption **key** is used. The use of two or more keys allows the sender, theoretically, to conceal or deny the existence of a controversial message in favor of a more benign decryption. For instance, a company may send an encrypted message to its high-level administrative staff whose key decrypts the message to read "We have no plans to change our business model," while the board of directors receives the same message that using its own key decrypts the same message to read "We are going bankrupt at this rate and need to let 20,000 people go, including high-level administrators." Deniable encryption is sometimes used for misinformation purposes when the sender anticipates, or even encourages, interception of a communication.

denial of service

On the Internet, a denial of service (DoS) attack is an incident in which a user or organization is deprived of the services of a resource they would normally expect to have. Typically, the loss of service is the inability of a particular network service, such as e-mail, to be available or the temporary loss of all network connectivity and services. In the worst cases, for example, a Web site accessed by millions of people can occasionally be forced to temporarily cease operation. A denial of service attack can also destroy programming and files in a computer system. Although usually intentional and malicious, a denial of service attack can sometimes happen accidentally. A denial of service attack is a type of security breach to a computer system that does not usually result in the theft of information or other security loss. However, these attacks can cost the target person or company a great deal of time and money.

Common forms of denial of service attacks are:

Buffer Overflow Attacks

The most common kind of DoS attack is simply to send more traffic to a network address than the programmers who planned its data **buffer**s anticipated someone might send. The attacker may be aware that the target system has a weakness that can be exploited or the attacker may simply try the attack in case it might work. A few of the better-known attacks based on the buffer characteristics of a program or system include:

- Sending e-mail messages that have attachments with 256-character file names to Netscape and Microsoft mail programs
- Sending oversized Internet Control Message Protocol (**ICMP**) **packet**s (this is also known as the Packet Internet or Inter-Network Groper (**PING**) of death)
- Sending to a user of the **Pine** e-mail progam a message with a "From" address larger than 256 characters

SYN Attack

When a session is initiated between the Transport Control Program (**TCP**) client and server in a network, a very small buffer space exists to handle the usually rapid "hand-shaking" exchange of messages that sets up the session. The session-establishing **packet**s include a SYN field that identifies the sequence in the message exchange. An attacker can send a number of connection requests very rapidly and then fail to respond to the reply. This leaves the first **packet** in the buffer so that other, legitimate connection requests can't be accommodated. Although the packet in the buffer is dropped after a certain period of time without a reply, the effect of many of these bogus connection requests is to make it difficult for legitimate requests for a session to get established. In general, this problem depends on the operating system providing correct settings or allowing the network administrator to tune the size of the buffer and the timeout period.

Teardrop Attack

This type of denial of service attack exploits the way that the Internet Protocol (**IP**) requires a packet that is too large for the next router to handle be divided into fragments. The fragment packet identifies an offset to the beginning of the first packet that enables the entire packet to be reassembled by the receiving system. In the teardrop attack, the attacker's IP puts a confusing offset value in the second or later fragment. If the receiving operating system does not have a plan for this situation, it can cause the system to crash.

Smurf Attack

In this attack, the perpetrator sends an IP ping (or "echo my message back to me") request to a receiving site. The ping packet specifies that it be broadcast to a number of hosts within the receiving site's local network. The packet also indicates that the request is from another site, the target site that is to receive the denial of service. (Sending a packet with someone else's return address in it is called **spoof**ing the return address.) The result will be lots of ping replies flooding back to the innocent, spoofed host. If the flood is great enough, the spoofed host will no longer be able to receive or distinguish real traffic.

Viruses

Computer **virus**es, which replicate across a network in various ways, can be viewed as denial-of-service attacks where the victim is not usually specifically targetted but simply a host unlucky enough to get the virus. Depending on the particular virus, the denial of service can be hardly noticeable ranging all the way through disastrous.

Physical Infrastructure Attacks

Here, someone may simply snip a fiber optic cable. This kind of attack is usually mitigated by the fact that traffic can sometimes quickly be rerouted.

There are ways of preventing many forms of DoS attacks.

denial-of-service attack

See "denial of service"

dense wavelength division multiplexing

Dense wavelength division multiplexing (DWDM) is a technology that puts data from different sources together on an **optical fiber**, with each signal carried on its own separate light **wavelength**. Using DWDM, up to 80 (and theoretically more) separate wavelengths or **channels** of data can be multiplexed into a lightstream transmitted on a single optical fiber. Each channel carries a time-division multiplexed (TDM) signal. In a system with each channel carrying 2.5 **Gbps** (billion bits per second), up to 200 billion bits can be delivered a second by the optical fiber. DWDM is also sometimes called *wave division multiplexing (WDM)*.

Since each channel is demultiplexed at the end of the transmission back into the original source, different data formats being transmitted at different data rates can be transmitted together. Specifically, Internet (IP) data, Synchronous Optical Network data (**SONET**), and asynchronous transfer mode (**ATM**) data can all be travelling at the same time within the optical fiber.

DWDM promises to solve the "**fiber exhaust**" problem and is expected to be the central technology in the all-optical networks of the future.

deploy

To deploy (from the French *deployer*) is "to spread out or arrange strategically." Long used in the context of military strategy, it has now gained currency in information technology, especially in **distributed** computing.

deprecated

Deprecated means tolerated but not recommended. A number of elements and attributes are deprecated in **HTML 4.0**, meaning that other methods of accomplishing the task are preferred. Deprecated features may become obsolete in future versions of HTML, though browsers that support the features may continue to support them.

DES

See "Data Encryption Standard"

desktop computer

Also see **portable computer** and **notebook computer**.

A desktop computer is a personal computer that is designed to fit conveniently on top of a typical office desk. A desktop computer typically comes in several units that are connected together during installation: (1) the **processor**, which can be in a *microtower* or *minitower* designed to fit under the desk or in a unit that goes on top of the desk, (2) the **display monitor**, (3) and input devices—usually a **keyboard** and a **mouse**. Today, almost all desktop computers include a built-in **modem**, a **CD-ROM** drive, a multi-**gigabyte** magnetic storage drive, and sometimes a **diskette** drive. At home, most desktop computer users also purchase a **printer**. In businesses and increasingly at home, desktop computers can be interconnected and can share resources such as printers by being connected to a local area network (**LAN**).

Desktop Management Interface

See "DMI"

desktop theme

A desktop theme is a customized graphical user inferface (**GUI**) that replaces a computer's ordinary sounds, icons, pointer, wallpaper or screensaver with something designed to reflect the interests of the user. For instance, if you were interested in bass fishing, you could have a picture of a lake for your computer wallpaper, icons that resemble different kinds of fishing lures, sounds that are related to boats, water and fishing reels, a screen saver from your favorite TV show about bass fishing, and a pointer that looks like a fish. Although desktop themes are popular for home use, many network administrators frown upon desktop themes, primarily because it is possible for a user to inadvertently introduce a virus by downloading a theme from an unknown source.

There are free desktop themes, as well as **shareware** themes, available on the Internet for all operating systems. It is also possible for users to create their own desktop themes. Microsoft used to require that users purchase an application called Microsoft Plus! to use desktop themes, but they included it as standard issue in Windows 98 and Windows Me. The initial release of Windows 2000 does not include the Plus! package (or its equivalent), although high customer demand leads some industry watchers to predict that the Plus! package will either be included in the next edition of Windows 2000, or be released separately (as it was for Windows 95). In Linux, the latest version of the KDE graphical desktop environment includes a tool to enable users to change their desktop theme.

development process

See "systems development method"

desktop

1) Using an office metaphor, a desktop is a computer display area that represents the kinds of objects one might find on a real desktop: documents, phonebook, telephone, reference sources, writing (and possibly drawing) tools, project folders. A desktop can be contained in a window that is part of the total display area or can be "full-screen" (the total display area). Conceivably, you can have multiple desktops (for different projects or work environments you may have) and switch among them.

In its Windows product, Microsoft provides what they call an Active Desktop. It includes representations of and access to desktop objects and also dynamic Web content as well, including integrated links to Web sites and information areas that are generated as the result of sites pushing requested information updates to the user.

2) Desktop is also an abbreviated form of *desktop computer*, a personal computer that fits on top of a desk.

device

1) In general, a device is a machine designed for a purpose. In a general context, a **computer** can be considered a device.

2) In the context of **computer** technology, a device is a unit of **hardware**, outside or inside the case or housing for the essential computer (processor, memory, and data paths) that is capable of providing input to the essential computer or of receiving output or of both. When the term is used generally (as in *computer devices*), it can include keyboards, mouses, display monitors, hard disk drives, CD-ROM players, printers, audio speakers and microphones, and other hardware units. Some devices such as a hard disk drive or a CD-ROM drive, while physically inside the computer housing, are considered devices because they are separately installable and replaceable. With notebook and smaller computers, devices tend to be more physically integrated with the "non-device" part of the computer.

The units of a computer to which the term *device* is not applied include the **motherboard**, the main **processor** and additional processors such as numeric coprocessors, and random access memory (**RAM**).

The term **peripheral** (a truncation of *peripheral device*) is sometimes used as a synonym for *device* or any input/output unit.

device driver

A device driver is a **program** that controls a particular type of **device** that is attached to your computer. There are device **driver**s for printers, displays, CD-ROM readers, diskette drives, and so on. When you buy an **operating system**, many device drivers are built into the product. However, if you later buy a new type of device that the operating system didn't anticipate, you'll have to install the new device driver. A device driver essentially converts the more general input/output instructions of the operating system to messages that the device type can understand.

Some Windows programs are **virtual device driver**s. These programs interface with the Windows Virtual Machine Manager. There is a virtual device driver for each main hardware device in the system, including the hard disk drive controller, keyboard, and serial and parallel ports. They're used to maintain the status of a hardware device that has changeable settings. Virtual device drivers handle software **interrupt**s from the system rather than hardware interrupts.

In Windows operating systems, a device driver file usually has a file name suffix of DLL or EXE. A virtual device driver usually has the suffix of VXD.

deviceCOM

DeviceCOM, from Intrinsyc Software, is a line of device and network integration products that is used to make Internet or PC devices work with each other on a network. Developed to provide Distributed Component Object Model (**DCOM**) services for **Windows CE**, Microsoft's embedded operating system for mobile devices, deviceCOM provides a development environment in which device-to-device communication is automatically managed so that application developers don't have to write programs to handle it. DCOM provides a development framework for distributed applications; deviceCOM supplies a connectivity framework between Windows CE-based devices and an enterprise's networked computers, through Microsoft's Web solution platform.

DeviceCOM was created specifically for distributed embedded applications and is said to have a small **footprint** and flexible **protocol** support, and to be **fault-tolerant** and **firewall**-friendly. Available for either Windows or Linux operating systems, deviceCOM is currently being used in a number of products, including industrial automation, mobile computing, and point-of-sale applications.

DFS

See "distributed file system"

DHCP

See "Dynamic Host Configuration Protocol"

DHTML

See "dynamic HTML"

Dialed Number Identification Service

DNIS (Dialed Number Identification Service) is a telephone service that identifies for the receiver of a call the number that the caller dialed. It's a common feature of 800 and 900 lines. If you have multiple 800 or 900 numbers to the same destination, DNIS tells which number was called. DNIS works by passing the touch tone digits (**dual tone multi frequency** or MF digits) to the destination where a special facility can read and display them or make them available for **call center** programming.

dial-up

Dial-up pertains to a telephone connection in a system of many lines shared by many users. A dial-up connection is established and maintained for a limited time duration. The alternative is a *dedicated* connection, which is continuously in place. Dial-up lines are sometimes called *switched* lines and dedicated lines are called *nonswitched* lines. A dedicated line is often a *leased line* that is rented from a telephone company.

A dial-up connection can be initiated manually or automatically by your computer's **modem** or other device.

dichotomizing search

See "binary search"

DICOM

DICOM (Digital Imaging and Communications in Medicine) is an application layer network protocol for the transmission of medical images, waveforms, and ancillary information. It was originally developed by the National Electrical Manufacturers Association (NEMA) and the American College of Radiology for CAT and MRI scan images. It is now controlled by the DICOM Standards Committee, and supports a wide range of medical images across the fields of radiology, cardiology, pathology and dentistry. DICOM uses TCP/IP as the lower-layer transport protocol.

DID

See "Direct Inward Dialing"

dielectric

See "dielectric material"

dielectric constant

The dielectric constant is the ratio of the **permittivity** of a substance to the permittivity of free space. It is an expression of the extent to which a material concentrates electric **flux**, and is the electrical equivalent of relative magnetic **permeability**.

As the dielectric constant increases, the electric flux density increases, if all other factors remain unchanged. This enables objects of a given size, such as sets of metal plates, to hold their electric charge for long periods of time, and/or to hold large quantities of charge. Materials with high dielectric constants are useful in the manufacture of high-value **capacitor**s.

A high dielectric constant, in and of itself, is not necessarily desirable. Generally, substances with high dielectric constants break down more easily when subjected to intense electric fields, than do materials with low dielectric constants. For example, dry air has a low dielectric constant, but it makes an excellent dielectric material for capacitors used in high-power radio-frequency (**RF**) transmitters. Even if air does undergo dielectric breakdown (a condition in which the dielectric suddenly begins to conduct **current**), the breakdown is not permanent. When the excessive electric field is removed, air returns to its normal dielectric state. Solid dielectric substances such as polyethylene or glass, however, can sustain permanent damage.

Also see **dielectric**, **capacitor**, **electric field**, and **permittivity**.

dielectric material

A dielectric material is a substance that is a poor conductor of electricity, but an efficient supporter of **electrostatic field**s. If the flow of **current** between opposite electric charge poles is kept to a minimum while the electrostatic lines of flux are not impeded or interrupted, an electrostatic field can store energy.This property is useful in **capacitor**s, especially at radio frequencies. Dielectric materials are also used in the construction of radio-frequency transmission lines.

In practice, most dielectric materials are solid. Examples include porcelain (ceramic), mica, glass, plastics, and the oxides of various metals. Some liquids and gases can serve as good dielectric materials. Dry air is an excellent dielectric, and is used in variable capacitors and some types of transmission lines. Distilled water is a fair dielectric. A vacuum is an exceptionally efficient dielectric.

An important property of a dielectric is its ability to support an electrostatic field while dissipating minimal energy in the form of heat. The lower the *dielectric loss* (the proportion of energy lost as heat), the more effective is a dielectric material. Another consideration is the *dielectric constant*, the extent to which a substance concentrates the electrostatic lines of flux. Substances with a low dielectric constant include a perfect vacuum, dry air, and most pure, dry gases such as helium and nitrogen. Materials with moderate dielectric constants include ceramics, distilled water, paper, mica, polyethylene, and glass. Metal oxides, in general, have high dielectric constants.

The prime asset of high-dielectric-constant substances, such as aluminum oxide, is the fact that they make possible the manufacture of high-value capacitors with small physical volume. But these materials are generally not able to withstand electrostatic fields as intense as low-dielectric-constant substances such as air. If the **voltage** across a dielectric material becomes too great—that is, if the electrostatic field becomes too intense—the material will suddenly begin to conduct current. This phenomenon is called *dielectric breakdown*. In components that use gases or liquids as the dielectric medium, this condition reverses itself if the voltage decreases below the critical point. But in components containing solid dielectrics, dielectric break-down usually results in permanent damage.

Difference Engine

The Difference Engine, designed in the 1820s by the English mathematician and inventor **Charles Babbage**, was intended to automatically compute mathematical tables which, until that time, had been tediously calculated by hand and were prone to error. Babbage saw an opportunity to revolutionize the field.

With good political contacts and the ear of Prime Ministers, Babbage was able to acquire initial funding for the construction of his machine, a task expected to last 3 years. The project turned into a nightmare, however, as setbacks piled up. In 1827, family tragedies, including the death of his wife, led Babbage to escape in travels to the Continent. When he returned and eventually secured further funding, a personality clash with his head engineer, Joseph Clement, saw construction of the engine halted. In the meantime, Babbage had designed a general-purpose computer, the Analytical Engine. He sought funds to either complete the Difference Engine or commence his new Analytical Engine. By this stage, the 1840's, times were hard and a government which had already spent as much as 17,000 English pounds with little reward declined to continue financing his plans.

The Difference Engine was eventually built in 1991, the bicentennial of Babbage's birth, using the technology of the era as proof that Babbage's designs were valid. A working model resides today in the Science Museum in London.

Differentiated Services

Differentiated Services (DiffServ, or DS) is a **protocol** for specifying and controlling network traffic by class so that certain types of traffic get precedence—for example, voice traffic, which requires a relatively uninterrupted flow of data, might get precedence over other kinds of traffic. Differentiated Services is the most advanced method for managing traffic in terms of what is called Class of Service (**CoS**). Unlike the earlier mechanisms of 802.1p tagging and Type of Service (ToS), Differentiated Services avoids simple priority tagging and depends on more complex **policy** or rule statements to determine how to forward a given network **packet**. An analogy is made to travel services, in which a person can choose among different modes of travel—train, bus, airplane—degree of comfort, the number of stops on the route, standby status, the time of day or period of year for the trip, and so forth. For a given set of packet travel rules, a packet is given one of 64 possible forwarding behaviors—known as per hop behaviors (PHBs). A six-bit field, known as the Differentiated Services Code Point (DSCP), in the Internet Protocol (**IP**) **header** specifies the per hop behavior for a given flow of packets.

Differentiated Services and the Class of Service approach provide a way to control traffic that is both more flexible and more **scalable** than the Quality of Service approach.

DiffServ

See "Differentiated Services"

digiboard

Digiboard or digicard is a generic name for a **serial port card** made by Digi International. While the typical PC comes with two serial ports, a compatible digiboard has the capability to add an additional four, eight, or 16 additional serial ports to a system.

A common use of a digiboard is to expand the services of a remote access server such as Microsoft RAS (Remote Access Server) for NT. It can also be used to expand a **terminal server** that accepts serial connections. Digiboards work with Windows, NetWare and most UNIX operating systems.

digicard

See "digiboard"

digital

Digital describes electronic technology that generates, stores, and processes data in terms of two states: positive and non-positive. Positive is expressed or represented by the number 1 and non-positive by the number 0. Thus, data transmitted or stored with digital technology is expressed as a string of 0's and 1's. Each of these state digits is referred to as a **bit** (and a string of bits that a computer can address individually as a group is a **byte**).

Prior to digital technology, electronic transmission was limited to **analog** technology, which conveys data as electronic signals of varying frequency or amplitude that are added to carrier waves of a given frequency. Broadcast and phone transmission has conventionally used analog technology.

Digital technology is primarily used with new physical communications media, such as *satellite* and **fiber optic** transmission. A **modem** is used to convert the digital information in your computer to analog signals for your phone line and to convert analog phone signals to digital information for your computer.

digital audio workstation

A digital audio workstation (DAW) is a computer that is specially equipped with a high-quality sound card and programming for editing and processing digital **audio** at a professional level. Digital audio workstations can range from a simple two-channel editor to a complete digital recording studio suite.

digital camera

A digital camera records and stores photographic images in digital form that can be fed to a computer as the impressions are recorded or stored in the camera for later loading into a computer. Currently, Kodak, Canon, and several other companies make digital cameras.

digital cash

Digital cash is a system of purchasing cash credits in relatively small amounts, storing the credits in your computer, and then spending them when making electronic purchases over the Internet. Theoretically, digital cash could be spent in very small increments, such as tenths of a cent (U.S.) or less. Most merchants accepting digital cash so far, however, use it as an alternative to other forms of payment for somewhat higher price purchases. There are several commercial approaches to digital cash on the Web.

Digital cash can also be stored on an electronically sensitive card. See **smart card** and **micropayment**.

digital certificate

A digital certificate is an electronic "credit card" that establishes your credentials when doing business or other transactions on the Web. It is issued by a certification authority (**CA**). It contains your name, a serial number, expiration dates, a copy of the certificate holder's **public key** (used for encrypting messages and **digital signature**s), and the digital signature of the certificate-issuing authority so that a recipient can verify that the certificate is real. Some digital certificates conform to a standard, X.509. Digital certificates can be kept in registries so that authenticating users can look up other users' public keys.

Digital Data Storage

Digital Data Storage (DDS) is a **format** for storing and backing up computer data on tape that evolved from the **Digital Audio Tape** (DAT) technology. DAT was created for CD-quality audio recording. In 1989, Sony and Hewlett Packard defined the DDS format for data storage using DAT tape cartridges. Tapes conforming to the DDS format can be played by either DAT or DDS tape drives. However, DDS tape drives cannot play DAT tapes since they can't pick up the audio on the DAT tape.

DDS uses a 4-mm tape. A DDS tape drive uses helical scanning for recording, the same process used by a video recorder (VCR). There are two read heads and two write heads. The read heads verify the data that has been written (recorded). If errors are present, the write heads rewrite the data. When restoring a backed-up file, the restoring software reads the directory of files located at the beginning of the tape, winds the tape to the location of the file, verifies the file, and writes the file onto the hard drive. DDS cannot update a backed-up file in the same place it was originally recorded. In general, DDS requires special software for managing the storage and retrieval of data from DDS tape drives.

There are four types of DDS drives:

- **DDS-1:** Stores up to 2 **gigabyte**s of uncompressed data on a 120-minute cartridge.

- **DDS-2:** Stores up to 8 GB of data in compressed format on a 120-minute cartridge. DDS-2 is ideal for small network servers.

- **DDS-3:** Stores up to 24 GB of data on a 125-minute cartridge. The DDS-3 drive is ideal for medium-sized servers. DDS-3 uses PRML (Partial Response Maximum Likelihood). PRML eliminates electronic **noise** for a cleaner data recording.

- **DDS-4:** The newest DDS drive, DDS-4 stores up to 40 GB of data on a 125-minute cartridge. Small to mid-size businesses benefit from the DDS-4 drive. A DDS cartridge needs to be retired after 2,000 passes or 100 full backups. You should clean your DDS tape drive every 24 hours with a cleaning cartridge and discard the cleaning cartridge after 30 cleanings. DDS tapes have an expected life of at least 10 years.

digital divide

The term "digital divide" describes the fact that the world can be divided into people who do and people who don't have access to—and the capability to use—modern information technology, such as the telephone, television, or the Internet. The digital divide exists between those in cities and those in rural areas. For example, a 1999 study showed that 86% of Internet delivery was to the 20 largest cities. The digital divide also exists between the educated and the uneducated, between economic classes, and, globally, between the more and less industrially developed nations.

Digital Enhanced Cordless Telecommunications

See "DECT"

Digital Equipment Corporation

See "DEC"

Digital Imaging and Communications in Medicine

See "DICOM"

digital library

A digital library is a collection of documents in organized electronic form, available on the Internet or on **CD-ROM** (compact-disk read-only memory) disks. Depending on the specific library, a user may be able to access magazine articles, books, papers, images, sound files, and videos.

On the Internet, the use of a digital library is enhanced by a **broadband** connection such as cable modem or DSL. Dial-up connections can be used to access plain-text documents and some documents containing images, but for complex files and those with animated video content, a downstream data speed of at least several hundred kilobits per second (**Kbps**) can make the user's experience less tedious, as well as more informative. Internet-based digital libraries can be updated on a daily basis. This is one of the greatest assets of this emerging technology.

On CD-ROM, the amount of data is limited to several hundred megabytes (**MB**) per disk, but access is generally much faster than on an Internet connection. Several CD-ROMs can be combined in a set, and because the disks are small, a large library can be accommodated in a reasonable physical space. The main limitation of CD-ROM is the fact that updating cannot be done as frequently as on the Internet. In addition, producing and distributing CD-ROMs involves overhead costs that are largely nonexistent in Internet-based libraries.

Some institutions have begun the task of converting classic books to electronic format for distribution on the Internet. Some files can be viewed directly in **HTML** format; others can be downloaded in **PDF** format and printed. Some publishers keep electronic files of books and produce them one unit at a time in printed and bound form on demand.

Electronic distribution of intellectual and artistic property has authors, agents, and publishers concerned about the possibility of copyright infringement. It is much easier to copy a CD-ROM, or to download an electronic book and make unauthorized copies of it, than it is to reproduce bound volumes and distribute them illegitimately. Fundamental changes in copyright law—and/or changes in the way in which the laws are enforced—are likely to occur as digital libraries expand and their use becomes more widespread.

digital loop carrier

DLC also is an abbreviation for **Data Link Control**.

Digital loop carrier (DLC) is equipment that bundles a number of individual phone line signals into a single multiplexed **digital** signal for local traffic between a telephone company **central office** and a business complex or other outlying service area. Typically, up to 24 analog voice calls are combined into a single signal and transmitted over a single copper **T-carrier system** or **E-carrier** line, an optical fiber cable, or a wireless connection. In a home, business, or other installation using digital loop carrier, the **analog** phone lines of individual users are connected to a local DLC box which then converts the analog signals into digital and combines (multiplexes) them into one signal that is sent to the phone company's central office on the single line. At the central office, the combined signal is separated back into the original signals. An estimated 20% of today's telephone users are being served by digital loop carriers.

Digital loop carrier can carry traffic for regular phone calls (**plain old telephone service**) and Integrated Services Digital Network (**ISDN**) service. More recently, approaches have been developed for using DLC to handle the higher **bandwidth** of Digital Subscriber Line (**DSL**) service.

Digital loop carrier is typically used as an efficient way to provide service to an office building or complex and to extend service to new areas outside the current **local loop**. DLC is also used to set up telephone service in emergency situations. Customers can easily migrate from a T-1 or E-1 line to fiber optic when it becomes needed and is available.

digital object identifier

A digital object identifier (DOI) is a permanent identifier given to a Web file or other Internet document so that if its Internet address changes, users will be redirected to its new address. You submit a DOI to a centrally-managed directory and then use the address of that directory plus the DOI instead of a regular Internet address. The DOI system was conceived by the Association of American Publishers in partnership with the Corporation for National Research Initiatives and is now administered by the International DOI Foundation. Essentially, the DOI system is a scheme for Web page redirection by a central manager.

Initially, the only central directory is the one maintained by the DOI Foundation. It's envisioned, however, that other directories might be created and maintained, perhaps by each major industry. Here's what a typical DOI might look like: 10.1002/ISBNJ0-471-58064-3

In this example, the "10.1002" identifies the directory and the part after the "/" is the rest of the DOI—in this case, the ISBN number of a particular book that has been published. The "-3" indicates a specific part or chapter in the book.

The DOI would be associated with a specific Web page or **Uniform Resource Locator** in the directory. If you wanted to link to the document in a Web page, you would link to this URL:

`http://www.doi.org/10.1002/ISBNJ0-471-58064-3`

Here, "www.doi.org" happens to be the current and only directory manager. A user clicking on this link would be linking to the directory page which in turn would locate and send back the URL associated with the DOI. Assuming the directory was up-to-date, the page owner and the user could both be sure that the latest page would be returned.

Early users of the DOI system are principally major publishers with thousands of documents to keep track of, many available on the Web. Relocating files from time to time for such a large number of documents would require many link changes on the publisher's site and perhaps a redirection page for users. With the DOI system, any future location change will require only updating the central directory and will not affect other site's links (if they also use the DOI in their link).

digital photo album

A digital photo album is a software application that allows the user to import **image** files from a **digital camera**, **memory card**, **scanner**, or computer **hard disk** to a central **database**. Album software applications typically allow the user to view, sort, edit, label, and arrange photos by using a book-like **interface** that resembles a traditional photo album. Album applications often offer special features, such as providing the user with the ability to create slide shows, order prints and gift items, or receive free online storage space.

Many Internet service providers (**ISP**s), e-mail providers, and Web **portal**s provide users with free tools to create and store online digital photo albums. Yahoo.com, for example, allows registered users 30MB for a digital photo album. Users do not need any special skills or software. After promising to use their digital photo album space in a manner that meets Yahoo community content standards, users click "upload" to place their **.gif** or **.jpeg** files in their photo album. Like most other online photo albums, Yahoo allows the album creator to choose whether to make their photo album public or keep it private. Public albums are given a universal resource locator (**URL**) address that users can share with others.

Smart frames are electronic picture frames that use universal plug and play (**UPnP**) to allow users to upload, exchange and print photos directly from their digital camera's memory card. **Smart** frames are portable and provide an alternative to **browser**-based digital photo albums. Smart frames often have the same features that online albums have, making them a good alternative for users who want to view their digital photos but do not want to be limited to viewing them on a computer.

Digital Powerline

Digital Powerline (DPL) technology provides the transmission of data to users over the same lines that bring electric power to homes and businesses. Using the Internet's **TCP/IP protocol**, companies using DPL across the mains electricity grid plan to deliver data at speeds up to 1 **Mbps**. DPL would allow a user to get Web pages and other Internet information over power lines with a 24-hour continuous connection (since your power lines are always connected). This would free your telephone for voice use. In addition, since many home appliances are attached to the power system, they could easily be addressed as Internet devices when plugged in.

NOR.WEB, a joint venture of Northern Telecom Limited (Nortel) and the UK-based United Utilities PLC, plans to offer a service to users in the UK. Trials of DPL are ongoing in Manchester, UK., and Milan, Italy. Utilities in Sweden and Germany have also shown interest and are planning trials.

The DPL technology has, however, been dogged by allegations that it has failed to overcome line noise on the power grid; in addition concerns have been addressed in certain countries that DPL will cause the power grid to emit unwanted radio frequency (**RF**) interference. NOR.WEB says, however, that their technology has overcome the line noise problem.

digital pulse wireless

See "ultra wideband radio"

digital rights management

Digital rights management (DRM) is a type of server software developed to enable secure distribution—and perhaps more importantly, to disable illegal distribution—of paid content over the Web. DRM technologies are being developed as a means of protection against the online piracy of commercially marketed material, which has proliferated through the widespread use of **Napster** and other **peer-to-peer** file exchange programs.

Although online content is protected by copyright laws, policing the Web and catching law-breakers is very difficult. DRM technology focuses on making it impossible to steal Web content in the first place, a much surer approach to the problem than the hit-and-miss strategies aimed at apprehending online poachers after the fact. A number of companies are releasing various DRM products based on a variety of approaches and technologies. In general, DRM products are turnkey packages that include everything needed for the operation, such as, for example, server software and user plug-ins.

A Brief Sampling of DRM Products:

ContentGuard (also the name of the company that sells it) DRM software uses XrML (Extensible Rights Markup Language), an **XML**-based language from Xerox's Palo Alto Research Center. Version 1.3 has four major components: a protection toolkit that allows users to decide on their own access and encryption rules, a distribution toolkit that helps users create interfaces for content distribution, a consumer toolkit that verifies authorization before content is distributed, and a **back-office** component that tracks usage and licensing.

InterTrust DRM, which is being developed by its own self-named company and British partner, Magex (of which Paul MacCartney is a prime investor), will focus on the protection of graphic and text content such as **JPEG**, **GIF**, and **PDF** files. The product will support a preview feature, as well as subscription capabilities.

EMediator DRM, from MediaDNA, works through a **plug-in** that users must download before they receive access to protected material. When the plug-in is downloaded, administrators can set various policies for access to different components of the content, such as print or copy restrictions set on material that may be freely viewed, or may set a time limit on access. Content sharing is disabled.

Vyou.com (pronounced *view dot com*) DRM software is made up of a mechanism (in this case called a *director*) that allows users to create their own policies regarding access, a server, and a protective plug-in that downloads automatically when a user attempts to download protected material.

digital signal processing

Digital signal processing (DSP) refers to various techniques for improving the accuracy and reliability of digital communications. Basically, DSP works by clarifying, or standardizing, the *levels* or *states* of a **digital** signal. A DSP circuit is able to differentiate between human-made signals, which are orderly, and **noise**, which is inherently chaotic.

All communications circuits contain some noise. This is true whether the signals are **analog** or digital, and regardless of the type of information conveyed. Noise is the eternal bane of communications engineers, who are always striving to find new ways to improve the **signal-to-noise ratio** in communications systems. Traditional methods of optimizing S/N ratio include increasing the transmitted signal power and increasing the receiver sensitivity. (In **wireless** systems, specialized antenna systems can also help.) Digital signal processing dramatically improves the sensitivity of a receiving unit. The effect is most noticeable when noise competes with a desired signal. A good DSP circuit can sometimes seem like an electronic miracle worker. But there are limits to what it can do. If the noise is so strong that all traces of the signal are obliterated, a DSP circuit cannot find any order in the chaos, and no signal will be received.

If an incoming signal is analog, for example a standard television broadcast station, the signal is first converted to digital form by an *analog-to-digital converter* (**ADC**). The resulting digital signal has two or more levels. Ideally, these levels are always predictable, exact voltages or currents. However, because the incoming signal contains noise, the levels are not always at the standard values. The DSP circuit adjusts the levels so they are at the correct values. This practically eliminates the noise. The digital signal is then converted back to analog form via a *digital-to-analog converter* (**DAC**).

If a received signal is digital, for example computer data, then the ADC and DAC are not necessary. The DSP acts directly on the incoming signal, eliminating irregularities caused by noise, and thereby minimizing the number of errors per unit time.

digital signal X

Digital signal X is a term for the series of standard digital transmission rates or levels based on DS0, a transmission rate of 64 **Kbps**, the **bandwidth** normally usedchannel. Both the North American **T-carrier system** system and the European **E-carrier** systems of transmission operate using the DS series as a base multiple. The digital signal is what is carried inside the carrier system.

DS0 is the base for the digital signal X series. DS1, used as the signal in the T-1 carrier, is 24 DS0 (64 Kbps) signals transmitted using pulse-code modulation (**PCM**) and time-division multiplexing (**TDM**). DS2 is four DS1 signals multiplexed together to produce a rate of 6.312 **Mbps**. DS3, the signal in the T-3 carrier, carries a multiple of 28 DS1 signals or 672 DS0s or 44.736 Mbps.

Digital signal X is based on the **ANSI** T1.107 guidelines. The **ITU-TS** guidelines differ somewhat. The following table summarizes the set of signals and relates them to the T-carrier and E-carrier systems.

Digital Signal Designator	Data Rate	DSo Multiple	T-Carrier	E-Carrier
DS0	64 Kbps	0	—	—
DS1	1.544 Mbps	24	T-1	—
—	2.048 Mbps	32	—	E1
DS1C	3.152 Mbps	48	—	—
DS2	6.312 Mbps	96	T-2	—
—	8.448 Mbps	128	—	E2
—	34.368 Mbps	512	—	E3
DS3	44.736 Mbps	672	T-3	—
—	139.264 Mbps	2048	—	E4
DS4/NA	139.264 Mbps	2176	—	—
DS4	274.176 Mbps	4032	—	—
—	565.148 Mbps	4 E4 channels	—	E5

digital signature legislation

See "Electronic Signatures in Global and National Commerce Act"

Digital Signature Standard

Digital Signature Standard (DSS) is the **digital signature algorithm** (DSA) developed by the U.S. National Security Agency (**NSA**) to generate a digital signature for the **authentication** of electronic documents. DSS was put forth by the National Institute of Standards and Technology (**NIST**) in 1994, and has become the U.S. government standard for authentication of electronic documents. DSS is specified in Federal Information Processing Standard (**FIPS**) 186.

DSA is a pair of large numbers that are computed according to the specified algorithm within parameters that enable the authentication of the signatory, and as a consequence, the **integrity** of the data attached. Digital signatures are generated through DSA, as well as verified. Signatures are generated in conjunction with the use of a **private key**; verification takes place in reference to a corresponding **public key**. Each signatory has their own paired public (assumed to be known to the general public) and private (known only to the user) keys. Because a signature can only be generated by an authorized person using their private key, the corresponding public key can be used by anyone to verify the signature.

A data summary of the information (called a *message digest*) is created through the use of a **hash function** (called the *Secure Hash Standard*, or *SHS*, and specified in FIPS 180). The data summary is used in conjuntion with the DSA algorithm to create the digital signature that is sent with the message. Signature verification involves the use of the same hash function.

digital signature

A digital signature (not to be confused with a **digital certificate**) is an electronic signature that can be used to authenticate the identity of the sender of a message or the signer of a document, and possibly to ensure that the original content of the message or document that has been sent is unchanged. Digital signatures are easily transportable, cannot be imitated by someone else, and can be automatically time-stamped. The ability to ensure that the original signed message arrived means that the sender cannot easily repudiate it later.

A digital signature can be used with any kind of message, whether it is **encrypted** or not, simply so that the receiver can be sure of the sender's identity and that the message arrived intact. A digital certificate contains the digital signature of the certificate-issuing authority so that anyone can verify that the certificate is real.

How It Works

Assume you were going to send the draft of a contract to your lawyer in another town. You want to give your lawyer the assurance that it was unchanged from what you sent and that it is really from you.

1. You copy-and-paste the contract (it's a short one!) into an e-mail note.

2. Using special software, you obtain a message hash (mathematical summary) of the contract.

3. You then use a private key that you have previously obtained from a public-private key authority to encrypt the hash.

4. The encrypted hash becomes your digital signature of the message. (Note that it will be different each time you send a message.)

At the other end, your lawyer receives the message.

1. To make sure it's intact and from you, your lawyer makes a hash of the received message.
2. Your lawyer then uses your public key to decrypt the message hash or summary.
3. If the hashes match, the received message is valid.

Also see **hashing** and **Digital Signature Standard**.

Digital Silhouettes

Digital Silhouettes is the trademarked name that Predictive Networks has given to its complex but anonymous user profiles that are established through gathered **click stream** data and artificial intelligence (**AI**) processes. The profile is built from analysis of an individual's Web site visits, and classifies a user in over 140 demographic (such as "45-year-old suburban female") and content affinity areas (such as "garden enthusiast"). The selected demographics fall into the six major categories of gender, age, income, education, and race—all of which break down to subcategories. There are more than 90 content affinity subcategories, such as golf, pets, and car accessories, for example. Every time a user visits a Web site that is listed in an extensive Predictive Networks database, demographic and content characterization congruent with that site are added to the user's Digital Silhouette. The more Web sites the user visits, and the longer the user is monitored, the more refined the Digital Silhouette will become. Once the profile reaches a critical level of determined accuracy, the user may be sent marketing messages targeted to their Digital Silhouette.

Because of the volume and sensitivity of data gathered, privacy issues have been raised about Digital Silhouettes. Predictive Networks categorizes information with the capacity to identify individuals (such as names and addresses, for example) as Personally Identifiable Information (PII). The company claims that Digital Silhouettes are identified only by randomly assigned and anonymous ID numbers. Nevertheless, the idea that so much individual data is being collected makes many people uneasy; furthermore, some industry insiders believe that identifying information will, in some circumstances, be divulged.

Digital Subscriber Line

DSL (Digital Subscriber Line) is a technology for bringing high-**bandwidth** information to homes and small businesses over ordinary copper telephone lines. xDSL refers to different variations of DSL, such as ADSL, HDSL, and RADSL. Assuming your home or small business is close enough to a telephone company **central office** that offers DSL service, you may be able to receive data at rates up to 6.1 megabits (millions of bits) per second (of a theoretical 8.448 megabits per second), enabling continuous transmission of motion video, audio, and even 3-D effects. More typically, individual connections will provide from 1.544 **Mbps** to 512 Kbps downstream and about 128 Kbps upstream. A DSL line can carry both data and voice signals and the data part of the line is continuously connected. DSL installations began in 1998 and will continue at a greatly increased pace through the next decade in a number of communities in the U.S. and elsewhere. Compaq, Intel, and Microsoft working with telephone companies have developed a standard and easier-to-install form of ADSL called **G.Lite** that is accelerating deployment. DSL is expected to replace **ISDN** in many areas and to compete with the **cable modem** in bringing multimedia and 3-D to homes and small businesses.

Digital Subscriber Line Access Multiplexer

A Digital Subscriber Line Access Multiplexer (DSLAM) is a network device, usually at a telephone company central office, that receives signals from multiple customer Digital Subscriber Line (**DSL**) connections and puts the signals on a high-speed **backbone** line using **multiplexing** techniques. Depending on the product, DSLAM multiplexers connect DSL lines with some combination of asynchronous transfer mode (**ATM**), **frame relay**, or **Internet Protocol** networks. DSLAM enables a phone company to offer business or homes users the fastest phone line technology (DSL) with the fastest backbone network technology (ATM).

digital switch

A digital switch is a device that handles digital signals generated at or passed through a telephone company **central office** and forwards them across the company's **backbone** network. It receives the digital signals from the office's **channel bank**s that have been converted from users' analog signals and switches them with other incoming signals out to the wide area network.

Digital switches are described in terms of classes based on the number of lines and features that are provided. A private branch exchange (**PBX**) is a digital switch owned by a private company. A **centrex** is a digital switch at the central office that manages switching for the private company from the central office.

digital television

Digital television (DTV) is the transmission of television signals using **digital** rather than conventional **analog** methods. Conventional standards—**National Television Standards Committee**, **Phase Alternation Line**, and **Sequential Couleur avec Memoire**—specify analog transmission. However, both the audio and video components of a television signal can be transmitted in **digital** form. Many engineers believe that DTV will become the industry standard within a few years.

Advantages of DTV over analog TV include:

- Superior image resolution (detail) for a given **bandwidth**
- Smaller bandwidth for a given image resolution
- Compatibility with computers and the Internet
- Interactivity
- Superior audio quality
- Consistency of reception over varying distances

Digital television is not the same thing as **HDTV** (high-definition television). HDTV describes a new television format (including a new aspect ratio and pixel size) but not how the format will be transmitted. HDTV can be transmitted in either analog or digital signals. However, since DTV technology is ideally suited for HDTV, it is likely that the names of the two technologies will continue to be used interchangeably.

digital versatile disc

DVD (digital versatile disc) is an optical disc technology that is expected to rapidly replace the **CD-ROM** disc (as well as the audio compact disc) over the next few years. The digital versatile disc (DVD) holds 4.7 **gigabytes** of information on one of its two sides, or enough for a 133-minute movie. With two layers on each of its two sides, it will hold up to 17 gigabytes of video, audio, or other information. (Compare this to the current CD-ROM disc of the same physical size, holding 600 **megabytes**. The DVD can hold more than 28 times as much information!)

DVD-Video is the usual name for the DVD format designed for full-length movies and is a box that will work with your television set. DVD-ROM is the name of the player that will (sooner or later) replace your computer's CD-ROM. It will play regular CD-ROM discs as well as DVD-ROM discs. DVD-RAM is the writeable version. DVD-Audio is a player designed to replace your compact disc player.

DVD uses the MPEG-2 file and compression standard. MPEG-2 images have four times the resolution of MPEG-1 images and can be delivered at 60 interlaced fields per second where two fields constitute one image frame. (MPEG-1 can deliver 30 noninterlaced frames per second.) Audio quality on DVD is comparable to that of current audio compact discs.

digital video

Digital video is part of digital versatile disc (**DVD**), a new optical disc technology that is expected to rapidly replace the **CD-ROM** over the next few years. The DVD holds 4.7 **gigabytes** of information on one of its two sides, or enough for a 133-minute movie. With two layers on each of its two sides, it will hold up to 17 gigabytes of video, audio, or other information. (Compare this to the current CD-ROM disc of the same physical size, holding 600 **megabytes**. The DVD can hold more than 28 times as much information.)

The DVD player will also play regular CD-ROM discs. DVDs can be recorded in any of three formats, variously optimized for: video (for example, continous movies) audio (for example, long-playing music), or a mixture (for example, interactive multimedia presentations). The DVD drive has a transfer rate somewhat faster than an eight-speed CD-ROM player.

DVD uses the **MPEG-2** file and compression standard. MPEG-2 images have four times the resolution of MPEG-1 images and can be delivered at 60 interlaced fields per second where two fields constitute one image frame. (MPEG-1 can deliver 30 noninterlaced frames per second.) Audio quality on DVD is comparable to that of current audio compact discs.

Digital Video Broadcasting

Digital Video Broadcasting (DVB) is a set of standards that define digital broadcasting using existing satellite, cable, and terrestrial infrastructures. In the early 1990s, European broadcasters, consumer equipment manufacturers, and regulatory bodies formed the European Launching Group (ELG) to discuss introducing **digital television** (DTV) throughout Europe. Today, the DVB Project consists of over 220 organizations in more than 29 countries worldwide. DVB-compliant digital broadcasting and equipment is widely available and is distinguished by the DVB logo. Numerous DVB broadcast services are available in Europe, North and South America, Africa, Asia, and Australia. The term *digital television* is sometimes used as a synonym for DVB. However, the Advanced Television Systems Committee (**ATSC**) standard is the digital broadcasting standard used in the U.S.

A fundamental decision of the DVB Project was the selection of MPEG-2, one of a series of **MPEG standards** for **compression** of audio and video signals. MPEG-2 reduces a single signal from 166 Mbits to 5 Mbits allowing broadcasters to transmit digital signals using existing cable, satellite, and terrestrial systems. MPEG-2 uses the **lossy compression** method, which means that the digital signal sent to the television is compressed and some data is lost. This lost data does not affect how the human eye perceives the picture. Two digital television formats that use MPEG-2 compression are standard definition television (**SDTV**) and high definition television (**HDTV**). SDTV's picture and sound quality is similar to digital versatile disc (**DVD**). HDTV programming presents five times as much information to the eye than SDTV, resulting in cinema-quality programming.

DVB uses **conditional access** (CA) systems to prevent external piracy. There are numerous CA systems available to content providers allowing them to choose the CA system that they feel is adequate for the services they provide. Each CA system provides a security module that scrambles and encrypts data. This security module is embedded within the receiver or is detachable in the form of a **PC card**. Inside the receiver, there is a **smart card** that contains the user's access information. The following describes the conditional access process:

- The receiver receives the digital data stream.

- The data flows into the conditional access module, which contains the content provider's unscrambling **algorithms**.

- The conditional access module verifies the existence of a smart card that contains the subscriber's authorization code.

- If the authorization code is accepted, the conditional access module unscrambles the data and returns the data to the receiver. If the code is not accepted, the data remains scrambled restricting access.

- The receiver then decodes the data and outputs it for viewing.

For years, smart cards have been used for pay TV programming. Smart cards are inexpensive allowing the content provider to issue updated smart cards periodically to prevent piracy. Detachable PC cards allow subscribers to use DVB services anywhere DVB technology is supported.

DVB is an **open** system as opposed to a closed system. Closed systems are content provider-specific, not expandable, and optimized only for television. Open systems such as DVB allows the subscriber to choose different content providers and allows integration of PCs and televisions. DVB systems are optimized for not only television but also for home shopping and banking, private network broadcasting, and interactive viewing. DVB offers the future possibilities of providing high-quality television display in buses, cars, trains, and hand-held devices. DVB allows content providers to offer their services anywhere DVB is supported regardless of geographic location, expand their services easily and inexpensively, and ensure restricted access to subscribers, thus reducing lost revenue due to unauthorized viewing.

Digital-Advanced Mobile Phone Service

See "D-AMPS"

digital-to-analog conversion

Digital-to-analog conversion is a process in which signals having a few (usually two) defined levels or states (**digital**) are converted into signals having a theoretically infinite number of states (**analog**). A common example is the processing, by a **modem**,of computer data into audio-frequency (AF) tones that can be transmitted over a **twisted pair** telephone line. The circuit that performs this function is a *digital-to-analog converter (DAC)*.

Basically, digital-to-analog conversion is the opposite of **analog-to-digital conversion**. In most cases, if an *analog-to-digital converter (ADC)* is placed in a communications circuit after a DAC, the digital signal output is identical to the

digital signal input. Also, in most instances when a DAC is placed after an ADC, the analog signal output is identical to the analog signal input.

Binary digital impulses, all by themselves, appear as long strings of ones and zeros, and have no apparent meaning to a human observer. But when a DAC is used to decode the binary digital signals, meaningful output appears. This might be a voice, a picture, a musical tune, or mechanical motion.

Both the DAC and the ADC are of significance in some applications of **digital signal processing**. The intelligibility or fidelity of an analog signal can often be improved by converting the analog input to digital form using a DAC, then clarifying the digital signal, and finally converting the "cleaned-up" digital impulses back to analog form using an ADC.

DIMM

A DIMM (dual in-line memory module) is a double **SIMM** (single in-line memory module). Like a SIMM, it's a **module** containing one or several random access **memory** (**RAM**) chips on a small circuit board with pins that connect it to the computer **motherboard**. A SIMM typically has a 32 data bit (36 bits counting **parity** bits) path to the computer that requires a 72-pin connector. For synchronous dynamic RAM (**SDRAM**) chips, which have a 64 data bit connection to the computer, SIMMs must be installed in in-line pairs (since each supports a 32-bit path). A single DIMM can be used instead. A DIMM has a 168-pin connector and supports 64-bit data transfer.

diode

A diode is a specialized electronic component with two electrodes called the *anode* and the *cathode*. Most diodes are made with **semiconductor** materials such as silicon, germanium, or selenium. Some diodes are comprised of metal electrodes in a chamber evacuated or filled with a pure elemental gas at low pressure. Diodes can be used as rectifiers, signal limiters, voltage regulators, **switch**es, signal modulators, signal mixers, signal demodulators, and **oscillators**.

The fundamental property of a diode is its tendency to conduct electric **current** in only one direction. When the cathode is negatively charged relative to the anode at a **voltage** greater than a certain minimum called *forward breakover*, then current flows through the diode. If the cathode is positive with respect to the anode, is at the same voltage as the anode, or is negative by an amount less than the forward breakover voltage, then the diode does not conduct current. This is a simplistic view, but is true for diodes operating as rectifiers, switches, and limiters. The forward breakover voltage is approximately six tenths of a volt (0.6 V) for silicon devices, 0.3 V for germanium devices, and 1 V for selenium devices.

The above general rule notwithstanding, if the cathode voltage is positive relative to the anode voltage by a great enough amount, the diode will conduct current. The voltage required to produce this phenomenon, known as the *avalanche voltage*, varies greatly depending on the nature of the semiconductor material from which the device is fabricated. The avalanche voltage can range from a few volts up to several hundred volts.

When an **analog** signal passes through a diode operating at or near its forward breakover point, the signal waveform is distorted. This *nonlinearity* allows for modulation, demodulation, and signal mixing. In addition, signals are generated at *harmonics*, or integral multiples of the input **frequency**. Some diodes also have a characteristic that is imprecisely termed *negative resistance*. Diodes of this type, with the application of a voltage at the correct level and the polarity, generate analog signals at microwave radio frequencies.

Semiconductor diodes can be designed to produce direct current (**DC**) when visible light, **infrared transmission** (IR), or ultraviolet (UV) energy strikes them. These diodes are known as *photovoltaic cells* and are the basis for solar electric energy systems and photosensors. Yet another form of diode, commonly used in electronic and computer equipment, emits visible light or IR energy when current passes through it. Such a device is the familiar *light-emitting diode* (LED).

dipole antenna

A dipole antenna is a straight electrical conductor measuring $1/2$ **wavelength** from end to end and connected at the center to a radio-frequency (**RF**) **feed line**. This antenna, also called a *doublet*, is one of the simplest types of **antennas**, and constitutes the main RF radiating and receiving element in various sophisticated types of antennas. The dipole is inherently a balanced antenna, because it is bilaterally symmetrical.

Ideally, a dipole antenna is fed with a balanced, parallel-wire RF transmission line. However, this type of line is not common. An unbalanced feed line, such as **coaxial cable**, can be used, but to ensure optimum RF **current** distribution on the antenna element and in the feed line, an RF transformer called a *balun* (contraction of the words "balanced" and "unbalanced") should be inserted in the system at the point where the feed line joins the antenna. For best performance, a dipole antenna should be more than $1/2$ wavelength above the ground, the surface of a body of water, or other horizontal, conducting medium such as sheet metal roofing. The element should also be at least several wavelengths away from electrically conducting obstructions such as supporting towers, utility wires, guy wires, and other antennas.

Dipole antennas can be oriented horizontally, vertically, or at a slant. The polarization of the **electromagnetic field** (EM) radiated by a dipole transmitting antenna corresponds to the orientation of the element. When the antenna is used to receive RF signals, it is most sensitive to EM fields whose polarization is parallel to the orientation of the element. The RF current in a dipole is maximum at the center (the point where the feed line joins the element), and is minimum at the ends of the element. The RF **voltage** is maximum at the ends and is minimum at the center.

direct access storage device

See "DASD"

direct access

In computer storage, direct access is the ability to obtain data from a storage device by going directly to where it is physically located on the device rather than by having to sequentially look for the data at one physical location after another. A direct access storage device (**DASD**) has the electrical or electromechanical means to be immediately positioned for reading and writing at any addressable location on the device.

An alternative to direct access is **sequential access**, in which a data location is found by starting at one place and seeking through every successive location until the data is found. Historically, **tape storage** is associated with sequential access, and **disk storage** is associated with direct access.

direct current

See "DC"

Direct Inward Dialing

Direct Inward Dialing (DID) is a service of a local phone company (or **local exchange carrier**) that provides a block of telephone numbers for calling into a company's **private branch exchange** (PBX) system. Using DID, a company can offer its customers individual phone numbers for each person or workstation within the company without requiring a physical line into the PBX for each possible connection.

For example, a company might rent 100 phone numbers from the phone company that could be called over eight physical telephone lines (these are called "trunk lines"). This would allow up to eight ongoing calls at a time; additional inbound calls would get a busy signal until one of the calls completed or be able to leave a voice mail message. The PBX automatically switches a call for a given phone number to the appropriate workstation in the company. A PBX switchboard operator is not involved.

A DID system can be used for **fax** and voice mail as well as for live voice connections. Compared to regular PBX service, DID saves the cost of a switchboard operator, calls go through faster, and callers feel they are calling a person rather than a company.

Direct Memory Access

Direct Memory Access (DMA) is a capability provided by some computer **bus** architectures that allows **data** to be sent directly from an attached device (such as a disk drive) to the **memory** on the computer's **motherboard**. The **microprocessor** is freed from involvement with the data transfer, thus speeding up overall computer operation.

Usually a specified portion of memory is designated as an area to be used for direct memory access. In the **ISA** bus standard, up to 16 megabytes of memory can be addressed for DMA. The **EISA** and **Micro Channel Architecture** standards allow access to the full range of memory addresses (assuming they're addressable with 32 bits). **Peripheral Component Interconnect** accomplishes DMA by using a **bus master** (with the microprocessor "delegating" I/O control to the PCI controller).

An alternative to DMA is the Programmed Input/Output (**PIO**) interface in which all data transmitted between devices goes through the processor. A newer protocol for the ATA/IDE interface is **Ultra DMA**, which provides a **burst** data transfer rate up to 33 MB (**megabytes**) per second.

Direct Rambus

See "DRDRAM"

direct sequence spread spectrum

Direct sequence spread spectrum, also known as direct sequence code division multiple access (DS-CDMA), is one of two approaches to **spread spectrum modulation** for digital signal transmission over the airwaves. In direct sequence spread spectrum, the stream of information to be transmitted is divided into small pieces, each of which is allocated across to a frequency channel across the spectrum. A data signal at the point of transmission is combined with a higher data-rate bit sequence (also known as a *chipping code*) that divides the data according to a spreading ratio. The redundant chipping code helps the signal resist interference and also enables the original data to be recovered if data bits are damaged during transmission.

Direct sequence contrasts with the other spread spectrum process, known as frequency hopping spread spectrum, or frequency hopping code division multiple access (**FH-CDMA**), in which a broad slice of the bandwidth spectrum is divided into many possible broadcast frequencies. In general, frequency-hopping devices use less power and are cheaper, but the performance of DS-CDMA systems is usually better and more reliable.

Spread spectrum first was developed for use by the military because it uses wideband signals that are difficult to detect and that resist attempts at jamming. In recent years, researchers have turned their attention to applying spread spectrum processes for commercial purposes, especially in local area wireless networks.

directory

A directory is, in general, an approach to organizing information, the most familiar example being a telephone directory.

1) On the World Wide Web, a directory is a subject guide, typically organized by major topics and subtopics. The best-known directory is the one at Yahoo (http://www.yahoo.com). Many other sites now use a Yahoo-like directory including major **portal** sites.

2) In computer file systems, a directory is a named group of related **files** that are separated by the naming convention from other groups of files.

3) In computer networks, a directory is a collection of users, user passwords, and, usually, information about what network resources they can access.

Directory Services Markup Language

See "DSML"

Directory-Enabled Networking

See "DEN"

DirectX

DirectX is an application program interface (**API**) for creating and managing graphic images and multimedia effects in **application**s such as games or active Web pages that will run in Microsoft's Windows **operating system**s. (Such an application program might be written in **C++**, or Visual C/C++, or **Java**.) The capability to "play" DirectX applications comes as an integrated part of Microsoft's Internet Explorer Web **browser**. (A 3-D player is optionally downloadable.)

The DirectX Software Development Kit (SDK) includes tools that let a developer create or integrate graphic images, overlays, **sprite**s, and other game elements, including sound. There is also a Driver Development Kit (DDK) that lets developers create **driver**s for display, audio, and other I/O devices.

DirectX is part of Microsoft's larger vision of an **object-oriented** development environment. For example, a sprite is created as an instance of a sprite **class**. Developers can also take advantage of Microsoft's set of prepackaged routines or small programs that are part of the **Microsoft Foundation Class Library**.

DirectX is designed so that some functions can be performed on a graphics accelerator **card**, freeing the microprocessor for other work. The accelerator manufacturer provides a **driver** especially for DirectX.

DirectX consists of five components:

- DirectDraw, an interface that lets you define two-dimensional images, specify textures, and manage double buffers (a technique for changing images)

- Direct3D, an interface for creating three-dimensional images

- DirectSound, an interface for integrating and coordinating sound with the images

- DirectPlay, a plug-in for end users, is also used by developers to test their application

- DirectInput, an interface for input from I/O devices

DirXML

DirXML is Novell's directory interchange software that uses **XML** to keep different directories synchronized. With DirXML, an IT manager can administer multiple user databases from a single interface, using Novell Directory Services (**NDS**) eDirectory to replicate the information. DirXML works within an existing network infrastructure and integrates NDS with directories in Microsoft Exchange, Lotus **Notes**, Windows 2000 **Active Directory**, and others.

As data flows into DirXML, it is translated into XML. The data is also converted into the target directory's native data format.

Novell is the first software vendor to utilize XML as the key language for directory **schema** publishing, data interchange, and query. Using DirXML, a company only has to enter information once and it will be identically replicated across its entire network. For instance, should a company insert address changes into a customer service database, those changes will automatically appear in its billing, shipping, and marketing directories. Thus, DirXML reduces manual labor costs, minimizes the possibility for human error, and saves in redundant data management expenses.

DirXML supports **Windows 2000**, **Windows NT**, Sun **Solaris**, **NetWare**, and **Linux**. Novell plans to add support for UNIX Tru64.

disaster recovery plan

A disaster recovery plan (DRP)—sometimes referred to as a Business Continuity Plan (BCP) or Business Process Contingency Plan (BPCP)—describes how an organization is to deal with potential disasters. Just as a disaster is an event that makes the continuation of normal functions impossible, a disaster recovery plan consists of the precautions taken so that the effects of a disaster will be minimized, and the organization will be able to either maintain or quickly resume **mission-critical** functions. Typically, disaster recovery planning involves an analysis of business processes and continuity needs; it may also include a significant focus on disaster prevention.

Disaster recovery is becoming an increasingly important aspect of enterprise computing. As devices, systems, and networks become ever more complex, there are simply more things that can go wrong. As a consequence, recovery plans have also become more complex. According to Jon William Toigo (the author of *Disaster Recovery Planning*), fifteen years ago a disaster recovery plan might consist of powering down a **mainframe** and other computers in advance of a threat (such as a fire, for example, or the sprinkler system), disassembling components, and subsequently drying circuit boards in the parking lot with a hair dryer. Current enterprise systems tend to be too complicated for such simple and hands-on approaches, however, and interruption of service or loss of data can have serious financial impact, whether directly or through loss of customer confidence.

Appropriate plans vary a great from one enterprise to another, depending on variables such as the type of business, the processes involved, and the level of security needed. Disaster recovery planning may be developed within an organization or purchased as a software application or a service. It is not unusual for an enterprise to spend 25% of its Information Technology (**IT**) budget on disaster recovery.

disaster recovery planning

See "disaster recovery plan"

discrete

Discrete (pronounced dihs-KREET, from the Latin *discretus* and perhaps *discernere*, meaning to separate) is an adjective meaning separate and distinct. *Discretion* and *discreet* derive from the same origin and have to do with the use of separate or individual judgement.

discrete multitone

Discrete multitone (DMT) is a method of separating a Digital Subscriber Line (**DSL**) signal so that the usable frequency range is separated into 256 frequency bands (or **channels**) of 4.3125 **KHz** each. DMT uses the fast Fourier transform (**FFT**) **algorithm** for **modulation** and demodulation. Dividing the frequency spectrum into multiple channels allows DMT to work better when AM radio transmitters are present. Within each channel, modulation uses quadratude amplitude modulation (**QAM**). By varying the number of bits per symbol within a channel, the modem can be rate-adaptive. Both **G.DMT** and **G.Lite** use DMT.

Other modulation technologies for DSL are carrierless amplitude modulation (**CAP**) and multiple virtual line (**MVL**). However, DMT is the most widely used and appears to be becoming the industry standard.

discussion board

A discussion board is a general term for any online "bulletin board" where you can leave and expect to see responses to messages you have left. Or you can just read the board. **Bulletin board service**s were invented for this purpose (as well as to allow for the exchange of uploaded/downloaded files). On the Internet, **Usenet** provides thousands of discussion boards. Discussion board software is now available that allows discussion boards to be added to a Web site.

dish antenna

A dish antenna, also known simply as a *dish*, is common in **microwave** systems. This type of antenna can be used for **satellite** communication and broadcast reception, space communications, radio astronomy, and radar.

A dish antenna consists of an active, or driven, element and a passive parabolic or spherical reflector. The driven element can be a **dipole antenna** or a **horn antenna**. If a horn is used, it is aimed back at the center of the reflecting dish. The reflector has a diameter of at least several **wavelength**s. As the wavelength increases (and the **frequency** decreases), the minimum required dish diameter becomes larger.

When the dipole or horn is properly positioned and aimed, incoming **electromagnetic field**s bounce off the reflector, and the energy converges on the driven element. If the horn or dipole is connected to a transmitter, the element emits electromagnetic waves that bounce off the reflector and propagate outward in a narrow beam.

A dish antenna is usually operated with an unbalanced **feed line**. For satellite television reception, **coaxial cable** is used. In applications such as radar where a high-power signal is transmitted, a feed system is preferred.

disintermediation

Disintermediation is giving the user or the consumer direct access to information that otherwise would require a mediator, such as a salesperson, a librarian, or a lawyer. Observers of the Internet and the World Wide Web note that these new technologies give users the power to look up medical, legal, travel, or comparative product information directly, in some cases removing the need for the mediator (doctor, lawyer, salesperson) or at the very least changing the relationship between the user and the product or service provider.

Also see **antidisintermediation**.

disk

See "diskette"

disk cache

A disk cache is a mechanism for improving the time it takes to read from or write to a **hard disk**. Today, the disk cache is usually included as part of the hard disk. A disk cache can also be a specified portion of random access memory (**RAM**). The disk cache holds data that has recently been read and, in some cases, adjacent data areas that are likely to be accessed next. Write caching is also provided with some disk caches.

The other type of hardware cache inside your computer is **cache memory**. Also see **cache**.

Disk Operating System

See "DOS"

disk striping

In computers that use multiple hard disk systems, disk striping is the process of dividing a body of data into blocks and spreading the data blocks across several **partition**s on several **hard disk**s. Each stripe is the size of the smallest partition. For example, if three partitions are selected with one partition equaling 150 **megabyte**s, another 100MB, and the third 50MB, each stripe will be 50 MB in size. It is wise to create the partitions equal in size to prevent wasting disk space. Each stripe created is part of the stripe set. Disk striping is used with redundant array of independent disks (RAID). RAID is a storage system that uses multiple disks to store and distribute data. Up to 32 hard disks can be used with disk striping.

There are two types of disk striping: single user and multi-user. Single user disk striping allows multiple hard disks to simultaneously service multiple **I/O** requests from a single workstation. Multi-user disk striping allows multiple I/O requests from several workstations to be sent to multiple hard disks. This means that while one hard disk is servicing a request from a workstation, another hard disk is handling a separate request from a different workstation.

Disk striping is used with or without **parity**. When disk striping is used with parity, an additional stripe that contains the parity information is stored on its own partition and hard disk. If a hard disk fails, a fault tolerance driver makes the lost partition invisible allowing reading and writing operations to continue which provides time to create a new stripe set. Once a hard disk fails, the stripe set is no longer fault tolerant, which means that if one or more hard disks fail after the first one, the stripe set is lost. Disk striping without parity provides no fault tolerance. The disk striping process is used in conjunction with software that lets the user know when a disk has failed. This software also allows the user to define the size of the stripes, the color assigned to the stripe set for recognition and diagnosing, and whether parity was used or not.

diskette

A diskette is a random access, removable data storage medium that can be used with personal computers. The term usually refers to the magnetic medium housed in a rigid plastic cartridge measuring 3.5 inches square and about 2 millimeters thick. Also called a "3.5-inch diskette," it can store up to 1.44 megabytes (MB) of data. Although most

personal computers today come with a 3.5-inch diskette drive pre-installed, some **network computers** now omit them.

Some older computers provide drives for magnetic diskettes that are 5.25 inches square, about 1 millimeter thick, and capable of holding 1.2 megabytes of data. These were sometimes called "floppy disks" or "floppies" because their housings are flexible. In recent years, 5.25-inch diskettes have been largely replaced by 3.5-inch diskettes, which are physically more rugged. Many people also call the newer hard-cased diskette a "floppy."

Magnetic diskettes are convenient for storing individual files and small programs. However, the **magneto-optical diskette** is more popular for mass storage, backup, and archiving. An MO diskette is only a little larger, physically, than a conventional 3.5-inch magnetic diskette. But because of the sophisticated read/write technology, the MO diskette can store many times more data.

displacement

Displacement (symbolized d or s), also called length or distance, is a one-dimensional quantity representing the separation betwen two defined points. The standard unit of displacement in the International System of Units (**SI**) is the **meter** (m).

Displacement is usually measured or defined along a straight line. For example, we might speak of the distance between the center of the earth and an orbiting **satellite**, and measure it as 13,000,000 meters. However, displacement is sometimes measured or defined along curved paths. The most common example is in expressions of the distance between geographic locations on the earth's surface; the equator is approximately 10,000,000 meters from the North Pole, for example. Other examples of nonlinear displacement include the circumference of a subatomic particle, the actual length (as opposed to the straight span) of a sagging rope, or the length of wire that comprises a coil.

When expressing large or small distances, **prefix multipliers** are attached to the meter. The table below shows the most common alternative displacement units and their relationship to the meter.

Unit (and symbol)	To convert to meters, multiply by:	Conversely, multiply by:
kilometer (km)	1000	0.001
centimeter (cm)	0.01	100
millimeter (mm)	0.001	1000
micrometer or micron (μ)	10^{-6}	10^6
nanometer (nm)	10^{-9}	10^9
Angström (Å)	10^{-10}	10^{10}

Compare **area**, and **volume**.

Also see **centimeter**, **meter**, **meter squared**, **meter cubed**, and International System of Units (**SI**).

display

A display is a computer output surface and projecting mechanism that shows text and often graphic images to the computer user, using a cathode ray tube (**CRT**), liquid crystal display (**LCD**), light-emitting diode, gas plasma, or other image projection technology. The display is usually considered to include the **screen** or projection surface and the device that produces the information on the screen. In some computers, the display is packaged in a separate unit called a **monitor**. In other computers, the display is integrated into a unit with the processor and other parts of the computer. (Some sources make the distinction that the monitor includes other signal-handling devices that feed and control the display or projection device. However, this distinction disappears when all these parts become integrated into a total unit, as in the case of notebook computers.) Displays (and monitors) are also sometimes called *video display terminals (VDTs)*. The terms *display* and *monitor* are often used interchangably.

Most computer displays use **analog** signals as input to the display image creation mechanism. This requirement and the need to continually refresh the display image mean that the computer also needs a display or **video adapter**. The video adapter takes the **digital** data sent by application programs, stores it in video random access memory (**video RAM**), and converts it to analog data for the display scanning mechanism using an digital-to-analog converter (**DAC**).

Displays can be characterized according to:

- Color capability
- Sharpness and viewability
- The size of the screen
- The projection technology

Color Capability

Today, most desktop displays provide color. Notebook and smaller computers sometimes have a less expensive *monochrome* display. Displays can usually operate in one of several **display modes** that determine how many bits are used to describe color and how many colors can be displayed. A display that can operate in SuperVGA mode can display up to 16,777,216 colors because it can process a 24-bit long description of a **pixel**. The number of bits used to describe a pixel is known as its *bit-depth*. The 24-bit bit-depth is also known as **true color**. It allows eight bits for each of the three additive primary colors—red, green, and blue. Although human beings can't really distinguish that many colors, the 24-bit system is convenient for graphic designers since it allocates one byte for each color. The Visual Graphics

Array (**VGA**) mode is the lowest common denominator of display modes. Depending on the resolution setting, it can provide up to 256 colors.

Sharpness and Viewability

The absolute physical limitation on the potential image sharpness of a screen image is the **dot pitch**, which is the size of an individual beam that gets through to light up a point of phosphor on the screen. (The shape of this beam can be round or a vertical, slot-shaped rectangle depending on the display technology.) Displays typically come with a dot pitch of .28 mm (millimeters) or smaller. The smaller the dot pitch in millimeters, the greater the potential image sharpness.

The actual sharpness of any particular overall display image is measured in dots-per-inch (**dpi**). The dots-per-inch is determined by a combination of the screen **resolution** (how many **pixel**s are projected on the screen horizontally and vertically) and the physical screen size. The same resolution spread out over a larger screen offers reduced sharpness. On the other hand, a high-resolution setting on a smaller surface will product a sharper image, but text readability will become more difficult.

Viewability includes the ability to see the screen image well from different angles. Displays with cathode ray tubes (**CRT**) generally provide good viewability from angles other than straight on. Flat-panel displays, including those using light-emitting diode and liquid crystal display technology, are often harder to see at angles other than straight on.

The Size of the Screen

On desktop computers, the display screen width relative to height, known as the *aspect ratio*, is generally standardized at 4 to 3 (usually indicated as "4:3"). Screen sizes are measured in either millimeters or inches diagonally from one corner to the opposite corner. Popular desktop screen sizes are 12-, 13-, 15-, and 17-inch. Notebook screen sizes are somewhat smaller.

The Projection Technology

Most displays in current use employ cathode ray tube (**CRT**) technology similar to that used in most television sets. The CRT technology requires a certain distance from the beam projection device to the screen in order to function. Using other technologies, displays can be much thinner and are known as *flat-panel displays*. Flat panel display technologies include light-emitting diode (**LED**), liquid crystal display (**LCD**), and gas plasma. LED and gas plasma work by lighting up display screen positions based on the voltages at different grid intersections. LCDs work by blocking light rather than creating it. LCDs require far less energy than LED and gas plasma technologies and are currently the primary technology for notebook and other mobile computers.

Displays generally handle data input as **character** maps or **bitmap**s. In character-mapping mode, a display has a preallocated amount of pixel space for each character. In bitmap mode, it receives an exact representation of the screen image that is to be projected in the form of a sequence of bits that describe the color values for specific **x and y coordinates** starting from a given location on the screen. Displays that handle bitmaps are also known as *all-points addressable* displays.

display modes

Displays for personal computers have steadily improved since the days of the monochrome monitors that were used in word processors and text-based computer systems in the 1970s. In 1981, IBM introduced the Color Graphics Adapter (CGA). This display system was capable of rendering four colors, and had a maximum **resolution** of 320 **pixel**s horizontally by 200 pixels vertically. While CGA was all right for simple computer games such as solitaire and checkers, it did not offer sufficient image resolution for extended sessions of word processing, desktop publishing, or sophisticated graphics applications.

In 1984, IBM introduced the Enhanced Graphics Adapter (EGA) display. It allowed up to 16 different colors and improved the resolution to 640 pixels horizontally by 350 pixels vertically. This improved the appearance of the display and made it possible to read text more easily than with CGA. Nevertheless, EGA did not offer sufficient image resolution for high-level applications such as graphic design and desktop publishing.

In 1987, IBM introduced the Video Graphics Array (VGA) display system. This has become the accepted minimum standard for PC clones. Many VGA monitors are still in use today. The maximum resolution depends on the number of colors displayed. You can choose between 16 colors at 640 × 480 pixels, or 256 colors at 320 × 200 pixels. All IBM-compatible computers support the VGA standard.

In 1990, IBM intoduced the Extended Graphics Array (XGA) display as a successor to its 8514/A display. A later version, XGA-2 offers 800 by 600 pixel resolution in **true color** (16 million colors) and 1,024 by 768 resolution in 65,536 colors.

Most PC displays sold today are described as Super Video Graphics Array (SVGA) displays. SVGA originally just meant "beyond "VGA" and was not a single standard. More recently, the Video Electronics Standards Assocation (**VESA**) has established a standard programming interface for SVGA displays, called the VESA BIOS Extension. Typically, an SVGA display can support a palette of up to 16,000,000 colors, although the amount of video memory in a particular computer may limit the actual number of displayed colors to something less than that. Image-resolution specifications vary. In general, the larger the diagonal screen measure of an SVGA monitor, the more pixels it can display horizontally and vertically. Small SVGA monitors (14-inch diagonal) usually display 800 pixels

horizontally by 600 pixels vertically. The largest monitors (20 inches or more diagonal measure) can display 1280 × 1024, or even 1600 × 1200, pixels.

distance

See "displacement"

distance education

Distance education is a formalized teaching system specifically designed to be carried out remotely. The students and the teacher are in different locations and lectures are transmitted through some type of technology such as closed-circuit or public television or an interactive Web site.

Distance education methods include:

- Voice-centered techniques, such as recordings, audioconferencing, and short-wave radio

- Video techniques, such as video cassettes, **videoconferencing**, or Web cameras

- Computer-centered techniques, such as computer-assisted instruction (CAI), which uses the computer as a teaching machine to present individual lessons, computer-mediated education (CME), which uses computer applications (e-mail, fax, or online chatting, for example) for delivery of instruction

- Print, such as books and hand-outs

Because distance education is less expensive to support and is not constrained by geographic considerations, it offers opportunities in situations where traditional education has difficulty operating. Students with scheduling or distance problems can benefit, as can workers, because distance education can be more flexible in terms of time and can be delivered virtually anywhere. Studies indicate that distance learning can be as effective as the traditional format when the methods are appropriate to the teaching tasks, there is student-teacher interaction, and the teachers provide students with appropriate and timely feedback.

distributed

Computing is said to be "distributed" when the computer programming and data that computers work on are spread out over more than one computer, usually over a network. Computing prior to low-cost computer power on the desktop, was organized in centralized "glass houses" (so-called because the computers were often shown to visitors through picture windows). Although these centers still exist, large and small enterprises over time are moving (distributing) applications and data to where they can operate most efficiently in the enterprise, to some mix of desktop workstations, local area network servers, regional servers, Web servers, and other servers. A popular trend has been **client/server** computing which is simply the view that a client computer can provide certain capabilities for a user

and request others from other computers that provide services for the clients. (The Web's **Hypertext Transfer Protocol** protocol is an example of this idea.)

The Distributed Computing Environment (**DCE**) is a particular industry standard for implementing a distributed computing environment. Today, major software makers are fostering an object-oriented view of distributed computing. As a distributed publishing environment with **Java** and other products that help companies create distributed applications, the World Wide Web is accelerating the trend toward distributed computing and the view that, as Sun Microsystem's slogan says, "The network is the computer."

distributed authoring

See "WebDAV"

Distributed Component Object Model

See "DCOM"

Distributed Computing Environment

See "DCE"

distributed denial-of-service attack

On the Internet, a distributed denial-of-service (DDoS) attack is one in which a multitude of compromised systems attack a single target, thereby causing **denial of service** for users of the targeted system. The flood of incoming messages to the target system essentially forces it to shut down, thereby denying service to the system to legitimate users.

A **hacker** (or, if you prefer, **cracker**) begins a DDoS attack by exploiting a vulnerability in one computer system and making it the DDoS "master." It is from the master system that the intruder identifies and communicates with other systems that can be compromised. The intruder loads cracking tools available on the Internet on multiple—sometimes thousands of—compromised systems. With a single command, the intruder instructs the controlled machines to launch one of many flood attacks against a specified target. The inundation of **packet**s to the target causes a denial of service.

While the press tends to focus on the target of DDoS attacks as the victim, in reality there are many victims in a DDoS attack—the final target and as well the systems controlled by the intruder.

distributed file system

A distributed file system is a **client/server**-based **application** that allows **clients** to access and process data stored on the **server** as if it were on their own computer. When a user accesses a file on the server, the server sends the user a copy of the file, which is **cached** on the user's computer while the data is being processed and is then returned to the server.

Ideally, a distributed file system organizes file and **directory** services of individual servers into a global directory in such a way that remote data access is not location-specific but is identical from any client. All files are accessible to all users of the global file system and organization is hierarchical and directory-based.

Since more than one client may access the same data simultaneously, the server must have a mechanism in place (such as maintaining information about the times of access) to organize updates so that the client always receives the most current version of data and that data conflicts do not arise. Distributed file systems typically use file or database replication (distributing copies of data on multiple servers) to protect against data access failures.

Sun Microsystems' Network File System (**NFS**), Novell **NetWare**, Microsoft's Distributed File System, and IBM/Transarc's DFS are some examples of distributed file systems.

Distributed interNet Applications Architecture

See "Web Solution Platform"

distributed learning

Distributed learning is a general term used to describe a multi-media method of instructional delivery that includes a mix of Web-based instruction, **streaming video** conferencing, face-to-face classroom time, distance learning through television or video, or other combinations of electronic and traditional educational models. Although distributed learning can be executed in a variety of ways, it is consistent in that it always accommodates a separation of geographical locations for part (or all) of the instruction, and focuses on learner-to-learner as well as instructor-to-learner interaction. Corporations and universities are using and promoting distributed learning for staff development, technical training, and advanced-degree coursework.

dithering

Dithering is the attempt by a computer program to approximate a color from a mixture of other colors when the required color is not available. For example, dithering occurs when a color is specified for a Web page that a **browser** on a particular **operating system** can't support. The browser will then attempt to replace the requested color with an approximation composed of two or more other colors it can produce. The result may or may not be acceptable to the graphic designer. It may also appear somewhat grainy since it's composed of different pixel intensities rather than a single intensity over the colored space.

Dithering also occurs when a display monitor attempts to display images specified with more colors than the monitor is equipped to handle.

Dithering is rather easy to confuse with **antialiasing**.

DKNF

See "normalization"

DLC

See "data link control"

DLL

See "dynamic link library"

DMA

See "Direct Memory Access"

DMI

Desktop Management Interface (DMI) is an industry framework for managing and keeping track of hardware and software components in a system of personal computers from a central location. DMI was created by the Desktop Management Task Force (DMTF) to automate system management and is particularly beneficial in a network computing environment where dozens or more computers are managed. DMI is hardware and operating system-independent, independent of specific management **protocol**, easy for vendors to adopt, mappable to existing management protocols such as the Simple Network Management Protocol (**SNMP**), and used on network and non-network computers. DMI consists of four components:

- **Management Information Format (MIF):** An MIF is a text file that contains specific information about the hardware and software being used on a computer. An MIF file consists of one or more groups containing attributes, which describe each component. By default, each MIF file contains the standard component ID group. This group contains the product name, version, serial number, and the time and date of the last installation. The ID number is assigned based on when the component was installed in relation to other components. Manufacturers can create their own MIFs specific to a component. For example, a manufacturer might write an MIF file for a fax/modem that contains two groups: a fax group and a modem group. Some group attributes include warranty information, support phone numbers, and any errors encountered. This information is then sent to an MIF database.

- **Service layer:** The service layer is memory-resident code that acts as a mediator for the management interface and the component interface and allows management and component software to access MIF files in the MIF database. The service layer is available as an operating system add-on and is a shared resource for all programs. Because the service layer must run all the time, it is designed not to use a lot of memory. The service layer also includes a common interface called the local agent, which is used to manage individual components.

- **Component interface (CI):** The CI is an **application program interface** (API) that sends status information to the appropriate MIF file via the service layer. Commands include the Get and Set command that modifies the MIF as needed and the Event command that notifies management software of critical events.

- **Management interface (MI):** The management software communicates with the service layer using the MI application program interface. The MI allows administrators to issue the Get and Set command and the List command that lists all the DMI-manageable devices.

To use DMI, you need a DMI-compliant management software package and a DMI-compliant computer. A DMI-compliant computer includes the CI, the MI, and the service layer. These drivers are available for download on the Internet.

Intel's **LANDesk Client Manager** is based on DMI.

DMP

See "dynamic multi-pathing"

DMR

See "digital rights management"

DMS

See "Defense Message System"

DMT

See "discrete multitone"

DMZ

In computer networks, a DMZ (demilitarized zone) is a computer host or small network inserted as a "neutral zone" between a company's private network and the outside public network. It prevents outside users from getting direct access to a server that has company data. (The term comes from the geographic buffer zone that was set up between North Korea and South Korea following the war in the early 1950s.) A DMZ is an optional and more secure approach to a **firewall** and effectively acts as a **proxy server** as well.

In a typical DMZ configuration for a small company, a separate computer (or **host** in network terms) receives requests from users within the private network for access to Web sites or other companies accessible on the public network. The DMZ host then initiates sessions for these requests on the public network. However, the DMZ host is not able to initiate a session back into the private network. It can only forward packets that have already been requested.

Users of the public network outside the company can access only the DMZ host. The DMZ may typically also have the company's Web pages so these could be served to the outside world. However, the DMZ provides access to no other company data. In the event that an outside user penetrated the DMZ host's security, the Web pages might be corrupted but no other company information would be exposed. Cisco, the leading maker of **router**s, is one company that sells products designed for setting up a DMZ.

DNA

See "Web Solution Platform"

DNIS

See "Dialed Number Identification Service"

DNS

See "domain name system"

docking station

A docking station is a hardware frame and set of electrical connection interfaces that enable a **notebook computer** to effectively serve as a **desktop computer**. The interfaces typically allow the notebook to communicate with a local printer, larger storage or backup drives, and possibly other devices that are not usually taken along with a notebook computer. A docking station can also include a network interface card (**NIC**) that attaches the notebook to a local area network (**LAN**).

Variations include the **port replicator**, an attachment on a notebook computer that expands the number of ports it can use, and the *expansion base*, which might hold a **CD-ROM** drive, a floppy disk drive, and additional storage.

DOCSIS

Now known as CableLabs Certified Cable Modems, DOCSIS (Data Over Cable Service Interface Specifications) is a **standard interface** for **cable modem**s, the devices that handle incoming and outgoing data signals between a cable TV operator and a personal or business computer or television set. DOCSIS 1.0 was ratified by the International Telecommunication Union (**ITU-TS**) in March of 1998. Although "DOCSIS" continues to be used, the newer name emphasizes that the standard is now being used to certify the products of cable modem makers. Cable modems conforming to DOCSIS are now being marketed.

Cable operators whose existing customers have non-standard cable modems can handle them by adding backwards-compatible support to the DOCSIS **card** at the cable operator's end. As DOCSIS continues to evolve to new versions, existing modems can be upgraded to the newer versions by changing the programming in the cable modem's **EEPROM memory**. DOCSIS-compliant cable modems are being integrated into **set-top box**es for use with television sets. DOCSIS must also support or converge with the high definition television (**HDTV**) standard. The set-top box itself follows a standard known as OpenCable.

DOCSIS specifies **modulation** schemes and the **protocol** for exchanging bidirectional signals over cable. It supports downstream-to-the-user data rates up to 27 **Mbps** (megabits per second). Since this data rate is shared by a number of users and because many cable operators will be limited by a **T1** connection to the Internet, the actual downstream data rate to an individual business or home will be more like 1.5 to 3 Mbps. Since the upstream data flow has to support much smaller amounts of data from the user, it's designed for an aggregate data rate of 10 Mbps with individual data rates between 500 **Kbps** and 2.5 Mbps.

Cisco and Microsoft have endorsed DOCSIS. They are collaborating on a DOCSIS-compliant cable hybrid fiber-coax (**HFC**) system, called the Multimedia Cable Network System (MCNS), that will deliver services to residential, commercial, and educational customers.

document

1) In general, a document (noun) is a record or the capturing of some event or thing so that the information will not be lost. Usually, a document is written, but a document can also be made with pictures and sound. A document usually adheres to some convention based on similar or previous documents or specified requirements. Examples of documents are sales invoices, wills and deeds, newspaper issues, individual newspaper stories, oral history recordings, executive orders, and product specifications.

A document is a form of **information**. A document can be put into an electronic form and stored in a computer as one or more **files**. Often a single document becomes a single file. An entire document or individual parts may be treated as individual **data** items. As files or data, a document may be part of a **database**. Electronic Document Management (**EDM**) deals with the management of electronically-stored documents.

When using certain computer application programs such as a **word processor**, a document is the unit of saved work. Each document is saved as a uniquely named file.

In the computer industry, **documentation** is the information provided to a customer or other users about a product or the process of preparing it.

2) To document (verb) a fact, event, or other thing is to record or annotate it, meaning to put it into some relatively permanent form so that it can be retrieved later.

Document Object Model

Document Object Model (DOM), a programming interface specification being developed by the World Wide Web Consortium (**W3C**), lets a programmer create and modify **HTML** pages and **XML document**s as full-fledged program **object**s. Currently, HTML (Hypertext Markup Language) and XML (Extensible Markup Language) are ways to express a document in terms of a data structure. As program objects, such documents will be able to have their contents and data "hidden" within the object, helping to ensure control over who can manipulate the document. As objects, documents can carry with them the object-oriented procedures called **method**s. DOM is a strategic and open effort to specify how to provide programming control over documents. It was inspired in part by the advent of the new HTML capabilities generally called **dynamic HTML** and as a way to encourage consistent **browser** behavior with Web pages and their elements.

The Document Object Model offers two levels of interface implementation: DOM Core, which supports XML and is the base for the next level, and DOM HTML, which extends the model to HTML documents. Here are some highlights:

- Any HTML or XML element (with the possibility of a few exceptions) will be individually addressable by programming.

- The specification will be language-independent. The specification, when available, will be described using the interface definition language (**IDL**) from the industry open standard **CORBA**.

- In addition, the interface will be described in terms of the **Java** programming language and ECMAScript, an industry-standard **script** language based on **JavaScript** and JScript.

- DOM is not to be confused with Microsoft's **Component Object Model** (COM) or **Distributed Component Object Model** (DCOM). COM and DCOM are language-independent ways to specifiy objects and could be used to create DOM objects (documents) just as specific languages like Java could.

Progress of the Document Object Model specification can be followed at the W3C Web site.

Document Style Semantics and Specification Language

See "DSSSL"

document type definition

A document type definition (DTD) is a specific definition that follows the rules of the Standard Generalized Markup Language (**SGML**). A DTD is a specification that accompanies a document and identifies what the funny little codes (or markup) are that separate paragraphs, identify

topic headings, and so forth and how each is to be processed. By mailing a DTD with a document, any location that has a DTD "reader" (or "SGML compiler") will be able to process the document and display or print it as intended. This means that a single standard SGML compiler can serve many different kinds of documents that use a range of different markup codes and related meanings. The compiler looks at the DTD and then prints or displays the document accordingly.

documentation

In computer hardware and software product development, documentation is the information that describes the product to its users. It consists of the product technical manuals and online information (including online versions of the technical manuals and help facility descriptions). The term is also sometimes used to mean the *source* information about the product contained in design documents, detailed code comments, white papers, and blackboard session notes.

The term is derived from the idea that engineers and programmers "document" their products in formal writing. The earliest computer users were sometimes simply handed the engineers' or programmers' "documentation." As the product audience grew, it became necessary to add professional technical writers and editors to the process. Today, IBM and other companies look at developing product information based on what users actually need to do when using the product. In this task-oriented view, product information can be divided into and sometimes physically organized into these task categories: evaluating, planning for, setting up or installing, customizing, administering, using, and maintaining the product. Documentation is now often built directly into the product as part of the user interface and in help pages. Printed technical manuals are increasingly available at company Web sites in the form of Adobe Acrobat Portable Document Format (**PDF**) files or in **HTML** pages. IBM and Microsoft are among the world's largest publishers.

dogcow

The dogcow is a drawing of a rather indiscriminate-looking animal (it looks mostly like a dog but is said to have the spots of a cow) that is or has been used in the Apple **Macintosh** operating system to help tell users about their printing options. If you have the right level of Macintosh, you can see the dogcow by going to the Finder, looking under "Page Setup...", and then looking under printer options. The dogcow is used to show you what kind of option you've selected. For example, "Flip Horizontal" flips the dogcow to upside down.

If you click on the dogcow, Macintosh sends you the animal's characteristic cry of "Moof!" The dogcow icon was originally created by graphic artist Susan Kare. (She is also the artist who created the graphic interface for everyone's favorite Windows 3.1 card game, Solitaire.) Microsoft has

adopted its own version of the dogcow and uses it to demonstrate slide transitions in its PowerPoint application, although Apple retains its copyright on the original image and, believe it or not, the "Moof!"

OS X creators originally dropped the dogcow, but on-line petitions and press coverage designed to "bring back the dogcow" have made Apple executives aware of the tremendous cult following of this hybrid icon. (Legend has it that development teams at Apple still use the dogcow to identify a partly completed program that is unique and worth checking out.) It is expected that the dogcow will return in the next version of OS X.

dog-food

For hardware and software developers, dog-food is jargon for trying out a product on yourself before giving it to others or in order to develop a customer view of the product, as in "Let's eat our own dog-food." Keith Dawson, who conducts a "Jargon Watch" in his e-mail newsletter, reports that the term is also used as a verb. Developers at Microsoft are quoted as saying, "We have to dog-food this architecture before we release it." At Rational, a software development company, a developer is quoted as saying "We have to dog-food this puppy."

DOI

See "digital object identifier"

Dolby Digital

Dolby Digital, formerly known as AC-3, is a digital audio coding technique that reduces the amount of data needed to produce high quality sound. Dolby Digital takes advantage of how the human ear processes sound. When coding **noise** is close to the frequency of an audio signal, that audio signal masks the noise so that the human ear hears only the intended audio signal. Sometimes the coding noise is not in the same frequency of an audio signal and must be reduced or eliminated. By reducing, eliminating, or masking the noise, the amount of data is reduced to one tenth of the data on a compact disk (CD). Dolby Digital is used with digital versatile discs (**DVDs**), **high definition television** (HDTV), and digital cable and satellite transmissions. It has been selected as the audio standard for digital television (**DTV**). The European DVB standard does not use Dolby Digital for audio, but instead uses MPEG standard technology for both the audio and video signals.

Dolby Digital provides five full bandwidth channels, front left, front right, center, surround left, and surround right, for true surround sound quality. A low frequency effect (LFE) channel is included that provides the sound needed for special effects and action sequences in movies. The LFE channel is one-tenth of the bandwidth of the other channels and is sometimes erroneously called the subwoofer channel. This multichannel scheme is known as 5.1 channel.

Because not everyone has the equipment needed to take advantage of Dolby Digital's 5.1 channel sound, developers included a downmixing feature that ensures compatibility with any playback device. The decoder in the playback device delivers the audio signal specific to that particular device's ability. For example, a 5.1 channel audio signal is delivered to a mono television. The playback device's decoder downmixes the 5.1 channel signal to a mono signal allowing the television to use the received audio signal. Because the playback device does the downmixing, producers do not have to create multiple audio signals for each playback device.

The ATSC selected Dolby Digital as a standard for DTV because of its popularity with film producers and consumers, its ability to use a single audio **streaming video** because of the downmixing feature, and its high quality sound. The U.S. cable television industry has also adopted Dolby Digital for DTV applications. Most television facilities are not equipped to produce 5.1 channel sound. For this reason, many DTV programs use two-channel sound. The 5.1 channel sound is used primarily for theatrical films on pay-per-view channels and at theaters.

To take advantage of Dolby Digital 5.1 channel sound for satellite broadcasts, a satellite receiver that provides a Dolby Digital output is necessary. For cable users, all digital **set-top box**es are equipped with a Dolby Digital two-channel decoder. To use 5.1 channel sound, a 5.1 channel-compliant set-top box is needed or an external 5.1 channel decoder unit. The proper sound equipment is also necessary.

DOLS

See "Domino Off-Line Services"

DOM

See "Document Object Model"

domain

Also see **domain name**.

In general, a domain is an area of control or a sphere of knowledge.

1) In computing and telecommunication in general, a domain is a sphere of knowledge identified by a name. Typically, the knowledge is a collection of facts about some program entities or a number of network points or addresses.

2) On the Internet, a domain consists of a set of network addresses. This domain is organized in levels. The top level identifies geographic or purpose commonality (for example, the nation that the domain covers or a category such as "commercial"). The second level identifies a unique place within the top level domain and is, in fact, equivalent to a unique address on the Internet (an **IP address**). Lower levels of domain may also be used.

Strictly speaking, in the Internet's domain name system (**DNS**), a domain is a name with which name server records are associated that describe subdomains or **hosts**. For example, "whatis.com" could be a domain with records for "www.whatis.com" and "www1.whatis.com," and so forth.

3) In Windows NT and Windows 2000, a domain is a set of network resources (applications, printers, and so forth) for a group of users. The user need only to log in to the domain to gain access to the resources, which may be located on a number of different servers in the network.

domain name

A **domain** name locates an organization or other entity on the Internet. For example, the domain name www.totalbaseball.com

locates an Internet address for "totalbaseball.com" at Internet point 199.0.0.2 and a particular host server named "www". The "com" part of the domain name reflects the purpose of the organization or entity (in this example, "commercial") and is called the **top-level domain** name. The "totalbaseball" part of the domain name defines the organization or entity and together with the top-level is called the **second-level domain** name. The second-level domain name maps to and can be thought of as the "readable" version of the Internet address.

A third level can be defined to identify a particular host server at the Internet address. In our example, "www" is the name of the server that handles Internet requests. (A second server might be called "www2".) A third level of domain name is not required. For example, the fully-qualified domain name could have been "totalbaseball.com" and the server assumed.

Subdomain levels can be used. For example, you could have "www.nyyankees.totalbaseball.com". Together, "www.totalbaseball.com" constitutes a *fully-qualified domain name*.

Second-level domain names must be unique on the Internet and registered with one of the **ICANN**-accredited registrars for the COM, NET, and ORG top-level domains. Where appropriate, a top-level domain name can be geographic. (Currently, most non-U.S. domain names use a top-level domain name based on the country the server is in.) To register a U.S. geographic domain name or a domain name under a country code, see an appropriate registrar.

On the Web, the domain name is that part of the Uniform Resource Locator(**URL**) that tells a domain name server using the domain name system (**DNS**) whether and where to forward a request for a Web page. The domain name is mapped to an IP address (which represents a physical point on the Internet).

More than one domain name can be mapped to the same Internet address. This allows multiple individuals, businesses, and organizations to have separate Internet identities while sharing the same Internet server.

To see the **IP address** for a domain name, use **ping**.

It may be worth noting that the domain name system contains an even higher level of domain than the top-level domain. The highest level is the *root domain*, which would be represented by a single dot (just as in many hierarchical file systems, a **root directory** is represented by a "/") if it were ever used. If the dot for the root domain were shown in the URL, it would be to the right of the top-level domain name. However, the dot is assumed to be there, but never shown.

domain name system

The domain name system (DNS) is the way that Internet **domain name**s are located and translated into **Internet Protocol** addresses. A domain name is a meaningful and easy-to-remember "handle" for an Internet address.

Because maintaining a central list of domain name/IP address correspondences would be impractical, the lists of domain names and IP addresses are distributed throughout the Internet in a hierarchy of authority. There is probably a DNS server within close geographic proximity to your access provider that maps the domain names in your Internet requests or forwards them to other servers in the Internet.

Domino

Domino is the name of the applications and messaging **server** program for IBM's Lotus **Notes** product, a sophisticated **groupware application** that is being installed in many corporations. Notes lets a corporation and its workers develop communications- and **database**-oriented applications so that users at different geographic locations can share files with each other, comment on them publicly or privately (to groups with special access), keep track of development schedules, work projects, guidelines and procedures, plans, white papers, and many other documents, including multimedia files. IBM uses the Domino name to refer to a set of Notes server applications. Notes itself refers to the overall product.

The Notes and Domino servers interact with other Notes/Domino servers in a **distributed** network. As changes are made to a database at one server, updates are continually forwarded to replicated copies of these databases at the other servers so that users are always looking at the same information. In general, Notes follows the **client/server** model. The replication updates are made using Remote Procedure Call (**RPC**) requests. Notes can be coordinated with Web servers and applications on a company's **intranet**.

Domino Extensible Language

See "DXL"

Domino Off-Line Services

Domino Off-Line Services (DOLS) is an **add-on** toolkit, based on **Domino replication** and security features, that allows users to access and interact with Domino Web applications through a **browser** without requiring a network connection, and to synchronize changes to source data when they reconnect. Applications such as **e-mail** and **discussion group**s are fully functional. Work completed offline is synchronized when the user next connects to the network through a tool called the **iNotes** Sync Manager. DOLS decreases demands on network resources, and facilitates interactivity for a mobile workforce.

Using DOLS, a mobile worker could, for example, bring up a Web form in a Domino-based application and work with it, offline, in a meeting with a client. Changes specified could be sent out to **work group** members through the iNotes sync manager when the worker next connects to the network. The work group might meet, through a **teleconference**, to discuss the changes. Online, after the discussion, the mobile worker could replicate the discussion database, and later, offline, respond to questions. The changes to the discussion database would be synchronized again whenever the worker next had an opportunity to connect to the network.

dongle

A dongle (pronounced DONG-uhl) is a mechanism for ensuring that only authorized users can copy or use specific software **applications**, especially very expensive programs. Common mechanisms include a hardware key that plugs into a parallel or serial port on a computer and that a software application accesses for verification before continuing to run; special key diskettes accessed in a similar manner; and registration numbers that are loaded into some form of **ROM** (read-only memory) at the factory or during system setup.

If more than one application requires a dongle, multiple dongles can be daisy-chained together from the same port. Dongles are not in frequent use partly because enterprises don't like to have a serial or parallel port preempted for this use.

Doppler effect

The frequency and wavelength of an **electromagnetic field** are affected by relative motion. This is known as the *Doppler effect*. Only the radial (approaching or receding) component of motion produces this phenomenon. The Doppler effect also occurs with acoustic waves.

The Doppler effect is significant in low-earth-orbit (LEO) **satellite** systems. All LEO satellites are constantly moving relative to each other and to points on the surface. This causes variations in the frequencies and wavelengths of received signals. In geostationary satellite systems, Doppler effect is not a factor unless the end user is on board a spacecraft or high-speed aircraft.

If the source of an EM field is approaching an observer, the **frequency** increases and the **wavelength** decreases. If the source is receding, the frequency decreases and the wavelength increases. If there are several observers, each moving radially at different speeds relative to the source of an EM field, every observer will perceive a unique frequency and wavelength for the EM field produced by the source.

A special type of **RADAR**, called *Doppler radar*, uses the Doppler effect to ascertain wind velocity in heavy thundershowers, tornadoes, and hurricanes. In a rotating storm such as a hurricane or tornado, the maximum sustained wind speed can be found by measuring the difference in frequency of echoes returned from approaching rain droplets and receding rain droplets. A more primitive form of Doppler radar is used by law enforcement personnel to enforce traffic speed limits.

DOS

DOS (Disk Operating System) was the first widely-installed **operating system** for personal computers. (Earlier, the same name had been used for an IBM operating system for a line of business computers.)

The first personal computer version of DOS, called **PC-DOS**, was developed for IBM by Bill Gates and his new Microsoft Corporation. He retained the rights to market a Microsoft version, called **MS-DOS**. PC-DOS and MS-DOS are almost identical and most users have referred to either of them as just "DOS." DOS was (and still is) a non-graphical line-oriented command- or menu-driven operating system, with a relatively simple interface but not overly "friendly" user interface. Its prompt to enter a command looks like this:

C:>

The first Microsoft Windows operating system was really an application that ran on top of the MS-DOS operating system. Today, Windows operating systems continue to support DOS (or a DOS-like user interface) for special purposes by emulating the operating system.

In the 1970s before the personal computer was invented, IBM had a different and unrelated DOS (Disk Operating System) that ran on smaller business computers. It was replaced by IBM's **VSE** operating system.

DOS Protected Mode Interface

DPMI (DOS Protected Mode Interface) is a program interface that allows an application program running under the Disk Operating System (DOS) to take advantage of a *DOS extender*, which lets the program address a larger range of random access memory (**RAM**) than the 640 kilobytes to which PC programs are basically constrained. To use the extender, the program must be in "protected mode," a mode

that ensures that program requests are not allowed to access certain portions of "protected" memory. (Programs running in the alternative "real mode" have access to all portions of memory, including system data.)

The first widely-distributed **operating system** for personal computers, DOS was designed to run on the Intel 8088 **microprocessor**. The 8088 provided a **megabyte** of RAM that could be addressed by a program instruction (that is, the total span of storage for storing and getting data back and forth between the microprocessor and RAM was a million bytes). Because certain space had to be reserved for "system" use (keeping track of applications, system status, and so forth), only 640 kilobytes was available for an application program. These bytes were contiguous in storage (that is, continuously adjacent to each other and not divided into different parts of RAM) and application programs were required to run and keep their data within this 640 kilobyte space. In fact, an instruction that violated the 640 kilobyte space would not be executed (thus protecting the system space in RAM). A program that ran in "real mode" could address the entire 1 megabyte of RAM including system data, but at the risk of writing data to the wrong place.

As new microprocessors such as the 80286 followed the 8088, DOS continued to preserve the 640 kilobyte addressing limitation so that newly-written application programs could continue to run on both the old as well as new microprocessors. The DOS extender program allowed application programs written for DOS to be freed from the 640K constraint by inserting memory management code into the application. Microsoft developed the DPMI for use on Windows 3.0 (which was itself a DOS application) and later gave the standard to an industry organization, the DPMI Committee.

Today's personal computers, using microprocessors that succeeded the 8088, typically contain 32 or more megabytes of RAM. Today's operating systems (including the latest DOS versions) come with extended memory management that frees the programmer from the original addressing constraints.

Besides the DPMI standard interface, two other standard extended memory management interfaces exist. Extended Memory Specification (XMS) is a program added to more recent versions of DOS and Windows when the system is loaded. It's called HIMEM.SYS. Another extended memory manager is the Virtual Control Program Interface (VCPI).

DOS/V and WIN/V

DOS/V is a version of **MS-DOS** that provides both English and Japanese language **command** interfaces and can be used for applications designed for either or both English and Japanese. DOS/V includes all the English-based commands and specific Japanese DOS/V commands. DOS/V gets its name because it requires a Video Graphics Array (**VGA**) display.

Before DOS/V, computers on the Japanese market were incompatible with machines made elsewhere and more expensive. Software developed for non-Japanese environments did not work on Japanese machines. In 1991, the Open Access Development Group (OADG), a consortium organized by IBM, developed DOS/V. Because DOS/V works on all IBM-compatible computers, foreign manufacturers were able to start selling their computers in the Japanese market. Competition brought prices down for computers, peripherals, and software. DOS/V also opened the door to Japanese versions of Windows 3.1, 95, and 98.

With the advent of Windows 3.1, a user was faced with new problems. A Windows user that needed Japanese capabilities had to juggle separate English and Japanese versions of Windows 3.1. This required installing Windows 3.1 twice in separate folders and rebooting when the other language version was needed. Installing separate English- and Japanese-based software applications was also necessary. WIN/V was developed to solve these problems.

WIN/V is an add-on to English versions of Windows 3.1 that emulates the Kanji-specific interface of Japanese versions of Windows 3.1, allowing users to use Japanese True Type fonts and Japanese applications without needing a Japanese version of Windows 3.1. WIN/V also allows users to use any printer that works with English versions of Windows 3.1. Since Windows 95 and 98 are truly multilingual, a WIN/V equivalent is no longer needed.

dot address

Tip: To find out the dot address (such as 205.245.172.72) for a given domain name, Windows users can go to their MS DOS prompt screen and enter: ping xxx.yyy where xxx is the second-level domain name like "whatis" and yyy is the top-level domain name like "com").

A dot address (sometimes known as a dotted quad address) refers to the notation that expresses the four-byte (32-bit) **IP address** as a sequence of four decimal numbers separated by dots. Each number represents the binary value of one of four bytes. Look at this Internet address, for example:

205.245.172.72

The first **byte** in the 32-bit sequence contains the binary equivalent of decimal 205, the second byte contains the equivalent of 245, the third of 172, and the fourth of 72.

The separation of the four numbers with dots makes the address easier to read. Of course, most of us remember an Internet location with a **domain name** rather than an Internet address. But we sometimes need the dot address form when we configure a Web browser or get set up with an access provider.

dot NET

See ".Net"

dot pitch

The dot pitch specification for a display monitor tells you how sharp the displayed image can be. The dot pitch is measured in millimeters (mm) and a smaller number means a sharper image. In desk top monitors, common dot pitches are .31mm, .28mm, .27mm, .26mm, and .25mm. Personal computer users will usually want a .28mm or finer. Some large monitors for presentation use may have a larger dot pitch (.48mm, for example). Think of the dot specified by the dot pitch as the smallest physical visual component on the display. A **pixel** is the smallest programmable visual element and maps to the dot if the display is set to its highest resolution. When set to lower resolutions, a pixel encompasses multiple dots.

Technically, in a cathode ray tube (**CRT**) display with a *shadow mask*, the dot pitch is the distance between the holes in the shadow mask, measured in millimeters (mm). The shadow mask is a metal screen filled with holes through which the three electron beams pass that focus to a single point on the tube's phosphor surface. In CRTs that use an *aperture grill* (a slotted form of mask), such as Sony's Trinitron flat-screen technology, the dot pitch is the difference between adjacent slots that pass through an electron beam of the same color.

dotcom

A dotcom is any **Web site** intended for business use and, in some usages, it's a term for any kind of Web site. The term is based on the **com** that forms the last part of the address for most commercial Web sites. The term is popular in news stories about how the business world is transforming itself to meet the opportunities and competitive challenges posed by the Internet and the World Wide Web. Beginning in mid-2000, as the stock market began to devalue many Internet stocks, the term became associated with a number of Web businesses that failed or suffered cutbacks.

Alternative spellings seen include: dot.com, dot-com, and dot com.

dots per inch

1) In computers, dots per inch (dpi) is a measure of the sharpness (that is, the density of illuminated points) on a display **screen**. The **dot pitch** determines the absolute limit of the possible dots per inch. However, the displayed **resolution** of **pixel**s (picture elements) that is set up for the display is usually not as fine as the dot pitch. The dots per inch for a given picture resolution will differ based on the overall screen size since the same number of pixels are being spread out over a different space. Some users prefer the term "pixels per inch (**ppi**)" as a measure of display image sharpness, reserving dpi for use with the print medium.

2) In printing, dots per inch (dpi) is the usual measure of printed image quality on the paper. The average personal computer printer today provides 300 dpi or 600 dpi. Choosing the higher print quality usually reduces the speed of printing each page.

dotted quad

See "dot address"

double data rate synchronous dynamic random access memory

See "DDR SDRAM"

Double Density CD

See "Double-Density Compact Disc"

Double-Density Compact Disc

Double-Density Compact Disc (DDCD) is a CD format that increases the storage capacity of the disc through means such as increasing the number of tracks and pits (scores on the disc that are used to encode the data). Philips and Sony described the DDCD specifications in their 2000 document (known informally as the **Purple Book**).

Although DDCD did not receive much industry notice until Philips and Sony produced the Purple Book specifications, the Optical Disc Corporation (ODC) released a similar format, High Density CD (HDCD) in 1993, and Nimbus Technology and Engineering introduced their own Double-Density CD format in 1994. The general feeling in the industry is that DDCD has been introduced as a stop-gap measure to tide over the market until DVD inevitably solves its problems (such as standardization and compatibility issues) and makes the CD obsolete.

downlink and uplink

In **satellite** telecommunication, a downlink is the **link** from a satellite down to one or more ground stations or receivers, and an uplink is the link from a ground station up to a satellite. Some companies sell uplink and downlink services to television stations, corporations, and to other telecommunication carriers. A company can specialize in providing uplinks, downlinks, or both.

The following table shows the main **frequency** bands used for satellite links.

Frequency Band	Downlink	Uplink
C	3,700-4,200 **MHz**	5,925-6,425 MHz
Ku	11.7-12.2 **GHz**	14.0-14.5 GHz
Ka	17.7-21.2 GHz	27.5-31.0 GHz

The C **band** is the most frequently used. The Ka and Ku bands are reserved exclusively for satellite communication but are subject to rain attenuation. Some satellites carry transponders for both C and Ku bands.

downloading

Downloading is the transmission of a file from one computer system to another, usually smaller computer system. From the Internet user's point-of-view, to download a file is to request it from another computer (or from a Web page on another computer) and to receive it.

Uploading is transmission in the other direction: from one, usually smaller computer to another computer. From an Internet user's point-of-view, uploading is sending a file to a computer that is set up to receive it. People who share images with others on bulletin board systems (**BBS**) upload files to the BBS.

The **File Transfer Protocol** (FTP) is the Internet protocol for downloading and uploading files and a number of special applications can furnish FTP services for you. (However, if you are downloading through a Web page, the FTP request is set up for you by the Web page. You are usually asked where you want the downloaded file placed on your hard disk, and then the downloading transmission takes place.)

When you send an attached file with an e-mail note, this is just an attachment, not a download or an upload. In practice, many people use "download" and "upload" rather indiscriminately so you just have to understand the context. For example, if someone says to you "Download (or upload) such–and–such a file to me by e-mail," they clearly mean "Send it to me as an attachment."

In general, from the ordinary workstation or small computer user's point-of-view, to download is to receive a file and to upload is to send a file.

downstream

1) In telecommunications generally, a transmission from an information **server** toward an **end user** is referred to as downstream and a transmission toward the server is referred to as upstream. In some transmission technologies, such as Digital Subscriber Line (**DSL**), the rates of data transfer upstream and downstream are not the same. In DSL, downstream data rates are higher since the kind of information that needs to get to the user (including still and video images and sound) requires a higher data rate. User responses back to the computer on the upstream path can be smaller since they are usually text-only.

2) In a **token ring**, a computer station is downstream from any station through which the token on the ring has already passed.

3) In **CATV**, a downstream **channel** is one used to transmit signals from the headend to the user. An upstream channel is one in another frequency band that is used to send signals from the user back to the headend.

dpi

See "dots per inch"

DPMI

See "DOS Protected Mode Interface"

draft document

See "working draft"

DRAM

Dynamic random access memory (DRAM) is the most common kind of random access memory (**RAM**) for personal computers and workstations. **Memory** is the network of electrically-charged points in which a computer stores quickly accessible data in the form of 0s and 1s. *Random access* means that the PC processor can access any part of the memory or data storage space directly rather than having to proceed sequentially from some starting place. DRAM is dynamic in that, unlike static RAM (**SRAM**), it needs to have its storage cells refreshed or given a new electronic charge every few milliseconds. Static RAM does not need refreshing because it operates on the principle of moving current that is switched in one of two directions rather than a storage cell that holds a charge in place. Static RAM is generally used for **cache memory**, which can be accessed more quickly than DRAM.

DRAM stores each bit in a storage cell consisting of a capacitor and a transistor. Capacitors tend to lose their charge rather quickly; thus, the need for recharging. A variety of other RAM interfaces to the computer exist. These include: **EDO RAM** and **SDRAM**.

DRDRAM

RDRAM (Rambus Dynamic Random Access Memory) is a **memory** subsystem that promises to transfer up to 1.6 billion bytes per second. The subsystem consists of the random access memory (**RAM**), the RAM controller, and the **bus** (path) connecting RAM to the **microprocessor** and devices in the computer that use it. Direct Rambus (DRDRAM), a technology developed and licensed by the Rambus Corporation, is the latest version and is expected to help accelerate the growth of visually intensive interfaces such as **3-D**, interactive games, and streaming multimedia. Rambus is intended to replace the current main memory technology of dynamic random access memory (**DRAM**). Much faster data transfer rates from attached devices such as videocams using **FireWire** and the Accelerated Graphics Port (**AGP**) make it important to reduce the bottleneck in getting data

into the computer, staging it in RAM, and moving it throught the microprocessor and to the display or other output devices.

Direct Rambus (DRDRAM) provides a two-byte (16 bit) bus rather than DRAM's 8-bit bus. At a RAM speed of 800 megahertz (800 million cycles per second), the peak data transfer rate is 1.6 billion bytes per second. Direct Rambus uses **pipelining** to move data from RAM to **cache** memory levels that are closer to the microprocessor or display. Up to eight operations may be underway at the same time. Rambus is designed to fit into existing **motherboard** standards. The components that are inserted into motherboard connections are called Rambus in-line memory modules (RIMMs). They can replace conventional **dual in-line memory module**.

An alternative to DRDRAM is SyncLink DRAM (**SDRAM**).

drilldown

As currently used in information technology, to drill down (verb) is to focus in on something. A drilldown (noun) is the act of focusing in.

The term is sometimes used when referring to moving down through a hierarchy of folders and files in a file system like that of Windows. It may also mean clicking through a series of dropdown menus in a graphical user interface.

Microsoft's Visual Studio Analyzer is said to "provide easy drilldown," possibly meaning that it allows the user to get quickly to a desired function or work unit.

The term *drillup* is also reported in the multi-dimensional data access query language (MDX), which contains the keywords DRILLDOWNMEMBER and DRILLUPMEMBER as well as TOGGLEDRILLSTATE.

driver

A driver is a program that interacts with a particular device or special (frequently optional) kind of software. The driver contains the special knowledge of the device or special software interface that programs using the driver do not. In personal computers, a driver is often packaged as a dynamic link library (**DLL**) file.

driver development kit

A driver development kit (DDK) is a set of programs and related files that are used to develop a new software or hardware **driver** or to update an existing **legacy application** driver for an **operating system**. (A driver is a relatively small program that addresses the unique requirements of a kind of hardware or a special software application.) Typically, DDKs are used by device manufacturers and software application developers. Some DDKs can be downloaded from the maker of the operating system. Others can be purchased from a third party. A DDK typically includes sample drivers, **source code**, a **debugging** utility, a **compiler**, testing tools, other utilities, and documentation.

In addition to the kit, a driver developer needs to be familiar with the operating system or application the driver is for. Building a driver is typically a complicated process. Testing and debugging should be thorough so that the driver is released with as few errors as possible. There are several steps in building a driver:

- Writing the driver code. Common programming languages for writing drivers are **C** and **C++**.

- Testing and debugging the driver on a *checked build*. A checked build is an operating system and **kernel**-mode driver that has extra error checking and debugging information in the code to aid testing and debugging of the driver. Running with a checked build is slower and uses more memory. A checked build is done in a separate computer from the free build.

- Testing and debugging the driver on a *free build*. A free build or *retail build* is the **end user** version of the operating system built with full optimization and all debugging information removed. A free build is faster and uses less memory. It also shows driver problems that a user might encounter such as error messages or a computer freeze.

- Fine-tuning and performance checking of the driver on the free build.

- Additional testing and debugging as necessary, using both the checked and free builds of the driver.

- Final testing using the free build. A driver needs testing on a multiprocessor computer as well as on a single processor computer.

DRM

See "digital rights management"

dropout

A dropout is a small loss of data in an audio or video file on tape or disk. A dropout can sometimes go unnoticed by the user if the size of the dropout is small. Error correction schemes can compensate for the dropout by filling in data where a dropout is detected. With a larger section of missing data, the user will see or hear the error.

The reason for a dropout can be bad tape stock, a bad block on a hard disk, dirt, the age of the tape or disk, or something else. Older tapes, especially those dating to the analog era, are more susceptible to dropouts as they age. The magnetic particles on the tape become detached from the backing material, resulting in what is commonly known as shedding. Larger dropouts can be quite serious. On the master tape of a vintage recording, a dropout could be large enough to

render a selection unusable. In a video studio, a dropout on the SMPTE Time Code track could cause the machines slaving to the Time Code track to stop momentarily.

DRP

See "disaster recovery plan"

DS (digital signal) levels

See "digital signal X"

DS

See "Differentiated Services"

DS0 – DS1 – DS2 – DS3 – DS4

See "digital signal X"

DS-CDMA

See "direct sequence spread spectrum"

DSL

See "Digital Subscriber Line"

DSLAM

See "Digital Subscriber Line Access Multiplexer"

DSML

DSML (Directory Services Markup Language) is an application of the Extensible Markup Language (**XML**) that enables different computer network directory formats to be expressed in a common format and shared by different directory systems.

In the latest DSML specification, the related XML schema defines types of information found in today's network and enterprise directories. It then defines a common XML document format that should be used to display the contents of each directory.

DSML has been heralded in industry press as a key component to the future of e-commerce and Web-based applications that link businesses and business processes together. Some examples of such business-to-business and business-to-customer applications include those in the area of supply chain management (SCM) or customer service, where someone in one company might use a Web interface to order items or to find out inventory levels on a vendor's products. Information in a variety of directories may need to be furnished in order to display the correct information to an end user.

Bowstreet Software was the primary company behind the initial draft of the DSML specification. With the support of such early members as IBM, Microsoft, Novell, Oracle, and the Sun-Netscape Alliance, they founded the DSML Working Group, an organization committed to gaining acceptance for DSML among a variety of standards bodies, including: XML.org, the World Wide Web Consortium (W3C), and OASIS.

DSML is part of a handful of other efforts currently underway to adopt standards that make it easier for the contents of different directories to be shared across platforms and over the Internet. Other such efforts include the Directory Interoperability Forum (DIF) and the Directory Enabled Networking (DEN) initiative. Proponents of DSML indicate that DSML also works synergistically with LDAP directories, allowing LDAP directory information to be transmitted beyond the traditional firewall and into Internet-based applications.

DSN

See "Deep Space Network"

DSP

See "digital signal processing"

DSS

See "Digital Signature Standard"

DSSSL

DSSSL (Document Style Semantics and Specification Language) is a standard for the processing of **SGML** (Standard Generalized Markup Language) documents. Whereas SGML is a standard for describing documents in terms of logical structure (rather than presentation), DSSSL describes how such a structured document might be presented visually, or converted to something else, or processed in some other way. SGML is a document structure language; DSSSL is a document processing language, especially for presentation or transformation.

A quick example: A Web page is an **HTML** (Hypertext Markup Language) document. HTML is a usage of SGML. Using DSSSL as a standard, someone could write a definition that would convert a Web page (HTML document) into a (let's call it) Tactile Markup Language (TML) document that could be processed by an online reader-and-sound converter for the blind. Or someone could write a definition that would transform the HTML document into a Microsoft Word document. DSSSL describes how you write such a definition, effectively how you map each markup tag from one definition (such as HTML) into some formatting process or markup tag in another "language."

DSSL contains separate parts and you can choose which parts of the standard to use when creating a DSSSL definition. It contains standards for:

- A style language
- Flow objects
- A transformation language
- A document model
- A query language

The style language lets you describe how each document element (heading, paragraph, list, and so forth) will be formatted for displaying, printing, or other presentation in terms of such things as fonts, colors, and space measurements. Flow objects are the formatted objects themselves—for example, the paragraph described in terms of its typographic fonts. Flow objects are usually described as part of a style specification. The transformation language is a language for mapping a document in one SGML format to a document in another SGML format. The document model is a view of how any document is organized that uses a "grove, tree, branch, leaf..." metaphor. The query language lets you access parts of a document just as **SQL** lets you access particular data from a database.

Several DSSSL processors have been written that are available for downloading from the Web.

DSTP

DSTP (Data Space Transfer Protocol) is a **protocol** that is used to index and retrieve data from a number of **databases**, **files**, and other data structures using a key that can find all the related data about a particular object across all of the data. The data is typically **distributed** among a number of **server**s in a network. The servers, called DSTP servers, understand how to index and retrieve appropriate data, using the key, which is called a Universal Correlation Key (UCK). DSTP can be considered a tool for **data mining**.

DSTP is similar in concept to the **NNTP**, which allows Internet users to access the online discussions known as Usenet newsgroups.

DSTP makes use of the Extensible Markup Language (**XML**). For an existing database, an XML file is created in which a UCK key or tag describes corresponding database columns.

DTD

See "document type definition"

DTE

In computer data transmission, DTE (Data Terminal Equipment) is the **RS-232C** interface that a computer uses to exchange data with a modem or other serial device. For further information about the DTE interface and its relationship to the Data Communication Equipment (DCE) interface, see **RS-232C**.

dual boot

A dual boot system is a computer system in which two **operating system**s are installed on the same hard drive, allowing either operating system to be loaded and given control. When you turn the computer on, a **boot** manager program displays a menu, allowing you to choose the operating system you wish to use. A boot manager works by replacing the original Master Boot Record (**MBR**) with its own so that the boot manager program loads instead of an operating system. Some popular boot manager programs are LILO, System Commander, and Partition Magic. Common combinations of operating systems used on dual boot systems include **Linux** and **Windows NT** and Windows 98 with one install of Windows being in a different language, such as Spanish. Since more than two operating systems can be installed on a computer, the term *multiboot system* is sometimes used.

dual in-line memory module

See "DIMM"

dual tone multi frequency

See "DTMF"

Dublin Core

Dublin Core is an initiative to create a digital "library card catalog" for the Web. Dublin Core is made up of 15 **metadata** (data that describes data) elements that offer expanded cataloging information and improved document indexing for **search engine** programs.

The 15 metadata elements used by Dublin Core are: title (the name given the resource), creator (the person or organization responsible for the content), subject (the topic covered), description (a textual outline of the content), publisher (those responsible for making the resource available), contributor (those who added to the content), date (when the resource was made available), type (a category for the content), format (how the resource is presented), identifier (numerical identifier for the content such as a URL), source (where the content originally derived from), language (in what language the content is written), relation (how the content relates to other resources, for instance, if it is a chapter in a book), coverage (where the resource is physically located), and rights (a link to a copyright notice).

Two forms of Dublin Core exist: Simple Dublin Core and Qualified Dublin Core. Simple Dublin Core expresses elements as attribute-value pairs using just the 15 metadata elements from the Dublin Core Metadata Element Set. Qualified Dublin Core increases the specificity of metadata by adding information about encoding schemes, enumerated lists of values, or other processing clues. While enabling searches to be more specific, qualifiers are also more complex and can pose challenges to interoperability.

Each method of recording or transferring Dublin Core metadata has its plusses and minuses. **HTML**, **XML**, **RDF**, and relational databases are among the more common methods.

The Dublin Core Metadata Initiative began in 1995, taking its name from the location of the original workshop, Dublin, Ohio. It has since become international in scope and has representatives from more than 20 countries now contributing. Dublin Core has always held that resource discovery should be independent from the medium of the resource. So, while Dublin Core targets electronic resources, it aims to be flexible enough to help in searches for more traditional formats of data too. Web sites, though, are the most common users of Dublin Core.

duh

In general, duh (pronounced DUH, prolonging the UH, pitching the voice a bit low, and inflecting it with an intonation of imbecility or sarcasm or both, depending on the usage, is a colloquial comment on one's (or someone else's) lack of knowledge or brain power.

Here are some usages:

1) It can be used as an epithet when confounded by new technology. For example, someone unfamiliar with computers looking at a **Windows 2000 desktop** for the first time, might say "Duh" out loud and to no one in particular. In this usage, duh expresses the state of what is, in the late 20th century vernacular, "being totally clueless."

2) A common use of duh is to confess an error.

3) Another common use is to suggest to someone that you are telling them something obvious, but you're telling them anyway because you don't expect that they are all that alert mentally.

duplex

In telecommunication, duplex communication means that both ends of the communication can send and receive **signal**s at the same time. **Full-duplex** communication is the same thing. **Half-duplex** is also bidirectional communication but signals can only flow in one direction at a time. Simplex communication means that communication can only flow in one direction and never flow back the other way.

An ordinary telephone conversation is a duplex communication. Most inexpensive speakerphones in conference rooms are half-duplex communication. (If you're speaking, you can't hear anyone else interrupt. You have to pause to let others speak.)

duty cycle

Duty cycle is the proportion of time during which a component, device, or system is operated. The duty cycle can be expressed as a ratio or as a percentage. Suppose a disk drive operates for 1 second, then is shut off for 99 seconds, then is run for 1 second again, and so on. The drive runs for one out of 100 seconds, or 1/100 of the time, and its duty cycle is therefore 1/100, or 1 percent.

The more a circuit, machine or component is used, the sooner it will wear out. Therefore, the higher the duty cycle, the shorter the useful life, all other things being equal. If the above-mentioned disk drive has a life expectancy of 1,000,000 hours based on a 1 percent duty cycle, that same device's expectancy would probably be about 500,000 hours based on a duty cycle of 2 percent, and 2,000,000 hours based on a duty cycle of 0.5 percent.

DVB

See "Digital Video Broadcasting"

DVD

See "digital versatile disc"

DVD Forum

The DVD Forum is an international organization made up of companies using or manufacturing digital versatile disc (**DVD**)-related products. The Forum, which was originally called the DVD Consortium, was created in 1995 when ten companies (Hitachi, Matsushita, Mitsubishi, Philips, Pioneer, Sony, Thomson Multimedia, Time Warner, Toshiba Corporation, and Victor) joined for the common purpose of promoting DVD worldwide and establishing standardized formats of each DVD application for the marketplace.

From ten founding members, the DVD Forum membership has grown to include some 230 companies worldwide. The Forum's activities are directed by a steering committee that is elected every second year. Separate working groups are established to define specifications, which currently include **DVD-Video** (this is the most familiar format), DVD-Read-Only Memory (**DVD-ROM**), DVD-Recordable (**DVD-R**), DVD-Rewritable (**DVD-RW**), and DVD-Audio (**DVD-A**). The DVD Forum issues specifications as separate books of the DVD specification, identified by letters (for example, DVD-R is laid out in Book D). A Verification Task Force (VTF) exists to define test specifications, tools, and procedures to be used and to ensure that products bearing the official DVD logo comply with all specifications.

DVD-A

See "DVD-Audio"

DVD-Audio

DVD-Audio (DVD-A) is a Digital Versatile Disc (**DVD**) format, developed by Panasonic, that is specifically designed to hold **audio** data, and particularly, high-quality music. The DVD Forum, consisting of 230 leading companies worldwide, released the final DVD-A specification in March of 1999. The new DVD format is said to provide at least twice the sound quality of audio CD on discs that can contain up to seven times as much information. Various types of DVD-A-compatible DVD players are being manufactured, in addition to the DVD-A players specifically developed for the format.

Almost all of the space on a DVD video disc is devoted to containing video data. As a consequence, the space allotted to audio data, such as a **Dolby Digital** 5.1 soundtrack, is severely limited. A **lossy compression** technique—so-called because some of the data is lost—is used to enable audio information to be stored in the available space, both on standard CDs and **DVD-Video** discs. In addition to using lossless compression methods, DVD-A also provides more complexity of sound by increasing the **sampling rate** and the frequency range beyond what is possible for the space limitations of CDs and DVD-Video. DVD-Audio is 24-bit, with a sampling rate of 96 kHz; in comparison, DVD-Video soundtrack is 16-bit, with a sampling rate of 48 kHz, and standard audio CD is 16-bit, with a sampling rate of 44.1 kHz.

Although DVD-A is designed for music, it can also contain other data, so that—similarly to **Enhanced CD**—it can provide the listener with extra information, such as liner notes and images. A variation on the format, DVD-AudioV, is designed to hold a limited amount of conventional DVD video data in addition to DVD-Audio. DVD-A is backed by most of the industry as the technology that will replace the standard audio CD. The major exceptions are Philips and Sony, whose Super Audio CD (**SACD**) provides similar audio quality. Like DVD-A, SACD offers 5.1 channel surround sound in addition to 2-channel stereo. Both formats improve the complexity of sound by increasing bit rates and sampling frequencies, and can be played on existing CD players, although only at quality levels similar to those of traditional CDs.

DVD-AudioV

See "DVD-Audio"

DWDM

See "dense wavelength division multiplexing"

DXL

DXL (Domino Extensible Language) is a specific version of Extensible Markup Language (**XML**) for Lotus Domino data. **Domino** is a server program for Lotus **Notes**, a **groupware** application that is used by many businesses.

The Document Type Definition (**DTD**) for DXL defines the **markup tag**s needed for working with XML within the Domino environment. This provides a consistent data format for non-Domino-equipped businesses when they access Domino data. Future versions of DXL will support Domino design elements, so non-Domino-equipped organizations can create or modify Domino documents.

DXL data must be converted to conventional XML when used outside the Domino environment. Conversely, XML data must be converted to DXL before it can be used in the Domino environment. Conversions in either direction are done by an Extensible Stylesheet Language Transformation (**XSLT**) processor.

dynamic and static

In general, *dynamic* means *energetic, capable of action and/or change*, or *forceful*, while *static* means *stationary* or *fixed*. In computer terminology, *dynamic* usually means *capable of action and/or change*, while *static* means *fixed*. Both terms can be applied to a number of different types of things, such as programming languages (or components of programming languages), Web pages, and application programs.

When a Web page is requested (by a computer user clicking a hyperlink or entering a **URL**), the **server** where the page is stored returns the **HTML** document to the user's computer and the **browser** displays it. On a static Web page, this is all that happens. The user may interact with the document through clicking available links, or a small program (an **applet**) may be activated, but the document has no capacity to return information that is not pre-formatted. On a dynamic Web page, the user can make requests (often through a **form**) for data contained in a **database** on the server that will be assembled **on the fly** according to what is requested. For example the user might want to find out information about a theatrical performance, such as theater locations and ticket availability for particular dates. When the user selects these options, the request is relayed to the server using an intermediary, such as an Active Server Page (**ASP**) **script** embedded in the page's HTML. The intermediary tells the server what information to return. Such a Web page is said to be dynamic.

A set of HTML capabilities are provided that help a designer create dynamic Web pages. This set of capabilities is generally known as **dynamic HTML**.

There are dynamic and static programming languages. In a dynamic language, such as **Perl** or **LISP**, a developer can create **variables** without specifying their type. This creates more flexible programs and can simplify **prototyping** and

some **object-oriented** coding. In a static programming language, such as **C** or **Pascal**, a developer must declare the type of each variable before the code is compiled, making the coding less flexible, but also less error-prone.

Dynamic Data Exchange

In the Windows, OS/2, and (with third-party development kits) other operating systems, Dynamic Data Exchange (DDE) allows information to be shared or communicated between programs. For example, when you change a form in your database program or a data item in a spreadsheet program, they can be set up to also change these forms or items anywhere they occur in other programs you may use. DDE is interprocess communication (**IPC**) that uses shared memory as a common exchange area and provides applications with a protocol or set of commands and message formats. DDE uses a client/server model in which the application requesting data is considered the client and the application providing data is considered the server.

Thousands of applications use DDE, including Microsoft's Excel, Word, Lotus 1-2-3, AmiPro, Quattro Pro, and Visual Basic.

Another facility, NetDDE, allows progams to converse across networks. For example, a Superbase program on one network node could be updated whenever an Excel program in network node was updated. Both nodes must have NetDDE installed.

dynamic DNS service

A dynamic **DNS** (domain name system) service is a company that charges a small fee to allow a user connecting to the Internet with a **dynamic IP address** to be able to use applications that require a **static IP address**.

Using a dynamic DNS service works as if there was an old-fashioned telephone message service at your computer's disposal. When a user registers with a DNS service and connects to the Internet with a dynamic IP address, the user's computer contacts the DNS service and lets them know what dynamic IP address it has been assigned from the pool; the service works with the DNS server to forward the correct address to the requesting computer. (Think of calling the message service and saying "Hi. I can be reached at 435.44.32.111 right now. Please tell anyone who tries to reach me to call that number.) Using a dynamic DNS service to arrange for computers to find you even though you are using a dynamic IP address is the next-best thing to having a static IP.

dynamic fonts

Dynamic fonts are a feature of Netscape's Communicator suite of products that enables a Web page designer to specify or create a special font style for a Web page or site. A **font** file (which describes how to display a particular set of font

images) is downloaded as a **plug-in** from the Web server along with the first page that uses it. Netscape's viewing support uses TrueDoc Technology from Bitstream.

Dynamic Host Configuration Protocol

Dynamic Host Configuration Protocol (DHCP) is a communications **protocol** that lets network administrators manage centrally and automate the assignment of Internet Protocol (**IP**) addresses in an organization's network. Using the Internet Protocol, each machine that can connect to the Internet needs a unique **IP address**. When an organization sets up its computer users with a connection to the Internet, an IP address must be assigned to each machine. Without DHCP, the IP address must be entered manually at each computer and, if computers move to another location in another part of the network, a new IP address must be entered. DHCP lets a network administrator supervise and distribute IP addresses from a central point and automatically sends a new IP address when a computer is plugged into a different place in the network.

DHCP uses the concept of a "lease" or amount of time that a given IP address will be valid for a computer. The lease time can vary depending on how long a user is likely to require the Internet connection at a particular location. It's especially useful in education and other environments where users change frequently. Using very short leases, DHCP can dynamically reconfigure networks in which there are more computers than there are available IP addresses.

DHCP supports static addresses for computers containing Web servers that need a permanent IP address.

DHCP is an alternative to another network IP management protocol, Bootstrap Protocol (**BOOTP**). DHCP is a more advanced protocol, but both configuration management protocols are commonly used. Some organizations use both protocols, but understanding how and when to use them in the same organization is important. Some operating systems, including Windows NT/2000, come with DHCP servers. A DHCP or BOOTP client is a program that is located in (and perhaps downloaded to) each computer so that it can be configured.

dynamic HTML

Dynamic HTML is a collective term for a combination of new Hypertext Markup Language (**HTML**) tags and options, that will let you create Web pages more animated and more responsive to user interaction than previous versions of HTML. Much of dynamic HTML is specified in HTML 4.0. Simple examples of dynamic HTML pages would include (1) having the color of a text heading change when a user passes a mouse over it or (2) allowing a user to "drag and drop" an image to another place on a Web page. Dynamic HTML can allow Web documents to look and act like desktop applications or multimedia productions.

The features that constitute dynamic HTML are included in recent versions of the Netscape, Internet Explorer, and other web browsers. While HTML 4.0 is supported by both Netscape and Microsoft browsers, some additional capabilities are supported by only one of the browsers. The biggest obstacle to the use of dynamic HTML is that, since many users are still using older browsers, a Web site must create two versions of each site and serve the pages appropriate to each user's browser version. The concepts and features in Dynamic HTML that both Netscape and Microsoft support are:

- An object-oriented view of a Web page and its elements
- Cascading style sheets and the layering of content
- Programming that can address all or most page elements
- Dynamic fonts

An Object-Oriented View of Page Elements

Each page element (division or section, heading, paragraph, image, list, and so forth) is viewed as an "object." (Microsoft calls this the "Dynamic HTML Object Model." Netscape calls it the "HTML Object Model." W3C calls it the "Document Object Model.") For example, each heading on a page can be named, given attributes of text style and color, and addressed by name in a small progam or "script" included on the page. This heading or any other element on the page can be changed as the result of a specified event such a mouse passing over or being clicked or a time elapsing. Or an image can be moved from one place to another by "dragging and dropping" the image object with the mouse. (These event possibilities can be viewed as the reaction capabilities of the element or object.) Any change takes place immediately (since all variations of all elements or objects have been sent as part of the same page from the Web server that sent the page). Thus, variations can be thought of as different properties of the object.

Not only can element variations change text wording or color, but everything contained within a heading object can be replaced with new content that includes different or additional HTML as well as different text. Microsoft calls this the "Text Range technology."

Style Sheets and Layering

A **style sheet** describes the default style characteristics (including the page layout and font type style and size for text elements such as headings and body text) of a document or a portion of a document. For Web pages, a style sheet also describes the default background color or image, hypertext link colors, and possibly the content of page. Style sheets help ensure consistency across all or a group of pages in a document or a Web site.

Dynamic HTML includes the capability to specify style sheets in a "**cascading style sheet**" fashion (that is, linking to or specifying different style sheets or style statements with predefined levels of precedence within the same or a set of related pages). As the result of user interaction, a new style sheet can be made applicable and result in a change of appearance of the Web page. You can have multiple layers of style sheet within a page, a style sheet within a style sheet within a style sheet. A new style sheet may only vary one element from the style sheet above it.

Layering is the use of alternate style sheets or other approaches to vary the content of a page by providing content layers that can overlay (and replace or superimpose on) existing content sections. Layers can be programmed to appear as part of a timed presentation or as the result of user interaction. In Internet Explorer, Microsoft implements layers through style sheets. Netscape supports the style sheet approach but also offers a new HTML ... tag set (that Microsoft does not support). Both approaches are being considered by the W3C Working Committee and both companies say they will support whatever W3C decides will be the recommended approach.

Programming

Although **JavaScript**, **Java applet**, and **ActiveX** controls were present in previous levels of Web pages, dynamic HTML implies an increased amount of programming in Web pages since more elements of a page can be addressed by a program.

Dynamic Fonts

Netscape includes **dynamic fonts** as part of dynamic HTML. This feature of Netscape's Navigator browser in its Communicator suite lets Web page designers include font files containing specific font styles, sizes, and colors as part of a Web page and to have the fonts downloaded with the page. That is, the font choice no longer is dependent on what the browser provides.

dynamic link library

In computers, a dynamic link library (DLL) is a collection of small programs, any of which can be called when needed by a larger program that is running in the computer. The small program that lets the larger program communicate with a specific device such as a printer or scanner is often packaged as a DLL program (usually referred to as a DLL file). DLL files that support specific device operation are known as **device driver**s.

The advantage of DLL files is that, because they don't get loaded into random access memory (**RAM**) together with the main program, space is saved in RAM. When and if a DLL file is needed, then it is loaded and run. For example, as long as a user of Microsoft Word is editing a document, the printer DLL file does not need to be loaded into RAM. If the user decides to print the document, then the Word application causes the printer DLL file to be loaded and run.

A DLL file is often given a ".dll" file name suffix. DLL files are dynamically linked with the program that uses them during program execution rather than being **compiler** with the main program. The set of such files (or the DLL) is somewhat comparable to the library routines provided with programming languages such as **C** and **C++**.

dynamic multi-pathing

Dynamic multi-pathing (DMP) is a type of communication **path control** software application. Path control is an approach to optimizing configuration and routing management for storage networks; DMP is used to automate these processes for storage network data backup and restoration. DMP was designed in response to the complex needs of storage networks as compared to ordinary data networks: Connection failures in data networks generally just mean that the connection must be retried; in storage networks, however, a failure is more likely to cause a system **crash**. The margin for error is smaller for storage networks as well: Whereas error recovery within minutes is acceptable for properly functioning data networks, for storage networks it should be within seconds—and preferably milliseconds.

To address these differences, storage networks should be designed to enable the greatest possible configuration flexibility and system availability. However, added flexibility also increases the possibility of connection failures: Where a storage system at one time might have consisted of a single storage device connected to a single **host** by a single cable, a storage system today typically consists of multiple diverse devices in an interconnected network **topology**. DMP software applications automatically reroute data through alternate paths in the event of a connection failure.

dynamic packet filter

A dynamic packet filter is a **firewall** facility that can monitor the state of active connections and use this information to determine which network **packet**s to allow through the firewall. By recording session information such as **IP address**es and **port** numbers, a dynamic packet filter can implement a much tighter security posture than a static packet filter.

For example, assume that you wish to configure your firewall so that all users in your company are allowed out to the Internet, but only replies to users' data requests are let back in. With a static packet filter, you would need to permanently allow in replies from all external addresses, assuming that users were free to visit any site on the Internet. This kind of filter would allow an attacker to sneak information past the filter by making the packet look like a reply (which can be done by indicating "reply" in the packet header).

By tracking and matching requests and replies, a dynamic packet filter can screen for replies that don't match a request. When a request is recorded, the dynamic packet filter opens up a small inbound hole so only the expected data reply is let back through. Once the reply is received, the hole is closed. This dramatically increases the security capabilities of the firewall.

dynamic port numbers

The dynamic port numbers (also known as the *private port numbers*) are the **port number**s that are available for use by any application to use in communicating with any other application, using the Internet's Transmission Control Protocol (**TCP**) or the User Datagram Protocol (**UDP**). When one application communicates with another application at another **host** computer on the Internet, it specifies that application in each data transmission by using its port number. The port numbers range from 0 through 65535. However, certain port numbers—the **well-known port numbers** and the **registered port numbers**—are registered and administered by the Internet Corporation for Assigned Names and Numbers (**ICANN**) for use by certain classes of applications. The dynamic port numbers are in the highest range, from 49152 through 65535.

Before the arrival of ICANN, the port numbers were administered by the Internet Internet Assigned Numbers Authority (**IANA**).

dynamic random access memory

See "DRAM"

dynamic range

Dynamic range describes the ratio of the softest sound to the loudest sound in a musical instrument or piece of electronic equipment. This ratio is measured in **decibels** (abbreviated as dB) units.

Dynamic range measurements are used in **audio** equipment to indicate a component's maximum output signal and to rate a system's noise floor. As a reference point, the dynamic range of human hearing, the difference between the softest sound we can perceive and the loudest, is about 120 dB.

Compressors, expanders, and noise gates are processing devices that are used in audio to alter the dynamic range of a given signal. This is done to achieve a more consistent sound when recording or as a special effect (by radically altering the dynamics of a sound, thereby creating a sound not possible from the original source).

E Ink

E Ink is an electronic device that is similar to a computer display, but with qualities that enable it to be used for applications such as **eBook**s, **electronic newspaper**s, portable signs, and foldable, rollable displays. E Ink Corp. (a Cambridge, Massachusetts company) and Lucent are developing the device, which combines E Ink's **electronic ink** with Lucent's **flexible transistor**s. Prototypes have featured 25-inch display areas involving several hundred **pixel**s. Although the new technology's more complex applications—such as electronic newspapers and improved e-books that are very similar to traditional books—are likely still at least 10 years in the future, E Ink is currently being tried for simpler applications, such as retail signage.

The E Ink prototypes combine thin, plastic transistors with **polymer LEDs** (**light-emitting diodes**) to create what are called **smart pixels**. The process involved—which is not dissimilar to traditional printing processes—uses silicon rubber stamps to actually print tiny computer circuits onto the surface. The electronic ink used is a liquid substance consisting of millions of tiny capsules floating in a substance like vegetable oil. The capsules, which are filled with a dark dye, contain negatively charged white chips that move either up or down within the capsules in response to a positive charge applied to the medium's surface. Information to be displayed is downloaded through a connection to a computer or a cell phone, or created with mechanical tools such as an electronic "pencil," and remains fixed until another charge is applied to change it. The devices use very low power: according to a spokesperson, prototypes of the device have been running on watch batteries.

Xerox, in partnership with 3M is working on a competing technology, called **Gyricon**.

e-

1) e- or E- (sometimes without the hyphen) is a prefix that has spread from **e-mail** to other forms of human enterprise as they emerge on the **Internet**. Well-known examples are **e-commerce**, **e-business**, **e-tailing**, and **ezine**. The e is a shortening of "electronic" and e-mail is still sometimes referred to as electronic mail. The sense of "electronic" in this usage generally had and has to do with telecommunications. Whatever it was you used to do before, now you can do it (send or receive it or have a transaction with others) electronically over a telecommunications line.

If the e- prefix denotes telecommunication, the *cyber* prefix denotes computing, although this often implicitly suggests network computing and telecommunication as well (as in **cyberspace**). The lower-case *i* (for Internet) prefix, which is usually without the hyphen, has also gained currency as a prefix for a name that instantly associates it with the Internet.

2) At least one user reports colloquial usage of the e alone as a verb, especially as a short form for "to email." For example: "I'll e it to you later, baby."

E1, E2, E3...

See "E-carrier system"

E2E

On the Internet, E2E has been used to mean exchange-to-exchange—that is, the exchange of information or transactions between Web sites that themselves serve as exchanges or brokers for goods and services between businesses. E2E can be thought of as a form of **B2B**.

E2K

E2K stands for the Exchange 2000 **messaging** and collaboration server product from Microsoft.

e3000

See "HP e3000"

EAI

EAI (enterprise application integration) is a business computing term for the plans, methods, and tools aimed at modernizing, consolidating, and coordinating the computer **applications** in an **enterprise**. Typically, an enterprise has existing **legacy applications** and **databases** and wants to continue to use them while adding or migrating to a new set of applications that exploit the Internet, **e-commerce**, **extranet**, and other new technologies. EAI may involve developing a new total view of an enterprise's business and its applications, seeing how existing applications fit into the new view, and then devising ways to efficiently reuse what already exists while adding new applications and data.

EAI encompasses methodologies such as **object-oriented programming**, distributed, cross-platform program communication using message brokers with **Common Object Request Broker Architecture** and **COM+**, the modification of enterprise resource planning (**ERP**) to fit new objectives, enterprise-wide content and data distribution using common databases and data standards implemented with the Extensible Markup Language (**XML**), **middleware**, message queueing, and other approaches.

Earth-Moon-Earth

See "moonbounce"

Easter egg

An Easter egg is an unexpected surprise, perhaps a message, an image, or a sound, hidden in a Web site or in an application program.

EBCDIC

EBCDIC (pronounced either "ehb-suh-dik" or "ehb-kuh-dik") is a **binary** code for alphabetic and numeric characters that IBM developed for its larger operating systems. It is the code for text files that is used in IBM's OS/390 operating system for its S/390 servers and that thousands of corporations use for their **legacy applications** and **databases**. In an EBCDIC file, each alphabetic or numeric character is represented with an 8-bit binary number (a string of eight 0's or 1's). 256 possible characters (letters of the alphabet, numerals, and special characters) are defined.

IBM's PC and workstation operating systems do not use IBM's proprietary EBCDIC. Instead, they use the industry standard code for text, **ASCII**. Conversion programs allow different operating systems to change a file from one code to another.

Also see **Unicode**.

e-biz

See "B2B"

eBook

An eBook is an *electronic* version of a traditional print book that can be read by using a personal computer or by using an eBook reader. (An eBook reader can be a software application for use on a computer, such as Microsoft's free *Reader* application, or a book-sized computer that is used solely as a reading device, such as Nuvomedia's **Rocket eBook**.) Users can purchase an eBook on diskette or CD, but the most popular method of getting an eBook is to purchase a downloadable file of the eBook (or other reading material) from a Web site (such as Barnes and Noble) to be read from the user's computer or reading device. Generally, an eBook can be downloaded in five minutes or less.

Although it is not necessary to use a reader application or device in order to read an Ebook (most books can be read as **PDF** files), they are popular because they enable options similar to those of a paper book—readers can bookmark pages, make notes, highlight passages, and save selected text. In addition to these familiar possibilities, eBook readers also include built-in dictionaries, and alterable font sizes and styles. Typically, an eBook reader hand-held device weighs from about twenty-two ounces to three or four pounds and can store from four thousand to over half a million pages of text and graphics. A popular feature is its back-lit screen (which makes reading in the dark possible).

Some eBooks can be downloaded for free or at reduced cost, however, prices for many eBooks—especially bestsellers—are similar to those of hardcover books, and are sometimes higher. Most eBooks at Barnes and Noble, for example, are comparable in price to their traditional print versions.

EBPP

On the Internet, electronic bill presentment and payment (EBPP) is a process that enables bills to be created, delivered, and paid over the Internet. The service has applications for many industries, from financial service providers to telecommunications companies and utilities.

Although buying products over the Internet with a credit card has become a common occurrence, viewing the credit card bill itself—and making payments to settle the bill electronically—has not. This is expected to dramatically change as new EBPP products are introduced that include features such as secure e-mail delivery, and also as EBPP technology becomes more common in business-to-business e-commerce.

One of the obstacles to widespread adoption of EBPP lies in the complexity of billing systems and processes used by competing banks and financial institutions. Some have resisted implementing EBPP for fear of being unable to cross-promote other services to customers, although experts claim EBPP appears ideal for this type of marketing. The banking industry also has been resistant for fear of losing out on lucrative cash-management services, reminiscent of the battle the industry fought and lost over credit card transactions. Disputes over adopting uniform security and implementation standards also have stalled the adoption of EBPP.

The common protocol known as the Open Financial Exchange would allow firms to integrate their systems. But the protocol has not been widely embraced, especially by banks, which are concerned about possibly losing control of their vital customer information. A second competing standard also is emerging. Spectrum, a joint venture of The Chase Manhattan Corp., First Union Corp. and Wells Fargo & Co., is adopting the Interactive Financial Exchange (IFX) protocol. The IFX Forum, an organization that comprises financial institutions, billers, insurance companies and vendors, is developing IFX.

Despite these difficulties, experts predict the industry will experience a growth spurt, driven by customers who want the convenience and time savings associated with being able to access, view and remit their bills directly online.

e-brokerage

An e-brokerage is a brokerage house that allows you to buy and sell stocks and obtain investment information from its Web site. Some e-brokerages are provided by traditional and well-established "offline" brokerage houses and a few are exclusively online only.

Traditional investing has experienced a revolution due to the rise of the e-brokerage industry, which enables investors to use the Internet to conduct secure trading. Two factors are contributing to the enormous growth of online investing. First, the Internet gives ready access to raw data. Second, investment houses can offer transactions at lower prices than traditional methods by eliminating the need for brokers or financial advisers.

The online brokerage industry has yet to attract mainstream investors, who represent 85 percent of the retail investment community. These investors prefer a combination of brokerage services, including not only online trading, but also financial advice and guidance.

Still, despite initial resistance, nearly every major investment firm offers trading with the click of a mouse. By 2003, it is estimated that about $3 trillion will be held in online brokerage accounts. The survival of brokerage firms may depend on how quickly they identify future customers.

e-business

E-business (electronic business), derived from such terms as "e-mail" and "e-commerce," is the conduct of business on the Internet, not only buying and selling but also servicing customers and collaborating with business partners. One of the first to use the term was IBM, when, in October 1997, it launched a thematic campaign built around the term. Today, major corporations are rethinking their businesses in terms of the Internet and its new culture and capabilities. Companies are using the Web to buy parts and supplies from other companies, to collaborate on sales promotions, and to do joint research. Exploiting the convenience, availability, and world-wide reach of the Internet, many companies, such as Amazon.com, the book sellers, have already discovered how to use the Internet successfully.

Increasingly, much direct selling (or **e-tailing**) is taking place on the Internet of computer-related equipment and software. One of the first to report sales in the millions of dollars directly from the Web was Dell Computer. Travel bookings directly or indirectly as a result of Web research are becoming significant. Custom-orderable golf clubs and similar specialties are considered good prospects for the immediate future.

With the security built into today's browsers and with **digital certificates** now available for individuals and companies from Verisign, a certificate issuer, much of the early concern about the security of business transaction on the Web has abated and e-business by whatever name is accelerating.

IBM considers the development of **intranets** and **extranets** to be part of e-business. e-business can be said to include *e-service*, the provision of services and tasks over the Internet by application service providers (**ASPs**).

ebXML

ebXML (Electronic Business XML) is a project to use the Extensible Markup Language (**XML**) to standardize the secure exchange of business data. Among other purposes, ebXML would encompass and perhaps replace a familiar standard called Electronic Data Interchange (**EDI**). ebXML is designed to enable a global electronic marketplace in which enterprises of any size, and in any location, could safely and securely transact business through the exchange of XML-based messages. The United Nations body for Trade Facilitation and Electronic Business Information Standards (UN/CEFACT) and the Organization for the Advancement of Structured Information Standards (**OASIS**) launched the project as a joint initiative. Its membership includes 75 companies, including major IT vendors and trade associations throughout the world.

Because ebXML relies on the Internet's existing standards such as HTTP, TCP/IP, MIME, SMTP, FTP, UML, and XML, it can be implemented and deployed on virtually any computing platform. The use of existing standards gives ebXML the advantage of being relatively inexpensive and easy to use.

A white paper on the official ebXML Web site explains that the initiative is built on three basic concepts: (1) provide an infrastructure that ensures data communication interoperability; (2) provide a semantics framework that ensures commercial interoperability; and (3) provide a mechanism that allows enterprises to find each other, agree to become trading partners and conduct business with each other. The core infrastructure specifications of ebXML are the messaging service, the registry and repository, and the collaborative partner agreement. The messaging service specification has been developed enough to enable early development work. The registry and repository and the collaborative partner specifications are nearing completion, with the complete set of ebXML specifications expected to be finished in May 2001.

E-carrier system

To see the relationship between the E-carrier system, the **T-carrier system**, and DS0 multiples, see **digital signal X**.

E1 (or E-1) is a European digital transmission format devised by the **ITU-TS** and given the name by the Conference of European Postal and Telecommunication Administration

(CEPT). It's the equivalent of the North American **T-carrier system** format. E2 through E5 are carriers in increasing multiples of the E1 format.

The E1 signal format carries data at a rate of 2.048 million bits per second and can carry 32 channels of 64 **Kbps*** each. E1 carries at a somewhat higher data rate than T-1 (which carries 1.544 million bits per second) because, unlike T-1, it does not do *bit-robbing* and all eight bits per channel are used to code the signal. E1 and T-1 can be interconnected for international use.

E2 (E-2) is a line that carries four multiplexed E1 signals with a data rate of 8.448 million bits per second.

E3 (E-3) carries 16 E1 signals with a data rate of 34.368 million bits per second.

E4 (E-4) carries four E3 channels with a data rate of 139.264 million bits per second.

E5 (E-5) carries four E4 channels with a data rate of 565.148 million bits per second.

*In international English outside the U.S., the equivalent usage is "kbps" or "kbits s^{-1}."

eCash

See "digital cash"

ECB

See "Electronic Code Book"

ECC

ECC (either "error correction [or correcting] code" or "error checking and correcting") allows data that is being read or transmitted to be checked for errors and, when necessary, corrected **on the fly**. It differs from **parity**-checking in that errors are not only detected but also corrected. ECC is increasingly being designed into data storage and transmission hardware as data rates (and therefore error rates) increase.

Here's how it works for data storage:

1. When a unit of data (or "**word**") is stored in RAM or peripheral storage, a code that describes the bit sequence in the word is calculated and stored along with the unit of data. For each 64-bit word, an extra 7 bits are needed to store this code.

2. When the unit of data is requested for reading, a code for the stored and about-to-be-read word is again calculated using the original algorithm. The newly generated code is compared with the code generated when the word was stored.

3. If the codes match, the data is free of errors and is sent.

4. If the codes don't match, the missing or erroneous bits are determined through the code comparison and the bit or bits are supplied or corrected.

5. No attempt is made to correct the data that is still in storage. Eventually, it will be overlaid by new data and, assuming the errors were transient, the incorrect bits will "go away."

6. Any error that recurs at the same place in storage after the system has been turned off and on again indicate a permanent hardware error and a message is sent to a log or to a system administrator indicating the location with the recurrent errors.

At the 64-bit word level, parity-checking and ECC require the same number of extra bits. In general, ECC increases the reliability of any computing or telecommunications system (or part of a system) without adding much cost. Reed-Solomon codes are commonly implemented; they're able to detect and restore "erased" bits as well as incorrect bits.

E-CD

See "enhanced CD"

eCheck

An eCheck is an electronic version of a paper check. It uses the same legal and business protocols associated with traditional paper checks—it can be used in any transactions where paper checks are used today—yet it capitalizes on the speed and processing efficiencies of all-electronic payments.

The technology used to standardize the implementation of eChecks was developed by the Financial Services Technology Consortium (FSTC), whose eCheck project is currently being used by the United States Treasury in a two-year pilot program. eChecks are based on the Financial Services Markup Language (**FSML**, the markup language developed to allow eCheck technology into the marketplace.

The FSTC's eCheck technology takes the basic, and nearly ubiquitous, concept and applies it to a markup-language-based document, thereby recognizing the need for basic signing, co-signing, and countersigning or notarizing. eChecks also utilize several different state-of-the-art security techniques including **authentication**, **public key infrastructure**, and **certificate authority** in order to ensure the integrity of each electronic transaction.

The path an eCheck takes looks something like this: the payer writes the eCheck on a computer, signs it, and e-mails it over the Internet. The payee receives it, verifies signatures, endorses it, writes a deposit slip, and signs it. The endorsed check is then sent by e-mail to the payee?s bank for deposit. Bank personnel verify signatures, credit the deposit, and then clear and settle the endorsed eCheck by sending it on to the payer's bank, where signatures are once again verified and the amount of the eCheck is debited from the payer's account.

The cryptographic certificates used with an eCheck enable a check payee to determine the validity of the signatures. Initially, these certificates are actually transmitted with the eCheck, but alternative models where the transmission, or possibly even issuance, of the certificate is not required are currently in the making.

eCheck technology also allows digital signatures to be applied to document blocks, rather than to the entire document. This allows parts of a document to be separated from the original, without compromising the integrity of the digital signature.

Echelon

According to such sources as the American Civil Liberties Union (ACLU) and the British Broadcasting Corporation (BBC), Echelon is a secret U.S.-led global spy network that operates an automated system for the interception and relay of electronic communications. Monitored transmissions are said to include up to 3 billion communications daily, including all the telephone calls, e-mail messages, faxes, satellite transmissions, and Internet downloads of both public and private organizations and citizens worldwide. Led by the U.S. National Security Agency (**NSA**), Echelon is operated collaboratively by the intelligence agencies of the United States, the United Kingdom, Australia, Canada, and New Zealand. The organization's name originated as the code name for the system component responsible for intercepting **satellite** communications.

Echelon collects information through an extensive system of radio antennae and satellites that monitor satellite communications and **sniffer** devices that collect Internet communications from **data packet**s. Some sources claim that the organization employs underwater devices to tap into transcontinental **fiber optic** phone cables. According to the ACLU, Echelon gathers huge volumes of data indiscriminately, and then filters out useful information through artificial intelligence (**AI**) technology. The system is also said to involve **voice recognition**, language translation, and keyword searching to select messages to study in their entirety. In October 1999, an e-mail based **hacktivism** campaign urged message recipients to include likely Echelon keywords ("manifesto," "revolution," and "Bill Clinton," for example) in any communications they sent on "Jam Echelon Day," with the intention of overwhelming the system. Because of the clandestine nature of Echelon, however, it is difficult to gauge the success of the campaign: whether or not Jam Echelon Day was effective, the organization itself has nothing to say about it—or about anything else, for that matter.

Although officials in both the United States and Britain have repeatedly denied the claims, the fact of Echelon's existence has been publicly admitted by the governments of both Australia and New Zealand. Although most people have no objection to some of Echelon's mandate (anti-terrorist surveillance, for example), many are made uneasy by claims that the organization practices economic espionage and monitors well-intentioned endeavors, such as Amnesty International. The Scientific and Technical Options Assessment program office (STOA) of the European Parliament recently commissioned two reports looking into Echelon. These reports found: that the organization exists; that it routinely intercepts both personal and business communications, in probable contravention of human rights; and that stringent **encryption** practices should be followed to protect against Echelon's transgressive invasions of privacy.

ECMAScript

ECMAScript is a standard **script** language, developed with the cooperation of Netscape and Microsoft and mainly derived from Netscape's **JavaScript**, the widely-used scripting language that is used in Web pages to affect how they look or behave for the user. Microsoft states that its latest version of **JScript** is the first implementation of the ECMAScript standard. The official standard, ECMA-262, was developed under the auspices of the European Computer Manufacturers Association (ECMA). Having the ECMAScript standard will help ensure more consistency between Netscape, Microsoft, and any other Web script implementations.

ECMAScript is **object-oriented** and conceived as a *core language* to which can be added the objects of any specific **domain** or context such as the idea of a "document." (for example, the World Wide Web Consortium's **Document Object Model**). ECMAScript together with the Document Object Model corresponds closely to the current implementations of JavaScript and JScript. Although likely to be used mainly as a standard script language for the World Wide Web, ECMAScript could also be used for any scripted application.

e-commerce

E-commerce (electronic commerce or EC) is the buying and selling of goods and services on the Internet, especially the World Wide Web. In practice, this term and a newer term, **e-business**, are often used interchangably. For online retail selling, the term **e-tailing** is sometimes used.

E-commerce can be divided into:

- E-tailing or "virtual storefronts" on Web sites with online catalogs, sometimes gathered into a "virtual mall"
- The gathering and use of demographic data through Web contacts
- Electronic Data Interchange (**EDI**), the business-to-business exchange of data
- **E-mail** and **fax** and their use as media for reaching prospects and established customers (for example, with newsletters)
- Business-to-business buying and selling
- The security of business transactions

E-tailing or The Virtual Storefront and the Virtual Mall

As a place for direct retail shopping, with its 24-hour availability, a global reach, the ability to interact and provide custom information and ordering, and multimedia prospects, the Web is rapidly becoming a multibillion dollar source of revenue for the world's businesses. A number of businesses already report considerable success. As early as the middle of 1997, Dell Computers reported orders of a million dollars a day. By early 1999, projected e-commerce revenues for business were in the billions of dollars and the stocks of companies deemed most adept at e-commerce were skyrocketing. Although many so-called **dotcom** retailers disappeared in the economic shakeout of 2000, Web retailing at sites such as Amazon.com, CDNow.com, and CompudataOnline.com continues to grow.

Market Research

In early 1999, it was widely recognized that because of the interactive nature of the Internet, companies could gather data about prospects and customers in unprecedented amounts -through site registration, questionnaires, and as part of taking orders. The issue of whether data was being collected with the knowledge and permission of market subjects had been raised. (Microsoft referred to its policy of data collection as "profiling" and a proposed standard has been developed that allows Internet users to decide who can have what personal information.)

Electronic Data Interchange (EDI)

EDI is the exchange of business data using an understood data format. It predates today's Internet. EDI involves data exchange among parties that know each other well and make arrangements for one-to-one (or point-to-point) connection, usually dial-up. EDI is expected to be replaced by one or more standard **XML** formats, such as **ebXML**. are

E-Mail, Fax, and Internet Telephony

E-commerce is also conducted through the more limited electronic forms of communication called e-mail, facsimile or fax, and the emerging use of telephone calls over the Internet. Most of this is business-to-business, with some companies attempting to use e-mail and fax for unsolicited ads (usually viewed as online junk mail or **spam**) to consumers and other business prospects. An increasing number of business Web sites offer e-mail newsletters for subscribers. A new trend is **opt-in e-mail** in which Web users voluntarily sign up to receive e-mail, usually sponsored or containing ads, about product categories or other subjects they are interested in.

Business-to-Business Buying and Selling

Thousands of companies that sell products to other companies have discovered that the Web provides not only a 24-hour-a-day showcase for their products but a quick way to reach the right people in a company for more information.

The Security of Business Transactions

Security includes authenticating business transactors, controlling access to resources such as Web pages for registered or selected users, **encrypting** communications, and, in general, ensuring the privacy and effectiveness of transactions. Among the most widely-used security technologies is the Secure Sockets Layer (**SSL**), which is built into both of the leading Web browsers.

e-commerce hosting

E-commerce hosting is a business in which a company provides other companies whatever they need to sell their products and services on the World Wide Web—including a **Web server** to serve a company's pages, possibly the Web site design (including catalog pages), and the special capabilities needed to accept, process, and confirm sales orders. **E-commerce hosting** usually includes providing templates for building virtual storefronts or online catalogs, providing software for customized electronic "shopping carts," taking and filling customer orders, arranging for secure credit-card purchasing, and providing tools for tracking and managing inventory.

Here's how it typically works:

A company contracts with an e-commerce hosting provider to purchase hosting space on its computer **server**. This space usually is billed monthly, along with any leasing of computer software for processing online orders. The computer server may be shared with other clients, or in the case of companies expecting a substantial amount of traffic, may be dedicated exclusively to one client.

To ensure secure payment processes, these providers also usually assist with setting up Internet merchant accounts, which are bank accounts established to process Visa, MasterCard, American Express and Discover credit-card transactions. Some hosting providers will register a company's domain name as part of the package.

E-commerce hosting firms customarily manage all the technical aspects of creating and maintaining a commercial Web site for its customers. For smaller companies, this is often more effective and cost-efficient than setting up and managing their own e-commerce site themselves since they are essentially sharing the cost of expensive equipment and Internet connections with other companies.

An e-commerce hosting provider may also provide services other than managing online transactions, including **EDI**, the gathering of demographic or other information (usually for marketing purposes), or transactions between businesses (business-to-business e-commerce).

e-copy

An e-copy is an electronic copy of a document. For example, when you send someone an **e-mail** note and specify that a copy of the note should be sent to someone else, the copy could be called an e-copy. The term does not seem to be very widely used, perhaps because, like e-mail, electronic copying is becoming so commonplace that identifying the copy as "electronic" seems unnecessary. Notice how often people today say "I'll send you a note" or "I'll send you some mail," because the electronic context is understood.

Edapt

Edapt is the trade name for an e-learning (electronic learning) program developed by Tcert of Atlanta, Georgia. The software employs artificial intelligence (**AI**) to stream-line the learning process for a student, and to make the program a better teacher as a student spends time with it.

Features of Edapt include an interface that keeps the student interested and helps the student follow specialized, nonlinear learning paths. The level of difficulty is constantly adjusted based on student performance, optimizing the amount of material learned per unit time. Students are given frequent opportunities to evaluate their progress. Animation, speech recognition, and interactivity enhance the flexibility of the program and keep users attentive. The learning environment has been described as structured yet not restrictive.

In a class setting, Edapt keeps track of the progress and needs of each individual student, and also of the group as a whole. Thus, the program can optimize curricula for small and large groups, as well as for individual students. Edapt is available for use in most natural languages, and most operating platforms. It can be used with individual computers, in a local area network (LAN), or on the Internet.

EDFA

See "erbium amplifier"

EDGE

EDGE (Enhanced Data GSM Environment), a faster version of the Global System for Mobile (**GSM**) wireless service, is designed to deliver data at rates up to 384 **Kbps** and enable the delivery of multimedia and other broadband applications to mobile phone and computer users. The EDGE standard is built on the existing GSM standard, using the same time-division multiple access (**TDMA**) **frame** structure and existing **cell** arrangements. Ericsson notes that its base stations can be updated with software.

EDGE is expected to be commercially available in 2001. It is regarded as an evolutionary standard on the way to Universal Mobile Telecommunications Service (**UMTS**).

edge router

A term used in asynchronous transfer mode (**ATM**) networks, an edge router is a device that routes data between one or more local area networks (**LANs**) and an ATM **backbone** network, whether a **campus** network or a wide area network (**WAN**). An edge router is an example of an *edge device* and is sometimes referred to as a *boundary router*. An edge router is sometimes contrasted with a *core router*, which forwards packets to computer hosts within a network (but not between networks).

EDI

EDI (Electronic Data Interchange) is a standard format for exchanging business data. The standard is **ANSI** X12 and it was developed by the Data Interchange Standards Association. ANSI X12 is either closely coordinated with or is being merged with an international standard, EDIFACT.

An EDI message contains a string of *data elements*, each of which represents a singular fact, such as a price, product model number, and so forth, separated by **delimiter**. The entire string is called a *data segment*. One or more data segments framed by a header and trailer form a *transaction set*, which is the EDI unit of transmission (equivalent to a *message*). A transaction set often consists of what would usually be contained in a typical business document or form. The parties who exchange EDI transmissions are referred to as *trading partners*.

EDI messages can be **encrypted**. EDI is one form of **e-commerce**, which also includes **e-mail** and **fax**.

EDM

1) EDM (Electronic Document Management) is the management of different kinds of **documents** in an **enterprise** using computer programs and storage. An EDM system allows an enterprise and its users to create a document or capture a hard copy in electronic form, store, edit, print, process, and otherwise manage documents in **image**, video, and **audio**, as well as in **text** form. An EDM system usually provides a single view of multiple **databases** and may include **scanners** for document capture, printers for creating hard copy, storage devices such as **redundant array of independent disks** systems, and computer **server** and server programs for managing the databases that contains the documents.

EDM may be needed in enterprises that capture and store a large number of documents such as invoices, sales orders, photographs, phone interviews, or video newsclips. EDM may be combined with or integrated into other applications. It may be combined with a **workflow** management approach. Capture may include document **imaging** and optical character recognition (**OCR**).

2) Engineering Data Management (EDM) is the management using computers and electronic storage media of documents or **data** that relate to engineering applications.

3) EDM (Electrical Discharge Machine or Machining) is a machine process driven by a computer program that is used in making high-precision molds, dies, or machine parts.

EDO RAM

EDO (extended data output) RAM is a type of random access memory (**RAM**) chip that improves the time to read from memory on faster **microprocessors** such as the Intel **Pentium**. EDO RAM was initially optimized for the 66 MHz Pentium. For faster computers, different types of synchronous dynamic RAM (**SDRAM**) are recommended.

Also see **BEDO DRAM**.

EDP

EDP (electronic data processing), an infrequently used term for what is today usually called "IS" (information services or systems) or "MIS" (management information services or systems), is the processing of **data** by a computer and its programs in an environment involving electronic communication. EDP evolved from "DP" (data processing), a term that was created when most computing input was physically put into the computer in punched card form and output as punched cards or paper reports.

EDRAM

EDRAM (enhanced dynamic random access memory) is **dynamic random access memory** (dynamic or power-refreshed **RAM**) that includes a small amount of static RAM (**SRAM**) inside a larger amount of DRAM so that many memory accesses will be to the faster SRAM. EDRAM is sometimes used as **L1 and L2** memory and, together with **enhanced synchronous dynamic DRAM**, is known as *cached DRAM*.

Data that has been loaded into the SRAM part of the EDRAM can be accessed by the **microprocessor** in 15 ns (nanoseconds). If data is not in the SRAM, it can be accessed in 35 ns from the DRAM part of the EDRAM.

edu

"edu" is one of the top-level **domain names** that can be used when choosing a domain name. It generally describes the entity owning the domain name as a four-year college or similar educational institution. (Educational institutions below four-year colleges are encouraged to use the geographic "us" top-level domain name.) Along with the second-level domain name (for example: "umich" in umich.edu), the top-level domain name is required in Web and e-mail addresses.

For more information, see **gTLD** (generic top-level domain name).

edutainment

Edutainment is a **neologism** (new term coinage), similar to **infotainment**, that expresses the marriage of education and entertainment in a work or presentation such as a television program or a Web site. The most educationally effective children's programs on television (Sesame Street, The Electric Company, Mr. Rogers) could be classed as edutainment. Outstanding Web sites that "edutain" include Learn2.com and HowStuffWorks.com.

EEPROM

EEPROM (electrically erasable programmable read-only memory) is user-modifiable read-only memory (**ROM**) that can be erased and reprogrammed (written to) repeatedly through the application of higher than normal electrical voltage. Unlike **EPROM** chips, EEPROMs do not need to be removed from the computer to be modified. However, an EEPROM chip has to be erased and reprogrammed in its entirety, not selectively. It also has a limited life—that is, the number of times it can be reprogrammed is limited to tens or hundreds of thousands of times. In an EEPROM that is frequently reprogrammed while the computer is in use, the life of the EEPROM can be an important design consideration.

A special form of EEPROM is **flash memory**, which uses normal PC voltages for erasure and reprogramming.

EFF

See "Electronic Frontier Foundation"

EFS

See "Encrypting File System"

EGA

See "display modes"

egosurfing

Egosurfing is looking to see how many places on the Web your name appears. On Alta Vista, you can also see how many times it appears in **Usenet** postings. On Alta Vista (http://www.altavista.com) and most other search engines, simply enter your name surrounded by double quotes in the search field like this:

"Your Name"

and you may be surprised to discover that you're a celebrated personage on someone's Web page or that the local task force report you helped write got put on the Web.

Egosurfing is also a way to find out how many of your site's Web pages are either indexed by the search engine or referred to by other sites. Just enter your second-level domain name, enclosed in quotes, like this:

"whatis.com" (but enter your own domain name)

e-government

See "B2G"

EGP

See "Exterior Gateway Protocol"

egress

Egress (pronounced EE-grehs, from Latin *egressus*, or going out) is the act of going out of something. For example, in telecommunications, an egress router is a router through which a data packet leaves one network for another network.

EIA

1) The Electronic Industries Association (EIA) comprises individual organizations that together have agreed on certain data transmission standards such as EIA/TIA-232 (formerly known as **RS-232**).

2) The Electronics Industries Alliance (EIA) is an alliance of trade organizations that lobby in the interest of companies engaged in the manufacture of electronics-related products.

EIDE

Enhanced (sometimes "Expanded") IDE is a standard electronic interface between your computer and its mass storage drives. EIDE's enhancements to Integrated Drive Electronics (**IDE**) make it possible to address a hard disk larger than 528 Mbytes. EIDE also provides faster access to the hard drive, support for Direct Memory Access (**DMA**), and support for additional drives, including CD-ROM and tape devices through the AT Attachment Packet Interface. When updating your computer with a larger hard drive (or other drives), an EIDE "controller" can be added to your computer in one of its **card slot**.

To access larger than 528 Mbyte drives, EIDE (or the **basic input/output system** that comes with it) uses a 28-bit logical block address (**LBA**) to specify the actual cylinder, head, and sector location of data on the disk. The 28 bits of the LBA provide enough information to specify unique sectors for a device up to 8.4 GB in size.

EIDE was adopted as a standard by **ANSI** in 1994. ANSI calls it Advanced Technology Attachment-2 (it's also referred to as "Fast **ATA**").

Also see **IDE**.

Eiffel

Eiffel is an **object-oriented** programming language developed by Bertrand Meyer, owner of Interactive Software Engineering (ISE), and named after Gustave Eiffel, the engineer who designed the Eiffel Tower. ISE Eiffel encompasses the Eiffel language, a method, and a programming environment. The language itself includes analysis, design, and implementation tools and was designed to create reusable code and to be **scalable**. The idea is that reusable components make writing programs more efficient because they save programming time and increase reliability. **Scalability** enables initially small programs to be expanded later to meet new needs. Eiffel is available for use on all major platforms.

Eiffel was designed to be simple, easy to learn, and powerful. It has the ability to incorporate program elements written in other languages. Features of Eiffel include **class**es, multiple **inheritance**, **polymorphism**, and a disciplined exception mechanism. ISE claims that Eiffel enables the fast production of bug-free software that is easy to change and extend in response to user requests, and can be reused in many different applications.

EIGRP

EIGRP (Enhanced Interior Gateway Routing Protocol) is a network **protocol** that lets **router**s exchange information more efficiently than with earlier network protocols. EIGRP evolved from IGRP (Interior Gateway Routing Protocol) and routers using either EIGRP and IGRP can interoperate because the **metric** (criteria used for selecting a route) used with one protocol can be translated into the metrics of the other protocol. EIGRP can be used not only for Internet Protocol (**IP**) networks but also for and Novell **NetWare** networks.

Using EIGRP, a router keeps a copy of its neighbor's routing tables. If it can't find a route to a destination in one of these tables, it queries its neighbors for a route and they in turn query their neighbors until a route is found. When a routing table entry changes in one of the routers, it notifies its neighbors of the change only (some earlier protocols require sending the entire table). To keep all routers aware of the state of neighbors, each router sends out a periodic "hello" packet. A router from which no "hello" packet has been received in a certain period of time is assumed to be inoperative.

EIGRP uses the Diffusing-Update Algorithm (DUAL) to determine the most efficient (*least cost*) route to a destination. A DUAL **finite state machine** contains decision information used by the algorithm to determine the least-cost route (which considers distance and whether a destination path is loop-free).

EIP

See "enterprise information portal"

EISA

EISA is a standard **bus** (computer interconnection) architecture that extends the **ISA** standard to a 32-bit interface. It was developed in part as an open alternative to the proprietary Micro Channel Architecture (**MCA**) that IBM introduced in its PS/2 computers.

EISA data transfer can reach a peak of 33 megabytes per second.

EJB

See "Enterprise JavaBeans"

electric field strength

Electric field strength is a quantitative expression of the intensity of an electric field at a particular location. The standard unit is the **volt per meter** (v/m or v ñ m⁻¹). A field strength of 1 v/m represents a potential difference of one **volt** between points separated by one meter.

Any electrically charged object produces an electric field. This field has an effect on other charged objects in the vicinity. The field strength at a particular distance from an object is directly proportional to the electric charge, in **coulomb**s, on that object. The field strength is inversely proportional to the distance from a charged object. The field-strength-vs-distance curve is a direct inverse function, and not an inverse-square function, because electric field strength is specified in terms of a linear displacement (per meter) rather than a surface area (per meter squared).

An alternative expression for the intensity of an electric field is **electric flux density**. This refers to the number of lines of electric **flux** passing orthogonally (at right angles) through a given surface area, usually one **meter squared** (1 m²). Electric flux density, like electric field strength, is directly proportional to the charge on the object. But flux density diminishes with distance according to the inverse-square law, because it is specified in terms of a surface area (per meter squared) rather than a linear displacement (per meter).

Sometimes the strength of an electromagnetic field (**EM field**) is specified in terms of the intensity of its electric-field component. This is done by engineers and scientists when talking about the radio-frequency field strength at a certain location arising from sources such as distant transmitters, celestial objects, high-tension utility lines, computer displays, or microwave ovens. In this context, electric field strength is usually specified in microvolts per meter (μV/m or μV · m⁻¹), nanovolts per meter (nV/m or nV · m⁻¹), or picovolts per meter (pV/m or pV · m⁻¹). The relationship among these units is shown in the table.

Unit	To convert to v/m, multiply by:	Conversely, multiply by:
v/m	1	1
μV/m	10^{-6}	10^{6}
nV/m	10^{-9}	10^{9}
pV/m	10^{-12}	10^{12}

Also see **coulomb**, **EM field**, **meter**, **volt**, and **SI** (International System of Units).

electrically erasable programmable ROM

See "EEPROM"

Electrohippies Collective

The Electrohippies Collective is an international group of **hacktivist**s based in Oxfordshire, England, whose purpose is to express its displeasure with the use of the Internet "as a tool for corporate communications and propaganda." A common form of protest used by The Electrohippies Collective is the Web sit-in. The group organizes volunteers who repeatedly access a target's Web site or who organize a **distributed denial-of-service attack**. There is some debate as to whether actions such as this are illegal. While The Electrohippies Collective agrees that DDoS attacks violate the First Amendment of the U.S. Constitution, the group is also relentless in identifying targets and fostering attacks.

electromagnetic field

An electromagnetic field, sometimes referred to as an EM field, is generated when charged particles, such as **electron**s, are accelerated. All electrically charged particles are surrounded by electric fields. Charged particles in motion produce magnetic fields. When the velocity of a charged particle changes, an EM field is produced.

Electromagnetic fields were first discovered in the 19th century, when physicists noticed that electric arcs (sparks) could be reproduced at a distance, with no connecting wires in between. This led scientists to believe that it was possible to communicate over long distances without wires. The first radio transmitters made use of electric arcs. These "spark transmitters" and the associated receivers were as exciting to people in the early 20th century as the Internet is today. This was the beginning of what we now call **wireless** communication.

Electromagnetic fields are typically generated by alternating current (**AC**) in electrical conductors. The **frequency** of the AC can range from one cycle in thousands of years (at the low extreme) to trillions or quadrillions of cycles per second (at the high extreme). The standard unit of EM frequency is the **hertz**, abbreviated Hz. Larger units are often used. A frequency of 1,000 Hz is one **kilohertz** (kHz); a frequency of 1,000 kHz is one **megahertz** (MHz); a frequency of 1,000 MHz is one **gigahertz** (GHz).

The **wavelength** of an EM field is related to the frequency. If the frequency f of an EM wave is specified in megahertz and the wavelength w is specified in meters (m), then in free space, the two are related according to the formula

$$w = 300/f$$

For example, a signal at 100 MHz (in the middle of the American **FM** broadcast band) has a wavelength of 3 m, or about 10 feet. This same formula applies if the frequency is given in gigahertz and the wavelength is specified in millimeters (mm). Thus, a signal at 30 GHz would have a wavelength of 10 mm, or a little less than half an inch.

The realm of EM field energy is called the **electromagnetic radiation spectrum**. In theory, this extends from arbitrarily long wavelengths to arbitrarily short wavelengths, or, as engineers sometimes imprecisely quip, "from DC to light."

electromagnetic interference

See "EMI"

electromagnetic radiation spectrum

The electromagnetic radiation spectrum is the complete range of the **wavelength**s of electromagnetic radiation, beginning with the longest radio waves (including those in the audio range) and extending through visible light (a very small part of the spectrum) all the way to the extremely short gamma rays that are a product of radioactive **atom**s.

Electromagnetic radiation results from the physics of the **electromagnetic field**.

electron

An electron is a negatively charged subatomic particle. It can be either free (not attached to any atom), or bound to the nucleus of an **atom**. Electrons in atoms exist in spherical shells of various radii, representing energy levels. The larger the spherical shell, the higher the energy contained in the electron.

In electrical conductors, **current** flow results from the movement of electrons from atom to atom individually, and from negative to positive electric poles in general. In semiconductor materials, current also occurs as a movement of electrons. But in some cases, it is more illustrative to envision the current as a movement of electron deficiencies from atom to atom. An electron-deficient atom in a semiconductor is called a **hole**. Holes "move" from positive to negative electric poles in general.

The charge on a single electron is considered as the unit electrical charge. It is assigned negative polarity. The charge on an electron is equal, but opposite, to the positive charge on a proton or hole. Electrical charge quantity is not usually measured in terms of the charge on a single electron, because this is an extremely small charge. Instead, the standard unit of electrical charge quantity is the coulomb, symbolized by C, representing about 6.24×10^{18} electrons. The electron charge, symbolized by e, is about 1.60×10^{-19} C. The mass of an electron at rest, symbolized m_e, is approximately 9.11×10^{-31} kilogram (kg). Electrons moving at an appreciable fraction of the speed of light, for example in a particle accelerator, have greater mass because of relativistic effects.

electronic bill presentment and payment

See "EBPP"

Electronic Code Book

Also see **cryptography**.

Electronic Code Book (ECB) is a mode of operation for a **block cipher**, with the characteristic that each possible block of **plaintext** has a defined corresponding **ciphertext** value and vice versa. In other words, the same plaintext value will always result in the same ciphertext value. Electronic Code Book is used when a volume of plaintext is separated into several blocks of data, each of which is then encrypted independently of other blocks. In fact, Electronic Code Book has the ability to support a separate **encryption key** for each block type.

However, Electronic Code Book is not a good system to use with small block sizes (for example, smaller than 40 bits) and identical encryption modes. This is because some words and phrases may be reused often enough so that the same repetitive part-blocks of ciphertext can emerge, laying the groundwork for a codebook attack where the plaintext patterns are fairly obvious. However, security may be improved if random pad bits are added to each block. On the other hand, 64-bit or larger blocks should contain enough unique characteristics (entropy) to make a codebook attack unlikely to succeed.

In terms of error correction, any bit errors in a ciphertext block affect decryption of that block only. Chaining dependency is not an issue in that reordering of the ciphertext blocks will only reorder the corresponding plaintext blocks, but not affect decryption.

Electronic Data Interchange

See "EDI"

electronic data processing

See "EDP"

Electronic Frontier Foundation

The Electronic Frontier Foundation is the primary watchdog for the preservation of civil liberties on the Internet. During its "Blue Ribbon" campaign in support of free speech on the Web, it was one of the four most-visited sites on the Web, according to Webcrawler. It develops positions on free speech, encryption, privacy, and intellectual property and lobbies for them.

The EFF was founded in 1990 by John Perry Barlow, Mitch Kapor (founder of Lotus 1-2-3), and others. Membership is open to the public.

Electronic Funds Transfer

Electronic Funds Transfer (EFT) is a system of transferring money from one bank account directly to another without any paper money changing hands. One of the most widely-used EFT programs is Direct Deposit, in which payroll is

deposited straight into an employee's bank account, although EFT refers to any transfer of funds initiated through an electronic terminal, including credit card, ATM, Fedwire and point-of-sale (POS) transactions. It is used for both credit transfers, such as payroll payments, and for debit transfers, such as mortgage payments.

Transactions are processed by the bank through the Automated Clearing House (ACH) network, the secure transfer system that connects all U.S. financial institutions. For payments, funds are transferred electronically from one bank account to the billing company's bank, usually less than a day after the scheduled payment date.

The growing popularity of EFT for online bill payment is paving the way for a paperless universe where checks, stamps, envelopes, and paper bills are obsolete. The benefits of EFT include reduced administrative costs, increased efficiency, simplified bookkeeping, and greater security. However, the number of companies who send and receive bills through the Internet is still relatively small.

The U.S. Government monitors EFT compliance through Regulation E of the Federal Reserve Board, which implements the Electronic Funds Transfer Act (EFTA). Regulation E governs financial transactions with electronic payment services, specifically with regard to disclosure of information, consumer liability, error resolution, record retention, and receipts at electronic terminals.

Electronic Industries Alliance

See "EIA"

Electronic Industries Association

See "EIA"

electronic ink

Electronic ink is a liquid substance, in development at MIT's Media Lab in partnership with a company called E Ink, that responds to electrical impulses to enable changeable text and image displays on a flexible surface. Electronic ink will be used for applications such as **e-book**s, **electronic newspaper**s, portable signs, and foldable, rollable displays. Electronic ink consists of millions of tiny capsules filled with dark dyes and containing negatively charged white chips, floating in a substance like vegetable oil. With a printer-like device, the electronic ink-coated material—which, according to researchers, could be just about any flat surface—is subjected to electrical impulses that act upon the white chips to make them display as light or dark-colored. A positive charge applied to an area on the top of the display medium causes the white chips to float to the top surface, and a charge applied to an area on the bottom of the medium causes them to drop to the bottom. The pattern of charges applied in concert enables the display of images and text.

Information to be displayed is downloaded through a connection to a computer or a cell phone, or created with mechanical tools such as an electronic "pencil."

Lucent and E Ink are developing a device (also called **E Ink**) that uses electronic ink and combines thin, plastic, **flexible transistor**s with **polymer LED**s (**light-emitting diode**s) to create what are called **smart pixel**s. The process involved—which is not dissimilar to traditional printing processes—uses silicon rubber stamps to actually print tiny computer circuits onto the surface. Electronic ink has been used for simple displays, such as retail signs. Researchers say that more complex displays using the technology are still several years away.

Displays written in electronic ink are bi-stable: they remain fixed until another charge is applied to change them. Once you had read the first section of your electronic newspaper you would select the next section that you wanted to read, download it from a wireless Internet connection and have the paper automatically refreshed to display, for example, the arts or sports news that you wanted to read. Another expected application of electronic ink is a more book-like version of the e-book. Consisting of a similar number of e-paper pages, and having the same look and feel as a traditional book, the future technology would allow the reader to download book after book to the same physical device. E Ink claims that a device written with electronic ink could be rewritten as many as 300 million times.

electronic newspaper

An electronic newspaper is a self-contained, reusable, and refreshable version of a traditional newspaper that acquires and holds information electronically. (The electronic newspaper should not be confused with newspapers that offer an online version at a Web site.) The near-future technology—researchers expect to have the product available as soon as 2003—will use **e-paper** (electronic paper) as the major component. Information to be displayed will be downloaded through a **wireless** Internet connection. A number of versions of the future technology are in development, although there are two frontrunners: Xerox's Palo Alto Research Center (PARC) is working on a newspaper that would consist of a single sheet of their e-paper (called **Gyricon**), while Lucent, in partnership with a company called E Ink, is working on a multi-page device (also called **E Ink**).

The Gyricon version consists of a single sheet of transparent plastic, containing millions of tiny bichromal (two color) beads in oil-filled pockets. Text and images are displayed through rotation of the beads that occurs in response to electrical impulses: a full rotation displays as black or white, and a partial rotation displays as gray shades. Nick Sheridon, a senior research fellow at PARC, has been working towards a viable electronic newspaper for over twenty years. Sheridon sees Xerox's device as consisting of a sheet of Gyricon wound around a spring mechanism in a lightweight cylinder. The user would pull the page out of a slit in the cylinder; in the process, the page would pass over a printer-like device which had downloaded data from the Internet through a wireless connection. To access another page, the reader would return the sheet to the cylinder, select the page, and draw the sheet from the scroll. The device could be carried like an umbrella, and would fit in a large purse or a briefcase. Sheridon projects that a Gyricon-based electronic newspaper could be available within three years. Currently, Gyricon uses 50-**micron** beads for a resolution of 200 **dpi** (dots per inch); the use of 30-micron beads will increase resolution to 300 dpi, slightly better than that of traditional newspapers.

Lucent's E Ink device uses **electronic ink** and combines thin, plastic, **flexible transistor**s with **polymer LEDs** (**light-emitting diodes**) to create what are called **smart pixel**s. The process involved—which is not dissimilar to traditional printing processes—uses silicon rubber stamps to actually print tiny computer circuits onto the surface. E Ink uses electronic ink for display: Millions of tiny capsules filled with light and dark dyes that change color—charged dye particles move either up or down within the capsules—when exposed to an electric charge. According to Paul Drzaic, the director of display technologies, prototypes of the device have been running on watch batteries. Although the technology has been used for retail signs, Lucent says that an E Ink-based electronic newspaper is still at least 10 years away, because electronic ink has not been sufficiently developed to make complex displays practical.

IBM is also working on an electronic ink-based device. IBM's electronic newspaper is in a book-like format, and is constructed of 16 pages of flexible, fiberglass-reinforced paper, each about 8.5" by 11". The lightweight pages are bound by a rigid metallic bar, and covered with a clear, protective cover sheet. Charged dye particles move either up or down within the capsules—causing light or dark areas to appear in the display—when exposed to an electric charge . The whole device could be rolled or folded similarly to a traditional newspaper. Like the E Ink-based electronic newspaper, IBM's version is several years away.

The challenge involved in creating a viable electronic newspaper is to develop a device that has the desirable characteristics of traditional paper in addition to its own inherent benefits (such as being automatically refreshable). Like traditional paper, the electronic newspaper must be lightweight, flexible, high-resolution, glare-free, and affordable, if it is to gain consumer approval. Sheridon proposes that the Gyricon version could cost about the same as a year's subscription to a regular newspaper.

electronic paper

See "e-paper"

electronic postmaster

An electronic postmaster is the capability in a program, usually a special program designated as an **e-mail** server, for handling the distribution, forwarding, and receiving of e-mail in a network. For example, an **Simple Mail Transfer Protocol** server at your access provider acts as an electronic postmaster by forwarding your outgoing messages to their destinations in the network and by collecting your incoming messages so that you can request them from a **POP3** server that holds your messages until you request that they be sent to your workstation client.

When you send a message with an e-mail address that can't be located, the term "electronic postmaster" may appear in the message sent to you by the SMTP server.

Electronic Signatures in Global and National Commerce Act

The Electronic Signatures in Global and National Commerce Act (often referred to as the e-signature bill) specifies that in the United States, the use of a **digital signature** is as legally valid as a traditional signature written in ink on paper. In effect since October 1, 2000, the U.S. law is expected to save companies that use e-signatures a significant amount of money by reducing the costs of mailing and handling hard-copy contracts and similar documents.

The Act does not specify a single digital signature technology. Many e-signature advocates expect that the public key infrastructure (**PKI**), used for authenticating credit card transactions over the Web, will play an important role in the development of secure e-signatures. Several third-party companies are now exploring other methods to verify a person's legal identity, including the use of personal smart cards, **PDA** encryption devices, and biometric verifications (fingerprint, voice, or iris scans). Experts agree that until the legality of e-signatures has been tested in the courts, the routine use of e-signatures is likely to be several years away, primarily because businesses lack confidence in present security and verification procedures.

electronic voting

See "e-voting"

Electronic Worldwide Switch Digital

See "EWSD"

electrostatic field

See also **dielectric material**.

When two objects in each other's vicinity have different electric charges, an electrostatic field exists between them. An electrostatic field also forms around any single object that is electrically charged with respect to its environment. An object is negatively charged (-) if it has an excess of

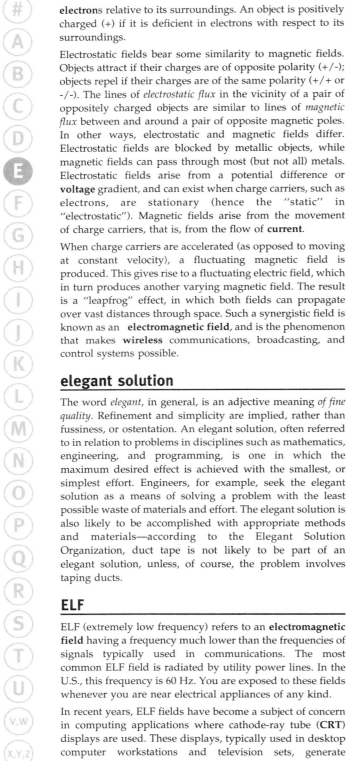

electrons relative to its surroundings. An object is positively charged (+) if it is deficient in electrons with respect to its surroundings.

Electrostatic fields bear some similarity to magnetic fields. Objects attract if their charges are of opposite polarity (+/-); objects repel if their charges are of the same polarity (+/+ or -/-). The lines of *electrostatic flux* in the vicinity of a pair of oppositely charged objects are similar to lines of *magnetic flux* between and around a pair of opposite magnetic poles. In other ways, electrostatic and magnetic fields differ. Electrostatic fields are blocked by metallic objects, while magnetic fields can pass through most (but not all) metals. Electrostatic fields arise from a potential difference or **voltage** gradient, and can exist when charge carriers, such as electrons, are stationary (hence the "static" in "electrostatic"). Magnetic fields arise from the movement of charge carriers, that is, from the flow of **current**.

When charge carriers are accelerated (as opposed to moving at constant velocity), a fluctuating magnetic field is produced. This gives rise to a fluctuating electric field, which in turn produces another varying magnetic field. The result is a "leapfrog" effect, in which both fields can propagate over vast distances through space. Such a synergistic field is known as an **electromagnetic field**, and is the phenomenon that makes **wireless** communications, broadcasting, and control systems possible.

elegant solution

The word *elegant*, in general, is an adjective meaning *of fine quality*. Refinement and simplicity are implied, rather than fussiness, or ostentation. An elegant solution, often referred to in relation to problems in disciplines such as mathematics, engineering, and programming, is one in which the maximum desired effect is achieved with the smallest, or simplest effort. Engineers, for example, seek the elegant solution as a means of solving a problem with the least possible waste of materials and effort. The elegant solution is also likely to be accomplished with appropriate methods and materials—according to the Elegant Solution Organization, duct tape is not likely to be part of an elegant solution, unless, of course, the problem involves taping ducts.

ELF

ELF (extremely low frequency) refers to an **electromagnetic field** having a frequency much lower than the frequencies of signals typically used in communications. The most common ELF field is radiated by utility power lines. In the U.S., this frequency is 60 Hz. You are exposed to these fields whenever you are near electrical appliances of any kind.

In recent years, ELF fields have become a subject of concern in computing applications where cathode-ray tube (**CRT**) displays are used. These displays, typically used in desktop computer workstations and television sets, generate

electromagnetic fields because of the strong, fluctuating currents in the electron-beam deflecting coils. The frequencies of these fields are on the order of a few kilohertz or less. Some studies suggest that ELF fields might have detrimental health effects on humans exposed to them for long periods of time. The claims vary from increased risk of cancer to premature births and miscarriages. However, as of this writing, conclusive proof has yet to be obtained that ELF fields are harmful at the levels encountered by computer users.

The ELF fields surrounding a CRT display tend to be stronger off the sides of the CRT than directly in front of it or behind it. The fields diminish rapidly in intensity with increasing distance from the CRT. As a general rule, computer users should sit at least 18 inches away from a CRT display. Side-by-side workstations should be at least five feet apart. These considerations are important for visual comfort and "breathing room" as much as for minimizing the potential risk posed by ELF fields.

Elm

Elm is a popular **e-mail** program for users of **UNIX**-based operating systems. Users of a UNIX-based system's non-graphical **shell** interface can enter the "elm" command to see menus from which they can choose to see their incoming mail or to create outgoing mail. Designed to run with **sendmail**, /bin/rmail, or any other Unix mail transport agent, elm includes programs like "frm" to show a table of contents of mail, and "printmail" to paginate mail files for printouts.

Originally developed by Dave Taylor, Elm is now developed by a cooperative of volunteers, called the Elm Development Group. Elm is freely distributable software. Its copyright is held by the USENET Community Trust, which assures that it is available to everyone.

EM field

See "electromagnetic field"

Emacs

Emacs (pronounced EE-maks and sometimes spelled "emacs" or "EMACS") is a popular **text editor** used mainly on **UNIX**-based systems by programmers, scientists, engineers, students, and system administrators. Like other UNIX text editors, Emacs provides typed commands and special key combinations that let you add, delete, insert, and otherwise manipulate words, letters, lines, and other units of text. Emacs is commonly used to enter the source statements for programs. Emacs itself is built using the **Lisp** programming language and users are invited to extend or personalize it using the same language. Emacs also offers a number of convenient capabilities such as the ability to initiate a program **compiler** and to handle e-mail from within the editor.

Emacs (derived from Editing **MACRoS**) was created by Richard Stallman at MIT. A popular version is called **GNU** Emacs. Emacs offers a much longer list of commands than the other widely-used UNIX text editor, **vi** and the ability to extend the interface. Like vi, the full capabilities of Emacs require a considerable investment in learning (or relearning if you don't use them continually). However, a beginning set of commands makes it possible to get to work immediately.

One or more versions of Emacs have been developed for use on Windows operating systems. A reader suggests another possible derivation for the letters in Emacs: Escape-Meta-Alt-Control-Shift—apparently referring to its use of key combination commands.

e-mail

E-mail (electronic mail) is the exchange of computer-stored messages by telecommunication. (Some publications spell it *email*; we prefer the currently more established spelling of *e-mail*.) E-mail messages are usually encoded in **ASCII** text. However, you can also send non-text files, such as graphic images and sound files, as attachments sent in **binary** streams. E-mail was one of the first uses of the Internet and is still the most popular use. A large percentage of the total traffic over the Internet is e-mail. E-mail can also be exchanged between **online service provider** users and in networks other than the Internet, both public and private.

E-mail can be distributed to lists of people as well as to individuals. A shared distribution list can be managed by using an **e-mail reflector**. Some mailing lists allow you to subscribe by sending a request to the mailing list administrator. A mailing list that is administered automatically is called a **list server**.

E-mail is one of the protocols included with the Transport Control Protocol/Internet Protocol (**TCP/IP**) suite of protocols. A popular protocol for sending e-mail is **Simple Mail Transfer Protocol** and a popular protocol for receiving it is **POP3**. Both Netscape and Microsoft include an e-mail utility with their Web browsers.

e-mail rage

E-mail rage is the online equivalent of "road rage"—in fact, the new social disorder is sometimes referred to as "road rage on the information superhighway." E-mail's immediacy and informal nature have made it a unique medium for messages: Communications are sent without the time for consideration involved in traditional written letters, and without the inhibiting social factors involved in face-to-face communication. In an Internet discussion group, sending a message under the influence of **e-mail** rage is sometimes called **flaming**.

As in incidents of road rage, e-mail rage happens when people are in an environment where they may tend to respond reflexively, rather than to stop and consider how to effectively react to a given situation. Also as with episodes of

road rage, e-mail rage can quickly escalate if the parties communicating both get caught up in the emotion, as the recipient of an offensive or angry e-mail can all too easily hit the "reply" button and have an irate response back to the sender within seconds. Although e-mail rage is less likely than road rage to result in actual physical carnage, careers and reputations have certainly been damaged by it and, at the very least, time has been taken up unnecessarily.

To avoid falling prey to e-mail rage, some experts advise that you should wait a while before sending—or replying to—an angry message, and always try to express yourself without resorting to abusive language.

e-mail reflector

An e-mail reflector is a program that acts as the forwarding broadcaster of e-mail messages to the names on a distribution list. Here's how it works:

1. One member of the distribution list composes an e-mail message or replies to one.

2. The user sends the message to the e-mail reflector (which to the user usually appears to be the list itself) on the server of whomever is managing the e-mail reflector.

3. The e-mail reflector receives the message and automatically forwards a copy to each person on the distribution list.

The advantage is that the distribution list can be centrally managed so that everyone will always have the most up-to-date version. Some Internet server products come with an e-mail reflector utility.

e-mail virus

An e-mail virus is computer code sent to you as an **e-mail** note attachment which, if activated, will cause some unexpected and usually harmful effect, such as destroying certain files on your hard disk and causing the attachment to be remailed to everyone in your address book. Although not the only kind of computer **virus**, e-mail viruses are the best known and undoubtedly cause the greatest loss of time and money overall. The best two defenses against e-mail viruses for the individual user are (1) a policy of never opening (for example, double-clicking on) an e-mail attachment unless you know who sent it and what the attachment contains, and (2) installing and using **anti-virus software** to scan any attachment before you open it. (However, some e-mail viruses may be so new when your receive them that your anti-virus software may not yet be familiar with it.) Business **firewall** servers also attempt, but not always successfully, to filter out e-mail that may carry a virus attachment.

The **Melissa virus macro virus** and the **ILOVEYOU virus** are among the best publicized of recent e-mail viruses. Each of these also spawned copycat variations with different words in the subject line.

Microsoft has been criticized for allowing its widely-used Outlook e-mail program to be so easily exploited by virus creators. Some users indicate that other e-mail programs such as Eudora offer the user more protection.

emanation monitoring

See "Tempest"

embedded systems programming

Embedded systems programming is the development of programs intended to be part of a larger **operating system** or, in a somewhat different usage, to be incorporated on a microprocessor that can then be included as part of a variety of hardware devices.

EME

See "moonbounce"

EMF

EMF (Enhanced MetaFile) and raw are terms for **spool** file formats used in printing by the Windows **operating system**. When a print job is sent to the **printer**, if it is already printing another file, the computer reads the new file and stores it, usually on the **hard disk** or in **memory**, for printing at a later time. Spooling allows multiple print jobs to be given to the printer at one time.

The EMF format is the 32-**bit** version of the original Windows **metafile** (WMF) format. The EMF format was created to solve the deficiencies of the WMF format in printing graphics from sophisticated graphics programs. The EMF format is device-independent. This means that the dimensions of a graphic are maintained on the printed copy regardless of the resolution in **dots per inch** of the printer. In a network, the smaller file size of the EMF format reduces network traffic. EMF is the spool file used by the Windows operating system.

A raw spool file is a one that is sent to the Windows spooler unprocessed (which is why it's called "raw"). The raw file is used to send **Postscript** commands to a Postscript printer. The Postscript commands are understood by the printer, but are just plain data to the Windows spooler. The raw format is device-dependent and slower. If printing problems occur while using the EMF format, they can sometimes be fixed by simply changing the format to "raw" in the printer Properties.

EMI

Any device or system that generates an **electromagnetic field** in the **radio frequency** spectrum has the potential to disrupt the operation of electronic components, devices, and systems in its vicinity. This phenomenon is known as *electromagnetic interference* or EMI.

The internal circuits of personal computers generate RF fields. Also, cathode ray tube (**CRT**) displays generate EM energy over a wide band of frequencies. These emissions can interfere with the performance of sensitive **wireless** receivers nearby. If you have a wireless receiver of any kind and use it at the same time as you operate your personal computer, you will probably hear RF noise in the receiver that originates in the PC system.

Moderate- or high-powered wireless transmitters can produce EM fields strong enough to upset the operation of electronic equipment nearby. If you live near a broadcast station or in the downtown area of a large city, you have probably experienced EMI from radio or television transmitters. Cordless telephones, home entertainment systems, computers, and certain medical devices can malfunction in the presence of strong RF fields.

Problems with EMI can be minimized by ensuring that all electronic equipment is operated with a good electrical ground system. In addition, cords and cables connecting the peripherals in an electronic or computer system should, if possible, be shielded to keep unwanted RF energy from entering or leaving. Specialized components such as line filters, **capacitors**, and **inductors** can be installed in power cords and interconnecting cables to reduce the EMI susceptibility of some systems. Before performing any modifications to equipment, contact the manufacturer for technical assistance. This is especially important if modifications might void an existing warranty, and it is imperative with medical devices of any kind.

emoticon

On the Internet in e-mail, chatting, and posted messages, an emoticon (sometimes referred to as a "smiley") is a short sequence of keyboard letters and symbols, usually emulating a facial expression, expressing a feeling that supplements the message. Most of these emoticons use several symbols to create a small face with an expression such as a smile, wink, or turned-down mouth.

One of our contributors says that to read these you can either tilt your head or turn the monitor on its side.

:-)	Smile
;-)	Smile with a wink
:<})	User with mustache, smiling
:-||	Mad
:-(	Sad
:' -(	Crying
:~	Also crying
:-))	Really happy
:-D	Big grin
:-*	A kiss
:-P~	A lick
:-o	Wow! or I'm surprised
:-|	Grim
:-P	Sticking out your tongue

:-	User happens to be Popeye
:-/	Perplexed
=:O	Frightened (hair standing on end)
=8O	Bug-eyed with fright
:-}	Embarassed smile
:-)<>>>>>>	Basic Smiley with a necktie
;-^)	Tongue in cheek
%*@:-(	Hung over
:-~~~	Drooling
>:)	Perplexed look
.)	Keeping an eye out for you
8:-)	Glasses on forehead
8:[	Normal smiling face of a gorilla
0:-)	Angel
]:-│[	Robot
(:V)	Duck
3:-o	Cow
:-]	Vampire
(_8-(│)	Homer Simpson
C│:-=	Charlie Chaplin
=│:-)=	Abe Lincoln
*<:-)	Santa Claus
-:-)	User sports a mohawk and admires Mr. T
(:)-)	Scuba diver
:-' │	User has a cold
:-{}	User with heavy lipstick
:-)8	User is well dressed
>:-	Mad
*#:-)	Scotsman wearing his Scottish tam
%-^	User is another Picasso
#-)	User partied all night
<:I	Dunce
:-│	"Have an ordinary day!" Smiley
:}{:	Kisses (stolen from June bug)
oooo(0) (0)oooo	Toes
(-_-)	Secret smile
#.-o	"Oh, nooooooo Mr. Bill!!!"

The Japanese have worked out another set of emoticons that fits the nuances of Japanese culture. See **Japanese emoticons**.

Finally, as a bonus, we share our "nose over fence" (or "Kilroy was here!") with you. Like emotions this expression is created by typing ordinary keyboard characters.

```
          ''' /
         (o o)
——————oOO–(_)–OOo——————
```

EMR-shielding

See "Tempest"

emulator

In computers, an emulator is a hardware device or a program that pretends to be another particular device or program that other components expect to interact with. For example, using a 3270 emulator, a program written to be used with the **3270** workstation can communicate with and control a **personal computer** as though it were a 3270. Typically, an emulator is provided when a popular hardware device becomes outdated and no longer marketed but **legacy application**s exist that still need to communicate with the older device. The practice of using an emulator to make an older program work with a new end-use device is called **terminal emulation**.

enantiomorph

An enantiomorph (pronounced en-ANT-i-o-morf) is a mirror image of something, an opposite reflection. The term, derived from the Greek *enantios* or "opposite," is used in a number of contexts, including architecture, molecular physics, and political theory. It is reported to also be used in computer system design.

encapsulation

In general, encapsulation is the inclusion of one thing within another thing so that the included thing is not apparent. Decapsulation is the removal or the making apparent a thing previously encapsulated.

1) In **object-oriented programming**, encapsulation is the inclusion within a program **object** of all the resources need for the object to function—basically, the **method**s and the data. The object is said to "publish its interfaces." Other objects adhere to these interfaces to use the object without having to be concerned with how the object accomplishes it. The idea is "don't tell me how you do it; just do it." An object can be thought of as a self-contained atom. The object interface consists of public methods and **instantiate** data.

2) In telecommunication, encapsulation is the inclusion of one data structure within another structure so that the first data structure is hidden for the time being. For example, a TCP/IP-formatted data **packet** can be encapsulated within an **ATM** frame (another kind of transmitted data unit). Within the context of transmitting and receiving the ATM frame, the encapsulated packet is simply a stream of bits beween the ATM data that describes the transfer.

encoder

In digital audio technology, an encoder is a program that converts an audio WAV file into an **MP3** file, a highly-compressed sound file that preserves the quality of a CD recording. (The program that gets the sound selection from a CD and stores it as a WAV file on a hard drive is called a **ripper**.) An MP3 encoder compresses the WAV file so that it is about one-twelfth the size of the original digital sound file.

The quality is maintained by an algorithm that optimizes for audio perception, losing data that will not contribute to perception. The program that plays the MP3 file is called a *player*. Some audio products provide all three programs together as a package.

Encrypting File System

The Encrypting File System (EFS) is a feature of the **Windows 2000 operating system** that lets any **file** or **folder** be stored in encrypted form and decrypted only by an individual user and an authorized recovery agent. EFS is especially useful for mobile computer users, whose computer (and files) are subject to physical theft, and for storing highly sensitive data.

EFS simply makes encryption an attribute of any file or folder. To store and retrieve a file or folder, a user must request a key from a program that is built into Windows 2000.

Although an encrypting file system has existed in or been an add-on to other operating systems, its inclusion in Windows 2000 is expected to bring the idea to a larger audience.

encryption

Encryption is the conversion of data into a form, called a **ciphertext**, that cannot be easily understood by unauthorized people. *Decryption* is the process of converting encrypted data back into its original form, so it can be understood.

The use of encryption/decryption is as old as the art of communication. In wartime, a **cipher**, often incorrectly called a "code," can be employed to keep the enemy from obtaining the contents of transmissions. (Technically, a *code* is a means of representing a signal without the intent of keeping it secret; examples are Morse code and **ASCII**.) Simple ciphers include the substitution of letters for numbers, the rotation of letters in the alphabet, and the "scrambling" of voice signals by inverting the sideband frequencies. More complex ciphers work according to sophisticated computer algorithms that rearrange the data bits in digital signals.

In order to easily recover the contents of an encrypted signal, the correct *decryption key* is required. The key is an **algorithm** that "undoes" the work of the encryption algorithm. Alternatively, a computer can be used in an attempt to "break" the cipher. The more complex the encryption algorithm, the more difficult it becomes to eavesdrop on the communications without access to the key.

Encryption/decryption is especially important in **wireless** communications. This is because wireless circuits are easier to "tap" than their hard-wired counterparts. Nevertheless, encryption/decryption is a good idea when carrying out any kind of sensitive transaction, such as a credit-card purchase online, or the discussion of a company secret between different departments in the organization. The stronger the cipher – that is, the harder it is for unauthorized people to break it – the better, in general. However, as the strength of encryption/decryption increases, so does the cost.

In recent years, a controversy has arisen over so-called *strong encryption*. This refers to ciphers that are essentially unbreakable without the decryption keys. While most companies and their customers view it as a means of keeping secrets and minimizing fraud, some governments view strong encryption as a potential vehicle by which terrorists might evade authorities. These governments, including that of the U.S., want to set up a *key-escrow* arrangement. This means everyone who uses a cipher would be required to provide the government with a copy of the key. Decryption keys would be stored in a supposedly secure place, used only by authorities, and used only if backed up by a court order. Opponents of this scheme argue that criminals could hack into the key-escrow database and illegally obtain, steal, or alter the keys. Supporters claim that while this is a possibility, implementing the key escrow scheme would be better than doing nothing to prevent criminals from freely using encryption/decryption.

end effector

In **robotics**, an end effector is a device or tool connected to the end of a robot arm. The structure of an end effector, and the nature of the programming and hardware that drives it, depends on the intended task.

If a robot is designed to set a table and serve a meal, then robotic hands, more commonly called grippers, are the most functional end effectors. The same or similar gripper might be used, with greater force, as a pliers or wrench for tightening nuts or crimping wire. In a **robot** designed to tighten screws, however, a driver-head end effector is more appropriate. A gripper is a hindrance in that application; the driver can be attached directly to the robot arm. The driver can be easily removed and replaced with a device that operates with similar motion, such as a bit for drilling or an emery disk for sanding.

A robot arm can accommodate only certain end-effector task modes without changes to the ancillary hardware and/or programming. It is not possible to directly replace a gripper with a screwdriver head, for example, and expect a favorable result. It is necessary to change the programming of the robot controller and use a different set of end-effector motors to facilitate torque rather than gripping force. Then the gripper can be replaced with a driver head.

Also see **eye-in-hand system** and **motion plan**.

end user

In information technology, the term *end user* is used to distinguish the person for whom a hardware or software product is designed from the developers, installers, and servicers of the product. The "end" part of the term probably derives from the fact that most information technologies involve a chain of interconnected product components at the end of which is the "user." Frequently, complex products require the involvement of other-than-end users such as installers, administrators, and system operators. The term *end user* thus distinguishes the user for which the product is designed from other users who are making the product possible for the end user. The term is used mostly with **mainframe** computer products and seldom with personal consumer products. Often, the term *user* would suffice.

End User License Agreement

An End User License Agreement (EULA) is a legal contract between a software application author or publisher and the user of that application. The EULA, often referred to as the "software license," is similar to a rental agreement; the user agrees to pay for the privilege of using the software, and promises the software author or publisher to comply with all restrictions stated in the EULA. The user is asked to indicate they that "accept" the terms of the EULA by opening the shrink wrap on the application package, breaking the seal on the CD case, sending a card back to the software publisher, installing the application, executing a downloadable file, or by simply using the application. The user can refuse to enter into the agreement by returning the software product for a complete refund or clicking "I do not accept" when prompted to accept the EULA during an install.

end-of-message

See "EOM"

energy

Energy is an expression of mechanical motion, thermal heat, or electrical **power** consumed, radiated, dissipated, or stored over a period of time. The common symbol for energy is the uppercase letter E. The standard unit is the **joule**, symbolized by J. In some systems, the British thermal unit (**Btu**) is specified instead; 1 Btu = 1055 J.

One joule is the energy resulting from the equivalent of one **watt** of power manifested for a period of one second. The energy in a direct-current (**DC**) circuit is equal to the product of the **voltage** in volts, the **current** in amperes, and the **time** in seconds. In alternating current (**AC**) circuits, the expression for energy is more complex.

The common symbol for current is I. When a DC source of V volts delivers I amperes for t seconds, the energy E expended in joules is:

$E = VIt$

When a direct current of I amperes passes through a **resistance** of R ohms for t seconds, the energy E lost in joules is:

$E = I^2 Rt$

When a DC potential difference of V volts appears across a component having a resistance of R ohms for t seconds, the energy E absorbed in joules is:

$E = V^2 t/R$

engine

In computer programming, *engine* is a jargon term for a program that performs a core or essential function for other programs. An engine can be a central or focal **program** in an **operating system**, subsytem, or **application program** that coordinates the overall operation of other programs. It is also used to describe a special-purpose program containing an **algorithm** that can sometimes be changed. The best known usage is the term **search engine** which uses an algorithm to search an index of topics given a search argument. A search engine is designed so that its approach to searching the index can be changed to reflect new rules for finding and prioritizing matches in the index. In **artificial intelligence**, the program that uses rules of logic to derive output from a knowledge base is called an **inference engine**.

The term connotes a comparison with mechanical engines. In 1844, Charles Babbage named his stored-program computer the **Analytical Engine**.

English system of units

See "foot-pound-second system of units"

Enhanced CD

Enhanced CD (E-CD) is a compact disc (**CD**) format that enables discs to be played on either a CD player or a multimedia-capable device, such as a **CD-i** player, or a **DVD-ROM**, or **CD-ROM** drive, where added material can be displayed. E-CD, technically known as *stamped multisession*, is used to refer to any audio CD that has CD-ROM data added. Most audio CDs use only about 60 minutes-worth of the disc's 74 available minutes-worth of space; E-CD takes advantage of the unused space to include extra data on audio CDs. Recording artists have used E-CD technology to include video clips, artist profiles, lyrics, interviews, animation, promotional material, and even games on audio disks.

E-CD specifications are described in the **Blue Book**, a 1995 supplement to the 1988 Philips and Sony **Orange Book**, that was intended as a separate definition for stamped **multisession** disc format. Because the discs are stamped (pressed from copies of the original recording), they are not user-recordable. The Blue Book, which called the new format *CD Plus* specified two recording sessions, one for audio data and one for any other included data. Like all CD formats, Enhanced CD is based on the original **Red Book** specifications. E-CD is sometimes called *CD-Extra, CD-Plus, stamped multisession*, or simply *Blue Book format*.

E-CD format is designed to overcome the problems of *mixed-mode* CDs, which also consisted of separate tracks for audio and other data. Mixed-mode discs were often responsible for speaker damage: when a CD player tried to read the data tracks, the result was loud static. Because E-CD data and audio tracks are written in separate sessions, the data track(s) can be made invisible to the CD player, so that only the audio tracks are played.

Enhanced Data GSM Environment

See "EDGE"

enhanced dynamic RAM

See "EDRAM"

Enhanced Integrated Drive Electronics

See "EIDE"

Enhanced Interior Gateway Routing Protocol

See "EIGRP"

Enhanced MetaFile

See "EMF"

Enhanced Specialized Mobile Radio

See "ESMR"

Enhanced Synchronous DRAM

See "ESDRAM"

entanglement

Entanglement is a term used in **quantum theory** to describe the way that particles of energy/matter can become *correlated* to predictably interact with each other regardless of how far apart they are.

Particles, such as photons, electrons, or qubits that have interacted with each other retain a type of connection and can be entangled with each other in pairs, in the process known as correlation. Knowing the spin state of one entangled particle—whether the direction of the spin is up or down—allows one to know that the spin of its mate is in the opposite direction. Even more amazing is the knowledge that, due to the phenomenon of **superposition**, the measured particle has no single spin direction before being measured, but is simultaneously in both a spin-up and spin-down state. The spin state of the particle being measured is decided at the time of measurement and communicated to the correlated particle, which simultaneously assumes the opposite spin direction to that of the measured particle. Quantum entanglement allows **qubits** that are separated by incredible distances to interact with each other immediately, in a communication that is not limited to the speed of light. No matter how great the distance between the correlated particles, they will remain entangled as long as they are isolated.

Entanglement is a real phenomenon (Einstein called it "spooky action at a distance"), which has been demonstrated repeatedly through experimentation. The mechanism behind it cannot, as yet, be fully explained by any theory. One proposed theory suggests that all particles on earth were once compacted tightly together and, as a consequence, maintain a connectedness. Much current research is focusing on how to harness the potential of entanglement in developing systems for **quantum cryptography** and **quantum computing**.

In 1997, Nicholas Gisin and colleagues at the University of Geneva used entangled photons to enable simple—but instantaneous—communication over a distance of seven miles.

enterprise

In the computer industry, an enterprise is an organization that uses computers. A word was needed that would encompass corporations, small businesses, non-profit institutions, government bodies, and possibly other kinds of organizations. The term *enterprise* seemed to do the job. In practice, the term is applied much more often to larger organizations than smaller ones.

enterprise application integration

See "EAI"

enterprise information portal

The enterprise information portal (EIP) is a concept for a **Web site** that serves as a single gateway to a company's information and knowledge base for employees and possibly for customers, business partners, and the general public as well.

In one model, an EIP is made up of these elements: access/search, categorization, collaboration, personalization, expertise and profiling, application integration, and security.

- **Access/search:** Access/search allows a user to get all the information needed (but no more) in the desired context. For example, a loan officer does not need marketing information to approve a loan. An EIP makes sure the loan officer gets only the information needed.

- **Categorization:** An EIP categorizes all information so that it is delivered to the user within the context needed (think of the subject structure on Yahoo)

- **Collaboration:** An EIP allows individuals to collaborate regardless of geographical location.

- **Personalization:** The information provided to individuals using an EIP is personalized to that person's role, preferences, and habits.

- **Expertise and profiling:** Expertise and profiling is essential for the collaboration element of an EIP. Individuals within an enterprise are profiled according to their experience and competencies. If an individual needs to collaborate with others, he can choose those that are qualified for the project.

- **Application integration:** This allows individuals to deliver, access, and share information regardless of applications used.

- **Security:** This provides information to users based on security clearance. The user logs on and is given access only to information that the user is authorized to access.

Enterprise JavaBeans

Enterprise JavaBeans (EJB) is an **architecture** for setting up program **component**s, written in the **Java** programming language, that run in the **server** parts of a computer network that uses the **client/server** model. Enterprise JavaBeans is built on the **JavaBeans** technology for distributing program components (which are called **Bean**s, using the coffee metaphor) to **client**s in a network. Enterprise JavaBeans offers **enterprise**s the advantage of being able to control change at the server rather than having to update each individual computer with a client whenever a new program component is changed or added. EJB components have the advantage of being reusable in multiple applications. To **deploy** an EJB Bean or component, it must be part of a specific application, which is called a **container**.

Originated by Sun Microsystems, Enterprise JavaBeans is roughly equivalent to Microsoft's **Component Object Model/Distributed Component Object Model** architecture, but, like all Java-based architectures, programs can be deployed across all major operating systems, not just Windows. EJB's program components are generally known as **servlet**s (little server programs). The application or container that runs the servlets is sometimes called an **application server**. A typical use of servlets is to replace Web programs that use the common gateway interface (**CGI**) and a **Practical Extraction and Reporting Language** script. Another general use is provide an interface between Web users and a **legacy application mainframe** application and its database.

In Enterprise JavaBeans, there are two types of beans: session beans and entity beans. An entity bean is described as one that, unlike a session bean, has *persistence* and can retain its original behavior or state.

enterprise relationship management

Enterprise relationship management (ERM) is software that analyzes data it has about its customers to develop a better understanding of the customer and how the customer is using its products and services. This kind of application may use **data mining** of its **data warehouse** or existing sales, marketing, service, finance, and manufacturing databases to generate new information about its customer relationships.

enterprise resource management

See "ERM"

enterprise resource planning

See "ERP"

enterprise risk management

Enterprise risk management (ERM) is the process of planning, organizing, leading, and controlling the activities of an organization in order to minimize the effects of risk on an organization's capital and earnings. Enterprise risk management expands the process to include not just risks associated with accidental losses, but also financial, strategic, operational, and other risks.

In recent years, external factors have fueled a heightened interest by organizations in ERM. Industry and government regulatory bodies, as well as investors, have begun to scrutinize companies' risk-management policies and procedures. In an increasing number of industries, boards of directors are required to review and report on the adequacy of risk-management processes in the organizations they administer.

Since they thrive on the business of risk, financial institutions are good examples of companies that can benefit from effective ERM. Their success depends on striking a balance between enhancing profits and managing risk.

Business risk management, holistic risk management and strategic risk management are synonyms.

enterprise server

1) An enterprise server is a computer containing programs that collectively serve the needs of an **enterprise** rather than a single user, department, or specialized application. Historically, **mainframe**-sized computers have been enterprise servers although they were not referred to as **server**s until recently. As smaller, usually **UNIX**-based servers and **Wintel** computers have become faster and have been provided with enterprise-wide program management capabilities, they also been referred to as enterprise servers. In this usage, an enterprise server is both the computer hardware and its main software, the operating system. Examples are Sun Microsystems' computers with their **UNIX**-based **Solaris** or **Linux** systems, Hewlett-Packard (**HP**) systems, the upper end of **Windows 2000** systems, and IBM's iSeries systems (the largest of which is the **zSeries 900**—formerly called the **S/390**).

2) Some companies use *enterprise server* to describe a "superprogram" that runs under the **operating system** in a computer and provides services for the system administrator and for the business **application program**s and more specialized **server**s that run in the computer. Before this usage originated, such services were sometimes considered part of the operating system itself or came in separate software packages. Originally, many services provided by an enterprise server tended to be available only on IBM or similar **mainframe** computers while less powerful computers ran specialized applications. As these smaller "server" computers (such as those from Sun Microsystems and H-P) became better adapted for business (and recently Internet) applications, the bundle of services required to manage a company-wide set of applications was renamed "the enterprise server." More specialized servers include the **Web server**, **firewall** server, **database** server, and so forth.

enterprise storage

Enterprise storage is a centralized repository for business information that provides common data management and protection, as well as data sharing functions, through connections to numerous (and possibly dissimilar) computer systems. Developed as a solution for the **enterprise** that deals with heavy workloads of business-critical information, enterprise storage systems should be scalable for workloads of up to 300 **gigabytes** without relying on excessive cabling or the creation of subsystems. Other important aspects of the enterprise storage system are unlimited connectivity and support for all the different platforms in operation.

Enterprise storage involves the use of a storage area network (**SAN**), rather than a distributed storage system, and includes benefits such as high availability and disaster recovery, data sharing, and efficient, reliable backup and restoration functions, as well as centralized administration and remote support. Through the SAN, multiple paths are created to all data, so that failure of a server never results in a loss of access to critical information.

entity

In general, an entity (pronounced N-tih-tee) is an existing or real thing. The word root is from the Latin, *ens*, or being, and makes a distinction between a thing's existence and its qualities. An entity exists and that's all it needs to do to be an entity. The fact that something exists also seems to connote separateness from other existences or entities. In programming, engineering, and probably many other contexts, the word is used to identify units, whether concrete things or abstract ideas, that have no ready name or label. In blackboard discussions, one can draw something as yet unnamed and refer to that drawing as the representation of an "entity." (If the entity being discussed later gets ascribed qualities and a name, reference to it as an "entity" may no longer be useful.)

In some usages, an entity is close in meaning to **object** as it is used in **object-oriented programming**.

Here are some of the usages we know of:

1) In the Standard Generalized Markup Language (**SGML**), an entity is a specific character string that has the effect of causing a formatting program (such as a print formatter or a Web browser—which formats for a display screen) to select and present a particular character or notation. In this usage, an entity is a certain string of characters that together specify a unique font to be selected and displayed or printed. A word was needed for such a character string and "entity" came in handy. In HTML (which is a usage of SGML), each special entity or character string is given a name and the entities are therefore called "named entities."

2) In relation to a **database**, an entity is a single person, place, or thing about which data can be stored.

3) In **data modeling** (a first step in the creation of a database), an entity is some unit of data that can be classified and have stated relationships to other entities.

4) In the Open Systems Interconnection (**OSI**) model of network communication, an entity is an active element within a subsystem that communicates with other entities using a defined protocol.

5) In IBM's **RACF** security product, an entity is a user, group, or resource that is defined to RACF.

6) In **FORTRAN**, almost every program element is referred to as an entity, such as a procedure, an operator, an interface block, an input-output unit, a symbolic constant, and a statement label.

entrepreneur

Entrepreneur, translated from its French roots, means "one who undertakes." The term is used to refer to anyone who undertakes the organization and management of an enterprise involving independence and risk as well as the opportunity for profit.

An entrepreneur, typically, is inspired to start a business because the entrepreneur perceives a consumer need that is not being adequately filled. This area of need—sometimes called an "opportunity niche"—can usually be expressed as a problem statement, such as "There is no online resource offering support for failed Web-based entrepreneurs." In fact, that statement was the basis for a new Web business startup recently.

entropy

Also see **Claude Shannon**.

Entropy has meanings in physics and in communications theory. More generally, entropy means a process in which order deteriorates with the passage of time. It has several special meanings in data communications.

Many scientists believe that the universe is naturally evolving toward a state of maximum entropy. The example commonly cited is the tendency for thermal differences to disappear. According to the so-called theory of entropy, everything in the universe will ultimately attain a uniform temperature. There will be no energy sources or absorbers. Stars and galaxies as we know them will cease to exist. There will be no life.

In data communications, the term entropy refers to the relative degree of randomness. The higher the entropy, the more frequent are **signaling** errors. Entropy is directly proportional to the maximum attainable data speed in bps (bits per second). Entropy is also directly proportional to **noise** and **bandwidth**. The entropy in a signal is inversely proportional to compressibility; the greater the entropy, the smaller the factor by which the data can be compressed. Entropy also refers to disorder deliberately added to data in certain **encryption** processes.

ENUM

ENUM is a standard adopted by the Internet Engineering Task Force (**IETF**) that uses the domain name system (**DNS**) to map telephone numbers to Web addresses or uniform resource locators (**URL**). The goal of the ENUM standard is to provide a single number to replace the multiple numbers and addresses for an individual's home phone, business phone, fax, cell phone, and e-mail.

The ENUM standard is a joint effort of Telecordia and Verisign. Every toll-free call in the United States depends on Telecordia software. Verisign is the leader in translating over 24 million **.com**, **.net**, and **.org domain name**s on the Internet. Verisign is also a leader in Internet security.

environment

In computers, the term *environment* when unqualified usually refers to the combination of **hardware** and **software** in a **computer**. In this usage, the term **platform** is a synonym. We often tend to think of *environment* as short for *operating system environment*, but, with the exception of **UNIX**-based operating systems, the operating system usually implies an underlying hardware **microprocessor** that the operating system is designed to run on.

environment variable

An environment **variable** defines some aspect of a user's environment that can vary. Generally set during the login procedure, the environment variable establishes some component of the user's working environment, such as the **default printer**, **browser**, or text editor to be used. Because these are preset as values specific to the identified user, they save time that would be used selecting them at each login. Environment variables are used across multiple languages and operating systems to provide information to applications that may be specific to the user request.

The **UNIX shell** uses environment variables to send information about the user's environment (such as the current working directory or the terminal type, for example) to the programs being run. The variable definitions are passed on to any program that is not built into the shell, and can be consulted, or modified by the program. For example, "TERM" (environment variables are expressed as upper case by programming convention) defines the type of terminal used, "PATH" defines the directories to be searched for programs corresponding to **command** names, and "USER" defines the particular user, so that access permissions may be checked for each request.

The common gateway interface (**CGI**) uses environment variables that are set when the server executes the gateway program, to pass information about requests from the server to the **script**. The server sends out environment variable definitions such as "SERVER_SOFTWARE," which identifies the name and version of the responding server software; "SERVER_NAME," which identifies the server's hostname, **DNS alias**, or Internet Protocol (**IP**) address; and "GATEWAY_INTERFACE," which identifies the CGI specification used. These environment variables are not request-specific, and are sent with every request. Other environment variables are specific to the type of request being sent, such as "SERVER_PROTOCOL," which identifies the name and revision of the **protocol** used for the request, and "REQUEST_METHOD," which identifies the **method** used for the request.

Environmental Resource Management

Environmental Resource Management (ERM) is the concern of a global organization of environmental, health, and safety experts, known as the ERM Group, with more than 110 worldwide locations. The Group has 2,400 professionally qualified staff. They work with industrial and other clients to create sound environmental, health, and safety programs. In addition to the ERM Group, a non-profit ERM Foundation supports noteworthy projects.

EOM

EOM stands for "end of message."

People who exchange a great deal of **e-mail** sometimes write a very short message in the subject line of an e-mail note and conclude it with: (EOM). This is a little faster to send and saves the receiver from having to take the time to open the note, since the entire message is visible in the subject line. The "(EOM)" is a signal that the message is wholly contained in the subject line.

e-outsourcing

For a business, e-outsourcing is buying information technology products and services that could be furnished in-house from one or a variety of sources on the Internet. For example, an organization might hire a **Web hosting** firm to

set up and run its **Web site**, an application service provider (**ASP**) to provide specific back- and front-office applications, and an outside security firm to install and maintain a **firewall** and a virtual private network (**VPN**). In a sense, the vendors act as the IT departments for the company, which is then free to focus on its **core competency**. E-outsourcing may also be provided in a package from one vendor that provides a wide range of services from other vendors.

Usually e-outsourcing enables a business running faster than if it tried to **deploy** the same technology using in-house staff. In the evolving Internet economy, where time to market is crucial and skilled IT labor is scarce, e-outsourcing is gaining in popularity. In fact, IBM CEO Lou Gerstner forecasts that the e-outsourcing market will soar to $55 billion in 2003 and predicts the movement will be "one of the really game-changing [IT] developments." Gerstner is so confident in the model that IBM is investing billions in new e-business hosting centers. Other top vendors are also making significant moves to enhance their e-outsourcing offerings.

E-outsourcing isn't without potential pitfalls, though. Some firms are less than confident when it comes to giving e-outsourcers access to their sensitive data. Also, some question how much responsibility an e-outsourcer will accept when its service isn't sufficient and whether it can integrate its offerings with a business's existing infrastructure and legacy applications.

epaper

See "e-paper"

e-paper

E-paper (sometimes called *radio paper* or just *electronic paper*) is a portable, reusable storage and display medium that looks like paper but can be repeatedly written on (refreshed)—by electronic means—thousands or millions of times. E-paper will be used for applications such as **e-books**, **electronic newspaper**s, portable signs, and foldable, rollable displays. Information to be displayed is downloaded through a connection to a computer or a cell phone, or created with mechanical tools such as an electronic "pencil". There are a number of different technologies being developed: Xerox, in partnership with 3M, has created an e-paper called **Gyricon** that is expected to be marketed in the not-distant future and Lucent, in partnership with a company called E Ink, is working on a device (also called **E Ink**) that is expected to be available within the next few years. Both of these technologies enable a black (or other color) and white display; Philips is working on a type of e-paper that will be full-color, but say that the product is at least 10-15 years away.

The Gyricon version consists of a single sheet of transparent plastic, containing millions of tiny bichromal (two color) beads in oil-filled pockets. Text and images are displayed through a rotation of the beads that occurs in response to an electrical impulse: A full rotation displays as black or white, and a partial rotation displays as gray shades. Like traditional paper, Gyricon has—and needs—no lighting component.

Lucent's E Ink device uses **electronic ink** and combines thin, plastic, **flexible transistor**s with **polymer LEDs** (**light-emitting diode**s) to create what are called **smart pixels**. The process involved—which is not dissimilar to traditional printing processes—uses silicon rubber stamps to actually print tiny (as small as those for the Pentium III processor) computer circuits onto the surface. E Ink uses electronic ink for display: A liquid plastic substance consisting of millions of tiny capsules filled with light and dark dyes that change color—charged dye particles move either up or down within the capsules—when exposed to an electric charge. According to Paul Drzaic, the director of display technologies, prototypes of the device have been running on watch batteries. The E Ink technology has been used for retail signs.

Neither the Lucent/E Ink version nor the Gyricon version require a constant power source; the initial charge creates the display, which then remains fixed until another charge is applied to change it. Low power demand is an important consideration for a technology that is intended to—at least partially—supplant a power-independent, standalone application like paper. The challenge involved in creating viable e-paper is to develop a material that has the desirable characteristics of traditional paper in addition to its own intrinsic benefits (such as being automatically refreshable). Like traditional paper, e-paper must be lightweight, flexible, glare-free, and affordable, if it is to gain consumer approval. Developers of both the competing e-papers claim to have accomplished most of these qualities in their products. The first e-paper products will be Gyricon-based: Portable, reusable pricing signs for stores that can be changed instantly through a computer link; the first Gyricon-based electronic newspaper is expected to be available within the next 3 years.

EPIC

EPIC (Explicitly Parallel Instruction Computing) is a 64-bit microprocessor instruction set, jointly defined and designed by **Hewlett Packard** and Intel, that provides up to 128 general and **floating point unit register**s and uses *speculative loading*, *predication*, and *explicit parallelism* to accomplish its computing tasks. By comparison, current 32-bit **CISC** and **RISC** microprocessor architectures depend on 32-bit registers, branch prediction, memory latency, and implicit parallelism, which are considered a less efficient approach in microarchitecture design.

IA-64 (Intel Architecture-64), Intel's first 64-bit CPU microarchitecture, is based on EPIC. Intel's first implementation, long expected and well-known as Merced (its code name), was christened with the **Itanium** brand name in October 1999. It is expected that Itanium-based systems will be compatible with versions of existing and future operating systems including HP-UX, 64-bit Windows, IA-64 Linux, Project Monterey, and Novell Modesto.

EPOC

EPOC is an **operating system** designed for small, portable computer-telephones with **wireless** access to phone and other information services. EPOC is based on an earlier operating system from Psion, the first major manufacturer of personal digital assistants (**PDAs**). The name derived from the company's belief that the world is entering "a new epoch of personal convenience." To earlier systems, EPOC adds wireless communication and an architecture for adding application programs. Psion declared its first version of EPOC to be an **open** operating system and licensed it to other equipment makers. Psion then formed a new company with Ericsson, Nokia, and later Motorola called Symbian, which now licenses EPOC and continues to develop it. For portable equipment manufacturers, EPOC is an alternative to Microsoft's **Windows CE.** (The popular **Palm** PDA uses its own proprietary operating system, **PalmOS.**)

Symbian refers to the class of hardware EPOC serves as "**wireless** information devices." EPOC is a 32-bit, **multitasking** operating system that supports a pen-based graphical user interface (**GUI**). It is written in the **C++** programming language using an **object-oriented programming** design. The code is very compact so that it can fit on a small **ROM** chip. In addition to basic services, the operating system comes with an "application suite," that includes a word processor, e-mail handler, spreadsheet program, a scheduling application, general purpose database, sketch program, world clock, voice recorder, spell checker, calculator, communication programs, and a Web browser. EPOC can be scaled from relatively large configurations for a fully-functional **handheld** computer to small configurations for **embedded systems programming** applications.

Although EPOC can be ported to other microprocessors, Symbian's preferred platform is the Advanced **RISC** Machines (ARM) architecture. Symbian considers ARM the best platform in terms of millions of instructions per second (**MIPS**) per watt and per dollar cost. Symbian provides development kits for C++, for OPL (a **BASIC**-like language), and for **Java**. Programmers write programs at a PC and use an emulator to test them.

EPP/ECP

EPP/ECP (Enhanced Parallel Port/Enhanced Capability Port) is a standard signaling method for bi-directional **parallel** communication between a **computer** and **peripheral** devices that offers the potential for much higher rates of data transfer than the original parallel signaling methods. EPP is for non-printer peripherals. ECP is for printers and scanners. EPP/ECP are part of **IEEE** Standard **1284**, which also specifies support for current signaling methods (including

Centronics, the de facto standard for printer communication) so that both old and new peripherals can be accommodated.

The new standard specifies five modes of data transfer. Three of them support the older mono-directional modes (a forward direction method from PC to Centronics printer and two reverse direction methods from peripheral to the PC). The fourth and fifth modes, EPP and ECP, are bi-directional (**half-duplex**) signaling methods, meaning that they are designed for back-and-forth communication. Partly because these are being implemented in hardware, EPP and ECP will provide much faster data transfer. The first three methods offer an effective data transfer rate of 50 to 100 kilobytes per second. EPP and ECP offer the possibility of rates "in excess of 1 **megabyte** per second," according to Warp Nine, a chip manufacturer.

In order to get the maximum advantage of EPP/ECP, both **operating system** (or an I/O **port** controller, or both) and peripheral device must support the standard. Initially, you may get the best effect from EPP and a **Zip drive**. Even printers that support ECP are limited by the mechanical aspects of printing. Nevertheless, even users of the compatibility modes of Standard 1284 are also expected to see some benefit in data transfer to and from peripherals.

Windows operating systems have built-in support for IEEE 1284 in their parallel **plug and play** feature. Windows also supports ECP in forward direction, assuming you have a printer and a parallel port with ECP. It is likely that other vendors will provide ECP or EPP software for other operating systems.

EPP/ECP is described fully in *IEEE Std. 1284-1994 Standard Signaling Method for a Bi-Directional Parallel Peripheral Interface for Personal Computers.*

e-procurement

E-procurement is the business-to-business purchase and sale of supplies and services over the Internet. An important part of many **B2B** sites, e-procurement is also sometimes referred to by other terms, such as *supplier exchange*. Typically, e-procurement Web sites allow qualified and registered users to look for buyers or sellers of goods and services. Depending on the approach, buyers or sellers may specify prices or invite bids. Transactions can be initiated and completed. Ongoing purchases may qualify customers for volume discounts or special offers.

E-procurement software may make it possible to automate some buying and selling. Companies participating expect to be able to control parts inventories more effectively, reduce purchasing agent overhead, and improve manufacturing cycles. E-procurement is expected to be integrated with the trend toward computerized *supply chain management*.

EPROM

EPROM (erasable programmable read-only memory) is programmable read-only memory (**programmable ROM**) that can be erased and re-used. Erasure is caused by shining an intense ultraviolet light through a window that is designed into the memory chip. (Although ordinary room lighting does not contain enough ultraviolet light to cause erasure, bright sunlight can cause erasure. For this reason, the window is usually covered with a label when not installed in the computer.)

A different approach to a modifiable ROM is electrically erasable programmable read-only memory (**EEPROM**).

erbium amplifier

An erbium amplifier, also called optical amplifier or an *erbium-doped fiber amplifier* or EDFA, is an optical or IR repeater that amplifies a modulated **laser** beam directly, without opto-electronic and electro-optical conversion. The device uses a short length of optical fiber doped with the rare-earth element erbium. When the signal-carrying laser beams pass through this fiber, external energy is applied, usually at IR wavelengths. This so-called *pumping* excites the **atom**s in the erbium-doped section of optical fiber, increasing the intensity of the laser beams passing through. The beams emerging from the EDFA retain all of their original modulation characteristics, but are brighter than the input beams.

In **fiber optic** communications systems, problems arise from the fact that no fiber material is perfectly transparent. The visible-light or infrared (**IR**) beams carried by a fiber are attenuated as they travel through the material. This necessitates the use of **repeater**s in spans of **optical fiber** longer than about 100 kilometers.

A conventional repeater puts a modulated optical signal through three stages: (1) optical-to-electronic conversion, (2) electronic signal amplification, and (3) electronic-to-optical conversion. (The term *optical* encompasses IR as well as visible-light energy in this context.) Repeaters of this type limit the **bandwidth** of the signals that can be transmitted in long spans of fiber optic cable. This is because, even if a **laser** beam can transmit several gigabits per second (**Gbps**) of data, the electronic circuits of a conventional repeater cannot.

Besides eliminating complex and inefficient conversion and electronic amplification stages, the EDFA allows the transmission of signals that employ wavelength-division multiplexing (**WDM**). This increases the realizable bandwidth relative to conventional repeaters still further.

erbium-doped fiber amplifier

See "erbium amplifier"

ergonomic

The ergonomic aspect of computers deals with their usability for humans. Ergonomics is the use of research in designing systems, programs, or devices that are easy to use for their intended purposes and contexts. The terms *human factors* and *usability* are related.

erlang

Also see **Erlang programming language**, a programming language.

In telecommunications, an erlang is a number between 0 and 1 that indicates how busy a telephone facility is over a period of time. An erlang of 1 applied to a particular telephone circuit would indicate *Busy 100% of the time*. An erlang can be applied to the group of lines in a telephone **trunk** line or to the traffic in a telephone call center.

The term is named after the Danish telephone engineer, A. K. Erlang, the originator of **queueing theory**.

Erlang B is a calculation for any one of these three factors if you know or predict the other two:

- Busy Hour Traffic (BHT), or the number of hours of call traffic during the busiest hour of operation
- Blocking, or the percentage of calls that are blocked because not enough lines are available
- Lines, or the number of lines in a trunk group

An extended version of Erlang B lets you add the factor of how many people who are blocked retry their calls immediately.

Erlang C is a calculation for how many call agents (answerers) you'll need in a call center that has a given number of calls per hour, a given average duration of call, and an acceptable level of delay in answering the call.

Erlang programming language

Also see **erlang**, a unit of telephone traffic.

Erlang is a programming language designed for developing **robust** systems of programs that can be distributed among different computers in a network. Named for the Danish mathematician Agner Krarup Erlang, the language was developed by the Ericsson Computer Sciences Lab to build software for its own telecommunication products. In use for a number of years at Ericsson and other companies, Erlang is taught in over 80 universities and colleges world-wide and is freely available as **Open Source** code.

Erlang is similar to **Java** in that it uses a **virtual machine** and supports **multithreading**. However, whereas the Java development community focuses on Web applications, Erlang is aimed at the market for extremely robust servers and embedded systems.

Erlang is described as a **functional programming** language, meaning that it emphasizes the evaluation of expressions rather than the execution of commands. The expressions use functions to derive basic values. (Two other well-known programming models are *procedural* and *object-oriented*.)

Here are some features of Erlang:

- Because the location of program threads can be either explicitly specified or invisible to the program, a program can easily be distributed and run at any point in a network.

- Erlang provides dynamic **data types**, allowing programmers to develop system components (such as message dispatchers) that do not care what type of data they are handling and others that strongly enforce **data type** restrictions or that decide how to act based on the type of data they receive.

- Pattern matching allows for extremely compact and clear programs (about 5-10 times shorter than equivalent programs in **C** or **Java**).

- Like Java, Erlang provides **garbage collecting**; programmers do not have to worry about returning allocated memory space.

- Upgrades to the Erlang software don't require stopping the system.

- Interfaces to other programming languages, such as C, C++ and Java, are provided.

- Erlang comes with design patterns or templates for client-server design, state machines, event distribution, and thread supervision.

- Erlang provides a framework that supports distribution of programs across a pool of servers, with automatic recovery and redistribution whenever a server fails.

- It also includes powerful components for a network system, including an **HTTP** server, an **Simple Network Management Protocol** agent, a **Common Object Request Broker Architecture** interface, an OAM subsystem, and a fully distributed **database** engine.

- Erlang's **bytecode** is identical on all platforms, and a network of Erlang nodes may consist of any mix of NT, UNIX, or other supported platforms.

- Erlang is relatively easy to learn compared to C, C++, and Java.

The proponents of Erlang claim that it is superior to Java when developing **back-end** systems that require: fault tolerance, distributed processing, a large amount of concurrent activity, real time response times in milliseconds, and non-stop operation.

ERM

See "enterprise risk management"

ERM Group

ERM (Environmental Resource Management) Group is a global organization of environmental, health, and safety experts, with more than 110 worldwide locations. The Group has 2,400 professionally qualified staff. They work with industrial and other clients to create sound environmental, health, and safety programs. In addition to the ERM Group, a non-profit ERM Foundation supports noteworthy projects.

ERP

ERP (enterprise resource planning) is an industry term for the broad set of activities supported by multi-module application software that helps a manufacturer or other business manage the important parts of its business, including product planning, parts purchasing, maintaining inventories, interacting with suppliers, providing customer service, and tracking orders. ERP can also include application modules for the finance and human resources aspects of a business. Typically, an ERP system uses or is integrated with a **relational database** system. The deployment of an ERP system can involve considerable business process analysis, employee retraining, and new work procedures.

In a recent trend, **SAP**, Peoplesoft, and J. D. Edwards are among ERP product providers offering ERP **outsourcing**.

error checking and correcting

See "ECC"

error correction code

See "ECC"

errors

See "Internet problems"

ESCD

In personal computers with Windows, ESCD (Extended System Configuration Data) is data that provides a computer's **BIOS** and the **operating system** with information for communicating with **plug and play** (PnP) devices. Full PnP capability requires a PnP BIOS. When a computer is started, the BIOS records in the ESCD information about how older devices are configured to the system. A pre-PnP device has an inflexible configuration (for example, a specified **interrupt request** setting). PnP-attached devices can automatically be configured around the existing older configurations (or, when necessary, configured manually).

ESCON

ESCON (Enterprise Systems Connection) is a marketing name for a set of IBM and vendor products that interconnect S/390 computers with each other and with attached storage, locally attached workstations, and other devices using **optical fiber** technology and dynamically modifiable switches called ESCON Directors. In IBM mainframes, the local interconnection of hardware units is known as **channel** connection (and sometimes as local connection to distinguish it from remote or telecommunication connection). ESCON's fiber optic cabling can extend this local-to-the-mainframe network up to 60 kilometers (37.3 miles) with chained Directors. The data rate on the link itself is up to 200 **Mbps** (million bits per second) and somewhat less when adapted to the channel interface. Vendor enhancements may provide additional distance and higher amounts of throughput.

ESCON, **Fibre Channel**, and **Small Computer System Interface** are three alternative technologies used in storage area networks (**SANs**).

In the early 1990s, ESCON replaced a much slower and more cumbersome system of interconnecting mainframes and attached devices known as the bus-and-tag cable. Bus-and-tag cable was copper, used a parallel bit attachment, and is usually referred to as a parallel environment in comparing it to the ESCON environment, which uses serial bit-by-bit technology.

ESDI

ESDI (Enhanced Small Device Interface) is a hardware **interface** for a computer disk drive based on the ST-506 standard, an early industry and later **ANSI** standard based on the Seagate disk drive. ESDI improved storage capacity and data transfer rates. It was used in IBM's higher-end PS/2 computers.

ESDI has generally been supplanted by the Enhanced Integrated Drive Electronics (**EIDE**) interface and the Small Computer Systems Interface (**SCSI**).

ESDRAM

ESDRAM (enhanced synchronous DRAM), made by Enhanced Memory Systems, includes a small static RAM in the SDRAM chip. This means that many accesses will be from the faster SRAM. In case the SRAM doesn't have the data, there is a wide **bus** between the SRAM and the SDRAM because they are on the same chip. ESDRAM is the synchronous version of Enhanced Memory Systems' **EDRAM** architecture. Both EDRAM and ESDRAM devices are in the category of **cache DRAM** and are used mainly for **L1 and L2**.

ESDRAM is apparently competing with **DDR SDRAM** as a faster SDRAM chip for **Socket 7** processors.

e-services

E-services, a business concept developed by Hewlett Packard (**HP**), is the idea that the World Wide Web is moving beyond **e-business** and **e-commerce** (that is, completing sales on the Web) into a new phase where many business services can be provided for a business or consumer using the Web. Some e-services, such as remote bulk printing, may be done at a Web site; other e-services, such as news updates to subscribers, may be sent to your computer. Other e-services will be done in the background without the customer's immediate knowledge. HP defines e-services as "modular, nimble, electronic services that perform work, achieve tasks, or complete transactions."

Using HP's e-services concept, any application program or information resource is a potential e-service and Internet service providers (**ISP**s) and other companies are logical distributors or access points for such services. The e-services concept also sees services being built into "cars, networked devices, and virtually anything that has a microchip in it." HP's vision is that IT departments will increasingly address their needs in a modular way so that individual modules can potentially be addressed by some e-service.

HP notes three trends:

1. The increasing availability of "**apps-on-tap**"—for accounting, payment systems, purchasing, and enterprise resource planning (**ERP**). (HP offers several of these services.)

2. An increase in the number of specialized Web **portal** sites such as OpenSkies (travel services) and Ariba.com's **e-procurement** services.

3. More **on-the-fly** handling of service requests that may require handling by several companies.

HP sees its **e-speak** application development facilities as supporting e-services. Also see **application service provider** (ASP).

e-signature

See "digital signature"

e-signature bill

See "Electronic Signatures in Global and National Commerce Act"

ESMR

Also see Specialized Mobile Radio (**SMR**).

ESMR (Enhanced Specialized Mobile Radio) is a **wireless** communication system in which numerous mobile/portable transceivers are linked in a network of repeaters. Each **repeater** has a range of approximately 5 to 10 miles. Operating frequencies are in the UHF (ultra-high-frequency) range, that is, between approximately 300 **MHz** and 3 **GHz**. Usually, the working band is near 900 MHz.

ESMR can function like its fundamentally simpler cousin, SMR, but it can also offer features similar to those of a **cellular telephone** network. The PTT (push-to-talk), **half-duplex** mode can be used; in this case the operation resembles communications between old style two-way radios. **Full-duplex** mode can also be used, so either party can listen and talk at the same time. Interconnection with the telephone networks is commonly done. In addition to voice communication, an ESMR system can offer paging, wireless fax, and data transmission.

ESMR systems use digital radio transmission. **Spread-spectrum** modes, such as frequency hopping, are common. In a well-designed ESMR system, connection is almost instantaneous, compared with the typical 15 to 20 seconds required to dial and set up a call in a public cellular network. The coverage of an ESMR system depends on the geographical distribution and needs of the users. Some systems are confined to single municipalities; others cover selected groups of metro areas; others operate over entire states or regions of a country.

Examples of ESMR networks include Ericsson's EDACS (Enhanced Digital Access Communications System), Motorola's IDEN (Integrated Dispatch Enhanced Network), and the Nextel System.

ESMTP

ESMTP, an abbreviation for Extended Simple Mail Transfer Protocol, specifies extensions to the original protocol for sending e-mail that supports graphics, audio and video files, and text in various national languages. The original Internet protocols for sending e-mail are described in Request for Comments **RFC** 822, Standard for the Format of ARPA Internet Text Messages, and in RFC 821, Simple Mail Transfer Protocol. As users began to want to attach various kinds of files to e-mail, the need for additional capabilities arose and resulted in RFC 1869, Extended Simple Mail Transfer Protocol.

ESMTP provides the capability for a **client** e-mail program to inquire of a **server** e-mail program about which capabilities it supports and then communicate accordingly. Currently, most commercial e-mail servers and clients support ESMTP.

e-speak

E-speak is an open software platform designed by **HP** to facilitate the delivery of e-services (electronic services) over the Internet. Based on Extensible Markup Language (**XML**) and often compared to Microsoft's **.Net** initiative, e-speak was designed to automate tasks people would have to complete personally by letting the computers involved talk to each other.

To understand e-speak, pretend you are thinking of taking a vacation to Paris. Instead of searching the Web for an airline, hotel, and rental car (and then spending hours looking through individual Web sites to see which services/prices fit your criteria), you would submit your criteria to a registered e-services site and and a services **agent** would find the registered providers that met your requirements. An added advantage of using a registered e-service site would be that if for some reason you missed your flight and had to take a later one, all the e-services site computers involved in your travel arrangements would notify each other and re-adjust your reservations accordingly.

Although HP has given up propriety rights to e-speak, it plans to sell servers, storage, and application solutions to developers who plan to use e-speak on their Web sites. HP is also using e-speak for its own product management.

e-tailing

E-tailing (less frequently: *etailing*) is the selling of retail goods on the Internet. Short for "electronic retailing," and used in Internet discussions as early as 1995, the term seems an almost inevitable addition to **e-mail**, **e-business**, and **e-commerce**. E-tailing is synonymous with business-to-consumer (**B2C**) transaction.

E-tailing began to work for some major corporations and smaller entrepreneurs as early as 1997 when Dell Computer reported multimillion dollar orders taken at its Web site. The success of Amazon.com hastened the arrival of Barnes and Noble's e-tail site. Concerns about secure order-taking receded. 1997 was also the year in which Auto-by-Tel reported that they had sold their millionth car over the Web, and CommerceNet/Nielsen Media reported that 10 million people had made purchases on the Web. Jupiter research predicted that e-tailing would grow to $37 billion by 2002.

E-tailing has resulted in the development of **e-tailware**—software tools for creating online catalogs and managing the business connected with doing e-tailing. A new trend is the price comparison site that can quickly compare prices from a number of different e-tailers and link you to them.

e-tailware

E-tailware is software for creating online catalogs, ordering forms, credit checking, and similar services for Web sites that sell goods and services to consumers. A number of e-tailware products provide a complete range of support so that a company that already has a Web site can easily add e-tailing capability to the site.

EtherExpress

EtherExpress is a technology from Intel that is used in network server adapters (devices that attach the **server** to the network cable) for **Ethernet**-based local area networks (LANs). The EtherExpress adapter has a built-in i960 **processor** (an Intel processor with 32-bit **RISC**-based architecture) that allows it to offload work from the server's

processor, improving network efficiency by reducing demands on server resources. Adapters that offload processor work are known as *intelligent* adapters.

Network adapter performance is usually assessed by comparing its data **throughput** (the rate at which data can be sent and received, measured in megabits per second or in frames per second) against the **host** CPU utilization, a measurement of the proportion of time the server's processor has to spend on network-related tasks. EtherExpress technology enhances adapter performance both by increasing throughput and by lowering CPU utilization, which increases the amount of time the server has for other requests.

EtherExpress server adapters are designed to take advantage of a number of advanced server technologies, such as:

- **Adapter Fault Tolerance (AFT)**, a method of protecting vital network links through the use of multiple adapters and redundant links which take over automatically if the first link fails

- **Adaptive Load Balancing (ALB)**, which allows as many as four adapters to handle outgoing server traffic, enabling scalable network bandwidth increases (up to 400 **Mbps**

- **Fast EtherChannel (FEC)**, a technology from Cisco Systems that balances incoming and outgoing traffic to increase throughput

- **PCI Hot Plug**, a technology from Compaq that makes it possible for a failed adapter to be hot swapped (replaced without powering down the server), allowing the network to function normally throughout the procedure.

EtherExpress server adapters include the EtherExpress PRO/100+ Server Adapter, the EtherExpress PRO/100 Intelligent Server Adapter, and the EtherExpress PRO/1000 Gigabit Server Adapter.

Ethernet

Ethernet is the most widely-installed **local area network** (LAN) technology. Specified in a standard, IEEE 802.3, Ethernet was originally developed by Xerox and then developed further by Xerox, DEC, and Intel. An Ethernet LAN typically uses **coaxial cable** or special grades of **twisted pair** wires. The most commonly installed Ethernet systems are called **10BASE-T** and provide transmission speeds up to 10 **Mbps**. Devices are connected to the cable and compete for access using a Carrier Sense Multiple Access with Collision Detection (**CSMA/CD**) protocol.

Fast Ethernet or 100BASE-T provides transmission speeds up to 100 megabits per second and is typically used for LAN **backbone** systems, supporting workstations with 10BASE-T cards. **Gigabit Ethernet** provides an even higher level of backbone support at 1000 megabits per second (1 gigabit or 1 billion bits per second).

ETL

See "extract, transform, load"

ETRN

ETRN (Extended Turn) is an extension to the Simple Mail Transfer Protocol (**SMTP**) that allows an SMTP **server** to send a request to another SMTP server to send any e-mail messages it has. Typically, SMTP is used with two other **protocols**, Post Office Protocol 3 (**POP3**) and Internet Message Access Protocol (**IMAP**), to request messages from a server because SMTP by itself cannot request mail to be sent.

ETRN is designed for use by anyone who is traveling and wants to get access to their mail. ETRN can only be used with Internet service providers that support ETRN. The latest version of the widely used SMTP server, **sendmail**, supports ETRN. The details of ETRN are in **Request for Comments** 1985 of the Internet Engineering Task Force (**IETF**), *SMTP Service Extension for Remote Message Queue Starting.*

ETSI

The European Telecommunications Standards Institute (ETSI) is a non-profit organization that establishes telecommunications standards for Europe. ETSI guidelines are voluntary and almost always comply with standards produced by international bodies.

ETSI initiatives touch on the following areas: aeronautical radio, API, ATM, electromagnetic compatibility, electronic signature, Generic Addressing and Transport protocol, maritime radio, service provider access, Telecommunications Management Network (TMN), **TETRA**, **VoIP**, and **xDSL**.

ETSI's structure includes a general assembly, a board, a technical organization, and a secretariat. Its technical organization has primary responsibility for devising standards.

ETSI is headquartered in southern France. It currently has 789 members from 52 countries and five continents. Its membership list features some of the biggest names in technology, including IBM Europe, Microsoft Europe, Hewlett-Packard France, Motorola, and Lucent Technologies. Membership is open to any firm with an interest in European telecommunications. Each member pays an annual fee to join ETSI.

EULA

See "End User License Agreement"

euro

The euro (pronounced YUR-oh) is now the official monetary unit of 11 member nations of the European Union. Having a common monetary unit is expected to make trade more efficient, make price comparisons easier, and stabilize interest rates overall. The euro is being phased in over a three-year period that began on January 1, 1999. Initially, the euro will be "bank money" only. Travellers can charge their credit cards in either euros or the local currency. Banks will need to be able to accept euros and convert them into their local money. Coin and note euros will not be available until 2002. (The coins have been designed, however, and candy makers are stamping them out in chocolate.)

Countries That Are Using the Euro

Austria, Belgium, Finland, France, Germany, Ireland, Italy, Luxembourg, the Netherlands, Portugal, and Spain are European Union member nations that have accepted the euro as their official currency. For the next three years, each country will use both the euro and the existing local currency. (For cash purchases, only the local currency will be available until 2002. For credit card charges, either the euro or the local currency can be used.)

Countries That Are Not Using the Euro

Britain, Denmark, Greece, and Sweden are not using the euro. Britain, Denmark, and Sweden may decide to join later. Greece did not meet the economic requirements.

What the Euro Means to Most of Us

If you trade or travel in Europe, you will be able to charge purchases in euros, using most major credit cards, including Visa International, the most popular credit card. American Express is printing travelers checks denominated in euros. Change will be returned in local currency. Since many prices will now be quoted in euros as well as in the local currency, you can easily compare prices for the same goods and services in different countries. Over time, this is expected to make prices more consistent among the countries that use the euro. For the time being, however, travellers can continue to deal entirely with local currencies.

Bank customers can have accounts in either euros or national currencies.

What the Euro Means to Large Businesses

Since many computer business applications involve accounting or sums of money that may now accept euros, these programs will need to be updated. The cost to business will be considerable, perhaps a third of the cost of the 2000 problem. In the beginning, businesses will tend to phase in the acceptance of or preference for euros over national currencies.

In terms of trading, the euro is expected to help stabilize the European economy as a whole. The 11 countries using the euro represent 290 million people.

What the Euro Means to the Financial Markets

European financial markets now quote stocks, bonds, and mutual funds in euros. Public debts are also expressed in euros.

Exchange Rates

Euros are now the only currency traded against other world currencies, such as the dollar and the Japanese yen. Exchange trading in German marks, French francs, and so forth no longer exists. Many stock market and finance Web sites post the latest exchange rates.

European Computer Driving License

The European Computer Driving License (ECDL) is a certification for qualified computer operators in the same way that a regular driving license is a certification for qualified vehicle operators—although it differs in that one may lawfully operate a computer without a computer driving license.

The ECDL Foundation, which was set up by the Council of European Professional Informatics Societies (CEPIS), developed the certification program as a way of to promote information technology skills among the general population and skill standardization within the IT industry. The ECDL Foundation developed from an earlier CEPIS group, the User Skills Task Force, and was established in Dublin in January 1997 as a non-profit organization.

The ECDLF syllabus claims: "A European Computer Driving Licence always certifies the same standard of competence, irrespective of a person's nationality, residence, education, age or sex." The original ECDLF members agreed on the standards to be met by license holders when the project began; subsequently the foundation issued a revised "Standards and Guidelines" report in March of 1998.

To obtain ECDL certification, an individual must pass a test about basic IT knowledge as well as six practice-based tests of competence using a computer and popular computer **application**s. Employers frequently require employees—or potential employees—to attain ECDL certification.

ECDLF has branches in most European countries; it also has a number of members internationally through its International Computer Driving License (ICDL) Foundation.

European Telecommunications Satellite Organization

See "EUTELSAT"

European Telecommunications Standards Institute

See "ETSI"

EUTELSAT

EUTELSAT (European Telecommunications Satellite Organization) refers to both the organization and its set of **satellite**s that were placed in geostationary orbits over Europe beginning in 1983. By early 1998, at least 48 countries had become members of EUTELSAT and the satellites were serving both public and private traffic, including telephone services, fax, data, land mobile service, and television and radio programming to home and business users with their own receivers. Since its first satellites, EUTELSAT has launched a succession of more capable and powerful spacecraft. Recently, EUTELSAT has begun offering Internet services including Web page transmission via digital television, using the **MPEG-2** DVB (Moving Picture Experts Group Direct Video Broadcasting) standard, a new European standard for digital television. Users are Internet service providers and cable companies that can redistribute Internet files via ground lines as well as private users with PC cards and set-top boxes.

EUVL

See "extreme ultraviolet lithography"

evergreen

On the Internet, *evergreen* is a term used by some ad agencies to describe a **Web site** that is updated on a daily or other frequent basis. A Web site that is evergreen is considered more likely to attract both first-time and repeat visitors. If a media buyer for an ad agency is selecting a number of sites for an ad campaign, whether a site is considered evergreen may determine whether it's included in the campaign. A Web site that is not updated frequently enough is termed *brown*.

Web sites or tools (such as Alexa) that evaluate other sites sometimes rate a site for *freshness*. One obvious way to change a site every day is to include **JavaScript** code on the home page that automatically changes the date. This is not usually enough to warrant a rating of "evergreen," however.

Evernet

The term *Evernet* has been used to describe the convergence of **wireless**, **broadband**, and **Internet telephony** technologies that will result in the ability to be continuously connected to the Web anywhere using virtually any information device. Considered the next generation of Internet access, the Evernet assumes the emergence of an amount of **bandwidth** that would enable millions of homes to access the Web through inexpensive **cable modem**, **DSL**, or wireless connections.

The "Evernet" can also be considered to include common household appliances and home and office networks that include devices that control the environment; such networks require an "always on" capability. In addition, portable devices that can connect quickly and easily without wires to other devices (see **Bluetooth**) might also be considered part of the Evernet.

e-voting

E-voting (sometimes called electronic voting, online voting, or Internet voting) is an election system that uses **encryption** to allow a voter to transmit his or her secure and secret ballot over the Internet. Critics of electronic voting express concerns about Web security and the lack of equal access to the Internet for all citizens (see **digital divide**). Advocates of e-voting cite the potential for reduced election costs, as well as the potential for increasing civic participation by making the voting process more convenient. Furthermore, they foresee that advances in **cryptography** will soon make submitting a governmental election ballot online just as common as filing an income tax return online is in the U. S.

At this time, e-voting is used primarily for conducting non-governmental elections, although a number of citizens in Switzerland and the U.S. (Arizona, parts of Alaska and California) have had the opportunity to be pioneers in the submission of governmental election ballots over the Internet, with varying degrees of success. Experts around the world agree that in governmental elections, the need to create a standardized, secure process for the verification, collection, and counting of votes must be addressed satisfactorily before online voting becomes a viable option.

There are several groups working to create online voting standards. In the U.S., the Federal Voting Assistance Program (FVAP) at the Pentagon, the California Secretary of State Internet voting task force, the NASED ITA subcommittee, and several third-party vendors are researching and testing voting models and software applications and examing standards to make online voting an option in time for the 2004 Presidential election. An international group of experts and companies, called *The Internet Voting Technology Alliance* is working on an open peer review of standards that could be used in e-voting throughout the world.

As of this writing, each of these groups has a different solution with different security standards and risks, although there are three Internet electronic voting models that each group seems to feel holds promise: automation of the current process, electronic voting at a secure Web site, and electronic voting at regional centers.

EWSD

EWSD (Electronic Worldwide Switch Digital, or, in German, Elektronisches WaehlSystem [Digital]) is a widely-installed telephonic **switch** system developed by Siemens. Siemens says that EWSD performs switching for over 160 million lines in more than 100 countries. EWSD is a **modular** system in which some switches in the system can be installed in a telephone company's **centrex** facility and other switches can be located at the customer.

Important features of EWSD include the following:

- Advanced Intelligent Network (**AIN**) 0.1 and 0.2 capabilities allow switching services to be added at Service Control Points, meaning that new services can be added and performed by the switching system without the customer having to buy new equipment.

- In addition to AIN capabilities, EWSD provides **ISDN**, CLASS, **SS7**, and **centrex** services.

- **Digital** and **analog** lines can be combined in the same line groups, allowing full **interoperability** between digital and analog terminals.

- Carriers using EWSD can provide **Automatic Call Distributor** services for customers with **call center**s.

- EWSD provides both **Bellcore** AIN 0.2 and Global System for Mobile (**GSM**) communications for **personal communications services**.

Line types supported include single or two-party analog, coin, TR08, and ISDN **Basic Rate Interface**. Unidirectional Digital Subscriber Line (**DSL**) support is planned. Any line type can be added by simply changing the line card.

exabyte

An exabyte (EB) is a large unit of computer data storage, two to the sixtieth power **bytes**. The prefix *exa* means one billion billion, or one quintillion, which is a decimal term. Two to the sixtieth power is actually 1,152,921,504,606,846,976 bytes in decimal, or somewhat over a quintillion (or ten to the eighteenth power) bytes. It is common to say that an exabyte is approximately one quintillion bytes. In decimal terms, an exabyte is a billion **gigabyte**s.

Exchange Rate Mechanism

The Exchange Rate Mechanism (ERM) is part of the European Monetary Union (EMU) that began operating in 1999.

exchange-to-exchange

See "E2E"

executable

In computers, to execute a **program** is to run the program in the computer, and, by implication, to start it to run. In usage, people run programs and systems execute them. That is, a system user asks the system to run the program (or sets it up so that this happens automatically at a certain time) and, as a result, the system executes the program. Typically, we don't say that a program is executing; we say that it is running.

A computer **processor** executes an **instruction**, meaning that it performs the operations called for by that instruction.

An executable is a **file** that contains a program—that is, a particular kind of file that is capable of being executed or run as a program in the computer. In a **Disk Operating System** or Windows operating system, an executable file usually has a file name extension of .bat, .com, or .exe. An executable file or a group of them are sometimes referred to as *binaries* as in "I'll download the binaries to you" since the file format of an executable is a solid sequence of binary values that cannot be easily read by anyone (unlike that of, for example, an ASCII text file which can be easily examined for information as it travels from one computer to another).

A file whose name ends in ".exe" is really a program that when "opened"—that is, selected by putting your mouse over the file name and then initiated by double-clicking your mouse, for example—causes the operating system to run the program. Users who receive an .exe file as an e-mail attachment should always be sure that the file comes from a trusted source and is not, in fact, a computer **virus**.

exit program

1) In computer programming, an exit program (or exit routine) is a named unit of programming code that is entered when a particular condition occurs, such as one that requires some screening for authorization. An exit program may be part of an **operating system** or part of an **application program**.

2) In the IBM **AS/400 operating system**, an exit program is a supplemental security measure that controls user access to applications, and prevents access outside of authorized applications. An AS/400 exit program (so called because the system exits to the program in the middle of a request from the user) is not used—as might be expected—to exit from a program, but to process user requests: It monitors user activity, checks to see if user requests comply with installation rules, and rejects those requests that contravene those rules.

expert system

An expert system is a computer program that simulates the judgement and behavior of a human or an organization that has expert knowledge and experience in a particular field. Typically, such a system contains a knowledge base containing accumulated experience and a set of rules for applying the knowledge base to each particular situation that is described to the program. Sophisticated expert systems can be enhanced with additions to the knowledge base or to the set of rules.

Among the best-known expert systems have been those that play chess and that assist in medical diagnosis.

Also see **AI**.

explicit parallelism

Explicit parallelism is a concept of **processor-compiler** efficiency in which a group of **instruction**s is sent from the compiler to the processor for simultaneous rather than sequential execution. Explicit parallelism is a feature of Explicitly Parallel Instruction Computing (**EPIC**) and Intel's EPIC-based architecture, **IA-64**.

Explicitly Parallel Instruction Computing

See "EPIC"

exploit

In computing, an exploit is an attack on a computer system, especially one that takes advantage of a particular vulnerability that the system offers to intruders. Used as a verb, the term refers to the act of successfully making such an attack.

Many **cracker**s (or **hacker**s, if you prefer that term) take pride in keeping tabs of such exploits and post their exploits (and discovered vulnerabilities) on a Web site to share with others.

Where an exploit takes advantage of a weakness in an **operating system** or vended **application program**, the owners of the system or application issue a "fix" or **patch** in response. Users of the system or application are responsible for obtaining the patch, which can usually be downloaded from the Web. Failure to install a patch for a given problem exposes the user to a security breach. (However, it can be difficult to keep up with all the required patches.)

exploratory model

The exploratory model is a systems development method (**SDM**) occasionally used to design and develop a computer system or product and basically consists of planning and trying different designs until one of them seems to be the right one to develop. This model works best in situations where few, or none, of the system or product requirements are known in detail ahead of time. This model is largely based on educated guesswork.

There are several steps in the exploratory model:

1. A starting point is determined for the work. All the information available is gathered together in an attempt to get an idea of what the new system will be expected to do, and how it can be done.

2. A rudimentary first-generation system is put together, based on the information gathered and the ideas formulated in the first step.

3. The first-generation system is tested to see how it performs, what it can and cannot do, and what might be done to improve it.

4. A second-generation system is developed from the first one, based on the improvements proposed in the previous step.

5. The second-generation system is tested, as was the first. Its performance is evaluated, and possible improvements determined.

6. The process is repeated as many times as necessary to obtain user satisfaction, or until it is decided that the project is unworkable.

7. Routine maintenance is carried out on a continuing basis to prevent large-scale failures and to minimize downtime.

This model resembles the prototyping model, but it begins at a more nebulous starting point, and proceeds in a less formal fashion. This scheme is not particularly cost-effective and sometimes results in less-than-optimal systems, so it should be used only when no viable alternative seems to exist.

exponential assembly

In **nanotechnology**, exponential assembly is a form of self-replication in which tiny devices called nanorobots repeatedly construct copies of themselves. Four conditions must be met for exponential assembly to take place in an orderly manner.

The first condition is that each nanorobot must construct at least two copies of itself during its operational life. These copies must be exact in every detail, including the ability to reproduce. The more copies each unit can produce, the more rapidly the population will grow.

The second condition is that there must exist sufficient energy and ingredients so the process can continue for the specified length of time, or until a specified population of nanorobots is reached. Because the population grows exponentially, the number of units will increase rapidly. For example, if a population begins with one nanorobot, and if each unit creates three copies of itself, then the population will grow by powers of three. Suppose replication takes place on a daily basis and each nanorobot ends its useful life as soon as it has reproduced. Then after two days the population will be $3^2 = 9$ units, after three days it will be $3^3 = 27$ units, after four days it will be $3^4 = 81$ units, and, in general, after n days the population will be 3^n units.

The third condition for exponential assembly is that the environment be controlled so the replication process can proceed efficiently. Excessive turbulence, temperature extremes, intense radiation, or other adverse circumstances might prevent the proper functioning of the nanorobots and cause the process to falter or fail before it is supposed to terminate.

The fourth condition is that the process be programmed to end at a certain point, or be modified so that the population cannot exceed a certain maximum number of units.

Otherwise, the nanorobots will eventually crowd each other out of their world, and the process will come to a catastrophic halt.

Compare **self-replication** and also see **nanotechnology**, **positional assembly**, and **self-assembly**.

exponential function

An exponential function is a mathematical function of the following form:

$$f(x) = a^x$$

where x is a variable, and a is a constant called the base of the function. The most commonly encountered exponential-function base is the **transcendental number** e, which is equal to approximately 2.71828. Thus, the above expression becomes:

$$f(x) = e^x$$

When the exponent in this function increases by 1, the value of the function increases by a factor of e. When the exponent decreases by 1, the value of the function decreases by this same factor (it is divided by e).

In electronics and experimental science, base-10 exponential functions are encountered. The general form is:

$$f(x) = 10^x$$

When the exponent increases by 1, the value of the base-10 function increases by a factor of 10; when the exponent decreases by 1, the value of the function becomes $1/10$ as great. A change of this extent is called one order of magnitude.

For a given, constant base such as e or 10, the exponential function "undoes" the **logarithm** function, and the logarithm undoes the exponential. Thus, these functions are inverses of each other. For example, if the base is 10 and $x = 3$:

$$\log (10^x) = \log (10^3) = \log 1000 = 3$$

If the base is 10 and $x = 1000$:

$$10^{(\log x)} = 10^{(\log 1000)} = 10^3 = 1000$$

extended binary-coded decimal interchange code

See "EBCDIC"

extended data output RAM

See "EDO RAM"

Extended Industry Standard Architecture

See "EISA"

Extended Simple Mail Transfer Protocol

See "ESMTP"

Extended System Configuration Data

See "ESCD"

extensible

In information technology, extensible describes something, such as a program, programming language, or protocol, that is designed so that users (or later designers) can extend its capabilities. Extensibility can be a primary reason for the system, as in the case of the Extensible Markup Language (**XML**), or it may be only a minor feature.

Approaches to extensibility include facilities (sometimes called **hook**s) for allowing users to insert their own program routines, the ability to define new **data type**s, and the ability to define new formatting **markup tag**s.

Extensible Business Reporting Language

See "XBRL"

Extensible Forms Description Language

See "XFDL"

Extensible Hypertext Markup Language

See "XHTML"

Extensible Markup Language

See "XML"

Extensible Stylesheet Language

See "XSL"

Extensible User-interface Language

See "XUL"

extension

1) In computer operating systems, a **file** name extension is an optional addition to the file name in a **suffix** of the form ".xxx" where "xxx" represents a limited number of alphanumeric characters depending on the operating system. (In Windows 3.1, for example, a file name extension or suffix can have no more than three characters, but in Windows 95 and later, it can have more.) The file name extension allows a file's format to be described as part of its name so that users can quickly understand the type of file it is without having to "open" or try to use it. The file name extension also helps an application program recognize whether a file is a type that it can work with.

2) In programming, an extension is a file containing programming that serves to extend the capabilities of or data available to a more basic program. Extensions are sometimes required to be stored in a separate extensions file so that

they're easy to locate. When installing software, you may be instructed to take one or more steps related to installing extensions (or these steps may automatically be done for you).

Exterior Gateway Protocol

Exterior Gateway Protocol (EGP) is a **protocol** for exchanging routing information between two neighbor **gateway hosts** (each with its own **router**) in a network of autonomous systems. EGP is commonly used between hosts on the Internet to exchange routing table information. The routing table contains a list of known routers, the addresses they can reach, and a cost **metric** associated with the path to each router so that the best available route is chosen. Each router polls its neighbor at intervals between 120 to 480 seconds and the neighbor responds by sending its complete routing table. EGP-2 is the latest version of EGP.

A more recent exterior gateway protocol, the Border Gateway Protocol (**BGP**), provides additional capabilities.

Also see Interior Gateway Protocol (**IGP**).

external storage

External storage is all addressable data **storage** that is not currently in the computer's **main storage** or **memory**. Synonyms are **auxiliary storage** and **secondary storage**.

extract, transform, load

In managing databases, extract, transform, load (ETL) refers to three separate functions combined into a single programming tool. First, the extract function reads data from a specified source **database** and extracts a desired subset of data. Next, the transform function works with the acquired data—using rules or lookup tables, or creating combinations with other data—to convert it to the desired state. Finally, the load function is used to write the resulting data (either all of the subset or just the changes) to a target database, which may or may not previously exist.

ETL can be used to acquire a temporary subset of data for reports or other purposes, or a more permanent data set may be acquired for other purposes such as: the population of a **data mart** or **data warehouse**; conversion from one database type to another; and the migration of data from one database or platform to another.

extranet

An extranet is a private network that uses the Internet **protocol** and the public telecommunication system to securely share part of a business's information or operations with suppliers, vendors, partners, customers, or other businesses. An extranet can be viewed as part of a company's **intranet** that is extended to users outside the

company. It has also been described as a "state of mind" in which the Internet is perceived as a way to do business with other companies as well as to sell products to customers.

An extranet requires security and privacy. These require **firewall** server management, the issuance and use of **digital certificate**s or similar means of user authentication, **encryption** of messages, and the use of virtual private networks (**VPN**) that tunnel through the public network.

Companies can use an extranet to:

- Exchange large volumes of data using Electronic Data Interchange (**EDI**)
- Share product catalogs exclusively with wholesalers or those "in the trade"
- Collaborate with other companies on joint development efforts
- Jointly develop and use training programs with other companies
- Provide or access services provided by one company to a group of other companies, such as an online banking application managed by one company on behalf of affiliated banks
- Share news of common interest exclusively with partner companies

Netscape, Oracle, and Sun Microsystems have announced an alliance to ensure that their extranet products can work together by standardizing on **JavaScript** and the Common Object Request Broker Architecture (**CORBA**). Microsoft supports the Point-to-Point Tunneling Protocol (**PPTP**) and is working with American Express and other companies on an Open Buying on the Internet (OBI) standard. The Lotus Corporation is promoting its groupware product, **Notes**, as well-suited for extranet use.

extrapolation and interpolation

Extrapolation is an estimation of a value based on extending a known sequence of values or facts beyond the area that is certainly known.

Interpolation is an estimation of a value within two known values in a sequence of values.

Extreme Programming

Extreme Programming (XP) is a pragmatic approach to program development that emphasizes business results first and takes an incremental, get-something-started approach to building the product, using continual testing and revision. The conception of Kent Beck, who has written a book about it, XP proceeds with the view that code comes first. Beck emphasizes that in order to write the code, however, you have to write a test for it first so that you will know when your code succeeds. Beck also introduces the relatively novel

idea that code should be written by pairs of programmers, forcing the main programmer to describe the code to the other programmer and perhaps to stimulate further ideas.

Beck calls Extreme Programming a "lightweight methodology" that challenges the assumption that getting the software right the first time is the most economical approach in the long run. Beck's fundamental idea is to start simply, build something real that works in its limited way, and then fit it into a design structure that is built as a convenience for further code building rather than as an ultimate and exhaustive structure after thorough and time-consuming analysis. Rather than specialize, all team members write code, test, analyze, design, and continually integrate code as the project develops. Because there is much face-to-face communication, the need for documentation is minimized, according to Beck.

extreme ultraviolet lithography

Extreme ultraviolet lithography (EUVL) is an advanced technology for making microprocessors a hundred times more powerful than those made today. Intel, **AMD**, and Motorola have joined with the U.S. Department of Energy in a three-year venture to develop a microchip with etched circuit lines smaller than 0.1 **micron** in width. (Today's circuits are generally .18 micron or greater.) A **microprocessor** made with the EUVL technology would be a hundred times more powerful than today's. **Memory** chips would be able to store 1,000 times more information than they can today. The aim is to have a commercial manfacturing process ready before 2005.

EUVL is one technology vying to replace the optical lithogaphy used to make today's microcircuits. It works by burning intense beams of ultraviolet light that are reflected from a circuit design pattern into a **silicon** wafer. EUVL is similar to optical lithography in which light is refracted through camera lenses onto the wafer. However, extreme ultraviolet light, operating at a different **wavelength**, has different properties and must be reflected from mirrors rather than refracted through lenses. The challenge is to build mirrors perfect enough to reflect the light with sufficient precision. Intel is working on some early prototypes. In the meantime, optical lithography will continue to advance over the next few years until replaced by newer technologies such as EUVL.

extremely low frequency

See "ELF"

eye candy

Eye candy is a term used in information technology for visual elements displayed on computer monitors that are aesthetically appealing or attention-compelling. There are several different usages:

1) Eye candy sometimes means any frill or decorative design intended to enhance the basic content of a presentation. In this usage, the connotation of "unnecessary" may or may not be present.

2) It is also used to refer to software that produces psychedelic or **fractal** images on a display as a screensaver or background. Some eye candy programs use audio input to generate sympathetic graphical output—in effect, sophisticated sound-to-light effects. In some cases, the software exists solely to provide visual entertainment or atmosphere as either a background or as a celebration of the technological possibilities.

eye-in-hand system

An eye-in-hand system is a **robot end effector** equipped with a close-range camera. The camera is designed for work at distances from a fraction of a millimeter to approximately one meter. A lamp is included in the gripper (robot hand) along with the camera to ensure that a good image is obtained in dim light. The camera has a lens that can be adjusted for proper focus, so the positioning error is minimized.

Eye-in-hand systems are used primarily to guide robot end effectors and grippers, and to ensure that grippers properly engage the intended targets. The system can also precisely measure the distance from the end effector or gripper to a target. In a robot equipped with a smart controller, the eye-in-hand system allows positive identification of a target. The controller compares the image from the camera with a set of images stored in memory.

Also see **motion plan** and **robotics**.

ezine

The term *ezine* is short for "electronic magazine." "E-zine" and "e-Zine" are spelling variations. A similar term is "ejournal." There are several usages of the term *ezine*. The term is similar to *zine*, which is derived from *magazine* and is used to describe "small press" or personally distributed magazines or newsletters.

1) An early use of the term *ezine* described a new kind of Web site that contained a stylized mixture of content (articles, pictures, poetry, fiction, and comment) conveyed in a way that exploited and celebrated the Web as a new information medium. Examples include Salon and HotWired.

2) Some ezines publishers saw ezines as an opportunity to reach an audience electronically and more economically than was possible with print medium. As a result, hundreds of Web site ezines were created, each devoted to a special cause, subject, or sensibility. This kind of ezine is roughly the cyberspace equivalent of the printed version and when printed out, is in fact, the equivalent.

3) The term is also used to describe any print magazine such as *National Geographic* or *Newsweek* that also has an electronic edition.

4) The term also sometimes includes e-mail newsletters, of which there are thousands that can be subscribed to. Some of these refer to themselves as zines or ezines.

F

See "farad"

failover

Failover is a backup operational mode in which the functions of a system component (such as a **processor**, **server**, network, or database, for example) are assumed by secondary system components when the primary component becomes unavailable through either failure or scheduled down time. Used to make systems more **fault-tolerant**, failover is typically an integral part of **mission-critical** systems that must be constantly available. The procedure involves automatically offloading tasks to a standby system component so that the procedure is as **seamless** as possible to the end user. Failover can apply to any aspect of a system: Within a personal computer, for example, failover might be a mechanism to protect against a failed processor; within a network, failover can apply to any network component or system of components, such as a connection **path**, storage device, or Web server.

Originally, stored data was connected to servers in very basic configurations: either point-to-point or cross-coupled. In such an environment, the failure (or even maintenance) of a single server frequently made data access impossible for a large number of users until the server was back online. More recent developments, such as the storage area network (**SAN**), make any-to-any connectivity possible among servers and data storage systems. In general, storage networks use many paths—each consisting of complete sets of all the components involved—between the server and the system. A failed path can result from the failure of any individual component of a path. Multiple connection paths, each with **redundant** components, are used to help ensure that the connection is still viable even if one (or more) paths fail. The capacity for automatic failover means that normal functions can be maintained despite the inevitable interruptions caused by problems with equipment.

Fair Information Practices

FIP (Fair Information Practices) is a general term for a set of standards governing the collection and use of personal data and addressing issues of privacy and accuracy. Different organizations and countries have their own terms for these concerns—the UK terms it "Data Protection," the European Union calls it "Personal Data Privacy," and the OECD has written *Guidelines on the Protection of Privacy and Transborder Flows of Personal Data*, which states these principles:

Collection Limitation Principle: There should be limits to the collection of personal data and any such data should be obtained by lawful and fair means and, where appropriate, with the knowledge or consent of the data subject.

Data Quality Principle: Personal data should be relevant to the purposes for which they are to be used, and, to the extent necessary for those purposes, should be accurate, complete and kept up-to-date.

Purpose Specification Principle: The purposes for which personal data are collected should be specified not later than at the time of data collection and the subsequent use limited to the fulfillment of those purposes or such others as are not incompatible with those purposes and as are specified on each occasion of change of purpose.

Use Limitation Principle: Personal data should not be disclosed made available or otherwise used for purposes other than those specified in accordance with the Purpose Specification Principle except:

a) with the consent of the data subject; or

b) by the authority of law.

Security Safeguards Principle: Personal data should be protected by reasonable security safeguards against such risks as loss or unauthorized access, destruction, use, modification or disclosure of data.

Openness Principle: There should be a general policy of openness about developments, practices and policies with respect to personal data. Means should be readily available of establishing the existence and nature of personal data, and the main purposes of their use, as well as the identity and usual residence of the data controller.

Individual Participation Principle: An individual should have the right:

a) to obtain from a data controller, or otherwise, confirmation of whether or not the data controller has data relating to him;

b) to have communicated to him, data relating to him within a reasonable time; at a charge, if any, that is not excessive; in a reasonable manner; and in a form that is readily intelligible to him;

c) to be given reasons if a request made under subparagraphs (a) and (b) is denied, and to be able to challenge such denial; and

d) to challenge data relating to him and, if the challenge is successful to have the data erased, rectified, completed or amended.

Accountability Principle: A data controller should be accountable for complying with measures which give effect to the principles stated above.

These principles are reprinted from http://www. junkbusters.com/ht/en/fip.html#OECD under the terms of the **GNU** General Public License.

FAQ

See "frequently-asked questions"

farad

The farad (symbolized F) is the standard unit of **capacitance** in the International System of Units (**SI**). Reduced to base SI units, one farad is the equivalent of one second to the fourth power **ampere** squared per kilogram per meter squared $(s^4 \cdot A^2 \cdot kg^{-1} \cdot m^{-2})$.

When the **voltage** across a 1 F capacitor changes at a rate of one **volt** per second (1 V/s), a **current** flow of 1 A results. A capacitance of 1 F produces 1 V of potential difference for an electric charge of one **coulomb** (1 C). The farad is an extremely large unit of capacitance. In practice, capacitors with values this large are almost never seen.

In common electrical and electronic circuits, units of microfarads (μF), where $1 \mu F = 10^{-6}$ F, and picofarads (pF), where $1 pF = 10^{-12}$ F, are used. At radio frequencies (**RF**), capacitances range from about 1 pF to 1,000 pF in tuned circuits, and from about 0.001 μF to 0.1 μF for blocking and bypassing. At audio frequencies (**AF**), capacitances range from about 0.1 μF to 100 μF. In power-supply filters, capacitances can be as high as 10,000 μF.

Also see **capacitor**, **inductor**, **reactance**, and **henry**.

fast retransmit and recovery

In **TCP/IP**, fast retransmit and recovery (FRR) is a congestion control **algorithm** that makes it possible to quickly recover lost data packets. Without FRR, the TCP uses a timer that requires a retransmission timeout if a packet is lost. No new or duplicate **packet**s can be sent during the timeout period. With FRR, if a receiver receives a data segment that is out of order, it immediately sends a duplicate acknowledgement to the sender. If the sender receives three duplicate acknowledgements, it assumes that the data segment indicated by the acknowledgements is lost and immediately retransmits the lost segment. With FRR, time is not lost waiting for a timeout in order for retransmission to begin.

FRR works most efficiently when there are isolated packet losses. It does not work efficiently when there are multiple data packet losses occurring over a short period of time. The fast retransmit/fast recovery algorithm was introduced in 4.3BSD Reno release and is described in RFC 2001 and RFC 2581.

Fast Ethernet

Fast Ethernet is a local area network (**LAN**) transmission standard that provides a data rate of 100 megabits per second (referred to as "100BASE-T"). Workstations with existing 10 megabit per second (10BASE-T) **Ethernet card** can be connected to a Fast Ethernet network. (The 100 megabits per second is a shared data rate; input to each workstation is constrained by the 10 Mbps card.)

fast packet technology

In data transmission, a fast **packet** is one that is transmitted without any error checking at points along the route. Assurance that the packet arrived without error is the responsibility of the receiver. Fast packet transmission is possible because of the extremely low incidence of error or data loss on **fiber optic** media and is a characteristic of high bandwidth transmission technologies such as **ATM**.

Fast Page Mode DRAM

See "FPM DRAM"

FastCGI

FastCGI is a programming interface that can speed up Web applications that use the most popular way to have the Web **server** call an application, the common gateway interface (**CGI**). According to one FastCGI implementor, user requests coming to a Web site and using a specific application program can be handled 3 to 30 times faster using FastCGI. FastCGI is a **plug-in** to the Web server. It requires only small changes to existing server applications (such as **Perl** or **Tcl** scripts and **C** and **C++** programs) to get the performance benefits.

Basically, FastCGI is a program that manages multiple CGI requests within a single **process**, saving many program instructions for each request. Without FastCGI, each instance of a user requesting a service causes the Web server to open a new process that gets control, performs the service, and then is closed. With FastCGI, the overhead for one process is shared among all currently processing requests. Unlike CGI, with FastCGI, a process runs independently of the Web server, isolating it and thus providing more security. FastCGI is language-independent. It was developed and is copyrighted by Open Market, Inc., which makes it freely available and offers it as an **open** standard. It offers a single non-proprietary approach for use across platforms and on any Web server.

FAT

See "file allocation table"

fat Mac

A fat Mac application is an application program for the **Macintosh** computer that is compiled to run on either a Mac containing the Motorola 68000 series microprocessor or the **PowerPC** microprocessor. The 68000 series is the traditional Macintosh microprocessor. The more recent and faster PowerPC microprocessor was developed by Apple, IBM, and Motorola to rival or exceed the Intel microprocessor series used in **PC**s. A fat Mac library is one that contains library routines (program code) that will run with either microprocessor.

fatal exception

In a computer error message, a fatal exception indicates an exceptional situation requiring that the program responsible for the situation be closed. In general, an *exception* is any uncontemplated situation (which includes but is not limited to program errors). A fatal exception simply means the exception can't really be handled so that the program can continue to run.

Software applications communicate with the operating system and other applications through several different layers of code. When an exception occurs at a certain layer of code, each layer sends the exception to the next layer in order to locate any exception handling code that can deal with the specific exception. If no exception handling code exists (at any layer) to deal with the exception, a fatal exception error message is generated by the operating system. This message can also contain some cryptic information about where the fatal exception error occurred (such as the hexadecimal location within the program's range of memory). This extra information has little value to the user, but may help support people or developers in debugging an application.

When a fatal exception occurs, the operating system has no other recourse but to shut down the application, and in some cases, its own operating system. When using a specific application, if you continue to experience fatal exception errors, report the problem to the software vendor.

fault-tolerant

Fault-tolerant describes a computer system or component designed so that, in the event that a component fails, a backup component or procedure can immediately take its place with no loss of service. Fault tolerance can be provided with software, or embedded in hardware, or provided by some combination. Leading vendors that specialize in fault-tolerant systems include Compaq Non-Stop (formerly Tandem), Marathon Technologies, and Stratus Computer.

In the software implementation, the **operating system** (for example, Tandem Guardian) provides an interface that allows a programmer to "checkpoint" critical data at pre-determined points within a transaction. In the hardware implementation (for example, with Stratus and its VOS operating system), the programmer does not need to be aware of the fault-tolerant capablilities of the machine.

At a hardware level, fault tolerance is achieved by duplexing each hardware component. Disks are mirrored. Multiple **processor**s are "lock-stepped" together and their outputs are compared for correctness. When an anomaly occurs, the faulty component is determined and taken out of service, but the machine continues to function as normal.

fax

Sometimes called "telecopying," a fax is the telephonic transmission of scanned-in printed material (text or images), usually to a telephone number associated with a printer or other output device. The original document is scanned with a fax machine, which treats the contents (text or images) as a single fixed graphic image, converting it into a **bitmap**. In this digital form, the information is transmitted as electrical signals through the telephone system. The receiving fax machine reconverts the coded image and prints a paper copy of the document.

Almost all **modem**s manufactured today are capable of sending and receiving fax data. Fax/modem software generates fax signals directly from disk files or the screen. Even if a document is text only, it is treated by the computer as a scanned image and is transmitted to the receiver as a bitmap. Faxing a message online works well if the recipient wants only to read the message. However, if the document requires editing, it must be converted into **ASCII** text by an OCR (optical character recognition) program, or it must be retyped manually into the computer. A more efficient method of sending documents that require modification is through the e-mail system. E-mail files are already ASCII text so they can be edited immediately in any text editor or word processing program.

The Internet now provides a new and cheaper way to send faxes in some cases. A number of free and commercial companies provide arrangements for using the Internet rather than the public telephone system for most or part of the path to the fax point. Some services also provide the ability to broadcast a fax to multiple addresses.

FC/IP

See "Fibre Channel over IP"

FCAPS

FCAPS (fault-management, configuration, accounting, performance, and security) is an acronym for a categorical model of the working objectives of **network management**. There are five levels, called the fault-management level (F), the configuration level (C), the accounting level (A), the performance level (P), and the security level (S).

At the F level, network problems are found and corrected. Potential future problems are identified, and steps are taken to prevent them from occurring or recurring. In this way, the network is kept operational, and downtime is minimized.

At the C level, network operation is monitored and controlled. Hardware and programming changes, including the addition of new equipment and programs, modification of existing systems, and removal of obsolete systems and programs, are coordinated. An inventory of equipment and programs is kept and updated regularly.

The A level, which might also be called the allocation level, is devoted to distributing resources optimally and fairly among network subscribers. This makes the most effective use of the systems available, minimizing the cost of operation. This level is also responsible for ensuring that users are billed appropriately.

The P level is involved with managing the overall performance of the network. **Throughput** is maximized, **bottleneck**s are avoided, and potential problems are identified. A major part of the effort is to identify which improvements will yield the greatest overall performance enhancement.

At the S level, the network is protected against **hacker**s, unauthorized users, and physical or electronic sabotage. Confidentiality of user information is maintained where necessary or warranted. The security systems also allow network administrators to control what each individual authorized user can (and cannot) do with the system.

Fcc

In Eudora and perhaps other e-mail facilities, you'll see the abbreviations "Fcc" and "Bcc." "Fcc" is the same as "cc" or **carbon copy**—that is, send a copy of the message to the address you fill in. "Bcc" stands for "Blind carbon copy" which says: Send a copy to another address...but in this case, don't indicate to the Fcc recipient that you also sent this copy.

FC-PGA

FC-PGA (flip chip-pin grid array) is a **microchip** design developed by Intel for its faster **microprocessor**s in which the hottest part of the chip is located on the side that is away from the **motherboard**.

According to Intel, the FC-PGA chip design is better than previous designs for several reasons:

- It protects the delicate circuitry of its microprocessor by making it easier to insert and remove the microprocessor within a computer. This is accomplished by way of its pin grid array construction, described below.

- It allows the microprocessor to operate more easily at its optimal temperatures by designing the processor core on the "flip side" (or backside) of the chip, facing away

from the motherboard. (The processor core, or **silicon** core, contains the delicate microprocessor engine that controls all of its actions.)

- Due to its flip-chip design, an FC-PGA microprocessor requires fewer hardware components (such as a thermal plate or heat spreader) than other chips in order to dissipate heat from the core and maintain its optimal temperature. In place of these components, an FC-PGA microprocessor allows a heatsink or other thermal device to be attached directly to the back of the processor, where the core resides. In general, PGA (pin grid array) chip packages (or PGA form factors, as they are also called), have 370 **pin**s "arrayed" in a series of square "grids" at the bottom of the microprocessor. This square-pin design allows a computer hardware technician to smoothly plug the microprocessor into a PGA370 socket on a computer's motherboard, using little-to-no force. PGA370 sockets are designed with a Zero Insertion Force (**ZIF**) feature that helps the PGA chip to slide easily in and out of its socket.

Currently, two types of PGA chip packages exist for Intel Celeron and Pentium III processors: **PPGA** (plastic pin grid array) and FC-PGA (flip chip-pin grid array). PPGA chip packages are designed with the processor core facing down toward the motherboard, whereas FC-PGA packages have the processor core flipped up on the back of the chip, facing away from the motherboard. Each PGA package requires different thermal designs and components in order to keep the chips cool.

Incidentally, in order to use either type of PGA microprocessor with its associated PGA370 socket, a computer's motherboard must support certain guidelines, known as VRM specifications. (For PPGA processors, the motherboard must support VRM 8.2 specifications. For FC-PGA processors, the motherboard must support VRM 8.4 specifications.)

FDDI

FDDI (Fiber Distributed Data Interface) is a standard for data transmission on **fiber optic** lines in a local area network (**LAN**) that can extend in range up to 200 km (124 miles). The FDDI protocol is based on the **token ring** protocol. In addition to being large geographically, an FDDI local area network can support thousands of users.

An FDDI network contains two token rings, one for possible backup in case the primary ring fails. The primary ring offers up to 100 **Mbps** capacity. If the secondary ring is not needed for backup, it can also carry data, extending capacity to 200 Mbps. The single ring can extend the maximum distance; a dual ring can extend 100 km (62 miles).

FDDI is a product of American National Standards Committee X3-T9 and conforms to the Open Systems Interconnection (*OSI*) model of functional layering. It can be used to interconnect LANs using other protocols. FDDI-II is a version of FDDI that adds the capability to add **circuit-switched** service to the network so that voice signals can also be handled. Work is underway to connect FDDI networks to the developing Synchronous Optical Network (**SONET**).

FDISK

WARNING: Use caution when repartitioning a hard disk drive that contains data. Repartitioning wipes out all data on the disk. Be sure to back up everything to another storage medium first.

FDISK is a **utility**, included in all versions of **MS-DOS** and Windows, for formatting (preparing) a **hard disk** drive to hold data and to logically **partition** the disk, specifying and naming major portions of it for different uses. FDISK is used to prepare and partition a brand new hard drive, and typically most personal computers today arrive with the drive already partitioned and loaded with the operating system and perhaps other software. A typical personal computer today arrives with a single partition that is addressed by the operating system as the logical C drive. (Some PCs also have one or two diskette drives addressed as the A and B drives. PCs with CD-ROMs also usually address the CD-ROM as the D drive. But a hard disk drive can be divided into and addressed as several "logical" drives, or partitions.)

In addition to setting up a new hard disk drive, FDISK is used for repartitioning the hard drive when you want to change something. For example, a computer can be set up as a **dual boot** system, with one **operating system** (for example, **Windows 2000**) in one partition and another operating system (for example, **Linux**) in another partition. Disk partitioning is also commonly used on **LAN** servers, where different sets of users share different files and applications. The maximum partition size in the first version of DOS to use FDISK was 16 **megabyte**s. Recent Windows systems support hard drives up to 2 **terabyte**s (2,000 **gigabyte**s) in size!

If you need to repartition your current hard drive, be sure to back up all data because it will be lost when you use FDISK. Be careful to follow the documented Microsoft and manufacturer directions.

The age of your computer and the operating system you use determines how difficult the hard drive installation will be. The Basic Input Output System (**BIOS**) in computers manufactured before 1994 does not support drives larger than 512 MB, which causes FDISK to display larger hard drives as only 512 MB in size. It is necessary to use disk management software that helps an older BIOS version to recognize a hard drive larger than 512 MB. Disk management software is usually included with your new hard drive or free upon request from the hard drive manufacturer. You can also purchase a BIOS upgrade such as an **EPROM** chip, **flash memory** BIOS software, a controller card, or a card with a BIOS chip on it depending

on the manufacturer's recommendation. Depending on your operating system, you may have to create multiple partitions in order to use your hard drive's full capacity:

- DOS version 6.22 and later supports drives greater than 8.4 GB. Versions earlier than 6.22 do not.

- Windows 95A does support drives larger than 8.4 GB, but you have to partition the drive into at least four partitions depending on the hard drive's size because of **FAT** 16 file system's limitations used by Windows 95A. Windows 95B supports FAT 32, which allows one large partition on new hard drives and supports hard drives up to 2,000 GB in size.

- The first and later editions of Windows 98 support FAT 32 and hard drives up to 2,000 GB.

- Windows NT version 5.0 and later also supports large hard drives.

FDISK has its limitations. You can't move applications from one partition to another without uninstalling and reinstalling the software. FDISK erases all data on your hard drive. And you can't delete or create new partitions without going through the entire FDISK and formatting process again. However, special partitioning software such as PartitionMagic can be used instead of FDISK. Partitioning software allows you to create, delete, and resize partitions without losing your data. You can move applications from one partition to another without uninstalling and reinstalling the application. You can hide partitions to protect data from other users. You can also use partitioning software as a boot manager. A boot manager allows you to install and use more than one operating system easily. Partition software also eliminates the need for a BIOS upgrade in older computers.

FDM

See "frequency-division multiplexing"

FDMA

FDMA (frequency division multiple access) is the division of the frequency band allocated for **wireless cellular telephone** communication into 30 channels, each of which can carry a voice conversation or, with digital service, carry digital data. FDMA is a basic technology in the **analog** Advanced Mobile Phone Service (**AMPS**), the most widely-installed cellular phone system installed in North America. With FDMA, each channel can be assigned to only one user at a time. FDMA is also used in the Total Access Communication System (TACS).

The Digital-Advanced Mobile Phone Service (**D-AMPS**) also uses FDMA but adds time division multiple access (**TDMA**) to get three channels for each FDMA channel, tripling the number of calls that can be handled on a channel.

FED

See "field emission display"

Federal Information Processing Standard

See "FIPS"

Federation of Telecommunications Engineers of the European Community

FITCE (Federation of Telecommunications Engineers of the European Community) is an international association that is committed to affecting telecommunication developments in a positive and constructive manner throughout Europe and the rest of the world. The FITCE Association informs and updates members and others engaged in the telecommunication industry. FITCE maintains a resource database for linking globally to telecommunication opportunities and contacts.

FITCE states that their aims are:

- To promote the development of science in the field of telecommunications.

- To enable each member to benefit from the experience acquired by the other members in all telecommunications fields (including associated areas, such as specialised buildings, power supplies and electrical machinery, electronic computers, and so forth) and to investigate new ideas that encourage the development of telecommunications in all countries represented.

- To study all aspects of problems arising from the recruitment, training, work assignments, and career structures of these telecommunications professionals.

- To develop cultural ties and to encourage friendly relations between telecommunications professionals who belong to the member associations, in order to enable themselves and their families to become better acquainted with one another.

feed line

In a **wireless** communications or broadcasting antenna system, the feed line connects the **antenna** to the receiver, transmitter, or transceiver. The line transfers radio-frequency (**RF**) energy from a transmitter to an antenna, and/or from an antenna to a receiver, but, if operating properly, does not radiate or intercept energy itself. There are three types of antenna feed lines, also called *RF transmission lines*, commonly used in wireless systems.

Coaxial line, also called **coaxial cable**, consists of a wire conductor surrounded by a tubular, braided metallic shield. The conductor is kept at the center of the shield by a **dielectric**, which is usually solid or foamed polyethylene. The shield is connected to RF ground, while the center conductor carries the **signal**. The shield, as its name implies, prevents the **electromagnetic field** (EM field) inside the

cable from escaping, and also prevents EM energy from entering the cable from outside. Coaxial cables are used at frequencies below approximately 1 **gigahertz**.

Parallel-wire line consists of two wires running alongside each other. At each point along the line, the RF **current** in the two wires are always equal in magnitude but opposite in direction. The two wires are spaced close together in terms of the EM **wavelength**. Because of this, the EM fields from the two wires practically cancel out each other in the region outside the line. This prevents the line from radiating RF energy. In receiving systems, EM fields from the external environment induce RF currents that flow in the same direction in each conductor. The receiver circuitry cancels out RF currents that flow in the same direction in both conductors, while responding to RF currents that flow in opposite directions. This prevents external EM fields from affecting the line. Parallel-wire line is rarely employed in commercial installations, but a prefabricated form, called *TV ribbon*, is sometimes used with television receivers in fringe areas for reception of channels 2 through 13. Another type of two-wire line, known as *window line, ladder line*, or *open wire*, is popular among **amateur radio** operators and shortwave listeners.

A **waveguide** is a hollow, metallic tube or pipe with a circular or rectangular cross section. The diameter of the waveguide is comparable to the wavelength of the EM field. The EM field travels along the inside of the waveguide in a manner somewhat analogous to the way sound waves propagate down a narrow tunnel. The metal structure prevents EM fields inside the waveguide from escaping, and also prevents external EM fields from penetrating to the interior. Waveguides are used at microwave frequencies, that is, at 1 GHz and above.

Because the currents in a parallel-wire line always exactly cancel or balance each other, this type of line constitutes a *balanced feed line*. Such lines work best with antenna systems that are bilaterally symmetrical; an example is the **dipole antenna**. Coaxial cables and waveguides are *unbalanced feed lines*. This type of line will work satisfactorily with antennas that are not symmetrical. With the use of a transformer called a **balun** (contraction of the words "balanced" and "unbalanced"), coaxial cables and waveguides can be used with symmetrical antennas.

femtosecond

(This definition follows U.S. usage in which a billion is a thousand million and a trillion is a 1 followed by 12 zeros.)

A femtosecond is one millionth of a nanosecond or 10^{-15} of a second and is a measurement sometimes used in laser technology.

For comparison, a millisecond (ms or msec) is one thousandth of a second and is commonly used in measuring the time to read to or write from a **hard disk** or a **CD-ROM** player or to measure **packet** travel time on the Internet.

A microsecond (μs) is one millionth (10^{-6}) of a second.

A nanosecond (ns or nsec) is one billionth (10^{-9}) of a second and is a common measurement of read or write access time to random access memory (**RAM**).

A picosecond is one trillionth (10^{-12}) of a second, or one millionth of a microsecond.

An attosecond is one quintillionth (10^{-18}) of a second and is a term used in photon research.

ferret

In a computer or a network, a ferret is a program that searches through selected files, databases, or search engine indexes for information that meets specified search criteria. The term derives from the name of a small furry animal, commonly a pet, that burrows under things. On the Internet, a ferret can forward a request simultaneously to a number of **search engine** sites and filter the results according to user-specified or program-designed guidelines.

Ferrets can be written to search a specific group of World Wide Web search engine sites, **Usenet** news groups, global e-mail directories, Internet Relay Channel (**IRC**) member lists, and any public, searchable database that can be efficiently selected.

A ferret should not be confused with a **crawler**, a program that search engines use to gather data from many Web pages that is then indexed for search retrieval.

ferroelectric RAM

See "FRAM"

ferrule

A ferrule (from Latin *viriola*, meaning *little bracelet*) is a ring or cap attached to an object to protect against damage, splitting, or wear. In **fiber optics**, a ferrule is a component (usually a rigid tube) used to align and protect the stripped end of a fiber.

A ferrule is used together with the connector that connects the fiber cable either to another cable or to a transmitter or receiver. The ferrule keeps the fibers accurately aligned within the connector. Ferrules can be made of glass, plastic, metal, or ceramic material. Ceramic is currently considered the best material for a number of reasons. For example, ceramic bonds well to glass and its expansion coefficient is close to that of the glass fibers, making it environmentally stable.

FET

See "field-effect transistor"

fetch

In computer technology, fetch has several meanings related to getting, reading, or moving data objects.

1) Fetch is the first of two stages involved in computer processing. The **processor** operates by processing **instruction**s in what is called the "fetch/execute cycle." The processor fetches (reads from memory) an instruction and then, depending on the instruction, executes it (takes some further action with it, such as shifting bits to the right or left). Then it fetches the next instruction, and so forth.

A **register** in the processor called the program counter holds information about where the processor is in the particular program being processed and the address (location) of the next instruction to be executed. At the beginning of the cycle, the program counter tells the processor which instruction to fetch; during the cycle, the instruction is executed and the information is updated to refer to the next instruction to be fetched.

In some newer processor designs, more than one instruction can be fetched at the same time and execution is done in parallel.

2) Fetch is a command used in embedded Structured Query Language (**SQL**) to retrieve rows sequentially. In SQL, a cursor is a pointer to a selected row in a collection retrieved by a SQL statement. The cursor advances through the rows, one at a time, to allow sequential processing of records. The fetch command retrieves the selected row from the cursor. The steps involved in using the fetch command are: Declare cursor, Open cursor, Fetch row (separate fetches may be executed for multiple rows) and Close cursor.

3) Fetch is a Macintosh program for transferring files between any networked Macintosh computers using the File Transfer Protocol (**FTP**). Its features include support of multiple connections, the capacity to restart interrupted transfers, and drag-and-drop functionality for transferring, bookmarking, and preference setting.

FH-CDMA

See "frequency-hopping spread spectrum"

Fiber Connectivity

See "FICON"

Fiber Distributed Data Interface

See "FDDI"

fiber optic

Fiber optic (or "optical fiber") refers to the medium and the technology associated with the transmission of information as light impulses along a glass or plastic wire or fiber. Fiber optic wire carries much more information than conventional copper wire and is far less subject to electromagnetic interference. Most telephone company long-distance lines are now fiber optic.

Transmission on fiber optic wire requires repeating at distance intervals. The glass fiber requires more protection within an outer cable than copper. For these reasons and because the installation of any new wiring is labor-intensive, few communities yet have fiber optic wires or cables from the phone company's branch office to local customers (known as **local loop**).

fiber to the curb

"Fiber to the curb" (FTTC) refers to the installation and use of **optical fiber** cable directly to the curbs near homes or any business environment as a replacement for "plain old telephone service" (**POTS**). Think of removing all the telephone lines you see in your neighborhood and replacing them with optical fiber lines. Such wiring would give us extremely high **bandwidth** and make possible movies-on-demand and online multimedia presentations arriving without noticeable delay.

The term "fiber to the curb" recognizes that optical fiber is already used for most of the long-distance part of your telephone calls and Internet use. Unfortunately, the last part—installing fiber to the curb—is the most expensive. For this reason, fiber to the curb is proceeding very slowly. Meanwhile, other less costly alternatives, such as **Asymmetric Digital Subscriber Line** on regular phone lines and satellite delivery, are likely to arrive much sooner in most homes.

Fiber to the curb implies that **coaxial cable** or another medium might carry the signals the very short distance between the curb and the user inside the home or business. "Fiber to the building" (FTTB) refers to installing optical fiber from the telephone company central office to a specific building such as a business or apartment house. "Fiber to the neighborhood" (FTTN) refers to installing it generally to all curbs or buildings in a neighborhood. Hybrid Fiber Coax (**HFC**) is an example of a distribution concept in which optical fiber is used as the **backbone** medium in a given environment and coaxial cable is used between the backbone and individual users (such as those in a small corporation or a college environment).

fiberless optics

Fiberless optics, a term that has been trademarked by Terabeam Networks, is a technology for transmitting large amounts of data on light waves sent through space rather than along an **optical fiber** cable, thus offering a surprising new solution to the so-called **last-mile technology** problem. Until now, optical fiber, cable TV, and various forms of **wireless** transmission have been the alternatives to consider in getting data back and forth between the backbone network and the home or business. TeraBeam Networks, a Seattle, Washington, company, expects to offer its "wireless optical fiber" system for mainly corporate use beginning in the summer of 2000 and to offer it in international markets over the next three years.

Terabeam describes the system as providing **broadband** services from a highly-directional point-to-multipoint beam using frequencies that "operate in a region of the **electromagnetic radiation spectrum** that is not subject to regulation by the FCC." The signal is **encryption** and said to be almost impossible to intercept. Multiple connections offer **scalability** and can be close together without interference concerns. The service will support the Internet Protocol (**IP**). As described by TeraBeam, fiberless optics seems like a laser beam (using a different part of the spectrum perhaps) that can be set up over a relatively long distance within a city-wide area. The system would involve fixed (not mobile) connections.

Fibre Channel over IP

Fibre Channel over IP (FC/IP, also known as *Fibre Channel tunneling* or *storage tunneling*) is an Internet Protocol (**IP**)-based storage networking technology developed by the Internet Engineering Task Force (**IETF**). FC/IP mechanisms enable the transmission of **Fibre Channel** (FC) information by **tunneling** data between storage area network (**SAN**) facilities over IP networks; this capacity facilitates data sharing over a geographically distributed enterprise. One of two main approaches to storage data transmission over IP networks, FC/IP is among the key technologies expected to help bring about rapid development of the storage area network market by increasing the capabilities and performance of storage data transmission.

FC/IP Versus iSCSI

The other method, **iSCSI**, generates **SCSI** codes from user requests and encapsulates the data into IP **packet**s for transmission over an **Ethernet** connection. Intended to link geographically distributed SANs, FC/IP can only be used in conjunction with Fibre Channel technology; in comparison, iSCSI can run over existing Ethernet networks. SAN connectivity, through methods such as FC/IP and iSCSI, offers benefits over the traditional point-to-point connections of earlier data storage systems, such as higher performance, availability, and **fault-tolerance**. A number of vendors, including Cisco, Nortel, and Lucent have introduced FC/IP-based products (such as **switch**es and **router**s). Both iSCSI and FC/IP are proposed standards, and are expected to be ratified by the end of 2001. A hybrid technology called *Internet Fibre Channel Protocol* (iFCP) is an adaptation of FC/IP that is used to move Fibre Channel data over IP networks using the iSCSI protocols.

Fibre Channel

Fibre Channel is a technology for transmitting data between computer devices at a data rate of up to 1 **Gbps**, or one billion bits per second. (A data rate of 10 Gbps has been proposed by the Fibre Channel Industry Association.) Fibre Channel is especially suited for connecting computer **server**s to shared storage devices and for interconnecting storage controllers and drives. Since Fibre Channel is three times as fast, it has begun to replace the Small Computer System Interface (**SCSI**) as the transmission interface between servers and clustered storage devices. Fibre channel is more flexible; devices can be as far as ten kilometers (about six miles) apart if **optical fiber** is used as the physical medium. Optical fiber is not required for shorter distances, however, because Fibre Channel also works using **coaxial cable** and ordinary telephone **twisted pair**.

Fibre Channel offers point-to-point, switched, and loop interfaces. It is designed to interoperate with SCSI, the Internet Protocol (**IP**) and other protocols, but has been criticized for its lack of compatibility—primarily because (like in the early days of SCSI technology) manufacturers sometimes interpret specifications differently and vary their implementations.

Standards for Fibre Channel are specified by the Fibre Channel Physical and Signalling standard, and the **ANSI** X3.230-1994, which is also **ISO** 14165-1.

FICON

FICON (for *Fiber Connectivity*) is a high-speed input/output (I/O) **interface** for **mainframe** computer connections to storage devices. As part of IBM's **S/390** server, FICON channels increase I/O capacity through the combination of a new architecture and faster physical link rates to make them up to eight times as efficient as **ESCON** (Enterprise System Connection), IBM's previous **fiber optic** channel standard.

FICON **channel** features include:

- A mapping layer based on the **ANSI** standard Fibre Channel-Physical and Signaling Interface (FC-PH), which specifies the signal, cabling, and transmission speeds

- 100 **Mbps** bi-directional link rates at distances of up to twenty kilometers, compared to the 3Mbps rate of ESCON channels at distances of up to three kilometers.

- More flexibility in terms of network layout, because of the greater distances

- Compatibility with any installed channel types on any S/390 G5 server

- Bridge feature, which enables support of existing ESCON control units

- Requires only one channel address

- Support for **full-duplex** data transfers, which enables simultaneous reading and writing of data over a single link

- **Multiplexing**, which enables small data transfers to be transmitted with larger ones, rather than having to wait until the larger transaction is finished

FidoNet

Started in 1984, FidoNet is a system for exchanging e-mail and discussion group and other files among users of over 30,000 bulletin board services. FidoNet messages are sent using the UNIX-to-UNIX Copy Protocol (**UUCP**). Messages can travel over the Internet after being converted to **TCP/IP** format by computer servers that act as Internet **gateway**.

field emission display

A field emission display (FED) is a new type of flat-panel display in which electron emitters, arranged in a grid, are individually controlled by "cold" cathodes to generate colored light. Field emission display technology makes possible the thin panel of today's liquid crystal displays (**LCD**), offers a wider field-of-view, provides the high image quality of today's cathode ray tube (**CRT**) displays, and requires less power than today's CRT displays.

Some FED products are now available and developers continue to refine the technology. Two companies working on this technology are Candescent Technologies and PixTech.

field

A field is an area in a fixed or known location in a unit of data such as a **record**, message **header**, or computer **instruction** that has a purpose and usually a fixed size. A field can be subdivided into smaller fields. Here are some examples:

1) In a form that you fill out on a Web site, each box that asks you for information is a text entry field.

2) In the **header** of a variable-length transmission unit, a two-byte subfield in the header (which is really a field itself) could identify the length in bytes of the message.

field-effect transistor

See also **bipolar transistor** and **transistor**.

A field-effect transistor (FET) is a type of **transistor** commonly used for weak-signal amplification (for example, for amplifying **wireless** signals). The device can amplify **analog** or **digital** signals. It can also switch DC or function as an oscillator.

In the FET, current flows along a semiconductor path called the *channel*. At one end of the channel, there is an electrode called the *source*. At the other end of the channel, there is an electrode called the *drain*. The physical diameter of the channel is fixed, but its effective electrical diameter can be varied by the application of a voltage to a control electrode called the *gate*. The conductivity of the FET depends, at any given instant in time, on the electrical diameter of the channel. A small change in gate voltage can cause a large variation in the current from the source to the drain. This is how the FET amplifies signals.

Field-effect transistors exist in two major classifications. These are known as the *junction FET (JFET)* and the *metal-oxide-semiconductor FET (MOSFET)*.

The junction FET has a channel consisting of N-type semiconductor (N-channel) or P-type semiconductor (P-channel) material; the gate is made of the opposite semiconductor type. In P-type material, electric charges are carried mainly in the form of **electron** deficiencies called *holes*. In N-type material, the charge carriers are primarily electrons. In a JFET, the junction is the boundary between the channel and the gate. Normally, this P-N junction is reverse-biased (a DC voltage is applied to it) so that no current flows between the channel and the gate. However, under some conditions there is a small current through the junction during part of the input signal cycle.

In the MOSFET, the channel can be either N-type or P-type semiconductor. The gate electrode is a piece of metal whose surface is oxidized. The oxide layer electrically insulates the gate from the channel. For this reason, the MOSFET was originally called the *insulated-gate FET (IGFET)*, but this term is now rarely used. Because the oxide layer acts as a dielectric, there is essentially never any current between the gate and the channel during any part of the signal cycle. This gives the MOSFET an extremely large input **impedance**. Because the oxide layer is extremely thin, the MOSFET is susceptible to destruction by electrostatic charges. Special precautions are necessary when handling or transporting MOS devices.

The FET has some advantages and some disadvantages relative to the **bipolar transistor**. Field-effect transistors are preferred for weak-signal work, for example in **wireless** communications and broadcast receivers. They are also preferred in circuits and systems requiring high impedance. The FET is not, in general, used for high-power amplification, such as is required in large wireless communications and broadcast transmitters.

Field-effect transistors are fabricated onto silicon integrated circuit (IC) chips. A single IC can contain many thousands of FETs, along with other components such as resistors, capacitors, and diodes.

field-programmable gate array

A field-programmable gate array (FPGA) is an integrated circuit (**IC**) that can be programmed in the field after manufacture. FPGAs are similar in principle to, but have vastly wider potential application than, programmable read-only memory (**PROM**) chips. FPGAs are used by engineers in the design of specialized ICs that can later be produced hard-wired in large quantities for distribution to computer manufacturers and end users. Ultimately, FPGAs might allow computer users to tailor microprocessors to meet their own individual needs.

FIFO

Also see **named pipe** (sometimes referred to as a "fifo").

In computer programming, FIFO (first-in, first-out) is an approach to handling program work requests from **queue**s or **stack**s so that the oldest request is handled next. LIFO (last-in, first-out) is an approach in which the most recent request is handled next and the oldest request doesn't get handled until it is the only remaining request on the queue (or in the stack). Although LIFO seems "unfair," it may be more efficient. A stack that is handled using LIFO is sometimes referred to as a *push-down* or *push-down pop-up* stack or list.

file

1) In data processing, using an office metaphor, a file is a related collection of records. For example, you might put the records you have on each of your customers in a file. In turn, each **record** would consist of *fields* for individual data items, such as customer name, customer number, customer address, and so forth. By providing the same information in the same fields in each record (so that all records are consistent), your file will be easily accessible for analysis and manipulation by a computer program. This use of the term has become somewhat less important with the advent of the **database** and its emphasis on the table as a way of collecting record and field data. In mainframe systems, the term **data set** is generally synonymous with file but implies a specific form of organization recognized by a particular **access method**. Depending on the operating system, files (and data sets) are contained within a **catalog**, **directory**, or **folder**.

2) In any computer system but especially in personal computers, a file is an entity of data available to system users (including the system itself and its application programs) that is capable of being manipulated as an entity (for example, moved from one file directory to another). The file must have a unique name within its own directory. Some operating systems and applications describe files with given formats by giving them a particular file name suffix. (The file name suffix is also known as a file name **extension**.) For example, a program or executable file is sometimes given or required to have an ".exe" suffix. In general, the suffixes tend to be as descriptive of the formats as they can within the limits of the number of characters allowed for suffixes by the operating system.

file allocation table

Also see: **fat Mac** and **Virtual File Allocation Table**.

A file allocation table (FAT) is a table that an **operating system** maintains on a **hard disk** that provides a map of the **cluster**s (the basic units of logical storage on a hard disk) that a file has been stored in. When you write a new file to a hard disk, the file is stored in one or more clusters that are not necessarily next to each other; they may be rather widely scattered over the disk. A typical cluster size is 2,048 **byte**s, 4,096 bytes, or 8,192 bytes. The operating system creates a FAT entry for the new file that records where each cluster is located and their sequential order. When you read a file, the operating system reassembles the file from clusters and places it as an entire file where you want to read it. For example, if this is a long Web page, it may very well be stored on more than one cluster on your hard disk.

Until Windows 95 **OSR2** (OEM Release 2), DOS and Windows file allocation table entries were 16 bits in length, limiting hard disk size to 128 **megabyte**s, assuming a 2,048 size cluster. Up to 512 megabyte support is possible assuming a cluster size of 8,192 but at the cost of using clusters inefficiently. DOS 5.0 and later versions provide for support of hard disks up to two **gigabyte**s with the 16-bit FAT entry limit by supporting separate FATs for up to four partitions.

With 32-bit FAT entry (FAT32) support in Windows 95 OSR2, the largest size hard disk that can be supported is two **terabyte**s! However, personal computer users are more likely to take advantage of FAT32 with 5 or 10 gigabyte drives.

file carbon copy

See "Fcc"

file sharing

File sharing is the public or private sharing of computer **data** or space in a **network** with various levels of **access** privilege. While **file**s can easily be shared outside a network (for example, simply by handing or mailing someone your file on a diskette), the term *file sharing* almost always means sharing files in a network, even if in a small local area network. File sharing allows a number of people to use the same file or file by some combination of being able to read or view it, write to or modify it, copy it, or print it. Typically, a file sharing system has one or more administrators. Users may all have the same or may have different levels of access privilege. File sharing can also mean having an allocated amount of personal file storage in a common file system.

File sharing has been a feature of **mainframe** and multi-user computer systems for many years. With the advent of the Internet, a file transfer system called the File Transfer Protocol (**FTP**) has become widely-used. FTP can be used to access (read and possibly write to) files shared among a particular set of users with a password to gain access to files shared from an FTP server site. Many FTP sites offer public file sharing or at least the ability to view or copy files by downloading them, using a public password (which happens to be "anonymous"). Most Web site developers use FTP to upload new or revised Web files to a Web server, and indeed the World Wide Web itself can be thought of as large-scale file sharing in which requested pages or files are constantly being downloaded or copied down to the Web user.

More usually, however, file sharing implies a system in which users write to as well as read files or in which users are allotted some amount of space for personal files on a common server, giving access to other users as they see fit. The latter kind of file sharing is common in schools and universities. File sharing can be viewed as part of file systems and their management.

Any multi-user operating system will provide some form of file sharing. Among the best known network file systems is (not surprisingly) the Network File System (**NFS**). Originally developed by Sun Microsystems for its **UNIX**-based systems, it lets you read and, assuming you have permission, write to sharable files as though they were on your own personal computer. Files can also be shared in file systems distributed over different points in a network. File sharing is involved in groupware and a number of other types of applications.

file system

1) In a computer, a file system is the way in which **file**s are named and where they are placed logically for storage and retrieval. The DOS, Windows, OS/2, Macintosh, and UNIX-based operating systems all have file systems in which files are placed somewhere in a hierarchical (tree) structure. A file is placed in a **directory** (*folder* in Windows) or subdirectory at the desired place in the tree structure.

File systems specify conventions for naming files. These conventions include the maximum number of characters in a name, which characters can be used, and, in some systems, how long the file name **suffix** can be. A file system also includes a format for specifying the **path** to a file through the structure of directories.

2) Sometimes the term refers to the part of an operating system or an added-on program that supports a file system as defined in (1). Examples of such add-on file systems include the Network File System (**NFS**) and the Andrew file system (**AFS**).

File Transfer Protocol

File Transfer Protocol (FTP), a standard Internet **protocol**, is the simplest way to exchange files between computers on the Internet. Like the Hypertext Transfer Protocol (**HTTP**), which transfers displayable Web pages and related files, and the Simple Mail Transfer Protocol (**SMTP**), which transfers e-mail, FTP is an application protocol that uses the Internet's **TCP/IP** protocols. FTP is commonly used to transfer Web page files from their creator to the computer that acts as their **server** for everyone on the Internet. It's also commonly used to **download** programs and other files to your computer from other servers.

As a user, you can use FTP with a simple command line interface (for example, from the Windows MS-DOS Prompt window) or with a commercial program that offers a graphical user interface. Your Web browser can also make FTP requests to download programs you select from a Web page. Using FTP, you can also update (delete, rename, move, and copy) files at a server. You need to **logon** to an FTP server. However, publicly available files are easily accessed using **anonymous FTP**.

Basic FTP support is usually provided as part of a suite of programs that come with TCP/IP. However, any FTP client program with a graphical user interface usually must be downloaded from the company that makes it.

file transfer

File transfer is the movement of one or more **file**s from one location to another. A collection of electronically-stored files can be moved by physically moving the electronic storage medium, such as a computer **diskette**, **hard disk**, or **compact disk** from one place to another or by sending the files over a telecommunications medium. On the Internet, the File Transfer Protocol (**FTP**) is a common way to transfer a single file or a relatively small number of files from one computer to another. For larger file transfers (a single large file or a large collection of files), file **compression** and aggregation into a single **archive** is commonly used. (A **zip file** is a popular implementation.)

Electronic Data Interchange (**EDI**) is a popular **protocol** for transferring files in a routine manner between businesses.

FileMaker

FileMaker (or its latest version, FileMaker Pro) is a **relational database** application known for being easy to use and for its ability to serve **Web page**s dynamically without requiring the use of additional third-party applications. With its built-in Web server (called "Web Companion") and out-of-the-box business **template**s, FileMaker Pro has received high praise for being the ideal application for beginning Web site administrators who want to quickly (literally with one click) add Web database publishing capabilities to their Web site or company intranet.

FileMaker was originally developed as a personal database application for the **Macintosh** computer by the Claris Corporation and has since moved into the Windows market. In an effort to build upon FileMaker's reputation for user friendliness, FileMaker Pro (now its latest version, FMP5) has been purposely redesigned so that its user interface more closely resembles that of Microsoft's Office. FMP5 has two Web publishing modes: Instant Web Publishing (which uses pre-designed templates and requires no knowledge of **HTML**) and Custom Web Publishing, which requires knowledge of HTML and Web Companion's proprietary programming language and is called Claris Dynamic Markup Language (CDML).

FMP5 can be used with a wide variety of **middleware** applications, common gateway interface (**CGI**) **script**s, and **application server**s to provide additional Web capabilities. For instance, to provide Secure Socket Layer (**SSL**) support, FMP5 can be connected to a **Mac OS** server by using WebStar, or be connected to a **Windows NT server** by using Microsoft's Web Server. To increase scalability, it is possible to set up a redundant array of inexpensive computers (**RAID**) to provide **load balancing** and to ensure consistent page serving with multiples copies of File Maker Pro 5 Unlimited.

FMP has also teamed up with **Palm** to provide database administrators with a way to seamlessly integrate information in a FMP database with Palm's Wireless Internet service.

filter

1) In computer programming, a filter is a program or section of code that is designed to examine each input or output request for certain qualifying criteria and then process or forward it accordingly. This term was used in **UNIX** systems and is now used in other operating systems. A filter is "pass-through" code that takes input data, makes some specific decision about it and possible transformation of it, and passes it on to another program in a kind of pipeline. Usually, a filter does no input/output operation on its own. Filters are sometimes used to remove or insert headers or control characters in data.

In Windows operating systems, using Microsoft's Internet Server Application Programming Interface (**ISAPI**), you can write a filter (in the form of a dynamic link library or **DLL** file) that the operating system gives control each time there is a Hypertext Transport Control (**HTTP**) request. Such a filter might log certain or all requests or encrypt data or take some other selective action.

2) In telecommunications, a filter is a device that selectively sorts signals and passes through a desired range of signals while suppressing the others. This kind of filter is used to suppress noise or to separate signals into **bandwidth** channels.

Financial Products Markup Language

See "FpML"

Financial Services Markup Language

FSML (Financial Services Markup Language) is a data description language based on the Standard Generalized Markup Language (**SGML**) that was developed to create financial documents for delivery over the Internet, including **eCheck** and their associated documentation. Like the Hypertext Markup Language (**HTML**), FSML is a set of **markup** symbols or codes that allows its users to define the individual items that compose a document, assemble items into larger document parts that take on a contextual meaning, and enable the screening of a document for **digital signatures**, endorsement, additions, or deletions.

FSML was created to ensure that eChecks could be transmitted by e-mail without being corrupted or invalidated by the particular e-mailing system in use. In order to make sure that all data contents are defined as specifically as possible and therefore may be processed by a software application in their entirety, FSML requires precise adherence to definitions of **syntax**, **semantics**, and all values associated with data elements.

FSML is designed to support a full range of payment mechanisms, including electronic checks, Automatic Clearing House (**ACH**) payment authorizations, ATM network transaction authorizations, and variations of a check, such as a postal money order or gift certificate. In the near future, FSML is expected to conform to the Extensible Markup Language (**XML**).

finger

Finger is a program that tells you the name associated with an **e-mail** address. It may also tell you whether they are currently logged in at their system or their most recent logon session and possibly other information, depending on the data that is maintained about users on that computer. Finger originated as part of **BSD UNIX**.

To finger another Internet user, you need to have the finger program on your computer or you can go to a finger **gateway** on the Web and enter the e-mail address. The server at the other end must be set up to handle finger requests. A ".plan" file can be created for any user that can be fingered. Commonly, colleges, universities, and large corporations set up a finger facility. Your own Internet access provider may also set up information about you and other subscribers that someone else can "finger." (To find out, enter your own e-mail address at a finger gateway.)

Ph and **LDAP** are somewhat similar facilities.

finite state machine

In general, a state machine is any device that stores the status of something at a given time and can operate on input to change the status and/or cause an action or output to take place for any given change. A **computer** is basically a state machine and each machine **instruction** is input that changes one or more states and may cause other actions to take place. Each computer's data register stores a state. The **read-only memory** from which a **boot** program is loaded stores a state (the boot program itself is an initial state). The **operating system** is itself a state and each **application** that runs begins with some initial state that may change as it begins to handle input. Thus, at any moment in time, a computer system can be seen as a very complex set of states and each program in

it as a state machine. In practice, however, state machines are used to develop and describe specific device or program interactions.

To summarize it, a state machine can be described as:

- An initial state or record of something stored someplace
- A set of possible input events
- A set of new states that may result from the input
- A set of possible actions or output events that result from a new state

In their book *Real-time Object-oriented Modeling*, Bran Selic & Garth Gullekson view a state machine as:

- A set of input events
- A set of output events
- A set of states
- A function that maps states and input to output
- A function that maps states and inputs to states (which is called a state transition function)
- A description of the initial state

A finite state machine is one that has a limited or finite number of possible states. (An infinite state machine can be conceived but is not practical.) A finite state machine can be used both as a development tool for approaching and solving problems and as a formal way of describing the solution for later developers and system maintainers. There are a number of ways to show state machines, from simple tables through graphically animated illustrations.

FIPS

FIPS (Federal Information Processing Standards) are a set of standards that describe document processing, provide standard algorithms for searching, and provide other information processing standards for use within U.S. government agencies.

firewall

A firewall is a set of related programs, located at a network **gateway server**, that protects the resources of a private network from users from other networks. (The term also implies the security policy that is used with the programs.) An enterprise with an **intranet** that allows its workers access to the wider Internet installs a firewall to prevent outsiders from accessing its own private data resources and for controlling what outside resources its own users have access to.

Basically, a firewall, working closely with a **router** program, examines each network **packet** to determine whether to forward it toward its destination. A firewall also includes or works with a **proxy server** that makes network requests on behalf of workstation users. A firewall is often installed in a specially designated computer separate from the rest of the network so that no incoming request can get directly at private network resources.

There are a number of firewall screening methods. A simple one is to screen requests to make sure they come from acceptable (previously identified) **domain name** and **Internet Protocol** addresses. For mobile users, firewalls allow remote access in to the private network by the use of secure logon procedures and authentication certificates.

A number of companies make firewall products. Features include logging and reporting, automatic alarms at given thresholds of attack, and a graphical user interface for controlling the firewall.

FireWire

FireWire is Apple Computer's version of a standard, **IEEE 1394**, High Performance Serial Bus, for connecting devices to your personal computer. FireWire provides a single plug-and-socket connection on which up to 63 devices can be attached with data transfer speeds up to 400 **Mbps** (**megabit**s per second). The standard describes a **serial bus** or pathway between one or more peripheral devices and your computer's **microprocessor**. Many peripheral devices now come equipped to meet IEEE 1394. FireWire and other IEEE 1394 implementations provide:

- A simple common plug-in serial connector on the back of your computer and on many different types of peripheral devices

- A thin serial cable rather than the thicker parallel cable you now use to your printer, for example

- A very high-speed rate of data transfer that will accommodate multimedia applications (100 and 200 megabits per second today; with much higher rates later)

- Hot-plug and **plug and play** capability without disrupting your computer

- The ability to chain devices together in a number of different ways without terminators or complicated set-up requirements

In time, IEEE 1394 implementations are expected to replace and consolidate today's serial and parallel interfaces, including **Centronics parallel**, **RS-232C**, and Small Computer System Interface (**SCSI**). The first products to be introduced with FireWire include **digital camera**s, digital video disks (**DVD**s), digital video tapes, digital camcorders, and music systems. Because IEEE 1394 is a **peer-to-peer** interface, one camcorder can dub to another without being plugged into a computer. With a computer equipped with the socket and bus capability, any device (for example, a video camera) can be plugged in while the computer is running.

Briefly How It Works

There are two levels of interface in IEEE 1394, one for the **backplane** bus within the computer and another for the point-to-point interface between device and computer on the serial cable. A simple bridge connects the two environments. The backplane bus supports 12.5, 25, or 50 megabits per second data transfer. The cable interface supports 100, 200, or 400 megabits per second. Each of these interfaces can handle any of the possible data rates and change from one to another as needed.

The serial bus functions as though devices were in slots within the computer sharing a common memory space. A 64-bit device address allows a great deal of flexibility in configuring devices in chains and trees from a single socket.

IEEE 1394 provides two types of data transfer: asynchronous and **isochronous**. Asynchronous is for traditional load-and-store applications where data transfer can be initiated and an application interrupted as a given length of data arrives in a **buffer**. Isochronous data transfer ensures that data flows at a pre-set rate so that an application can handle it in a timed way. For multimedia applications, this kind of data transfer reduces the need for buffering and helps ensure a continuous presentation for the viewer.

The 1394 standard requires that a device be within 4.5 meters of the bus socket. Up to 16 devices can be connected in a single chain, each with the 4.5 meter maximum (before signal attenuation begins to occur) so theoretically you could have a device as far away as 72 meters from the computer.

Another new approach to connecting devices, the Universal Serial Bus (**USB**), provides the same "hot plug" capability as the 1394 standard. It's a less expensive technology but data transfer is limited to 12 Mbps (million bits per second). Small Computer System Interface offers a high data transfer rate (up to 40 megabytes per second) but requires address preassignment and a device terminator on the last device in a chain. FireWire can work with the latest internal computer **bus** standard, Peripheral Component Interconnect (**PCI**), but higher data transfer rates may require special design considerations to minimize undesired buffering for transfer rate mismatches.

firmware

Firmware is programming that is inserted into programmable read-only memory (programmable **ROM**), thus becoming a permanent part of a computing device. Firmware is created and tested like software (using microcode simulation). When ready, it can be distributed like other software and, using a special user interface, installed in the programmable read-only memory by the user. Firmware is sometimes distributed for printers, modems, and other computer devices.

IBM prefers the term **microcode**.

first mover

In the business world, a first mover is a company that aims to gain an advantageous and perhaps insurmountable market position by being the first to establish itself in a given market. Since the arrival of the World Wide Web, many new companies (called "start-ups" until their **IPO**) have established themselves as first movers in their respective marketplace on the Web. Perhaps the quintessential example of being a first mover on the Web is Yahoo, which provided early Web users with the first popular directory and search engine. Although Yahoo has competition from Alta Vista, Google, and several other companies, its well-entrenched position as the one that got there first along with its easy-to-remember brand name and aggregation of content combine to make it difficult to compete with.

Other examples of first movers include Amazon.com (books), Travelocity (airline tickets), and eBay (online auctions). Although each of these has encountered competition, their early arrival and commitment to becoming the predominant owner of their market has seemed to assure their success.

One of the usual creeds of companies that attempt to be a first mover and command a market niche is "go big or stay home (**GOBOSH**)." Once a first mover has become established, the fact that someone has already arrived becomes in itself a **barrier to entry** for prospective competitors.

fixed wireless

Fixed wireless refers to the operation of **wireless** devices or systems in fixed locations such as homes and offices. Fixed wireless devices usually derive their electrical power from the utility mains, unlike **mobile wireless** or **portable wireless** which tend to be battery-powered. Although mobile and portable systems can be used in fixed locations, efficiency and **bandwidth** are compromised compared with fixed systems. Mobile or portable, battery-powered wireless systems can serve as emergency backups for fixed systems in case of a power blackout or natural disaster.

The technology for wireless connection to the Internet is as old as the Internet itself. Amateur radio operators began "patching" into telephone lines with fixed, mobile, and portable two-way voice radios in the middle of the 20th century. A wireless modem works something like an amateur-radio "phone patch," except faster. High-end fixed wireless employs broadband modems that bypass the telephone system and offer Internet access hundreds of times faster than twisted-pair hard-wired connections or cell-phone modems.

Some of the most important assets of fixed wireless are as follows.

- Subscribers can be added or moved (to a certain extent) without modifying the infrastructure.
- Subscribers in remote areas can be brought into a network without the need for stringing new cables or optical fibers across the countryside.
- Broad bandwidth is possible because there are no wires or cables to introduce **reactance** into the connection (reactance limits bandwidth by preventing signals higher than a certain **frequency** from efficiently propagating).
- As the number of subscribers increases, the connection cost per subscriber goes down.

flag

In programming, a flag is a predefined **bit** or bit sequence setting in a small data area that is used by a program either to remember something or to leave a sign for another program. For example, a three-bit flags field or data area in a message being exchanged by two programs might be set to one of three bit configurations or flags:

001 (meaning "I'm a self-contained message")
011 (meaning "I'm one of several chunks of data in this message")
111 (meaning "I'm the last chunk of data in this message")
Flags have many uses.

flamebait

On the Internet, flamebait is a "posting" or note on a **Web site** discussion forum, an online **bulletin board**, a **Usenet newsgroup**, or other public forum that is intended to elicit the extremely strong responses characteristic of **flaming** and active public discussions. To be effective, flamebait should be a bit subtle (but not too subtle) so that potential flamers will "take the bait." This term is similar to **troll**, which is an effort to get a reaction from readers but not necessarily for the purpose of eliciting flames.

Sometimes flamebait is used just to get a discussion started.

flaming

On the Internet, flaming is giving someone a verbal lashing in public. Often this is on a **Usenet** newsgroup but it could be on a Web forum or perhaps even as e-mail with copies to a distribution list. Unless in response to some rather obvious **flamebait**, flaming is poor **netiquette**. Certain issues tend to provoke emphatically stated responses, but flaming is often directed at a self-appointed expert rather than at the issues or information itself and is sometimes directed at unwitting but opinionated **newbie**s who appear in a newsgroup.

flanging

Flanging is an **audio** process that combines two copies of the same **signal**, with the second delayed slightly, to produce a swirling effect. The process originated before digital effect

boxes and computer editing were available. The effect, invented in the early 1950s by Les Paul and later used by artists such as Jimi Hendrix and The Beatles, was originally created using two tape recorders.

Here's how the nondigital process worked: While the original sound was being played from Tape Recorder #1, a second copy of the same audio material was played back from Tape Recorder #2. This process alone creates a hollow sound caused by the slight irregularities in the phase relationship of the audio waveforms. To get the flanging effect, the speed of the second recording was altered slightly. This was done most often by pressing a finger lightly on the tape reel's "flange," the large metal circle that surrounds and contains the tape on its hub. This created a time delay in addition to the phase differences, making the effect more pronounced.

Today, digital simulations of the process have replaced the flanging effect that was created using reel-to-reel tape recorders. The basic concept remains the same. The software or hardware device delays a copy of the source audio, but instead uses a low frequency **oscillator** (LFO) to vary the speed of the copy's playback. (The oscillator moves in the range of 1-20 cycles per seconds to get the effect.) Feeding the processed signal back into the device to be processed again can get a more intense effect.

Guitarist Les Paul invented flanging. He and Mary Ford first made it popular in the early 1950s. Les Paul also invented the solid body electric guitar and many sound techiques in use today. The first completely digital electronic flanging unit was the Delta Lab Research CompuEffectron, introduced in the 1970s.

Flash

Flash, a popular authoring software developed by Macromedia, is used to create **vector graphics**-based animation programs with full-screen navigation interfaces, graphic illustrations, and simple interactivity in an antialiased, resizable file format that is small enough to stream across a normal modem connection. The software is ubiquitous on the Web, both because of its speed (vector-based animations, which can adapt to different display sizes and resolutions, play as they download) and for the smooth way it renders graphics. Flash files, unlike animated but rasterized **GIF** and **JPEG** files, are compact, efficient, and designed for optimized delivery.

flash memory

Flash memory (sometimes called "flash RAM") is a type of constantly-powered **nonvolatile memory** that can be erased and reprogrammed in units of memory called *blocks*. It is a variation of electrically erasable programmable read-only memory (**EEPROM**) which, unlike flash memory, is erased and rewritten at the byte level, which is slower than flash memory updating. Flash memory is often used to hold

control code such as the Basic Input/Output System (**BIOS**) in a personal computer. When BIOS needs to be changed (rewritten), the flash memory can be written to it in block (rather than byte) sizes, making it easy to update. On the other hand, flash memory is not useful as random access memory (**RAM**) because RAM needs to be addressable at the byte (not the block) level.

Flash memory gets its name because the microchip is organized so that a section of memory cells are erased in a single action or "flash." The erasure is caused by Fowler-Nordheim tunneling in which electrons pierce through a thin **dielectric material** to remove an electronic charge from a *floating gate* associated with each memory cell. Intel offers a form of flash memory that holds two bits (rather than one) in each memory cell, thus doubling the capacity of memory without a corresponding increase in price.

Flash memory is used in digital cellular phones, digital cameras, LAN switches, **PC Card** for notebook computers, digital set-up boxes, embedded controllers, and other devices.

flat file

Also see **flat file system**, an entirely different term.

A flat file is a **file** containing **record**s that have no structured interrelationship. The term is frequently used to describe a textual document from which all word processing or other structure characters or **markup** have been removed. In usage, there is some ambiguity about whether such markings as line breaks can be included in a "flat file." In any event, many users would call a Microsoft Word document that has been saved as "text only" a "flat file." The resulting file contains records (lines of text of a certain uniform length) but no information, for example, about what size to make a line that is a title or that a program could use to format the document with a table of contents.

Another form of flat file is one in which table data is gathered in lines of ASCII text with the value from each table cell separated by a comma and each row represented with a new line. This type of flat file is also known as a **comma-separated values file** (CSV) file.

In *SQL for Dummies*, an introduction to **Structured Query Language**, Allen G. Taylor notes that the advantage of a flat file is that it takes up less space than a structured file. However, it requires the application to have knowledge of how the data is organized within the file. By using SQL and a **database** (rather than a collection of files in a file system), a user or an application is free from having to understand the location and layout of data (for example, the length of each item of data, its type of data, and its relationship to other data items).

In relational databases, *flat file* is sometimes used as a synonym for a *relation*.

flat file system

Also see **flat file**, an entirely different term.

A flat file system is a system of files in which every **file** in the system must have a different name. In Windows 95 and most other **operating systems** today, files are managed in a hierarchical file system with a hierarchy of directories and subdirectories, each containing a number of files (or subdirectories). The operating system allows more than one file to have the same name as long as it is stored in a different directory. Early versions of the Macintosh and DOS operating systems used a flat file system.

The term *flat file directory* is used to describe a file directory that can contain only files (no subdirectories).

flexible transistor

A flexible transistor is one which, unlike present, rigidly-structured **transistor**s, can be successfully used in packages that can be curled up, wrapped, or bent, a quality that will enable users to—for example—have a display screen that can be rolled up. In October 1999, IBM announced that they had developed a very thin, flexible and inexpensive type of transistor that could actually be sprayed onto plastic.

Cherie Kagan, a materials scientist at IBM, led a study that was featured in the journal *Science*. Kagan wrote that the combination of an inorganic **semiconductor** that conducts electricity and an organic material that modulates the structure makes the procedure possible at room temperature. Researchers used a compound composed of an organic material, phenethylammonium, and an inorganic material, tin iodide. The two materials were combined in separate layers, to create a coating thinner than a human hair. Current research is exploring other materials that could be used in the same fashion.

Currently available transistors are made of materials that must undergo high-temperature processing, and consequently can only be placed on heat-resistant surfaces. The flexible transistor could be used to replace the amorphous silicon used in computer displays. Future applications of the technology could include, among numerous other possibilities, a computer screen that could be rolled up and carried in the user's pocket.

flip chip-pin grid array

See "FC-PGA"

floating point unit

An floating point unit (FPU), also known as a *numeric coprocessor*, is a **microprocessor** or special circuitry in a more general microprocessor that manipulates numbers more quickly than the basic microprocessor your computer uses. It does so by having a special set of instructions that focus entirely on large mathematical operations. A floating point

unit is often built into today's personal computers, but it is needed only for special applications such as graphic image processing or display. Personal computers that don't have floating point units can sometimes handle software that requires them by installing a floating point **emulator**.

Floating point numbers are numbers that are carried out to a certain decimal position (such as 2.17986). They are stored in three parts: the *sign* (plus or minus), the *significant* or *mantissa* which is the digits that are meaningful, and the *exponent* or order of magnitude of the significant, which determines the place to which the decimal point floats. Floating point numbers are binary (expressed in powers of 2).

Some software you might download from the World Wide Web, such as Macromedia's **Shockwave**, may require that your computer have a floating point unit. If it doesn't, you may be able to download an FPU emulator that will fool the software into thinking you have one.

floating-point operations per second

See "FLOPS"

floating-point unit

See "floating point unit"

flooding

In a **network**, flooding is the forwarding by a **router** of a **packet** from any **node** to every other node attached to the router except the node from which the packet arrived. Flooding is a way to distribute routing information updates quickly to every node in a large network. It is also sometimes used in **multicast** packets (from one source node to many specific nodes in a real or virtual network).

The Internet's Open Shortest Path First (**OSPF**) protocol, which updates router information in a network, uses flooding.

floppy

See "diskette"

FLOPS

In computers, FLOPS are floating-point operations per second. Floating-point is, according to IBM, "a method of encoding real numbers within the limits of finite precision available on computers." Using floating-point encoding, extremely long numbers can be handled relatively easily. A floating-point number is expressed as a basic number or *mantissa*, an exponent, and a number base or *radix* (which is often assumed). The number base is usually ten but may also be 2. Floating-point operations require computers with floating-point *registers*. The computation of floating-point numbers is often required in scientific or real-time processing applications and FLOPS is a common measure for any computer that runs these applications.

In larger computers and parallel processing, computer operations can be measured in **megaflops**, **gigaflops**, and **teraflops**. Some computer scientists have at least begun to think about **petaflops**.

flow control

Flow control is the management of data flow between computers or devices or between nodes in a network so that the data can be handled at an efficient pace. Too much data arriving before a device can handle it causes data overflow, meaning the data is either lost or must be retransmitted. For serial data transmission locally or in a network, the **Xon/Xoff** protocol can be used. For **modem** connections, either Xon/ Xoff or CTS/RTS (Clear to Send/Ready to Send) commands can be used to control data flow.

In a network, flow control can also be applied by refusing additional device connections until the flow of traffic has subsided.

flowchart

A flowchart is a formalized graphic representation of a program logic sequence, work or manufacturing process, organization chart, or similar formalized structure. In computer programming, flowcharts were formerly used to describe each processing path in a program (the main program and various subroutines that could be branched to). Programmers were admonished to always flowchart their logic rather than carry it in their heads. With the advent of object-oriented programming (**OOP**) and visual development tools, the traditional program flowchart is much less frequently seen. However, there are new flowcharts that can be used for the data or class modeling that is used in object-oriented programming.

Traditional program flowcharting involves the use of simple geometric symbols to represent the beginning or end of a program (an oval), a process (a rectangle), a decision (a diamond), or an I/O process (a parallelogram). These symbols are defined in **ANSI** x 3.5 and **ISO** 1028.

flux

Flux is the presence of a force field in a specified physical medium, or the flow of energy through a surface. In electronics, the term applies to any **electrostatic field** and any **magnetic field**. Flux is depicted as "lines" in a plane that contains or intersects electric charge poles or magnetic poles. Three examples of *flux lines* are shown in the illustration.

Drawing A shows the geometric orientation of the lines of flux in the vicinity of an electrically charged object. The intensity of the field is inversely proportional to the separation between the lines of flux. The *flux density*, and hence the electrostatic field strength, decreases as the distance from the charged object increases. Electrostatic flux density is inversely proportional to the distance from the charge center.

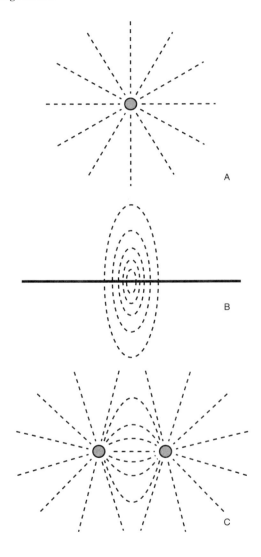

Drawing B illustrates flux lines surrounding a current-carrying conductor as they appear in a plane perpendicular to the conductor. As with the flux surrounding an electrically charged object, the separation between the flux lines increases as the distance from the conductor increases. Magnetic flux density is inversely proportional to the distance from a current-carrying conductor, as measured in a plane perpendicular to the conductor.

Drawing C shows the general orientation of the lines of flux of an electrostatic field between two oppositely charged poles in a plane containing the centers of both poles. In a magnetic field between opposite poles, the flux lines have the same general shape and orientation, so this drawing also applies to that situation. The flux density is greatest near the poles. The flux density is considerable along and near a line connecting the poles. As the distance from the line connecting the poles increases, the flux density decreases.

Flux lines are intangible; they cannot be seen. But they can be observed indirectly, and they produce demonstrable effects. If you place iron filings on a sheet of paper and place the paper on a magnet so both magnetic poles are near the paper, the filings line up in a pattern resembling illustration C. This demonstration is common in school science classes.

FM

See "frequency modulation"

FMP

See "FileMaker"

fnord

Certain words are intended to be undefinable and "fnord" is one of them. First used in Robert Anton Wilson' trilogy, *The Illuminati Papers*, fnord has developed a group of devotees that meet at certain pages in **cyberspace** to celebrate the word's sense of the apparent but indefinite. The editors of whatis.com have spent far too much chasing the meaning of this elusive term, and this is what we are left with:

- Fnord is the space between the pixels on your screen.
- Fnord is the "ooo" in varooom of race cars.
- Fnord is the smallest number greater than zero.
- Fnord keeps a spare eyebrow in his pocket.

In Wilson's trilogy (based on reports from users), truth is revealed to those who know where to look. The enlightened can see *fnord* in the empty spaces between unjustified columns of text in newspapers and magazines. Called sticky spots, these spaces are not really blank, but contain fnord, visible only to those privy to heavily guarded secrets and occult powers. Fans of the novel began using the word as a private joke and the concept spread to many who had never read the book but had no trouble discovering new places where *fnord* must clearly exist.

folder

In the Windows, Macintosh, and some other operating systems, a folder is a named collection of related **files** that can be retrieved, moved, and otherwise manipulated as one entity. **Mainframe** operating systems such as **OS/390** and most **UNIX**-based operating systems use the term **directory** rather than folder.

font

A font is a set of printable or displayable **text characters** in a specific style and size. The type design for a set of fonts is the **typeface** and variations of this design form the *typeface family*. Thus, Helvetica is a typeface family, Helvetica italic is a typeface, and Helvetica italic 10-point is a font. In practice, *font* and *typeface* are often used without much precision, sometimes interchangably.

An *outline font* is a software typeface that can generate a scalable range of font sizes. A **bitmap** *font* is a digital representation of a font that is already fixed in size or a limited set of sizes. The two most popular outline font software programs on today's computers are TrueType and Adobe's Type 1. TrueType fonts come with both Windows and Macintosh operating systems. However, Type 1 is a standard outline font (ISO 9541). Both TrueType and Type 1 fonts can be used by Adobe's PostScript printers (although Adobe says that Type 1 fonts makes fuller use of the PostScript language).

Independent developers and graphic designers create new typefaces for both TrueType and Type 1. Adobe states that there are over 30,000 Type 1 fonts available. Fonts (in addition to those that come with your computer) can be purchased as individual typeface families or in typeface collections.

foo

Just as economists sometimes use the term "widget" as the ultimate substitute for "something" that is being measured, programmers tend to use the term "foo" (pronounced FOO) as a universal substitute for something real when discussing ideas or presenting examples. Suppose you are defining a **template** for any group of programmers to follow when creating a new user command, you might specify that the **syntax** for the command should be in the form:

Command foo (arg1, arg2)

where the "foo" would mean "the name you give to this command." In other words, "foo" is a nonsense kind of placeholder for some value that will be provided when using this template to define a real command. (And the "arg1" and "arg2" are arguments or information you would define that would be passed along with the command.) Because "foo" has no rational meaning of its own and because "foo" is conventionally used as such a placeholder, the idea will be clear to any programmer.

Foo or any such word used this way is formally known as a *metasyntactic variable*. Eric Raymond, probably the world's greatest authority on foo and other metasyntactic variables, also lists qux, waldo, fred, xyzzy, and thud among others that are occasionally used. Although foo is the **canonical** metasyntactic variable, Raymond notes that cultures outside the United States have their own preferences. Fred, barney, and wombat seem common in the U.K. Toto, tata, titi, and tutu reportedly are used by the French. Blarg and wibble are used in New Zealand.

The origin of foo seems wrapped in the mists of time, but Raymond observes (and we remember) that in Bill Holman's comic strip of the 1930-50 era, Smokey Stover, the letters "FOO" commonly appeared, unexplained and as a kind of running gag, on license plates, in picture frames, and on the backs of sandwich board signs.

foot-pound-second system of units

The foot-pound-second (fps) system of units is a scheme for measuring dimensional and material quantities. The fundamental units are the foot for length, the pound for weight, and the second for time.

The fps system has two variants, known as the American version and the Imperial version. Neither scheme is often used by scientists nowadays; the International System of Units (**SI**) is preferred. However, fps units are used to some extent by the general public, especially in the U.S.

Foot
One foot (1 ft) represents a length of 12 inches. The inch was originally defined as the length of three typical barleycorns laid end-to-end. A foot was also approximately equal to three hand widths or $2/3$ of a cubit (the distance from an average person's elbow to the tips of the fingers). Nowadays, a foot is considered to be 0.3048 meter, where the **meter** is the fundamental unit of displacement in the **metric system** and International System of Units (SI).

Pound
One pound (1 lb) is the force that produces an acceleration of 32.1740 feet per second squared (32.1740 ft/sec^2) when applied against a known standard mass. The acceleration of 32.1740 ft/sec^2 is approximately the value of the earth's gravitational acceleration at 45 degrees north latitude.

Second
One second (1 s or 1 sec) is the time that elapses during 9.192631770×10^9 cycles of the radiation produced by the transition between two levels of Cesium 133. It is also 1/86,400 of a mean solar day. (There are 60 seconds in a minute, 60 minutes in an hour, and 24 hours in a day; $60 \times 60 \times 24 = 86,400$.)

footprint

In information technology, a footprint is the amount of space a particular unit of hardware or software occupies. Marketing brochures frequently state that a new hardware control unit or desktop display has a "smaller footprint," meaning that it occupies less space in the closet or on your desk. More recently, the term is used to describe microcomponents that take less space inside a computer and software that occupies less space in **memory** (whether **random access memory** or **read-only memory**).

footprinting

1) In the study of DNA, footprinting is the method used to identify the nucleic acid sequence that binds with proteins.

2) In computers, footprinting is the process of accumulating data regarding a specific network environment, usually for the purpose of finding ways to intrude into the environment. Footprinting can reveal system vulnerabilities and improve the ease with which they can be exploited.

Footprinting begins by determining the location and objective of an intrusion. Once this is known, specific information about the organization is gathered using non-intrusive methods. For example, the organization's own Web page may provide a personnel directory or employee bios, which may prove useful if the hacker needs to use **social engineering** to reach the objective. Conducting a whois query on the Web provides the domain names and associated networks related to a specific organization.

Other information obtained may include learning the Internet technologies being used; the operating system and hardware being used; IP addresses; e-mail addresses and phone numbers; and policies and procedures.

for your information

This term is included in our list of chat term and other **chat abbreviations**.

FYI (pronounced EFF-WAI-AI) is an abbreviation for "For your information," and is often used in forwarding **e-mail** or printed material to colleagues or friends. It usually means that information is simply being shared and that no immediate action is required or expected.

force

Force is an action that causes a free object with nonzero, finite mass to accelerate, relative to a non-accelerating frame of reference. Examples of force include the thrust of a rocket engine, the impetus that causes a car to speed up when you step on the accelerator, and the pull of gravity on your body. Force is the effect that produces the phenomenon of weight for objects with nonzero, finite **mass**.

The standard unit of force is the **newton**. One newton is equivalent to one kilogram-meter per second squared (kg · m/s^2 or kg · m · s^{-2}). Alternatively, the **dyne** is sometimes used to express force; one dyne is equal to one gram-centimeter per second squared (g · cm/s^2 or g · cm · s^{-2}). To convert from newtons to dynes, mulitiply by 100,000 (10^5). Conversely, multiply by 0.00001 (10^{-5}).

Force is defined in mechanical terms, but it can result from the action of electric fields, magnetic fields, thermal heating, particle bombardment, and various other phenomena. In all cases, force has the property of imparting acceleration to particles or objects. If an object is anchored so it cannot move, a force against it produces pressure.

Also see **impulse**, **mass**, **newton**, **pressure**, **weight**, **SI** (International System of Units), and **Table of Physical Units**.

form factor

1) In computers, the form factor (sometimes hyphenated as form-factor) is the size, configuration, or physical arrangement of a computer hardware object. The term is commonly used in describing the size and/or arrangement of a computer case or chassis or one of its internal components such as a *daughterboard*. If you see the term applied to software or programming, it will usually mean the size of the program or the amount of memory required to run the program effectively. When used to refer to the size of a free-standing computer or other device, it's close in meaning to **footprint**.

2) In electric motor terminology, a form factor is the amount of rectified current emitted from a direct current (DC) power source and is expressed as a ratio of the root-mean square (rms) value of the current to the average (av) current or Irms/Iav. If the form factor differs much from pure non-pulsating DC (a value of 1.0), it indicates the possibility that motor and brush life will be shorter.

format

1) A format (noun, pronounced FOHR-mat) is a pre-established layout for data. **Program**s accept data as input in a certain format, process it, and provide it as output in the same or another format. All data is stored in some format with the expectation that it will be processed by a program that knows how to handle that format. Generically, data formats tend to fall into **bitmap**s (strings of 0s and 1s) that describe images or sound patterns (or both), text formats (in which usually each **byte** value is mapped to a **character**), and numeric data formats (used by spreadsheet and other **database** programs).

Hard disk and other storage devices are also said to be formatted when their space has been organized and divided into pieces that can be controlled for convenient storage and access. For example, a hard disk may be formatted into areas called sectors, tracks, and clusters.

2) To format (verb) a document or file for printing or displaying is to add the necessary information to it so that the output device will know how to present the output.

3) To format (verb) a hard disk or diskette is to set up the space divisions on the medium and initiate a space allocation table that will know exactly how to reach each bit of data that may be stored there later.

Fortezza

Fortezza, Italian for "fortress," is a family of security products trademarked by the US government's National Security Agency. Fortezza-enabled security is popular with government agencies, especially the military. The Fortezza crypto card (similar to a **PC Card**) works in PCs loaded with Talisman software, which **encrypts** every file on the computer. Then, only a user with the correct Fortezza crypto card and password can gain access to the encrypted data.

Currently, the main use of Fortezza is for encrypting e-mail, but Fortezza security is also included in digital cellular telephones, Web browsers, and databases. The technology hasn't gained widespread acceptance in the corporate world, primarily because many businesses simply don't trust government-developed technology. However, the latest version of Microsoft's Windows 2000 Web server, the Internet Information Server (**IIS**), supports Fortezza.

Forth

Forth is a high-level programming language that works like reverse Polish notation (RPN) on a calculator. It differs from typical programming languages, like **C** and **FORTRAN**, because it is interactive. Using Forth, a user doesn't need to recompile a program to add new functionality; the user defines a new command and it is available right away.

Forth has one of the simplest syntaxes of any computer language. The syntax can be stated as: Forth code is a bunch of words with spaces between them. Each word is equivalent to a function or subroutine in a language like C. Functions are executed in the order they appear in the code. The following statement is an example that could appear in a Forth program: WAKE.UP EAT.BREAKFAST WORK EAT.DINNER PLAY SLEEP. The dots between WAKE and UP and the other words simply connect the two words to make one. Forth word names can have any combination of letters, numbers, or punctuation.

FORTRAN

FORTRAN (FORmula TRANslation) is a third-generation (**3GL**) programming language that was designed for use by engineers, mathematicians, and other users and creators of scientific algorithms. It has a very succinct and spartan syntax. Today, the **C** language has largely displaced FORTRAN.

forward carbon copy

See "Fcc"

forward compatible

Also see **backward compatible**.

Forward compatible describes a system that is designed in such a way that it fits with planned future versions of itself. Forward compatible usually implies that dependent systems, such as application programs developed for a specific operating system, will work in a satisfactory way in future as well as in the current, forward compatible system.

Forward DNS lookup

Forward DNS lookup is using an Internet **domain name** to find an **IP address**. Reverse DNS lookup is using an Internet IP address to find a domain name. When you enter the address for a Web site at your browser (the address is formally called the Uniform Resource Locator, or **URL**), the address is transmitted to a nearby **router** which does a forward DNS lookup in a routing table to locate the IP address. Forward **DNS** (which stands for domain name system) lookup is the more common lookup since most users think in terms of domain names rather than IP addresses. However, occasionally you may see a Web page with a URL in which the domain name part is expressed as an IP address (sometimes called a **dot address**) and want to be able to see its domain name. An Internet facility that lets you do either forward or reverse DNS lookup yourself is called **nslookup**. It comes with some operating systems or you can download the program and install it in your computer.

FPGA

See "field-programmable gate array"

FPM DRAM

Prior to newer forms of DRAM, FPM DRAM (Fast Page Mode DRAM) was the most common kind of dynamic RAM in personal computers. *Page mode* DRAM essentially accesses a row of RAM without having to continually respecify the row. A row access strobe (**RAS**) signal is kept active while the column access strobe (**CAS**) signal changes to read a sequence of contiguous memory cells. This reduces access time and lowers power requirements. Clock timings for FPM DRAM are typically 6-3-3-3 (meaning 3 clock cycles for access setup, and 3 clock cycles for the first and each of three successive accesses based on the initial setup).

FpML

Financial Products Markup Language (FpML) is a business information exchange standard based on Extensible Markup Language (**XML**) that enables **business-to-business** over-the-counter (OTC) financial derivative transactions using the **Internet**. FpML is used between participating companies for communicating OTC transaction details, within a company for the purpose of sharing OTC transaction information, and between a participating company and an outside firm offering a service related to the OTC transaction. FpML is freely licensed and, because it is independent of the software or hardware used by participating companies, ensures **interoperability**. FpML focuses on interest rate swaps and Forward Rate Agreements (FRA) but will eventually be used for all aspects of OTC transactions.

OTC contracts shared between two companies are highly customized based on the needs of the parties involved. For this reason, prior to the arrival of the Internet and XML, it was not feasible to efficiently carry out the OTC contract process online. Today, companies can electronically structure and negotiate the terms of an OTC contract, execute and confirm the contract, communicate settlement details, and analyze risks using FpML.

Chase Manhattan Bank has reviewed and adopted FpML for their OTC Interest Rate Derivative applications. Fuji Capital Markets Corporation used the FpML definition to design their XML-based FRA confirmation prototype. And J.P. Morgan developed an FpML interest rate swap prototype application. Organizations participating in the development and application of FpML include Bank of America, Citigroup, Deutsche Bank, IBM, PricewaterhouseCoopers, J.P. Morgan, Reuters, and UBS Warburg.

fps system of units

See "foot-pound-second system of units"

FPU

See "floating point unit"

FQDN

See "fully-qualified domain name"

fractional T-1

A fractional T-1 or T-3 line is a T-1 or T-3 digital phone line in the North American **T-carrier system** that is leased to a customer at a fraction of its data-carrying capacity and at a correspondingly lower cost. A T-1 line contains 24 channels, each with a data transfer capacity of 64 **Kbps**. The customer can rent some number of the 24 channels. The transmission method and speed of transfer remain the same. Overhead bits and framing are still used, but the unrented channels simply contain no data.

T-3 lines (which offer 672 64 Kbps channels) are also sometimes offered as a fractional service. T-1 and fractional T-1 service are sometimes advertised as "point-to-point" service (from the customer to the service provider).

FRAD

A FRAD (frame relay access device; also sometimes referred to as a frame relay assembler/dissembler) is a box that encapsulates (puts **frame relay** header and trailer information on) outgoing data **packets** and decapsulates (removes frame relay headers and trailers from) incoming packets. Frame relay is a system in which data (in the form of packets) from different protocols such as **Ethernet**, X.25, and the Internet Protocol (**IP**) is collected into "frames" or larger units of transmission that are delivered in burst-like mode over a switched connection that is, however, a "permanent virtual circuit" (PVC). A PVC ensures that packets always arrive in the right order so that they can be

reassembled successfully. Since frame relay does not take responsibility for error detection, the FRAD sometimes includes error detection.

The FRAD is a box, usually close to the user, that provides the interface between the user and a network that uses frame relay. The FRAD is sometimes included as part of a **router**.

FRAM

FRAM (ferroelectric RAM) is **random access memory** that combines the fast read and write access of dynamic RAM (**DRAM**)—the most common kind of personal computer memory—with the ability to retain data when power is turned off (as do other non-volatile memory devices such as **ROM** and **flash memory**). Because FRAM is not as dense (can not store as much data in the same space) as DRAM and **SRAM**, it is not likely replace these technologies. However, because it is fast memory with a very low power requirement, it is expected to have many applications in small consumer devices such as personal digital assistants (**PDA**s), handheld phones, power meters, and **smart cards**, and in security systems. FRAM is faster than flash memory. It is also expected to replace **EEPROM** and SRAM for some applications and to become a key component in future **wireless** products.

In spite of its name, ferroelectric RAM does not contain iron. Today's FRAM uses lead zirconate titanate (PZT); other materials are being considered. The main developer of FRAM is Ramtron International.

frame

See **frames** for the use of multiple Web pages on a single display screen.

1) In telecommunications, a frame is **data** that is transmitted between network points as a unit complete with addressing and necessary **protocol** control information. A frame is usually transmitted **serial bit** by bit and contains a header field and a trailer field that "frame" the data. (Some control frames contain no data.)

Here is a simple representation of a frame, based on the frame used in the **frame relay** access standard:

———Header———   ———Trailer———

| Flag (01111110) | Address field | Information (data) field (0-4096 bytes) | Frame check sequence | Flag (01111110) |

In the figure above, the flag and address fields constitute the header. The frame check sequence and second flag fields constitute the trailer. The information or data in the frame may contain another encapsulated frame that is used in a higher-level or different protocol. In fact, a frame relay frame typically carries data that has been framed by an earlier protocol program.

2) In time-division multiplexing (**TDM**), a frame is a complete cycle of events within the time division period.

3) In film and video recording and playback, a frame is a single image in a sequence of images that are recorded and played back.

4) In computer video display technology, a frame is the image that is sent to the display image rendering devices. It is continuously updated or refreshed from a *frame buffer*, a highly accessible part of video RAM.

5) In artificial intelligence (**AI**) applications, a frame is a set of data with information about a particular object, process, or image. An example is the iris-print visual recognition system used to identify users of certain bank automated teller machines. This system compares the frame of data for a potential user with the frames in its database of authorized users.

frame rate

In motion pictures, television, and in computer video displays, the frame rate is the number of frames or images that are projected or displayed per second. Frame rates are used in synchronizing **audio** and pictures, whether film, television, or video. In motion pictures and television, the frame rates are standardized by the Society of Motion Picture and Television Editors (SMPTE). SMPTE Time Code frame rates of 24, 25 and 30 frames per second are common, each having uses in different portions of the industry. The professional frame rate for motion pictures is 24 frames per second and, for television, 30 frames per second (in the U.S.).

In computer video streams, the frame rate describes playback rates for AVI and QuickTime movies. The video playback rate for an AVI or QuickTime movie directly relates to the perceived smoothness of its playback. The higher the number of frames playing per second, the smoother the video playback appears to the user. Lower rates result in a choppy playback. (As a reference point, film uses 24 frames per second to allow the viewer to perceive smooth playback.) Several factors affect the actual frame rate you get on your computer. For example, your PC **processor** or graphics hardware may only be capable of playing 10−15 frames per second without acceleration.

In developing motion pictures, television, and video, frame rate information is used as a reference for audio signals. The recorded signal includes information about location in time using a 24-hour clock, and individual frame numbers. This signal is used to synchronize multiple audio and video machines during the recording and editing process. Using a master synchronizing device, the operator can issue location commands from a central machine and have all slaved machine follow the master.

frame relay

Frame relay is a telecommunication service designed for cost-efficient data transmission for intermittent traffic between local area networks (**LAN**s) and between end-points in a wide area network (**WAN**). Frame relay puts data

in a variable-size unit called a **frame** and leaves any necessary error correction (retransmission of data) up to the end-points, which speeds up overall data transmission. For most services, the network provides a permanent virtual circuit (**PVC**), which means that the customer sees a continous, dedicated connection without having to pay for a full-time leased line, while the service provider figures out the route each frame travels to its destination and can charge based on usage. An enterprise can select a level of service quality—prioritizing some frames and making others less important. Frame relay is offered by a number of service providers, including AT&T. Frame relay is provided on **fractional T-1** or full **T-carrier system** carriers. Frame relay complements and provides a mid-range service between **ISDN**, which offers **bandwidth** at 128 Kbps, and Asynchronous Transfer Mode (**ATM**), which operates in somewhat similar fashion to frame relay but at speeds from 155.520 Mbps or 622.080 Mbps.

Frame relay is based on the older **X.25** packet-switching technology which was designed for transmitting **analog** data such as voice conversations. Unlike X.25 which was designed for analog signals, frame relay is a **fast packet technology**, which means that the protocol does not attempt to correct errors. When an error is detected in a frame, it is simply "dropped" (thrown away). The end points are responsible for detecting and retransmitting dropped frames. (However, the incidence of error in digital networks is extraordinarily small relative to analog networks.)

Frame relay is often used to connect local area networks with major backbones as well as on public wide area networks and also in private network environments with leased lines over T-1 lines. It requires a dedicated connection during the transmission period. It's not ideally suited for voice or video transmission, which requires a steady flow of transmissions. However, under certain circumstances, it is used for voice and video transmission.

Frame relay relays packets at the **Data Link layer** of the Open Systems Interconnection (**OSI**) model rather than at the **Network layer**. A frame can incorporate packets from different protocols such as **Ethernet** and **X.25**. It is variable in size and can be as large as a thousand bytes or more.

frame relay access device

See "FRAD"

frames

See **frame** for additional meanings.

In creating a Web site, frames is the use of multiple, independently controllable sections on a Web presentation. This effect is achieved by building each section as a separate **HTML** file and having one "master" HTML file identify all of the sections. When a user requests a Web page that uses frames, the address requested is actually that of the "master" file that defines the frames; the result of the request is that multiple HTML files are returned, one for each visual section. Links in one frame can request another file that will appear in another (or the same) frame. A typical use of frames is to have one frame containing a selection menu in one frame and another frame that contains the space where the selected (linked to) files will appear.

Frames, originally created by Netscape as an HTML extension and now part of the **HTML 4.0**, specification are defined with HTML FRAMESET and FRAME tags. Sites that use frames need to create an alternative scheme of pages for requests from browsers that don't support them and possibly for users that prefer a non-frames version.

Free Software Foundation

The Free Software Foundation (FSF) was founded in 1983 along with its demonstration **GNU** project. Richard Stallman, an MIT professor, had worked as a student on projects where software was freely exchanged without copying or modifying stipulations. Why, he asked himself and others, should software users be prohibited from copying it for friends, looking at the source code and copying it, and redistributing the results? Taking this idea to the group level, Stallman and others created the FSF and set out to demonstrate that an entire **operating system** could be developed and shared freely. The result was the **UNIX**-like GNU, which, in August 1996, became complete by adding a **kernel**.

The "free" does not mean at no charge. The Free Software Foundation does charge an initial distribution price for GNU. "Free" refers to the use the person who acquires the software has with it. The Free Software Foundation believes that individuals and society would benefit from, and moreover have the right to study a program's source code to discover how it works, to make changes that enhance the program in some way, and to redistribute and even to sell improved versions to others as long as they in turn make their software free of reuse restrictions.

freemail

Freemail is a service that provides free **e-mail** delivery to anyone in exchange for exposure to advertising on the site where you request your e-mail and, in some cases, for some personal information. Assuming you currently get e-mail as part of your Web **browser**, the advantage to freemail is that you can log in to the freemail provider from anyone's Internet access and don't have to use your own **Internet service provider** or remember its phone number. If you don't have your own Web account, you can use someone else's computer but still get your own e-mail from the freemail Web site. For example, college students who don't have their own computers or Internet access can register for freemail and send and receive e-mail at their nearest **cybercafe**.

Unlike your regular e-mail interface which is a separate program (although it comes integrated with the popular Web browsers), most freemail providers require using a forms interface with a Web site that is more time-consuming than programs designed expressly for e-mail. In general, freemail is simpler but offers fewer services than when using the e-mail program with your browser and being connected to your own Internet access provider.

Among the most popular freemail providers are Hotmail, apparently the most popular and according to a recent RelevantKnowledge survey, the 13th most visited site on the Web; Rocketmail, also very popular; and Juno, one of the first freemail providers. Juno requires you to use its own software interface rather than a Web browser.

freeware

Freeware is programming that is offered at no cost. However, it is copyrighted so that you can't incorporate its programming into anything you may be developing. The least restrictive "no-cost" programs are uncopyrighted programs that are in the public domain. These include a number of small UNIX programs. When reusing public domain software in your own programs, it's good to know the history of the program so that you can be sure it really is in the public domain.

Also see **liteware**, **postcardware**, and **shareware**.

free-space optics

Free-space optics (FSO), also called free-space photonics (FSP), refers to the transmission of modulated visible or infrared (**IR**) beams through the atmosphere to obtain **broadband** communications. **Laser** beams are generally used, although non-lasing sources such as light-emitting diodes (**LED**s) or IR-emitting diodes (IREDs) will serve the purpose.

The theory of FSO is essentially the same as that for **fiber optic** transmission. The difference is that the energy beam is collimated and sent through clear air or space from the source to the destination, rather than guided through an optical fiber. If the energy source does not produce a sufficiently parallel beam to travel the required distance, collimation can be done with lenses. At the source, the visible or IR energy is modulated with the data to be transmitted. At the destination, the beam is intercepted by a photodetector, the data is extracted from the visible or IR beam (demodulated), and the resulting signal is amplified and sent to the hardware.

FSO systems can function over distances of several kilometers. As long as there is a clear line of sight between the source and the destination, communication is theoretically possible. Even if there is no direct line of sight, strategically positioned mirrors can be used to reflect the energy. The beams can pass through glass windows with little or no attenuation (as long as the windows are kept clean!).

Although FSO systems can be a good solution for some broadband networking needs, there are limitations. Most significant is the fact that rain, dust, snow, fog, or smog can block the transmission path and shut down the network.

free-space photonics

See "free-space optics"

frequency

For an oscillating or varying **current**, frequency is the number of complete cycles per second in alternating current direction. The standard unit of frequency is the **hertz**, abbreviated Hz. If a current completes one cycle per second, then the frequency is 1 Hz; 60 cycles per second equals 60 Hz (the standard alternating-current utility frequency in some countries).

Larger units of frequency include the **kilohertz** (kHz) representing thousands (1,000's) of cycles per second, the **megahertz** (MHz) representing millions (1,000,000's) of cycles per second, and the **gigahertz** (GHz) representing billions (1,000,000,000's) of cycles per second. Occasionally the **terahertz** (THz) is used; 1 THz = 1,000,000,000,000 cycles per second. Note that these prefixes represent specific powers of 10, in contrast to the prefixes for multiples of bytes, which represent specific powers of 2.

Computer clock speed is generally specified in megahertz and, more recently, in gigahertz.

Frequency is important in **wireless** communications, where the frequency of a signal is mathematically related to the **wavelength**. If f is the frequency of an **electromagnetic field** in free space as measured in megahertz, and w is the wavelength as measured in meters, then

$w = 300/f$

and conversely

$f = 300/w$

Also see the definitions of **signal** and **electromagnetic radiation spectrum**.

frequency division multiple access

See "FDMA"

frequency modulation

Also see **modulation** and frequency-shift keying (**FSK**).

Frequency modulation (FM) is a method of impressing data onto an alternating-current (**AC**) **wave** by varying the instantaneous **frequency** of the wave. This scheme can be used with **analog** or **digital** data.

In analog FM, the frequency of the AC **signal** wave, also called the *carrier*, varies in a continuous manner. Thus, there are infinitely many possible carrier frequencies. In *narrowband FM*, commonly used in two-way **wireless** communications, the instantaneous carrier frequency varies by up to 5 kilohertz (kHz, where 1 kHz = 1000 **hertz** or alternating cycles per second) above and below the frequency of the carrier with no modulation. In *wideband FM*, used in wireless broadcasting, the instantaneous frequency varies by up to several megahertz (MHz, where 1 MHz = 1,000,000 Hz). When the instantaneous input wave has positive **polarity**, the carrier frequency shifts in one direction; when the instantaneous input wave has negative polarity, the carrier frequency shifts in the opposite direecion. At every instant in time, the extent of carrier-frequency shift (the *deviation*) is directly proportional to the extent to which the signal amplitude is positive or negative.

In digital FM, the carrier frequency shifts abruptly, rather than varying continuously. The number of possible carrier frequency states is usually a power of 2. If there are only two possible frequency states, the mode is called frequency-shift keying (**FSK**). In more complex modes, there can be four, eight, or more different frequency states. Each specific carrier frequency represents a specific digital input data state.

Frequency modulation is similar in practice to phase modulation (**PM**). When the instantaneous frequency of a carrier is varied, the instantaneous phase changes as well. The converse also holds: When the instantaneous phase is varied, the instantaneous frequency changes. But FM and PM are not exactly equivalent, especially in analog applications. When an FM receiver is used to demodulate a PM signal, or when an FM signal is intercepted by a receiver designed for PM, the audio is distorted. This is because the relationship between frequency and phase variations is not linear; that is, frequency and phase do not vary in direct proportion.

frequency-division multiplexing

Frequency-division multiplexing (FDM) is a scheme in which numerous signals are combined for transmission on a single communications line or channel. Each signal is assigned a different frequency (subchannel) within the main channel.

A typical **analog** Internet connection via a **twisted pair** telephone line requires approximately three kilohertz (3 kHz) of **bandwidth** for accurate and reliable data transfer. Twisted-pair lines are common in households and small businesses. But major telephone cables, operating between large businesses, government agencies, and municipalities, are capable of much larger bandwidths.

Suppose a long-distance cable is available with a bandwidth allotment of three megahertz (3 **MHz**). This is 3,000 kHz, so in theory, it is possible to place 1,000 signals, each 3 kHz wide, into the long-distance channel. The circuit that does

this is known as a **multiplexer**. It accepts the input from each individual end user, and generates a signal on a different frequency for each of the inputs. This results in a high-bandwidth, complex signal containing data from all the end users. At the other end of the long-distance cable, the individual signals are separated out by means of a circuit called a demultiplexer, and routed to the proper end users. A two-way communications circuit requires a multiplexer/demultiplexer at each end of the long-distance, high-bandwidth cable.

When FDM is used in a communications network, each input signal is sent and received at maximum speed at all times. This is its chief asset. However, if many signals must be sent along a single long-distance line, the necessary bandwidth is large, and careful engineering is required to ensure that the system will perform properly. In some systems, a different scheme, known as **time-division multiplexing**, is used instead.

frequency-hopping spread spectrum

Frequency hopping is one of two basic **modulation** techniques used in **spread spectrum signal** transmission. It is the repeated switching of frequencies during radio transmission, often to minimize the effectiveness of "electronic warfare"—that is, the unauthorized interception or jamming of telecommunications. It also is known as frequency hopping-code division multiple access (**FH-CDMA**).

Spread spectrum modulation techniques have become more common in recent years. Spread spectrum enables a signal to be transmitted across a **frequency band** that is much wider than the minimum **bandwidth** required by the information signal. The transmitter "spreads" the energy, originally concentrated in **narrowband**, across a number of frequency band channels on a wider **electromagnetic spectrum**. Benefits include improved privacy, decreased narrowband interference, and increased signal capacity.

In an FH-CDMA system, a transmitter "hops" between available frequencies according to a specified **algorithm**, which can be either random or preplanned. The transmitter operates in synchronization with a receiver, which remains tuned to the same center frequency as the transmitter. A short burst of data is transmitted on a narrowband. Then, the transmitter tunes to another frequency and transmits again. The receiver thus is capable of hopping its frequency over a given bandwidth several times a second, transmitting on one frequency for a certain period of time, then hopping to another frequency and transmitting again. Frequency hopping requires a much wider bandwidth than is needed to transmit the same information using only one carrier frequency.

The spread spectrum approach that is an alternative to FH-CDMA is direct sequence code division multiple access (**DS-CDMA**), which chops the data into small pieces and spreads them across the frequency domain. FH-CDMA devices use less power and are generally cheaper, but the performance of DS-CDMA systems is usually better and more reliable. The biggest advantage of frequency hopping lies in the coexistence of several access points in the same area, something not possible with direct sequence.

Certain rules govern how frequency-hopping devices are used. In North America, the Industrial, Scientific, and Medial (ISM) waveband is divided into 75 hopping channels, with power transmission not to exceed 1 watt on each **channel**. These restrictions ensure that a single device does not consume too much bandwidth or linger too long on a single frequency.

The Federal Communications Commission (**FCC**) has amended rules to allow frequency hopping spread spectrum systems in the unregulated 2.4 **GHz** band. The rule change is designed to allow wider bandwidths, thus enabling Internet devices to operate at higher speeds and fostering development of **wireless LAN**s and wireless cable modems.

Movie star Hedy Lamarr is generally credited as co-originator of the idea of spread spectrum transmission. She and her pianist were issued a patent for the technique during World War II. They discovered the technique using a player piano to control the frequency hops, and envisioned it as a way to provide secure communications during wartime. The pair never made any money off the invention and their patent eventually expired. Sylvania introduced a similar concept in the 1950s and coined the term "spread spectrum."

frequency-shift keying

See also phase-shift keying (**PSK**).

Frequency-shift keying (FSK) is a method of transmitting **digital** signals. The two **binary** states, logic 0 (low) and 1 (high), are each represented by an **analog waveform**. Logic 0 is represented by a wave at a specific **frequency**, and logic 1 is represented by a wave at a different frequency. A **modem** converts the binary data from a computer to FSK for transmission over telephone lines, cables, **optical fiber**, or wireless media. The modem also converts incoming FSK signals to digital low and high states, which the computer can "understand."

The FSK mode was introduced for use with mechanical teleprinters in the mid-1900s. The standard speed of those machines was 45 **baud**, equivalent to about 45 bits per second. When personal computers became common and networks came into being, this signaling speed was tedious. Transmission of large text documents and programs took hours; image transfer was unknown. During the 1970s, engineers began to develop modems that ran at faster speeds, and the quest for ever-greater **bandwidth** has continued ever since. Today, a standard telephone modem operates at thousands of bits per second. Cable and wireless modems work at more than 1,000,000 bps (one megabit per second or 1 Mbps), and optical fiber modems function at many Mbps. But the basic principle of FSK has not changed in more than half a century.

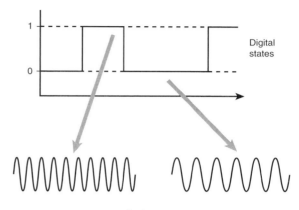

Digital states

Analog waves

frequently-asked questions

The FAQ (pronounced FAK) or list of "frequently-asked questions" (and answers) has become a feature of the Internet. The FAQ seems to have originated in many of the **Usenet** groups as a way to acquaint new users with the rules. Today, there are thousands of FAQs on the World Wide Web.

To see the range and variety of topics for which FAQs have been written, go to Yahoo or any major **search engine**, and enter "faq" or "faqs" in the search entry box. To find a FAQ on a subject of interest (for example, hedgehogs), enter "faq and hedgehogs"(without the quotes). Also note that the number of subjects on which you will NOT find is FAQ is also large. The most useful FAQs are often found at a Web site you've discovered through other search approaches.

front-end

Front-end and back-end are terms used to characterize program interfaces and services relative to the initial user of these interfaces and services. (The "user" may be a human being or a program.) A "front-end" **application** is one that application users interact with directly. A "back-end" application or program serves indirectly in support of the front-end services, usually by being closer to the required resource or having the capability to communicate with the required resource. The back-end application may interact directly with the front-end or, perhaps more typically, is a program called from an intermediate program that mediates front-end and back-end activities.

For example, the Telephony Application Program Interface (TAPI) is sometimes referred to as a front-end interface for telephone services. A program's TAPI requests are mapped

by Microsoft's TAPI Dynamic Link Library programs (an intermediate set of programs) to a "back-end" program or **driver** that makes the more detailed series of requests to the telephone hardware in the computer.

As another example, a front-end application might interface directly with users and forward requests to a remotely-located back-end program in another computer to get requested data or perform a requested service. Relative to the **client/server** computing model, a front-end is likely to be a client and a back-end to be a server.

frontside bus

See also: **backside bus**

In a personal computer with an Intel **processor chipset** that includes a Dual Independent Bus (DIB), the frontside **bus** is the data path and physical interface between the processor and the main memory (**RAM**).

FRR

See "fast retransmit and recovery"

FSB

See "frontside bus"

FSK

See "frequency-shift keying"

FSML

See "Financial Services Markup Language"

FSO

See "free-space optics"

FSP

On the Internet, an FSP (full-service provider) is an application service provider (**ASP**) that offers a wide range of Web-based information technology services to other companies—including the planning and creation of a Web presence, providing needed software applications, and **hosting** and maintaining the site. The FSP aims to consolidate and streamline a customer's Internet operations and to offer a single point of contact for an array of services.

FTP

See "File Transfer Protocol"

FTP cable

FTP (foil screened twisted pair) cable is a cable containing multiple pairs of copper wire enclosed in a sheath of aluminum foil. It's used in wiring systems in buildings or other environments where heavy noise adjacent to the wire might cause interference. The foil provides insulation not afforded by **UTP** (unshielded twisted pair), the most common kind of structural wiring. The disadvantage of FTP is that it requires somewhat more care in "earthing" (grounding) than UTP and electrical impedances must be matched when connecting to UTP. Typically, FTP might be used in a factory setting and UTP in an office setting.

FTTC

See "fiber to the curb"

FUBAR

FUBAR is an acronym that originated in the military to stand for the words "f***ed up beyond all repair." This is often softened to "fouled up beyond all repair" in reference to hardware. The programming and documentation equivalent is "fouled up beyond all recognition." Sometimes the last word is "recovery" or "reconciliation" or "reason."

In a Virtual Address Extension (VAX), the acronym FUBAR has been adapted to refer to the words "failed UniBus address register." Some programmers apparently managed to sneak this by humorless higher-ups, and the term stuck.

F.U.B.A.R. International is the name of a film company founded in 1989 by several businessmen seeking adventure. They went on location to film natural disasters. Some of the disasters were artificially created, especially avalanches, which could be triggered by explosives. Company executives vacation in Vail, Colorado every year, and have become local celebrities. These days, F.U.B.A.R. International markets clothing and novelty items.

Because **foo**, an unrelated term, appears phonetically in FUBAR, programmers have taken to using both *foo* and **bar** as metasyntactic variables when two such variables are needed.

FUD

FUD (Fear, Uncertainty, and Doubt) is the term for any strategy intended to make a company's customers insecure about future product plans with the purpose of discouraging them from adopting competitors' products. For example, "You can try using X instead of our product, but you may lose all your data."

full-duplex

Full-duplex data transmission means that data can be transmitted in both directions on a signal carrier at the same time. For example, on a local area network with a technology that has full-duplex transmission, one workstation can be sending data on the line while another workstation is receiving data. Full-duplex transmission necessarily implies a bidirectional line (one that can move data in both directions).

full-service provider

See "FSP"

fully-qualified domain name

A fully-qualified domain name (FQDN) is that portion of an Internet Uniform Resource Locator (**URL**) that fully identifies the **server** program that an Internet request is addressed to. The FQDN includes the second-level **domain name** (such as "whatis.com") and any other levels (for example, "www.whatis.com" or "www1.somesite.com"). The prefix "http://" added to the fully-qualified domain name completes the URL.

Fullerene

A Fullerene is a pure carbon molecule composed of at least 60 **atom**s of carbon. Because a Fullerene takes a shape similar to a soccer ball or a geodesic dome, it is sometimes referred to as a *buckyball* after the inventor of the geodesic dome, Buckminster Fuller, for whom the Fullerene is more formally named. Fullerenes are seen as promising components of future micro-electromechanical systems (**MEMS**) and in **nanotechnology**. Current work on the Fullerene is largely theoretical and experimental.

NASA, in co-operation with geochemist Lynn Becker from the University of Hawaii, has discovered naturally-occuring Fullerenes in ancient meteorites that hit the Earth. Recent research has suggested many uses for Fullerenes, including medical applications, superconductors, and fiber-optics.

function

In information technology, the term *function* (pronounced FUHNK-shun) has a number of meanings. It's taken from the Latin "functio"—to perform.

1) In its most general use, a function is what a given **entity** does in being what it is.

2) In **C** language and other programming, a function is a named procedure that performs a distinct service. The language statement that requests the function is called a *function call*. Programming languages usually come with a **compiler** and a set of "canned" functions that a programmer can specify by writing language statements. These provided functions are sometimes referred to as *library routines*. Some functions are self-sufficient and can return results to the requesting program without help. Other functions need to make requests of the **operating system** in order to perform their work.

3) In mathematics, a function is an association between two sets of values in which each element of one set has one assigned element in the other set so that any element selected becomes the independent variable and its associated element is the dependent variable. Thus, in:

$$y = f(x)$$

y is said to be a function of x.

4) In a hardware device, a function is one complete physical movement that has a discernible consequence relative to the device's purposes. In a printer, for example, this might be a carriage return or a line feed.

function key

On a computer **keyboard**, a function key is one of a sequence of special keys labeled "F1" or higher (usually up to "F12" on most keyboards) that can be assigned a specific use in order to save a user time. Some function keys have uses assigned by an operating system such as Windows and somewhat different uses when interacting with an application program. In some cases, the meaning of a function key can be described by the user to an application program.

A function key may be assigned a second use when it is pressed in combination with the shift key, ALT key, or Control key. A function key is sometimes considered to be a form of **hot key**.

functional programming

1) Functional programming is a style of programming that emphasizes the evaluation of expressions rather than the execution of commands. **Erlang programming language** is described as a functional programming language. Erlang avoids the use of global variables that can be used in common by multiple functions since changing such a variable in part of a program may have unexpected effects in another part.

2) In an earlier definition from the **ITU-TS**, functional programming is "a method for structuring programs mainly as sequences of possibly nested function procedure calls." A function procedure is a relatively simple program that is called by other programs and derives and returns a value to the program that called it.

functional specification

A functional specification (or sometimes *functional specifications*) is a formal document used to describe in detail for software developers a product's intended capabilities, appearance, and interactions with users. The functional specification is a kind of guideline and continuing reference point as the developers write the programming code. (At least one major product development group used a "Write the manual first" approach. Before the product existed, they wrote the user's guide for a word processing system, then declared that the user's guide was the functional specification. The developers were challenged to create a product that matched what the user's guide described.) Typically, the functional specification for an application program with a series of interactive windows and dialogs with a user would show the visual appearance

of the user interface and describe each of the possible user input actions and the program response actions. A functional specification may also contain formal descriptions of user tasks, dependencies on other products, and usability criteria. Many companies have a guide for developers that describes what topics any product's functional specification should contain.

For a sense of where the functional specification fits into the development process, here are a typical series of steps in developing a software product:

- **Requirements**. This is a formal statement of what the product planners informed by their knowledge of the marketplace and specific input from existing or potential customers believe is needed for a new product or a new version of an existing product. Requirements are usually expressed in terms of narrative statements and in a relatively general way.

- **Objectives**. Objectives are written by product designers in response to the Requirements. They describe in a more specific way what the product will look like. Objectives may describe architectures, protocols, and standards to which the product will conform. *Measurable objectives* are those that set some criteria by which the end product can be judged. Measurability can be in terms of some index of customer satisfaction or in terms of capabilities and task times. Objectives must recognize time and resource constraints. The development schedule is often part or a corollary of the Objectives.

- **Functional specification**. The functional specification (usually *functional spec* or just *spec* for short) is the formal response to the objectives. It describes all *external* user and programming interfaces that the product must support.

- **Design change requests**. Throughout the development process, as the need for change to the functional specification is recognized, a formal change is described in a design change request.

- **Logic specification**. The structure of the programming (for example, major groups of code modules that support a similar function), individual code modules and their relationships, and the data parameters that they pass to each other may be described in a formal document called a logic specification. The logic specification describes *internal interfaces* and is for use only by the developers, testers, and, later, to some extent, the programmers that service the product and provide code fixes to the field.

- **User documentation**. In general, all of the preceding documents (except the logic specification) are used as source material for the technical manuals and online information (such as help pages) that are prepared for the product's users.

- **Test plan**. Most development groups have a formal test plan that describes test cases that will exercise the programming that is written. Testing is done at the module (or unit) level, at the component level, and at the system level in context with other products. This can be thought of as *alpha testing*. The plan may also allow for **beta test**. Some companies provide an early version of the product to a selected group of customers for testing in a "real world" situation.

- **The final product**. Ideally, the final product is a complete implementation of the functional specification and design change requests, some of which may result from formal testing and beta testing. The cycle is then repeated for the next version of the product, beginning with a new Requirements statement, which ideally uses feedback from customers about the current product to determine what customers need or want next.

Most software makers adhere to a formal development process similar to the one described above. The hardware development process is similar but includes some additional considerations for the outsourcing of parts and verification of the manufacturing process itself.

functionality

In information technology, functionality (from Latin *functio* meaning "to perform") is the sum or any aspect of what a product, such as a software application or computing device, can do for a user.

A product's functionality is used by marketers to identify product features and enables a user to have a set of capabilities. Functionality may or may not be easy to use.

Also see **function**.

Furby

Furby (pronounced FURR-bee) is the name of an electronic toy, five inches tall, that is covered with simulated fur, has big eyes and ears, a vocabulary of over 200 words, and a limited ability to react to its environment. Created by toy designer Dave Hampton and made by Tiger Electronics. Furby was designed to appeal to 7- to 9-year old girls but, based on early sales, the toy also appeals to anyone fascinated by technology. Each Furby contains **embedded systems programming** and six sensors so that it can:

- Dance, wiggle, and squirm in reaction to pokes and prods

- Talk in English and in its own language, Furbish

- Tell when the lights go out, when it's being petted, or when music is played—and react accordingly

- Hold a conversation with other Furbies (using **infrared transmission** signals)

- Catch another Furby's cold

Furby requires batteries and costs about $30 US.

futzing

Futzing or "futzing around" is unstructured, playful, often experimental interaction between a human being and a computer, product, or any technology, sometimes but not always with a productive purpose in mind. Futzing can be pure play, learning by trying, or an attempt to achieve breakthrough insights. When someone says "Oh, I'm just futzing," they may be just wasting time or they may be working on a hard problem or they may not even know.

fuzzy logic

Fuzzy logic is an approach to computing based on "degrees of truth" rather than the usual "true or false" (1 or 0) **Boolean** logic on which the modern computer is based. The idea of fuzzy logic was first advanced by Dr. Lotfi Zadeh of the University of California at Berkeley in the 1960s. Dr. Zadeh was working on the problem of computer understanding of natural language. Natural language (like most other activities in life and indeed the universe) is not easily translated into the absolute terms of 0 and 1. (Whether everything is ultimately describable in binary terms is a philosophical question worth pursuing, but in practice much data we might want to feed a computer is in some state in between and so, frequently, are the results of computing.)

Fuzzy logic includes 0 and 1 as extreme cases of truth (or "the state of matters" or "fact") but also includes the various states of truth in between so that, for example, the result of a comparison between two things could be not "tall" or "short" but ".38 of tallness."

Fuzzy logic seems closer to the way our brains work. We aggregate data and form a number of partial truths which we aggregate further into higher truths which in turn, when certain thresholds are exceeded, cause certain further results such as motor reaction. A similar kind of process is used in artificial computer **neural network** and expert systems.

It may help to see fuzzy logic as the way reasoning really works and binary or Boolean logic is simply a special case of it.

fuzzy number

See also **fuzzy logic**.

A fuzzy number is a quantity whose value is imprecise, rather than exact as is the case with "ordinary" (single-valued) numbers. Any fuzzy number can be thought of as a function whose domain is a specified **set** (usually the set of real numbers) and whose range is the span of non-negative real numbers between, and including, 0 and 1000. Each numerical value in the domain is assigned a specific "grade of membership" where 0 represents the smallest possible grade, and 1000 is the largest possible grade.

In many respects, fuzzy numbers depict the physical world more realistically than single-valued numbers. Suppose, for example, that you are driving along a highway where the speed limit is 55 miles an hour (mph). You try to hold your speed at exactly 55 mph, but your car lacks "cruise control," so your speed varies from moment to moment. If you graph your instantaneous speed over a period of several minutes and then plot the result in rectangular coordinates, you will get a function that looks like one of the curves shown below.

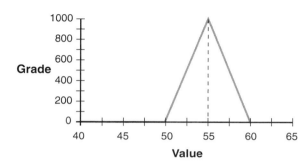

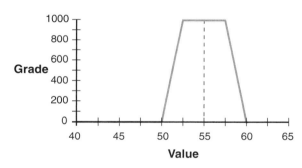

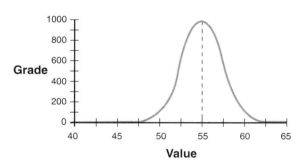

The curve at the top represents a triangular fuzzy number; the curve in the middle shows a trapezoidal fuzzy number; the curve at the bottom illustrates a bell-shaped fuzzy number. These three functions, known as *membership functions*, are all convex (the grade starts at zero, rises to a maximum, and then declines to zero again as the domain increases). However, some fuzzy numbers have concave, irregular, or even chaotic membership functions. There is no

restriction on the shape of the membership curve, as long as each value in the domain corresponds to one and only one grade in the range, and the grade is never less than 0 nor more than 1000.

Fuzzy numbers are used in statistics, computer programming, engineering (especially communications), and experimental science. The concept takes into account the fact that all phenomena in the physical universe have a degree of inherent uncertainty.

G.lite

For more information, see **Digital Subscriber Line**.

G.Lite is the informal name for what is now a standard way to install Asymmetric Digital Subscriber Line (**ADSL**) service. Also known as Universal ADSL, G.Lite makes it possible to have Internet connections to home and business computers at up to 1.5 **Mbps** (millions of bits per second) over regular phone lines. Even at the lowest downstream rate generally offered of 384 **Kbps** (thousands of bits per second), G.Lite is about seven times faster than regular phone service with a **V.90** modem and three times faster than an Integrated Services Digital Network (**ISDN**) connection. Upstream speeds from the computer are at up to 128 Kbps. (Theoretical speeds for ADSL are much higher, but the data rates given here are what is realistically expected.)

With G.Lite, your computer's analog-to-digital **modem** is replaced with an "ADSL modem" and the transmission from the phone company is **digital** rather than the analog tranmission of "plain old telephone service." G.Lite is also known as "splitterless DSL" because, unlike other DSL technologies, it does not require that a technician come to install a splitter, a device that separates voice from data signals, at the home or business (sometimes referred to as "the truck roll").

The G.Lite standard was developed by the Universal ADSL Working Group, whose members include major phone companies in the U.S. and globally, including Ameritech, Bell Atlantic, BellSouth, GTE, MCI, USWest, Sprint, SBC Communications, Deutsche Telekom, France Telecom, British Telecommunications, Singapore Telecom, and Nippon Telegraph and Telephone. Microsoft, Intel, and Compaq are also represented in the Working Group.

The telephone companies and ADSL are competing with the cable TV companies and the **cable modem**s to capture the market for fast Internet access. While phone companies conceded the early lead to the cable TV companies, most industry experts believe that G.lite and ADSL will eventually become the dominant technology for most homes and businesses.

The G.Lite standard is officially known as G.992.2.

G

See "gauss"

gain

See "amplification factor"

gallium arsenide field-effect transistor

Also see **metal-oxide semiconductor field-effect transistor**.

A gallium arsenide field-effect transistor (GaAsFET) is a specialized type of field-effect transistor (**FET**) that is used in **amplifier** circuits at very-high, ultra-high, and **microwave** radio frequencies. This spans the **electromagnetic radiation spectrum** from approximately 30 **MHz** up to the infrared band. The GaAsFET is known for its sensitivity, and especially for the fact that it generates very little internal noise. This is because **gallium arsenide** has exceptional carrier mobility. The **electron**s and **hole**s move through the **semiconductor** material easily and fast. The GaAsFET is a *depletion-mode* device. This means that it conducts when no **voltage** is applied to the control electrode (gate), and when a voltage appears at the gate, the channel conductivity decreases.

In weak-signal **wireless** communications and broadcast reception, GaAsFET devices perform better than most other types of FET. Some types of GaAsFET are used as radio-frequency (**RF**) power amplifiers. GaAsFETs are employed in space communications, in radio astronomy, and in experiments conducted by amateur radio operators.

gallium arsenide

Gallium arsenide (chemical formula GaAs) is a **semiconductor** compound used in some **diode**, **field-effect transistor**s (FETs), and **integrated circuit**s (ICs). The charge carriers, which are mostly **electron**s, move at high speed among the **atom**s. This makes GaAs components useful at ultra-high radio frequencies, and in fast electronic switching applications. GaAs devices generate less **noise** than most other types of semiconductor components. This is important in weak-signal amplification.

Gallium arsenide is used in the manufacture of **light-emitting diode**s (LEDs), which are found in optical communications and control systems. Gallium arsenide can replace silicon in the manufacture of linear ICs and **digital** ICs. Linear (also called **analog**) devices include **oscillator**s and **amplifier**s. Digital devices are used for electronic switching, and also in computer systems.

gallium nitride

See also **gallium arsenide**.

Gallium nitride (GaN) is a **semiconductor** compound expected to make possible miniaturized, high-power **wireless** transmitters. These transmitters will be combined with sensitive receivers into telephone sets capable of

directly accessing communications **satellite**. The compound can also be used in light-emitting diodes (**LED**s) and other semiconductor devices.

The advantages of GaN devices include high output power with small physical volume, and high efficiency in power amplifiers at ultra-high and **microwave** radio frequencies.

The main problem with GaN technology is cost. A special process is required to grow a GaN crystal or wafer on which **transistor**s and integrated circuits (**IC**s) can be fabricated. Once the process is implemented on a large scale, the cost should come down.

GaN

See "gallium nitride"

Gantt chart

A Gantt chart is a horizontal bar chart developed as a production control tool in 1917 by Henry L. Gantt, an American engineer and social scientist. Frequently used in project management, a Gantt chart provides a graphical illustration of a schedule that helps to plan, coordinate, and track specific tasks in a project. Gantt charts may be simple versions created on graph paper or more complex automated versions created using project management applications such as Microsoft Project or Excel.

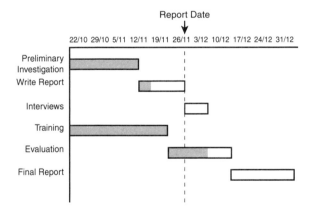

A Gantt chart is constructed with a horizontal axis representing the total time span of the project, broken down into increments (for example, days, weeks, or months) and a vertical axis representing the tasks that make up the project (for example, if the project is outfitting your computer with new software, the major tasks involved might be: conduct research, choose software, install software). Horizontal bars of varying lengths represent the sequences, timing, and time span for each task. Using the same example, you would put "conduct research" at the top of the verticle axis and draw a bar on the graph that represents the amount of time you expect to spend on the research, and then enter the other

tasks below the first one and representative bars at the points in time when you expect to undertake them. The bar spans may overlap, as, for example, you may conduct research and choose software during the same time span. As the project progresses, secondary bars, arrowheads, or darkened bars may be added to indicate completed tasks, or the portions of tasks that have been completed. A vertical line is used to represent the report date.

Gantt charts give a clear illustration of project status, but one problem with them is that they don't indicate task dependencies—you cannot tell how one task falling behind schedule affects other tasks. The **PERT chart**, another popular project management charting method, is designed to do this. Automated Gantt charts store more information about tasks, such as the individuals assigned to specific tasks, and notes about the procedures. They also offer the benefit of being easy to change, which is helpful. Charts may be adjusted frequently to reflect the actual status of project tasks as, almost inevitably, they diverge from the original plan.

garbage collecting

Garbage collecting is the recovery of pooled computer **storage** that is being used by a program when that program no longer needs the storage. This frees the storage for use by other programs (or processes within a program). It also ensures that a program using increasing amounts of pooled storage does not reach its quota (in which case it may no longer be able to function).

Some programming languages such as **Java** provide built-in garbage collecting so that the programmer does not have to write code for it.

garbage

In computers, garbage has two related meanings:

1) From a user's perceptual point-of-view, garbage is often used to mean anything on your display screen that looks unreadable or unviewable. This can include looking at a graphics file, such as a Web **Graphics Interchange Format** file, with a text reader. Although this is simply an instance of using the wrong program to view a perfectly good file, the viewer is likely to think that what's presented is "garbage."

2) From a programming point-of-view, garbage is data that has been placed in **random access memory** space obtained from the operating system that is no longer needed. Freeing the space for reuse is called "garbage collecting." In the past, programmers have had to write programs that explicitly requested storage and then returned it to the system when it was no longer needed. (Programs that neglect to return unused storage can be shut down by the operating system.) The term "garbage collecting" apparently was first used in the LISP programming language. **Java** is a newer

programming language that, like LISP, handles garbage-collecting for the program, freeing the programmer from being concerned about it.

gateway

A gateway is a **network** point that acts as an entrance to another network. On the Internet, a **node** or stopping point can be either a gateway node or a **host** (end-point) node. Both the computers of Internet users and the computers that serve pages to users are host nodes. The computers that control traffic within your company's network or at your local Internet service provider (**ISP**) are gateway nodes.

In the network for an **enterprise**, a computer **server** acting as a gateway node is often also acting as a **proxy server** and a **firewall** server. A gateway is often associated with both a **router**, which knows where to direct a given **packet** of data that arrives at the gateway, and a **switch**, which furnishes the actual path in and out of the gateway for a given packet.

gauss

The gauss (symbolized G) is the centimeter-gram-second (cgs) unit of magnetic flux density. A flux density of 1 G represents one **maxwell** per centimeter squared $(1 \ Mx - cm^{-2})$. The gauss was named for the German scientist Karl Friedrich Gauss.

The gauss is used when expressing the flux density produced by magnets of the sort commonly encountered in consumer products. The flux density of the earth's magnetic field at the surface is about 1 G. In industrial electromagnetics, the **tesla** (T), a much larger unit, is used to express magnetic flux density. The gauss is one ten-thousandth of a tesla $(1 \ G = 10^{-4} \ T)$.

Also see **magnetic field**, **tesla**, and **International System of Units**.

GB

See "gigabyte"

GBIC

See "gigabit interface converter"

Gbps

Gbps stands for *billions of bits per second* and is a measure of **bandwidth** on a digital data transmission medium such as **optical fiber**. With slower media and protocols, bandwidth may be in the Mbps (millions of bits or megabits per second) or the Kbps (thousands of bits or kilobits per second) range.

GDMO

GDMO (Guidelines for Definition of Managed Objects) is a standard for defining **object**s in a network in a consistent way. With a consistent "language" for describing such objects as workstations, LAN servers, and switches, programs can be written to control or sense the status of network elements throughout a network. Basically, GDMO prescribes how a network product manufacturer must describe the product formally so that others can write programs that recognize and deal with the product. Using GDMO, you describe the **class** or classes of the object, how the object behaves, its attributes, and classes that it may inherit.

GDMO is part of the Open Systems Interconnection (**OSI**) Common Management Information Protocol (**CMIP**) and also the guideline for defining network objects under the Telecommunications Management Network (**TMN**), a comprehensive and strategic series of international standards for network management. The object definitions created using GDMO and related tools form a Management Information Base (**MIB**). GDMO uses Abstract Syntax Notation One (**ASN.1**) as the rules for **syntax** and attribute encoding when defining the objects.

GDMO is specified in ISO/IEC standard 10165/x.722.

geek speak

Chat abbreviations could be considered a special branch of geek speak.

Geek speak is how the uninitiated refer to the jargon and special vocabulary used by those immersed in computers and other fields of information technology. Geek speak is usually something that someone else uses. (That person may be viewed as a **geek** or just someone who knows more than you.) As a person learns about computers, the terms they use become familiar and only the ones they haven't mastered yet continue to be geek speak. The term was used in press coverage of the 1998 (and ongoing) Microsoft antitrust case in which a great deal of industry jargon was heard from witnesses and in e-mail introduced as evidence.

Geek speak often sounds like normal English that doesn't quite make sense because familiar words have been given a new meaning. A **port** is no longer where a ship docks and a **spool** is no longer what thread comes on. And for that matter, a **thread** is no longer a thin strand of cotton. And executing a program is not at all the same thing as killing it.

geek

In computers and the Internet, a geek is a person who is inordinately dedicated to and involved with technology to the point of sometimes not appearing to be normal. Being a geek also implies a capability with the technology. Although historically, computer and Internet programming and hacking has been a male thing, there are now many "girl geeks." The term "hacker" generally connotes competence more strongly than "geek" does. The term "geek" emphasizes dedication and weirdness, although recent use of the term suggests greater social acceptance and tolerance for geeks. (Historically, a geek was a circus person whose

role in the side-show was to bite off chicken's heads or perform other bizarre feats. Eric Raymond describes "computer geek" as "one who eats (computer) bugs for a living.")

The term seems to be used by many in the general populace for anyone who spends a lot of or too much time at a computer.

geekosphere

Assuming you're a computer, Internet, or programming **geek** at least some of the time, the geekosphere is the physical ambiance around you and your workstation monitor, including the pasted-up notes, inspirational quotes, family photos, software cheat templates, coffee cup(s), old cans of **Jolt**, mouse pad, pencils, diskettes, more notes, and so forth. The term was mentioned in a *Wired Magazine* article.

geekspeak

See "geek speak"

General Packet Radio Services

See "GPRS"

general protection fault

"General protection fault" (or *general protection error*) is a phrase that users of personal computers see when an application program they are running (for example, Microsoft Word or the Netscape Web browser) tries to access storage that is not designated for their use. An operating system (such as Windows 95) manages the use of random access memory (**RAM**) for its own needs and for those of the application programs that it manages. The application programs are actually managed as **task**. When a task attempts to write to a place in RAM that is outside its assigned storage area, the operating system requires that the task or application be closed. Users usually get a message that tells you this is happening, but there isn't much you can do about it other than to restart the program and hope it will run successfully the next time.

If an application program were to be able to write outside of its assigned storage area, it could overwrite other applications' or the operating system's instructions and data. (If that should happen, the operating system would "crash" or close down in some way and you would have to reboot the operating system.) Closing down the errant application protects other applications and the operating system.

A general protection fault is more likely to occur when you are trying out **beta test**-version software. However, even well-seasoned applications can cause a general protection fault because a user hits some combination of keys in quick succession that the programmer could not easily anticipate. A general protection fault can also occur because a system

setting is wrong. If you repeatedly encounter the same general protection fault message, record the details (you are usually given a string of digits that identify exactly where in storage the error is occurring) and call the company that makes the software that seems to be causing the message.

Generalized Markup Language

See "GML"

generic top-level domain name

See "gTLD"

genetic programming

Genetic programming is a model of programming which uses the ideas (and some of the terminology) of biological evolution to handle a complex problem. Of a number of possible programs (usually small program functions within a larger application), the most effective programs survive and compete or cross-breed with other programs to continually approach closer to the needed solution. Genetic programming is an approach that seems most appropriate with problems in which there are a large number of fluctuating variables such as those related to **artificial intelligence**. The genetic programming model is mostly used with the **LISP** and Scheme programming languages. However, it can also be used with **C** and other programming languages.

Genetic programming can be viewed as an extension of the *genetic algorithm*, a model for testing and selecting the best choice among a set of results, each represented by a **string**. Genetic programming goes a step farther and makes the program or "function" the unit that is tested. Two approaches are used to select the successful program— cross-breeding and the tournament or competition approach. A difficult part of using genetic programming is determining *the fitness function*, the degree to which a program is helping to arrive at the desired goal. A simple example of a task suited for genetic programming would be devising a program to fire a gun. The distance by which the bullet misses its target would determine the fitness function.

Genetic programming is a challenging new approach that requires a considerable learning investment for the programmer.

geographic information system

See "GIS"

George Boole

George Boole (1815-1864) was a British mathematician and is known as the founder of mathematical logic. Boole, who came from a poor family and was essentially a self-taught mathematician, made his presence known in the world of mathematics in 1847 after the publication of his book, "The

Mathematical Analysis of Logic." In his book, Boole successfully demonstrated that logic, as Aristotle taught it, could be represented by algebraic equations. In 1854, Boole firmly established his reputation by publishing "An Investigation of the Laws of Thought, on Which Are Founded the Mathematical Theories of Logic and Probabilities," a continuation of his earlier work.

In 1855 Boole, the first professor of mathematics at The College of Cork, Ireland, married Mary Everest, who is now known as a mathematician and teacher in her own right. Mary, who was 18 years younger than Boole, served as sounding-board and editor for her husband throughout their nine years of marriage. Unfortunately, Mary's poor choice of medical treatment may have hastened Boole's death. After getting caught in the rain and catching a cold, Boole was put to bed by his wife, who dumped buckets of water on him based on the theory that whatever had caused the illness would also provide the cure. (It seemed logical to her.) George and Mary had five daughters; the third daughter, Alicia Boole Stott, became well-known for her work in the visualization of geometric figures in hyperspace.

Boole's work in symbolic logic, collectively known as "Boolean algebra," is widely regarded to be based on the work of earlier mathematician G.W. Leibniz. Although Boole's work was well-received during his lifetime, it was considered to be "pure" mathematics until 1938, when **Claude Shannon** published his thesis at MIT. Shannon demonstrated that Boole's symbolic logic, as it applies to the representation of TRUE and FALSE, could be used to represent the functions of switches in electronic circuits. This became the foundation for **digital** electronic design, with practical applications in telephone switching and computer engineering.

Today, when using a search engine on the Internet, we use Boole's mathematical concepts to help us locate information by defining a relationship between the terms we enter. For instance, searching for George AND Boole would find every article in which both the word George and the word Boole appear. Searching for George OR Boole would find every article in which either the word George or the word Boole appears. We call this a **Boolean** search.

gesture recognition

Gesture recognition is human interaction with a computer in which human gestures, usually hand motions, are recognized by the computer. Recognizing gestures as input might make computers more accessible for the physically-impaired and make interaction more natural for young children. It could also provide a more expressive and nuanced communication with a computer. Several companies have developed prototype products. Gesture recognition is already being used for interaction with a **3-D** immersion environment.

A prototype motion processor developed by Toshiba allows a computer to recognize hand motions and to display them in real-time on the computer's display. Proposed applications include word processing using input with hand sign language, games, and other entertainment and educational approaches in which hand motion could result in multimedia effects.

Toshiba's motion processor works by emitting an **infrared transmission** light near the hand area and "reading" the light reflected back from the hand. Reflections from areas beyond the hand don't occur because the light is quickly dissipated over distance. The reflected light allows the computer to continuously build a 3-D motion image of the hand, which can be displayed or not.

Other forms of gesture recognition than hand gestures are being studied. Finger pointing is one area of study as a way to select or move objects around. Face tracking, eye motion, and lip reading are also being considered as ways to provide interaction. There have also been multimedia experiments in which the entire human body and its range of motions was used to produce computer effects.

ghost

The word "ghost" derives from Old English *gast* and means a disembodied spirit or soul. In information technology, the term has several special meanings:

1) Ghost, a product from Symantec, can clone (copy) the entire contents of a **hard disk** to another computer's hard disk, automatically formatting and partitioning the target disk. This product is especially useful where one system is to be replicated on a number of computers.

2) On the Web's live chat medium, the Internet Relay Chat (**IRC**), a ghost is a vacated user session that the server believes is still active.

3) Ghostscript is a program for **UNIX** systems that interprets a **Postscript** file (which is a file formatted for a Postscript printer) so that, using a related program, Ghostview, you can view it on a display screen.

ghost imaging

Also see **ghost**.

Ghost imaging is the copying of the contents of a computer's **hard disk** into a single compressed **file** or set of files (referred to as an *image*) so that the contents of the hard disk, including configuration information and applications, can be copied to the hard disk of other computers.

An example of ghost imaging software is Norton Ghost, a product from Symantec. Using this product, you can clone (copy) the entire contents of a hard disk to a portable medium such as a writeable CD or to a server. The portable image can then be used to set up each hard disk in other computers, automatically formatting and partitioning each target disk. Ghost imaging is useful where one system is to

be replicated on a number of computers in a classroom or for a team of notebook computer users who all need the same system and applications.

ghost site

Also see **ghost**.

A ghost site is a **Web site** that is no longer maintained but that remains available for viewing. Since many sites don't identify their date of last update, it's not always easy to tell whether a site is a ghost site or just resting. A ghost site is not to be confused with a retired or invisible site (one which doesn't exist anymore and results in a "Not found" message). It's possible to have a ghost site that continues to be useful or appealing because its content doesn't date easily.

A ghost site that for some reason seems to have moved to another location is a **zombie**.

GHz

See "gigahertz"

giant

In networks, a giant is a **packet**, **frame**, cell, or other transmission unit that is too large. Network protocols specify maximum and minimum sizes (and sometimes a single uniform size) for any transmission unit. For example, **ATM** packages all data into 53-byte cells. Any cell larger than that is discarded and recorded as a giant by network monitoring tools. The Remote Network Monitoring (**RMON**) standard information base for network adminstration calls them "oversize packets."

Also see **runt**.

giant magnetoresistive effect

GMR is the newest generation of **hard disk** drive **storage**. It provides almost three times the data density of its immediate predecessor, **magnetoresistive head technology**.

Disk storage technology strives to improve areal density—in other words, how much data can be packed into a given space. And where MR technology can store up to 3.3 **gigabyte**s per square inch, GMR squeezes in 10 gigabytes per square inch—over 40 gigabytes per drive.

As more data is squeezed into the same amount of space, the devices needed to accurately read the data also must keep pace. GMR is designed to pack as much data onto a disk that can be retrieved accurately—with as few moving parts as possible.

The technology is based on a discovery made by two scientists in the late 1980s. The two—Peter Gruenberg of Julich, Germany and Albert Fert of Paris—figured out that

materials made up of very thin, alternating layers of various metallic and nonmetallic elements experienced significant variations in **resistance**.

Disk drives that are based on GMR use these properties to help control a sensor that responds to very small rotating on the disk. The magnetic rotation yields a very large change in sensor resistance, which in turn provides a signal that can be picked up by the electric circuits in the drive.

GID

1) In a **UNIX** system, a GID (group ID) is a name that associates a system user with other users sharing something in common (perhaps a work project or a department name). It's often used for accounting purposes. A user can be a member of more than one group and thus have more than one GID. Any user using a UNIX system at a given time has both a user ID (UID) and a group ID (GID).

2) In Windows 95, a file with a ".gid" suffix is a global index file. Windows 95 sometimes creates these files to hold information about a help file (the global index file has the same name as the help file but with the .gid suffix) and stores them as hidden files in the same directory as the help files.

GIF

The GIF (the original and preferred pronunciation is DJIF; it stands for Graphics Interchange Format) is one of the two most common file **format**s for graphic images on the World Wide Web. The other is the **JPEG**.

On the Web and elsewhere on the Internet (for example, bulletin board services), the GIF has become a de facto standard form of image. The **LZW compression algorithm** used in the GIF format is owned by Unisys, and companies that make products that exploit the algorithm (including the GIF format) need to license its use from Unisys. In practice, Unisys has not required users of GIF images to obtain a license, although their licensing statement indicates that it is a requirement. Unisys says that getting a license from them does not necessarily involve a fee.

The GIF uses the 2D **raster** data type and is encoded in **binary**. There are two versions of the format, 87a and **GIF89a**. Version 89a (July, 1989) allows for the possibility of an **animated GIF**, which is a short sequence of images within a single GIF file. A **GIF89a** can also be specified for **interlaced GIF** presentation.

A patent-free replacement for the GIF, the Portable Network Graphics (**PNG**) format, has been developed by an Internet committee and major browsers support it or soon will. Meanwhile, many GIF downloaders and Web site builders on the Web continue to be ignorant of or indifferent to the requirement to get a license from Unisys for the use of their algorithm.

GIF89a

A GIF89a graphics file is an image formatted according to Graphics Interchange Format (**GIF**) Version 89a (July, 1989). There was an earlier Version, 87a, from May of 1987, but most images you will see on the Web have probably been created in the newer format. One of the chief advantages of the newer format is the ability to create an animated image that can be played after transmitting to a viewer.page that moves—for example, a twirling icon or a banner with a hand that waves or letters that magically get larger. In particular, an **animated GIF** is a file in the Graphics Interchange Format specified as GIF89a that contains within the single file a set of images that are presented in a specified order.

gigabit

In data communications, a gigabit is one billion **bit**s, or 1,000,000,000 (that is, 10^9) bits. It's commonly used for measuring the amount of data that is transferred in a second between two telecommunication points. For example, **Gigabit Ethernet** is a high-speed form of **Ethernet** (a local area network technology) that can provide data transfer rates of about 1 gigabit per second. Gigabits per second is usually shortened to Gbps.

Some sources define a gigabit to mean 1,073,741,824 (that is, 2^{30}) bits. Although the bit is a unit of the binary number system, bits in data communications are discrete signal pulses and have historically been counted using the decimal number system. For example, 28.8 kilobits per second (**Kbps**) is 28,800 bits per second. Because of computer architecture and memory address boundaries, bytes are always some multiple or exponent of two. See **kilobyte**, etc.

Gigabit Ethernet

Gigabit Ethernet, a transmission technology based on the **Ethernet** frame format and protocol used in local area networks (**LAN**s), provides a data rate of 1 billion bits per second (one **gigabit**). Gigabit Ethernet is defined in the **IEEE 802.3** standard and is currently being used as the **backbone** in many enterprise networks.

Gigabit Ethernet is carried primarily on **optical fiber** (with very short distances possible on copper media). Existing Ethernet LANs with 10 and 100 Mbps cards can feed into a Gigabit Ethernet backbone. An alternative technology that competes with Gigabit Ethernet is **ATM**. A newer standard, **10-Gigabit Ethernet**, is also becoming available.

gigabit interface converter

A gigabit interface converter (GBIC) is a **transceiver** that converts electric currents (digital highs and lows) to optical signals, and optical signals to digital electric currents. The GBIC is typically employed in **fiber optic** and **Ethernet** systems as an interface for high-speed networking. The data transfer rate is one gigabit per second (1 **Gbps**) or more.

GBIC modules allow technicians to easily configure and upgrade electro-optical communications networks. The typical GBIC transceiver is a plug-in module that is **hot-swapp**able (it can be removed and replaced without turning off the system). The devices are economical, because they eliminate the necessity for replacing entire boards at the system level. Upgrading can be done with any number of units at a time, from an individual module to all the modules in a system.

gigabyte

A gigabyte (pronounced GIG-a-bite with hard G's) is a measure of computer data storage capacity and is "roughly" a billion bytes. A gigabyte is two to the 30th power, or 1,073,741,824 in decimal notation.

Also see **gigabit**, **megabyte**, **terabyte**, and **exabyte**.

gigaflop

As a measure of computer speed, a gigaflop is a billion floating-point operations per second (**FLOPS**).

gigahertz

The gigahertz, abbreviated GHz, is a unit of alternating current (**AC**) or electromagnetic (EM) wave frequency equal to one thousand million **hertz** (1,000,000,000 Hz). The gigahertz is used as an indicator of the frequency of ultra-high-frequency (UHF) and **microwave** EM signals and also, in some computers, to express microprocessor **clock speed**.

An EM signal having a **frequency** of 1 GHz has a **wavelength** of 300 millimeters, or a little less than a foot. An EM signal of 100 GHz has a wavelength of 3 millimeters, which is roughly $1/8$ of an inch. Some radio transmissions are made at frequencies up to hundreds of gigahertz. Personal computer clock speeds are increasing month by month as the technology advances, and reached the 1 GHz point in March of 2000, with a processor from **AMD**, closely followed by a 1 GHz **Pentium 3** from Intel.

Other commonly-used units of frequency are the **kHz**, equal to 1,000 Hz or 0.000001 GHz, and the **MHz**, equal to 1,000,000 Hz or 0.001 GHz.

GIMP

GIMP, sometimes referred to as "The Gimp," is a freely available **open source** application for created and manipulating graphic images that runs on **Linux** and other **UNIX**-based operating systems. GIMP is distributed under licensing terms defined by the **GNU** project. You are likely to find GIMP as one of the optional applications that come in any large Linux package such as those distributed by **Debian** and **Red Hat**. You can also download it directly. GIMP offers photo retouching, image composition, and

image authoring and is favorably compared by users to Adobe's Photoshop and Illustrator applications. GIMP was created by Peter Mattis and Spencer Kimball.

GIS

A GIS (geographic information system) enables you to envision the geographic aspects of a body of data. Basically, it lets you query or analyze a and receive the results in the form of some kind of map. Since many kinds of data have important geographic aspects, a GIS can have many uses: weather forecasting, sales analysis, population forecasting, and land use planning, to name a few.

In a GIS, geographic information is described explicitly in terms of geographic coordinates (latitude and longitude or some national grid coordinates) or implicitly in terms of a street address, postal code, or forest stand identifier. A geographic information system contains the ability to translate implicit geographic data (such as a street address) into an explicit map location. GIS developers sometimes obtain the map data from public sources or companies that specialize in collecting and organizing geographic information. The process of converting implicit geographic data into explicit or map-form images is called *geocoding*.

Geographic data can be stored in a **vector graphics** or a **raster graphics** format. Using a vector format, two-dimensional data is stored in terms of **x and y coordinates**. A road or a river can be described as a series of x,y coordinate points. Nonlinear features such as town boundaries can be stored as a closed loop of coordinates. The vector model is good for describing well-delineated features. A raster data format expresses data as a continuously-changing set of grid cells. The raster model is better for portraying subtle changes such as soil type patterns over an area. Most geographic information systems make use of both kinds of data.

GISs do these kinds of things:

- They accept geographic input in the form of scanned-in and digitized map images. Often this data is supplied by a source that may own maps and has already digitized them.

- They rescale or otherwise manipulate geographic data for different purposes.

- They include a database manager, usually a relational database management system (**RDBMS**).

- They include query and analysis programs so that you can retrieve answers to simple questions such as the distance between two points on a map or more complicated questions that require analysis, such as determining the traffic pattern at a given intersection.

- They provide answers visually, usually as maps or graphs.

glass house

Glass house is a term for centralized computing in an **enterprise** and the mindset of those who plan and administer it. The term originated from the glass windows that, beginning in the 1950s, corporations began to build into their large central computer rooms to let visitors peer in on their impressive rows of **mainframe** computers, direct access storage devices and tape racks, and other hardware. These large rooms were built with an elevated floor that could accommodate, underneath the floorboards, telecommunications and local channel cabling as well as water pipes for cooling the larger water-cooled mainframes. As hardware technology and physical footprints have changed, the physical glass house has changed or even disappeared into smaller spaces and closets. However, much computing in an enterprise remains (and is expected to remain) centrally administered and, to the extent that it does, the glass house point-of-view remains in fashion.

glitch

In several usages in information technology, a *glitch* (pronounced GLIHTCH) is a sudden break in function or continuity, sometimes of a transient nature, with a varying degree of seriousness. According to Eric Raymond, author of *The New Hacker's Dictionary*, glitch is from the German "glitschen," meaning "to slip," via Yiddish "glitshen," meaning "to slide or skid."   In different contexts, the term has different meanings.

1) In electrical service, a glitch, sometimes called a *power glitch*, is a momentary power failure.

2) In network service, a glitch can be any temporary loss of service in the network.

3) In a computer program, a glitch can be a **bug** that isn't encountered very often, resulting in a problem that sometimes goes away because next time the combination of events is different. Glitches like this are often encountered with Web **browsers**. (Browser glitches are often fixed by closing the browser program and then reopening it, or by restarting the operating system.) A glitch can also be an intentionally planned trap or other program device that results in exposing a user's password or in some other security breach.

4) In computer **audio**, a glitch is a quick temporary noise in a file that sounds like a "snap."

Glite

See "G.lite"

Global Positioning System

The GPS (Global Positioning System) is a "constellation" of 24 well-spaced satellites that orbit the Earth and make it possible for people with ground receivers to pinpoint their

geographic location. The location accuracy is anywhere from 100 to 10 meters for most equipment. Accuracy can be pinpointed to within one (1) meter with special military-approved equipment. GPS equipment is widely used in science and has now become sufficiently low-cost so that almost anyone can own a GPS receiver.

The GPS is owned and operated by the U.S. Department of Defense but is available for general use around the world. Briefly, here's how it works:

- 21 GPS satellites and three spare satellites are in orbit at 10,600 miles above the Earth. The satellites are spaced so that from any point on Earth, four satellites will be above the horizon.

- Each satellite contains a computer, an atomic clock, and a radio. With an understanding of its own orbit and the clock, it continually broadcasts its changing position and time. (Once a day, each satellite checks its own sense of time and position with a ground station and makes any minor correction.)

- On the ground, any GPS receiver contains a computer that "triangulates" its own position by getting bearings from three of the four satellites. The result is provided in the form of a geographic position—longitude and latitude—to, for most receivers, within 100 meters.

- If the receiver is also equipped with a display screen that shows a map, the position can be shown on the map.

- If a fourth satellite can be received, the receiver/computer can figure out the altitude as well as the geographic position.

- If you are moving, your receiver may also be able to calculate your speed and direction of travel and give you estimated times of arrival to specified destinations.

The GPS is being used in science to provide data that has never been available before in the quantity and degree of accuracy that the GPS makes possible. Scientists are using the GPS to measure the movement of the arctic ice sheets, the Earth's tectonic plates, and volcanic activity.

GPS receivers are becoming consumer products. In addition to their outdoor use (hiking, cross-country skiing, ballooning, flying, and sailing), receivers can be used in cars to relate the driver's location with traffic and weather information.

global spy network

See "Echelon"

Global System for Mobile communication

See "GSM"

Global Tag

See "GTAG"

global unique identifier

See "GUID"

glyph

In information technology, a glyph (pronounced GLIHF) is a graphic symbol that provides the appearance or form for a **character**. A glyph can be an alphabetic or numeric **font** or some other symbol that pictures an encoded character. The following quote is from a document written as background for the **Unicode** character set standard.

An ideal characterization of characters and glyphs and their relationship may be stated as follows:

1. A character conveys distinctions in meaning or sounds. A character has no intrinsic appearance.

2. A glyph conveys distinctions in form. A glyph has no intrinsic meaning.

3. One or more characters may be depicted by one or more glyph representations (instances of an abstract glyph) in a possibly context dependent fashion.

Glyph is from a Greek word for "carving."

GML

GML (Generalized Markup Language) is an IBM document-formatting language that describes a document in terms of its organization structure and content parts and their relationship. GML **markup** or **tag**s describe such parts as chapters, important sections and less important sections (by specifying heading levels), paragraphs, lists, tables, and so forth. GML frees document creators from specific document formatting concerns such as **font** specification, line spacing, and page layout required by IBM's printer formatting language, SCRIPT.

GML Starter Set is the name of IBM's set of GML tags. GML Starter Set input is processed by the Document Composition Facility (DCF) which formats printer-ready output. A later and more capable set of GML tags is provided by IBM's BookMaster product.

GML preceded and was an inspiration for the industry-developed Standard Generalized Markup Language (**SGML**), today's strategic set of rules for creating any structured document description language. This Web page is marked up with Hypertext Markup Language (**HTML**) tags and is an example of a document that makes use of GML concepts. The Extensible Markup Language (**XML**) also has roots in GML.

GMT

See "Coordinated Universal Time"

GNOME

GNOME (**GNU** Network Object Model Environment, pronounced gah-NOHM) is a graphical user interface (**GUI**) and set of computer **desktop application**s for users of the **Linux** computer operating system. It's intended to make a Linux operating system easy to use for non-programmers and generally corresponds to the Windows desktop interface and its most common set of applications. In fact, GNOME allows the user to select one of several desktop appearances. With GNOME, the user interface can, for example, be made to look like **Windows 98** or like **Mac OS**. In addition, GNOME includes a set of the same type of applications found in the Windows Office 97 product: a **word processor**, a spreadsheet program, a **database** manager, a presentation developer, a Web **browser**, and an **e-mail** program.

GNOME is derived from a long-running volunteer effort under the auspices of the **Free Software Foundation**, the organization founded by Richard Stallman. Stallman and fellow members of the Free Software Foundation believe that software **source code** should always be public and **open** to change so that it can continually be improved by others. GNOME is in part an effort to make Linux a viable alternative to Windows so that the desktop operating system market is not controlled by a single vendor. **GNU** is the Free Software Foundations's own operating system and set of applications. **Linux**, the operating system, was developed by Linus Torvalds who, assisted by contributors, added a **kernel** to additional operating system components from GNU.

GNOME comes with an object request broker (**ORB**) supporting the Common Object Request Broker Architecture (**CORBA**) so that GNOME programs and programs from other operating system platforms in a network will be able to interoperate. GNOME also includes a **widget** library that programmers can use to develop applications that use the GNOME user interface. In addition to a desktop version, GNOME also comes as a user interface and set of applications for the handheld PalmPilot.

GNU Network Object Model Environment

See "GNOME"

GNU

GNU is a **UNIX**-like **operating system** that comes with source code that can be copied, modified, and redistributed. The GNU project was started in 1983 by Richard Stallman and others, who formed the **Free Software Foundation**. Stallman believes that users should be free to do whatever they want with software they acquire, including making copies for friends and modifying the source code and repackaging it with a distribution charge. The FSF uses a stipulation that it calls **copyleft**. Copyleft stipulates that anyone redistributing free software must also pass along the freedom to further copy and change the program, thereby ensuring that no one can claim ownership of future versions and place restrictions on users.

The "free" means "freedom," but not necessarily "no charge." The Free Software Foundation does charge an initial distribution price for GNU. Redistributors can also charge for copies either for cost recovery or for profit. The essential idea of "free software" is to give users freedom in how they modify or repackage the software along with a restriction that they in turn do not restrict user freedom when they pass copies or modified versions along.

One of the results of the free software philosophy, Stallman believes, would be free programs put together from other free programs. GNU is an example of this idea. It became a complete operating system in August 1996, when a **kernel**, consisting of GNU Hurd and Mach, was added. The FSF plans to continue developing their free software in the form of application programs. A free spreadsheet program is now available.

The **Linux** operating system consists of GNU components and the kernel developed by Linus Torvalds.

Gnutella

Gnutella is a system in which individuals can exchange files over the Internet directly without going through a Web site in an arrangement sometimes described as **peer-to-peer** (here meaning "person-to-person"). Like **Napster** and similar Web sites, Gnutella is often used as a way to download music files from or share them with other Internet users and has been an object of great concern for the music publishing industry. Unlike Napster, Gnutella is not a Web site, but an arrangement in which you can see the files of a small number of other Gnutella users at a time, and they in turn can see the files of others, in a kind of daisy-chain effect. Gnutella also allows you to download any file type, whereas Napster is limited to **MP3** music files.

After installing and launching Gnutella, a user's computer (node) becomes both a **client** and a **server** in the network (which is called GnutellaNet) and is able to share files that other Gnutella users have set up to make available. Gnutella, whose name pays homage to both the hazelnut/chocolate spread "Nutella" and the **GNU** project of the Free Software Foundation, was originally developed by Nullsoft (creators of MP3 and WinAMP). It was never publicly released because Nullsoft's parent corporation (AOL) declared the work an "unauthorized publication." However, the **beta** version that was made available for preview was an **open source** program, which resulted in any number of clone variations becoming available that AOL does not own.

Although Gnutella and its variants have incurred the wrath of some musicians and the music industry, the defenders of the peer-to-peer approach view it as a new movement that frees individuals to exchange information with each other directly without the supervision and restrictions of brokering Web sites or other third-parties.

go bosh

Go bosh is cyberspeak for "Go Big or Stay Home," meaning that if you don't commit enough resources to your enterprise, you'll probably fail in your objectives. The term is sometimes used to refer to new Web sites or enterprises that need to gain enough traffic to be able to compete for advertising with similar sites. Web analysts predict that in any given market niche only a few Web sites will be able to establish themselves well enough to succeed in the long run.

going forward

Going forward is a relatively new and apparently convenient way to indicate a progression in time from the present. The term suggests a continuing and progressive movement rather than, as *in the future* can sometimes mean, some specific future date. Like many such expressions, it means enough to be useful while also being suitably vague. The term is widely used in annual reports and other corporate statements and, like such terms as *venue* and *cautionary tale*, seems to have been readily adopted by news media writers. The term has become increasingly popular in press releases from Internet start-ups and newly public companies.

"Going forward" also has a longer-standing usage as the starting, continuing, or resumption of activity on something that has been planned previously, such as an engineering project or a summit conference.

googol and googolplex

A googol is 10 to the 100th power (which is 1 followed by 100 zeros). The term was invented by Milton Sirotta, the 9-year nephew of mathematician Edward Kasner, who had asked his nephew what he thought such a large number should be called. Such a number, Milton apparently replied after a short thought, could only be called something as silly as...a *googol*! A googol is larger than the number of elementary particles in the universe, which amount to only 10 to the 80th power.

Later, another mathematician devised the term *googolplex* for 10 to the power of googol—that is, 1 followed by 10 to the power of 100 zeros. Frank Pilhofer has determined that, given **Moore's Law** (which is that computer processor power doubles about every 1 to 2 years), it would make no sense to try to print out a googleplex for another 524 years—since all earlier attempts to print a googleplex out would be overtaken by the faster processor.

gov

"gov" is one of the top-level **domain name**s that can be used when choosing a domain name. It generally describes the entity owning the domain name as a branch or an agency of the U.S. Federal government. (Other U.S. government levels are encouraged to use the geographic top-level domain name of "us".) Along with the second-level domain name (for example: "whitehouse" in whitehouse.gov), the top-level domain name is required in Web and e-mail addresses.

For more information, see **gTLD** (generic top-level domain name).

GPRS

General Packet Radio Services (GPRS) is a **packet**-based **wireless** communication service that promises data rates from 56 up to 114 **Kbps** and continuous connection to the Internet for mobile phone and computer users. The higher data rates will allow users to take part in video conferences and interact with multimedia Web sites and similar applications using mobile **handheld** devices as well as notebook computers. GPRS is based on Global System for Mobile (**GSM**) communication and will complement existing services such **circuit-switched** cellular phone connections and the Short Message Service (**SMS**).

In theory, GPRS packet-based service should cost users less than circuit-switched services since communication channels are being used on a shared-use, as-packets-are-needed basis rather than dedicated only to one user at a time. It should also be easier to make applications available to mobile users because the faster data rate means that **middleware** currently needed to adapt applications to the slower speed of wireless systems will no longer be needed. As GPRS becomes available, mobile users of a virtual private network (**VPN**) will be able to access the private network continuously rather than through a dial-up connection.

GPRS will also complement **Bluetooth**, a standard for replacing wired connections between devices with wireless radio connections. In addition to the Internet Protocol (**IP**), GPRS supports **X.25**, a packet-based protocol that is used mainly in Europe. GPRS is an evolutionary step toward Enhanced Data GSM Environment (**EDGE**) and Universal Mobile Telephone Service (**UMTS**).

GPS

See "Global Positioning System"

Grace Hopper

Grace Murray Hopper, one of the pioneers of computer science, is generally credited with developments that led to **COBOL**, the programming language for business applications on which the world's largest corporations ran for more than a generation. By the time of her death in 1992, Rear Admiral Grace Hopper had left many contributions to

the field of software engineering and was arguably the world's most famous programmer. After receiving her Ph.D. in mathematics at Yale, Hopper worked as an associate professor at Vassar College before joining the U.S. Naval Reserve in 1943. She went on to work as a researcher and mathematician at the Eckert-Mauchly Computer Corp. and the Sperry Corporation. Having retired from the Navy after World War II, she returned in 1967 to work at the Naval Data Automation Command.

At Eckerd-Mauchly, Hopper developed programs for the first large-scale digital computer, the Mark I. She also developed the first **compiler**, the A-O. She published the first paper on compilers in 1952. The successor to the the A-O, named FLOW-MATIC, lead to the development of the COBOL programming language. Until then programming was done using **assembler** language. Admiral Hopper's idea was to make a programming language closer to ordinary language so that it could be used by non-technical people, thus opening the practice of programming to the business world and freeing it from the rarefied environments of science and engineering.

Admiral Hopper remained in the Navy until 1986 and then worked as a senior consultant for **DEC** until shortly before her death. She was highly sought after as an enthusiastic and entertaining public speaker and educator of young programmers. Hopper was an early advocate of the use of shared code libraries and developed compiler verification software and compiler standards. Hopper is also sometimes mistakenly credited with inventing the term **bug**, a flaw in a computer or a program.

gram

The gram (abbreviation, g or gm) is the **cgs** (centimeter/gram/second) unit of **mass**. A force of one **dyne** (1 dyn), applied to a mass of one gram (1 g), will cause that mass to accelerate at one centimeter per second squared (1 cm/s^2).

Mass is often specified in larger or smaller units than the gram, by changing the power-of-10 **prefix multiplier**. A mass of one kilogram (1 kg) is 1000 g. A mass of one milligram (1 mg) is 0.001 g. A mass of one microgram (1 µg) is 10^{-6} g. A mass of one nanogram (1 ng) is 10^{-9} g. In the International System of Units (**SI**), the kilogram is the preferred unit of mass.

Also see **kilogram**, **mass**, **small-unit metric system**, and International System of Units (**SI**).

granularity

Granularity is the relative size, scale, level of detail, or depth of penetration that characterizes an object or activity. It may help to think of it as: Which type of "granule" are we looking at? This term is used in astronomy, photography, physics, linguistics, and fairly often in information technology. It can refer to the level of a hierarchy of objects or actions, to the fineness of detail in a photograph, or to the amount of

information that is supplied in describing a person's age. Its meaning is not always immediately clear to those unfamiliar with the context in which it's being used.

graphical user interface

See "GUI"

graphics accelerator

A graphics accelerator (a **chipset** attached to a *video board*) is a computer microelectonics component to which a computer program can offload the sending and refreshing of images to the display monitor and the computation of special effects common to 2-D and **3-D** images. Graphics accelerators speed up the displaying of images on the monitor making it possible to achieve effects not otherwise possible—for example, the presentation of very large images or of interactive games in which images need to change quickly in response to user input. Many new personal computers are now sold with a graphics accelerator built in. The power of a graphics accelerator can be extended further if the personal computer is equipped with the Accelerated Graphics Port (**AGP**), a bus (data path) interface between the computer components involved in image display.

Each graphics accelerator provides an application program interface (**API**). Some support more than one API. Among the most popular API's are the industry standard **OpenGL** and Microsoft's **DirectX** and Direct3D.

Graphics Interchange Format

See "GIF"

grasping plan

A grasping plan is an **algorithm** used by a **robot** arm and gripper to get hold of a specific object. The details of such a program depend on the type of robot arm and gripper, on the size of the robot's work area, and on the type of object(s) to be grasped.

As an example, imagine you own a mobile, autonomous personal robot. You are having spaghetti with lots of sauce for supper, so you feel compelled to instruct the machine to get you six paper napkins. The robot must use a certain program to find the kitchen, another program to locate the cabinet or drawer in which the napkins are stored, and another program to determine which objects in the drawer are the paper napkins. Then the gripper must pick up exactly six napkins without upsetting the other contents of the drawer or cabinet. This is a simple process for a human being, even a child, to carry out, but it is complex when reduced to digital components. There are myriad ways in which the robot might execute this assignment wrong, but only one way to do it right.

A grasping plan can be enhanced by **machine vision**. Tactile sensors, pressure sensors, and texture sensors can also help ensure that the gripper picks up the correct object in the right way. An efficient and reliable grasping plan involves the use of a detailed, three-dimensional map of the robot's entire work environment, stored in the robot controller's memory. The grasping plan can then assign every object or set of objects a range of coordinate values.

Also see **artificial intelligence**, fine-motion plan, gross-motion plan, and **robotics**.

grating light valve

Using grating light valve (GLV) technology, picture elements (**pixel**s) are formed on the surface of a silicon chip and become the source for display projection on anything from an auditorium scrreen down to a handheld computer display. Using GLV, displays of the future may cost much less, require less space, and make high-resolution images possible in handheld personal communication devices. GLV was developed by David Bloom together with his students at Stanford University. Bloom has since founded Silicon Light Machines, which is developing the technology further.

GLV uses micro-electromechanical systems (**MEMS**) technology and optical physics to vary how light is reflected from each of multiple ribbon-like structures that represent a particular "image point" or pixel. The ribbons can move a tiny distance, changing the wavelength of reflected light. Grayscale tones are achieved partly by varying the speed at which given pixels are switched on and off. The resulting image can be projected in a large auditorium with a bright light source or on a small appliance using low-power LEDs as a light source.

gravesite

In the context of the World Wide Web, a gravesite is either:

1) A **Web site** that has been abandoned or forgotten by its originators that is nevertheless still accessible on a server. (There is a vast but untold number of these.) A synonym is **ghost site**.

2) A Web site that, in the eyes of marketers, has failed to get sufficient traffic to be interesting to advertisers or other revenue providers, possibly by not finding an audience niche or building an audience community, or by failing to find a distribution partner such as America Online, Yahoo, or Netscape.

gray hat

Gray hat describes a **cracker** (or, if you prefer, **hacker**) who exploits a security weakness in a computer system or product in order to bring the weakness to the attention of the owners. Unlike a **black hat**, a gray hat acts without malicious intent. The goal of a gray hat is to improve system and network security. However, by publicizing a

vulnerability, the gray hat may give other crackers the opportunity to exploit it. This differs from the **white hat** who alerts system owners and vendors of a vulnerability without actually exploiting it in public.

gray

The gray (symbolized Gy) is the standard unit of absorbed ionizing-radiation dose, equivalent to one **joule** per kilogram (1 J · kg^{-1}). Reduced to base units in the International System of Units (**SI**), 1 Gy is equivalent to one **meter squared per second** squared (1 m^2 · s^{-2}).

In general, ionizing-radiation dose is the amount of X-ray, gamma-ray, or high-speed-particle **energy** absorbed per unit **mass**. The gray supersedes the **rad**, an older unit of radiation dose. In some documents the rad is still used; the gray is 100 times larger. If D_g is the radiation dose in grays and D_r is the radiation dose in rads, then the following formulas can be used for conversion:

$$D_r = 100 \; D_g$$
$$D_g = 0.01 \; D_r$$

Also see **gray per second**, **sievert**, International System of Units (**SI**).

Gregorian calendar

The Gregorian calendar is the calendar in current use in the Western world, both as the civil and Christian ecclesiastical calendar. Instituted by Pope Gregory XIII in 1582, the calendar has 365 days with an extra day every four years (the leap year) except in years divisible by 100 but not divisible by 400. Thus, the calendar year has an average length of 365.2422 days. The Gregorian calendar replaced the **Julian calendar**, which had become 10 days out of synchrony with the solar cycle. In October, 1582, 10 days were dropped from the calendar. England and the American colonies were late in adopting the calendar. In 1752, they dropped 11 days.

grep

Grep, a **UNIX** command and also a utility available for Windows and other operating systems, is used to search one or more files for a given character string or pattern and, if desired, replace the character string with another one. For example, a UNIX system user can enter on a command line:

grep html homepage.htm

html specifies the character string to search for on each line. *homepage.htm* specifies the file to search. The result would be to display any line in the *homepage.htm* file that includes the character string *html*. The entire line is displayed.

Grep can be used simply as a way of searching, especially through multiple files. (In the above command, we could have specified additional files besides *homepage.htm*.) It can also be used to search for word or string occurrences that need to be replaced. If you are not sure exactly what the effect might be of making the replacement, grep identifies the lines and you can decide what further action to take for each occurrence. grep can also be used as the first step in an automatic procedure to search and replace a word or phrase. The output from grep can be the input (perhaps using the UNIX **pipe** symbol) for a replacement command.

Grep allows the string argument to be specified as a *regular expression*, which is a way of specifying a string that allows certain *metacharacters* (special keyboard characters such as the period) to stand for other characters or to further define the way the pattern-matching should work. For example:

Grep ".*hood" essay1 would search the *essay1* file and display every line containing a word with the string *hood*. The period (dot) indicates that any character may precede the string *hood* and the asterisk (*) says that any number of the "any characters" indicated by the dot can precede the string. (The quote marks around the string argument in this example are optional, but quotes are required where the argument is a phrase or contains a blank.)

grep originated from a UNIX text editor that provided a command sequence *g/re/p* for *global/regular expression/print*.

grey hat

See "gray hat"

grok

To grok (pronounced GRAHK) something is to understand something so well that it is fully absorbed into oneself. In Robert Heinlein's science-fiction novel of 1961, *Stranger in a Strange Land*, the word is Martian and literally means "to drink" but metaphorically means "to take it all in," to understand fully, or to "be at one with." Today, grok sometimes is used to include acceptance as well as comprehension—to "dig" or appreciate as well as to know.

As one character from Heinlein's novel says:

> 'Grok' means to understand so thoroughly that the observer becomes a part of the observed—to merge, blend, intermarry, lose identity in group experience. It means almost everything that we mean by religion, philosophy, and science—and it means as little to us (because we are from Earth) as color means to a blind man.

In common usage, "Do you grok?" seems close in meaning to "Do you get it?"

ground-plane antenna

A ground-plane antenna is a variant of the **dipole antenna**, designed for use with an unbalanced **feed line** such as **coaxial cable**. It resembles a **coaxial antenna** whose lower section consists of straight elements called *radials* instead of a hollow conducting cylinder. There are two or more radials, each measuring $^1/_4$ **wavelength**. The main element can be any length, but it must be adjusted to function at and near a

specific **frequency**. This adjustment is done using a tuning coil. The radials are connected to the outer conductor or shield of the feed line cable; the main element is connected to the center conductor.

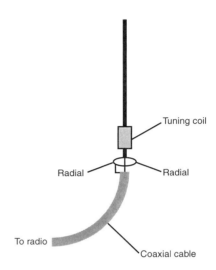

The main element of a ground-plane antenna is almost always oriented vertically. This results in transmission of, and optimum response to, vertically polarized **wireless** signals. When the base of the antenna is placed at least $^1/_4$ wavelength above the ground or other conducting surface, the radials behave as a near-perfect ground system for an **electromagnetic field**, and the antenna is highly efficient. It works equally well in all horizontal directions. Ground-plane antennas are favored at frequencies above approximately 10 **MHz** where the dimensions are manageable. This type of antenna is especially popular among Citizens Band radio operators for fixed-station use in the class-D band at 27 MHz.

groupware

Groupware refers to programs that help people work together collectively while located remotely from each other. Groupware services can include the sharing of calendars, collective writing, e-mail handling, shared database access, electronic meetings with each person able to see and display information to others, and other activities.

Some product examples of groupware include Lotus Notes and Microsoft Exchange, both of which facilititate calendar sharing, e-mail handling, and the replication of files across a distributed system so that all users can view the same information. Electronic "face-to-face" meetings are facilitated by **CU-SeeMe** and Microsoft NetMeeting.

GSM

GSM (Global System for Mobile communication) is a **digital** mobile telephone system that is widely used in Europe and other parts of the world. GSM uses a variation of time division multiple access (**TDMA**) and is the most widely used of the three digital **wireless** telephone technologies (TDMA, GSM, and CDMA). GSM digitizes and compresses data, then sends it down a channel with two other streams of user data, each in its own time slot. It operates at either the 900 **MHz** or 1800 MHz frequency band.

GSM is the de facto wireless telephone standard in Europe. GSM has over 120 million users worldwide and is available in 120 countries, according to the GSM MoU Association. Since many GSM network operators have roaming agreements with foreign operators, users can often continue to use their mobile phones when they travel to other countries.

American Personal Communications (APC), a subsidiary of Sprint, is using GSM as the technology for a **broadband** personal communications service (**PCS**). The service will ultimately have more than 400 base stations for the palm-sized handsets that are being made by Ericsson, Motorola, and Nokia. The handsets include a phone, a text pager, and an answering machine.

GSM together with other technologies is part of an evolution of wireless mobile telemmunication that includes High-Speed Circuit-Switched Data (**HCSD**), General Packet Radio System (**GPRS**), Enhanced Data GSM Environment (**EDGE**), and Universal Mobile Telecommunications Service (**UMTS**).

GTAG

GTAG (Global Tag) is a standardization initiative of the Uniform Code Council (UCC) and the European Article Numbering Association (**EAN**) for asset tracking and logistics based on radio frequency identification (**RFID**). EAN and UCC launched the GTAG project in March of 2000, and—along with input from international companies including Philips Semiconductors, Intermec, and Gemplus —are expected to publish their final guidelines by May 2002. The Initiative intends to increase the range and complexity of typical current RFID applications, such as automatic road toll collection and anti-theft technologies, to sophisticated *smart tag* RFID products as small as a postage stamp that can be used to track inventory and deter theft, among a myriad of potential uses.

The RFID smart tag devices are basically very small database applications that receive information via radio frequency (**RF**) waves. In the future, this capability will automate an increasing number of tasks. For example, a library patron or store customer would no longer have to stop at a cash register or a library check out. RFID devices would store information about both the patron and their selections, which would be transmitted to electronic equipment and updated in all associated system components. The RFID

devices are still much more expensive than the magnetic tags commonly used now (about $1 per tag, compared to $.03), but as prices come down and the practical and cost benefits of RFID smart tags become more widely known, they are likely to be seen in an increasing number of applications. There are still some privacy and security issues to be resolved however, since the information stored in tags—which may not be encrypted—can be read by anyone with the requisite equipment, to a distance of several feet.

gTLD

A gTLD (generic top-level domain name) is the **top-level domain** name of an Internet address that identifies it generically as associated with some domain class, such as .com (commercial), .net (originally intended for Internet service providers, but now used for many purposes), .org (for non-profit organizations, industry groups, and others), .gov (U.S. government agencies), .mil (for the military), .edu (for educational institutions); and .int (for international treaties or databases and not much used). For example, in the domain name, www.ibm.com, .com is the chosen gTLD. In addition to the gTLD, there is the ccTLD (country code top-level domain name) that identifies a specific national domicile for an address. (For instance, .fr for France and .mx for Mexico.)

In November 2000, the Internet Corporation for Assigned Names and Number (**ICANN**), a Los Angeles-based non-profit group that oversees the distribution of domain names, approved seven additional gTLDs. The new gTLDs are .biz, restricted to businesses; .info, open to anyone; .name, for personal registrations; .pro, for licensed professionals such as lawyers, doctors and accountants; .aero, for anything related to air transport; .museum, for museums; and .coop, for co-operative businesses such as credit unions. The group selected these new gTLDs from among more than 40 proposed suffixes. It rejected gTLDs such as .kid, .site, .xxx, .home, .dot, and .site. ICANN is currently negotiating registry agreements with the gTLD applicants it chose.

Proponents of adding new gTLDs argue that they are easy to create and free up new space for Internet addresses. Those opposed say more gTLDs only lead to confusion and pose an increased risk of trademark infringement, **cybersquatting**, and cyberpiracy.

ICANN has approved several organizations to register domain names for individuals and businesses. The group has not yet accredited anyone to pre-register names in any of the new gTLDs, and those attempting it do so at their own risk.

GUI

Also see **HCI** (human-computer interaction).

A GUI (usually pronounced GOO-ee) is a graphical (rather than purely textual) user interface to a computer. The term came into existence because the first interactive user interfaces to computers were not graphical; they were text-and-keyboard oriented and usually consisted of commands you had to remember and computer responses that were infamously brief. The command interface of the **DOS** operating system (which you can still get to from your Windows operating system) is an example of the typical user-computer interface before GUIs arrived. An intermediate step in user interfaces between the command line interface and the GUI was the non-graphical *menu-based interface*, which let you interact by using a **mouse** rather than by having to type in keyboard commands.

Today's major operating systems provide a graphical user interface. Applications typically use the elements of the GUI that come with the operating system and add their own graphical user interface elements and ideas. A GUI sometimes uses one or more metaphors for objects familiar in real life, such as the **desktop**, the view through a window, or the physical layout in a building. Elements of a GUI include such things as: windows, pull-down menus, buttons, scroll bars, iconic images, wizards, the mouse, and no doubt many things that haven't been invented yet. With the increasing use of multimedia as part of the GUI, sound, voice, motion video, and virtual reality interfaces seem likely to become part of the GUI for many applications. A system's graphical user interface along with its input devices is sometimes referred to as its "look-and-feel."

The GUI familiar to most of us today in either the Mac or the Windows operating systems and their applications originated at the Xerox Palo Alto Research Laboratory in the late 1970s. Apple used it in their first Macintosh computers. Later, Microsoft used many of the same ideas in their first version of the Windows operating system for IBM-compatible PCs.

When creating an application, many object-oriented tools exist that facilitate writing a graphical user interface. Each GUI element is defined as a **class widget** from which you can create **object** instances for your application. You can code or modify prepackaged methods that an object will use to respond to user stimuli.

GUID

A GUID (global unique identifier) is a term used by Microsoft for a number that its programming generates to create a unique identity for an entity such as a Word document. GUIDs are widely used in Microsoft products to identify interfaces, replica sets, records, and other objects. Different kinds of objects have different kinds of GUIDs—for instance, a Microsoft Access database uses a 16-byte field to establish a unique identifier for replication.

The nature of certain of Microsoft's GUIDs, the use made of GUIDs, and the potential for abuse arising out of GUIDs, have raised concern among privacy advocates. In March 1999, a request was made to the U.S. Federal Trade Commission to investigate Microsoft's use of GUIDs.

The controversy relates especially to GUIDs attached to Office 97 and Office 2000 documents. The GUID numbers generated for Office documents on Mac and networked PCs have been found to incorporate the unique identification number of the computer's card. The fact that Office documents, such as a Word file or an Excel spreadsheet, contain a GUID is not made evident to users. There are a number of reported incidents in which the author of a document could be traced by the GUID in the document, even in circumstances where the author had taken exceptional care to maintain their anonymity.

In response to expressed concerns, Microsoft has released a patch for Office 97 SR2 which disables the GUID function, and a utility to remove GUIDs from existing documents.

Concerns about the GUID parallel similar concerns about the potential for abuse of Intel's processor serial number.

Guidelines for Definition of Managed Objects

See "GDMO"

Gyricon

Gyricon is a type of electronic paper (sometimes called **e-paper**) developed at Xerox's Palo Alto Research Center (PARC). The Xerox technology is expected to yield the first complex e-paper products, although other companies (such as Lucent and Philips) are also working on their own versions of e-paper. Gyricon will be used for products such as **e-book**s, **electronic newspaper**s, portable signs, and foldable, rollable displays.

Gyricon consists of a double sided plastic sheet almost as thin as a standard transparency. Within the sheet are millions of bichromal (two color) balls just .1 mm wide, contained in tiny oil-filled pockets in the material. The balls are rotated by exposure to an electrical charge; they rotate fully to display as black or white, or partially (in response to lower electrical pulses), to display a range of grey shades. Images and text are created by the combined display, and are bi-stable: They remain fixed in position until another electrical pulse is applied to change the orientation of the balls. Data will be downloaded to the ePaper through a wireless connection to a computer or a cell phone.

PARC, in conjunction with 3M, has already manufactured a large roll of Gyricon, to prove the viability of volume production of the ePaper. Xerox has created a subsidiary company, Gyricon Media Inc. to develop and market the technology, which will be seen as early as the end of 2001 in portable, reusable pricing signs for stores that can be changed instantly through a computer link. Nick Sheridon, a senior research fellow at PARC, projects that a Gyricon-based electronic newspaper could be available within the next few years.

H

See "henry"

H.323

H.323 is a standard approved by the International Telecommunication Union (**ITU**) in 1996 to promote compatibility in **videoconference** transmissions over **IP** networks. H.323 was originally promoted as a way to provide consistency in audio, video and data **packet** transmissions in the event that a local area network (**LAN**) did not provide guaranteed service quality (**QoS**). Although it was doubtful at first whether manufacturers would adopt H.323, it is now considered to be the standard for interoperability in audio, video and data transmissions as well as Internet phone and voice-over-IP (**VoIP**) because it addresses call control and management for both point-to-point and multipoint conferences as well as gateway administration of media traffic, bandwidth and user participation.

H.323, which describes how multimedia communications occur between **terminals**, network equipment and services, is part of a larger group of ITU recommendations for multimedia interoperability called H.3x. The latest of these recommendations, H.248, is a recommendation to provide a single standard for the control of **gateway** devices in multimedia packet transmissions to allow calls to connect from a LAN to a public switched telephone network (**PSTN**), as well as to other standards-based terminals. This recommendation was announced in August 2000, by the ITU-TU Study Group 16 and the Megaco Working Group of the Internet Engineering Task Force (**IETF**).

hacker

Hacker is a term used by some to mean "a clever programmer" and by others, especially journalists or their editors, to mean "someone who tries to break into computer systems."

1) Eric Raymond, compiler of *The New Hacker's Dictionary*, defines a hacker as a clever programmer. A "good hack" is a clever solution to a programming problem and "hacking" is the act of doing it. Raymond lists five possible characteristics that qualify one as a hacker, which we paraphrase here:

- A person who enjoys learning details of a programming language or system
- A person who enjoys actually doing the programming rather than just theorizing about it
- A person capable of appreciating someone else's hacking

- A person who picks up programming quickly
- A person who is an expert at a particular programming language or system, as in "**UNIX** hacker" Raymond deprecates the use of this term for someone who attempts to crack someone else's system or otherwise uses programming or expert knowledge to act maliciously. He prefers the term **cracker** for this meaning.

2) Journalists or their editors almost universally use hacker to mean someone who attempts to break into computer systems. Typically, this kind of hacker would be a proficient programmer or engineer with sufficient technical knowledge to understand the weak points in a security system. For more on this usage, see **cracker**.

hacktivism

Hacktivism is the act of **hacking**, or breaking into a computer system, for a politically or socially motivated purpose. The individual who performs an act of hacktivism is said to be a *hacktivist*.

A hacktivist uses the same tools and techniques as a **hacker**, but does so in order to disrupt services and bring attention to a political or social cause. For example, one might leave a highly visible message on the home page of a Web site that gets a lot of traffic or which embodies a point-of-view that is being opposed. Or one might launch a **denial-of-service attack** to disrupt traffic to a particular site.

A recent demonstration of hacktivism followed the death of a Chinese airman when his jet fighter collided with a U.S. surveillance plane in April 2001. Chinese and American hacktivists from both countries hacked Web sites and used them as "blackboards" for their statements.

Whether hacktivism is a crime may be debated. Opponents argue that hacktivism causes damage in a forum where there is already ample opportunity for nondisruptive free speech. Others insist that such an act is the equivalent of a protest and is therefore protected as a form of free speech.

hacktivist

See "hacktivism"

HailStorm

Part of Microsoft's **.Net** initiative, HailStorm is the company's plan to provide a single place on the Web where any individual user (who pays a fee) may securely store personal and financial information that can be shared with others when desired (for example, to pay for something at an

online store). HailStorm makes use of the Extensible Markup Language (**XML**) and the Simple Object Access Protocol (**SOAP**).

The initial set of HailStorm services includes the storing of subscribers' personal information, contacts, locations, profiles, favorite Web sites, and device settings. HailStorm also can provide calendar services and management of inbox items such as e-mail and voice mail. Users pay for all selected services.

An example of a HailStorm service might involve an individual booking an airline flight using an online travel reservation service. With the user's permission, the flight is automatically scheduled into his HailStorm-enabled calendar. If the flight is delayed or canceled, the user is automatically notified. HailStorm services can be accessed from any computer, **smartphone**, personal digital assistant (**PDA**), or other Internet-connected device.

Microsoft believes that HailStorm offers users online privacy that is not currently available at most Web sites. Today, any information entered into an online form at a Web site becomes the property of that Web site. With HailStorm, the user controls all personal information and decides who gets to use it, how long they may use it, and how they may use it. A user can also revoke access to personal information. Microsoft binds HailStorm licensees to specific terms of use that control how data is used. HailStorm services are expected to be available as a **beta test** in late 2001. Full release is expected in 2002.

Industry commentators and competitors express concerns about Microsoft's ability to keep its users' personal information secure and about the need for an **open** cross-competitor standard as opposed to a proprietary service that becomes a de facto standard.

half-duplex

Half-duplex data transmission means that data can be transmitted in both directions on a signal carrier, but not at the same time. For example, on a local area network using a technology that has half-duplex transmission, one workstation can send data on the line and then immediately receive data on the line from the same direction in which data was just transmitted. Like **full-duplex** transmission, half-duplex transmission implies a bidirectional line (one that can carry data in both directions).

HALO

A HALO (High Altitude Long Operation) aircraft is an aircraft designed to act as a very high altitude receiving and transmitting tower, circling a metropolitan area and providing **broadband** telecommunication service at data rates up to 5 **Mbps** to homes and up to 25 Mbps to business users with dedicated lines. Angel Technologies plans to launch a HALO-based series of metropolitan area networks (**MAN**s). In each city, a single aircraft flying at about 52,000

feet will be able to service home and business users over a 60 mile area. Three aircraft will take turns, each flying an 8-hour shift. Users on the ground will mount a small external antenna outside their home or building. The airplane will link users with each other or with Internet service providers (**ISP**s) and telephone company offices for connection to networks outside the metropolitan area. Tens or even hundreds of thousands of users can be serviced. Rates are not yet announced.

The aircraft, called the Proteus, is being built in California by Scaled Composites, a subsidiary of Wyman-Gordon Company. It is powered by twin turbofan engines and is designed to have an "efficient high-altitude loiter," to be easy to maneuver, and to sustain flight at altitudes as high as 60,000 feet for 14 hours with a payload of up to 2,000 pounds. Extendible wings allow it to carry a range of payloads. The first "proof of concept" Proteus has been successful in preliminary flight tests.

Unlike the telecommunication **satellite** systems now being developed, a HALO system can be launched for one city at a time. (The HALO aircraft flies at about a tenth of the lowest altitude of the LEO satellite.) An advantage of a high-altitude plane over other wireless solutions is that there is almost no interference. Transmitters will be powered with 40 kilowatts at the 28 and 38 GHz frequency bands. An antenna can receive a signal through trees and during rainstorms. Angel plans to offer three levels of service:

- For home and small business users using dial-up, 1 to 5 Mbps, providing low-cost Internet service, video on demand, and 2-way video conferencing

- For larger businesses using dial-up or dedicated connection, 5 to 12.5 Mbps

- For businesses with dedicated connections, up to 25 Mbps

ham radio

See "amateur radio"

Handheld Device Markup Language

See "HDML"

handheld

A handheld computer is a computer that can conveniently be stored in a pocket (of sufficient size) and used while you're holding it. Today's handheld computers, which are also called personal digital assistants (**PDA**s), can be divided into those that accept handwriting as input and those with small keyboards. The original handheld that accepted handwriting was Apple's Newton, which was later withdrawn from the market. Today, the most popular handheld that accepts handwritten input is the PalmPilot. Philips, Casio, NEC, Compaq, and other companies make handhelds with small keyboards.

Windows **CE** and **EPOC** are two of the most widely used **operating system**s in handheld computers.

Handheld computers are typically used for personal information manager (PIM) types of applications: maintaining schedules, keeping names and phone numbers, doing simple calculations, taking notes, and, with a modem, exchanging e-mail and getting information from the Web. Keyboards have tiny keys that take getting used to. Those that handle handwriting also impose constraints and require some learning. Nevertheless, this class of computer is widely sold and appreciated by many users.

Hewlett-Packard has recently introduced the first handheld computer with a color display. A number of companies now combine voice and data telephone service using **cellular telephone** or other **wireless** technologies with the handheld computer in a single device.

handie talkie

A handie talkie, often referred to by its abbreviation, HT, is a handheld, portable two-way radio transceiver. This type of radio is sometimes called a "walkie talkie" or a "handheld." Handie talkies are popular among **amateur radio** operators, especially on their VHF and UHF bands at 144 and 432 MHz. Handie talkies are widely used by security personnel, military personnel, and police officers. Most HTs are used in conjunction with repeaters for extended range. Some HTs are designed for the 27-MHz **Citizens Band** (CB) radio service.

A typical HT is a rectangular box about the size and weight of an old-fashioned telephone handset. The antenna protrudes from the top end, and consists of a coiled-up element encased in rubber and wound around a flexible rod. This type of antenna, known as a "rubber duck," is not particularly efficient, but is convenient and rugged. Volume and squelch controls are usually placed next to the antenna. The frequency control knob or buttons are on the top end or the front. A speaker/microphone is contained within the box, as is a battery power supply. A small display shows the frequency or channel, received signal strength, and relative RF output power. The transmitter produces RF power output ranging from about 100 milliwatts (100 mW) to five watts (5 W), depending on the service and the intended use.

Rechargeable nickel-cadmium (NiCd), nickel-metal-hydride (NiMH), or lithium (Li) batteries (see **battery**) are employed as the power supply for a typical HT, with a nominal voltage of 12 to 14 volts DC. Most HTs can be operated while recharging, which is usually done using an adapter connecting the HT to a 117-volt AC utility outlet. Some HTs have adapters that allow recharging from automotive batteries.

handoff

In an ideal **cellular telephone** network, each end user's telephone set or **modem** (the subscriber's hardware) is always within range of a base station. The region covered by each base station is known as its **cell**. The size and shape of each cell in a network depends on the nature of the terrain in the region, the number of base stations, and the transmit/receive range of each base station. In theory, the cells in a network overlap; for much of the time, a subscriber's hardware is within range of more than one base station. The network must decide, from moment to moment, which base station will handle the signals to and from each and every subscriber's hardware.

Each time a mobile or portable cellular subscriber passes from one cell into another, the network automatically switches coverage responsibility from one base station to another. Each base-station transition, as well as the switching process or sequence itself, is called handoff. In a properly functioning network, handoff occurs smoothly, without gaps in communications and without confusion about which base station should be dealing with the subscriber. Subscribers to a network need not do anything to make handoff take place, nor should they have to think about the process or about which base station is dealing with the signals at any given moment.

handshaking

In telephone communication, handshaking is the exchange of information between two **modem**s and the resulting agreement about which **protocol** to use that precedes each telephone connection. You can hear the handshaking in those crunching and other sounds when you make a dial-out call from your computer.

Since the modems at each end of the line may have different capabilities, they need to inform each other and settle on the highest transmission speed they can both use. At higher speeds, the modems have to determine the length of line delays so that echo cancellers can be used properly.

The most common modem standards are briefly described in our **V.xx** page.

Handspring

Handspring is a company that manufactures portable computer/organizer hardware. The principal Handspring product is a handheld computer called the Visor, which is similar to the **Palm** computer and uses the Palm operating system (**Palm OS**). Data can be easily transferred between the Visor and other computers, including Palm handhelds, using **HotSync** technology. Interfacing is possible with Macintosh as well as with IBM-compatible desktop and notebook computers.

The Visor can be tailored to meet the needs of the individual user. It contains an expansion slot called Springboard that allows the addition of modules, each of which is designed for a specific function. The modules are **plug-and-play** and are hot-swappable (they are automatically recognized by the Visor, and they can be exchanged without powering-down or rebooting). Data can be stored and backed up with an optional flash-memory module.

haptics

Haptics (pronounced HAP-tiks) is the science of applying touch (tactile) sensation and control to interaction with computer applications. (The word derives from the Greek *haptein* meaning "to fasten.") By using special input/output devices (joysticks, data gloves, or other devices), users can receive feedback from computer applications in the form of felt sensations in the hand or other parts of the body. In combination with a visual display, haptics technology can be used to train people for tasks requiring hand-eye coordination, such as surgery and space ship maneuvers. It can also be used for games in which you feel as well as see your interactions with images. For example, you might play tennis with another computer user somewhere else in the world. Both of you can see the moving ball and, using the haptic device, position and swing your tennis racket and feel the impact of the ball.

A number of universities are experimenting with haptics. The Immersion Corporation offers a joystick product that is used in laboratories and in arcade games. Haptics offers an additional dimension to a virtual reality or 3-D environment.

hard disk

A hard disk is part of a unit, often called a "disk drive," "hard drive," or "**hard disk drive**," that stores and provides relatively quick access to large amounts of data on an electromagnetically charged surface or set of surfaces. Today's computers typically come with a hard disk that contains several billion bytes (**gigabyte**s) of **storage**.

A hard disk is really a set of stacked "disks," each of which, like phonograph records, has data recorded electromagnetically in concentric circles or "tracks" on the disk. A "head" (something like a phonograph arm but in a relatively fixed position) records (writes) or reads the information on the tracks. Two heads, one on each side of a disk, read or write the data as the disk spins. Each read or write operation requires that data be located, which is an operation called a "seek." (Data already in a **disk cache**, however, will be located more quickly.)

A hard disk/drive unit comes with a set rotation speed varying from 4500 to 7200 rpm. Disk access time is measured in milliseconds. Although the physical location can be identified with cylinder, track, and sector locations, these are actually mapped to a logical block address (**LBA**) that works with the larger address range on today's hard disks.

hard disk drive

In a personal computer, a hard disk drive (HDD) is the mechanism that controls the positioning, reading, and writing of the **hard disk**, which furnishes the largest amount of data **storage** for the PC. Although the hard disk drive (often shortened to "hard drive") and the hard disk are not the same thing, they are packaged as a unit and so either term is sometimes used to refer to the whole unit.

hardcode

In computer programming or text markup, to hardcode (less frequently, *hard code*) is to use an explicit rather than a symbolic name for something that is likely to change at a later time. Such coding is sometimes known as hardcode (noun) and it is more difficult to change if it later becomes necessary. In most programming languages, it is possible to equate a symbol with a particular name (which may also represent a number) value. If the name changes, the symbol stays the same and only the equate line of code needs to be changed to reflect the new name. When the program is recompiled, the new name is picked up wherever the symbol occurs in the code. Although there are search-and-replace tools that can change all occurrences of a given name, program code is very unforgiving in case a small error is introduced, and it is safer to have a single place in which such a change can be made. For this reason, hardcoding is usually a practice to be avoided.

Hardcode is also sometimes used in describing more difficult programming languages such as **C** or **C++** rather than such "softcode" languages as **Visual Basic**.

hardware

Hardware is the physical aspect of computers, telecommunications, and other information technology devices. The term arose as a way to distinguish the "box" and the electronic circuitry and components of a computer from the program you put in it to make it do things. The program came to be known as the **software**.

Hardware implies permanence and invariability. Software or programming can easily be varied. You can put an entirely new program in the hardware and make it create an entirely new experience for the user. You can, however, change the modular configurations that most computers come with by adding new adapters or **card** that extend the computer's capabilities.

Like software, hardware is a collective term. Hardware includes not only the computer proper but also the cables, connectors, power supply units, and peripheral devices such as the keyboard, mouse, audio speakers, and printers.

Hardware is sometimes used as a term collectively describing the physical aspects of telephony and telecommunications network infrastructure.

hardware abstraction layer

1) In computers, a hardware abstraction layer (HAL) is a layer of programming that allows a computer **operating system** to interact with a hardware device at a general or abstract level rather than at a detailed hardware level. **Windows 2000** is one of several operating systems that include a hardware abstraction layer. The hardware abstraction layer can be called from either the operating system's **kernel** or from a **device driver**. In either case, the calling program can interact with the device in a more general way than it would otherwise.

2) "HAL" was the name of the computer that ran the spaceship in Stanley Kubrick and Arthur C. Clarke's film *2001*.

harmonic

A harmonic is a signal or wave whose **frequency** is an integral (whole-number) multiple of the frequency of some reference signal or wave. The term can also refer to the ratio of the frequency of such a signal or wave to the frequency of the reference signal or wave.

Let f represent the main, or fundamental, frequency of an alternating current (**AC**) signal, **electromagnetic field**, or sound wave. This frequency, usually expressed in **hertz**, is the frequency at which most of the energy is contained, or at which the signal is defined to occur. If the signal is displayed on an oscilloscope, the **waveform** will appear to repeat at a rate corresponding to f Hz.

For a signal whose fundamental frequency is f, the second harmonic has a frequency $2f$, the third harmonic has a frequency of $3f$, and so on. Let w represent the **wavelength** of the signal or wave in a specified medium. The second harmonic has a wavelength of $w/2$, the third harmonic has a wavelength of $w/3$, and so on. Signals occurring at frequencies of $2f$, $4f$, $6f$, etc. are called even harmonics; the signals at frequencies of $3f$, $5f$, $7f$, etc. are called odd harmonics. A signal can, in theory, have infinitely many harmonics.

Nearly all signals contain energy at harmonic frequencies, in addition to the energy at the fundamental frequency. If all the energy in a signal is contained at the fundamental frequency, then that signal is a perfect sine wave. If the signal is not a perfect sine wave, then some energy is contained in the harmonics. Some waveforms contain large amounts of energy at harmonic frequencies. Examples are square waves, sawtooth waves, and triangular waves.

In **wireless** communications and broadcasting, transmitters are designed so they emit a minimum of energy at harmonic frequencies. Normally, a wireless device is intended for use at only one frequency. Signal output at harmonic frequencies can cause interference to other communications or broadcasting. For example, a broadcast signal at 90.5 MHz (in the standard FM band) would have a second harmonic at

181 MHz, a third harmonic at 271.5 MHz, a fourth harmonic at 362 MHz, and so on. Some or all of these harmonic signals could, if strong, disrupt activities in other wireless services.

hash function

See "hashing"

hashing

Hashing is the transformation of a string of **characters** into a usually shorter fixed-length value or key that represents the original string. Hashing is used to index and retrieve items in a **database** because it is faster to find the item using the shorter hashed key than to find it using the original value. It is also used in many **encryption** algorithms.

As a simple example of the using of hashing in databases, a group of people could be arranged in a database like this:

```
Abernathy, Sara
Epperdingle, Roscoe
Moore, Wilfred
Smith, David
(and many more sorted into alphabetical order)
```

Each of these names would be the key in the database for that person's data. A database search mechanism would first have to start looking character-by-character across the name for matches until it found the match (or ruled the other entries out). But if each of the names were hashed, it might be possible (depending on the number of names in the database) to generate a unique four-digit key for each name. For example:

```
7864 Abernathy, Sara
9802 Epperdingle, Roscoe
1990 Moore, Wilfred
8822 Smith, David
(and so forth)
```

A search for any name would first consist of computing the hash value (using the same hash function used to store the item) and then comparing for a match using that value. It would, in general, be much faster to find a match across four digits, each having only 9 possibilities, than across an unpredictable value length where each character had 26 possibilities.

The hashing **algorithm** is called the *hash function* (and probably the term is derived from the idea that the resulting hash value can be thought of as a "mixed up" version of the represented value). In addition to faster data retrieval, hashing is also used to **encrypt** and decrypt digital signatures (used to authenticate message senders and receivers). The **digital signature** is transformed with the hash function and then both the hashed value (known as a message-digest) and the signature are sent in separate transmissions to the receiver. Using the same hash function as the sender, the receiver derives a message-digest from the signature and compares it with the message-digest it also received. They should be the same.

The hash function is used to index the original value or key and then used later each time the data associated with the value or key is to be retrieved. Thus, hashing is always a one-way operation. There's no need to "reverse engineer" the hash function by analyzing the hashed values. In fact, the ideal hash function can't be derived by such analysis. A good hash function also should not produce the same hash value from two different inputs. If it does, this is known as a *collision*. A hash function that offers an extremely low risk of collision may be considered acceptable.

Here are some relatively simple hash functions that have been used:

- The division-remainder method: The size of the number of items in the table is estimated. That number is then used as a divisor into each original value or key to extract a quotient and a remainder. The remainder is the hashed value. (Since this method is liable to produce a number of collisions, any search mechanism would have to be able to recognize a collision and offer an alternate search mechanism.)

- Folding: This method divides the original value (digits in this case) into several parts, adds the parts together, and then uses the last four digits (or some other arbitrary number of digits that will work) as the hashed value or key.

- Radix transformation: Where the value or key is digital, the number base (or radix) can be changed resulting in a different sequence of digits. (For example, a decimal numbered key could be transformed into a hexadecimal numbered key.) High-order digits could be discarded to fit a hash value of uniform length.

- Digit rearrangement: This is simply taking part of the original value or key such as digits in positions 3 through 6, reversing their order, and then using that sequence of digits as the hash value or key.

A hash function that works well for database storage and retrieval might not work as for cryptographic or error-checking purposes. There are several well-known hash functions used in cryptography. These include the message-digest hash functions MD2, MD4, and MD5, used for hashing digital signatures into a shorter value called a message-digest, and the Secure Hash Algorithm (SHA), a standard algorithm, that makes a larger (60-bit) message digest and is similar to MD4.

HAVi

HAVi is a standard, developed by several leading electronics and computer manufacturers, that allows a number of different home-entertainment and communication devices to operate from a single controller device such as your TV set. The specification uses IEEE **1394** (**FireWire** or **i.LINK**) as the interconnection medium.

With a HAVi-based system, users of home appliances will be able to add new devices without going through complicated installation processes or wading through arcane instruction manuals or help files. Personal computers may be part of a HAVi-based home system, but it will not be necessary for such a system to function.

Here are some examples of how a HAVi system might work:

- You are watching a show on television, and a phone call comes in. You have programmed the television set to automatically mute, so you can carry on the phone conversation without distraction. If you wish, you can carry on the conversation in video-phone mode, and use the television screen as the display.

- Someone rings the buzzer at your front door. You walk over to a wall-based video intercom unit that is playing the five o'clock television news. The screen is switched to a video camera located over the front door so you can see who is there. The audio switches from the television show to a two-way link with the front door.

- You are watching an educational television show, and a scientist uses a word that you do not recognize. You speak the word into a microphone, and an Internet-based dictionary, complete with speech recognition, looks the word up and displays the meaning(s) in the corner of the screen or announces the definition(s) in a synthesized voice.

The HAVi specification will be easy to upgrade. As is the case with popular Web **browser**s today, updates will be available for downloading from the Internet. You might even program the system to automatically download the updates as they become available.

HAVi will be operational across devices from all participating manufacturers. Users will be able to choose their own favorite hardware brands. The video disk recorder (VDR), television set, telephone, home video intercom system, computer (if wanted), and telephone set (with or without video) might all be manufactured by different companies, but they will function seamlessly in the HAVi-based network. When a new device, such as a printer/scanner/fax machine, is installed, the system will configure itself to accommodate it.

Somewhat similar standards for interconnecting devices include Home API (HAPI), **Jini**, Open Services Gateway Initiative (OSGi), Universal PlugnPlay, and Vesa Home Network. HAVi and Vesa are specifically aimed at the home entertainment environment. The other standards are aimed at remote interconnection and make use of Internet protocols.

HCI

Also see **GUI** (graphical user interface).

HCI (human-computer interaction) is the study of how people interact with computers and to what extent computers are or are not developed for successful interaction with human beings. A significant number of major corporations and academic institutions now study HCI. Historically and with some exceptions, computer system developers have not paid much attention to computer ease-of-use. Many computer users today would argue that computer makers are still not paying enough attention to making their products "user-friendly." However, computer system developers might argue that computers are extremely complex products to design and make and that the demand for the services that a computers can provide has always outdriven the demand for ease-of-use.

One important HCI factor is that different users form different conceptions or mental models about their interactions and have different ways of learning and keeping knowledge and skills (different "cognitive styles" as in, for example, "left-brained" and "right-brained" people). In addition, cultural and national differences play a part. Another consideration in studying or designing HCI is that user interface technology changes rapidly, offering new interaction possibilities to which previous research findings may not apply. Finally, user preferences change as they gradually master new interfaces.

HDD

See "hard disk drive"

HDLC

HDLC (High-level Data Link Control) is a group of **protocol**s or rules for transmitting **data** between **network** points (sometimes called **node**s). In HDLC, data is organized into a unit (called a *frame*) and sent across a network to a destination that verifies its successful arrival. The HDLC protocol also manages the flow or pacing at which data is sent. HDLC is one of the most commonly-used protocols in what is layer 2 of the industry communication reference model called Open Systems Interconnection (**OSI**). (Layer 1 is the detailed physical level that involves actually generating and receiving the electronic signals. Layer 3 is the higher level that has knowledge about the network, including access to **router** tables that indicate where to forward or send data. On sending, programming in layer 3 creates a frame that usually contains source and destination network addresses. HDLC (layer 2) encapsulates the layer 3 frame, adding data link control information to a new, larger frame.)

Now an **ISO** standard, HDLC is based on IBM's SDLC protocol, which is widely used by IBM's large customer base in **mainframe** computer environments. In HDLC, the protocol that is essentially SDLC is known as Normal Response Mode (NRM). In Normal Response Mode, a primary station (usually at the mainframe computer) sends data to secondary stations that may be local or may be at remote locations on dedicated leased lines in what is called a multidrop or multipoint network. (This is not the network we usually think of; it's a nonpublic closed network. In this arrangement, although communication is usually **half-duplex**.)

Variations of HDLC are also used for the public networks that use the **X.25** communications protocol and for **frame relay**, a protocol used in both and **wide area network**, public and private.

In the X.25 version of HDLC, the data frame contains a **packet**. (An X.25 network is one in which packets of data are moved to their destination along routes determined by network conditions as perceived by **router**s and reassembled in the right order at the ultimate destination.) The X.25 version of HDLC uses **peer-to-peer** communication with both ends able to initiate communication on **duplex** links. This mode of HDLC is known as Link Access Procedure Balanced (LAPB).

The following table summarizes the HDLC variations and who uses them.

HDLC SUBSET	USES
NRM (Normal Response Mode)	Multipoint networks that typically use SDLC
LAP (Link Access Procedure)	Early X.25 implementations
LAPB (Link Access Procedure, Balanced)	Current X.25 implementations
LAPD (Link Access Procedure for the **ISDN** D channel)	ISDN D channel and frame relay
LAPM (Link Access Procedure for Modems)	Error-correcting modems (specified as part of V.42)

HDML

HDML (Handheld Device Markup Language)—often compared to Wireless Markup Language (WML)—is a language that allows the text portions of Web pages to be presented on **cellular telephone**s and personal digital assistants (**PDAs**) via **wireless** access. Developed by Unwired Planet, HDML is an open language offered royalty-free. According to UP's president Chuck Parrish, any programmer with working knowledge of **HTML**, **CGI**, and **SQL** should be able to write a presentation layer using HDML. One major difference between HDML and WML is that WML is **XML**-based, while HDML is not. Another

difference between HDML and WML is that HDML does not allow scripting, while WML allows it's own version of **JavaScript**, called WMLScript. Although Unwired Planet has changed their name to Phone.com, specifications for HDML are still available on their Web site in **pdf** format.

HD-ROM

HD-ROM (High-Density—Read Only Memory) is a high-capacity storage technology developed at Norsam Technologies in conjunction with an IBM research group that enables a disc to store hundreds of times as much information as a **CD-ROM**. HD-ROM uses a very narrow, finely-focused particle beam (charged gallium ions) to write data. HD-ROM technology can be used to write data on different types of media, such as metal or other durable materials, to create virtually indestructible storage.

HD-ROM's particle beam, at a size of 50 nanometers, enables a storage capacity of 165 gigabytes on discs the same size as a CD or digital versatile disc (**DVD**). In comparison, CD-ROM uses an 800-nanometer **wavelength laser** beam for a storage capacity of 650 megabytes, and **DVD-ROM** uses a 350-nanometer wavelength laser for a storage capacity of 4.7 gigabytes. HD-ROM was designed to store large databases, such as those required by government agencies, banks, insurance companies, scientific users, and libraries. In addition to the enormous storage capacity, HD-ROM's benefits over traditional archival storage systems (such as magnetic tape and **RAID**) include faster access times, greater durability, and lower costs.

HDSL

HDSL (High bit-rate Digital Subscriber Line), one of the earliest forms of DSL, is used for wideband digital transmission within a corporate site and between the telephone company and a customer. The main characteristic of HDSL is that it is symmetrical: an equal amount of bandwidth is available in both directions. For this reason, the maximum data rate is lower than for Asymmetric DSL (**ADSL**). HDSL can carry as much on a single wire of **twisted-pair** cable as can be carried on a **T1** line in North America or an **E1** line in Europe (2,320 Kbps).

head-end

See "cable head-end"

header

In information technology, a header is, in general, something that goes in front of something else and is usually repeated as a standard part of the units of something else. A header can consist of multiple **field**s, each containing its own value. Here are four common uses:

1) In a **document**, a header is some combination of **text** and **image**s that can be made to appear at the top of each page when displayed or printed.

2) In **e-mail**, the header is the part of a message that describes the originator, the addressee and other recipients, message priority level, and so forth.

3) In a computer file, a header may be a field that precedes the main file content and describes the length of the content or other characteristics of the file.

4) In a network transmission unit, a header precedes the data or control signals and describes something about the file or transmission unit, such as its length and whether there are other files or transmission units logically or physically associated with this one.

heap

In certain programming languages including **C** and **Pascal**, a heap is an area of pre-reserved computer **main storage** (**memory**) that a program **process** can use to store data in some variable amount that won't be known until the program is running. For example, a program may accept different amounts of input from one or more users for processing and then do the processing on all the input data at once. Having a certain amount of heap storage already obtained from the operating system makes it easier for the process to manage storage and is generally faster than asking the **operating system** for storage every time it's needed. The process manages its allocated heap by requesting a "chunk" of the heap (called a *heap block*) when needed, returning the blocks when no longer needed, and doing occasional "garbage collecting," which makes blocks available that are no longer being used and also reorganizes the available space in the heap so that it isn't being wasted in small unused pieces.

The term is apparently inspired by another term, **stack**. A stack is similar to a heap except that the blocks are taken out of storage in a certain order and returned in the same way. In Pascal, a *subheap* is a portion of a heap that is treated like a stack.

helical antenna

Also see **satellite**.

A helical antenna is a specialized **antenna** that emits and responds to **electromagnetic field**s with rotating (circular) polarization. These antennas are commonly used at earth-based stations in satellite communications systems. This type of antenna is designed for use with an unbalanced **feed line** such as **coaxial cable**. The center conductor of the cable is connected to the helical element, and the shield of the cable is connected to the reflector.

To the casual observer, a helical antenna appears as one or more "springs" or helixes mounted against a flat reflecting screen. The length of the helical element is one **wavelength** or greater. The reflector is a circular or square metal mesh or sheet whose cross dimension (diameter or edge) measures at least $^3/_4$ wavelength. The helical element has a radius of $^1/_8$ to $^1/_4$ wavelength, and a pitch of $^1/_4$ to $^1/_2$ wavelength. The minimum dimensions depend on the lowest **frequency** at which the antenna is to be used. If the helix or reflector is too small (the frequency is too low), the efficiency is severely degraded. Maximum radiation and response occur along the axis of the helix.

Helical antennas are commonly connected together in so-called *bays* of two, four, or occasionally more elements with a common reflector. The entire assembly can be rotated in the horizontal (azimuth) and vertical (elevation) planes, so the system can be aimed toward a particular satellite. If the satellite is not in a geostationary orbit, the azimuth and elevation rotators can be operated by a computerized robot that is programmed to follow the course of the satellite across the sky.

helical scan

Helical scan is a way of recording information onto magnetic tape. It was used to record TV programs in the 1960s, and has been used by several storage vendors (including IBM, Exabyte, StorageTek and others) in their high-end tape-backup products. It's also the same technology used in digital audio tapes (**Digital Audio Tape**).

Helical scan began in the VCR world and uses a spinning read/write head and diagonal tracks. But the recording and playback heads touch the tape, and an IBM scientist concluded in the mid-1990s that helical-scan cartridges can start to deteriorate after being used from 50 to 250 times. For this reason, IBM introduced its follow-on to helical scan in 1995. Called linear technology, it doesn't store as much data as helical scan but the heads don't touch the tape. Helical scan remains a viable option for high-capacity tape backup.

help desk

In a business enterprise, a help desk is a place that a user of information technology can call to get help with a problem. In many companies, a help desk is simply one person with a phone number and a more or less organized idea of how to handle the problems that come in. In larger companies, a help desk may consist of a group of experts using software to help track the status of problems and other special software to help analyze problems (for example, the status of a company's telecommunications network).

Typically, the term is used for centralized help to users within an enterprise. A related term is **call center**, a place that customers call to place orders, track shipments, get help with products, and so forth.

The World Wide Web offers the possibility of a new, relatively inexpensive, and effectively standard user interface to help desks (as well as to call centers) and appears to be encouraging more automation in help desk service.

Some common names for a help desk include: Computer Support Center, IT Response Center, Customer Support Center, IT Solutions Center, Resource Center, Information Center, and Technical Support Center.

henry

The henry (symbolized H) is the International System of Units (**SI**) unit of **inductance**. Reduced to base SI units, one henry is the equivalent of one kilogram meter squared per second squared per ampere squared ($kg \cdot m^2 \cdot s^{-2} \cdot A^{-2}$).

In a **circuit** where the **current** is changing at a constant rate of one **ampere** per second (A/s), an inductance of 1 H results in the generation of one **volt** (1 V) of potential difference across an inductor. More rapid current changes produce much greater surges of electromotive force. This is the principle by which a spark coil generates a high and dangerous voltage.

The henry is a large unit of inductance. In audio-frequency (**AF**) and radio-frequency (**RF**) applications, units of millihenrys (mH), where $1 \text{ mH} = 10^{-3}$ H, and microhenrys (μH), where $1 \mu\text{H} = 10^{-6}$ H, are common. Occasionally, the filter choke in a power supply, or a field coil designed to produce a large voltage upon release of its stored magnetic energy, will be found whose value can be expressed in henrys. In very-high-frequency (**VHF**), ultra-high-frequency (**UHF**), and **microwave** devices and systems, units of nanohenrys (nH), where $1 \text{ nH} = 10^{-9}$ H, and picohenrys (pH), where $1 \text{ pH} = 10^{-12}$ H, are used.

Also see **capacitor**, **inductor**, **reactance**, and **farad**.

henry per meter

The henry per meter (symbolized H/m) is the unit of magnetic **permeability** in the International System of Units (**SI**). Reduced to base units in SI, 1 H/m is the equivalent of one kilogram meter per second squared per ampere squared (kg times m times s^{-2} times A^{-2}).

Permeability is a characteristic of matter, and is important in the design and construction of electromagnets, inductors, and alternating-current (**AC**) **transformer**s. The permeability of a vacuum (also known as free space) is equal to approximately 1.257×10^{-6} H/m, or 1.257 microhenrys per meter (1.257 μH/m).

The henry per meter is a large unit of permeability. Virtually all substances have permeability far less than 1 (unity). However, permeability can also be expressed as the ratio of the number of henrys per meter in a particular substance to

1.257×10^{-6} H/m. In this scheme, free space has a relative permeability of 1, and most substances have relative permeability greater than or equal to this.

Also see **inductor**, **henry**, **magnetic field**, **meter**, **permeability**, and International System of Units (**SI**).

Herman Hollerith

Born in 1860 in Buffalo, NY, Herman Hollerith was the creator of the Hollerith Electric Tabulating System, the ancestor to computers as we know them today. The system used cards with punched holes to tabulate data. Though first used in 1887 for calculating mortality statistics, Hollerith's punch card system became widely known when it was used to tabulate the U.S. population during the 1890 census.

Hollerith founded the Tabulating Machine Company in 1896. His punch card machine, now fitted with automatic card feeders, was used again in the 1900 census. But by 1910, the U.S. Census Bureau decided to build their own machines because Hollerith was charging too much money for use of his machines.

In 1911, Hollerith's Tabulating Machine Company merged with another machine manufacturer to form Computer Tabulating Recording Company. The new company struggled to gain market share for nearly ten years, and it wasn't until 1920 that it became a leader in the counting machine industry. Hollerith retired in 1921. In 1924, under the direction of Thomas Watson, Sr., the company was renamed International Business Machines Corporation (IBM).

As a primary form of data input for computers, the punch card existed well into the early 1970s before the interactive display terminal began its ascendance. Hollerith died in 1929 in Washington, D.C., and is widely known today as the father of information processing.

hertz

Hertz is a unit of frequency (of change in state or cycle in a sound wave, alternating current, or other cyclical waveform) of one cycle per second. It replaces the earlier term of "cycle per second (cps)."

For example, in the U.S., common house electrical supply is at 60 hertz (meaning the current changes direction or polarity 120 times, or 60 cycles, a second). (In Europe, line frequency is 50 hertz, or 50 cycles per second.) Broadcast transmission is at much higher frequency rates, usually expressed in kilohertz (KHz) or megahertz (MHz).

In acoustic sound, the range of human hearing is from 0 Hz to roughly 20 KHz (depending on many factors, including age and how loud the drummer in your high school rock band played!). The pitch of Middle C on a piano is 263 Hz. Hertz is also used frequently when describing the individual bands of an audio equalizer. To make that Middle C louder, you could boost other frequencies to around 263 Hz with an equalizer.

The unit of measure is named after Heinrich Hertz, German physicist.

heterogeneous

Heterogeneous (pronounced HEH-tuh-roh-DJEEN-ee-uhs, from the Greek *heteros* or "other" and *genos* or "kind") is the characteristic of containing dissimilar constituents. A common use of this word in information technology is to describe a product as able to contain or be part of a "heterogeneous network," consisting of different manufacturers' products that can "interoperate." Heterogeneous networks are made possible by standards-conforming hardware and software interfaces used in common by different products, thus allowing them to communicate with each other. The Internet itself is an example of a heterogeneous network.

A similar word is *heterogenous*, which means "originating elsewhere."

heuristic

As an adjective, heuristic (pronounced hyu-RIS-tik and from the Greek "heuriskein" meaning "to discover") pertains to the process of knowing by trying rather than by following some preestablished formula. (Heuristic can be contrasted with **algorithmic**.) The term seems to have two usages:

1) Describing an approach to learning by trying without necessarily having an organized hypothesis or way of proving that the results proved or disproved the hypothesis. That is, "seat-of-the-pants" or "trial-by-error" learning.

2) Pertaining to the use of the general knowledge gained by experience, sometimes expressed as "using a rule-of-thumb." (However, heuristic knowledge can be applied to complex as well as simple everyday problems. Human chess players use a heuristic approach.)

As a noun, a heuristic is a specific rule-of-thumb or argument derived from experience.

hexadecimal

Hexadecimal describes a base-16 number system. That is, it describes a numbering system containing 16 sequential numbers as base units (including 0) before adding a new position for the next number. (Note that we're using "16" here as a decimal number to explain a number that would be "10" in hexadecimal.) The hexadecimal numbers are 0-9 and then use the letters A-F. We show the equivalence of binary, decimal, and hexadecimal numbers in the table below.

Hexadecimal is a convenient way to express **binary** numbers in modern computers in which a **byte** is almost always defined as containing eight **binary digit**s. When showing the contents of computer storage (for example, when getting a

core dump of storage in order to **debug** a new computer program or when expressing a string of **text character**s or a string of binary values in coding a program or HTML page), one hexadecimal digit can represent the arrangement of four binary digits. Two hexadecimal digits can represent eight binary digits, or a byte.

Binary	Decimal	Hexadecimal
0	0	0
1	1	1
10	2	2
11	3	3
100	4	4
101	5	5
110	6	6
111	7	7
1000	8	8
1001	9	9
1010	10	A
1011	11	B
1100	12	C
1101	13	D
1110	14	E
1111	15	F
10000	16	10
10001	17	11
etc	etc	etc

HFC

See "hybrid fiber coaxial network"

hiccup

In information technology, hiccup is an informal term for a non-recurring problem of indeterminate cause that usually does not cause a significant disruption of work or activity. A hiccup might be due to a transient power level change, a program bug that is only encountered under very rare circumstances, or something else. Unlike hiccups in human beings, a hiccup in a computer or a network tends not to be followed by additional hiccups. If it does, then it may rise to the level of a "problem."

A hiccup is similar to a **glitch** in terms of its temporariness, but is usually less serious.

Hierarchical Storage Management

See "HSM"

High Altitude Long Operation

See "HALO"

High bit-rate DSL

See "HDSL"

high definition television

See "HDTV"

High Level Assembler

High Level Assembler (HLASM) is IBM's **assembler** programming language and the assembler itself for the IBM **OS/390**, **MVS**, **VM**, and VSE operating systems. Released in June 1992, HLASM was the first new assembler language from IBM in twenty years. Version 4 was released in September 2000.

In common with other assembler (sometimes known as assembly) programs, HLASM translates basic computer instructions (such as Load, for example, which instructs the processor to move data from memory to a register) to **machine code**, the **binary** information that is all that computers understand.

HLASM replaced IBM's earlier assembler programs, Assembler H Version 2, Assembler XF, DOS/VSE, and VSE/AF. IBM claims that HLASM features a number of improvements over other assembler programs. HLASM includes support for existing applications through such measures as extensions to earlier IBM assemblers. Automation of common tasks and cross-reference features was included to make programming and administrative tasks easier and less time-consuming, while improved diagnostics were developed to find common, but hard-to-find coding errors more quickly. The HLASM Toolkit, an optional feature, includes additional development, diagnosis, and recovery tools.

High Performance File System

HPFS (High Performance File System) is the **file system** introduced with IBM's **OS/2** Version 1.2. HPFS is noted for handling large files (2 **gigabytes**) across multiple hard disk volumes (addressable up to 2 **terabyte**) and long file names (up to 256 bytes). OS/2 was designed to get around several limitations at the time in MS-DOS, among them its eight-character name. HPFS uses a centrally located **root directory** and B-tree lookup to speed access. HPFS can coexist with the MS-DOS file system, File Allocation Table (**file allocation table**), or run independently.

Among the benefits of HPFS:

- Contiguous storage of extended attributes (without the EA DATA.SF file used by FAT)
- Resistance to file fragmentation
- Small cluster size
- Support for larger file storage devices (up to 512 GB)
- Speedier disk operation

Among the drawbacks:

- Requires more system memory

- HPFS partitions are not visible to MS-DOS, so if you need to boot from a floppy disk, it could be inconvenient.

- Native DOS needs a special utility (Partition Magic from PowerQuest) to access a HPFS partition

High Performance Storage System

See "HPSS"

High-Level Data Link Control

See "HDLC"

High-Performance Parallel Interface

See "HIPPI"

High-Speed Circuit-Switched Data

High-Speed Circuit-Switched Data (HSCSD) is **circuit-switched wireless** data transmission for mobile users at data rates up to 38.4 **Kbps**, four times faster than the standard data rates of the Global System for Mobile (**GSM**) communication standard in 1999. HSCSD is comparable to the speed of many computer **modem**s that communicate with today's fixed telephone networks.

HSCSD is an evolutionary technology on the way to Universal Mobile Telecommunications Service (**UMTS**).

High-Speed Serial Interface

High-Speed Serial Interface (HSSI) is a short-distance communications **interface** that is commonly used to interconnect routing and switching devices on local area networks (**LAN**s) with the higher-speed lines of a wide area network (**WAN**). HSSI is used between devices that are within fifty feet of each other and achieves data rates up to 52 **Mbps**. Typically, HSSI is used to connect a **LAN router** to a **T-3** line. HSSI can be used to interconnect devices on **token ring** and **Ethernet** LANs with devices that operate at Synchronous Optical Network (**SONET**) **OC-1** speeds or on **T-3** lines. HSSI is also used for host-to-host linking, image processing, and disaster recovery applications.

Like **ISDN** and **DSL**, HSSI operates at the **physical layer** of a network, using the standard Open Systems Interconnection (**OSI**) model. The electrical connection uses a 50-**pin** connector. The HSSI transmission technology uses *differential emitter-coupled logic (ECL)*. (ECL is a circuit design in which two **transistor** emitters are connected to a **resistor** that is switched between the emitters, producing high bit rates.) HSSI uses gapped timing. Gapped timing allows a Data Communications Equipment (**DCE**) device to control the flow of data being transmitted from a Data Terminating Equipment (**DTE**) device such as a terminal or computer by adjusting the **clock speed** or deleting clock impulses.

For diagnosing problems, HSSI offers four **loopback** tests. The first loopback tests the cable by looping the signal back after it reaches the DTE port. The second and third loopbacks test the line ports of the local DCE and the remote DTE. The fourth tests the DTE's DCE port. HSSI requires two control signals ("DTE available" and "DCE available") before the data circuit is valid.

The HSSI cable uses the same number of pins and wires as a **SCSI**-2 cable, but uses the HSSI electrical interface. It is not recommended to use a SCSI-2 cable with an HSSI interface.

hijacking

Hijacking is a type of network security attack in which the attacker takes control of a communication—just as an airplane hijacker takes control of a flight—between two entities and masquerades as one of them. In one type of hijacking (also known as a **man in the middle** attack), the perpetrator takes control of an established connection while it is in progress. The attacker intercepts messages in a public key exchange and then retransmits them, substituting their own **public key** for the requested one, so that the two original parties still appear to be communicating with each other directly. The attacker uses a program that appears to be the server to the client and appears to be the client to the server. This attack may be used simply to gain access to the messages, or to enable the attacker to modify them before retransmitting them.

Hijacking is also used to make it appear that one or more Web sites have been taken over. There are two different types of domain name system (**DNS**) hijacking. In one, the attacker gains access to DNS records on a server and modifies them so that requests for the genuine Web page will be redirected elsewhere—usually to a fake page that the attacker has created. This gives the impression to the viewer that the Web site has been compromised, when in fact, only a server has been. In February 2000, an attacker hijacked RSA Security's Web site by gaining access to a DNS server that was not controlled by RSA. By modifying DNS records, the attacker diverted requests to a **spoof** Web site. It appeared to users that an attacker had gained access to the actual RSA Web site data and changed it—a serious problem for a security enterprise. This type of hijacking is difficult to prevent, because administrators control only their own DNS records, and have no control over **upstream** DNS servers. In the second type of DNS hijack, the attacker spoofs valid e-mail accounts and floods the inboxes of the technical and administrative contacts. This type of attack can be prevented by using **authentication** for **InterNIC** records.

In another type of Web site hijack, the perpetrator simply registers a **domain name** similar enough to a legitimate one that users are likely to type it, either by mistaking the actual name or through a typo. This type of hijack is currently being employed to send many unwary citizens to porn sites when they were attempting to visit official Web sites such as Amazon, Dow Jones, and the White House, among others.

HiperLAN

HiperLAN is a set of wireless local area network (**WLAN**) communication standards primarily used in European countries. There are two specifications: HiperLAN/1 and HiperLAN/2. Both have been adopted by the European Telecommunications Standards Institute (ETSI).

The HiperLAN standards provide features and capabilities similar to those of the **IEEE 802.11** wireless local area network (**LAN**) standards, used in the U.S. and other adopting countries. HiperLAN/1 provides communications at up to 20 **Mbps** in the 5-GHz range of the radio frequency (**RF**) spectrum. HiperLAN/2 operates at up to 54 Mbps in the same RF band. HiperLAN/2 is compatible with **3G** (third-generation) WLAN systems for sending and receiving data, images, and voice communications. HiperLAN/2 has the potential, and is intended, for implementation worldwide in conjunction with similar systems in the 5-GHz RF band.

Also see **802.11**.

HIPPI

HIPPI (High-Performance Parallel Interface) is a standard point-to-point **protocol** for transmitting large amounts of data at up to billions of bits per second over relatively short distances, mainly on local area networks (**LAN**s). The proponents of HIPPI believe that its use can make computers, interconnected storage devices, and other resources on a local area network function as though they were all within a single supercomputer. (One firm has coined the term *SuperLAN* for this idea.) HIPPI is considered an ideal technology for the transfer of "big data," such as data warehouse updating, audio and video streams, and data backup within a range up to 10 kilometers.

HIPPI uses a point-to-point link. The original HIPPI standard specifies data transfer at 800 **Mbps** with a 32-bit data **bus** or 1600 Mbps with a 64-bit data bus. Basic HIPPI uses 50 **twisted pair** copper wires with a maximum range limited to 25 meters. Data is sent in bursts of 1024 or 2048 bytes on a unidirectional channel. **Full duplex** can be achieved using two channels. An important part of HIPPI is the use of a network **switch** that will allow data to be forwarded in the network with minimal processing (the switches are called *nonblocking crossbar switches*). Error detection is provided, but error correction is left to a higher protocol level. HIPPI packets can be encapsulated and sent over **ATM** and **Fibre Channel** networks.

Serial HIPPI, a later version of HIPPI, is designed for networks up to 10 kilometers using **optical fiber** cable. An even faster technology is HIPPI-6400, which promises up to 6.4 **Gbps**. (See the table that follows.)

HIPPI defines interfaces at the Physical layer (layer 1) and for part of the Data-Link Control (**DLC**) (layer 2) levels of the Open Systems Interconnection (**OSI**) communications

model. In addition to the standard HIPPI specification, there are working papers for proposed standards for related aspects of using HIPPI at the application level.

The following table summarizes HIPPI technologies.

HIPPI Technology	Speed	Maximum Distance	Physical Medium
HIPPI-800	800 **Mbps** (100 megabytes per second)	25 meters	One 50-pair **twisted pair** copper wire
HIPPI-1600	1600 Mbps (200 Mbytes per second)	25 meters	Two 50-pair **twisted pair** copper wire
HIPPI-800 Serial	800 Mbps	1 kilometer with... 10 kilometers with...	**multimode fiber** **optical fiber** **single mode fiber** optical fiber
HIPPI-1600 Serial	1600 Mbps	1 kilometer with... 10 kilometers with...	**multimode** fiber **optical fiber** **single mode fiber** optical fiber
HIPPI-6400	6.4 **Gbps**	50 meters	**twisted pair copper wire**
HIPPI-6400	6.4 Gbps	1 kilometer	**optical fiber**

history

In a Web **browser**, the history is a detailed list of Web sites the computer has visited which remains in a computer's memory for a pre-determined number of days. (The number of days the computer retains its history can be set in the browser's preferences.) History can be used to backtrack where you have gone on the Web; the list of Web sites in a browser's history can be viewed by date, time of day, title, address (**URL**), alphabetical order, or number of repeat visits. Many parent groups advocate checking the history of a family computer to monitor where children have gone online. Internet Explorer history can be viewed by clicking on the History **icon** (which resembles a sun dial) in the browser **toolbar**. Netscape history can be viewed by clicking on the word "Communicator" followed by "Tools" and then "History."

hit

A hit is a single file request in the **access log** of a Web **server**. A request for an **HTML page** with three graphic images will result in four hits in the log: one for the HTML text file and one for each of the graphic image files. While a hit is a meaningful measure of how much traffic a server handles, it can be a misleading indicator of how many pages are being

looked at. Instead, advertising agencies and their clients look at the number of pages delivered and ad **impression**s or views.

HLASM

See "High Level Assembler"

HOLAP

See "hybrid online analytical processing"

hole

In physics, a hole is an electric charge carrier with a positive charge, equal in magnitude but opposite in **polarity** to the charge on the **electron**. Holes and electrons are the two types of charge carriers responsible for **current** in **semiconductor** materials.

A hole is the absence of an electron in a particular place in an **atom**. Although it is not a physical particle in the same sense as an electron, a hole can be passed from atom to atom in a semiconductor material. Electrons orbit the nucleus at defined energy levels called *bands* or *shells*. A hole forms in an atom when an electron moves from the so-called *valence band* (the shell outside the closed shells that is partially or completely filled with electrons) into the *conduction band* (the outer "cloud" from which electrons most easily escape from, or are accepted by, the atom).

Both electrons and holes are present in any semiconductor substance. Electrons flow from minus to plus, and holes "flow" from plus to minus. The more abundant charge carriers are called *majority carriers*; the less abundant are called *minority carriers*. In N-type semiconductor material, electrons are the majority carriers and holes are the minority carriers. In P-type semiconductor material, the opposite is true.

In the processing of semiconductors, the number of charge carriers can be increased by a process known as *doping*, which consists of adding minute amounts of elements called *impurities*. Certain impurities, when added to a semiconducting element such as silicon, increase the number of electrons and produce an N-type material; other impurities increase the number of holes and produce a P-type material. Both N-type and P-type material are important in the manufacture of solid-state electronic components.

hologram

A hologram (pronounced HOL-o-gram) is a three-dimensional image, created with photographic projection. The term is taken from the Greek words *holos* (whole) and *gramma* (message). Unlike **3-D** or **virtual reality** on a two-dimensional computer display, a hologram is a truly three-dimensional and free-standing image that does not simulate spatial depth or require a special viewing device.

Theoretically, holograms could someday be transmitted electronically to a special display device in your home and business.

The theory of holography was developed by Dennis Gabor in 1947. The development of laser technology made holography possible.

holographic storage

Holographic storage is computer storage that uses laser beams to store computer-generated data in three dimensions. The goal is to store a lot of data in a little bit of space.

Perhaps you have a bank credit card containing a logo in the form of a **hologram**. The idea is to use this type of technology to store computer information.

Although no one has yet mass-commercialized this technology, many vendors—including Lucent and IBM—are working on it. Prototypes of holographic storage devices can store at least 12 times the amount of information on today's largest magnetic hard disk drives, with input/output rates more than 10 times faster than what is possible today.

home network

A home network is two or more computers interconnected to form a local area network (**LAN**) within the home. In the U.S., for example, it is estimated that 15 million homes have more than one computer. A home network allows computer owners to interconnect multiple computers so that each can share files, programs, printers, other peripheral devices, and Internet access with other computers, reducing the need for redundant equipment and, in general, making everything easier to use. For example, if you have an older computer without a CD-ROM, you can access your newer computer's CD-ROM instead of purchasing one for your older computer. Sharing files across a home network is also easier than copying a file to a floppy and running to the other computer to use the file. A new trend, sometimes referred to as an *intelligent network*, extends the home network to include controls for the home ambient environment, security systems, and kitchen devices. In general, a home network is distinguished from a small office-home office (**SOHO**) network only by its more general purpose and possibly by the kinds of devices that are interconnected.

Before deciding what kind of home network you want, you must ask yourself if it bothers you to drill holes and run wire throughout your house? Do you mind opening your computer and installing network cards? Are your computers in the same room? What is your budget for a home network? Do you mind paying someone to come in and do the setup for you?

There are five types of home networks, two that use wire connections and three that use **wireless** connections:

- **Direct cable connection:** This allows you to connect both computers with a $10 **null modem** that plugs into both computers' **serial, parallel,** or **Universal Serial Bus port**. You simply configure the Windows 9x/NT Direct Cable Connection feature and you're ready to go. You lose your printer's parallel port if you use a parallel port connection. USB is faster than both serial and parallel, but you must make sure you are using Windows 95B or Windows 98 when using a USB network. This is a possible choice when two computers are in the same room.

- **Traditional Ethernet:** A **peer-to-peer Ethernet** network requires installing network interface cards (**NIC**) inside each computer and interconnecting them with a **coaxial cable** cable or a **twisted pair** cable. You have to install **driver** and configure Windows 9x/NT. The drawback to an Ethernet network is the difficulty of hardware installation. Will your computers recognize the new cards? If your computers have several cards installed already, you might run into hardware conflicts. This type of network is suitable for use with two to twelve computers. You can have your computers scattered throughout your house, but you will have to wire each room that has a computer. Beginning cost of an Ethernet network is $100.

- **AC network:** An **AC** (alternating current) network is a possibility when computers are in different locations in your house. You don't need to drill any holes or wire any rooms. You simply plug one end of an adapter into the parallel port of your computer and plug the other end into an outlet. You do the same for each computer. Your data is transmitted through the power lines. You can have a ready-made network anywhere in the house at any time. When purchasing the equipment and software for your AC network, make sure it includes extra outlet strips and an adapter for your printer. The software setup can be difficult for AC networks. The cost of an AC network is $200 for two computers.

- **Phoneline network** This type of wireless network was developed by the Home Phoneline Networking Alliance (HomePNA) to offer an easy and inexpensive (starting at $150 for two computers) solution that uses existing phone lines. For example, Action Tec's ActionLink Home Networking Kit provides **PCI card** that share a single **registered jack** with your **modem** and telephone. The HomePNA technology is designed to not interfere with your voice and data transmissions. This means that you can talk on the phone and use your Internet connection at the same time without any noticeable decrease in modem speed. A phoneline network does require you to install PCI cards and software drivers. The data transfer rate of a phoneline network is 10 **Mbps**.

- **Radio Free (RF) network:** This type of wireless network uses radio frequency (**RF**) waves to transmit through walls and floors up to 800 feet. The only hardware is a special card inserted into each computer or a **transceiver** plugged into each computer's parallel port. If you purchase an RF network that uses transceivers, make sure equipment is included for connecting your printer. The problem with an RF network is interference from other wireless communication devices. Some RF network packages promise no interference from other wireless devices. RF networks start at $100.

A number of companies offer approaches to an *intelligent network* in the home. For example, IBM is partnering with home developers to equip new houses with Home Director Model 200, which includes the distribution of video and satellite connections throughout your house, using your DVD player in the living room to watch a movie in your bedroom, automatically turning on and off your lights, and lowering your thermostat at night.

home page

1) For a Web user, the home page is the first Web **page** that is displayed after starting a Web **browser** like Netscape's Navigator or Microsoft's Internet Explorer. The browser is usually preset so that the home page is the first page of the browser manufacturer. However, you can set it to open to any **Web site**. For example, you can specify "http://www.yahoo.com" or "http://whatis.com" as your home page. You can also specify that there be no home page (a blank space will be displayed) in which case you choose the first page from your bookmark list or enter a Web address.

2) For a Web site developer, a home page is the first page presented when a user selects a **site** or **presence** on the World Wide Web. The usual address for a Web site is the home page address, although you can enter the address (**Uniform Resource Locator**) of any page and have that page sent to you.

Home Phoneline Networking Alliance

The HPNA (Home Phoneline Networking Alliance) is an industry group that promotes standards for using existing phone lines and jacks to interconnect computers within a home. The HPNA's **HomePNA** standard is one of several leading technologies for **home network**.

HPNA's approach is one of several competing home networking approaches. Others include **Ethernet**, the powerline protocol, or the **Bluetooth** standard. Ethernet is a widely-used standard for a local area nework (**LAN**) that requires each computer to be equipped with an interface card and the installation of thicker cabling. Powerline is a slower data transmission method that uses the home's electrical wiring. Bluetooth uses wireless technology to transmit data between devices within a 30-foot range. In addition to HomePNA, there are other proprietary approaches to home networks using existing phone lines.

The Home Phoneline Networking Alliance is a consortium with over 100 members, including 3Com, AT&T Wireless, IBM, Intel, Compaq, Lucent Technologies, and Hewlett-Packard.

homecam

See "cam"

HomePNA

HomePNA is an industry standard for interconnecting computers within a home using existing telephone lines and **registered jacks**. Using HomePNA, multiple computer users in a home can share a single Internet connection, open or copy files from different computers, share printers, and play multiuser computer games. The latest version, HomePNA 2.0, allows data transmission at a rate of 10 **Mbps** over a standard telephone line's home wiring system using the **Ethernet CSMA/CD** framing and transmission protocol. HomePNA can be used without interrupting normal voice or fax services. One user can talk on the phone at the same time other users are sharing the same line to access the Web or share other computer resources. A Quality of Service (**QoS**) feature assigns higher-level priorities to applications that are latency-sensitive like packetized voice and streaming audio and video. The **home network** standard is sponsored by members of the Home Phoneline Networking Alliance (**HPNA**).

The shared phone line approach is one of several home network approaches. Others include the regular Ethernet local area network, the powerline protocol, or the **Bluetooth** standard. Ethernet is a widely-used standard for a local area network (**LAN**) that ordinarily requires each computer to be equipped with an interface card, connected to a **hub**, and sometimes the use of thicker cabling. (HomePNA uses the Ethernet line protocol with existing phone cabling.) Powerline is a slower data transmission method that uses the home's electrical wiring. Bluetooth uses wireless technology to transmit data between devices within a 30-foot range. In addition to HomePNA, there are other proprietary approaches to home networks using existing phone lines.

HomeRF

HomeRF (for *home radio frequency*) is a home networking standard developed by Proxim Inc. that combines the **802.11b** and Digital Enhanced Cordless Telecommunication (**DECT**) portable phone standards into a single system. HomeRF uses a **frequency-hopping** technique to deliver speeds of up to 1.6 **Mbps** over distances of up to 150 ft—too short a range for most business applications, but suitable for the home market that it was specifically developed for.

HomeRF is one of two standards currently vying for the wireless home network market share. The other main contender, **Wi-Fi** uses a direct sequence spread spectrum (**DSSS**) transmission method to deliver speeds of up to 11

Mbps. HomeRF is said to have better mechanisms in place to deal with interference (from microwave ovens, for example) and to handle voice, video, and audio data better than Wi-Fi. Nevertheless, Wi-Fi is significantly faster than Home-RF—albeit more expensive as well. Wi-Fi products have already become fairly well established in corporate wide area networks (**WANs**), which tend to support the older standard for home networks, since consumers tend to prefer to use the same technologies in both home and work settings. Although industry support is split between the two technologies, a number of companies (such as IBM and Proxim itself) have begun to back both standards.

honey pot

A honey pot is a computer system on the Internet that is expressly set up to attract and "trap" people who attempt to penetrate other people's computer systems. (This includes the **hacker**, **cracker**, and **script kiddy**.) To set up a honey pot, it is recommended that you:

- Install the **operating system** without **patch**es installed and using typical defaults and options
- Make sure that there is no data on the system that cannot safely be destroyed
- Add the application that is designed to record the activities of the invader

Maintaining a honey pot is said to require a considerable amount of attention and may offer as its highest value nothing more than a learning experience (that is, you may not catch any hackers).

hook

In programming, a hook is a place and usually an interface provided in packaged code that allows a programmer to insert customized programming. For example, a programmer might want to provide code that analyzed how often a particular logic path was taken within a program. Or a progammer might want to insert an additional capability. Typically, hooks are provided for a stated purpose and are documented for the programmer.

Some writers use hook to also mean the program that gets inserted.

hoot and holler

See "hoot-n-holler"

hoot-n-holler

In telecommunications, a hoot-n-holler is a dedicated "always on" connection used for two-way business-to-business voice communication. Hoot-n-holler networks evolved from a type of crude point-to-point plain old telephone system (**POTS**) used by small businesses with large inventories in the mid-1900's. A plumbing supply company in the 1950's, for instance, might use a full-duplex, transmit-and-receive device commonly called a "squawk box" or "shout down" to allow the front desk person to have two-way communication with the warehouse supervisor over a dedicated open phone line without having to pick up a receiver or dial a phone. Hoot-n-holler found a home at brokerage firms in the 1960's, where it became more sophisticated and grew into the speakerphone and conference-call technology many businesses use today.

Hoot-n-holler is still used extensively in the financial community to share market updates and trading orders and is also used at news agencies, weather bureaus, transportation providers, and in manufacturing work environments. According to Cisco Systems, some larger financial firms budget 2−3 million dollars a year just for distribution of their hoot-n-holler feeds to remote branch offices. Voice over IP (**VoIP**) hoot-n-holler is slowly gaining popularity and is being promoted as a cost-effective solution for "party-line" communication because it still allows users in a hoot-n-holler network to talk simultaneously if they want to, but also allows any idle bandwidth to be reclaimed and used by data applications.

hop

1) In a packet-switching network, a hop is the trip a **data packet** takes from one **router** or intermediate point to another in the network. On the Internet (or a network that uses **TCP/IP**), the number of hops a packet has taken toward its destination (called the "hop count") is kept in the packet header. A packet with an exceedingly large hop count is discarded.

2) Using Cellular Digital Packet Data (CDPD), a hop is a switch to another radio frequency (RF) channel.

Hopper, Grace

See "Grace Hopper"

horn antenna

A horn antenna is used for the transmission and reception of **microwave** signals. It derives its name from the characteristic flared appearance. The flared portion can be square, rectangular, or conical. The maximum radiation and response corresponds with the axis of the horn. In this respect, the antenna resembles an acoustic horn. It is usually fed with a **waveguide**.

In order to function properly, a horn antenna must be a certain minimum size relative to the **wavelength** of the incoming or outgoing **electromagnetic field**. If the horn is too small or the wavelength is too large (the **frequency** is too low), the antenna will not work efficiently.

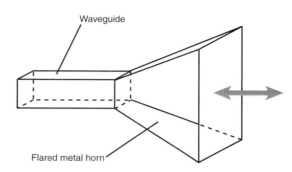

Waveguide

Flared metal horn

Horn antennas are commonly used as the active element in a **dish antenna**. The horn is pointed toward the center of the dish reflector. The use of a horn, rather than a **dipole antenna** or any other type of antenna, at the focal point of the dish minimizes loss of energy (leakage) around the edges of the dish reflector. It also minimizes the response of the antenna to unwanted signals not in the favored direction of the dish.

Horn antennas are used all by themselves in short-range radar systems, particularly those used by law-enforcement personnel to measure the speeds of approaching or retreating vehicles.

host

The term "host" is used in several contexts, in each of which it has a slightly different meaning:

1) In Internet protocol specifications, the term "host" means any computer that has full two-way access to other computers on the Internet. A host has a specific "local or host number" that, together with the network number, forms its unique **IP address**. If you use **Point-to-Point Protocol** to get access to your access provider, you have a unique IP address for the duration of any connection you make to the Internet and your computer is a host for that period. In this context, a "host" is a **node** in a network.

2) For companies or individuals with a **Web site**, a host is a computer with a **Web server** that serves the pages for one or more Web sites. A host can also be the company that provides that service, which is known as **hosting**.

3) In IBM and perhaps other mainframe computer environments, a host is a mainframe computer (which is now usually referred to as a "large server"). In this context, the mainframe has intelligent or "dumb" workstations attached to it that use it as a host provider of services. (This does not mean that the host only has "servers" and the workstations only have "clients." The server/client relationship is a programming model independent of this contextual usage of "host.")

4) In other contexts, the term generally means a device or program that provides services to some smaller or less capable device or program.

hosting

Hosting (also known as *Web site hosting*, *Web hosting*, and *Webhosting*) is the business of housing, serving, and maintaining files for one or more **Web sites**. More important than the computer space that is provided for Web site files is the fast connection to the Internet. Most hosting services offer connections on **T-carrier system** lines. Typically, an individual business hosting its own site would require a similar connection and it would be expensive. Using a hosting service lets many companies share the cost of a fast Internet connection for serving files.

A number of Internet access providers, such as America Online, offer subscribers free space for a small Web site that is hosted by one of their computers. Geocities is a Web site that offers registered visitors similar free space for a Web site. While these services are free, they are also very basic.

A number of hosting companies describe their services as **virtual hosting**. Virtual hosting usually implies that their services will be transparent and that each Web site will have its own **domain name** and set of e-mail addresses. In most usages, *hosting* and *virtual hosting* are synonyms. Some hosting companies let you have your own **virtual server**, the appearance that you are controlling a **server** that is dedicated entirely to your site.

Dedicated hosting is the provision of a **dedicated server** machine that is dedicated to the traffic to your Web site. Only very busy sites require dedicated hosting. Many companies purchase their own servers and place them on a site that provides fast access to the Internet. This practice is called **colocation**.

hosting reseller

See "reseller hosting"

hot fix

See "hotfix"

hot key

A hot key is a key or a combination of keys on a computer **keyboard** that, when pressed at one time, performs a task (such as starting an application) more quickly than by using a **mouse** or other input device. Hot keys are sometimes called shortcut keys. Hot keys are supported by many **operating system** and applications.

The specific task performed by a particular hot key varies by operating system or application. However, there are commonly-used hot keys. For example, pressing the F1 key in any application running Windows usually brings up a help menu. The "Alt + F4" combination results in closing the

current application or, if no application is open, shutting down Windows. To find out which hot keys are used in an application, search the index in that application's help menu using the words "hot keys" or "shortcut keys."

The "F" or **function key** that come on most computer keyboards can be viewed as a built-in set of hot keys or potential hot keys whose use is determined by the operating system or the current application. Some operating systems or applications allow certain hot keys to be set up to perform a task specified by the user or to start a specific application. For example, a user could set up one hot key to start a music compact disk (CD) and another to adjust the speaker volume.

Microsoft's sales literature refers to hot keys as though they are keys separate from function keys.

hot site and cold site

A hot site is a commercial disaster recovery service that allows a business to continue computer and network operations in the event of a computer or equipment disaster. For example, if an enterprise's data processing center becomes inoperable, that enterprise can move all data processing operations to a hot site. A hot site has all the equipment needed for the enterprise to continue operation, including office space and furniture, telephone jacks, and computer equipment.

A cold site is a similar type of disaster recovery service that provides office space, but the customer provides and installs all the equipment needed to continue operations. A cold site is less expensive, but it takes longer to get an enterprise in full operation after the disaster.

Typically, a business has an annual contract with a company that offers hot and cold site services with a monthly service charge. Some disaster recovery services offer **backup** services so that all company data is available regardless of whether a hot site or cold site is used. If an enterprise must use a hot or cold site, there are usually daily fees and other incidental fees in addition to the basic service charge.

Hot Standby Router Protocol

Hot Standby Router Protocol (HSRP) is a routing **protocol** that allows **host** computers on the Internet to use multiple **router**s that act as a single virtual router, maintaining connectivity even if the first **hop** router fails, because other routers are on "hot standby"—ready to go. Configured on Cisco routers running the Internet Protocol (**IP**) over **Ethernet**, Fiber Distributed-Data Interface (**FDDI**), and **token ring** local area networks (**LAN**s), HSRP provides automatic router backup. The protocol is fully compatible with Novell's Internetwork Packet Exchange (**IPX**), **AppleTalk**, and Banyan VINES, and (in some configurations) with Xerox Network Systems (XNS) and **DECnet**.

Developed by **Cisco** and specified in **IETF** Request for Comments (**RFC**) 2281, HSRP ensures that only a single router (called the *active router*) is forwarding **packets** on behalf of the virtual router at any given time. A standby router is chosen to be ready to become the active router, in the event that the current active router fails. HSRP defines a mechanism used to determine active and standby routers by referring to their **IP address**es. Once these are determined, the failure of an active router will not cause any significant interruption of connectivity.

On any given LAN, there may be multiple, possibly overlapping, hot standby groups, each with a single Media Access Control (**MAC**) address and IP address; the IP address should belong to the primary **subnet**, but must be different from any actual or virtual addresses allocated to any routers or hosts on the network.

hot swap

A hot swap is the replacement of a hard drive, CD-ROM drive, power supply, or other device with a similar device while the computer system using it remains in operation. The replacement can be because of a device failure or, for storage devices, to substitute other data.

Hot swapping works by providing a rack or enclosure for the device that provides an appearance to the computer's **bus** or I/O controller that the device is still there while it's being removed and replaced with another device. A hot swap arrangement is sometimes provided where multiple devices are shared on a local area network. Hot swap arrangements are sold for both **SCSI** and **IDE** hard drives. Hot swap versions of a redundant array of independent devices (**RAID**) are also available.

hotfix

In Microsoft products, a hotfix is code (sometimes called a **patch**) that fixes a **bug** in the product. Users of the products are typically notified or can obtain information about current hotfixes at Microsoft's Web site and download the hotfixes they wish to apply. Hotfixes are sometimes packaged as a set of fixes called a combined hotfix or a **service pack**.

Quick fix engineering (QFE) is a newer Microsoft term for a hotfix.

HotSync

HotSync is the registered trade name for a sophisticated method of linking between a **Palm** handheld computer and a more substantial notebook, desktop, or other computer. Such a link can be done using a so-called HotSync cable, or using a wireless connection. If the portable computer and the larger machine are in the same room, the link can use infrared radiation (**IR**).

Direct linking between computers eliminates the need for cumbersome disks or tapes when data must be copied from one **hard drive** to another. But the versatility of the scheme goes beyond simple data transfer. In a network, direct linking allows each portable computer to take advantage of the resources of the whole system, and also allows communication between or among end users.

HP 9000

The HP 9000 is a line of **UNIX**-based business **server**s from **Hewlett-Packard** (HP) with server models that span **enterprise** applications from the "entry-level" (branch or department-level computers, Web hosting servers, and so forth) through the **midrange** with needs for handling advanced enterprise resource planning (**ERP**) and analytical customer resource management (**CRM**) up to its high-end servers for very computing-intensive applications. Within the entry-level, midrange, and high-end categories, a customer can choose one of several "classes" of server. In all cases, the **operating system** is **HP-UX**.

The HP 9000 uses HP's 8600 processor with PA-**RISC** architecture. At the high end, HP offers **SuperDome**, a product that consists of up to 64 HP 9000 processors that can do **parallel processing**. The customer can choose to use as many processors as are needed and is charged accordingly.

The HP 9000 represents HP's newest line of computer servers. Its well-known line of HP 3000 computers has also been updated as the **HP e3000** and continue to support older applications as well as new ones.

HP e3000

The HP e3000 is a line of **midrange** business **server**s that carries on the well-known series of 3000 computers from **Hewlett-Packard** (HP). The e3000 uses HP's **MPE/iX operating system**, which can run applications written for the first 3000 systems that date as far back as the early 1970s and also run **POSIX**-conforming (**UNIX**-based) applications as well.

The HP e3000 servers are offered in a compact, entry-level ("a-class") model and several larger ("n-class") models. The "a-class" model is also suggested as a replacement for HP's older 3000 models, which will no longer be supported after April 30, 2002.

MPE/iX provides "Web connectivity" (support for **TCP/IP**) as well as the ability to develop and run applications written in **Java**.

HP OpenView

HP OpenView is a suite of business computer management or "**e-services**" programs from **Hewlett-Packard** (HP), which states that the suite is "among the world's 20 largest software businesses." The OpenView programs are frequently sold to **HP 9000** and **e3000** business server

customers. An HP customer's IT professionals can use OpenView to manage applications, device availability, network conditions and status, system performance, service and program maintenance, and storage resources. Altogether, there are about 30 different OpenView products.

HP9000

See "HP 9000"

HPSS

HPSS (High Performance Storage System) is a storage management system especially designed for moving large files and large amounts of data around a network that may consist of **parallel processing** computers, **supercomputer**s, and clusters of high-end **workstation**s. HPSS is especially valuable for moving around large amounts of data for scientific and other complex applications and for moving large video files across the network.

Geared to work with both directly-connected and **network-attached storage** devices, HPSS supports data transfer rates greater than 1 gigabytes per second and is aimed at enterprises that handle quantities of data in the **petabyte** range. The HPSS technology makes use of "data movers," which are specialized software modules geared to sending very large data streams.

A joint development of industry and the U.S. government, HPSS is the result of contributions from more than 20 organizations, including Transarc, Objectivity, IBM, Los Alamos National Laboratory, and the San Diego Supercomputer Center. HPSS vendors include Cray, SGI, Sun Microsystems, and Intel.

HP-UX

HP-UX is the **UNIX**-based **operating system** for the **HP 9000** series of business **server**s from **Hewlett-Packard**. The 9000 series spans a spectrum of business needs and server sizes, ranging from an "entry-level" server appropriate for an Internet **firewall**, **Web hosting**, or branch office use to a **midrange** server appropriate for advanced enterprise resource planning (**ERP**) or Web commerce, to a high-end model for larger-scale and more computing-intensive applications. HP's **SuperDome** computer is based on parallel operation of up to 64 9000 processors. All of these servers run HP-UX.

HP also offers the e3000 line of servers, evolved from its long-established HP3000. The e3000 servers use HP's **MPE/iX** operating system.

HS

See "modem lights"

HSB

See "hue, saturation, and brightness"

HSCSD

See "High-Speed Circuit-Switched Data"

HSM

HSM (Hierarchical Storage Management) is **policy**-based management of file **backup** and **archiving** in a way that uses storage devices economically and without the user needing to be aware of when files are being retrieved from backup storage media. Although HSM can be implemented on a standalone system, it is more frequently used in the distributed network of an enterprise. The hierarchy represents different types of storage media, such as **redundant array of independent disks** systems, optical storage, or tape, each type representing a different level of cost and speed of retrieval when access is needed. For example, as a file ages in an archive, it can be automatically moved to a slower but less expensive form of storage. Using an HSM product, an administrator can establish and state guidelines for how often different kinds of files are to be copied to a backup storage device. Once the guideline has been set up, the HSM software manages everything automatically.

HSM adds to archiving and file protection for disaster recovery the capability to manage storage devices efficiently, especially in large-scale user environments where storage costs can mount rapidly. It also enables the automation of backup, archiving, and migration to the hierarchy of storage devices in a way that frees users from having to be aware of the storage policies. Older files can automatically be moved to less expensive storage. If needed, they appear to be immediately accessible and can be restored transparently from the backup storage medium. The apparently available files are known as *stubs* and point to the real location of the file in backup storage. The process of moving files from one storage medium to another is known as *migration*.

An administrator can set high and low thresholds for hard disk capacity that HSM software will use to decide when to migrate older or less-frequently used files to another medium. Certain file types, such as **executable** files (programs), can be excluded from those to be migrated.

HSRP

See "Hot Standby Router Protocol"

HSSI

See "High-Speed Serial Interface"

HT

See "handie talkie"

htaccess

.htaccess is the default name for a file that is used to indicate who can or cannot access the contents of a specific file directory from the Internet or an intranet. The .htaccess file is a configuration file that resides in a directory and indicates which users or groups of users can be allowed access to the files contained in that directory.

.htaccess was introduced as a directory-level, user authentication method along with the original programs developed for retrieving Web pages over the Internet, such as **Hypertext Transfer Protocol daemon**. When users type in a **Uniform Resource Locator** (the name of a Web site they want to go to), the URL begins with "http://". This command is recognized by the underlying Web server software program, HTTPd (for HyperText Transfer Protocol daemon). (A **daemon** is a program that sits waiting for requests for other programs.)

The main access control file used by HTTPd is the global access configuration file, which often resides at the **root directory** of the HTTPd server. .htaccess files are additional, directory-level access control files used by HTTPd.

When the HTTPd server receives a user's request for a document, it looks in the document's own directory, as well as higher up in the chain of directories for these types of access control files. If it finds .htaccess, it will look there to see whether or not the user is allowed to access the file. Based on the information it finds, it may ask the user for his or her user name and password first, before sending the requested document.

.htaccess is the default file name used by HTTPd when no other name has been indicated in the HTTPd server's resource configuration file, srm.conf. Another file name can be specified in this file, under the AccessFileName <file> line, where <file> would normally indicate .htaccess or another name. (In Netscape servers, this file name is called .nsconfig, and uses a different syntax from .htaccess.)

Whether or Not to Use .htaccess

.htaccess is often used in settings where a group network administrator wants to control who views or changes the contents of the directories that relate to his or her groups or users. In these settings, it is not practical or advisable to give the administrator primary access to all of the HTTPd server's functions, and all of its other directories and configuration files. Having the local-level control provided by .htaccess files allows more flexibility for the administrator to create and change directory access controls, as needed.

Some disadvantages to using *.htaccess* files have been noted: If an organization has several hundred .htaccess files on several hundred directories, each granting or denying user access to their own contents, it is more difficult for the company's network administrators to prepare a global access or authentication strategy and keep up with changes. Also, .htaccess files can be overwritten very easily, causing problems for users who once could access a directory's contents, but now cannot. Finally, .htaccess files are more likely to be opened or retrieved by unauthorized users.

htm

htm is sometimes used as a short form of the file name **suffix** for an **HTML** file. For example, the file for our definition of *computer* might be named "computer.htm" instead of "computer.html". The main advantage is that it's one character shorter. The disadvantage is that it's not quite as easy to recognize as an HTML file. Prior to wide-spread use of Windows 95 and later systems, there was another reason to prefer the three-character suffix rather than the four-character. Certain operating systems, such as Windows 3.1 and OS/2 used the original DOS **operating system** naming conventions, in which names were limited to eight characters and suffixes to three characters. So it was safer to create file names and suffixes that met this "8.3" limitation. (For example, if you created an HTML page coding hypertext links to your other pages based on a four-character suffix (".html") system and then moved that page to a Web **server** that only allowed a three-character suffix, your file name suffixes would all be shortened and your links would no longer work. And if you created links with the three-character suffix and moved it to a server that always required four-character suffixes for HTML files, you would be in trouble again.)

Today, the operating systems most people are likely to create HTML pages on and serve them from are all operating systems (such as Windows 95/98/NT, Mac OS, and UNIX-based systems) that support longer file names and suffixes. So if you were building a new Web site, you would most likely use the four-character html suffix for clarity (unless you preferred the brevity of the three-character suffix) because you could know that you could safely use either suffix—as long as the suffixes in your links and your file names matched.

However, if you have an existing Web site that started out using the three-character suffix, you may prefer to leave everything as it is. If you do move to a server that requires a four-character suffix for server consistency, you could do a search-and-replace at that time.

HTML

HTML (Hypertext Markup Language) is the set of **markup** symbols or codes inserted in a file intended for display on a World Wide Web **browser** page. The markup tells the Web browser how to display a Web page's words and images for the user. Each individual markup code is referred to as an element (but many people also refer to it as a **tag**). Some elements come in pairs that indicate when some display effect is to begin and when it is to end.

HTML is a formal Recommendation by the World Wide Web Consortium (**W3C**) and is generally adhered to by the major browsers, Microsoft's Internet Explorer and Netscape's Navigator, which also provide some additional non-standard codes. The current version of HTML is **HTML 4.0**. However, both Internet Explorer and Netscape implement some features differently and provide non-standard extensions. Web developers using the more advanced features of HTML 4 may have to design pages for both browsers and send out the appropriate version to a user. Significant features in HTML 4 are sometimes described in general as **dynamic HTML**. What is sometimes referred to as HTML 5 is an extensible form of HTML called Extensible Hypertext Markup Language (**XHTML**).

HTML 4.0

HTML 4.0 was the final version of the Hypertext Markup Language (**HTML**) before the Extensible Markup Language (**XHTML**) and remains the set of **markup** on which most large Web sites today are based. Like all HTML levels, HTML 4.0 was the official "recommendation" of the World Wide Web Consortium (**W3C**), the group that suggests industry standards for the Web.

Among new features introduced in HTML 4.0 were:

- The **cascading style sheet**, the ability to control Web page content at multiple levels
- The ability to create richer forms
- Support for **frames** (which is already supported by the major browsers)
- Enhancements for tables that make it possible to use captions to provide table content for Braille or speech users
- The capability to manage pages so that they can be distributed in different languages

In practice, the two leading browsers, Netscape and Internet Explorer, support HTML 4.0 somewhat differently or offer non-standard approaches. These require Web developers that use more advanced features to create pages for each browser and send the appropriate pages to the user.

HTML comment

You can include a comment in an HTML document. A comment will not be displayed and will help you remember why you coded something a particular way. A comment might look like this:

```
<!-The following table gives us precise control of
figure placement.->
```

Hint: Be sure to include two hyphens after the exclamation point and two hyphens before the greater-than sign. Not all browsers are picky about this, but some may be.

HTTP

See "Hypertext Transfer Protocol"

HTTP 1.1

HTTP (**Hypertext Transfer Protocol**), the World Wide Web application protocol that runs on top of the Internet's **TCP/IP** suite of protocols, now exists in a newer version, HTTP 1.1, that promises to bring Web pages a little faster to your browser and reduce some of the Web's enormous traffic. Developed by a committee of the Internet Engineering Task Force (**IETF**) that includes the Web's chief creator Tim Berners-Lee, HTTP 1.1 exists as a "proposal," but in fact, most major Web servers and browser clients are at some stage of supporting it.

Here's a summary of how HTTP 1.1 makes information flow faster:

- Instead of opening and closing a connection for each application request, HTTP 1.1 provides a *persistent connection* that allows multiple requests to be batched or *pipelined* to an output **buffer**. The underlying **Transmission Control Protocol** layer can put multiple requests (and responses to requests) into one TCP *segment* that gets forwarded to the **Internet Protocol** layer for packet transmission. Because the number of connection and disconnection requests for a sequence of "get a file" requests is reduced, fewer packets need to flow across the Internet. Since requests are pipelined, TCP segments are more efficient. The overall result is less Internet traffic and faster performance for the user.

Persistent connection is similar to Netscape's HTTP 1.0 extension called KeepAlive, but provides better handling of requests that go through **proxy servers**.

- When a browser supporting HTTP 1.1 indicates it can decompress HTML files, a server will compress them for transport across the Internet, providing a substantial aggregate savings in the amount of data that has to be transmitted. (Image files are already in a compressed format so this improvement applies only to HTML and other non-image data types.)

In addition to persistent connections and other performance improvements, HTTP 1.1 also provides the ability to have multiple **domain names** share the same Internet address (**IP address**). This will simplify processing for Web servers that host a number of Web sites in what is sometimes called **virtual hosting**.

HTTPD

See "Hypertext Transfer Protocol daemon"

HTTPS

HTTPS (Secure Hypertext Transfer Protocol) is a Web **protocol** developed by **Netscape** and built into its **browser** that **encrypts** and decrypts user page requests as well as the pages that are returned by the Web server. HTTPS is really just the use of Netscape's Secure Socket Layer (**SSL**) as a sublayer under its regular HTTP application **layering**. (HTTPS uses **port** 443 instead of HTTP port 80 in its interactions with the lower layer, **TCP/IP**.) SSL uses a 40-bit key size for the RC4 stream encryption **algorithm**, which is considered an adequate degree of encryption for commercial exchange.

Suppose you use a Netscape browser to visit a Web site to view their online catalog. When you're ready to order, you will be given a Web page order form with a Uniform Resource Locator (**URL**) that starts with https://. When you click "Send," to send the page back to the catalog retailer, your browser's HTTPS layer will encrypt it. The acknowledgement you receive from the server will also travel in encrypted form, arrive with an https:// URL, and be decrypted for you by your browser's HTTPS sublayer.

HTTPS and SSL support the use of X.509 **digital certificate**s from the server so that, if necessary, a user can authenticate the sender. SSL is an **open**, nonproprietary protocol that Netscape has proposed as a standard to the World Wide Consortium (**W3C**). HTTPS is not to be confused with SHTTP, a security-enhanced version of HTTP developed and proposed as a standard by EIT.

hub

Also see **stackable hub**.

In general, a hub is the central part of a wheel where the spokes come together. The term is familiar to frequent fliers who travel through airport "hubs" to make connecting flights from one point to another. In data communications, a hub is a place of convergence where data arrives from one or more directions and is forwarded out in one or more other directions. A hub usually includes a **switch** of some kind. (And a product that is called a "switch" could usually be considered a hub as well.) The distinction seems to be that the hub is the place where data comes together and the switch is what determines how and where data is forwarded from the place where data comes together. Regarded in its switching aspects, a hub can also include a **router**.

1) In describing network topologies, a hub **topology** consists of a **backbone** (main circuit) to which a number of outgoing lines can be attached ("dropped"), each providing one or more connection **port** for **device** to attach to. For Internet users not connected to a local area network, this is the general topology used by your access provider. Other common network topologies are the **bus** network and the **ring** network. (Either of these could possibly feed into a hub network, using a **bridge**.)

2) As a network product, a hub may include a group of **modem** cards for dial-in users, a gateway card for connections to a local area network (for example, an **Ethernet** or a **token ring**), and a connection to a line (the main line in this example).

hue, saturation, and brightness

Hue, saturation, and brightness are aspects of color in the red, green, and blue (**RGB**) scheme. These terms are most often used in reference to the color of each **pixel** in a cathode ray tube (**CRT**) display. All possible colors can be specified according to hue, saturation, and brightness (also called *brilliance*), just as colors can be represented in terms of the R, G, and B components.

Most sources of visible light contain energy over a band of wavelengths. Hue is the **wavelength** within the visible-light spectrum at which the energy output from a source is greatest. This is shown as the peak of the curves in the accompanying graph of intensity versus wavelength. In this example, all three colors have the same hue, with a wavelength slightly longer than 500 nanometers, in the yellow-green portion of the spectrum.

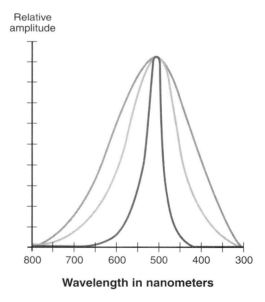

Wavelength in nanometers

Saturation is an expression for the relative bandwidth of the visible output from a light source. In the diagram, the saturation is represented by the steepness of the slopes of the curves. Here, the outside curve represents a color having low saturation, the middle curve represents a color having greater saturation, and the inside curve represents a color with fairly high saturation. As saturation increases, colors appear more "pure." As saturation decreases, colors appear more "washed-out."

Brightness is a relative expression of the intensity of the energy output of a visible light source. It can be expressed as a total energy value (different for each of the curves in the diagram), or as the amplitude at the wavelength where the intensity is greatest (identical for all three curves). In the RGB color model, the amplitudes of red, green, and blue for a particular color can each range from 0 to 100 percent of full brilliance. These levels are represented by the range of decimal numbers from 0 to 255, or hexadecimal numbers from 00 to FF.

human factors

In industry, human factors (also known as **ergonomic**s) is the study of how humans behave physically and psychologically in relation to particular environments, products, or services. Many large manufacturing companies have a Human Factors department or hire a consulting firm to study how any major new product will be accepted by the users that it is designed for. A human factors specialist typically has an advanced academic degree in Psychology or has special training. The term *usability* is now sometimes used as an alternative to *human factors*, although human factors is really a larger area of study, including responses that are unrelated to usability, such as reactions and preferences in relation to visual and other sensory stimuli.

In a typical human factors or usability study, a group of hired or volunteer test subjects that represent future end users is given tasks to do with a working prototype or early version of a product. Typically, a test subject is observed while doing a task, asked to react verbally as any problems occur or as observations are made, and interviewed after each test. (Test subjects have to be assured that it is the product—and not their own skills or capabilities—that is being tested.) Usually, the test is videotaped for later study. In some cases, successive corrections to the product are made during the course of testing.

Human factors study can focus on general human behavior in relation to technology (such as studies of how people react to various type styles and sizes), on a generic type of product (such as **wearable computer**s), on specific environment or product designs as a whole, or on some specific design aspects of a particular environment or product. Depending on objectives, the result of human factors study can include suggestions on how to redesign the object of study or a general guideline for designing such an object.

In addition to relatively formal human factors study, human factors can be said to be underway any time a designer thinks about the effects of the design on the end user, and, in fact, much corrective design work goes on without formal testing. A relatively new object of study is the design of a **Web site**, either as a general problem or in order to build a specific Web site that meets user needs.

human-computer interaction

See "HCI"

humanware

Humanware is **hardware** and **software** that emphasizes user capability and empowerment and the design of the user interface. The process of building humanware generally consists of these steps:

1. Define users (age, mindset, environmental context, previous product experience and expectations, and so forth) and what they really want to do

2. Identify tasks they will need to do or capabilities they will want

3. Specify usability objectives (if possible, these should be measurable, such as how long to do something or how many mouse clicks to get to a specified task point) for each task or capability

4. Build a prototype of the user interface (it can be a paper or simulated prototype if time is short)

5. Test and verify or correct the prototype

6. Provide the prototype and usability objectives to the program designers and coders

7. Test the code against the prototype and objectives and, if necessary, redesign or recode the software

8. Test the product with users or valid test subjects and revise as necessary

9. Get feedback from users and continually improve the product

Philips Research uses the term for both software and hardware that is specially designed to interact with users, including its speech synthesis and speech recognition microchips.

Hungarian notation

In programming, Hungarian notation is a set of conventions for naming data objects in which a programmer adds a meaningful prefix of one or several characters to the object's name to identify what type of object it is. The conventions suggest, among other things, that programmers choose prefixes that are suggestive of the type of object named and are easy to remember. Consistency in naming is very important.

In one programmer's version of Hungarian notation, a form might have the prefix "frm" and, if the form name is "Switchboard," the extended name would be "frmSwitchboard." This makes it clear that the reference is to a form called "Switchboard," and not to some other type of object with the same name, such as a label (which might be called "lblSwitchboard"). The conventions were developed to define naming procedures that would help programmers create prefixes that would be easy to remember and would make objects easy to identify, both for themselves and for other programmers that might work with their code in the future.

Dr. Charles Simonyi developed the convention at Microsoft, where it is used in the Windows source code. Microsoft says it's known as Hungarian notation because the prefixes make the names seem to be non-English and also because Simonyi is from Hungary. Since Microsoft uses it extensively, many programmers outside Microsoft use it. Charles Petzold's use of Hungarian notation in his book, "Programming Windows," also has influenced many Windows programmers.

hybrid fiber coaxial network

A hybrid fiber coaxial (HFC) network is a telecommunication technology in which **optical fiber** cable and **coaxial cable** are used in different portions of a **network** to carry **broadband** content (such as video, **data**, and voice). Using HFC, a local **CATV** company installs fiber optic cable from the cable head-end (distribution center) to serving nodes located close to business and residential users and from these nodes uses coaxial cable to individual businesses and homes. An advantage of HFC is that some of the characteristics of fiber optic cable (high **bandwidth** and low noise and interference susceptibility) can be brought close to the user without having to replace the existing coaxial cable that is installed all the way to the home and business.

Both cable TV and telephone companies are using HFC in new and upgraded networks and, in some cases, sharing the same infrastructure to carry both video and voice conversations in the same system. Scientific Atlanta lists four reasons why cable TV and telephone companies are upgrading facilities to HFC:

1) The use of fiber optic cable for the **backbone** paths allows more data to be carried than coaxial cable alone.

2) The higher bandwidth supports reverse paths for interactive data flowing back from the user.

3) That portion of the infrastructure with fiber optic cable is more reliable than coaxial cable. Reliability is perceived as more important in an interactive environment.

4) Fiber optic cable is more efficient for interconnecting cable TV or phone companies that are consolidating with geographically adjacent companies.

hybrid online analytical processing

Hybrid online analytical processing (HOLAP) is a combination of relational OLAP (**ROLAP**) and multi-dimensional OLAP (usually referred to simply as **OLAP**). HOLAP was developed to combine the greater data capacity of ROLAP with the superior processing capability of OLAP.

HOLAP can use varying combinations of ROLAP and OLAP technology. Typically it stores data in a both a **relational database** (RDB) and a **multidimensional database** (MDDB) and uses whichever one is best suited to the type of processing desired. The databases are used to store data in the most functional way. For data-heavy processing, the data is more efficiently stored in a RDB, while for speculative processing, the data is more effectively stored in an MDDB.

HOLAP users can choose to store the results of queries to the MDDB to save the effort of looking for the same data over and over which saves time. Although this technique—called "materializing cells"—improves performance, it takes a toll on storage. The user has to strike a balance between performance and storage demand to get the most out of HOLAP. Nevertheless, because it offers the best features of both OLAP and ROLAP, HOLAP is increasingly preferred.

Hydra

See "Terminal Server product"

hyper

1) As an adjective, *hyper* is slang for "keyed up" or "overwrought."

2) Hyper is also a prefix, from the Greek *hyper-*, meaning over, above, or excessive, used in such terms as *hyperbole* (exaggeration in describing something) and **hypertext** (text that extends to point to or include other text).

3) In science, also as a prefix, hyper- is something that exists in a space of four or more dimensions, such as a *hyperplane*.

HyperCard

HyperCard is an early (1986) Macintosh **application** that enables users to author **hypertext** pages, called cards, without any programming knowledge. A set of cards, called a stack, can be linked together to allow readers to navigate through the stack in a non-linear manner by clicking on buttons or objects associated with an action script.

Hyper-G

Hyper-G is a publishing system with **hypertext** features more advanced than those available with the **Hypertext Transfer Protocol** and today's Web **browser**. Hyper-G was inspired in part by the ideas of Ted Nelson, who coined the term "hypertext," and was developed in Graz, Austria, by a team of researchers at the Institute for Information Processing and Computer Supported New Media (**IICM**) and the Institute for HyperMedia Systems (IHM) of Joanneum Research. Assistance was provided by developers elsewhere.

Using Hyper-G:

- You can have bi-directional links between HTML pages (or other hypertext documents). That is, you can know for any page what other HTML pages (including those at other Web sites) link to the page. The latter kind of link is known as a **backlink**.

- You can create *link types* (for example, for a single link, you might have one type called "definition" and another link type called "picture").

- Links can be defined as separate objects or files, allowing them to be easily filtered or changed for an entire document or set of files.

- One link type can be an annotation that an editor or a reviewer can create or modify. Thus, a number of collaborating reviewers or writers can share each others comments, made visible by the links they create.

- Links can overlap each other. For example, "client-server" could contain a link for "client," for "server," and another for the term "client-server" as a whole.

- The structure of a document can be viewed graphically and even in 3-D.

- The author can control who can see a document, who can see a link, who can edit the document, and who can edit the links.

Hyper-G is available in a commercial version called HyperWave. HyperWave consists of a server and clients that run on Windows and UNIX platforms. A version for Macintosh is in preparation. The most advanced client is the UNIX version; it can be run on **Linux** systems. HyperWave is compatible with **HTML**.

Among other applications, HyperWave has ideal features for online peer or technical reviews and collaborative writing. Among the early users of Hyper-G or derivative versions were Oxford University Press and the European Space Agency.

hyperlink

On the Web or other hypertext systems, hyperlink is a synonym for both **link** and **hypertext link**. Possibly, the term originated because "link" was not felt to be specific enough. And it's shorter than "hypertext link."

hypermedia

Hypermedia, a term derived from **hypertext**, extends the notion of the hypertext **link** to include links among any set of multimedia objects, including sound, motion video, and virtual reality. It can also connote a higher level of user/ network interactivity than the interactivity already implicit in hypertext.

hyperspace

Hyperspace is a term that describes the total number of individual locations and all of their interconnections in a **hypertext** environment. It also connotes a perceived sense of this potentially confusing totality. If you've ever started out somewhere on the World Wide Web and gradually lost the sense that you know where you are going or where you are, you are in the condition known as "lost in hyperspace." (Studies, however, show that the "lost in hyperspace" problem is relatively low on users' lists of "things to improve.")

Hyperspace can be considered the hypertextual or architectural aspect of **cyberspace**, a term that has even richer connotations.

hypertext

Hypertext is the organization of information units into connected associations that a user can choose to make. An instance of such an association is called a **link** or hypertext link. (And the highlighted word "link" in the previous sentence is an example of a hypertext link.)

Hypertext was the main concept that led to the invention of the World Wide Web, which is, after all, nothing more (or less) than an enormous amount of information content connected by an enormous number of hypertext links.

The term was first used by Ted Nelson in describing his **Xanadu** system.

Also see **hypermedia**.

Hypertext Transfer Protocol daemon

On the Web, each **server** has an *HTTPD* or **Hypertext Transfer Protocol** daemon that waits in attendance for requests to come in from the rest of the Web. A *daemon* is a program that is "an attendant power or spirit" (Webster's). It sits waiting for requests to come in and then forwards them to other processes as appropriate.

Hypertext Transfer Protocol

The Hypertext Transfer Protocol (HTTP) is the set of rules for exchanging files (text, graphic images, sound, video, and other multimedia files) on the **World Wide Web**. Relative to the **TCP/IP** suite of protocols (which are the basis for information exchange on the Internet), HTTP is an application **protocol**.

Essential concepts that are part of HTTP include (as its name implies) the idea that files can contain references to other files whose selection will elicit additional transfer requests. Any **Web server** machine contains, in addition to the HTML and other files it can serve, an HTTP **daemon**, a program that is designed to wait for HTTP requests and handle them when they arrive. Your Web **browser** is an HTTP **client**, sending requests to server machines. When the browser user enters file requests by either "opening" a Web file (typing in a **Uniform Resource Locator**) or clicking on a **hypertext link**, the browser builds an HTTP request and sends it to the **Internet Protocol address** indicated by the URL. The HTTP daemon in the destination server machine receives the request and, after any necessary processing, the requested file is returned.

The latest version of HTTP is **HTTP 1.1**.

Hz

See "hertz"

i.LINK

i.LINK is the Sony Corporation implementation of a standard, **IEEE 1394**, High Performance Serial Bus, for connecting devices to your personal computer. i.LINK provides a single plug-and-socket connection on which up to 63 devices can be attached with data transfer speeds up to 400 **Mbps** (**megabit**s per second). The standard describes a **serial bus** or pathway between one or more peripheral devices and your computer's **microprocessor**. Many peripheral devices now come equipped to meet IEEE 1394. i.LINK, Apple's **FireWire**, and other IEEE 1394 implementations provide:

- A simple common plug-in serial connector on the back of your computer and on many different types of peripheral devices

- A thin serial cable rather than the thicker parallel cable you now use to your printer, for example

- A very high-speed rate of data transfer that will accommodate multimedia applications (100 and 200 megabits per second today; with much higher rates later)

- Hot-plug and **plug and play** capability without disrupting your computer

- The ability to chain devices together in a number of different ways without terminators or complicated set-up requirements

In time, IEEE 1394 implementations are expected to replace and consolidate today's serial and parallel interfaces, including **Centronics parallel**, **RS-232C**, and Small Computer System Interface (**SCSI**). The first products to be introduced with FireWire include **digital camera**s, digital video discs (**DVD**s), digital video tapes, digital camcorders, and music systems. Because IEEE 1394 is a **peer-to-peer** interface, one camcorder can dub to another without being plugged into a computer. With a computer equipped with the socket and bus capability, any device (for example, a video camera) can be plugged in while the computer is running.

Briefly How It Works

There are two levels of interface in IEEE 1394, one for the **backplane** bus within the computer and another for the point-to-point interface between device and computer on the serial cable. A simple bridge connects the two environments. The backplane bus supports 12.5, 25, or 50 megabits per second data transfer. The cable interface supports 100, 200, or 400 megabits per second. Each of these interfaces can handle any of the possible data rates and change from one to another as needed.

The serial bus functions as though devices were in slots within the computer sharing a common memory space. A 64-bit device address allows a great deal of flexibility in configuring devices in chains and trees from a single socket.

IEEE 1394 provides two types of data transfer: asynchronous and **isochronous**. Asynchronous is for traditional load-and-store applications where data transfer can be initiated and an application interrupted as a given length of data arrives in a **buffer**. Isochronous data transfer ensures that data flows at a pre-set rate so that an application can handle it in a timed way. For multimedia applications, this kind of data transfer reduces the need for buffering and helps ensure a continuous presentation for the viewer.

The 1394 standard requires that a device be within 4.5 meters of the bus socket. Up to 16 devices can be connected in a single chain, each with the 4.5 meter maximum (before signal attenuation begins to occur) so theoretically you could have a device as far away as 72 meters from the computer.

Another new approach to connecting devices, the Universal Serial Bus (**USB**), provides the same "hot plug" capability as the 1394 standard. It's a less expensive technology but data transfer is limited to 12 Mbps (million bits per second). Small Computer System Interface offers a high data transfer rate (up to 40 megabytes per second) but requires address preassignment and a device terminator on the last device in a chain. FireWire can work with the latest internal computer **bus** standard, Peripheral Component Interconnect (**PCI**), but higher data transfer rates may require special design considerations to minimize undesired buffering for transfer rate mismatches.

I18N

See "internationalization"

I2C bus

The I2C (Inter-IC) bus is a bi-directional two-wire **serial bus** that provides a communication link between integrated circuits (**IC**s). Phillips introduced the I2C bus 20 years ago for mass-produced items such as televisions, VCRs, and audio equipment. Today, I2C is the de-facto solution for embedded applications.

There are three data transfer speeds for the I2C bus: standard, fast-mode, and high-speed mode. Standard is 100 **Kbps**. Fast-mode is 400 Kbps, and high-speed mode supports speeds up to 3.4 **Mbps**. All are **backward compatible**. The I2C bus supports 7-**bit** and 10-bit **address** space devices and devices that operate under different voltages.

I2C

See "I2C bus"

IA-64

IA-64 is a **64-bit processor** architecture developed at Intel that is based on Explicitly Parallel Instruction Computing (**EPIC**) and designed as the foundation for Intel's line of microprocessors through 2005. The **Itanium** is the first in Intel's line of IA-64 processors.

IAB

The IAB (Internet Architecture Board) is the **Internet Society** overseer of the technical evolution of the Internet. The IAB supervises the Internet Engineering Task Force (**IETF**), which oversees the evolution of **TCP/IP**, and the Internet Research Task Force (**IRTF**), which works on network technology.

IANA

IANA (Internet Assigned Numbers Authority) is the organization under the Internet Architecture Board (**IAB**) of the **Internet Society** that, under a contract from the U.S. government, has overseen the allocation of **Internet Protocol** addresses to Internet service providers (**ISP**s). IANA also has had responsibility for the registry for any "unique parameters and protocol values" for Internet operation. These include **port number**s, character sets, and **MIME** media access types.

Partly because the Internet is now a global network, the U.S. government has withdrawn its oversight of the Internet, previously contracted out to IANA, and lent its support to a newly-formed organization with global, non-government representation, the Internet Corporation for Assigned Names and Numbers (**ICANN**). ICANN has now assumed responsibility for the tasks formerly performed by IANA.

IAP

An IAP (Internet access provider) is a company that provides individuals and other ISP companies access to the Internet. An IAP is a type of Internet service provider (**ISP**). (The other main service that an ISP provides is **Web site** building and **virtual hosting**.) An IAP has the equipment and the telecommunication line access required to have **POP** on the Internet for the geographic area served. The larger IAPs have their own high-speed leased lines so that they are less dependent on the telecommunication providers and can provide better service to their customers. Among the largest national and regional ISPs are AT&T WorldNet, IBM Global Network, MCI, Netcom, UUNet, and PSINet.

IAPs also include regional providers such as New England's NEARNet and the San Francisco Bay area BARNet. They also include thousands of local providers. In addition, Internet users can also get access through online service providers (**OSP**) such as America Online.

The larger IAPs interconnect with each other through **MAE** (ISP switching centers run by MCI WorldCom) or similar centers. The arrangements they make to exchange traffic are known as **peering** agreements. There are several very comprehensive lists of IAPs (usually identified as ISPs) available to Web users.

iButton

An iButton is a **microchip** similar to those used in a **smart card** but housed in a round stainless steel button of 17.35mm × 3.1mm—5.89mm in size (depending on the function). The iButton was invented and is still manufactured exclusively by Dallas Semiconductor mainly for applications in harsh and demanding environments.

Like a smart card, an iButton does not have an internal power source. It requires connection to a reader (known as a Blue Dot Receptor) in order to be supplied with power and to receive input and send output. Unlike some smart cards, there are currently no contactless iButtons: They require physical contact with a reader to function.

There are iButtons that measure temperature (for food storage and transport); have an electronic ID (for physical access to buildings); and store e-cash (for purchases both in stores and via the web). For **e-commerce** applications, the iButton can support JavaCard 2.0/OpenCard standards in addition to proprietary software.

iButtons have an advantage over conventional smart cards in term of durability and longevity. The stainless steel casing gives iButton a far greater ability to survive in a range of temperatures—all versions are functional from -40 C to +70 C—and in a much harsher range of environments (such as exposure to salt water and long term exposure to physical impacts) than the plastic smart card. For e-commerce and personal ID usage, iButtons can be mounted on a range of personal accessories: Watch, ring, key chain, or dog tag.

As of early 2000, Dallas Semiconductor had shipped over 27 million iButtons around the world. This figure is below that of smart cards because of a larger installed user base for smart cards, the comparatively high cost of iButtons, the fact that iButtons have a long life, and because Dallas Semiconductor has not licensed the patents for external manufacture. Thus far, the major successes for iButton have been in Turkey as an e-purse for the mass transit system; in Argentina and Brazil for parking meters; and in the U.S. as Blue Mailbox attachments that improve postal efficiency.

IC

See "integrated circuit"

ICANN

ICANN (Internet Corporation for Assigned Names and Numbers) is the private (non-government) non-profit corporation with responsibility for **IP address** space allocation, **protocol** parameter assignment, **domain name system** management, and **root server system** management functions, the services previously performed by the Internet Assigned Numbers Authority (**IANA**). (ICANN is usually pronounced EYE-can, as in "I can at least try to manage the Internet.")

Initial members of the ICANN board were chosen by the late Dr. Jonathon Postel, who headed IANA. IANA derived its authority under a contract from the U.S. government which financed the original research network, **Advanced Research Projects Agency Network**, from which the Internet grew. The need to internationalize the governing of the Internet (among other concerns) led the U.S. government to recommend the origin of ICANN as a global, government-independent entity to manage the systems and protocols that keep the Internet going. The U.S. government is essentially turning over control of the Internet to ICANN although domain name registration performed by Network Solutions, Inc. will continue to be under U.S. government contract for a limited time.

ICANN has a board of nineteen Directors, nine At-Large Directors, nine to be nominated by Supporting Organizations, and the President/CEO (ex officio). The nine At-Large Directors of the Initial Board are serving one-year terms and will be succeeded by At-Large Directors elected by an at-large membership organization.

Since its beginning, ICANN has had to deal with controversial issues (such as what new top-level domain names should be permitted and whether alternative root server systems should be allowed).

ice

For ICE, see **Information and Content Exchange**.

Ice, jello, and liquid are related terms describing three approaches to controlling content placement on a Web page. Because the **browser** user can control and change both screen resolution and window size, the Web page designer is challenged to design a page that will achieve its intended effect in spite of user resizing.

An ice page is one in which the primary content has a fixed width in **pixels** and assumes a left margin alignment. Such a page is designed to display optimally on one particular display resolution setting and window size and either specifies or assumes that size. If the resolution is set to a different setting, the page may have unneeded space on the right size of the display window, but this is a risk that the designer chooses to take.

A jello page is one in which the primary content is centered on the page. It also has a fixed-width column, but it is always centered in any size window and at any display resolution. Its center alignment eliminates the excessive right margin seen in an "ice" page (when viewed on a large monitor). But it can have excessive margins on both sides of the centered content.

A liquid page, according to Glenn Davis of Project Cool, is (to paraphrase slightly): ..."a Web page that will reflow to fit no matter what size window you pour it into." Unlike the ice and jello approaches, a liquid page or content area leaves no blank margin on the right or the left. However, unless special care is taken, elements in a liquid page can sometimes have too much or too little space between them.

More sophisticated designers sometimes use a combination of tables and tables-within-tables to define and control layout space and element placement in the various resolutions and windows sizes users may choose to use. To create liquid content spaces or pages, you may be able to determine the window size and dynamically adjust your content layout to meet each user's requirements.

ICM file

In Windows 95 and possibly other operating systems, an ICM (Image Color Matching) file contains a color system profile for a particular application or device such as a color printer or scanner. This profile is matched to a common profile that in turn can be mapped to other device's individual profiles. This allows the color system used by one computer device to match the colors used by other applications and devices on the same or other computer platforms. A profile commonly adopted by some programs and devices is the Kodak Professional Color System profile. An ICM file usually carries the suffix ".icm".

Microsoft, Apple, and Adobe are among the manufacturers who adhere to the ICC's color profiling system.

ICMP

ICMP (Internet Control Message Protocol) is a message control and error-reporting protocol between a **host** server and a **gateway** to the Internet. ICMP uses Internet Protocol (**IP**) **datagram**s, but the messages are processed by the IP software and are not directly apparent to the application user.

icon

1) In a computer's graphical user interface (**GUI**), an icon (pronounced EYE-kahn) is an image that represents an application, a capability, or some other concept or specific

entity with meaning for the user. An icon is usually selectable but can also be a nonselectable image such as a company's logo.

2) On a Web page, an icon is often a graphical image that represents the topic or information category of another Web page. Frequently, the icon is a hypertext **link** to that page. Typically, icons are gathered in one or two places on a page, either as separate graphic files or as a single **image map**.

3) Icon is also a lexical programming language, commonly thought to be an evolution of the SNOBOL programming language.

ICP

An ICP (Internet commerce provider) is a company that sells software and services that enable a merchant with a **Web site** to build an online store on the merchant's own site or on the provider's site. Products and services can be pre-packaged or customized or some combination. Typically, a pre-packaged ICP product lets a merchant set up an online store using one of several design templates, arranges for secure credit card transactions, and provides order tracking. An ICP may also provide services related to order fulfillment, such as shipping and customer relations.

Some Internet access providers (**IAP**) and Web design shops also act as ICPs, offering customized services or serving as a vendor of packaged products.

ICQ

ICQ ("I Seek You") is a program you can download that will let you know when friends and contacts are also online on the Internet. ICQ allows you to page them, chat with them, and initiate and participate in PC-to-PC calls, PC-to-phone and phone-to-phone calling cards calls. Like AOL's Instant Messenger (**AIM**), in order to use ICQ, both parties must have downloaded the program.

ICQ enables you to send messages, files (single, multiple or whole directories), and URLs directly to your friends. In addition, you can initiate an IRC-style chat session or voice and video-voice connection and play games with other ICQ members that you are in touch with. Your contact is signaled of an incoming event in real time and has immediate access to it.

IDE

IDE (Integrated Drive Electronics) is a standard electronic **interface** used between a computer **motherboard**'s data paths or **bus** and the computer's disk storage devices. The IDE interface is based on the IBM PC Industry Standard Architecture (**ISA**) 16-bit **bus** standard, but it is also used in computers that use other bus standards. Most computers sold today use an enhanced version of IDE called Enhanced

Integrated Drive Electronics (**EIDE**). IDE gets its name because the disk drive controller is built into the logic board in the disk drive.

IDE was adopted as a standard by American National Standards Institute (**ANSI**) in November 1990. The ANSI name for IDE is Advanced Technology Attachment (**ATA**). The IDE (ATA) standard is one of several related standards maintained by the T10 Committee.

IDEA

See "International Data Encryption Algorithm"

iDEN

iDEN (Integrated Digital Enhanced Network) is a **wireless** technology from Motorola combining the capabilities of a digital **cellular telephone**, two-way radio, alphanumeric **pager**, and data/fax **modem** in a single network. iDEN operates in the 800 **MHz**, 900MHz, and 1.5 **GHz** bands and is based on time division multiple access (**TDMA**) and **GSM** architecture. It uses Motorola's Vector Sum Excited Linear Predictors (VSELP) **vocoder** for voice compression and **QAM** modulation to deliver 64 **Kbps** over a 25 KHz channel.

iDEN is designed to give the mobile user quick access to information without having to carry around several devices. In early 2001, a new iDEN handset is scheduled for release that will tackle added business needs like logistics management and alerts.

Currently, iDEN systems work in more than a dozen countries.

IDF

See "interface device"

IDL

1) IDL (interface definition language) is a generic term for a language that lets a program or **object** written in one language communicate with another program written in an unknown language. In distributed object technology, it's important that new objects be able to be sent to any platform environment and discover how to run in that environment. An Object Request Broker (**ORB**) is an example of a program that would use an interface definition language to "broker" communication between one object program and another one.

An interface definition language works by requiring that a program's interfaces be described in a **stub** or slight extension of the program that is compiled into it. The stubs in each program are used by a broker program to allow them to communicate.

2) IDL (Interactive Data Language) is a language for creating visualizations based on scientific or other data.

3) IDL (interactive distance learning) is a general term for learning that takes place through remote telecommunication and that allows students to participate from a distance. Television has been used for many years for non-interactive distance learning. Teleconference classes are becoming more common where higher bandwidth and such technologies as **ISDN** and satellite communication permit. The World Wide Web, with or without multimedia, offers new possibilities.

idoru

An idoru is a virtual (computer-created) media star. If real pop music stars sometimes seem to become the conception of their producers' dreams, perhaps it would be simpler to start from scratch and design your own media star to perform (think of a fully-developed **hologram** singing and dancing before tens of thousands of insane fans in Central Park), be interviewed by *Rolling Stone*, and even evolve and grow older! The idea is explored in the novel, *Idoru*, by science-fiction writer William Gibson.

IDSL

IDSL is a system in which digital data is transmitted at 128 **Kbps** on a regular copper telephone line (**twisted pair**) from a user to a destination using digital (rather than analog or voice) transmission, bypassing the telephone company's central office equipment that handles analog signals. IDSL uses the Integrated Services Digital Network (**ISDN**) **Basic Rate Interface in ISDN** transmission code.

IDSL is a technology developed by Ascend Communications (now part of Lucent Technologies). IDSL is an expedient approach that allows use of existing ISDN card technology for data-only use.

The differences between IDSL and ISDN are:

- ISDN passes through the phone company's central office voice network; IDSL bypasses it by plugging into a special router at the phone company end

- ISDN requires call setup; IDSL is a dedicated service

- ISDN may involve per-call fees; IDSL may be billed at a flat rate with no usage charges

IEC

See "International Electrotechnical Commission"

IEEE

The IEEE (Institute of Electrical and Electronics Engineers) describes itself as "the world's largest technical professional society—promoting the development and application of electrotechnology and allied sciences for the benefit of humanity, the advancement of the profession, and the well-being of our members."

The IEEE fosters the development of standards that often become national and international standards. The organization publishes a number of journals, has many local chapters, and several large societies in special areas, such as the IEEE Computer Society.

IEEE 1394

IEEE 1394, High Performance Serial Bus, is an electronics standard for connecting devices to your personal computer. IEEE 1394 provides a single plug-and-socket connection on which up to 63 devices can be attached with data transfer speeds up to 400 **Mbps** (**megabit**s per second). The standard describes a **serial bus** or pathway between one or more peripheral devices and your computer's **microprocessor**. Many peripheral devices now come equipped to meet IEEE 1394. Two popular implementations of IEEE 1394 are Apple's **FireWire** and Sony's **i.LINK**. IEEE 1394 implementations provide:

- A simple common plug-in serial connector on the back of your computer and on many different types of peripheral devices

- A thin serial cable rather than the thicker parallel cable you now use to your printer, for example

- A very high-speed rate of data transfer that will accommodate multimedia applications (100 and 200 megabits per second today; with much higher rates later)

- Hot-plug and **plug and play** capability without disrupting your computer

- The ability to chain devices together in a number of different ways without terminators or complicated set-up requirements

In time, IEEE 1394 implementations are expected to replace and consolidate today's serial and parallel interfaces, including **Centronics parallel**, **RS-232C**, and Small Computer System Interface (**SCSI**). The first products to be introduced with FireWire include **digital camera**s, digital video discs (**DVD**s), digital video tapes, digital camcorders, and music systems. Because IEEE 1394 is a **peer-to-peer** interface, one camcorder can dub to another without being plugged into a computer. With a computer equipped with the socket and bus capability, any device (for example, a video camera) can be plugged in while the computer is running.

Briefly How It Works

There are two levels of interface in IEEE 1394, one for the **backplane** bus within the computer and another for the point-to-point interface between device and computer on the serial cable. A simple bridge connects the two environments. The backplane bus supports 12.5, 25, or 50 megabits per second data transfer. The cable interface supports 100, 200, or 400 megabits per second. Each of these interfaces can handle any of the possible data rates and change from one to another as needed.

The serial bus functions as though devices were in slots within the computer sharing a common memory space. A 64-bit device address allows a great deal of flexibility in configuring devices in chains and trees from a single socket.

IEEE 1394 provides two types of data transfer: asynchronous and **isochronous**. Asynchronous is for traditional load-and-store applications where data transfer can be initiated and an application interrupted as a given length of data arrives in a **buffer**. Isochronous data transfer ensures that data flows at a pre-set rate so that an application can handle it in a timed way. For multimedia applications, this kind of data transfer reduces the need for buffering and helps ensure a continuous presentation for the viewer.

The 1394 standard requires that a device be within 4.5 meters of the bus socket. Up to 16 devices can be connected in a single chain, each with the 4.5 meter maximum (before signal attenuation begins to occur) so theoretically you could have a device as far away as 72 meters from the computer.

Another new approach to connecting devices, the Universal Serial Bus (**USB**), provides the same "hot plug" capability as the 1394 standard. It's a less expensive technology but data transfer is limited to 12 Mbps (million bits per second). Small Computer System Interface offers a high data transfer rate (up to 40 megabytes per second) but requires address preassignment and a device terminator on the last device in a chain. FireWire can work with the latest internal computer **bus** standard, Peripheral Component Interconnect (**PCI**), but higher data transfer rates may require special design considerations to minimize undesired buffering for transfer rate mismatches.

IETF

The IETF (Internet Engineering Task Force) is the body that defines standard Internet operating **protocol**s such as **TCP/IP**. The IETF is supervised by the **Internet Society's** Internet Architecture Board (**IAB**). IETF members are drawn from the Internet Society's individual and organization membership. Standards are expressed in the form of Requests for Comments (**RFC**s).

IGMP

See "Internet Group Management Protocol"

IGP

An IGP (Interior Gateway Protocol) is a protocol for exchanging routing information between **gateway**s (**host**s with **router**s) within an autonomous network (for example, a system of corporate local area networks). The routing information can then be used by the Internet Protocol (**IP**) or other network protocols to specify how to route transmissions.

There are two commonly used IGPs: the **Routing Information Protocol** (RIP) and the Open Shortest Path First (**OSPF**) protocol.

Also see the Exterior Gateway Protocol (**EGP**).

IIOP

IIOP (Internet Inter-ORB Protocol) is a **protocol** that makes it possible for **distributed** programs written in different programming languages to communicate over the Internet. IIOP is a critical part of a strategic industry standard, the Common Object Request Broker Architecture (**CORBA**). Using CORBA's IIOP and related protocols, a company can write programs that will be able to communicate with their own or other company's existing or future programs wherever they are located and without having to understand anything about the program other than its service and a name. CORBA and IIOP compete with a similar strategy from Microsoft called the Distributed Component Object Model (**DCOM**). (Microsoft and the Object Management Group, sponsors of CORBA, have agreed to develop software bridges between the two models so that programs designed for CORBA can communicate with programs designed for DCOM.)

CORBA and IIOP assume the **client/server** model of computing in which a client program always makes requests and a server program waits to receive requests from clients. When writing a program, you use an interface called the General Inter-ORB Protocol (GIOP). The GIOP is implemented in specialized mappings for one or more network transport layers. Undoubtedly, the most important specialized mapping of GIOP is IIOP, which passes requests or receives replies through the Internet's transport layer using the Transmission Control Protocol (**TCP**). Other possible transport layers would include IBM's Systems Network Architecture (**SNA**) and Novell's **IPX**.

For a client to make a request of a program somewhere in a network, it must have an address for the program. This address is known as the Interoperable Object Reference (IOR). Using IIOP, part of the address is based on the server's port number and **IP address**. In the client's computer, a table can be created to map IORs to proxy names that are easier to use. The GIOP lets the program make a connection with an IOR and then send requests to it (and lets servers send replies). A Common Data Representation (CDR) provides a way to encode and decode data so that it can be exchanged in a standard way.

A somewhat similar protocol, the Remote Method Invocation (**RMI**), was developed by Sun Microsystems to serve its cross-platform framework for the **Java** programming language. Sun has provided a way so that programming that uses the RMI can be mapped to IIOP.

IIS

IIS (Internet Information Server) is a group of Internet **server**s (including a Web or **Hypertext Transfer Protocol** server and a **File Transfer Protocol** server) with additional capabilities for Microsoft's **Windows NT** and **Windows 2000** Server operating systems. IIS is Microsoft's entry to compete in the Internet server market that is also addressed by **Apache**, Sun Microsystems, O'Reilly, and others. With IIS, Microsoft includes a set of programs for building and administering Web sites, a search engine, and support for writing Web-based applications that access **database**s. Microsoft points out that IIS is tightly integrated with the Windows NT and 2000 Servers in a number of ways, resulting in faster Web page serving.

A typical company that buys IIS can create pages for Web sites using Microsoft's Front Page product (with its **WYSIWYG** user interface). Web developers can use Microsoft's **Active Server Page** (ASP) technology, which means that applications—including **ActiveX control**s—can be imbedded in Web pages that modify the content sent back to users. Developers can also write programs that filter requests and get the correct Web pages for different users by using Microsoft's Internet Server Application Program Interface (**ISAPI**) interface. ASPs and ISAPI programs run more efficiently than common gateway interface (**CGI**) and server-side include (**SSI**) programs, two current technologies. (However, there are comparable interfaces on other platforms.)

Microsoft includes special capabilities for server administrators designed to appeal to Internet service providers (**ISP**s). It includes a single window (or "console") from which all services and users can be administered. It's designed to be easy to add components as **snap-in**s that you didn't initially install. The administrative windows can be customized for access by individual customers.

IIS works closely with the **Microsoft Transaction Server** to access databases and provide control at the transaction level. It also works with Microsoft's Netshow in the delivery of streaming audio and video, delayed or live.

ILEC

An ILEC (incumbent local exchange carrier) is a telephone company in the U.S. that was providing local service when the **Telecommunications Act of 1996** was enacted. ILECs include the former Bell operating companies (**BOC**s) which were grouped into holding companies known collectively as the regional Bell operating companies (**RBOC**s) when the Bell System was broken up by a 1983 consent decree. ILECs are in contradistinction to **CLEC**s (competitive local exchange carriers).

A "local exchange" is the local "central office" of an LEC. Lines from homes and businesses terminate at a local exchange. Local exchanges connect to other local exchanges within a local access and transport area (**LATA**) or to interexchange carriers (**IXC**s) such as long-distance carriers AT&T, MCI, and Sprint.

iLINK

See "i.LINK"

illegal operation

An illegal operation, a term often seen in error messages, is a command to the **operating system** or an instruction to the computer **processor** that specifies an operation that is unknown to the operating system or processor and that therefore can't be performed. The result is that the operating system or processor usually terminates the program that made the "illegal" request. If that program was an application that you were using, you may find that data you were entering was lost or, in some cases, can be recovered from a backed-up copy that the system made for you.

A computer's processor knows what operation to perform as the result of an operation code (or *opcode*) within the instruction. Failing to recognize an opcode, the processor will return information to the operating system which in turn will usually terminate the application program that sent the bad instruction and issue a message to the user about the illegal operation. An illegal operation may mean a **bug** in the application program (or occasionally in the operating system) or it may be the result of a combination of unusual circumstances that the program and operating system could or did not anticipate. In the latter case, the problem may not be repeated or may be intermittent.

The usual practice if you get an illegal operation message is to continue working if the application is still running, or to restart the program if it has been terminated, and, if the problem recurs, to reboot the operating system and try again. If you continue to experience illegal operation errors with an application, report the problem to the software vendor.

ILOVEYOU virus

The ILOVEYOU virus comes in an e-mail note with "I LOVE YOU" in the subject line and contains an attachment that, when opened, results in the message being re-sent to everyone in the recipient's Microsoft Outlook address book and, perhaps more seriously, the loss of every **JPEG**, **MP3**, and certain other files on the recipient's hard disk. Because Microsoft Outlook is widely installed as the e-mail handler in corporate networks, the ILOVEYOU **virus** can spread rapidly from user to user within a corporation. On May 4, 2000, the virus spread so quickly that e-mail had to be shut down in a number of major enterprises such as the Ford Motor Company. The virus reached an estimated 45 million users in a single day.

The attachment in the ILOVEYOU virus is a **VBScript** program that, when opened (for example, by double-clicking on it with your mouse), finds the recipient's Outlook address book and re-sends the note to everyone in it. It then overwrites (and thus destroys) all files of the following file types: JPEG, MP3, VPOS, JS, JSE, CSS, WSH, SCT and HTA. Users who don't have a backup copy will have lost these files. (In March 1999, a virus named **Melissa virus** also replicated itself by using Outlook address books, but was less harmful in destroying user files.) The ILOVEYOU virus also resets the recipient's Internet Explorer start page in a way that may cause further trouble, resets certain Windows **registry** settings, and also acts to spread itself through Internet Relay Chat (**Internet Relay Chat**).

One of the first steps companies used to ward off the ILOVEYOU virus was to screen out notes with ILOVEYOU in the subject line. However, hackers quickly introduced copycat variations with subject lines variously identifying "JOKE" and "Mother's Day!" as the content, but containing the same or similar VBScript code. At least 12 variations have been identified. The most sinister mutation is undoubtedly the one with the subject line containing "VIRUS ALERT!!!" Posing as a virus fix from Symantec, the note starts out with "Dear Symantec Customer." The attachment (which should not be opened) is "protect.vbs."

Companies and users are advised to get or update **anti-virus software** that can help screen for the virus and remove it for users whose systems have been infected. Users are always advised never to open an e-mail attachment without screening it with anti-virus software or knowing exactly who sent it and what it is.

IM

See "instant messaging"

iMac

Now offered in multiple designer colors, the iMac is a low-cost version of Apple Computer's **Macintosh**. The iMac was designed to attract people who have never owned a personal computer and also to win back former Mac users who have moved to **personal computers**. Released in mid-August 1998, the initial version of the iMac featured a sleekly-molded designer-colored translucent case with a built-in 15-inch display, a fast 233 **MHz** processor, and the Mac OS **operating system**. Traditionally, somewhat higher in price than Intel-based PCs, a low-priced Mac symbolized Apple's determination to compete in and increase its share of the personal computer market. The iMac's designers have omitted a floppy disk drive with the idea that few users will miss it. Apple is advertising the iMac as easy to set up and ideal for simple applications and surfing the Web (the "i" in its name is said to stand for "Internet").

image

Also see **imaging**.

An image is a visual representation of something. In information technology, the term has several usages:

1) An image is a picture that has been created or copied and stored in electronic form. An image can be described in terms of **vector graphics** or **raster graphics**. An image stored in raster form is sometimes called a **bitmap**. An **image map** is a file containing information that associates different locations on a specified image with **hypertext** links.

2) An image is a section of random access memory (**RAM**) that has been copied to another memory or storage location.

image compression

Image compression is minimizing the size in bytes of a graphics file without degrading the quality of the image to an unaccceptable level. The reduction in file size allows more images to be stored in a given amount of disk or memory space. It also reduces the time required for images to be sent over the Internet or downloaded from Web pages.

There are several different ways in which image files can be compressed. For Internet use, the two most common compressed graphic image formats are the **JPEG** format and the **GIF** format. The JPEG method is more often used for photographs, while the GIF method is commonly used for line art and other images in which geometric shapes are relatively simple.

Other techniques for image compression include the use of **fractal**s and **wavelet**s. These methods have not gained widespread acceptance for use on the Internet as of this writing. However, both methods offer promise because they offer higher compression ratios than the JPEG or GIF methods for some types of images. Another new method that may in time replace the GIF format is the **PNG** format.

A text file or program can be compressed without the introduction of errors, but only up to a certain extent. This is called *lossless compression*. Beyond this point, errors are introduced. In text and program files, it is crucial that compression be lossless because a single error can seriously damage the meaning of a text file, or cause a program not to run. In image compression, a small loss in quality is usually not noticeable. There is no "critical point" up to which compression works perfectly, but beyond which it becomes impossible. When there is some tolerance for loss, the compression factor can be greater than it can when there is no loss tolerance. For this reason, graphic images can be compressed more than text files or programs.

image map

In Web page development, an image map is a graphic image defined so that a user can click on different areas of the image and be linked to different destinations. You make an image map by defining each of the sensitive areas in terms of their **x and y coordinates** (that is, a certain horizontal distance and a certain vertical distance from the left-hand corner of the image). With each set of coordinates, you specify a **Uniform Resource Locator** or Web address that will be linked to when the user clicks on that area.

The X and Y coordinates are expressed in **pixel**s either in a separate file called a map file or in the same HTML file that contains the link to the image map. Popular tools like MapEdit provide a graphical interface for creating an image map (so that you don't have to figure out the X and Y coordinate numbers yourself).

Originally, the map file had to be sent to the server. Now the creator can place the map information either at the server or at the client (a "client-side map").

Image maps are used widely on many Web sites as a more adventuresome form of main menu.

imaginary number

An imaginary number is a quantity of the form ix, where x is a **real number** and i is the positive square root of -1. The term "imaginary" probably originated from the fact that there is no real number z that satisfies the equation $z^2 = 1$. But imaginary numbers are no less "real" than real numbers. The quantity i is called the *unit imaginary number*. In engineering, it is denoted j, and is known as the j *operator*.

The unit imaginary number has some intriguing properties. For example:

$(-i)^2 = -1$

but $-i$ is different from i

$i^3 = i^2 i = (-1)i = -i$

$i^4 = i^2 i^2 = (-1)(-1) = 1$

$i^5 = i^3 i^2 = (i^3)(-1) = (-i)(-1) = i$

$i^n = i^{(n-4)}$

when n is a **natural number** larger than 4

As i is raised to higher natural-number powers, the resultant cycles through four values: i, -1, $-i$, and 1 in that order. No real number behaves like that!

The set **I** of imaginary numbers consists of the set of all possible products iw, where w is an element of the set **R** of real numbers. Therefore, the sets **I** and **R** are in one-to-one correspondence. The sum $v + iw$ of a real number v and an imaginary number iw forms a **complex number**. The set **C** of all complex numbers corresponds one-to-one with the set R **?** R of all ordered pairs of real numbers. The set **C** also corresponds one-to-one with the points on a geometric plane.

Imaginary and complex numbers are used in engineering, particularly in electronics. Real numbers denote electrical **resistance**, imaginary numbers denote **reactance**, and complex numbers denote **impedance**.

imaging

Imaging is the capture, storage, manipulation, and display of **image**s. In document imaging, the emphasis is on capturing, storing, and retrieving information from the images (which are often mainly images of text). In graphical imaging, the emphasis is on the manipulation of created images in order to achieve special effects through rotating, stretching, blurring, resizing, twirling, and other changes to the original image.

IMAP

See "Internet Message Access Protocol"

IMHO

Like FYI (for your information), IMHO (in my humble opinion) is an abbreviation for a phrase sometimes used in online chatting and e-mail. Variations include IMNSHO (in my not so humble opinion).

For similar terms, see **chat abbreviations**.

IMing

See "instant messaging"

i-Mode

i-Mode is the **packet**-based service for mobile phones offered by Japan's leader in wireless technology, NTT DoCoMo. Unlike most of the key players in the wireless arena, i-Mode eschews the Wireless Application Protocol (**WAP**) and uses a simplified version of HTML, Compact Wireless Markup Language (CWML) instead of WAP's Wireless Markup Language (**WML**). NTT DoCoMo has said that eventually it will support WAP and WML, but the company has not said exactly when this will happen.

First introduced in 1999, i-Mode was the world's first smart phone for Web browsing. The i-Mode wireless data service offers color and video over many phones. Its mobile computing service enables users to do telephone banking, make airline reservations, conduct stock transactions, send and receive e-mail, and have access to the Internet. As of early 2000, i-Mode had an estimated 5.6 million users.

impedance

Impedance, denoted Z, is an expression of the opposition that an electronic component, circuit, or system offers to alternating and/or direct electric **current**. Impedance is a vector (two-dimensional)quantity consisting of two independent scalar (one-dimensional) phenomena: **resistance** and **reactance**.

Resistance, denoted R, is a measure of the extent to which a substance opposes the movement of electrons among its atoms. The more easily the atoms give up and/or accept electrons, the lower the resistance, which is expressed in positive **real number** ohms. Resistance is observed with alternating current (**AC**) and also with direct current (**DC**). Examples of materials with low resistance, known as electrical conductors, include copper, silver, and gold. High-resistance substances are called insulators or dielectrics, and include materials such as polyethylene, mica, and glass. A material with an intermediate levels of resistance is classified as a **semiconductor**. Examples are **silicon**, germanium, and **gallium arsenide**.

Reactance, denoted X, is an expression of the extent to which an electronic component, circuit, or system stores and releases energy as the current and voltage fluctuate with each AC cycle. Reactance is expressed in **imaginary number** ohms. It is observed for AC, but not for DC. When AC passes through a component that contains reactance, energy might be stored and released in the form of a magnetic field, in which case the reactance is inductive (denoted $+jX_L$); or energy might be stored and released in the form of an electric field, in which case the reactance is capacitive (denoted $-jX_C$). Reactance is conventionally multiplied by the positive square root of -1, which is the unit imaginary number called the *j operator*, to express Z as a **complex number** of the form $R + jX_L$ (when the net reactance is inductive) or $R - jX_C$ (when the net reactance is capacitive).

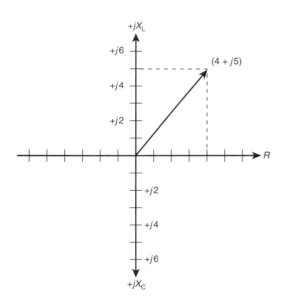

The illustration shows a coordinate plane modified to denote complex-number impedances. Resistance appears on the horizontal axis, moving toward the right. (The left-hand half of this coordinate plane is not normally used because negative resistances are not encountered in common practice.) Inductive reactance appears on the positive imaginary axis, moving upward. Capacitive reactance is

depicted on the negative imaginary axis, moving downward. As an example, a complex impedance consisting of 4 ohms of resistance and $+j5$ ohms of inductive reactance is denoted as a vector from the origin to the point on the plane corresponding to $4 + j5$.

In series circuits, resistances and reactances add together independently. Suppose a resistance of 100.00 ohms is connected in a series circuit with an inductance of 10.000 μH. At 4.0000 MHz, the complex impedance is:

$Z_{RL} = R + jX_L = 100.00 + j251.33$

If a capacitor of 0.0010000 μF is put in place of the inductor, the resulting complex impedance at 4.0000 MHz is:

$Z_{RC} = R - jX_C = 100.00 - j39.789$

If all three components are connected in series, then the reactances add, yielding a complex impedance of:

$Z_{RLC} = 100 + j251.33 - j39.789 = 100 + j211.5$

This is the equivalent of a 100-ohm resistor in series with an inductor having $+j211.5$ ohms of reactance. At 4.0000 MHz, this reactance is presented by an inductance of 8.415 μH, as determined by plugging the numbers into the formula for inductive reactance and working backwards. (See the definition of for this formula, and for the corresponding formula for capacitive reactance.)

Parallel RLC circuits are more complicated to analyze than are series circuits. To calculate the effects of capacitive and inductive reactance in parallel, the quantities are converted to *inductive susceptance* and *capacitive susceptance*. Susceptance is the reciprocal of reactance. Susceptance combines with *conductance*, which is the reciprocal of resistance, to form *complex admittance*, which is the reciprocal of complex impedance. Entire volumes have been devoted to the theoretical and practical aspects of resistance, conductance, reactance, susceptance, impedance, and admittance. An intermediate electronics text or reference book is recommended for further study.

impression

In Web advertising, the term *impression* is sometimes used as a synonym for *view*, as in *ad view*. Online publishers offer and their customers buy advertising measured in terms of ad views or impressions. Since a single Web page can contain multiple ads (depending on its design), a site usually registers more ad views per unit of time than Web pages per unit of time. (*Hits* is the term for any requested file, including each of a page's images. Although hits are of interest for traffic measurement purposes, they have no significance for advertisers.)

Page or ad impressions are logged in a log that is maintained by the site server. Programs like Web Trends read the log, abstract meaning from it, and generate a report about site usage. Other programs, such as Central Ad, can keep track of all ad impressions that have been sent and how many of these were clicked on by users.

IMT-2000 direct spread

See "WCDMA"

in the wild

According to noted computer **virus** expert Paul Ducklin, in order for a virus to be considered *in the wild*, "it must be spreading as a result of normal day-to-day operations on and between the computers of unsuspecting users." Although there are an estimated 47,000 computer viruses, fewer than 600 are said to be circulating outside of laboratories and research facilities—hence, in the wild. Experts say these wild viruses pose the most significant threat to computers. Wild viruses typically contain a damaging **payload** and the ability to wipe out all computer files, sometimes even damaging a computer's **BIOS**.

The Wild List Organization International has compiled a cumulative list of viruses considered to be in the wild. New viral strains are added as they are reported and can be verified. Recent examples of computer viruses in the wild include **Melissa**, CIH, and W.32 Navidad (the **Kriz virus**).

in-band signaling

In the public switched telephone network, (**PSTN**), in-band signaling is the exchange of **signaling** (call control) information on the same **channel** that the telephone call itself is using. Today, most long-distance communication uses **out-of-band signaling** as specified in various Signaling System 7 (**SS7**) standards.

incubator

In the business world, an incubator is an enterprise that is set up to provide office space, equipment, and sometimes mentoring assistance and capital to new businesses that are just getting started. (The term is familiar in poultry farming, where an incubator is a specially-equipped home for baby chickens.) Business incubators are set up by universities, non-profit groups, and increasingly by venture capitalists, especially for new Web businesses.

On the Web, the pace of growth and competition, especially of retail and business-to-business (**B2B**) Web sites, is fostering software packages for the creation of "out-of-the-box" Web sites. For more ambitious Web sites and technology product development, venture capitalists are discovering that the incubation idea provides an organized way to finance and monitor the progress of its fledgling "chicks."

In early 2000, the number of incubators in the U.S. was approaching 1,000, with the largest located in major cities and many university-sponsored incubators scattered throughout the country. There are also incubators in the UK and elsewhere.

incumbent local exchange carrier

See "ILEC"

Indefeasible Right of Use

In telecommunications, Indefeasible Right of Use (IRU) is the effective long-term lease (temporary ownership) of a portion of the capacity of an international cable. IRUs are specified in terms of a certain number of **channel**s of a given **bandwidth**. IRU is granted by the company or consortium of companies that built the (usually **optical fiber**) cable. Some IRU legal agreements forbid resale of the capacity ownership. For at least one major international cable owner, an IRU ownership period is granted for 25 years.

An IRU gives a large-scale Internet service provider (**ISP**) the ability to assure its own customers of international service on a long-term basis.

Indeo

Indeo is a **compression** algorithm developed by Intel and used by Microsoft's Video for Windows.

Other digital video compression algorithms include **MPEG** and PLV.

independent software vendor

See "ISV"

Indexed Sequential Access Method

See "ISAM"

inductance

See "inductor"

inductor

An inductor is a passive electronic component that stores energy in the form of a magnetic field. In its simplest form, an inductor consists of a wire loop or coil. The inductance is directly proportional to the number of turns in the coil. Inductance also depends on the radius of the coil and on the type of material around which the coil is wound.

For a given coil radius and number of turns, air cores result in the least inductance. **Dielectric** materials such as wood, glass, and plastic are essentially the same as air for the purposes of inductor winding. Ferromagnetic substances such as iron, laminated iron, and powdered iron increase the inductance obtainable with a coil having a given number of turns. In some cases, this increase is on the order of thousands of times. The shape of the core is also significant. Toroidal (donut-shaped) cores provide more inductance, for a given core material and number of turns, than solenoidal (rod-shaped) cores.

The standard unit of inductance is the **henry**, abbreviated H. This is a large unit. More common units are the microhenry, abbreviated μH (1 μH =10^{-6}H) and the millihenry, abbreviated mH (1 mH =10^{-3} H). Occasionally, the nanohenry (nH) is used (1 nH = 10^{-9} H).

It is difficult to fabricate inductors onto integrated circuit (**IC**) chips. Fortunately, **resistor**s can be substituted for inductors in most microcircuit applications. In some cases, inductance can be simulated by simple electronic circuits using **transistor**s, resistors, and **capacitor**s fabricated onto IC chips.

Inductors are used with capacitors in various **wireless** communications applications. An inductor connected in series or parallel with a capacitor can provide discrimination against unwanted signals. Large inductors are used in the power supplies of electronic equipment of all types, including computers and their peripherals. In these systems, the inductors help to smooth out the rectified utility **AC**, providing pure, battery-like **DC**.

industrial strength

In information technology, *industrial strength* is the ability of a hardware or software product or a system to work capably and dependably in the operational world of business. Prior to the advent of today's information technology revolution, the term was used to describe such products as cleansers, lubricants, and stepladders.

In the world of **mainframe** computers, IBM's flagship **operating system**, OS/390 (and its predecessor versions of **MVS**), has been described as having industrial strength.

Industry Standard Architecture

See "ISA"

InfiniBand

InfiniBand is an architecture and specification for data flow between processors and I/O devices that promises greater **bandwidth** and almost unlimited expandability in tomorrow's computer systems. In the next few years, InfiniBand is expected to gradually replace the existing Peripheral Component Interconnect (**PCI**) shared-**bus** approach used in most of today's personal computers and servers. Offering throughput of up to 2.5 **gigabyte**s per second and support for up to 64,000 addressable devices, the architecture also promises increased reliability, better sharing of data between clustered processors, and built-in security. InfiniBand is the result of merging two competing designs, Future I/O, developed by Compaq, IBM, and Hewlett-Packard, with Next Generation I/O, developed by Intel, Microsoft, and Sun Microsystems. For a short time before the group came up with a new name, InfiniBand was called System I/O.

Existing PCs and server systems are hampered with an inflexible and relatively slow internal data flow system, including today's 64-bit, 66 **MHz** PCI bus. As the amount of data coming into and flowing between components in the computer increases, the existing bus system becomes a bottleneck. InfiniBand provides a revolutionary new approach. Instead of sending data in parallel (typically 32 bits at a time, but in some computers 64 bits) across the **backplane** bus (data path), InfiniBand specifies a serial (bit-at-a-time) bus. Fewer **pin**s and other electrical connections are required, saving manufacturing cost and improving reliability. The serial bus can carry multiple **channel**s of data at the same time in a **multiplexing** signal. InfiniBand also supports multiple **memory** areas, each of which can addressed by both processors and storage devices.

Unlike the present I/O subsystem in a computer, InfiniBand seems like a full-fledged network. The InfiniBand Trade Organization describes the new bus as an I/O network and views the bus itself as a **switch** since control information will determine the route a given message follows in getting to its destination address. In fact, InfiniBand uses Internet Protocol Version 6 (**IPv6**) with its 128-bit address, allowing an almost limitless amount of device expansion.

With InfiniBand, data is transmitted in **packet**s that together form a communication called a *message*. A message can be a remote direct memory access (RDMA) read or write operation, a channel send or receive message, a transaction-based operation (that can be reversed), or a **multicast** transmission. Like the channel model many mainframe users are familiar with, all transmission begins or ends with a channel adapter. Each processor (your PC or a data center server, for example) has what is called a *host channel adapter* (HCA) and each peripheral device has a *target channel adapter* (TCA). These adapters can potentially exchange information that ensures security or work with a given Quality of Service level.

infomediary

An infomediary is a **Web site** that provides specialized information on behalf of producers of goods and services and their potential customers. The term is a composite of *information* and *intermediary*. The advent of the Web has made possible quick 24-hour access to information databases that previously were not available. Gathering these information aggregates and adding services to them is now the business of companies like the Thomas Register of Manufacturers that can bring a base of information from the print medium to the Web. Perhaps more importantly as infomediaries are Web sites that are gathering, organizing, and linking to the new information and services that is being added to the Web.

Infomediaries can be divided into those intended for consumers and those intended for businesses. Any consumer **e-commerce** site that provides information as well as an order form could be classed as an infomediary. However, the term is more frequently used to refer to sites that offer information for businesses about suppliers and other businesses.

infomercial

On television, an infomercial is a short or regular-length television program that combines information presentation with an integrated suggestion to buy a particular product or service. Exercise equipment and correspondence courses are two products sometimes sold through infomercials.

In the print media, the equivalent to an infomercial is the multi-page "advertising supplement" that is formatted to look like the news part of the medium and contains real information content.

The Internet analog of the infomercial appears to be what advertisers generally refer to as "rich media," including interactive banner ads that sometimes include **Flash** animations.

Similar neologisms include **infotainment** and **edutainment**.

infonesia

Infonesia is an inability to remember where you saw or heard an item of information. The condition is usually temporary but can recur frequently. It is more common in "information societies", with their flows of **e-mail**, seasonal catalogs, **personal digital assistant**s, and trial magazine subscriptions. Possibly the most pernicious form of infonesia is **internesia**, the inability to remember which Web site you saw an item of information on.

A person who is racking their brain to remember the information source could properly be termed an infonesiac, although this usage is not common.

information

Information is stimuli that has meaning in some context for its receiver. Some (if not all) kinds of information can be converted into **data** and passed on to another receiver. Relative to the computer, we can say that: Information is made into data, put into the computer where it is stored and processed as data, and then put out as data in some form that can be perceived as information.

Knowledge is information that is readily accessible to its user (for example, either in one's brain or in a nearby dictionary).

Information and Content Exchange

Information and Content Exchange (ICE) is an **XML**-based standard **protocol** for electronic business-to-business (**B2B**) asset management. ICE defines an architecture and a common language that can be used as a means of automating Web content **syndication** (information sharing and reuse between Web sites) for publishing and **e-commerce** uses. Members of the ICE Authoring Group (which includes representatives from Adobe Systems, Microsoft, Sun Microsystems, Vignette, and National Semiconductor) are committed to the further development of ICE as an **open** standard. ICE version 1.1 was released in June 2000.

ICE enables the automation of data supplying, exchanging, updating, and controlling without requiring the supplier to manually package content, or to maintain knowledge about the structure of recipient Web sites. ICE specifies creation of a trust relationship based on the Open Profiling System (**OPS**). Use of the ICE protocol enables data sharing between servers, so that, for example, syndicated portions of a Web page can be automatically updated when the source is updated, or new content can be automatically entered and integrated with existing content on a Web page. Each protocol message between servers consists of a valid (conforming to **namespace** criteria) XML document. XML **tags** are used to format data to be processed by the servers involved in the transaction.

ICE is intended to make it possible for almost every aspect of B2B asset exchange to be automated. Use of the protocol allows information service providers to specify content, customize it for specific recipients, schedule its delivery, and maintain it. Nevertheless, the success of content syndication is still reliant on the development of a standard **metadata** vocabulary, considered to be another essential element. The Publishing Requirements for Industry Standard Metadata (PRISM) working group (an organization made up of content providers and vendors) is collaborating to develop such a standard.

information architecture

1) In technical writing, information architecture is the set of ideas about how all information in a given context should be treated philosophically and, in a general way, how it should be organized. In the context of a company making computer products, an information architect might say that "All of our product information should serve customer needs as expressed by tasks that they have to do with our products," and would then develop a framework for organizing all existing and future product information in modules related to customer tasks. The results of this thinking would be expressed in an information architecture document.

For product information in the example just discussed, the information architecture document would become the foundation for *information planning*, which focuses on using the architecture for a specific division, set of products, or individual product. In addition to information architecture and information planning, **information design** focuses more narrowly on activities that support the architecture and planning, such as style guidelines, graphic design motifs, page design, and the information aspects of industrial design (labels, knobs, and other physical aspects of the user interface).

2) In Web site design, information architecture has a meaning similar to (1), but focused somewhat more narrowly on Web content as building blocks to be fit into a site's visual design and navigation scheme.

In technical writing in general and in Web site design in particular, information architecture is related to and generally supports the overlapping areas of **content management**, **content distribution** or **syndication**, and **electronic publishing**. Information architecture is also related to the treatment of information modules or building blocks as "objects" that can be described in one or a set of data definitions, typically using the Extensible Markup Language (**XML**). For example, an encyclopedic topic could be treated as a building block that could be distributed electronically using an XML definition that described each of the items in the topic (title, main content, author, date of authorship, and so forth).

information design

Information design is the detailed planning of specific **information** that is to be provided to a particular audience to meet specific objectives. The information designer may or may not have available (or may create) an information architecture that defines the overall pattern or structure that is imposed on the information design and an information plan that defines information units and how they are to be completed. The output of an information design is sometimes expressed in written instructions, plans, sketches, drawings, or formal specifications. However, on very small projects, information design is likely to be much less formal.

Information design can be distinguished from *information architecture* and *information planning*. In one view, there are three hierarchical levels of activity:

1. *Information architecture*, which is the general set of ideas about how all information in a given context should be organized. For example, one might say that "All of our product information should serve customer needs as expressed by tasks they have to do with our products," and then develop a pattern that organizes all product information in modules related to customer tasks. The output is an information architecture document.

2. *Information planning*, which focuses on all aspects required to prepare and support the information of a specific set of products, single product, or event over the product life or other time span. This generally includes understanding the product or event goals, studying the audience and their needs, considering possible information media, defining specific information "units" (books, chapters, Web pages, visualizations, and so forth), specifying the people who will work on them, what the schedule is, and how this work will relate to the work of others. The output is an information plan.

3. *Information design*, which focuses more narrowly on the information itself in one or more information units, and may encompass the information aspects of industrial design (labels, knobs, and the physical interface), information content design, page design, Web site design, illustration design, typography decisions, and so forth. Information design can be applied to a single work, such as a city map, or to a corporation's entire set of customer information. The output may be part of an information plan, a separate information design document, or simply the designed object or set of objects.

Information design ideas can often be tested in a usability laboratory by observing surrogate users trying to use the designed information and getting their feedback. The practice of information design invites questions into how people learn or prefer to learn and how they use information. It also raises questions about how to design information for different cultural and other contextual differences in the audience.

Since information is now commonly delivered using electronic media with new possibilities for user interaction and as product designers have become more aware of the importance of usability, a new term, *interaction design*, has arisen as a corollary of information design. A number of universities now offer courses or degree programs centered on information design.

Information Technology Information Sharing and Analysis Center

See "IT-ISAC"

Information Technology Infrastructure Library

See "ITIL"

information technology

See "IT"

infosurfing

Infosurfing is using the Internet and World Wide Web so that you get maximum information in the shortest amount of time, which for many people means favoring textual content over images. Infosurfing is practiced by librarians, professional researchers, journalists, people addicted to news, and almost anyone that gets impatient with multimedia or likes the focus of just plain text.

The simplest way to infosurf is to turn the pictures (images) off, using your browser option. Many sites specify an alternate text string in the HTML image tag that provides a brief textual descripion of each image in the space allocated for it. Otherwise, you'll get a broken image icon from your browser. Turning off graphics is best when you're familiar with most sites and know what you're missing.

Some infosurfers also turn off Java and JavaScript, turning them back on only when wanted. Once you get the idea of turning things off, some infosurfers also turn off **cookie** though cookies don't in themselves impede the downloading of text. If you have the latest levels of Netscape Communicator and Microsoft Internet Explorer, you can specify that cookies be disabled entirely or that you be prompted about whether to accept one.

If you infosurf for certain kinds of information, you'll obviously want to bookmark the sites that specialize in what you're interested in. You may want to subscribe to e-mail newsletters such as those at ZDNet, Women's Wire, or whatis.com. These newsletters summarize stories you can choose to link to or not.

Other techniques include: opening the browser several times and looking in one window while downloading to another and increasing the size of your browser **cache**. If you're constantly checking the latest news, you might set your start page at a news site. If you like to learn new words every day, you might start with whatis.

infotainment

Infotainment, combining *information* with *entertainment*, is a fairly recent **neologism** for a television program, Web site feature, or other presentation that combines information with entertainment. Most of today's popular fact-based television shows, such as those on the Animal Planet channel, could be classed as infotainment.

Serious information publishing sites such as those of TechTarget.com (including whatis.com) provide a limited amount of infotainment in the form of user polls, quizzes, and contests.

Also see **infomercial** and **edutainment**.

infranet

Infranet is a term used to refer to the **infrastructure** of a **network**, especially the **Internet**. For the Internet, the infranet is that portion of the public telephone network on which data **packet**s are exchanged using Internet **protocol**s. It can also be said to include private network infrastructures that use the Internet set of protocols, **TCP/IP**, whether or not these interconnect with the public Internet. The term was used to describe the major **switch**ing hardware and technologies, such as **frame relay** and **asynchronous transfer mode**, in an April 1999 article, "The Next Net," in *Wired* magazine. John Chambers, head of Cisco Systems, is credited with coining the term.

infrared radiation

Infrared radiation (IR) or the term *infrared* alone refers to energy in the region of the **electromagnetic radiation spectrum** at wavelengths longer than those of visible light, but shorter than those of radio waves. Correspondingly, the frequencies of IR are higher than those of microwaves, but lower than those of visible light.

Scientists divide the IR spectrum into three regions. The wavelengths are specified in microns (symbolized μ, where 1 $\mu = 10^{-6}$ meter) or in nanometers (abbreviated nm, where 1 nm = 10^{-9} meter = 0.001 μ). The *near IR band* contains energy in the range of wavelengths closest to the visible, from approximately 0.750 to 1.300 μ (750 to 1300 nm). The *intermediate IR band* (also called the *middle IR band*) consists of energy in the range 1.300 to 3.000 μ (1300 to 3000 nm). The *far IR band* extends from 2.000 to 14.000 μ (3000 nm to 1.4000 x 10^4 nm).

Infrared is used in a variety of **wireless** communications, monitoring, and control applications. A few of the applications include home-entertainment remote-control boxes, wireless local area networks, links between notebook computers and desktop computers, cordless **modem**s, intrusion detectors, motion detectors, and fire sensors.

infrastructure

In information technology and on the Internet, infrastructure is the physical **hardware** used to interconnect **computer**s and users. Infrastructure includes the transmission media, including telephone lines, cable television lines, and **satellite**s and antennas, and also the **router**s, **aggregator**s, **repeater**s, and other devices that control transmission paths. Infrastructure also includes the **software** used to send, receive, and manage the **signal**s that are transmitted.

In some usages, infrastructure refers to interconnecting hardware and software and not to computers and other devices that are interconnected. However, to some information technology users, infrastructure is viewed as everything that supports the flow and processing of information.

Infrastructure companies play a significant part in evolving the Internet, both in terms of where the interrconnections are placed and made accessible and in terms of how much information can be carried how quickly.

ingress

Ingress (pronounced IHN-grehs, from Latin *ingressus* or stepping into) is the act of entering something. For example, in telecommunications, an ingress router is a **router** through which a data packet enters a network from another network.

inheritance

In **object-oriented programming**, inheritance is the concept that when a **class** of **object**s is defined, any subclass that is defined can inherit the definitions of one or more general classes. This means for the programmer that an object in a subclass need not carry its own definition of data and methods that are generic to the class (or classes) of which it is a part. This not only speeds up program development; it also ensures an inherent validity to the defined subclass object (what works and is consistent about the class will also work for the subclass).

initial public offering

See "IPO"

initialization

Initialization is the process of locating and using the defined values for variable **data** that is used by a computer program. For example, an **operating system** or application program is installed with **defaults** or user-specified values that determine certain aspects of how the system or program is to function. Typically, these values are stored in initialization files (in Windows, these can be identified as files with an INI suffix). When the operating system or an application program is first loaded into memory, a part of the program performs initialization—that is, it looks in the initialization files, finds definite values to substitute for variable values, and acts accordingly. For example, the desktop appearance and application programs that are to be started along with the operating system are identified and loaded.

The process of the user specifying initialization values is sometimes called *configuration*.

inode

In a **UNIX**-based **operating system**, an inode is a computer-stored description of an individual file in a UNIX file system.

iNotes

See "Shimmer"

Input/Output Supervisor

See "IOS"

insect robot

See "robot"

InstallAnywhere

InstallAnywhere is a program that can used by software developers to package a product written in **Java** so that it can be installed on any major **operating system**. As its name indicates, a big advantage of InstallAnywhere is that the developer does not have to package different distribution versions of a product for different operating systems. InstallAnywhere refers to this idea as a "universal installer." The idea is possible because programs written in **Java** can be compiled into Java **bytecode** that is independent of operating system differences. Since major operating systems today come with a Java, one InstallAnywhere-packaged Java-based product will install on any of the systems.

InstallAnywhere is intended to be easy for developers to use. Customized installers will **deploy** a package from the Web or CD-ROM. An InstallAnywhere-packaged Java-based product will install on Windows 95/98/NT, Solaris, Linux, AIX, HP-UX, IRIX, OS/2 and any other Java-enabled platform.

Installfest

An Installfest is a special occasion when computer users get together to help each other install new programming, usually the **Linux operating system** and related programs, often together with experts and the resources to download programming from the Internet. The Installfest idea was originated by Linux enthusiasts and has been well supported by Linux distributors, which include Red Hat, S. U. S. E., Slackware, Debian, and Caldera. Typically, an Installfest is sponsored by a local computer club. The Installfest idea has caught on, and, at some computer club meetings, the Installfest is an ongoing part of each regular meeting.

InstallShield

InstallShield is a product used by software developers to package software so that users can install it easily and safely. (It can also be used to uninstall a product.)

InstallShield provides the developer with templates and pre-built interface objects that make it easy to package the software. Users who receive software packaged with InstallShield are assured that it will be installed quickly and without affecting other applications or system characteristics.

instant messaging

See also **IRC** (Internet Relay Chat) and **ICQ** (I Seek You).

Instant messaging (sometimes called IM or IMing) is the ability to easily see whether a chosen friend or co-worker is connected to the Internet and, if they are, to exchange messages with them. Instant messaging differs from ordinary **e-mail** in the immediacy of the message exchange and also makes a continued exchange simpler than sending e-mail back and forth. Most exchanges are text-only. However, some services allow attachments. AOL first popularized instant messaging and, with its large membership, is likely to be the most popular service for some time to come. AOL's Instant Messenger can be used by AOL members but there is no requirement to be connected to the Internet through AOL. An **Open Source** alternative to AOL's instant messaging is called **Jabber**.

In order for IMing to work, both users (who must subscribe to the service) must be online at the same time, and the intended recipient must be willing to accept instant messages. (It is possible to set your software to reject messages.) An attempt to send an IM to someone who is not online, or who is not willing to accept IMs, will result in notification that the transmission cannot be completed. If the online software is set to accept IMs, it alerts the recipient with a distinctive sound, a window that indicates that an IM has arrived and allowing the recipient to accept or reject it, or a window containing the incoming message.

Under most conditions, IMing is truly "instant." Even during peak Internet usage periods, the delay is rarely more than a second or two. It is possible for two people to have a real-time online "conversation" by IMing each other back and forth.

instant translation

Also see **automatic language translation**.

Instant translation is the translation from one language to another of Web pages, e-mail, and online chat text by a computer program so that the translated results appear almost instantly. Instant translation services are gaining in popularity because they help people who work for global businesses communicate and enable e-commerce sites to appeal to customers in other countries. Because much of the material on the Web is written in English and the majority of the world speaks other languages, most instant translation is from English to another language. IDC estimates that the machine translation industry will grow to $378 million by 2003.

Most instant translation tools store frequently-encountered words, sentences, and phrases in a database that is accessed when a new document is translated. Until recently, vendors like Lernout & Hauspie, Systran, and Transparent Language dominated the instant translation space. However, IBM is entering the arena with the WebSphere Translation Server, targeting Internet service providers and other companies that run their own servers. The IBM product creates and distributes Web content globally without the need for special Web pages or separate infrastructure. WebSphere Translation Server translates material from English to French, Spanish, German, Italian, Chinese, Japanese, and Korean but does not convert material into English.

Some companies are especially cautious when using instant translation software, having discovered that even small translation errors can result in big business problems.

instantiate

An instance is a particular realization of an abstraction or **template** such as a **class** of **object**s or a computer **process**. To instantiate is to create such an instance by, for example, defining one particular variation of object within a class, giving it a name, and locating it in some physical place.

1) In **object-oriented programming**, some writers say that you instantiate a **class** to create an **object**, a concrete instance of the class. The object is an executable file that you can run in a computer.

2) In the object-oriented programming language, **Java**, the object that you instantiate from a class is, confusingly enough, called a class instead of an object. In other words, using Java, you instantiate a class to create a specific class that is also an executable file you can run in a computer.

3) In approaches to data modeling and programming prior to object-oriented programming, one usage of *instantiate* was to make a real (data-filled) object from an abstract object as you would do by creating an entry in a table (which, when empty, can be thought of as a kind of class template for the objects to be filled in).

Institute of Electrical and Electronics Engineers

See "IEEE"

instruction

An instruction is an order given to a **computer processor** by a computer **program**. At the lowest level, each instruction is a sequence of 0s and 1s that describes a physical operation the computer is to perform (such as "Add") and, depending on the particular instruction type, the specification of special storage areas called "registers" that may contain data that to be used in carrying out the instruction or the location in computer **memory** of data that is to be used in carrying out the instruction, or a direct or indirect reference to the location in memory of the data.

In a computer's **assembler** language, each language statement generally corresponds to a single processor instruction. In higher-level languages, a language statement generally results (after program compilation) in multiple processor instructions.

In assembler language, a "macro instruction" is one that, during processing by the assembler program, expands to become multiple instructions (based on a previously coded "macro definition").

int

"int" is one of the top-level **domain name**s that can be used when choosing a domain name. This domain name is intended for sites related to international treaties or containing international databases. (For this reason, the domain name is not widely used.) Along with the second-level domain name, the top-level domain name is required in Web and e-mail addresses.

For more information, see **gTLD** (generic top-level domain name).

integer

An integer (pronounced IN-tuh-jer) is a whole number (not a fractional number) that can be positive, negative, or zero.

Examples of integers are: -5, 1, 5, 8, 97, and 3,043.

Examples of numbers that are not integers are: -1.43, $1\,^3/_4$, 3.14, .09, and 5,643.1.

The **set** of integers, denoted Z, is formally defined as follows:

$$Z = \{..., -3, -2, -1, 0, 1, 2, 3, ...\}$$

In mathematical equations, unknown or unspecified integers are represented by lowercase, italicized letters from the "late middle" of the alphabet. The most common are p, q, r, and s.

The set Z is a *denumerable* set. Denumerability refers to the fact that, even though there might be an infinite number of elements in a set, those elements can be denoted by a list that implies the identity of every element in the set. For example, it is intuitive from the list $\{..., -3, -2, -1, 0, 1, 2, 3, ...\}$ that 356,804,251 and $-67,332$ are integers, but 356,804,251.5, $-67,332.89$, $-^4/_3$, and 0.232323 ... are not.

The elements of Z can be paired off one-to-one with the elements of N, the set of natural numbers, with no elements being left out of either set. Let $N = \{1, 2, 3, ...\}$. Then the pairing can proceed in this way:

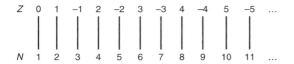

In infinite sets, the existence of a one-to-one correspondence is the litmus test for determining **cardinality**, or size. The set of natural numbers and the set of rational numbers have the same cardinality as Z. However, the sets of real numbers, imaginary numbers, and complex numbers have cardinality larger than that of Z.

integrated circuit

An integrated circuit (IC), sometimes called a *chip* or **microchip**, is a **semiconductor** wafer on which thousands or millions of tiny resistors, **capacitor**s, and **transistor**s are fabricated. An IC can function as an **amplifier, oscillator,** timer, counter, computer **memory**, or **microprocessor**. A particular IC is categorized as either linear (**analog**) or **digital**, depending on its intended application.

Linear ICs have continuously variable output (theoretically capable of attaining an infinite number of states) that depends on the input signal level. As the term implies, the output signal level is a linear function of the input signal level. Ideally, when the instantaneous output is graphed against the instantaneous input, the plot appears as a straight line. Linear ICs are used as audio-frequency (**AF**) and radio-frequency (**RF**) amplifiers. The *operational amplifier* (op amp) is a common device in these applications.

Digital ICs operate at only a few defined levels or states, rather than over a continuous range of signal amplitudes. These devices are used in computers, computer networks, modems, and frequency counters. **Logic gate**s are the fundamental building blocks of digital ICs that work with binary data, that is, signals that have only two different states, called low (logic 0) and high (logic 1).

integrated development environment

(The abbreviation *IDE* also stands for **Integrated Drive Electronics**.)

An integrated development environment (IDE) is a programming environment that has been packaged as an application program, typically consisting of a code editor, a **compiler**, a debugger, and a graphical user interface (**GUI**) builder. The IDE may be a standalone application or may be included as part of one or more existing and compatible applications. The **BASIC** programming language, for example, can be used within Microsoft Office applications, which makes it possible to write a WordBasic program within the Microsoft Word application. IDEs provide a user-friendly framework for many modern programming languages, such as **Visual Basic**, **Java**, and **PowerBuilder**.

IDEs for developing **HTML** applications are among the most commonly used. For example, many people designing Web sites today use an IDE (such as HomeSite, DreamWeaver, or FrontPage) for Web site development that automates many of the tasks involved.

Integrated Digital Enhanced Network

See "iDEN"

Integrated Drive Electronics

See "IDE"

Integrated Services Digital Network

See "ISDN"

integration

Integration (from the Latin *integer*, meaning whole or entire) generally means combining parts so that they work together or form a whole. In information technology, there are several common usages:

1) Integration during product development is a process in which separately produced components or subsystems are combined and problems in their interactions are addressed.

2) Integration is an activity by companies that specialize in bringing different manufacturers' products together into a smoothly working system.

3) In marketing usage, products or components said to be integrated appear to meet one or more of the following conditions:

A) They share a common purpose or set of objectives. (This is the loosest form of integration.)

B) They all observe the same standard or set of standard **protocols** or they share a mediating capability, such the Object Request Broker (**ORB**) in the Common Object Request Broker Architecture (**CORBA**).

C) They were all designed together at the same time with a unifying purpose and/or architecture. (They may be sold as piece-parts but they were designed with the same larger objectives and/or architecture.)

D) They share some of the same programming code.

E) They share some special knowledge of code (such as a lower-level program interface) that may or may not be publicly available. (If not publicly available, companies have been known to sue to make it available in order to make competition fair.)

In describing its Internet Information Manager (**IIS**), Microsoft says that it is "tightly integrated," apparently meaning that it meets conditions (A), (B), to some extent (C), possibly a bit of (D), and, if any, an unstated amount of (E).

integrity

Integrity, in terms of data and network security, is the assurance that information can only be accessed or modified by those authorized to do so. Measures taken to ensure integrity include controlling the physical environment of networked terminals and servers, restricting access to data, and maintaining rigorous **authentication** practices. Data integrity can also be threatened by environmental hazards, such as heat, dust, and electrical surges.

Practices followed to protect data integrity in the physical environment include: Making servers accessible only to network administrators, keeping transmission media (such as cables and connectors) covered and protected to ensure that they cannot be tapped, and protecting hardware and storage media from power surges, electrostatic discharges, and magnetism.

Network administration measures to ensure data integrity include: maintaining current authorization levels for all users, documenting system administration procedures, parameters, and maintenance activities, and creating disaster recovery plans for occurrences such as power outages, server failure, and virus attacks.

intellectual capital

Intellectual capital is **knowledge** that can be exploited for some money-making or other useful purpose. The term combines the idea of the intellect or brain-power with the economic concept of capital, the saving of entitled benefits so that they can be invested in producing more goods and services. Intellectual capital can include the skills and knowledge that a company has developed about how to make its goods or services; individual employees or groups of employees whose knowledge is deemed critical to a company's continued success; and its aggregation of documents about processes, customers, research results, and other information that might have value for a competitor that is not common knowledge.

intelligent agent

On the Internet, an intelligent agent (or simply an *agent*) is a program that gathers information or performs some other service without your immediate presence and on some regular schedule. Typically, an agent program, using parameters you have provided, searches all or some part of the Internet, gathers information you're interested in, and presents it to you on a daily or other periodic basis. An agent is sometimes called a **bot** (short for robot).

Other agents have been developed that personalize information on a Web site based on registration information and usage analysis. Other types of agents include specific site watchers that tell you when the site has been updated or look for other events and analyst agents that not only gather but organize and interpret information for you.

The practice or technology of having information brought to you by an agent is sometimes referred to as **push** technology.

Intelligent Network

Intelligent Network (IN) is a telephone network architecture originated by Bell Communications Research (Bellcore) in which the service logic for a call is located separately from the switching facilities, allowing services to be added or changed without having to redesign switching equipment. According to Bell Atlantic, IN is a "service-specific" architecture. That is, a certain portion of a dialed phone number, such as 800 or 900, triggers a request for a specific service. A later version of IN called Advanced Intelligent

Network (**AIN**) introduces the idea of a "service-independent" architecture in which a given part of a telephone number can interpreted differently by different services depending on factors such as time of day, caller identity, and type of call. AIN makes it easy to add new services without having to install new phone equipment.

Bellcore called its network IN/1. It included this model:

- The customer's telephone
- The switching system (starting with the switch a call is handled by first, usually at a telephone company central office (CO)
- A database called a service control point (SCP) that defines the possible services and their logic
- A service management system (SMS)

For more information, see **AIN**.

intelligent peripheral interface

See "IPI"

Interactive System Productivity Facility

See "ISPF"

interactive TV

Interactive TV means allowing the viewer to interact with the television set in ways other than simply controlling the channel and the volume and handling videotapes. Typical interactive TV uses are selecting a video film to view from a central bank of films, playing games, voting or providing other immediate feedback through the television connection, banking from home, and shopping from home.

Interactive TV involves adding a special "set-top unit" to the existing television set. In addition, other installation and infrastructure arrangements are required, depending on the particular approach. Most services involve offering special programming, news, and home shopping and a number offer video-on-demand and home banking. Since interactive TV still requires a considerable investment by both the service provider and the consumer and because interactive applications are still being explored, it is somewhat difficult to predict how soon it will become widely deployed.

Interactive Voice Response

Interactive Voice Response (IVR) is a software application that accepts a combination of voice telephone input and touch-tone keypad selection and provides appropriate responses in the form of voice, fax, callback, e-mail and perhaps other media. IVR is usually part of a larger application that includes **database** access. Common IVR applications include:

- Bank and stock account balances and transfers
- Surveys and polls

- Call center forwarding
- Simple order entry transactions
- Selective information lookup (movie schedules, etc.)

An IVR application provides pre-recorded voice responses for appropriate situations, keypad signal logic, access to relevant data, and potentially the ability to record voice input for later handling. Using computer telephony integration (**CTI**), IVR applications can hand off a call to a human being who can view data related to the caller at a display.

interactivity

In computers, interactivity is the sensory dialog that occurs between a human being (or possibly another live creature) and a computer **program**. (Programs that run without immediate user involvement are not interactive; they're usually called **batch** or background programs.) Games are usually thought of as fostering a great amount of interactivity. However, order entry applications and many other business applications are also interactive, but in a more constrained way (offering fewer options for user interaction).

On the World Wide Web, you not only interact with the **browser** (the Web application program) but also with the pages that the browser brings to you. **Hypertext** or the word and picture links you can connect to are the most common form of interactivity when using the Web (which can be thought of as a giant, interconnected application progam).

In addition to hypertext, the Web (and many non-Web applications in any computer system) offer other possibilities for interactivity. Any kind of user input, including typing commands or clicking the mouse, is a form of input. Displayed images and text, printouts, motion video sequences, and sounds are output forms of interactivity.

The earliest form of interaction with computers was indirect and consisted of submitting commands on punched cards and letting the computer read them and perform the commands. Later computer systems were designed so that average people (not just programmers) could interact immediately with computers, telling them what programs to run and then interacting with those programs, such as word processors (then called "editors"), drawing programs, and other interactive programs. The first interactive human-computer interfaces tended to be input text sequences called "commands" (as in "DOS commands") and terse one-line responses from the system.

In the late 1970's, the first graphical user interfaces (**GUI**) emerged from the Xerox PARC Lab, found their way into the Apple Mcintosh personal computer, and then into Microsoft's Windows operating systems and thus into almost all personal computers available today. GUIs inherently promoted interactivity because they offered the user more interaction options.

interexchange carrier

An interexchange carrier (IXC) is a telephone company that provides connections between **local exchange**s in different geographic areas. IXCs provide *inter***LATA** service as described in the **Telecommunications Act of 1996**. They're commonly referred to as "long-distance carriers." IXCs include AT&T, MCI, Sprint, and others.

interface

As a noun, an interface is either:

1. A user interface, consisting of the set of dials, knobs, operating system commands, graphical display formats, and other devices provided by a computer or a program to allow the user to communicate and use the computer or program. A graphical user interface (**GUI**) provides its user a more or less "picture-oriented" way to interact with technology. A GUI is usually a more satisfying or user-friendly interface to a computer system.

2. A programming interface, consisting of the set of statements, functions, options, and other ways of expressing program instructions and data provided by a program or language for a programmer to use.

3. The physical and logical arrangement supporting the attachment of any device to a connector or to another device.

As a verb, to interface means to communicate with another person or object. With hardware equipment, to interface means making an appropriate physical connection so that two pieces of equipment can communicate or work together effectively.

interface device

An interface device (IDF) is a hardware component or system of components that allows a human being to interact with a computer, a telephone system, or other electronic information system. The term is often encountered in the mobile communication industry where designers are challenged to build the proper combination of portability, capability, and ease of use into the interface device. The overall set of characteristics provided by an interface device is often referred to as the *user interface* (and, for computers—at least, in more academic discussions—the human-computer interface or **HCI**). Today's desktop and notebook computers have what has come to be called a graphical user interface (**GUI**) to distinguish it from earlier, more limited interfaces such as the command line interface (**CLI**).

An interface device generally must include some form or forms of output interface, such as a display screen or audio signals, and some form or forms of input interface, such as buttons to push, a keyboard, a voice receiver, or a handwriting tablet. Harmonia, a company that makes a program for developing Web pages that can be formatted **on**

the fly for different kinds of interface devices, defines six generic classes of interface devices that characterize today's technology:

- **The personal computer** (desktop or notebook, abundant memory and external storage, keyboard, large display)
- **Handheld** (much smaller, still has a keyboard)
- **Palm** (smaller still, can fit in some pockets, handwriting is primary input interface, display very small and usually landscape rather than portrait)
- **Smart Phone** (digital cellular phone with little or no computing, accepts Wireless Markup Language-coded pages from Web servers)
- **Smart Pager** (also known as a *two-way pager*, has the ability to respond by pressing buttons or by using a tiny keyboard)
- **Standard Telephone** (voice and key input interface, no computer capability)
- **Hybrid** (often a combined phone and handheld computer)

If you are creating content for a human receiver, you need at least a general understanding of the type or types of interface devices that your audience may be using. The Extensible Markup Language (**XML**) is designed to allow Web or other content to be created independently of the type of interface device that may be used. An individual **style sheet** designed for specific interface device types can be created using the Extensible Stylesheet Language (**XSL**). Then, when a user requests a page, that user's interface device type can be recognized and the appropriate style sheet used to format the page that is sent. Harmonia has developed a User Interface Markup Language (UIML) that facilitates this process.

Inter-IC bus

See "I2C bus"

Interior Gateway Protocol

See "IGP"

interlaced display

An interlaced display is a cathode-ray tube (**CRT**) display in which the lines are scanned alternately in two interwoven rasterized lines.

In a CRT display, there are several hundred horizontal lines in a frame (full screen). These lines are scanned from left to right, and from top to bottom. The refresh rate (number of frames scanned per second) varies, but it is normally between 60 and 100 **hertz**. Refresh rates slower than 60 Hz produce distracting screen flicker, which can cause headaches and eye fatigue.

Most CRT computer monitors scan each line in turn from top to bottom at the lowest **resolution** levels (640 × 480 and 800 × 600 **pixel**). However, at the higher resolutions, such as 1024 × 768 or 1200 × 800, the frame is sometimes scanned in interlaced fashion: first the odd-numbered lines, and then the even-numbered lines. This allows for a lower refresh rate without producing flicker. With text and fixed graphics displays, this scheme can work well. However, with animated graphics—especially images that move or change form rapidly—interlacing can produce a fluttering effect at least as irritating as screen flicker.

For serious animated-graphics work and video editing, a non- interlaced CRT display is recommended. The refresh rate should be as high as the system will allow, ideally 70 Hz or more.

interlaced GIF

An interlaced GIF (**Graphics Interchange Format**) is a GIF image that seems to arrive on your display like an image coming through a slowly-opening Venetian blind. A fuzzy outline of an image is gradually replaced by seven successive waves of bit streams that fill in the missing lines until the image arrives at its full resolution. Among the advantages for the viewer using 14.4 Kbps and 28.8 Kbps modems are that the wait time for an image seems less and the viewer can sometimes get enough information about the image to decide to click on it or move elsewhere. For users with faster connections, there is little difference in effect between an interlaced GIF and a non-interlaced GIF.

intermediate distribution frame

IDF also stands for **interface device**.

An intermediate distribution frame (IDF) is a free-standing or wall-mounted rack for managing and interconnecting the telecommunications cable between end user devices and a main distribution frame (MDF). For example, an IDF might be located on each floor of a multi-floor building routing the cabling down the walls to an MDF on the first floor. The MDF would contain cabling that would interconnect to the phone company or to other buildings.

Intermediate System-to-Intermediate System protocol

See "IS-IS"

international callback

See "callback"

International Data Encryption Algorithm

IDEA (International Data Encryption Algorithm) is an **encryption algorithm** developed at ETH in Zurich, Switzerland. It uses a **block cipher** with a 128-bit **key**, and is generally considered to be very secure. It is considered

among the best publicly known algorithms. In the several years that it has been in use, no practical attacks on it have been published despite of a number of attempts to find some. IDEA is patented in the United States and in most of the European countries. The patent is held by Ascom-Tech. Non-commercial use of IDEA is free. Commercial licenses can be obtained by contacting Ascom-Tech.

International Electrotechnical Commission

On the Internet, "IEC" usually means the International Electrotechnical Commission.

In telephony, IEC may also refer to an "interexchange carrier" (a long-distance carrier).

International Organization for Standardization

See "ISO"

International Standard Book Number

See "ISBN"

International Standard Recording Code

The International Standard Recording Code (ISRC) is an international code used to identify sound and audio-visual recordings on compact discs (**CDs**), music videos, and other media, primarily to ensure royalty payments. ISRC was developed because of the need to reliably identify all recordings, especially digital recordings. ISRC was developed by the International Organization for Standardization (**ISO**) in 1986 and is also known as ISO 3901.

The ISRC code is contained in the subcode of each track or recording. The ISRC code is made up of letters and numbers and is 12 characters in length. The code consists of characters for the country, registrant, year of reference, and designation code separated by dashes. An example of an ISRC code is GB-Z03-01-53900.

The country code identifies the country of residence of the registrant of the recording such as the producer or owner. It consists of two letters that are allocated to each country by the ISO. For example, FR is the code for France. The registrant code identifies the producer of the recording. It consists of three characters, which contain both letters and numbers. The year of reference is the code that identifies the year in which the ISRC code was assigned to that recording. The code is the last two digits of the year. For 2001, the year of reference code is 01. The final code is the designation code. This code must be five digits in length and is assigned by the producer or owner of the recording.

An ISRC code may not be reused. For example, if a recording is remixed or the playing time changes, a new ISRC code must be assigned. The same ISRC code may be used if a

recording is sold or recompiled without any editing. The owner of the recording, copyright organizations, broadcasting organizations, and libraries use ISRC codes.

The ISO Technical Committee (TC) in charge of ISRC is ISO/ TC 46.

International System of Units

The International System of Units (abbreviated "SI" from the French version of the name) is a scientific method of expressing the magnitudes or quantities of seven important natural phenomena. This system was formerly called the meter-kilogram-second (MKS) system.

All SI units can be expressed in terms of standard multiple or fractional quantities, as well as directly. Multiple and fractional SI units are defined by prefix multipliers according to powers of 10 ranging from 10^{-24} to 10^{24}.

Meter

The meter (abbreviation, m) is the SI unit of displacement or length. One meter is the distance traveled by a ray of electromagnetic (EM) energy through a vacuum in $1/_{299,792,458}$ ($3.33564095 \times 10^{-9}$) second. The meter was originally defined as one ten-millionth (0.0000001 or 10^{-7}) of the distance, as measured over the earth's surface in a great circle passing through Paris, France, from the geographic north pole to the equator.

Kilogram

The kilogram (abbreviation, kg) is the SI unit of mass. It is defined as the mass of a particular international prototype made of platinum-iridium and kept at the International Bureau of Weights and Measures. It was originally defined as the mass of one liter (10^{-3} cubic meter) of pure water.

Second

The second (abbreviation, s or sec) is the SI unit of time. One second is the time that elapses during 9.192631770×10^9 cycles of the radiation produced by the transition between two levels of Cesium 133. It is also the time required for an EM field to propagate 299,792,458 (2.99792458×10^8) meters through a vacuum.

Kelvin

The Kelvin (abbreviation K), also called the degree Kelvin (abbreviation, °K), is the SI unit of temperature. One Kelvin is $1/_{273.16}$ (3.6609×10^{-3}) of the thermodynamic temperature of the triple point of pure water (H_2O).

Ampere

The ampere (abbreviation, A) is the SI unit of electric current. One ampere is the current that would produce a force of 0.0000002 (2×10^{-7}) newton between two straight, parallel, perfectly conducting wires having infinite length and zero diameter, separated by one meter in a vacuum. One ampere represents 6.24×10^{18} unit electric charge carriers, such as electrons, passing a specified fixed point in one second.

Candela

The candela (abbreviation, cd) is the SI unit of luminous intensity. It is the electromagnetic radiation, in a specified direction, that has an intensity of 1/683 (1.46×10^{-3}) watt per steradian at a frequency of 540 terahertz (5.40×10^{14} hertz).

Mole

The mole (abbreviation, mol) is the SI unit of material quantity. One mole is the number of atoms in 0.012 kilogram of the most common isotope of elemental carbon (C-12). This is approximately 6.022169×10^{23}, and is also called the Avogadro constant.

Also see **prefix multiplier**s.

internationalisation

See "internationalization"

internationalization

Internationalization (sometimes shortened to "I18N, meaning "I—eighteen letters -N") is the process of planning and implementing products and services so that they can easily be adapted to specific local languages and cultures, a process called **localization**. The internationalization process is sometimes called translation or localization *enablement*. Enablement can include:

- Allowing space in user interfaces (for example, hardware labels, help pages, and online menus) for translation into languages that require more characters

- Developing with products (such as Web editors or authoring tools) that can support international character sets (**Unicode**)

- Creating print or Web site graphic images so that their text labels can be translated inexpensively

- Using written examples that have global meaning

- For software, ensuring data space so that messages can be translated from languages with single-byte character codes (such as English) into languages requiring multiple-byte character codes (such as Japanese Kanji)

internesia

Internesia is an inability to remember which Web site or other Internet facility you saw an item of information on. It is an important form of the more general condition known as **infonesia**, which is the inability to remember where you saw an item of information from any source (newspapers, television, and so forth).

Infojunkies are especially susceptible to internesia. A person who can never remember a Web site is an internesiac. Bookmarks may help, but many internesiacs bookmark so many sites, they can't find anything on their bookmark list or remember the right search word.

Internet

The Internet, sometimes called simply "the Net," is a worldwide system of computer networks—a network of networks in which users at any one computer can, if they have permission, get information from any other computer (and sometimes talk directly to users at other computers). It was conceived by the Advanced Research Projects Agency (ARPA) of the U.S. government in 1969 and was first known as the **ARPANet**. The original aim was to create a network that would allow users of a research computer at one university to be able to "talk to" research computers at other universities. A side benefit of ARPANet's design was that, because messages could be routed or rerouted in more than one direction, the network could continue to function even if parts of it were destroyed in the event of a military attack or other disaster.

Today, the Internet is a public, cooperative, and self-sustaining facility accessible to hundreds of millions of people worldwide. Physically, the Internet uses a portion of the total resources of the currently existing public telecommunication networks. Technically, what distinguishes the Internet is its use of a set of protocols called **TCP/IP** (for Transmission Control Protocol/Internet Protocol). Two recent adaptations of Internet technology, the **intranet** and the **extranet**, also make use of the TCP/IP protocol.

For many Internet users, electronic mail (**e-mail**) has practically replaced the Postal Service for short written transactions. Electronic mail is the most widely used application on the Net. You can also carry on live "conversations" with other computer users, using Internet Relay Chat (**IRC**). More recently, **Internet telephony** hardware and software allows real-time voice conversations.

The most widely used part of the Internet is the **World Wide Web** (often abbreviated "WWW" or called "the Web"). Its outstanding feature is **hypertext**, a method of instant cross-referencing. In most Web sites, certain words or phrases appear in text of a different color than the rest; often this text is also underlined. When you select one of these words or phrases, you will be transferred to the site or page that is relevant to this word or phrase. Sometimes there are buttons, images, or portions of images that are "clickable." If you move the pointer over a spot on a Web site and the pointer changes into a hand, this indicates that you can click and be transferred to another site.

Using the Web, you have access to millions of pages of information. Web browsing is done with a Web **browser**, the most popular of which are Microsoft Internet Explorer and Netscape Navigator. The appearance of a particular Web site may vary slightly depending on the browser you use. Also, later versions of a particular browser are able to render more "bells and whistles" such as animation, virtual reality, sound, and music files, than earlier versions.

Internet access provider

See "IAP"

Internet Advertising Bureau

The IAB (Internet Advertising Bureau) is an organization that fosters the growth of advertising on the Internet. Membership is available to corporations engaged in selling, measuring, monitoring, or producing advertising on the Internet. The IAB recommends a set of standard-size banner ads for World Wide Web pages.

Internet Architecture Board

See "IAB"

Internet Assigned Numbers Authority

See "IANA"

Internet commerce provider

See "ICP"

Internet Control Message Protocol

See "ICMP"

Internet Corporation for Assigned Names and Numbers

See "ICANN"

Internet Engineering Task Force

See "IETF"

Internet Explorer Administration Kit

Internet Explorer Administration Kit (IEAK) is a product from Microsoft that enables an organization to centrally manage the customizing, deployment, and maintenance of Microsoft's Web **browser**, Internet Explorer, for users on different computer **platform**s. There is no royalty on the deployed copies. Using IEAK, a company can set up every user's browser the same way. Microsoft offers a step-by-step process for using the kit.

Internet Explorer

See "Microsoft Internet Explorer"

Internet Group Management Protocol

The Internet Group Management Protocol (IGMP) is an Internet **protocol** that provides a way for an Internet computer to report its **multicast** group membership to adjacent **router**s. Multicasting allows one computer on the Internet to send content to multiple other computers that have identified themselves as interested in receiving the originating computer's content. Multicasting can be used for such applications as updating the address books of mobile computer users in the field, sending out company newsletters to a distribution list, and "broadcasting" high-bandwidth programs of **streaming media** to an audience that has "tuned in" by setting up a multicast group membership.

Using the Open Systems Interconnection (**OSI**) communication model, IGMP is part of the **Network layer**. IGMP is formally described in the Internet Engineering Task Force (**IETF**) Request for Comments (**RFC**) 2236.

Internet Information Server

See "IIS"

Internet Inter-ORB Protocol

See "IIOP"

Internet maps

Since the Internet began developing about 25 years ago, there has always been some kind of map showing what it looks like. Maps, even partial ones, of today's enormous Internet, whether of its physical wiring, its information content, or some other aspect, challenge both creator and user. Yet a map, even a complicated one, has a way of bounding chaos and giving us a ready-packaged mental construct. Some time ago, we discovered Martin Dodge's remarkable collection of Internet maps at the Centre for Advanced Spatial Analysis, University College London. His Atlas of Cyberspaces (http://www.cybergeography.org/atlas/atlas.html) contains separate collections for maps of:

- ISP and Internet backbone networks
- Three-dimensional information spaces
- Information landscapes or visualizations
- Cyberspace using geographic metaphors

The Atlas of Cyberspaces also includes examples of Web site maps and several other map categories.

Internet Message Access Protocol

Internet Message Access Protocol (IMAP) is a standard **protocol** for accessing **e-mail** from your local server. IMAP (the latest version is IMAP4) is a **client/server** protocol in which e-mail is received and held for you by your Internet server. You (or your e-mail client) can view just the heading and the sender of the letter and then decide whether to download the mail. You can also create and manipulate folders or mailboxes on the server, delete messages, or search for certain parts or an entire note. IMAP requires continual access to the server during the time that you are working with your mail.

A less sophisticated protocol is Post Office Protocol 3 (**POP3**). With POP3, your mail is saved for you in your mail box on the server. When you read your mail, all of it is immediately downloaded to your computer and, unless you request it, no longer maintained on the server.

IMAP can be thought of as a remote file server. POP can be thought of as a "store-and-forward" service.

POP and IMAP deal with the receiving of e-mail from your local server and are not to be confused with Simple Mail Transfer Protocol (**SMTP**), a protocol for transferring e-mail between points on the Internet. You send e-mail with SMTP and a mail handler receives it on your recipient's behalf. Then the mail is read using POP or IMAP.

Internet Open Trading Protocol

Internet Open Trading Protocol (IOTP) is a set of standards that makes all electronic purchase transactions consistent for customers, merchants, and other involved parties, regardless of payment system. IOTP accommodates a wide range of payment systems such as **Secure Electronic Transaction**, **digital cash**, e-checks, and debit cards. Payment system data is encapsulated within IOTP messages. IOTP is designed to handle a transaction that involves a number of different parties: the customer, merchant, credit checker and certifier, bank, and delivery handler. IOTP uses the Extensible Markup Language (**XML**) to define data that encompasses everything that may be needed in a transaction.

In the "real world," you can negotiate certain factors when considering a purchase. These include choosing who you conduct business with, whether it will be conducted in person or by phone, the method of payment, the provision of a payment receipt, and the delivery of the product. In the virtual world, IOTP is designed to ensure that all of these factors are successfully and securely performed.

Companies contributing to the development of IOTP include Hewlett Packard, IBM, JCP, MasterCard International, Smart Card Integrations, Sun Microsystems, and Wells Fargo Bank.

Internet presence provider and promoter

See "IPPP"

Internet presence provider

See "IPP"

Internet problems

Here are:

- Three rules-of-thumb for dealing with Internet problems
- A table showing the most common codes and messages you're likely to see on your Web browser (**HTTP**), when accessing **Usenet**, using **e-mail**, or using the **FTP** protocol to upload or download files

A Table Showing the Most Common Codes and Messages

Error message	What it means	What you can do
400—Bad request	You entered a **URL** that is not accepted as correct. Possibly the server being contacted doesn't recognize the document you are asking for or it may no longer exist. It is also possible that it is correct but you aren't authorized to access it.	Check the URL to see if it's correctly spelled and that every letter is in the right (upper- or lower-) case. Check colons, numbers of slashes, and tildes.
401—Unauthorized	The site being accessed is protected and you either entered the incorrect password or the host does not want users coming from your domain to enter. Some sites will only allow specific domains to access the site. For example, some U.S. government sites (with the .gov top-level domain name) will only permit users coming from .gov or .edu (educational sites) to gain access. Or some educational sites only allow access from other educational sites.	If you are sure you have access to the site, try typing the password again. If you don't have a password or your domain does not have access to the site, you won't be able to access it.
403—Forbidden	You are not permitted to access this document. It is either password-protected or the host does not want your domain to enter.	See above.
404—Not found	The host server can't find the HTML document at the URL you've entered. Either you have mistyped the URL, the document no longer exists, or you've been given the wrong URL.	If your URL ends in ".htm", try ".html" (and vice versa). To find out whether the site hosting the document is still active, delete everything after the last slash in the URL. If this doesn't work, try deleting the slash and adding .htm or .html to the end. If the site is still running, try and find the page from another location on the site that you can reach.
550—xxxxxxxx is not a known user	Using e-mail, you sent a note to an e-mail address that isn't recognized at the mail server you've specified. The e-mail note got all the way to the mail server (so that part's right), but you may have entered the user part of the e-mail address incorrectly or the user may no longer have an account on that server.	Make sure you entered the correct e-mail user name. If you suspect it's an old address or was mistyped in a note sent to you, try looking up a new address using the person's name. Try **e-mail address finding tools**.
Bad file request	The form you're trying to access is not supported by your browser or there is an error in the form.	Try using a different browser. If the problem persists or another browser is not available, send an e-mail note to the site's Webmaster.
Cannot add form submission result to book-mark list	This error message occurs when you've submitted a search request and then try to save the result as a bookmark. Even hough it may look like a valid address, the resulting page does not have a URL that can be reused so it can't be added to your bookmark list.	Use the **Save As** command to save the page to your hard drive. Then you can open the saved HTML page in your browser and add that to your bookmark list.
Connection refused by host	You're not permitted to access this document either because it's password-protected or the host doesn't permit your domain to enter.	If you have access to the site and you know the password, try again, making sure you type it correctly and with the correct case.
Failed DNS lookup	The **URL** you requested could not be translated into a valid Internet address by the domain name system. This is either a result of a mistake in the system or you could have mistakenly entered an incorrect URL.	Mistakes in **DNS** lookups are a common occurrence. Simply clicking the Reload button may correct the error. If the error persists, you may have entered an incorrect host name. Try typing the URL again.
File contains no data	The site you accessed doesn't ontain any Web pages on it. It's possible that you're trying to access the site while the page is being uploaded.	Try waiting a minute and clicking on the Reload button. Make sure that the URL is typed in correctly. If the problem persists, try again later.

Error message	What it means	What you can do
Helper application not found	You're trying to load a file of a type that your browser doesn't recognize. Most browsers can be enabled to view or load file types that they don't otherwise recognize. These files can be sound files, movie clips, graphics, ZIP archive files, or any other type of file you are trying to download.	The dialog box that carries this message will tell you the file type that is missing. You can then follow your browser's instructions for assigning a viewer for each file format you wish to view online. It's often better to have certain file formats not assigned to helper applications for Internet browsers. When files are not assigned to helper applications, the dialog box you receive has a "Save to Disk" option. This can often be useful when you want to download files, such as ZIP archive files, to save them instead of extracting them right away.
Host unavailable	The server computer that hosts this site could not be reached. The server may be offline or down for maintenance.	Try clicking on the Reload button. If it still doesn't work, try again later.
Host unknown	The server you're trying to reach is not connected, or you have lost your own connection. You may have also entered the URL incorrectly.	Click the Reload button and try again. Occasionally, packets don't arrive on the Internet and a second try will work. Next, make sure you are connected to the Internet. If you have lost your connection, simply reconnect and try the URL again. If you still receive the error, check the URL for typos and case-sensitivity.
Network connection was refused by the server	Some servers have limits on the number of people or request they can handle at a time. If you get this message, the server is probably too busy to handle one more user. When the server doesn't create its own message to handle this error, this generic message is displayed instead.	Try clicking the Reload button until you connect. Or try again later.
NNTP server error	This error occurs when you are trying to log on to a Usenet newsgroup. An **NNTP** server is part of your Internet service provider's software, so if this error occurs the software may be malfunctioning or the newsgroup does not exist.	Make sure that the URL is typed correctly. If you still receive the error, wait a while and try again. If the problem still persists, contact your access provider and make them aware of the problem.
Permission denied	This error occurs when you are connected with an FTP site and you are either uploading or downloading. Sometimes the site administrator doesn't want you to upload to the site, download a certain file, or access a certain directory. The site may also be too busy.	Check that you are using the correct procedure to upload or download the file. Then keep trying until you succeed. If you still receive the error and know that you're able to upload or download to that site, contact the Webmaster by phone or e-mail.
Too many connections—try again later	The limit to the number of people who can use the site at one time has been exceeded. You'll have to wait your turn.	Keep clicking the Reload button until you connect or try again later when there is likely to be less traffic.
Too many users	To avoid slow uploading and downloading rates, site administrators set a maximum number of users that can access the site at one time. Your request is one too many.	Keep trying until you connect or try again later when there is less Internet traffic. Check to see whether the site has mirrors, and try one of those.
Unable to locate host	The server is either down for maintenance or you may have lost your connection.	Click the Reload button; sometimes there is an intermittent problem on the Internet. Then make sure you're connected to the Internet. If you have lost your connection, simply reconnect and try the URL again. If you still receive the error, check the URL for typos and case-sensitivity.

Error message	What it means	What you can do
Unable to locate the server	The server indicated in the URL you typed or clicked from either no longer exists or was entered incorrectly.	Check the URL to see if everything is correct. Make sure that everything is correctly spelled and in the correct case (some servers are case-sensitive). You can also check with the source of the URL to verify that it is correct.
Viewer not found	Your browser doesn't recognize files of this type. Most browsers can be extended to be able to view or load file types that are not otherwise recognized by browsers, such as movie or sound files.	When this dialog box appears, search for a helper application that will open files of this format. Then follow your browser's instructions for assigning this viewer to open files of that format online.
You can't log on as an anonymous user	This is another FTP error message. Most browsers submit "anonymous" as your user ID and your email address as your password. The FTP site you are connecting to may not allow "anonymous" access. This error will also occur when the FTP server is currently at its limit of "anonymous" users. Another possibility is that your browser doesn't support anonymous FTP access (for example, America Online's browser).	Keep trying to access the FTP site until you succeed. Sometimes the FTP server is too busy. However, if you don't have a browser that allows anonymous FTP access or the site is password-protected, enter your user ID and password manually using FTP software such as WS_FTP or CuteFTP.

Three Rules-of-Thumb for Dealing with Internet Problems

1. If you get a message saying the domain name server (**DNS**) can't find your page and you're sure you've typed it in correctly or clicked on a valid link, try it again—TWO more times! (Sometimes **packets** don't get there!)

2. If you get a "Not found" message, the page may be temporarily missing because of miscoding at the target site. Try it again tomorrow...or try the home page for the site and send e-mail asking them to restore the page.

3. Be aware that sometimes a page you've visited recently may be coming from your **cache** (or the cache on a **proxy** server within your company). To get the "fresh" version of the page, click on "Reload" in your tool bar.

Internet Protocol

The Internet Protocol (IP) is the method or **protocol** by which **data** is sent from one computer to another on the **Internet**. Each computer (known as a **host**) on the Internet has at least one **IP address** that uniquely identifies it from all other computers on the Internet. When you send or receive data (for example, an e-mail note or a Web page), the message gets divided into little chunks called packets. Each of these packets contains both the sender's Internet address and the receiver's address. Any **packet** is sent first to a **gateway** computer that understands a small part of the Internet. The gateway computer reads the destination address and forwards the packet to an adjacent gateway that in turn reads the destination address and so forth across the Internet until one gateway recognizes the packet as belonging to a computer within its immediate neighborhood or **domain**. That gateway then forwards the packet directly to the computer whose address is specified.

Because a message is divided into a number of packets, each packet can, if necessary, be sent by a different route across the Internet. Packets can arrive in a different order than the order they were sent in. The Internet Protocol just delivers them. It's up to another protocol, the Transmission Control Protocol (**TCP**) to put them back in the right order.

IP is a connectionless protocol, which means that there is no continuing connection between the end points that are communicating. Each packet that travels through the Internet is treated as an independent unit of data without any relation to any other unit of data. (The reason the packets do get put in the right order is because of TCP, the connection-oriented protocol that keeps track of the packet sequence in a message.) In the Open Systems Interconnection (**OSI**) communication model, IP is in **layer 3**, the Networking Layer.

The most widely used version of IP today is Internet Protocol Version 4 (IPv4). However, IP Version 6 (**IPv6**) is also beginning to be supported. IPv6 provides for much longer addresses and therefore for the possibility of many more Internet users and devices. IPv6 includes the capabilities of IPv4 and any server that can support IPv6 packets can also support IPv4 packets.

Internet Protocol Security

See "IPsec"

Internet Relay Chat

For terms frequently used in online keyboard chatting, see **chat abbreviations**.

Internet Relay Chat (IRC) is a system for **chatting** that involves a set of rules and conventions and **client/server** software. On the Web, certain sites such as Talk City or IRC networks such as the **Undernet** provide **servers** and help you download an IRC **client** to your PC. Talk City also offers an IRC client **applet** that it downloads for you as part of their home page so that you can start chatting right away.

You can start a chat group (called a **channel**) or join an existing one. There is a protocol for discovering existing chat groups and their members. Depending on the type of network, nicknames can be reserved (registered) or just used during the session. Some channels encourage you to register a nickname that you always use and even offer space for a personal profile, picture, and personal home page link.

Popular ongoing IRC channels are #hottub and #riskybus. A number of channels are set up and conducted in foreign languages. The most common IRC networks are IRCnet (mostly European), EFnet (mostly North American), Undernet, and Dalnet. Popular IRC clients include mIRC for Windows, IRCle for Mac OS, and irc2 (the original client) for UNIX-base operating systems.

The IRC protocol uses **Transmission Control Protocol** (you can IRC via a **Telnet** client), usually on **port** 6667.

Internet Research Task Force

The IRTF is an activity of the of the **Internet Society**. The Internet Research Task Force (IRTF) works on network technology.

You can find out more about the IRTF at the Internet Society's home page.

Internet Server Application Program Interface

See "ISAPI"

Internet service provider

See "ISP"

Internet Society

The Internet Society is an international non-profit organization that acts as a guide and conscience for the workings of the Internet. It was founded in 1992 and is based on Reston, Virginia. The Internet Society supports the Internet Architecture Board (**IAB**), which supervises technical and other issues. Among the IAB's activities is the Internet Engineering Task Force (**IETF**), which oversees the evolution of **TCP/IP**.

Internet time

Internet time is the concept that events occur at a faster rate on the Internet than elsewhere or that, everywhere, the Internet is affecting the pace of change. Andy Grove, CEO of Intel, is quoted as saying, "The world now runs on Internet time."

Internet traffic

Several major Internet **backbone** providers have Web sites that post hourly or more frequent statistics on how fast data is travelling on their backbone lines and the percentage of data **packet** that are being lost. Our table summarizes these sites, the information they provide, and how often they are updated.

This Internet traffic statistics site...	Gives you this information
AT&T Internet Network Status http://ipnetwork. bgtmo.ip.att.net/delay. html or http:// ipnetwork.bgtmo.ip.att. net/loss.html	Backbone delay (**latency**) or **packet** loss between specified U.S. cities (both pages updated every 30 minutes)

This Internet traffic statistics site...	Gives you this information
Cable and Wireless Global Internet Backbone `http://sla.cw.net`	Backbone delay (latency) and packet loss by global region (updated every 10 minutes)
UUNET `http://www.uunet.com/ lang.en/customers/sla/ latency.html`	Monthly statistics for North America, Trans-atlantic, and Europe

Internet voting

See "e-voting"

Internet2

Internet2 is a collaboration among more than 100 U.S. universities to develop networking and advanced applications for learning and research. Since much teaching, learning, and collaborative research may require real-time multimedia and high-**bandwidth** interconnection, a major aspect of Internet2 is adding sufficient network infrastructure to support such applications. But Internet2 also intends to investigate and develop new ways to use the Internet and the Internet2 infrastructure for its educational purposes. Although Internet2 is not envisioned as a future replacement for the Internet, its organizers hope to share their developments with other networks, including the Internet. Internet2 will include and further develop the National Science Foundation's very high-speed Backbone Network Service (**vBNS**) that currently interconnects research **supercomputer centers** in the U.S. The involved institutions plan to continue using the existing Internet for "ordinary" services such as e-mail, personal Web access, and newsgroups.

Internet2 collaborators plan to use Quality-of-Service (**QoS**) tools so that participants can reserve and use bandwidth for special events or in certain time periods. Here are some possibilities envisioned by Internet2:

Distributed learning modules: Conceptually, teachers and students can be share materials in cyberspace with students learning in a self-directed manner under the supervision of an educational system or teacher. Internet2 foresees tools that would make it easy to create what they call LearningWare, using existing methodologies. Internet2 may also help realize the Instructional Management System (IMS), a standard process for using the Internet in developing and delivering learning packages and tracking outcomes. One can think of the IMS as a more structured way to exploit the potential learning materials on the World Wide Web.

New ways to envision and retrieve information: In the future, today's text-oriented models of information structure could be replaced by interactive pictures of information structure (compare a textual taxonomy or table of contents with illustrations of interlinked and explodable animal forms, for example). With Internet2's high-bandwidth connections, experiments in such information visualization will be possible; new ideas can be tried out. In environments where up-to-date information is valuable, information can be pushed to users at their request.

Virtual environment sharing: Sometimes called *tele-immersion*, participants in teleconferences could share the perception that everyone was in the same physical place, possibly with virtual (but somewhat real) models of shared work objects such as architectural models or multimedia storyboards. You would be able to see yourself with others in a far-away conference room, talking and perhaps manipulating objects in the room.

Virtual laboratory: A virtual laboratory would allow scientists in a number of different physical locations, each with unique expertise, computing resources, and/or data to collaborate efficiently not simply at a meeting but in an ongoing way. Effectively, such a project would extend and pool resources while engendering orderly communication and progress toward shared goals. For example, a group of astronomers and computer scientists at the supercomputing centers in the U.S. are attempting to share experiments and knowledge about the origin of the universe. Shared visualizations of alternative possibilities could conceivably suggest additional or refined alternatives. Virtual laboratories are also envisioned for the design and manufacturing of complex systems such as airplanes and for studying and forecasting weather patterns.

Internetwork Packet Exchange

See "IPX"

internetworking

Internetworking is a term used by Cisco, BBN, and other providers of network products and services as a comprehensive term for all the concepts, technologies, and generic devices that allow people and their computers to communicate across different kinds of **networks**. For example, someone at a computer on a **token ring** local area network may want to communicate with someone at a computer on an **Ethernet** local area network in another country using a **wide area network** interconnection. The common internetwork **protocols**, routing tables, and related network devices required to achieve this communication constitute internetworking.

The standard reference model for internetworking is Open Systems Interconnection (**OSI**), which could also be used as a model for intranetworking as well. OSI enables any technology to be related to another technology because each

can be related to the standard communication model. OSI provides a **layering** approach to the problem of exchanging data across a network or a network of networks so that the problem can be broken down into easier-to-understand components and so that boundaries between components can be more easily determined.

InterNIC

Unitl recently, InterNIC (Internet Network Information Center), a cooperative activity between the U.S. government and Network Solutions, Inc., was the organization responsible for registering and maintaining the **com**, **net**, and **org top-level domain** names on the World Wide Web. The actual registration was performed by Network Solutions, Inc. As a result of a new U. S. Government Statement of Policy (known as "the white paper") in October 1998, competition will be introduced in domain name registration for these top-level domains and a new, non-profit global organization, the Internet Corporation of Assigned Names and Numbers (**ICANN**), has been designated to conduct the registrar accreditation process. ICANN has initially designated five new registrar companies—in addition to Network Solutions—for a two-month test period. After that period, additional registrars are expected to be accredited.

In addition to the com, net, and org domain name, geographically identified domains in the U.S. such as those for cities and towns are administered by US Domain Name Registration Services. There are also registries for Canada, Mexico, Europe, Asia Pacific countries, and other countries.

interoperability

Interoperability (pronounced IHN-tuhr-AHP-uhr-uh-BIHL-ih-tee) is the ability of a system or a product to work with other systems or products without special effort on the part of the customer. Interoperability becomes a quality of increasing importance for information technology products as the concept that "The network is the computer" becomes a reality. For this reason, the term is widely used in product marketing descriptions.

Products achieve interoperability with other products using either or both of two approaches:

- By adhering to published **interface** standards
- By making use of a "broker" of services that can convert one product's interface into another product's interface "on the fly"

A good example of the first approach is the set of standards that have been developed for the World Wide Web. These standards include **TCP/IP**, **Hypertext Transfer Protocol**, and **HTML**. The second kind of interoperability approach is exemplified by the Common Object Request Broker Architecture (**CORBA**) and its Object Request Broker (**ORB**).

Compatibility is a related term. A product is compatible with a standard but interoperable with other products that meet the same standard (or achieve interoperability through a broker).

interpreted

An interpreted program, sometimes called a *script*, is a program whose instructions are actually a logically sequenced series of operating system commands, handled one at a time by a **command interpreter**. In turn, the command interpreter requests services from the operating system. The writer of the interpreted program need not be concerned by low-level storage management considerations. On the other hand, an interpreted program can not be as efficient as a *compiled* program, which has been processed by a language compiler. A language compiler converts source statements into something close to the strings of 0's and 1's that a processor ultimately is given to work on. Because this work is already done before a compiled program is run, it runs much more quickly.

An interpreted program in a language such as **Perl** is much easier to write than a program written for a compiler. Interpreted programs are ideal for small tasks and for "gluing together" a succession of compiled programs that are run from the interpreted program.

interprocess communication

Interprocess communication (IPC) is a set of programming **interface**s that allow a programmer to create and manage individual program **process**es that can run concurrently in an **operating system**. This allows a program to handle many user requests at the same time. Since even a single user request may result in multiple processes running in the operating system on the user's behalf, the processes need to communicate with each other. The IPC interfaces make this possible. Each IPC method has its own advantages and limitations so it is not unusual for a single program to use all of the IPC methods. IPC methods include:

- **Pipe**s and **named pipe**s
- **Message queueing**
- **Semaphore**s
- **Shared memory**
- **Sockets**

interrupt

An interrupt is a signal from a device attached to a computer or from a program within the computer that causes the main program that operates the computer (the *operating system*) to stop and figure out what to do next. Almost all personal (or larger) computers today are *interrupt-driven*—that is, they start down the list of computer instructions in one program (perhaps an application such as a word processor) and keep running the instructions until either (A) they can't go any further or (B) an interrupt signal is sensed. After the interrupt signal is sensed, the computer either resumes running the program it was running or begins running another program.

Basically, a single computer can perform only one computer instruction at a time. But, because it can be interrupted, it can take turns in which programs or sets of instructions that it performs. This is known as *multitasking*. It allows the user to do a number of different things at the same time. The computer simply takes turns managing the programs that the user effectively starts. Of course, the computer operates at speeds that make it seem as though all of the user's tasks are being performed at the same time. (The computer's operating system is good at using little pauses in operations and user think time to work on other programs.)

An operating system usually has some code that is called an *interrupt handler*. The interrupt handler prioritizes the interrupts and saves them in a *queue* if more than one is waiting to be handled. The operating system has another little program, sometimes called a *scheduler*, that figures out which program to give control to next.

In general, there are hardware interrupts and software interrupts. A hardware interrupt occurs, for example, when an I/O operation is completed such as reading some data into the computer from a tape drive. A software interrupt occurs when an application program terminates or requests certain services from the operating system. In a personal computer, a hardware interrupt request (**IRQ**) has a value associated with it that associates it with a particular device.

interrupt request

See "IRQ"

interstitial

An interstitial (something "in between") is a page that is inserted in the normal flow of editorial content structure on a Web site for the purpose of advertising or promotion. It can be more or less intrusive and the reaction of viewers usually depends on how welcome or entertaining the message is. An interstitial is usually designed to move automatically to the page the user requested after allowing enough time for the message to register or the ad(s) to be read.

intrabody signaling

See "personal area network"

intranet

An intranet is a private **network** that is contained within an **enterprise**. It may consist of many interlinked **local area networks** and also use leased lines in the **wide area network**. Typically, an intranet includes connections through one or more **gateway** computers to the outside Internet. The main purpose of an intranet is to share company information and computing resources among employees. An intranet can also be used to facilitate working in groups and for teleconferences.

An intranet uses **TCP/IP**, **HTTP**, and other Internet protocols and in general looks like a private version of the Internet. With **tunneling**, companies can send private messages through the public network, using the public network with special encryption/decryption and other security safeguards to connect one part of their intranet to another.

Typically, larger enterprises allow users within their intranet to access the public Internet through **firewall** servers that have the ability to screen messages in both directions so that company security is maintained. When part of an intranet is made accessible to customers, partners, suppliers, or others outside the company, that part becomes part of an **extranet**.

intrusion detection

Intrusion detection (ID) is a type of security management system for computers and networks. An ID system gathers and analyzes information from various areas within a computer or a network to identify possible security breaches, which include both intrusions (attacks from outside the organization) and misuse (attacks from within the organization). ID uses *vulnerability assessment* (sometimes refered to as *scanning*), which is a technology developed to assess the security of a computer system or network.

Intrusion detection functions include:

- Monitoring and analyzing both user and system activities
- Analyzing system configurations and vulnerabilities
- Assessing system and file integrity
- Ability to recognize patterns typical of attacks
- Analysis of abnormal activity patterns
- Tracking user policy violations

ID systems are being developed in response to the increasing number of attacks on major sites and networks, including those of the Pentagon, the White House, NATO, and the U.S. Defense Department. The safeguarding of security is becoming increasingly difficult, because the possible technologies of attack are becoming ever more sophisticated; at the same time, less technical ability is required for the novice attacker, because proven past methods are easily accessed through the Web.

Typically, an ID system follows a two-step process. The first procedures are host-based and are considered the *passive* component, these include: inspection of the system's configuration files to detect inadvisable settings; inspection of the password files to detect inadvisable passwords; and inspection of other system areas to detect policy violations. The second procedures are network-based and are

considered the *active* component: mechanisms are set in place to reenact known methods of attack and to record system responses.

In 1998, ICSA.net, a leading security assurance organization, formed the Intrusion Detection Systems Consortium (IDSC) as an open forum for ID product developers with the aim of disseminating information to the end user and developing industry standards.

inverse multiplexing

Inverse multiplexing speeds up data transmission by dividing a data stream into multiple concurrent streams that are transmitted at the same time across separate channels (such as a **T-1** or **E-1** lines) and are then reconstructed at the other end back into the original data stream. Just the reverse of ordinary **multiplexing**, which combines multiple signals into a single signal, inverse multiplexing is a technique commonly used where data in a high-speed local area network (**LAN**) flows back and forth into a wide area network (**WAN**) across the "bottleneck" of a slower line such as a T-1 (1.544 **Mbps**). By using multiple T-1 lines, the data stream can be load-balanced across all of the lines at the same time. As a general rule, inverse multiplexing across up to 8 T-1 lines (or E-1 lines in Europe and elsewhere) is said to be less expensive than the cost of renting a T-3 (45 Mbps) line (or E-3 line in Europe and elsewhere).

Inverse multiplexing is also sometimes used in combination with **frame relay** and asynchronous transfer mode (**ATM**) transmission.

Inverse multiplexing is sometimes called *inverse muxing* or *imuxing*.

inverse-square law

The inverse-square law is a principle that expresses the way radiant energy propagates through space. The rule states that the power intensity per unit area from a point source, if the rays strike the surface at a right angle, varies inversely according to the square of the distance from the source.

Imagine a 40-**watt** lamp at the center of a spherical enclosure. The total **power** striking the surface of the sphere is 40 watts, no matter what the size of the sphere. Some people find this counter-intuitive, but it becomes obvious when we consider that all the radiated power (no more and no less) from the source must strike an enclosure of any size that completely surrounds the source. Thus, the power striking the interior of a sphere 10 meters across is the same (40 watts in this hypothetical example) as the power striking the interior of a sphere 100 meters across, 100 kilometers across, or 100,000 kilometers across. The power per unit area, however, does depend on the size of the sphere.

The surface area A (in meters squared) of a sphere having radius r (in meters) is given by:

$$A = (4 \text{ pi}) \, r^2$$

where **pi** is the ratio of a sphere's circumference to its diameter, and is approximately equal to 3.14159. If the radius of a sphere is multiplied by some factor n, then the surface area increases by a factor of n^2. This decreases the power per unit area by a factor of n^2. Another way of saying this is that the power per unit area becomes n^{-2} times as great.

Increasing the diameter of a sphere from 10 to 100 meters makes it 10 times as large in diameter, and gives it 100 times the surface area. This cuts the light power per unit area from a lamp at the sphere's center by a factor of 100. The power landing on, say, one square centimeter of the sphere's interior becomes $1/100$, or 0.01 times, as great, if the sphere's diameter grows from 10 to 100 meters. The law applies only as long as the point source is at the center of the sphere, so the rays from the source strike the sphere's surface at right angles.

Also see **meter**, **square meter**, and International System of Units (**SI**).

I/O

I/O (input/output), pronounced "eye-oh," describes any operation, program, or device that transfers data to or from a computer. Typical I/O devices are printers, hard disks, keyboards, and mouses. In fact, some devices are basically input-only devices (keyboards and mouses); others are primarily output-only devices (printers); and others provide both input and output of data (hard disks, diskettes, writable CD-ROMs).

IO.SYS

In the **Windows 95 operating system**, IO.SYS is an **executable binary file** (in other words, a program) that, when the operating system is **booted** (started), processes **instruction**s that tell the operating system how the computer is set up. In Windows 95, IO.SYS replaced the older **MS-DOS** system files, IO.SYS and MSDOS.SYS. The newer IO.SYS contains all the information needed to start your computer and eliminates the need for the **CONFIG.SYS** and **autoexec.bat** files because the values in CONFIG.SYS and AUTOEXEC.BAT are in IO.SYS instead. Both of these files still come with Windows for older applications and drivers that need them.

In computers using DOS or Windows 3.x, the IO.SYS is loaded with the MSDOS.SYS file when the computer is booted. MSDOS.SYS is a text file that determines whether DOS or Windows is loaded. Because IO.SYS is a sequence of executable code rather than readable text, it is not editable like MSDOS.SYS, CONFIG.SYS, and AUTOEXEC.BAT.

To change **default** values that come with IO.SYS, you must change the CONFIG.SYS file. In loading IO.SYS, the system picks up any changed values that are present in the CONFIG.SYS file.

IOS

IOS (Input/Output Supervisor) is a Microsoft Windows program that supervises the interaction between **file system** requests and events and **input/output** device **driver**s.

IP

See "Internet Protocol"

IP address

This definition is based on Internet Protocol Version 4. See Internet Protocol Version 6 (**IPv6**) for a description of the newer 128-bit IP address. Note that the system of IP address classes described here, while forming the basis for IP address assignment, is generally bypassed today by use of Classless Inter-Domain Routing (**CIDR**) addressing.

In the most widely installed level of the Internet Protocol (**IP**) today, an IP address is a 32-**bit** number that identifies each sender or receiver of information that is sent in **packets** across the Internet. When you request an HTML page or send e-mail, the Internet Protocol part of **TCP/IP** includes your IP address in the message (actually, in each of the packets if more than one is required) and sends it to the IP address that is obtained by looking up the **domain name** in the **Uniform Resource Locator** you requested or in the e-mail address you're sending a note to. At the other end, the recipient can see the IP address of the Web page requestor or the e-mail sender and can respond by sending another message using the IP address it received.

An IP address has two parts: the identifier of a particular network on the Internet and an identifier of the particular device (which can be a server or a workstation) within that network. On the Internet itself—that is, between the **router** that move packets from one point to another along the route—only the network part of the address is looked at.

The Network Part of the IP Address

The Internet is really the interconnection of many individual networks (it's sometimes referred to as an *internetwork*). So the Internet Protocol (**IP**) is basically the set of rules for one network communicating with any other (or occasionally, for broadcast messages, all other networks). Each network must know its own address on the Internet and that of any other networks with which it communicates. To be part of the Internet, an organization needs an Internet network number, which it can request from the Network Information Center (NIC). This unique network number is included in any packet sent out of the network onto the Internet.

The Local or Host Part of the IP Address

In addition to the network address or number, information is needed about which specific machine or host in a network is sending or receiving a message. So the IP address needs both the unique network number and a host number (which is unique within the network). (The host number is sometimes called a *local* or *machine address*.)

Part of the local address can identify a subnetwork or **subnet** address, which makes it easier for a network that is divided into several physical subnetworks (for example, several different local area networks) to handle many devices.

IP Address Classes and Their Formats

Since networks vary in size, there are four different address formats or classes to consider when applying to NIC for a network number:

- **Class A** addresses are for large networks with many devices.
- **Class B** addresses are for medium-sized networks.
- **Class C** addresses are for small networks (fewer than 256 devices).
- **Class D** addresses are multicast addresses.

The first few bits of each IP address indicate which of the address class formats it is using. The address structures look like this:

Class A	0	Network (7 bits)	Local address (24 bits)
Class B	10	Network (14 bits)	Local address (16 bits)
Class C	110	Network (21 bits)	Local address (8 bits)
Class D	1110	Multicast address (28 bits)	

The IP address is usually expressed as four decimal numbers, each representing eight bits, separated by periods. This is sometimes known as the **dot address** and, more technically, as *dotted quad notation*. For Class A IP addresses, the numbers would represent "network.local.local.local"; for a Class C IP address, they would represent "network.network.network.local". The number version of the IP address can (and usually is) represented by a name or series of names called the **domain name**.

The Internet's explosive growth makes it likely that, without some new architecture, the number of possible network addresses using the scheme above would soon be used up (at least, for Class C network addresses). However, a new IP version, **IPv6**, expands the size of the IP address to 128 bits, which will accommodate a large growth in the number of network addresses. For hosts still using IPv4, the use of **subnet**s in the host or local part of the IP address will help reduce new applications for network numbers. In addition, most sites on today's mostly IPv4 Internet have gotten around the Class C network address limitation by using the Classless Inter-Domain Routing (**CIDR**) scheme for address notation.

Relationship of the IP Address to the Physical Address

The machine or physical address used within an organization's local area networks may be different than the Internet's IP address. The most typical example is the 48-bit **Ethernet** address. TCP/IP includes a facility called the Address Resolution Protocol (**ARP**) that lets the administrator create a table that maps IP addresses to physical addresses. The table is known as the *ARP cache*.

Static versus Dynamic IP Addresses

The discussion above assumes that IP addresses are assigned on a static basis. In fact, many IP addresses are assigned dynamically from a pool. Many corporate networks and online services economize on the number of IP addresses they use by sharing a pool of IP addresses among a large number of users. If you're an America Online user, for example, your IP address will vary from one logon session to the next because AOL is assigning it to you from a pool that is much smaller than AOL's base of subscribers.

IP telephony

IP telephony (**Internet Protocol** telephony) is a general term for the technologies that use the Internet Protocol's **packet**-switched connections to exchange voice, fax, and other forms of information that have traditionally been carried over the dedicated circuit-switched connections of the public switched telephone network (**PSTN**). Using the Internet, calls travel as packets of data on shared lines, avoiding the tolls of the PSTN. The challenge in IP telephony is to deliver the voice, fax, or video packets in a dependable flow to the user. Much of IP telephony focuses on that challenge.

IP telephony service providers include or soon will include local telephone companies, long distance providers such as AT&T, cable TV companies, Internet service providers (**ISPs**), and fixed service **wireless** operators. IP telephony services also affect vendors of traditional **handheld** devices.

Currently, unlike traditional phone service, IP telephony service is relatively unregulated by government. In the U.S., the Federal Communications Commission (FCC) regulates phone-to-phone connections, but says they do not plan to regulate connections between a phone user and an IP telephony service provider.

VoIP is an organized effort to standardize IP telephony. IP telephony is an important part of the **convergence** of computers, telephones, and television into a single integrated information environment. Also see another general term, computer-telephony integration (**CTI**), which describes technologies for using computers to manage telephone calls.

IPC

See "interprocess communication"

IPI

IPI (Intelligent Peripheral Interface) is a high-**bandwidth** interface between a computer and a **hard disk** or a tape device. Devices using IPI can transfer data between the hard drive and **RAM** in the range between 3 and 25 **megabyte**s per second.

The latest version of IPI is IPI-3, which supports **redundant array of independent disks**. The official IPI standards are:

- ANSI/ISO 9318-3 Intelligent Peripheral Interface— Device Generic Command Set for Magnetic and Optical Disk Drives

- ANSI/ISO 9318-4 Intelligent Peripheral Interface— Device Generic Command Set for Magnetic Tape Drives

IPL

IPL (initial program load) is a **mainframe** term for the loading of the **operating system** into the computer's main **memory**. A mainframe operating system (such as OS/390) contains many megabytes of code that is customized by each installation, requiring some time to load the code into the memory. On a personal computer, **booting** or re-booting (re-starting) is the equivalent to IPLing (the term is also used as a verb).

In earlier operating systems, when you added devices to the hardware system, you had to stop the system, change the configuration file, and then "re-IPL," an activity that meant the system would be unavailable for some period of time. Today's systems provide dynamic reconfiguration so that the system can keep running.

IPng

See "IPv6"

IPO

See "IPO"

IPP

An Internet presence provider (IPP) is a company that provides the disk space, high-speed Internet connection, and possibly the **Web site** design and other services for companies, organizations, or individuals to have a visible **presence** (meaning Web site) on the Internet. Using an IPP means that the owner of the Web site doesn't need to have the files for it served from the owner's computer. Although one can maintain a Web site from a smaller computer if site traffic is very low, most moderate- to high-traffic Web sites require a relatively expensive, higher-speed connection to the Internet. For this reason alone, most individuals and organizations put their sites on a server at an Internet presence provider.

Many Internet service providers (**ISPs**) act as both Internet access provider (IAP) and Internet presence provider, although some provide only one or the other service. An IPP sometimes offers design and production services for a Web site as a package or on a consulting basis. Some Internet presence providers use the term *hosting* or **virtual hosting** for the "housing and maintenance" aspects of presence providing. Typical service packages at different prices include assistance with **domain name** registration, a specific amount of hard disk space for Web pages, a number of e-mail addresses, the arrangement of server application or database access from Web pages, **e-commerce** shopping page setup, a specific amount of allowable Web data traffic, and assistance in setting up and maintaining the site.

Some presence providers let you put your own server machine (or lease one to you) at their location and they manage it for you. This is called *co-location*.

IPPP

An IPPP (Internet presence provider and promoter) is a company that helps an enterprise create a **Web site**, arrange for **hosting** (housing, maintaining, and providing Internet access) for the Web site, and promote an audience for it. Many Internet service providers (**ISPs**) are also IPPPs, but some ISPs simply offer users **access** to the Internet.

IPsec

IPsec (Internet Protocol Security) is a developing standard for security at the network or **packet** processing layer of network communication. Earlier security approaches have inserted security at the **Application** layer of the communications model. IPsec will be especially useful for implementing **virtual private network**s and for remote user access through dial-up connection to private networks. A big advantage of IPsec is that security arrangements can be handled without requiring changes to individual user computers. Cisco has been a leader in proposing IPsec as a standard (or combination of standards and technologies) and has included support for it in its network **routers**.

IPsec provides two choices of security service: Authentication Header (AH), which essentially allows authentication of the sender of data, and Encapsulating Security Payload (ESP), which supports both authentication of the sender and encryption of data as well. The specific information associated with each of these services is inserted into the packet in a header that follows the IP packet header. Separate key protocols can be selected, such as the ISAKMP/Oakley protocol.

Officially spelled IPsec by the IETF, the term often appears as IPSec and IPSEC.

IPv6

IPv6 (Internet Protocol Version 6) is the latest level of the Internet Protocol (**IP**) and is now included as part of IP support in many products including the major computer **operating system**s. IPv6 has also been called "IPng" (IP Next Generation). Formally, IPv6 is a set of specifications from the Internet Engineering Task Force (**IETF**). IPv6 was designed as an evolutionary set of improvements to the current IP Version 4. Network **hosts** and intermediate **node**s with either IPv4 or IPv6 can handle **packet**s formatted for either level of the Internet Protocol. Users and service providers can update to IPv6 independently without having to coordinate with each other.

The most obvious improvement in IPv6 over the IPv4 is that **IP address**es are lengthened from 32 bits to 128 bits. This extension anticipates considerable future growth of the Internet and provides relief for what was perceived as an impending shortage of network addresses.

IPv6 describes rules for three types of addressing: **unicast** (one host to one other host), **anycast** (one host to the nearest of multiple hosts), and **multicast** (one host to multiple hosts). Additional advantages of IPv6 are:

● Options are specified in an extension to the header that is examined only at the destination, thus speeding up overall network performance.

● The introduction of an "anycast" address provides the possibility of sending a message to the nearest of several possible gateway hosts with the idea that any one of them can manage the forwarding of the packet to others. Anycast messages can be used to update routing tables along the line.

● Packets can be identified as belonging to a particular "flow" so that packets that are part of a multimedia presentation that needs to arrive in "real time" can be provided a higher quality-of-service relative to other customers.

● The IPv6 header now includes extensions that allow a packet to specify a mechanism for authenticating its origin, for ensuring data integrity, and for ensuring privacy.

IPX

IPX (Internetwork Packet Exchange) is a networking **protocol** from Novell that interconnects networks that use Novell's **NetWare** clients and servers. IPX is a datagram or **packet** protocol. IPX works at the Network layer of communication protocols and is connectionless (that is, it doesn't require that a connection be maintained during an exchange of packets as, for example, a regular voice phone call does).

Packet acknowledgment is managed by another Novell protocol, the Sequenced Packet Exchange (**SPX**). Other related Novell NetWare protocols are: the Routing Information Protocol (RIP), the Service Advertising Protocol (SAP), and the NetWare Link Services Protocol (NLSP).

IR

See "infrared radiation"

IRC

See "Internet Relay Chat"

IRQ

An IRQ (**interrupt request**) value is an assigned location where the computer can expect a particular device to interrupt it when the device sends the computer signals about its operation. For example, when a printer has finished printing, it sends an **interrupt** signal to the computer. The signal momentarily interrupts the computer so that it can decide what processing to do next. Since multiple signals to the computer on the same interrupt line might not be understood by the computer, a unique value must be specified for each device and its path to the computer. Prior to Plug-and Play (**PnP**) devices, users often had to set IRQ values manually (or be aware of them) when adding a new device to a computer.

If you add a device that does not support Pnp, the manufacturer will hopefully provide explicit directions on how to assign IRQ values for it. If you don't know what IRQ value to specify, you'll probably save time by calling the technical support phone number for the device manufacturer and asking.

irrational number

An irrational number is a **real number** that cannot be reduced to any ratio between an **integer** p and a **natural number** q. The union of the set of irrational numbers and the set of **rational number**s forms the set of real numbers. In mathematical expressions, unknown or unspecified irrationals are usually represented by u through z. Irrational numbers are primarily of interest to theoreticians. Abstract mathematics has potentially far-reaching applications in communications and computer science, especially in data encryption and security.

Examples of irrational numbers are $2^{1/2}$ (the square root of 2), $3^{1/3}$ (the cube root of 3), the circular ratio **pi**, and the natural **logarithm** base e. The quantities $2^{1/2}$ and $3^{1/3}$ are examples of **algebraic number**s. Pi and e are examples of special irrationals known as a **transcendental number**s. The decimal expansion of an irrational number is always nonterminating (it never ends) and nonrepeating (the digits display no repetitive pattern).

If x and z are irrationals such that $x\ z$, then there always exists an irrational y such that $x\ y\ z$. The set of irrationals is "dense" like the set **Q** of rationals. But theoretically, the set of irrationals is "more dense." Unlike **Q**, the set of irrationals is *nondenumerable*. There are more nonterminating, nonrepeating decimals than is possible to list, even by implication. To prove this, suppose there is an implied list of all the nonterminating, nonrepeating decimal numbers between 0 and 1. Every such number consists of a zero followed by a decimal point, followed by an infinite sequence of digits from the set {0, 1, 2, 3, 4, 5, 6, 7, 8, 9}. Suppose the elements of the list are denoted x_1, x_2, x_3, ... and the digits in the numbers are denoted a_{ii}. The list can be written like this:

$$x_1 = 0.a_{11}a_{12}a_{13}a_{14}a_{15}a_{16} \ldots$$
$$x_2 = 0.a_{21}a_{22}a_{23}a_{24}a_{25}a_{26} \ldots$$
$$x_3 = 0.a_{31}a_{32}a_{33}a_{34}a_{35}a_{36} \ldots$$
$$x_4 = 0.a_{41}a_{42}a_{43}a_{44}a_{45}a_{46} \ldots$$
$$x_5 = 0.a_{51}a_{52}a_{53}a_{54}a_{55}a_{56} \ldots$$
$$x_6 = 0.a_{61}a_{62}a_{63}a_{64}a_{65}a_{66} \ldots$$
$$\ldots$$

Even though we don't know the actual values of any of the digits, it is easy to imagine a number between 0 and 1 that can't be in this list. Think of a number **y** of the following form:

$$y = 0.b_{11}b_{22}b_{33}b_{44}b_{55}b_{66} \ldots$$

such that no b_{ii} in **y** is equal to the corresponding a_{ii} in the list. The resulting number **y** is nonterminating and nonrepeating, is between 0 and 1, but is not equal to any x_i in the list, because there is always at least one digit that does not match.

The non-denumerability of the set of irrational numbers has far-reaching implications. Perhaps most bizarre is the notion that "not all infinities are created equal." Although the set of rationals and the set of irrationals are both infinite, the set of irrationals is larger in a demonstrable way.

IRTF

See "Internet Research Task Force"

IRU

See "Indefeasible Right of Use"

IS

1) IS (information system) is the collection of technical and human resources that provide the storage, computing, distribution, and communication for the information required by all or some part of an **enterprise**. A special form of IS is a management information system (**MIS**), which provides information for managing an enterprise.

2) IS (information services) is a common name for an organization within an enterprise that is responsible for its data processing and information system or systems.

ISA

See "ISA"

ISAM

ISAM (Indexed Sequential Access Method) is a file management system developed at IBM that allows **record**s to be accessed either sequentially (in the order they were entered) or randomly (with an index). Each index defines a different ordering of the records. An employee database may have several indexes, based on the information being sought. For example, a name index may order employees alphabetically by last name, while a department index may order employees by their department. A key is specified in each index. For an alphabetical index of employee names, the last name field would be the key.

ISAM was developed prior to **VSAM** (Virtual Storage Access Method) and relational databases.

ISAPI

ISAPI (Internet Server Application Program Interface) is a set of Windows program calls that let you write a Web server application that will run faster than a common gateway interface (**CGI**) application. A disadvantage of a CGI application (or "executable file," as it is sometimes called) is that each time it is run, it runs as a separate process with its own address space, resulting in extra instructions that have to be performed, especially if many instances of it are running on behalf of users. Using ISAPI, you create a dynamic link library (**DLL**) application file that can run as part of the Hypertext Transport Protocol (**HTTP**) application's process and address space. The DLL files are loaded into the computer when HTTP is started and remain there as long as they are needed; they don't have to be located and read into storage as frequently as a CGI application.

Existing CGI applications can be converted into ISAPI application DLLs without having to rewrite their logic. However, they do need to be written to be **thread**-safe so that a single instance of the DLL can serve multiple users.

A special kind of ISAPI DLL is called an ISAPI **filter**, which can be designated to receive control for every HTTP request. You can create an ISAPI filter for **encryption** or decryption, for logging, for request screening, or for other purposes.

ISBN

The ISBN (International Standard Book Number) is a unique number assigned to a book title by its publisher for tracking and ordering purposes. An example is:

ISBN 0-385-49531-5

which is the ISBN for Simon Singh's *The Code Book*, a book about crypography.

Publishers, retailers, libraries, and readers use the ISBN as a way to specify a particular book without confusion.

The principles and procedures for international standard book numbering are contained in the International Organization for Standardization's Recommendation 2108.

iSCSI

iSCSI is Internet SCSI (Small Computer System Interface), a new Internet Protocol (**IP**)-based storage networking standard for linking data storage facilities, developed by the Internet Engineering Task Force (**IETF**). By carrying **SCSI** commands over IP networks, iSCSI is used to facilitate data transfers over intranets and to manage storage over long distances. The iSCSI **protocol** is among the key technologies expected to help bring about rapid development of the storage area network (**SAN**) market, by increasing the capabilities and performance of storage data transmission. Because of the ubiquity of IP networks, iSCSI can be used to transmit data over local area networks (**LAN**s), wide area networks (**WAN**s), or the Internet and can enable location-independent data storage and retrieval.

How iSCSI Works:

When an end user or application sends a request, the **operating system** generates the appropriate SCSI commands and data request, which then go through **encapsulation** and, if necessary, **encryption** procedures. A **packet header** is added before the resulting IP packets are transmitted over an **Ethernet** connection. When a packet is received, it is decrypted (if it was encrypted before transmission), and disassembled, separating the SCSI commands and request. The SCSI commands are sent on to the SCSI controller, and from there to the SCSI storage device. Because iSCSI is bi-directional, the protocol can also be used to return data in response to the original request.

iSCSI is one of two main approaches to storage data transmission over IP networks; the other method, Fibre Channel over IP (**FC/IP**), translates **Fibre Channel** control codes and data into IP packets for transmission between geographically distant Fibre Channel SANs. FC/IP (also known as *Fibre Channel tunneling* or *storage tunneling*) can only be used in conjunction with Fibre Channel technology; in comparison, iSCSI can run over existing Ethernet networks. A number of vendors, including Cisco, IBM, and Nishan have introduced iSCSI-based products (such as **switch**es and **router**s). Both iSCSI and FC/IP are proposed standards, and are expected to be ratified by the end of 2001.

ISDN

ISDN (Integrated Services Digital Network) is a set of **CCITT/ITU** standards for digital transmission over ordinary telephone copper wire as well as over other media. Home and business users who install an ISDN **adapter** (in place of a **modem**) can see highly-graphic Web pages arriving very

quickly (up to 128 **Kbps**). ISDN requires adapters at both ends of the transmission so your access provider also needs an ISDN adapter. ISDN is generally available from your phone company in most urban areas in the United States and Europe.

There are two levels of service: The Basic Rate Interface (**BRI**), intended for the home and small enterprise, and the Primary Rate Interface (**PRI**), for larger users. Both rates include a number of B-channels and a D-channels. Each **B-channel** carries data, voice, and other services. Each **D-channel** carries control and signaling information.

The Basic Rate Interface consists of two 64 Kbps B-channels and one 16 Kbps D-channel. Thus, a Basic Rate user can have up to 128 Kbps service. The Primary Rate consists of 23 B-channels and one 64 Kpbs D-channel in the U.S. or 30 B-channels and 1 D-channel in Europe.

Integrated Services Digital Network in concept is the integration of both analog or voice data together with digital data over the same network. Although the ISDN you can install is integrating these on a medium designed for analog transmission, **broadband** ISDN (**BISDN**) will extend the integration of both services throughout the rest of the end-to-end path using fiber optic and radio media. Broadband ISDN will encompass **frame relay** service for high-speed data that can be sent in large bursts, the Fiber Distributed-Data Interface (**FDDI**), and the Synchronous Opical Network (**SONET**). BISDN will support transmission from 2 Mbps up to much higher, but as yet unspecified, rates.

IS-IS

One of the most commonly used **routing protocol**s, the Intermediate System-to-Intermediate System protocol (IS-IS) is based on a routing method known as *DECnet Phase V* routing, in which routers known as *intermediate systems* exchange data about routing using a single **metric** to determine the network **topology**. IS-IS was developed by the International Organization for Standardization (**ISO**) as part of their Open Systems Interconnection (**OSI**) model. The first versions of IS-IS were used to manage routing within ISO Connectionless Network Protocol (CLNP) networks. IS-IS was ratified as a standard in 1990 (OSI IS-IS Intra-domain Routing Protocol, **IETF**RFC 1142 [2], **ISO/IEC** 10589 [3]).

In the OSI context, an *intermediate system* refers to a router, as opposed to an *end system* (ES), which refers to a **node**. ES-IS protocols allow routers and nodes to identify each other; IS-IS performs the same service between nodes for routing purposes. In common with other routing protocols such as **OSPF** (Open Shortest Path First), IS-IS is a *link state* protocol: it stores information about the state of links and uses that data to select paths. IS-IS is used to intermittently send out link state information across the network, so that each router can maintain a current picture of network topology. Optional metrics can be used to identify network delay, expense, and error involved with the use of a particular link.

ISO

ISO (International Organization for Standardization), founded in 1947, is a worldwide federation of national standards bodies from some 100 countries, one from each country. Among the standards it fosters is Open Systems Interconnection (**OSI**), a universal reference model for communication protocols. Many countries have national standards organizations such as the American National Standards Institute (**ANSI**) that participate in and contribute to ISO standards making.

"ISO" is not an abbreviation. It is a word, derived from the Greek *isos*, meaning "equal," which is the root for the prefix "iso-" that occurs in a host of terms, such as "isometric" (of equal measure or dimensions) and "isonomy" (equality of laws, or of people before the law). The name ISO is used around the world to denote the organization, thus avoiding the assortment of abbreviations that would result from the translation of "International Organization for Standardization" into the different national languages of members. Whatever the country, the short form of the Organization's name is always ISO.

ISO 14000 and 14001

ISO 14000 is a series of environmental management standards developed and published by the International Organization for Standardization (**ISO**) for organizations. The ISO 14000 standards provide a guideline or framework for organizations that need to systematize and improve their environmental management efforts. The ISO 14000 standards are not designed to aid the enforcement of environmental laws and do not regulate the environmental activities of organizations. Adherence to these standards is voluntary.

The ISO 14001 standard is the most important standard within the ISO 14000 series. ISO 14001 specifies the requirements of an environmental management system (EMS) for small to large organizations. An EMS is a systemic approach to handling environmental issues within an organization. The ISO 14001 standard is based on the Plan-Check-Do-Review-Improve cycle.

The Plan cycle deals with the beginning stages of an organization becoming ISO 14001-compliant. The Check cycle deals with checking and correcting errors. The Do cycle is the implementation and operation of the ISO 14001 standard within an organization. The Review cycle is a review of the entire process by the organization's top management. And the Improve cycle is a cycle that never ends as an organization continually finds ways to improve their EMS.

The entire process can take several months to several years depending on the size of the organization. If an organization is already ISO 9000-certified, the implementation of ISO 14001 does not take as long. When an organization is compliant, they can either register with a third-party registrar or self-declare their compliance. The ISO 14001 standard is the only ISO 14000 standard that allows an organization to be registered or "certified."

The Technical Committee (TC) behind ISO 14000 is TC 207.

ISO 9000

ISO 9000 is a series of standards, developed and published by the International Organization for Standardization (**ISO**), that define, establish, and maintain an effective quality system for manufacturing and service industries. The ISO 9000 standard is the most widely known and has perhaps had the most impact of the 13,000 standards published by the ISO. It serves many different industries and organizations as a guide to quality products, service, and management.

An organization can be ISO 9000-certified if it successfully follows the ISO 9000 standards for its industry. In order to be certified, the organization must submit to an examination by an outside assessor. The assessor interviews staff members to ensure that they understand their part in complying with the ISO 9000 standard, and the assessor examines the organization's paperwork to ensure ISO 9000 compliance. The assessor then prepares a detailed report that describes the parts of the standard the organization missed. The organization then agrees to correct any problems within a specific time frame. When all problems are corrected, the organization can then be certified. Today, there are approximately 350,000 ISO 9000-certified organizations in over 150 countries.

The Technical Committee (TC) behind ISO 9000 is TC 176.

ISO 9660

An ISO 9660 file system is a standard **CD-ROM file system** that allows you to read the same CD-ROM whether you're on a PC, Mac, or other major computer platform. The standard, issued in 1988, was written by an industry group named High Sierra. Almost all computers with CD-ROM drives can read files from an ISO 9660 file system.

There are several specification levels. In Level 1, file names must be in the 8.3 format (no more than eight characters in the name, no more than three characters in the suffix) and in capital letters. Directory names can be no longer than eight characters. There can be no more than eight nested directory levels. Level 2 and 3 specifications allow file names up to 32 characters long.

ISO date format

The **International Organization for Standardization** (ISO) date format is a standard way to express a numeric calendar date that eliminates ambiguity. For example, North Americans usually write the month before the date. Europeans write the date before the month as in "30.3.1998" for March 30, 1998. The separators used between numbers

also vary between countries. The question of how to express a date in numbers that precedes "1/1/1" also arises (how to express a date that is "B.C."). ISO 8601 provides a standard cross-national approach that says:

- A general-to-specific approach, forming a date that is easier to process—thus, the year first, followed by month, then day
- With each separated by a hyphen ("-")
- Numbers less than 10 preceded by a leading zero
- Years expressed as "0" prior to year 1 and as "-1" for the year prior to year 0 (and so forth). Thus, March 30, 1998 would be: 1998-03-30.

To express whether the date reflects the **Julian calendar** or the **Gregorian calendar**, the date can be followed with a "J" or a "G".

isochronous

In information technology, isochronous (from the Greek "equal" and "time"; pronounced "eye-SAH-krun-us") pertains to processes that require timing coordination to be successful, such as voice and digital video transmission. A sound or picture going from a peripheral computer device or across a network into a computer or television set needs to arrive at close to the same rate of data flow as the source. In feeding digital image data from a peripheral device (such as a video camera) to a display mechanism within a computer, isochronous data transfer ensures that data flows continously and at a steady rate in close timing with the ability of the display mechanism to receive and display the image data. (**FireWire**, the IEEE 1394 High Performance Serial Bus, includes an isochronous interface.)

Isochronous can be distinguished from **asynchronous**, which pertains to processes that proceed independently of each other until a dependent process has to "interrupt" the other process, and **synchronous**, which pertains to processes in which one process has to wait on the completion of an event in another process before continuing.

isotropic radiator

An isotropic radiator is a **transducer** that produces useful **electromagnetic field** output in all directions with equal intensity, and at 100-percent efficiency, in three-dimensional space. If used for signal reception, the device is equally sensitive in all directions. In **wireless** communications and broadcasting, the isotropic radiator (also called an isotropic **antenna**) is a theoretical ideal. It is sometimes referred to as a *point source*.

In wireless applications, an isotropic radiator can be approximated by constructing a single-turn square loop with a circumference of $^1/_2$ **wavelength**, and then giving the loop a half-twist along an axis that lies in the plane of the loop.

The isotropic radiator is useful primarily as a standard laboratory reference source. The behavior and performance of more complex antennas is measured against it. A **dipole antenna**, for example, has signal output and sensitivity approximately 2.15 **decibel**s greater, in its favored directions, than the output and sensitivity of an isotropic antenna.

ISP

An ISP (Internet service provider) is a company that provides individuals and other companies access to the Internet and other related services such as Web site building and **virtual hosting**. An ISP has the equipment and the telecommunication line access required to have a **point-of-presence** on the Internet for the geographic area served. The larger ISPs have their own high-speed leased lines so that they are less dependent on the telecommunication providers and can provide better service to their customers. Among the largest national and regional ISPs are AT&T WorldNet, IBM Global Network, MCI, Netcom, UUNet, and PSINet.

ISPs also include regional providers such as New England's NEARNet and the San Francisco Bay area BARNet. They also include thousands of local providers. In addition, Internet users can also get access through online service providers (**OSP**) such as America Online and Compuserve.

The larger ISPs interconnect with each other through **MAE** (ISP switching centers run by MCI WorldCom) or similar centers. The arrangements they make to exchange traffic are known as **peering** agreements. There are several very comprehensive lists of ISPs world-wide available on the Web.

An ISP is also sometimes referred to as an IAP (Internet access provider). ISP is sometimes used as an abbreviation for *independent service provider* to distinguish a service provider that is an independent, separate company from a telephone company.

ISPF

ISPF (Interactive System Productivity Facility) is the **user interface** and supporting programs that come with IBM's **OS/390** operating system and that allow a company to configure and manage its system, add new system or application programs and test them, and access system files (data sets). ISPF consists of the Dialog Manager (DM), the Program Development Facility (PDF), and the Software Configuration and Library Management (SCLM) facility.

IBM also offers an ISPF that will run on an **OS/2** system so that developers can work "offline" from the OS/390.

ISPs

See "ISP"

ISRC

See "International Standard Recording Code"

ISV

An ISV (independent software vendor) makes and sells software products that run on one or more computer hardware or **operating system platform**s. The companies that make the platforms like Microsoft, IBM, Hewlett-Packard, Apple, and others encourage and lend support to ISVs, often with special "business partner" programs. In general, the more applications that run on a platform, the more value it offers to customers. Of course, platform manufacturers such as Microsoft and IBM make applications, too, but don't have the resources and, in many cases, the special knowledge required, to make them all. Think of all the programs that run on your Windows 2000 or Mac platform and you'll realize how many ISVs there are. Some ISVs focus on a particular operating system like IBM's small business **AS/400** for which there are thousands of ISV applications. Other ISVs specialize in a particular application area, such as engineering, and develop software primarily for high-end **UNIX**-based workstation platforms.

ISVs make and sell software that is added to platforms. Original equipment manufacturers (**OEM**s) use hardware platform components to build larger products. Value-added resellers (**VAR**s) incorporate platform software into their own software product packages.

IT

IT (information technology) is a term that encompasses all forms of technology used to create, store, exchange, and use **information** in its various forms (business data, voice conversations, still images, motion pictures, multimedia presentations, and other forms, including those not yet conceived). It's a convenient term for including both telephony and computer technology in the same word. It is the technology that is driving what has often been called "the information revolution."

IT Infrastructure Library

See "ITIL"

Itanium

Itanium is Intel's first **microprocessor** that is based on the **64-bit** architecture known as **IA-64**. Developed under the code name of **Merced**, Itanium and its underlying **architecture** are expected to provide a foundation for the next-generation of software for the **server** and high-end **workstation** markets.

Intel plans to follow Itanium with additional IA-64 microprocessors, which have the code names of McKinley, Madison, and Deerfield.

In addition to supporting a 64-bit processor **bus** and a set of 28 **register**s, the 64-bit design allows access to a very large **memory** (VLM). In addition, the architecture exploits features in Explicitly Parallel Instruction Computing (**EPIC**), a joint Intel and Hewlett-Packard development effort. These provide advances in the **parallel processing** handling of computer **instruction**s known as **predication** and **speculation**.

An additional Itanium feature includes a Level 3 (L3) **cache memory**, to supplement the current **L1** and **L2** cache memories found in most of today's microcomputers.

Most applications in use today are based on a 32-bit microprocessor architecture, and are designed for up to 4 gigabytes of memory. However, with application access to ever-larger databases becoming more important, many of the leading software and hardware suppliers in the computer industry have already begun to develop systems and applications for the Itanium and its ability to handle 64-bit address space.

One feature of Itanium is its use of a "smart **compiler**" to optimize how instructions are sent to the processor. This approach allows Itanium and future IA-64 microprocessors to process more instructions per clock cycle (IPCs). (IPCs can be used along with clock speed in terms of megahertz (MHz) to indicate a microprocessor's overall performance.)

Itanium is viewed by Intel and industry observers as a new level of hardware platform for the UNIX and Windows server market and also for the high-end PC workstation market with its memory- and graphics-intensive scientific, technical, and high-end graphics applications. Observers say Itanium-based servers will be especially suited for today's large enterprise computing environments with data warehouses and a requirement for intensive processing for complex queries and transactions.

Virtually all of the major manufacturers and suppliers of today's applications, high-end systems, operating systems, and computer hardware have endorsed Itanium and the IA-64 line of processors. More than 30 Itanium-based systems are expected to come to the marketplace in 2001. Some reports indicate that Itanium's IA-64 architecture will own its market through 2003, at which point some competitive "next-generation" microprocessors may begin to be seen. This window of opportunity allows Intel to capitalize on the popularity of IA-64, and to develop profitable **original equipment manufacturer** arrangements with other vendors, suppliers, and manufacturers in the computer industry. Itanium and IA-64 also support 32-bit applications.

iterative

Iterative (prounounced IT-ter-a-teev) is an adjective that means repetitious.

1) In computer programming, iterative is used to describe a situation in which a sequence of instructions can be executed multiple times. One pass through the sequence is called an iteration. If the sequence of instructions is executed repeatedly, it is called a **loop**, and we say that the computer iterates through the loop.

2) In software development, iterative is used to describe a **heuristic** planning and development process where an **application** is developed in small sections called iterations. Each iteration is reviewed and critiqued by the software team and potential end-users; insights gained from the critique of an iteration are used to determine the next step in development. Data models or sequence diagrams, which are often used to map out iterations, keep track of what has been tried, approved, or discarded, and eventually serve as a kind of blueprint for the final product.

The challenge in iterative development is to make sure all the iterations are compatible. As each new iteration is approved, developers may employ a technique known as backwards engineering, which is a systematic review and check procedure to make sure each new iteration is compatible with previous ones. The advantage of using iterative development is that the end-user is involved in the development process. Instead of waiting until the application is a final product, when it may not be possible to make changes easily, problems are identified and solved at each stage of development. Iterative development is sometimes called circular or evolutionary development.

ITIL

ITIL (Information Technology Infrastructure Library) is a set of **best practice**s standards for information technology (**IT**) service management. The United Kingdom's Central Computer and Telecommunications Agency (CCTA) created the ITIL in response to the growing dependence on information technology to meet business needs and goals. The ITIL provides businesses with a customizable framework of best practices to achieve quality service and overcome difficulties associated with the growth of IT systems. Hewlett-Packard and Microsoft are two businesses that use ITIL as part of their own best practices frameworks.

The ITIL is organized into "sets" of texts which are defined by related functions: service support, service delivery, managerial, software support, computer operations, security management, and environmental. In addition to texts, which can be purchased online, ITIL services and products include training, qualifications, software tools, and user groups such as the IT Service Management Forum (itSMF).

While owned by the CCTA since the mid-1980s, the ITIL is currently maintained and developed by The National Exam Institute for Informatics (EXIN), a non-proprietary and non-profit organization based in the Netherlands.

IT-ISAC

IT-ISAC (Information Technology Information Sharing and Analysis Center) is a facility founded in January 2001 by nineteen prominent IT industry companies (including

Oracle, IBM, EDS, and Computer Sciences) to serve as a central repository for security-related information. The group's purpose is to share each organization's information about security attacks and vulnerabilities among all the members. Member companies are expected to report information concerning security problems that they have or solutions to such problems that they have found. IT-ISAC should increase security levels and decrease monetary losses for its membership, at a time when—according to FBI estimates—the average security attack can cost an organization $400,000.

President Clinton, in May 1998, issued Presidential Decision Directive 63, appealing to U.S. industry leaders to form information sharing and analysis groups to protect the nation's critical infrastructures against attacks, and establishing that purpose as a national security policy. Because much of the nation's infrastructure is privately owned and operated, effective security measures depend upon collaboration between the public and private sectors. In response to the directive, the Financial Services industry formed FS-ISAC (Financial Services Information Sharing and Analysis Center) in 1999. The effectiveness of the new group was demonstrated in February 2000, when it saved its membership from falling victim to the widespread **denial of service attack**s that affected much of the industry.

IT-ISAC is modeled on the financial services group, which distributes much of its information anonymously. Anonymity helps members to be more comfortable sharing information in a traditionally competitive industry where the security of organization-critical information has been very closely guarded.

ITU-T

The ITU-T (for Telecommunication Standardization Sector of the International Telecommunications Union) is the primary international body for fostering cooperative standards for telecommunications equipment and systems. It was formerly known as the **CCITT**. It is located in Geneva, Switzerland.

IVR

See "Interactive Voice Response"

IXC

See "interexchange carrier"

J/Direct

J/Direct is an application programming interface (**API**) from Microsoft that allows applications written in the **Java** programming language to make programming requests for Windows **operating system** services. Introduced in June 1997, J/Direct allows Java applications to make calls on Windows dynamic link libraries (**DLL**s). The existing DLLs do not need to be changed manually, because J/Direct automatically converts many commonly-used data types, according to Microsoft. Unlike earlier Java-to-Windows tools, J/Direct eliminates the need for programmers to write **wrapper** code around existing Windows applications.

J/Direct supports Microsoft's Windows 32-bit APIs and has been included in the software developer's kit (**SDK**) for Internet Explorer.

J2EE

J2EE (Java 2 Platform, Enterprise Edition) is a Java **platform** designed for the **mainframe**-scale computing typical of large **enterprise**s. Sun Microsystems (together with industry partners such as IBM) designed J2EE to simplify application development in a **thin client tier**ed environment. J2EE simplifies application development and decreases the need for programming and programmer training by creating standardized, reusable modular components and by enabling the tier to handle many aspects of programming automatically.

J2EE includes many components of the Java 2 Platform, Standard Edition (J2SE):

- The Java Development Kit (**JDK**) is included as the core language package.
- *Write Once Run Anywhere* technology is included to ensure **portability**.
- Support is provided for Common Object Request Broker Architecture (**CORBA**), a predecessor of Enterprise JavaBeans (**EJB**), so that Java objects can communicate with CORBA objects both locally and over a network through its *interface broker*.
- Java Database Connectivity 2.0 (**JDBC**), the Java equivalent to Open Database Connectivity (**ODBC**), is included as the standard interface for Java databases.
- A security model is included to protect data both locally and in Web-based applications.

J2EE also includes a number of components added to the J2SE model, such as the following:

- Full support is included for Enterprise JavaBeans. EJB is a server-based technology for the delivery of program components in an enterprise environment. It supports the Extensible Markup Language (**XML**) and has enhanced deployment and security features.
- The Java **servlet API** (application programming interface) enhances consistency for developers without requiring a graphical user interface (**GUI**).
- Java Server Pages (**JSP**) is the Java equivalent to Microsoft's **Active Server Page**s (ASP) and is used for dynamic Web-enabled data access and manipulation.

The J2EE architecture consists of four major elements:

- The J2EE Application Programming Model is the standard programming model used to facilitate the development of multi-tier, thin client applications.
- The J2EE Platform includes necessary policies and APIs such as the Java servlets and Java Message Service (**JMS**).
- The J2EE Compatibility Test Suite ensures that J2EE products are compatible with the platform standards.
- The J2EE Reference Implementation explains J2EE capabilities and provides its operational definition.

J2ME

J2ME (Java 2 Platform, Micro Edition) is a technology that allows programmers to use the **Java** programming language and related tools to develop programs for mobile **wireless** information devices such as cellular phones and personal digital assistants (PDAs). J2ME consists of programming specifications and a special **virtual machine**, the K Virtual Machine, that allows a J2ME-encoded program to run in the mobile device.

There are two programming specifications: Connected, Limited Device Configuration (CLDC) and the Mobile Information Device Profile (MIDP). CLDC lays out the application program interface (**API**) and virtual machine features needed to support mobile devices. MIDP adds to the CLDC the user interface, networking, and **messaging** details needed to interface with mobile devices. MIDP includes the idea of a **midlet**, a small Java application similar to an **applet** but one that conforms with CLDC and MIDP and is intended for mobile devices.

Devices with systems that exploit J2ME are already available and are expected to become even more available in the next few years.

Jabber

Also see **jabber (in networks)**.

Jabber is an initiative to produce an **open source**, XML-based **instant messaging** platform. Similar to the **Linux** and **Apache** projects, Jabber developers volunteer their time to work with the code over the Internet. As a result of their efforts, anyone can download the Jabber client and server for free. Creator Jeremie Miller first started Jabber.org in 1998.

Jabber operates differently than other proprietary instant messaging systems and works in a fashion similar to e-mail, using a distributed architecture. It adds a suffix to each address after the "@" sign (for instance user@msn) just like an **e-mail** addressing system. This enables a Jabber server to read addresses from different messaging systems and know where they can be found.

Even though Jabber is offered for free, many businesses need a contact for packaged software, technical support, and other services. That's the niche that Jabber.com hopes to fill. The company calls its relationship to Jabber.org similar to the one **Red Hat** has with Linux. Jabber.com has already released an instant messaging server that it vows will be compatible with many existing platforms, including America Online's closely guarded ICQ and AOL Instant Messenger. Miller now works for Jabber.com.

In September 2000, Jabber.com signed a deal with an open-source application service provider (**ASP**) and a wireless application developer to make a version for mobile devices.

jabber (in networks)

Also see **Jabber**, an open source program for instant messaging.

In networks, a jabber is any device that is handling electrical signals improperly, usually affecting the rest of the network. In an **Ethernet** network, devices compete for use of the line, attempting to send a signal and then retrying in the event that someone else tried at the same time. A jabber can look like a device that is always sending, effectively bringing the network to a halt. A jabber is usually the result of a bad network interface card (**NIC**). Occasionally, it can be caused by outside electrical interference.

jam

In an Ethernet network, a jam is a signal from one device to all other devices that a **collision** has occurred (it was trying to send a frame while another device was also trying to put a frame on the line). The jam signal results in additional collisions in any other frames in process of being put on the line and warns non-transmitting devices to wait. Effectively, a jam provides a way to force all devices to restart any bids to get control of the line.

jam sync

In **audio** (sound) production, jam sync is a mode of device synchronization using SMPTE time code in which a slave device can furnish its own timing during the time that a master device is temporarily unstable. Jam sync is usually an optional mode that the user can select.

In a basic SMPTE synchronization scenario, time code is fed from one device (the master) to a second device (the slave). The slave device follows the time locations as transmitted by the master device. If the master device goes to one hour and thirteen minutes (expressed as 01:13:00:00; Hours:Minutes:Seconds:Frames), the slave device follows it there.

The problem arises when the master device's SMPTE time code has an error in it, caused by a small bad portion of tape, for example. In most situations, the slave device would not know what to do for a split second since it has missing instructions from its host. It would stutter or stop completely.

By using jam syncing, the slave device can be instructed to ignore small dropouts of time code from the master, thus ensuring smooth synchronization. To do this, it generates its own time code whenever the master's time code is missing.

Japanese emoticons

In Japan, users have worked out **emoticon**s (or keyboard "smiley faces") adapted to their culture. According to *The New York Times* (August 12, 1996), the Japanese are using emoticons even more than Westerners. Because their PC keyboards handle the two-byte characters of Kanji, users can choose between single- and double-byte versions of certain characters such as underscore characters, allowing a further degree of expression.

Here are some examples of Japanese emoticons:

^_^	Smile
^o^;>	Excuse me
^^;	Cold sweat
^o^	Happy
*^o^*	Exciting
(^_^)/	Banzai smiley

JAR file

A JAR (Java ARchive) file is a file that contains the **class**, image, and sound files for a **Java applet** gathered into a single file and compressed for faster **downloading** to your Web browser. An applet that comes as part of a Web page that you may happen to request may include several files, each of which would have to be downloaded along with the Web page. By putting the applet components in a single file and compressing that file, download time is saved.

When a programmer gets a Java program development kit, a small program or utility called "jar" is included. The jar utility lets you create, list, and extract the individual files from a JAR file. Ordinarily, a browser user will not need to "open" or view a JAR file directly. It is opened when the Web page is received and the applet is in some manner initiated.

The JAR format is based on the popular **zip** file format.

Java

Java is a programming language expressly designed for use in the **distributed** environment of the Internet. It was designed to have the "look and feel" of the **C++** language, but it is simpler to use than C++ and enforces an **object-oriented programming** model. Java can be used to create complete applications that may run on a single computer or be distributed among servers and clients in a network. It can also be used to build a small application module or **applet** for use as part of a Web page. Applets make it possible for a Web page user to interact with the page.

The major characteristics of Java are:

- The programs you create are portable in a network. (See **portability**.) Your source program is compiled into what Java calls **bytecode**, which can be run anywhere in a network on a **server** or **client** that has a Java **virtual machine**. The Java virtual machine interprets the bytecode into code that will run on the real computer hardware. This means that individual computer platform differences such as instruction lengths can be recognized and accommodated locally just as the program is being executed. Platform-specific versions of your program are no longer needed.

- The code is **robust**, here meaning that, unlike programs written in C++ and perhaps some other languages, the Java objects can contain no references to data external to themselves or other known objects. This ensures that an instruction can not contain the address of data storage in another application or in the operating system itself, either of which would cause the program and perhaps the operating system itself to terminate or "crash." The Java virtual machine makes a number of checks on each object to ensure integrity.

- Java is object-oriented, which means that, among other characteristics, an **object** can take advantage of being part of a **class** of objects and inherit code that is common to the class. Objects are thought of as "nouns" that a user might relate to rather than the traditional procedural "verbs." A **method** can be thought of as one of the object's capabilities or behaviors.

- In addition to being executed at the client rather than the server, a Java applet has other characteristics designed to make it run fast.

- Relative to C++, Java is easier to learn. (However, it is not a language you'll pick up in an evening!)

Java was introduced by Sun Microsystems in 1995 and instantly created a new sense of the interactive possibilities of the Web. Both of the major Web browsers include a Java virtual machine. Almost all major operating system developers (IBM, Microsoft, and others) have added Java compilers as part of their product offerings.

The Java virtual machine includes an optional **just-in-time compiler** that dynamically compiles bytecode into executable code as an alternative to interpreting one bytecode instruction at a time. In many cases, the dynamic JIT compilation is faster than the virtual machine interpretation.

JavaScript should not be confused with Java. JavaScript, which originated at Netscape, is interpreted at a higher level, is easier to learn than Java, but lacks some of the portability of Java and the speed of bytecode. Because Java applets will run on almost any operating system without requiring recompilation and because Java has no operating system-unique extensions or variations, Java is generally regarded as the most strategic language in which to develop applications for the Web. (However, JavaScript can be useful for very small applications that run on the Web client or server.)

Java 2 Platform, Enterprise Edition

See "J2EE"

Java 2 Platform, Micro Edition

See "J2ME"

Java chip

The Java chip is a **microchip** that, when included in or added to a computer, will accelerate the performance of **Java** programs (including the **applet**s that are sometimes included with Web pages). The special chip can execute all or some of the instructions in the Java **bytecode** directly without requiring interpretation by a software **virtual machine**.

The Java chip may be particularly important as part of **embedded system**s in **handheld** devices such as **smart phone**s.

Java Database Connectivity

JDBC (Java Database Connectivity) is an application program interface (**API**) specification for connecting programs written in **Java** to the data in popular **database**. The application program interface lets you encode access request statements in structured query language (**SQL**) that are then passed to the program that manages the database. It returns the results through a similar interface. JDBC is very similar to the SQL Access Group's Open Database Connectivity (**ODBC**) and, with a small "bridge" program, you can use the JDBC interface to access databases through

the ODBC interface. For example, you could write a program designed to access many popular database products on a number of **operating system platform**s. When accessing a database on a PC running Microsoft's Windows 2000 and, for example, a Microsoft Access database, your program with JDBC statements would be able to access the Microsoft Access database.

JDBC actually has two levels of interface. In addition to the main interface, there is also an API from a JDBC "manager" that in turn communicates with individual database product "**driver**s," the JDBC-ODBC bridge if necessary, and a JDBC network driver when the Java program is running in a network environment (that is, accessing a remote database).

When accessing a remote database, JDBC takes advantage of the Internet's file addressing scheme and a file name looks much like a Web page address (or **Uniform Resource Locator**). For example, a Java SQL statement might identify the database as:

```
jdbc:odbc://www.somecompany.com:400/databasefile
```

JDBC specifies a set of **object-oriented class**es for the programmer to use in building SQL requests. An additional set of classes describes the JDBC driver API. The most common SQL **data type**s, mapped to Java data types, are supported. The API provides for implementation-specific support for **Microsoft Transaction Server** requests and the ability to commit or roll back to the beginning of a transaction.

Java Foundation Classes

Using the **Java** programming language, Java Foundation Classes (JFC) are pre-written code in the form of **class** libraries (coded routines) that give the programmer a comprehensive set of graphical user interface (**GUI**) routines to use. The Java Foundation Classes are comparable to the Microsoft Foundation Class (**MFC**) library. JFC is an extension of the original Java Abstract Windowing Toolkit (**AWT**). Using JFC and **Swing**, an additional set of program components, a programmer can write programs that are independent of the **windowing system** within a particular **operating system**.

Java Message Service

Java Message Service (JMS) is an application program interface (**API**) from Sun Microsystems that supports the formal communication known as **messaging** between computers in a network. Sun's JMS provides a common interface to standard messaging protocols and also to special messaging services in support of **Java** programs. Sun advocates the use of the Java Message Service for anyone developing Java applications, which can be run from any major operating system platform.

The messages involved exchange crucial data between computers—rather than between users—and contain information such as event notification and service requests.

Messaging is often used to coordinate programs in dissimilar systems or written in different programming languages.

Using the JMS interface, a programmer can invoke the messaging services of IBM's **MQSeries**, Progress Software's SonicMQ, and other popular messaging product vendors. In addition, JMS supports messages that contain serialized Java **object** and messages that contain Extensible Markup Language (**XML**) pages.

Java Naming and Directory Interface

See "JNDI"

Java Server Page

Java Server Page (JSP) is a technology for controlling the content or appearance of Web pages through the use of **servlet**s, small programs that are specified in the Web page and run on the Web server to modify the Web page before it is sent to the user who requested it. Sun Microsystems, the developer of **Java**, also refers to the JSP technology as the Servlet application program interface (**API**). JSP is comparable to Microsoft's Active Server Page (**ASP**) technology. Whereas a Java Server Page calls a Java program that is executed by the Web server, an Active Server Page contains a **script** that is **interpreted** by a script interpreter (such as **VBScript** or **JScript**) before the page is sent to the user.

An HTML page that contains a link to a Java servlet is sometimes given the file name suffix of .JSP.

JavaBeans

JavaBeans is an **object-oriented programming** interface from Sun Microsystems that lets you build re-useable applications or program building blocks called **component**s that can be deployed in a network on any major operating system platform. Like **Java applet**, JavaBeans components (or "**Bean**s") can be used to give World Wide Web pages (or other applications) interactive capabilities such as computing interest rates or varying page content based on user or **browser** characteristics.

From a user's point-of-view, a component can be a button that you interact with or a small calculating program that gets initiated when you press the button. From a developer's point-of-view, the button component and the calculator component are created separately and can then be used together or in different combinations with other components in different applications or situations.

When the components or Beans are in use, the properties of a Bean (for example, the background color of a window) are visible to other Beans and Beans that haven't "met" before can learn each other's properties dynamically and interact accordingly.

Beans are developed with a Beans Development Kit (BDK) from Sun and can be run on any major operating system platform (Windows, UNIX, Mac) inside a number of application environments (known as *containers*), including browsers, word processors, and other applications.

To build a component with JavaBeans, you write language statements using Sun's **Java** programming language and include JavaBeans statements that describe component *properties* such as user interface characteristics and *events* that trigger a bean to communicate with other beans in the same container or elsewhere in the network.

Beans also have *persistence*, which is a mechanism for storing the state of a component in a safe place. This would allow, for example, a component (bean) to "remember" data that a particular user had already entered in an earlier user session.

JavaBeans gives Java applications the *compound document* capability that the OpenDoc and **ActiveX** interfaces already provide.

JavaScript

JavaScript is an **interpreted** programming or **script** language from Netscape. It is somewhat similar in capability to Microsoft's **Visual Basic**, Sun's **Tcl**, the UNIX-derived **Perl**, and IBM's **REX**. In general, script languages are easier and faster to code in than the more structured and **compiled** languages such as **C** and **C++**. Script languages generally take longer to process than compiled languages, but are very useful for shorter programs.

JavaScript is used in Web site development to do such things as:

- Automatically change a formatted date on a Web page
- Cause a linked-to page to appear in a popup window
- Cause text or a graphic image to change during a **mouse rollover**

JavaScript uses some of the same ideas found in **Java**, the compiled **object-oriented programming** derived from C++. JavaScript code can be imbedded in **HTML** pages and interpreted by the Web browser (or client). JavaScript can also be run at the server as in Microsoft's **Active Server Page**s before the page is sent to the requestor. Both Microsoft and Netscape browsers support JavaScript, but sometimes in slightly different ways.

Jaz drive

A Jaz drive is a small, portable **hard disk drive** used primarily for backing up and archiving personal computer files. The Jaz drive is sold by Iomega Corporation, the same company that developed the **Zip drive**. Both the Jaz drive and the disks come in two sizes, 1 **GB** and 2 GB. The two sizes look similar, but a 2 GB disk is not compatible with a 1 GB Jaz drive. The 2 GB Jaz drive can use both disk sizes.

Internal and external Jaz drives are available. The Jaz drive uses the Small Computer System Interface (**SCSI**) and requires a SCSI controller.

A Jaz drive comes with software to back up the hard disk, to record and playback voice, music and video files, to temporarily use the Jaz drive on another computer, and to duplicate Jaz disks using one Jaz drive. Jaz drives are also used to exchange files with others, to store unusually large files, and to keep certain files separate from files on your hard disk. The Jaz drive is different from a Zip drive in that the computer recognizes it as another hard disk, which allows the user to install and use applications from the Jaz drive. The Jaz drive runs at speeds near or equal to traditional hard disks.

JBOD

JBOD (for "just a bunch of disks," or sometimes "just a bunch of drives") is a derogatory term—the official term is "spanning"—used to refer to a computer's hard disks that haven't been configured according to the **RAID** (for "redundant array of independent disks") system to increase fault tolerance and improve data access performance.

The RAID system stores the same data redundantly on multiple disks that nevertheless appear to the **operating system** as a single disk. Although JBOD also makes the disks appear to be a single one, it accomplishes that by combining the drives into one larger logical one. JBOD doesn't deliver any advantages over using separate disks independently and doesn't provide any of the fault tolerance or performance benefits of RAID.

JCL

JCL (job control language) is a language for describing **jobs** (units of work) to the **MVS**, **OS/390**, and VSE **operating system**s, which run on IBM's **S/390** large **server** (**mainframe**) computers. These operating systems allocate their time and space resources among the total number of jobs that have been started in the computer. Jobs in turn break down into job steps. All the statements required to run a particular program constitute a job step. Jobs are *background* (sometimes called **batch**) units of work that run without requiring user interaction (for example, print jobs). In addition, the operating system manages interactive (*foreground*) user requests that initiate units of work. In general, foreground work is given priority over background work.

One IBM manual compares a set of JCL statements to a menu order in a restaurant. The whole order is comparable to the job. Back in the kitchen, the chefs divide the order up and work on individual dishes (job steps). As the job steps complete, the meal is served (but it has to be served in the order prescribed just as some job steps depend on other job steps being performed first).

JCL statements mainly specify the input *data sets* (files) that must be accessed, the output data set to be created or updated, what resources must be allocated for the job, and the programs that are to run, using these input and output data sets. A set of JCL statements for a job is itself stored as a data set and can be started interactively. MVS and OS/390 provide an interactive menu-like interface, ISPF, for initiating and managing jobs.

In MVS and OS/390, the part of the operating system that handles JCL is called the Job Entry Subsystem (**JES**). There are two versions, JES2 and a later version with additional capabilities, JES3.

JDBC

See "Java Database Connectivity"

JEDEC SDRAM

JEDEC (Joint Electron Device Engineering Council) SDRAM is an industry standard synchronous DRAM. It has a dual-bank architecture and several burst mode accesses that can be preset. JEDEC SDRAM chips operate at either 83 MHz or 100 MHz. JEDEC SDRAM is also known as PC66 SDRAM because it was originally rated for 66 MHz bus operation and to distinguish it from Intel's PC100 architecture.

jello

See "ice"

JES

See "Job Entry Subsystem"

JES2

See "Job Entry Subsystem"

JES3

See "Job Entry Subsystem"

JFC

See "Java Foundation Classes"

JHTML

JHTML (Java within Hypertext Markup Language) is a standard for including a **Java** program as part of a Web page (a page written using the Hypertext Markup Language, or **HTML**). A Web site developer can write a small program using the Java programming language and insert the program within a Web page. When a user requests the page, the Web site server, observing a request for a file with the .jhtml suffix, passes the code to a special Java program designed to handle JHML. This program, called the PageCompileServlet, calls the Java **compiler**, which quickly compiles the code. (If the code has previously been compiled by an earlier page request, this step is unnecessary.) The code is then executed, typically modifying the contents of the Web page in some way before it is sent to the requestor.

JHTML is comparable to Microsoft's **Active Server Page** and to **PHP** in that all are approaches to modifying a Web page at the server before it is sent rather than at the **client** (the user's Web browser) with **JavaScript**. To access a **database** from the Web page, the Java code might use the Java Database Connectivity (**JDBC**) interface.

JHTML requires installing a Java compiler on the Web server. JHTML is part of JavaSoft's Java WebServer Application Program Interface.

Jigsaw

Jigsaw is a **Web server** from the World Wide Web Consortium (**W3C**) that is designed for the purpose of demonstrating new Web **protocols** and other features. Jigsaw is written in the **Java** programming language and made available as **open source software**. You can download it from the W3C site in either a **UNIX** or a **Windows 2000** version.

Although Jigsaw is intended to be a demonstration platform rather than a fully capable Web server, the W3C reports that it performs as well as the **CERN** server and provides much of the usual Web server support such as **proxy server** capability, **virtual hosting**, and support for **common gateway interface**. Jigsaw can also be used for delivering pages built or modified with **Personal Home Page** and JSP scripts.

Jikes

Jikes is an **open source Java compiler** from IBM that adheres strictly to the Java specification and promises an "extremely fast" compilation. Although Sun Microsystems, the inventor of Java, offers its own proprietary compiler, IBM's compiler uses the open source idea, meaning that anyone can acquire IBM's Jikes **source code** for free and redistribute it with modifications (if these adhere to the Java specifications). Jikes is included as part of several different variations of **Linux**, including the popular version from Red Hat.

IBM says that Jikes adheres to both the Java Language Specification and the Java Virtual Machine Specification, and does not support subsets, supersets, or other variations of the language. In addition to fast compilation, Jikes analyzes source code that is being compiled for dependencies on other source code files that may be needed. Jikes is available for most major **operating system** platforms. IBM points out that Jikes is not a Java development environment, but just a Java compiler.

Jini

Jini (pronounced DJEE-nee like the Arabic word for "magician") is a new idea that Sun Microsystems calls "spontaneous networking." Using the Jini architecture, users will be able to plug printers, storage devices, speakers, and any kind of device directly into a network and every other computer, device, and user on the network will know that the new device has been added and is available. Each pluggable device will define itself immediately to a network device registry. When someone wants to use or access the resource, their computer will be able to download the necessary programming from it to communicate with it. No longer will the special device support software known as a **device driver** need to be present in an **operating system**. The operating system will know about all accessible devices through the network registry.

Jini can be viewed as the next step after the **Java** programming language toward making a network look like one large computer. Jini promises to enable manufacturers to make devices that can attach to a network independently of an operating system like Windows 95. Equipped with its own small, special-purpose and possibly microchip-embedded operating system, a printer could be plugged into a network and immediately shared by users at a mix of computers: Windows, Macintosh, UNIX. Mobile devices could be transported and easily plugged into a network so that others could use the device.

How It Works

Jini consists of four program layers:

- Directory Service
- JavaSpace
- Remote Method Invocation (RMI)
- Boot, Join, and Discover Protocol

Any device with an operating system that supports a Java can be plugged into the network. (For many devices, the operating system can be much smaller than Windows 2000, for example, since it is serving only the functions that device requires.) When a device is plugged into the Jini network, it is immediately registered by the Directory Service layer as a member of the network. Its necessary program **objects** are placed in a JavaSpace layer so that other network members can discover and download them when that network member wants to use the device. The actual communication with objects in JavaSpace is done using the Remote Method Invocation (RMI) interface and layer. The layer supporting the boot, join, and discover protocols enables devices, users, and applications to announce and register themselves and to discover others.

JIT

See "just-in-time compiler"

jitter

Jitter is the deviation in or displacement of some aspect of the pulses in a high-frequency **digital signal**. As the name suggests, jitter can be thought of as shaky pulses. The deviation can be in terms of amplitude, phase timing, or the width of the signal pulse. Another definition is that it is "the period frequency displacement of the signal from its ideal location." Among the causes of jitter are electromagnetic interference (**EMI**) and crosstalk with other signals. Jitter can cause a display **monitor** to flicker; affect the ability of the **processor** in a personal computer to perform as intended; introduce clicks or other undesired effects in **audio** signals, and loss of transmitted data between network devices. The amount of allowable jitter depends greatly on the application.

JMS

See "Java Message Service"

JNDI

JNDI (Java Naming and Directory Interface) enables **Java** platform-based applications to access multiple naming and directory services. Part of the Java Enterprise application programming interface (**API**) set, JNDI makes it possible for developers to create **portable** applications that are enabled for a number of different naming and directory services, including: **file system**s; **directory** services such as Lightweight Directory Access Protocol (**LDAP**), **Novell Directory Services**, and Network Information System (**NIS**); and distributed object systems such as the Common Object Request Broker Architecture (**CORBA**), Java Remote Method Invocation (**RMI**), and Enterprise JavaBeans (**EJB**).

As an illustration of what JNDI does, Todd Sundsted (in a JavaWorld article, *JNDI overview, Part 1: An introduction to naming services*) uses the analogy of a library's file system. Sundsted says that JNDI organizes and locates components within a distributed computing environment similarly to the way that card catalogs (and increasingly computer applications) organize and represent the locations of books within a library. A distributed application needs a means of locating components in the same way that the library patron needs a means of locating the book: Just rummaging around inside a library—or an application—is not an efficient way to find a particular object. JNDI makes it possible for application components to find each other. Because different naming and directory service providers can be seamlessly connected through the API, Java applications using it can be easily integrated into various environments and coexist with **legacy application**s. The current version, JNDI 1.2, was specified with input from Netscape, Novell, Tarantella, Sun, and BEA. JNDI is considered an industry standard.

job

In certain computer operating systems, a job is the unit of work that a computer **operator** (or a program called a **job scheduler**) gives to the **operating system**. For example, a job could be the running of an **application program** such as a weekly payroll program. A job is usually said to be run in **batch** (rather than interactive) mode. The operator or job scheduler gives the operating system a "batch" of jobs to do (payroll, cost analysis, employee file updating, and so forth) and these are performed in the **background** when time-sensitive interactive work is not being done. In IBM mainframe operating systems (**MVS**, **OS/390**, and successors) a job is described with job control language (**JCL**). Jobs are broken down into **job step**s. An example of a job step might be to make sure that a particular data set or database needed in the job is made accessible.

Typically, the development programmer who writes a program that is intended to be run as a batch job also writes the JCL that describes for the operating system how to run the job (for example, what data sets or databases it uses). The use of a job scheduler usually provides greater flexibility and the ability to monitor and report batch job operations.

A similar term is **task**, a concept usually applied to interactive work. A **multitasking** operating system serving one or more interactive users can at the same time perform batch jobs in the background.

job control language

See "JCL"

Job Entry Subsystem

Job Entry Subsystem (JES) is a subsystem of the **OS/390** and **MVS mainframe** operating systems that manages *jobs* (units of work) that the system does. Each job is described to the operating system by system administrators or other users in job control language (**JCL**). The operating system then sends the job to the JES program. The JES program receives the job, performs the job based on priority, and then purges the job from the system.

There are two versions, JES2 and JES3. JES3 allows central control of the processing of jobs using a common work queue. Both OS/390 and MVS provide an interactive menu for initiating and managing jobs.

job scheduler

A job scheduler is a program that enables an enterprise to schedule and, in some cases, monitor computer "batch" **jobs** (units of work, such as the running of a payroll program). A job scheduler can initiate and manage jobs automatically by processing prepared **job control language** statements or through equivalent interaction with a human operator.

Today's job schedulers typically provide a graphical user interface and a single point of control for all the work in a **distributed** network of computers.

Some features that may be found in a job scheduler include:

- Continuously automatic monitoring of jobs and completion notification
- Event-driven job scheduling
- Performance monitoring
- Report scheduling

job step

In certain computer operating systems, a job step is part of a **job**, a unit of work that a computer **operator** (or a program called a **job scheduler**) gives to the **operating system**. For example, a job could be the running of an **application program** such as a weekly payroll program. A job is usually said to be run in **batch** (rather than interactive) mode. The operator or job scheduler gives the operating system a "batch" of jobs to do (payroll, cost analysis, employee file updating, and so forth) and these are performed in the **background** when time-sensitive interactive work is not being done. In IBM mainframe operating systems (**MVS**, **OS/390**, and successors) a job is described with job control language (**JCL**). Jobs are broken down into **job step**s. An example of a job step might be to make sure that a particular data set or database needed in the job is made accessible.

John von Neumann

John von Neumann was the scientist who conceived a fundamental idea that serves all modern computers—that a computer's **program** and the **data** that it processes do not have to be fed into the computer while it is working, but can be kept in the computer's **memory**—a notion generally referred to as *the stored-program computer*. In his short life, von Neumann became one of the most acclaimed and lauded scientists of the 20th century. He left an indelible mark on the fields of mathematics, quantum theory, game theory, nuclear physics, and computer science. Born in Budapest, von Neumann was a child prodigy who went on to study chemistry in Berlin and Zurich, where he earned a Diploma in Chemical Engineering in 1926. His doctorate in mathematics (on set theory) from the University of Budapest followed in the same year. After lecturing at Berlin and Hamburg, von Neumann emigrated to the U.S. in 1930 where he worked at Princeton and was one of the founding members of the Institute for Advanced Studies.

At Princeton, von Neumann lectured in the nascent field of **quantum theory** and through his work on rings of operators (later renamed Neumann algebras) he helped develop the mathematical foundations of that theory which were unveiled in the paper *"Mathematische Grundlagen der*

Quantenmechanik" (1932). His seminal publication on game theory, *"Theory of Games and Economic Behaviour"* was published in 1934 with co-author Oskar Morgenstern.

Spurred by an interest in hydrodynamics and the difficulty of solving the non-linear partial differential equations involved, von Neumann turned to the emerging field of computing. His first introduction to computers was Howard Aiken's Harvard Mark I. As a consultant to Eckert and Mauchly on the ENIAC, he devised a concept for computer architecture that remains with us to this day. Known subsequently as the "von Neumann architecture," the stored-program computer (where both the instructions and the data they operate upon reside together in memory) with its central controller, I/O, and memory was outlined in a "Draft Report" and paved the way for the modern era of computing. von Neumann was a pioneer in the field of cellular automata (an n-dimensional array of cells where the contents of a cell depend of the contents of neighboring cells) and also popularized the **binary digit** as the unit of computer memory.

von Neumann was constantly busy with both his extensive consulting career and his varied research interests. Among his employers was the U.S. military, for whom he worked on the development of the hydrogen bomb. He received the Enrico Fermi award in 1956, the latest in a long line of honors (including 7 honorary doctorates and 2 Presidential Awards). John von Neumann died on February 8, 1957 in Washington D.C.

Joint Photographic Experts Group

See "JPEG"

Jolt

Jolt, an American soft drink that contains the equivalent of two cups of coffee, has a following with programmers, college students, Internet surfers, and anyone else who needs to keep awake in the late night or early morning hours. One of our contributors describes it as "the fuel on which the Internet is run." A typical can or bottle of Jolt contains about twice the amount of caffeine as Pepsi Cola or Coca Cola.

Yahoo lists a number of Web sites created by Jolt devotees.

joule

The joule (pronounced DJOOL) is the standard unit of **energy** in electronics and general scientific applications. One joule is defined as the amount of energy exerted when a force of one **newton** is applied over a displacement of one meter. One joule is the equivalent of one watt of **power** radiated or dissipated for one second.

In some applications, the British thermal unit (**Btu**) is used to express energy. One Btu is equivalent to approximately 1055 joules.

journaling file system

A journaling file system is a fault-resilient **file system** in which data integrity is ensured because updates to directories and bitmaps are constantly written to a serial log on disk before the original disk log is updated. In the event of a system failure, a full journaling filesystem ensures that the data on the disk has been restored to its pre-crash configuration. It also recovers unsaved data and stores it in the location where it would have gone if the computer had not crashed, making it an important feature for mission-critical applications.

Not all operating systems provide the same journaling technology. Windows NT offers a less robust version of the full system. If your Windows NT system crashes, you may not lose the entire disk volume, but you will likely lose all the data that hadn't yet been written to the disk prior to the crash. By the same token, the default Linux system, ext2fs, does not journal at all. That means, a system crash—although infrequent in a Linux environment—can corrupt an entire disk volume.

However, XFS, a journaling file system from Silicon Graphics, became a part of the open-source community in 1999 and, therefore, has had important implications for Linux developers, who previously lacked such insurance features. Capable of recovering from most unexpected interruptions in less than a second, XFS epitomizes the high-performance journaling filesystem of the future.

The earliest journaling file systems, created in the mid-1980s, included Veritas, Tolerant, and IBM's JFS. With increasing demands being placed on file systems to support terabytes of data, thousands upon thousands of files per directory and 64-bit capability, it is expected that interest will continue to grow in high-performance journaling file systems like XFS.

JPEG

A JPEG (pronounced JAY-peg) is a graphic image file created by choosing from a range of **compression** qualities (actually, from one of a suite of compression **algorithm**s). When you create a JPEG or convert an image from another format to a JPEG, you are asked to specify the quality of image you want. Since the highest quality results in the largest file, you can make a trade-off between image quality and file size. Formally, the JPEG file format is **ISO** standard 10918. The JPEG scheme includes 29 distinct coding processes although a JPEG implementor may not use them all. JPEG is an acronym for Joint Photographic Experts Group, the committee that established the baseline algorithms.

Together with the Graphic Interchange Format (**GIF**) and Portable Network Graphics (**PNG**) file formats, the JPEG is one of the image file formats supported on the World Wide Web, usually with the file suffix of ".jpg". You can create a **progressive JPEG** that is similar to an **interlaced GIF**.

JPG

See "JPEG"

JScript

JScript is a **script** language from Microsoft that is expressly designed for use within Web pages. It adheres to the **ECMAScript** standard and is basically Microsoft's equivalent to Netscape's earlier and more widely used **JavaScript**.

JSP

See "Java Server Page"

Julian calendar

The Julian calendar was the 365-day calendar that Julius Caesar made official in 46 B.C. It replaced a calendar based on lunar cycles. The Julian calendar provided for a leap year with an extra day every four years. Thus, the Julian calendar included an average of 365.25 days each year. By 1582 A.D., however, the Julian calendar had become out of step with the seasonal cycle by 10 days. The adjustment, ordered by Pope Gregory XIII in October, 1582, subtracted ten days from the calendar. The new **Gregorian calendar** removes a leap year every one hundred years except for years divisible by four hundred.

The Julian calendar has no relation to the **Julian date** format sometimes used in computing.

Julian date

1) Not to be confused with the **Julian calendar**, a Julian date or day number is the number of elapsed days since the beginning of a cycle of 7,980 years invented by Joseph Scaliger in 1583. The purpose of the system is to make it easy to compute an integer (whole number) difference between one calendar date and another calendar date. The 7,980 year cycle was derived by combining several traditional time cycles (solar, lunar, and a particular Roman tax cycle) for which 7,980 was a common multiple. The starting point for the first Julian cycle began on January 1, 4713 B.C. (**Gregorian calendar**—expressed in the ISO date format as "-4713-01-01 G") and will end on January 22, 3268 (3268-01-22 G). The following day will begin the first day of the second Julian date period (or 7,980 year cycle).

A Julian date or day number for a certain time of day on January 9, 2001, looked like this:
2451919.3423000001348555
meaning 2,451,919 elapsed days since the beginning of the Julian cycle. The ".3423000001348555" represented the time of day ("15:12:54 EST").

It is not certain whether the Julian date or day number system was named after Joseph Scaliger's father, Julius Caesar Scaliger, or after the Julian calendar. Julian day numbers are widely used in astronomy.

2) Commonly in computer programming, Julian date has been corrupted to mean the number of elapsed days since the beginning of a particular year. For example, in this usage, the Julian date for the calendar date of 1998-02-28 would be day 59.

jumbogram

Using the Internet Protocol version 6 (**IPv6**), a jumbogram is a transmission **packet** that contains a **payload** larger than 65,535 eight-bit bytes (also known as **octet**s).

jump page

1) In Web site design, jump page is a term that is sometimes used to describe a Web site page that provides a "jumping off" point for users who need to locate information on the Web quickly and efficiently. Thus, a **portal** site or the **home page** for a site that specializes in gathering resources for a specific area of interest might be referred to as jump pages. whatis.com and other TechTarget.com sites can be considered jump pages for IT-specific information on the Web.

2) In Web site maintenance, a jump page can be a page that is posted temporarily to redirect the user when the page's address (its **URL**) has been changed.

3) In Internet advertising and marketing, a jump page (also called a landing page) is a Web page that is posted temporarily to capture the user's attention as a promotion or lead-in to a Web site. A jump page may be a **splash page** that contains a **Flash** animation. According to industry expert Robbin Zeff, a jump page on the Web is temporary, it is directly related to products or services that are currently being promoted, and it is designed to reinforce other ad promotions the user may have been exposed to.

jumper setting

1) In a computer, a jumper is a pair of prongs that are electrical contact points set into the computer **motherboard** or an **adapter card**. When you set a jumper, you place a plug on the prongs that completes a contact. Jumper settings tell the computer how it is configured and what operations can be performed. Computers come with jumpers preset. Instructions are sometimes provided so that the owner can reset the jumpers when new equipment is added. The latest trend, however, is **plug and play** equipment that does not require manual setting of jumpers. A group of jumpers is sometimes called a *jumper block*.

Finding the right jumper settings for a particular computer configuration usually requires having some technical information that comes with each product for which a jumper setting has to be set or changed. Where this information isn't available, you may be able to find information at the Web site of the manufacturer.

2) In electronic test equipment, a jumper cable is used to make a temporary contact between two points for the purpose of testing a circuit.

junk

See "spam"

just a bunch of disks

See "JBOD"

just-in-time compiler

In the **Java** programming language and environment, a just-in-time (JIT) compiler is a program that turns Java **bytecode** (a program that contains instructions that must be interpreted) into instructions that can be sent directly to the **processor**. After you've written a Java program, the source language statements are compiled by the Java **compiler** into *bytecode* rather than into code that contains instructions that match a particular hardware platform's processor (for example, an Intel **Pentium** microprocessor or an IBM System/390 processor). The bytecode is platform-independent code that can be sent to any platform and run on that platform.

In the past, most programs written in any language have had to be recompiled, and sometimes, rewritten for each computer platform. One of the biggest advantages of Java is that you only have to write and compile a program once. The Java on any platform will interpret the compiled bytecode into instructions understandable by the particular processor. However, the virtual machine handles one bytecode instruction at a time. Using the Java just-in-time compiler (really a second compiler) at the particular system platform compiles the bytecode into the particular system code (as though the program had been compiled initially on that platform). Once the code has been (re-)compiled by the JIT compiler, it will usually run more quickly in the computer.

The just-in-time compiler comes with the virtual machine and is used optionally. It compiles the bytecode into platform-specific executable code that is immediately executed. Sun Microsystems suggests that it's usually faster to select the JIT compiler option, especially if the method executable is repeatedly reused.

K Desktop Environment

K Desktop Environment (KDE) is an **Open Source** graphical **desktop** environment for **UNIX workstations**. Initially called the Kool Desktop Environment, KDE is an ongoing project with development taking place on the Internet and discussions held through the official KDE mailing list, numerous newsgroups, and Internet Relay Chat (**IRC**) channels. KDE has a complete graphical user interface (**GUI**) and includes a file manager, a window manager, a help system, a configuration system, tools and utilities, and several **applications**. The most popular suite of KDE applications is KOffice, which includes a word processor, a spreadsheet application, a presentation application, a **vector** drawing application, and image editing tools. KOffice was released with KDE version 2.0 in October 2000. On December 5, 2000, KDE 2.0.1 was released.

Matthias Ettrich launched the KDE project in October 1996 with the goal of making the UNIX **platform** more attractive and easy to use for computer users who are familiar with a graphical interface instead of typed commands. Today, KDE is used with **Linux**, **Solaris**, FreeBSD, OpenBSD, and LinuxPPC. Several hundred software programmers from all over the world contribute to the development of KDE.

K-12

K-12, a term used in education and educational technology in the United States, Canada, and possibly other countries, is a short form for the publicly-supported school grades prior to college. These grades are kindergarten (K) and the 1st through the 12th grade (1-12). (If the term were used, "13th grade" would be the first year of college.)

Most communities in the United States and Canada (and wherever else the term is used) are just beginning to provide modern information technology at the K-12 levels.

K6

K6 (referred to by its manufacturer as AMD-K6) is a line of **microprocessors** from **AMD** that compete with Intel's **Pentium** series of microprocessors. The successor to the K6 is the **Athlon**.

K7

K7 was the development name for the **Athlon** personal computer **microprocessor** from **AMD**, the microprocessor and **flash memory** maker. The Athlon became the first microprocessor for mainstream PCs to support a 200 **MHz** system **bus** and to achieve a 1 **gigahertz clock speed**. As Athlon, different versions of the K7 are built with either the

0.25 **micron** infrastructure that is used in the popular **K6** microprocessor or, as for the 1 GHz model, with a 0.18 micron infrastructure.

Katmai

See "Pentium 3"

Kbps

*Note: In international English outside the U.S., the equivalent usage is "kbps" or "kbits s⁻¹."

In the U.S., Kbps stands for **kilobits** per second (thousands of bits per second) and is a measure of **bandwidth** (the amount of data that can flow in a given time) on a data transmission medium. Higher bandwidths are more conveniently expressed in **megabits** per second (**Mbps**, or millions of bits per second) and in **gigabits** per second (**Gbps**, or billions of bits per second).

k-business

See "knowledge management"

Kbyte

See "kilobyte"

KDE

See "K Desktop Environment"

Keep It Simple, Stupid

See "KISS Principle"

keiretsu

In corporate culture, keiretsu refers to a uniquely Japanese form of corporate organization. A keiretsu is a grouping or family of affiliated companies that form a tight-knit alliance to work toward each other's mutual success. The keiretsu system is also based on an intimate partnership between government and businesses. It can best be understood as the intricate web of relationships that links banks, manufacturers, suppliers, and distributors with the Japanese government.

These ironclad corporate alliances have caused much debate and have been called "government-sponsored cartels." While some think keiretsu are a menace to trade, others see them as a model for change. Features common to most keiretsu include "main bank," stable shareholding, and seconded directors. Some keiretsu concepts have no

American parallel such as "general trading company." The keiretsu system is one of the profound differences between Japanese and U.S. business structures.

Keiretsu operate globally and are integrated both vertically and horizontally. They are organized around their own trading companies and banks. Each major keiretsu is capable of controlling nearly every step of the economic chain in a variety of industrial, resource and service sectors.

There are horizontal and vertical keiretsu. Horizontal keiretsu are headed by major Japanese banks and include the "Big Six"—Mitsui, Mitsubishi, Sumitomo, Fuyo, Sanwa, and Dai-Ichi Kangyo Bank Groups. Vertical keiretsu are industrial groups connecting manufacturers and part suppliers or manufacturers, wholesalers and retailers. These verticle keiretsu include car and electronics producers (Toyota, Nissan, Honda–Matsushita, Hitachi, Toshiba, Sony) and their "captive" subcontractors. Distribution keiretsu, a subgroup of vertical keiretsu, control much of Japanese retailing, determining what products will appear in stores and showrooms—and at what price.

kelvin

The kelvin (abbreviation K), less commonly called the degree Kelvin (symbol, ^{o}K), is the International System (**SI**) unit of thermodynamic temperature. One kelvin is formally defined as $1/_{273.16}$ (3.6609×10^{-3}) of the thermodynamic temperature of the triple point of pure water (H_2O).

The kelvin scale differs from the more familiar Celsius or centigrade (^{o}C) temperature scale; there is no such thing as a below-zero Kelvin figure. A temperature of 0 K represents absolute zero, the absence of all heat. However, the size of the kelvin "degree" is the same as the size of the Celsius "degree." A change of plus-or-minus 1 ^{o}C is the same as a change of plus-or-minus 1 K.

At standard Earth-atmospheric sea-level pressure, water freezes at 0 ^{o}C or +273.15 K, and boils at +100 ^{o}C or +373.15 K. A temperature of 0 K thus corresponds to -273.15 ^{o}C. To convert a kelvin temperature figure to Celsius, subtract 273.15. To convert a Celsius temperature figure to kelvin, add 273.15.

Kerberos

Kerberos is a secure method for authenticating a request for a service in a computer network. Kerberos was developed in the Athena Project at the Massachusetts Institute of Technology (MIT). The name is taken from Greek mythology; Kerberos was a three-headed dog who guarded the gates of Hades. Kerberos lets a user request an encrypted "ticket" from an **authentication** process that can then be used to request a particular service from a server. The user's **password** does not have to pass through the network. A version of Kerberos (client and server) can be downloaded from MIT or you can buy a commercial version.

Briefly and approximately, here's how Kerberos works:

1. Suppose you want to access a server on another computer (which you may get to by sending a **Telnet** or similar login request). You know that this server requires a Kerberos "ticket" before it will honor your request.

2. To get your ticket, you first request authentication from the Authentication Server (AS). The Authentication Server creates a "session key" (which is also an encryption key) basing it on your password (which it can get from your user name) and a random value that represents the requested service. The session key is effectively a "ticket-granting ticket."

3. You next send your ticket-granting ticket to a ticket-granting server (TGS). The TGS may be physically the same server as the Authentication Server, but it's now performing a different service. The TGS returns the ticket that can be sent to the server for the requested service.

4. The service either rejects the ticket or accepts it and performs the service.

5. Because the ticket you received from the TGS is time-stamped, it allows you to make additional requests using the same ticket within a certain time period (typically, eight hours) without having to be reauthenticated. Making the ticket valid for a limited time period make it less likely that someone else will be able to use it later.

The actual process is much more complicated than just described. The user procedure may vary somewhat according to implementation.

Kermit

Kermit is a popular file transfer and management **protocol** and suite of communications software programs with advantages over existing Internet protocols such as **File Transfer Protocol** and **Telnet**. It is **freeware**, developed and maintained by members of the Kermit Project at Columbia University. (However, you're invited to purchase shrink-wrapped versions and/or the manuals to help support the project.) The Kermit protocol is described as "fast, robust, extensible, tunable, and medium-independent." In addition to the protocol support, the Kermit suite includes **terminal emulation**, character-set translation, and scripting. The suite can be installed on almost any **operating system**, including Windows, UNIX, DOS, VMS, OS/2, and a number of mainframe operating systems. Most versions support both direct or dialed serial connections (with a modem) and network connections (**Telnet** and often others such as Rlogin, LAT, or **X.25**).

Some advantages of Kermit are:

- You can write a script that will allow a sequence of file transfers to happen with a single command

- You can transfer an entire file directory and its subdirectories with a single command

- Text and binary files can be sent in the same file transfer

- Character-sets can be translated as part of the transfer (for example, from **EBCDIC** to **ASCII**)
- Files can be transferred through **firewall**s and network address translators

kernel

The kernel is the essential center of a computer **operating system**, the core that provides basic services for all other parts of the operating system. A synonym is *nucleus*. A kernel can be contrasted with a **shell**, the outermost part of an operating system that interacts with user commands. *Kernel* and *shell* are terms used more frequently in **UNIX** and some other operating systems than in IBM mainframe systems.

Typically, a kernel (or any comparable center of an operating system) includes an interrupt handler that handles all requests or completed I/O operations that compete for the kernel's services, a scheduler that determines which programs share the kernel's processing time in what order, and a supervisor that actually gives use of the computer to each process when it is scheduled. A kernel may also include a manager of the operating system's address spaces in memory or storage, sharing these among all components and other users of the kernel's services. A kernel's services are requested by other parts of the operating system or by **applications** through a specified set of program interfaces sometimes known as *system calls*.

Because the code that makes up the kernel is needed continuously, it is usually loaded into computer storage in an area that is protected so that it will not be overlaid with other less frequently used parts of the operating system.

The kernel is not to be confused with the basic input/output system (**BIOS**).

Some kernels have been developed independently for use in any operating system that wants to use it. A well-known example is the *Mach kernel*, developed at Carnegie-Mellon University, and currently used in a version of the **Linux** operating system for Apple's PowerMac computers.

key

In cryptography, a key is a variable value that is applied using an **algorithm** to a string or **block** of unencrypted text to produce **encrypted** text, or to decrypt encrypted text. The length of the key is a factor in considering how difficult it will be to decrypt the text in a given message.

keyboard

On most computers, a keyboard is the primary **text** input device. (The **mouse** is also a primary input device but lacks the ability to easily transmit textual information.) The keyboard also contains certain standard function keys, such as the Escape key, tab and cursor movement keys, shift and control keys, and sometimes other manufacturer-customized keys.

The computer keyboard uses the same key arrangement as the mechanical and electronic typewriter keyboards that preceded the computer. The standard arrangement of alphabetic keys is known as the Qwerty (pronounced KWEHR-tee) keyboard, its name deriving from the arrangement of the five keys at the upper left of the three rows of alphabetic keys. This arrangement, invented for one of the earliest mechanical typewriters, dates back to the 1870s. Another well-known key arrangement is the Dvorak (pronounced duh-VOR-ak, not like the Czech composer) system, which was designed to be easier to learn and use. The Dvorak keyboard was designed with the most common consonants on one side of the middle or home row and the vowels on the other side so that typing tends to alternate key strokes back and forth between hands. Although the Dvorak keyboard has never been widely used, it has adherents.

Because many keyboard users develop a **cumulative trauma disorder**, such as *carpal tunnel syndrome*, a number of **ergonomic** keyboards have been developed. Approaches include keyboards contoured to alleviate stress and foot-driven pedals for certain keys or keyboard functions.

kHz

The kilohertz, abbreviated kHz or KHz*, is a unit of alternating current (**AC**) or electromagnetic (EM) wave frequency equal to one thousand **hertz** (1,000 Hz). The unit is also used in measurements or statements of signal **bandwidth**.

An AC signal having a frequency of 1 kHz is within the range of human hearing. If a signal at this frequency is input to a headset or loudspeaker, the resulting tone has a pitch that falls into the so-called "audio midrange." An EM signal at a frequency of 1 kHz has a **wavelength** of 300 kilometers, or about 190 miles. The standard amplitude-modulation (**AM**) broadcast band extends from 535 kHz to 1,605 kHz. Some EM transmissions are made at millions of kHz.

The kilohertz is a relatively small unit of frequency; more common units are the **MHz**, equal to 1,000,000 Hz or 1,000 kHz, and the **GHz**, equal to 1,000,000,000 Hz or 1,000,000 kHz.

The kilohertz is often used to specify bandwidth for **digital** as well as **analog** signals. The bandwidth of a digital signal, in kilohertz, is related to the data speed in **bits per second**. In general, the greater the data speed, the larger the bandwidth. Data speed is not, however, the same thing as bandwidth. A modem operating at a speed of 28,800 bps has, in a certain sense, a nominal frequency of 28.8 kHz. But the bandwidth is generally much smaller, because it depends on variations in the individual data characters, not on the number of data bits per unit time.

*The engineer's society, **IEEE**, and most other sources prefer "kHz" to "KHz." This apparently makes it less likely that users will confuse "kilo" (decimal 1,000) with the computer "K" (1,024).

killer app

A "killer app" is jargon in the computer industry for an **application program** that intentionally or unintentionally gets you to make the decision to buy the system the application runs on. A classic example of a killer app was the **spreadsheet** program, the first of which was called VisiCalc, followed later by Lotus 1-2-3. The spreadsheet application helped introduce the personal computer into the department level of large and small businesses. A killer app can refer to a generic type of application that hasn't existed before, to a particular product that first introduces a new application type, or to any application with wide appeal.

When a new kind of computer hardware product comes out, such as a hand-held computer, manufacturers offer or hope to entice others to develop what they believe will be the killer app that will motivate potential customers to buy the new computer. In recent ads, IBM says that the killer app for **e-business** (which is both a concept and an array of Internet products and services that IBM sells) is "an application deployed over the Web that makes it easier to do the things you already do." Clearly, the Web **browser** and the Internet servers it communicates with became the killer app of the 1990s.

kilobit

In data communications, a kilobit is a thousand (10^3) **bit**s. It's commonly used for measuring the amount of data that is transferred in a second between two telecommunication points. Kilobits per second is usually shortened to **Kbps**.*

Some sources define a kilobit to mean 1,024 (that is, 2^{10}) bits. Although the bit is a unit of the binary number system, bits in data communications are discrete signal pulses and have historically been counted using the decimal number system. For example, 28.8 kilobits per second (**Kbps**) is 28,800 bits per second. Because of computer architecture and memory address boundaries, bytes are always some multiple or exponent of two. See **kilobyte**, etc.

*Note:** In international English outside the U.S., the equivalent usage is "kbps" or "kbits s^{-1}."

kilobits per second

See "Kbps"

kilobyte

As a measure of computer **memory** or storage, a kilobyte (KB or Kbyte*) is approximately a thousand **byte**s (actually, 2 to the 10th power, or decimal 1,024 bytes).

*Note:** In international English outside the U.S., the equivalent usage is sometimes "kbyte."

kilogram per meter cubed

The kilogram per meter cubed (symbolized kg/m^3) is the standard unit of material density in the International System of Units (SI). Material density is expressed directly in base SI units, and cannot be further reduced.

A substance with a density of 1 kg/m^3 is extremely light for its size. Even styrofoam or bubble-wrap has a density greater than this. A cubic meter of water has a mass of about 1000 kg, more than a conventional English ton in the gravitational field of the earth.

Alternative units are often used to express density. The most common of these is the gram per centimeter cubed (g/cm^3). A substance with a density of 1 g/cm^3 has a density of 1000 kg/m^3. Conversely, a substance with a density of 1 kg/m^3 has a density of 0.001 g/cm^3.

Also see **kilogram**, **meter**, **specific gravity**, and **SI** (International System of Units).

kilogram

The kilogram (abbreviation, kg) is the International System of Units (**SI**) unit of mass. It is defined as the mass of a particular international prototype made of platinum-iridium and kept at the International Bureau of Weights and Measures. It was originally defined as the mass of one liter (10^{-3} cubic meter) of pure water.

At the Earth's surface, a mass of 1 kg weighs approximately 2.20 pounds (lb). Conversely, an object that weighs 1 lb at the Earth's surface has a mass of approximately 0.454 kg. There is a qualitative as well as a quantitative difference between kilograms and pounds. Kilograms denote mass, but pounds denote weight, the force a mass exerts against a barrier in the presence of an acceleration field acting perpendicular to the barrier. On the surface of Mars, where the gravitational acceleration is 37 percent of that on the surface of the Earth, a mass of 1 kg weighs 0.814 lb. In orbit, or in a vehicle coasting through space, the net acceleration is zero and a mass of 1 kg has no weight. In other words, it is weightless.

Mass is often specified in smaller units than the kilogram, by changing the power-of-10 **prefix multiplier**. A mass of one gram (1 g) is 10^{-3} kg. A mass of one milligram (1 mg) is 10^{-6} kg, or 10^{-3} g. A mass of one microgram (1 μg) is 10^{-9} kg, or 10^{-6} g. A mass of one nanogram (1 ng) is 10^{-12} kg, or 10^{-9} g.

kiosk

In information technology, a kiosk (pronounced KEE-ahsk) is a small physical structure (often including a computer and a display screen) that displays information for people walking by. Kiosks are common near the entrances of shopping malls in North America where they provide shoppers with directions. Kiosks are also used at trade shows and professional conferences. The word is of Turkish and earlier Persian origin, where it meant an outdoor pavilion or a portico. The kiosks best known to travellers are those that display show and movie posters on the streets of Paris.

More sophisticated kiosks let users interact and include touch screens, sound, and motion video. A number of companies specialize in creating **multimedia** kiosks. A simple kiosk can be created using **HTML** pages and graphics, setting the typesize large enough to attract people from a short distance, and removing the Web browser's tool bar so that the display screen is effectively in "kiosk mode." The presentation can be designed to simply loop through a series of pages or to allow user interaction and exploration. Having a separate printed sign that invites people to your home-made kiosk may help.

Kirchhoff's Laws for current and voltage

Also see **Ohm's Law**.

Kirchhoff's Laws for current and voltage are two principles that apply to DC circuits and networks.

The total **current** flowing into any DC circuit node, also called a branch point, is always the same as the total current flowing out of the node. An example is shown in the top illustration. There are four current-carrying conductors (**a**, **b**, **c**, and **d**) leading into the node (black dot), and two conductors (**e** and **f**) leading out. Direct currents in parallel add together arithmetically. Therefore, the total current flowing into the node is **a + b + c + d**, and the total current flowing out is **e + f**. These total currents, according to *Kirchhoff's First Law*, must be equal.

Kirchhoff's Second Law deals with **voltage**. An example is shown in the bottom illustration. A source having voltage equal to **a** is connected in a circuit with five passive components having voltage differences **b**, **c**, **d**, **e**, and **f** across them. The voltages across the passive components add together arithmetically because they are connected in series. According to the Second Law, the total voltage across the set of passive components is always equal and opposite to the source voltage. Therefore, the sum of the voltage differences across all the circuit elements (including the source) is always zero.

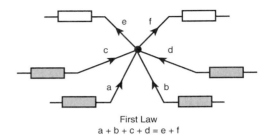

First Law
a + b + c + d = e + f

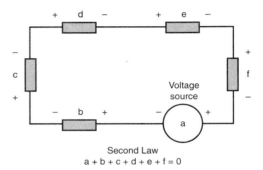

Second Law
a + b + c + d + e + f = 0

KISS Principle

The KISS (Keep It Simple, Stupid) Principle is self-descriptive and recognizes two things:

1. People (including product and service users) generally want things that are simple, meaning easy to learn and use.

2. A company that makes products or furnishes services may find simplicity an advantage for the company as well, since it tends to shorten time and reduce cost. (Where the company is trying to use the principle on behalf of users, however, design time may take longer and cost more, but the net effect will be beneficial since easy-to-learn-and-use products and services tend to be cheaper to produce and service in the long run.)

The New Hacker's Dictionary, edited by Eric Raymond, says the the KISS Principle is sometimes cited on a development project to fend off "creeping featurism."

The somewhat related idea of **Ockham's razor** is about always looking for the simplest explanation.

KLOC

KLOC (thousands of lines of code) is a traditional measure of how large a computer **program** is or how long or how many people it will take to write it. The code measured is usually **source code**. Since a higher-level source language (such as C++) **compiles** into more lines of **machine code** than a lower-level language (such as **assembler** language), a KLOC of C++ statements would generate a larger program (in number of **byte**s) than a KLOC of assembler language statements.

KLOC has been used as a rough measure of programmer productivity, as in "How many lines of code can you write a day?" However, this measure does not consider the efficiency of the code. Many other factors obviously affect productivity.

Defects per KLOC is a common measure used as a target or for evaluating code quality.

kludge

In information technology, a kludge (pronounced KLOOdzh) is an awkward or clumsy (but at least temporarily effective) solution to a programming or hardware design or implementation problem. According to Eric Raymond, the term is indirectly derived from the German *klug* meaning clever. Raymond considers "kludge" an incorrect spelling of *kluge*, a term of the 1940s with the same general meaning and possibly inspired by the Kluge paper feeder, a "fiendishly complex assortment of cams, belts, and linkages...devilishly difficult to repair...but oh, so clever!"

A kludge originates because another, more elegant or appropriate solution is not currently possible (perhaps because of time constraints). Hardware and software products are sometimes the result of adding a new and basically incompatible design to the original design rather than redesigning the product completely. What is a kludge can be a matter of opinion. Users often have a different opinion than the designers, who understand the problems that had to be overcome. To the extent that information technology products are combinations of elements originating from a variety of design philosophies and constraints, almost any product is bound to contain some element of kludginess.

knowbot

A knowbot is a program that automatically searchs Internet sites and gathers information from them according to user-specified criteria. A knowbot is more frequently called an **intelligent agent** or simply an **agent**. A knowbot should not be confused with a **search engine crawler** or **spider**. A crawler or spider progam visits Web sites and gathers information according to some generalized criteria and this information is then indexed so that it can be used for searching by many individual users. A knowbot works with specific and easily changed criteria that conform to or anticipate the needs of the user or users. Its results are then organized for presentation but not necessarily for searching. An example would be a knowbot (sometimes also called a *newsbot*) that visited major news-oriented Web sites each morning and provided a digest of stories (or links to them) for a personalized news page.

knowledge

In information technology, knowledge is, to an enterprise or an individual, the possession of **information** or the ability to quickly locate it. This is essentially what Samuel Johnson, compiler of the first comprehensive English dictionary, said when he wrote that:

> Knowledge is of two kinds: We know a subject ourselves, or we know where we can find information upon it.

In the context of the business enterprise or the personal computer user, knowledge tends to connote possession of experienced "know-how" as well as possession of factual information or where to get it. Enterprises have recently begun to treat their accumulated knowledge as an asset and to develop **knowledge management** plans and applications. A new kind of application, called **data mining**, attempts to develop knowledge from a company's accumulated business transactions and other **data**.

In philosophy, the theory of knowledge is called *epistemology* and deals with such questions as how much knowledge comes from experience or from innate reasoning ability; whether knowledge needs to be believed or can simply be used; and how knowledge changes as new ideas about the same set of facts arise.

knowledge base

In general, a knowledge base is a centralized repository for information: A public library, a database of related information about a particular subject, and whatis.com could all be considered to be examples of knowledge bases. In relation to information technology (**IT**), a knowledge base is a machine-readable resource for the dissemination of information, generally **online** or with the capacity to be put online. An integral component of **knowledge management** systems, a knowledge base is used to optimize information collection, organization, and retrieval for an organization, or for the general public.

A well-organized knowledge base can save an **enterprise** money by decreasing the amount of employee time spent trying to find information about—among myriad possibilities—tax laws or company policies and procedures. As a customer relationship management (**CRM**) tool, a knowledge base can give customers easy access to information that would otherwise require contact with an organization's staff; as a rule, this capacity should make the interaction simpler for both the customer and the organization. A number of software applications are available that allow users to create their own knowledge bases, either separately (these are usually called *knowledge management software*) or as part of another application, such as a CRM package.

In general, a knowledge base is not a static collection of information, but a dynamic resource that may itself have the capacity to learn, as part of an artificial intelligence (**AI**) **expert system**, for example. According to the World Wide Web Consortium (**W3C**), in the future the Internet may become a vast and complex global knowledge base. Tim Berners-Lee calls this the **Semantic Web**.

knowledge management

Knowledge management is the name of a concept in which an **enterprise** consciously and comprehensively gathers, organizes, shares, and analyzes its **knowledge** in terms of resources, documents, and people skills. In early 1998, it was believed that few enterprises actually had a comprehensive knowledge management practice (by any name) in operation. Advances in technology and the way we access and share information have changed that; many enterprises now have some kind of knowledge management framework in place.

Knowledge management involves **data mining** and some method of operation to **push** information to users. Some vendors are offering products to help an enterprise inventory and access knowledge resources. The Lotus Knowledge Discovery System, for example, advertises that it can locate and organize relevant content and expertise required to address specific business tasks and projects. It will analyze the relationships between content, people, topics, and activity, and produce a knowledge map report, based on a point system, that can be shared.

In an *Information Week* article, Jeff Angus and Jeetu Patel describe a four-process view of knowledge management that we have put into a table:

This major process...	Includes these activities....
Gathering	• Data entry
	• OCR and scanning
	• Voice input
	• Pulling information from various sources
	• Searching for information to include
Organizing	• Cataloging
	• Indexing
	• Filtering
	• Linking
Refining	• Contextualizing
	• Collaborating
	• Compacting
	• Projecting
	• Mining
Disseminating	• Flow
	• Sharing
	• Alert
	• Push

A knowledge management plan involves a survey of corporate goals and a close examination of the tools, both traditional and technical, that are required for addressing the needs of the company. The challenge is to select or build software that fits the context of the overall plan and encourage employees to share information.

knowledge worker

A knowledge worker is anyone who works for a living at the tasks of developing or using **knowledge**. For example, a knowledge worker might be someone who works at any of the tasks of planning, acquiring, searching, analyzing, organizing, storing, programming, distributing, marketing, or otherwise contributing to the transformation and commerce of information and those (often the same people) who work at using the knowledge so produced. A term first used by Peter Drucker in his 1959 book, *Landmarks of Tomorrow*, the knowledge worker includes those in the information technology fields, such as programmers, systems analysts, technical writers, academic professionals, researchers, and so forth. The term is also frequently used to include people outside of information technology, such as lawyers, teachers, scientists of all kinds, and also students of all kinds.

Korn shell

The Korn shell is the **UNIX shell** (command execution program, often called a *command interpreter*) that was developed by David Korn of Bell Labs as a comprehensive combined version of other major UNIX shells. Incorporating all the features of **C shell** (*csh*) and Tab C-shell (*tcsh*) with the script language features similar to that of the **Bourne shell**, the Korn shell is considered the most efficient shell. Korn, Bourne, and C are the three most commonly used UNIX shells.

The Korn shell is considered a member of the Bourne shell family and uses as its shell prompt (character displayed to indicate readiness for user input) the $ symbol. Because it is the easiest shell to use, inexperienced users usually prefer the Korn shell and, not surprisingly, it is the one most often used in commercial environments.

Sometimes known by its program name *ksh*, the Korn is the default shell on many UNIX systems.

KVM switch

A KVM (keyboard, video, mouse) switch allows a single **keyboard**, video display **monitor**, and **mouse** to be switched to any of a number of computers when typically a single person interacts with all the computers but only one at a time. The switch provides more table space in addition to saving the cost of multiple keyboards and monitors. KVM switches are commonly used at Web and other **server** locations with multiple computers but usually a single administrator or Webmaster. The switches range in price

from about $200 U.S. for a system in which up to eight computers can be daisy-chained to about $2,000 for a switch that controls up to 10 Sun workstations. Larger configurations can cost more.

L1 and L2

L1 and L2 are levels of **cache memory** in a computer. If the computer processor can find the data it needs for its next operation in cache memory, it will save time compared to having to get it from **random access memory**. L1 is "level-1" cache memory, usually built onto the microprocessor chip itself. For example, the Intel **MMX** microprocessor comes with 32 thousand bytes of L1.

L2 (that is, level-2) cache memory is on a separate **chip** (possibly on an expansion **card**) that can be accessed more quickly than the larger "main" memory. A popular L2 cache memory size is 1,024 kilobytes (one megabyte).

L2TP

See "Layer Two Tunneling Protocol"

lambda

LAMBDA

Upper Case Λ

Lower Case λ

Lambda, the 11th letter of the Greek alphabet, is the symbol for **wavelength**. In **optical fiber** networking, the word lambda is used to refer to an individual optical wavelength.

lambda calculus

Lambda calculus, considered to be the mathematical basis for programming language, is a calculus developed by Alonzo Church and Stephen Kleene in the 1930s to express all computable functions. In an effort to formalize the concept of computability (also known as constructibility and effective calculability), Church and Kleene developed a powerful language with a simple **syntax** and few grammar restrictions. The language deals with the application of a **function** to its arguments (a function is a set of rules) and expresses any **entity** as either a variable, the application of one function to another, or as a "lambda abstraction" (a function in which the Greek letter lambda is defined as the abstraction operator). Lambda calculus, and the closely related theories of combinators and type systems, are important foundations in the study of mathematics, logic, and computer programming language.

lambda switching

Lambda switching (sometimes called *photonic* switching, or *wavelength* switching) is the technology used in optical networking to switch individual wavelengths of light onto separate paths for specific routing of information. In conjunction with technologies such as dense wavelength division multiplexing (**DWDM**)—which enables 80 or more separate light **wavelength**s to be transmitted on a single optical fiber—lambda switching enables a light path to behave like a **virtual circuit**.

Although the ability to redirect specific wavelengths intelligently is, in itself, a technological breakthrough, lambda switching works in much the same way as traditional routing and switching. Lambda **router**s—which are also called *wavelength* routers, or *optical cross-connects* (OXC)—are positioned at network junction points. The lambda router takes in a single wavelength of light from a specific **fiber optic** strand and recombines it into another strand that is set on a different path. Lambda routers are being manufactured by a number of companies, including Ciena, Lucent, and Nortel.

Multiprotocol Lambda Switching is a variation of multiprotocol label switching (**MPLS**, confusingly, the abbreviation for both variants) in which specific wavelengths serve in place of labels as unique identifiers. The specified wavelengths, like the labels, make it possible for routers and switches to perform necessary functions automatically, without having to extract instructions regarding those functions from **IP address**es or other **packet** information.

Lambda switching gets its name from *lambda*, the 11th letter of the Greek alphabet, which has been adopted as the symbol for *wavelength*. In networking, the word is used to refer to an individual optical wavelength.

lamer

Lamer is a term used on interactive Web sites to describe an irritating or immature participant. Among users of Internet Relay Chat (**IRC**), a lamer is someone who irritates other users by typing in all caps or iN pART cAPS, by insulting and **flaming** other users, by typing abbreviations for almost every word, or by performing other annoying acts in chat rooms. Some IRC **channels** use **bots** to monitor any "lame" behavior and kick lamers out.

Lamer is also used by **crackers** and **warez** d00dz. Warez d00dz (that is, "wares dudes") are people who strip software of its copyright protection and then distribute the pirated software on the Internet for downloading. Warez d00dz sometimes compete to distribute the pirated software before other warez d00dz groups. People who create warez sites sometimes call them "warez sitez" and use "z" in other pluralizations. A lamer according to the warez d00dz culture is an individual who tries to distribute software that is several years old or software infected with a virus. Crackers use the term in a non-derogatory way to refer to cracker aspirants who are in the larval or beginning stage of computer cracking.

LAN

See "local area network"

LAN server

A local area network (LAN) server is a program (and by implication usually the computer it runs in) that serves resources (files, storage, application programs, printers, and other devices) to a number of attached workstations.

In an enterprise, a LAN server has an administrator (or someone who fills that role) and typically LAN services and the setting up and administration of the local area network are managed on behalf of users but not directly by the users.

A LAN server can also be housed in a computer that has other servers such as a **proxy server**.

LANDesk Client Manager

LDCM (LANDesk Client Manager) is a software product from Intel that lets a system administrator for a local area network (**LAN**) see the configurations and monitor the status of **personal computers** on the LAN. LDCM is an implementation of the Desktop Management Interface (**DMI**) standard established by the Desktop Management Task Force, an industry group. To take advantage of DMI, product components must provide a Management Information Format (MIF) file.

Using LDCM, a LAN administrator can be notified automatically when a workstation is nearing problem status. LDCM's "PC health monitoring" can notify the administrator of the status of low **memory**, any recoverable **parity** error, any **boot virus** that may be present, the **motherboard** and **central processing unit** temperatures, and other status information. LDCM also allows an inventory to be kept of all software and hardware characteristics of all workstations.

The first releases of LDCM have been pre-installed on PCs by original equipment manufacturers. LDCM requires a **BIOS** that supports System Management BIOS Specification Version 2.0.

landing page

See "jump page"

Langmuir-Blodgett film

A Langmuir-Blodgett (LB) film is a set of monolayers, or layers of organic material one molecule thick, deposited on a solid substrate. An LB film can consist of a single layer or many, up to a depth of several visible-light **wavelength**s.

The term Langmuir-Blodgett comes from the names of a research scientist and his assistant, Irving Langmuir and Katherine Blodgett, who discovered unique properties of thin films in the early 1900s. Langmuir's original work involved the transfer of monolayers from liquid to solid substrates. Several years later, Blodgett expanded on Langmuir's research to include the deposition of multi-layer films on solid substrates.

By transferring monolayers of organic material from a liquid to a solid substrate, the structure of the film can be controlled at the molecular level. Such films exhibit various electrochemical and photochemical properties. This has led some researchers to pursue LB films as a possible structure for integrated circuits (**IC**s). Ultimately, it might be possible to construct an LB-film memory chip in which each data bit is represented by a single molecule. Complex switching networks might be fabricated onto multilayer LB-films chips.

laptop computer

This definition is very similar to our definition for **notebook computer**. Aso see **portable computer**.

A laptop computer, usually called a *notebook computer* by manufacturers, is a battery-powered personal computer generally smaller than a briefcase that can easily be transported and conveniently used in temporary spaces such as on airplanes, in libraries, temporary offices, and at meetings. A laptop typically weighs less than 5 pounds and is 3 inches or less in thickness. Among the best-known makers of laptop computers are IBM, NEC, Dell, Toshiba, and Hewlett-Packard.

Laptop computers generally cost more than desktop computers with the same capabilities because they are more difficult to design and manufacture. A laptop can effectively be turned into a desktop computer with a **docking station**, a hardware frame that supplies connections for peripheral input/output devices such as a printer or larger monitor. The less capable *port replicator* allows you to connect a laptop to a number of peripherals through a single plug.

Laptops usually come with displays that use thin-screen technology. The **thin film transistor** or active matrix screen is brighter and views better at different angles than the STN or dual-scan screen. Laptops use several different approaches for integrating a **mouse** into the keyboard, including the **touch pad**, the **trackball**, and the pointing stick. A serial port also allows a regular mouse to be attached. The **PC Card** is insertable hardware for adding a **modem** or **NIC** to a laptop. CD-ROM and **digital versatile disk** drives may be built-in or attachable.

laser

The acronym *laser* stands for "light amplification by stimulated emission of radiation." Lasers work as a result of resonant effects. The output of a laser is a coherent **electromagnetic field**. In a coherent beam of electromagnetic energy, all the waves have the same **frequency** and **phase**.

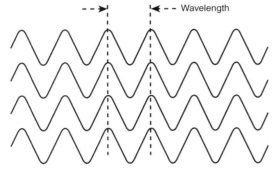

Coherent electromagnetic waves have identical frequency, and are aligned in phase.

In a basic laser, a chamber called a *cavity* is designed to internally reflect infrared (IR), visible-light, or ultraviolet (UV) waves so they reinforce each other. The cavity can contain gases, liquids, or solids. The choice of cavity material determines the wavelength of the output. At each end of the cavity, there is a mirror. One mirror is totally reflective, allowing none of the energy to pass through; the other mirror is partially reflective, allowing approximately 5 percent of the energy to pass through. Energy is introduced into the cavity from an external source; this is called *pumping*.

As a result of pumping, an electromagnetic field appears inside the laser cavity at the natural (resonant) frequency of the atoms of the material that fills the cavity. The waves reflect back and forth between the mirrors. The length of the cavity is such that the reflected and re-reflected wavefronts reinforce each other in phase at the natural frequency of the cavity substance. Electromagnetic waves at this resonant frequency emerge from the end of the cavity having the partially-reflective mirror. The output may appear as a continuous beam, or as a series of brief, intense pulses.

The *ruby laser*, a simple and common type, has a rod-shaped cavity made of a mixture of solid aluminum oxide and chromium. The output is in pulses that last approximately 500 microseconds each. Pumping is done by means of a helical flash tube wrapped around the rod. The output is in the red visible range.

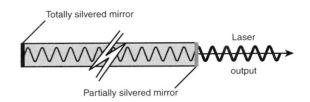

A simple laser works via resonant effects in a cavity with mirrors at either end.

The *helium-neon laser* is another popular type, favored by electronics hobbyists because of its moderate cost. As its name implies, it has a cavity filled with helium and neon gases. The output of the device is bright crimson. Other gases can be used instead of helium and neon, producing beams of different wavelengths. Argon produces a laser with blue visible output. A mixture of nitrogen, carbon dioxide, and helium produces IR output.

Lasers are one of the most significant inventions developed during the 20th century. They have found a tremendous variety of uses in electronics, computer hardware, medicine, and experimental science.

laser diode

Also see **diode**.

A laser diode, also known as an *injection laser* or *diode laser*, is a **semiconductor** device that produces coherent radiation (in which the waves are all at the same frequency and phase) in the visible or **infrared** (IR) spectrum when **current** passes through it. Laser diodes are used in **optical fiber** systems, compact disc (**CD**) players, **laser printer**s, remote-control devices, and **intrusion detection** systems.

Laser diodes differ from conventional lasers, such as the helium-neon (He-Ne), ruby, and gas types, in several ways.

- **Small size and weight**: A typical laser diode measures less than one millimeter across and weighs a fraction of a gram, making it ideal for use in portable electronic equipment.

- **Low current, voltage, and power requirements**: Most laser diodes require only a few milliwatts of power at 3 to 12 volts DC and several milliamperes. Therefore, they can operate using small battery power supplies.

- **Low intensity**: A laser diode cannot be used for spectacular purposes such as burning holes in metal, bringing down satellites, or blinding aircraft pilots. Nevertheless, its coherent output results in high efficiency and ease of **modulation** for communications and control applications.

- **Wide-angle beam**: A laser diode produces a "cone" rather than a "pencil" of visible light or IR, although this "cone" can be collimated using convex lenses.

laser printer

A laser printer is a popular type of personal computer **printer** that uses a non-impact (keys don't strike the paper), photocopier technology. When a document is sent to the printer, a laser beam "draws" the document on a selenium-coated drum using electrical charges. After the drum is charged, it is rolled in toner, a dry powder type of ink. The toner adheres to the charged image on the drum. The toner is transferred onto a piece of paper and fused to the paper with heat and pressure. After the document is printed, the electrical charge is removed from the drum and the excess toner is collected. Most laser printers print only in monochrome. A color laser printer is up to 10 times more expensive than a monochrome laser printer.

IBM introduced the first laser printer in 1975 for use with its **mainframe** computers. In 1984, Hewlett-Packard revolutionized laser-printing technology with its first LaserJet, a compact, fast, and reliable printer that personal computer users could afford. Since then, laser printers have decreased further in price and increased in quality. Hewlett Packard continues to be the leading manufacturer with competitors including Lexmark, Okidata, and Xerox.

The laser printer is different from an inkjet printer in a number of ways. The toner or ink in a laser printer is dry. In an inkjet, it is wet. Over time, an inkjet printer is about ten times more expensive to operate than a laser printer because ink needs replenishing more frequently. The printed paper from an inkjet printer will smear if wet, but a laser-printed document will not. Both types of printer operate quietly and allow fonts to be added by using **font** cartridges or installing soft fonts. If your printing needs are minimal, an inkjet printer is sufficient. But if your printing volume is high, consider buying a laser printer.

When buying a laser printer, these are some important features to consider:

Print capacity and speed: Personal laser printers are sufficient for printing an average of 200 pages per week. These are low-end and cost $200 and up. They can print up to eight ppm (pages per minute). A workgroup printer is needed if an average of 1000 pages per week is needed. These print up to 24 ppm and cost $1000 to $6000 and more. Production printers are needed for printing 50,000 or more pages per week. These are quite expensive and are used by commercial publishers. They can print up to 700 ppm and cost $100,000 and up. They can print 24 hours a day, seven days a week.

Resolution: The standard **resolution** in most laser printers today is 600 dots-per-inch (**dpi**). This resolution is sufficient for normal everyday printing including small desktop publishing jobs. A high-end production printer might have a resolution of 2400 dpi. Some laser printers still use a resolution of 300 dpi. This resolution can cause jagged lines to appear on the outer edge of an image. Hewlett Packard created RET (Resolution Enhancement Technology) to correct this. RET inserts smaller dots at the edges of lines and to smooth the rough edges. RET does not improve the resolution, but the document looks better. If you purchase a printer with 300 dpi, make sure it has RET.

Printer languages: Printer Control Language (**PCL**) is the standard printer language for Hewlett Packard and most other laser printers (which are mostly HP-compatible). PCL is used for printing letters, database printouts, spreadsheets, and simple graphics. **Postscript** printers are used with desktop publishing software and drawing packages. Postscript printers are the norm for Apple **Macintosh** printers. A laser printer that comes with Postscript installed is more expensive. A laser printer that uses PCL can be upgraded to Postscript by installing a software driver provided by the manufacturer of the laser printer. The printer might require more **memory** when upgraded to use Postscript. This is because a laser printer needs the entire image in memory before printing, and a Postscript printer requires more memory to process than a PCL printer does. The application being used must support Postscript in order for the laser printer to print Postscript documents.

Paper handling: Paper handling is important when shopping for a laser printer. Most laser printers use letter-size, cut-sheet paper. High-end production printers use continuous sheet paper. Laser printers can print on transparencies, adhesive labels, and lightweight cards. A laser printer with duplex printing can print on one side of the paper, turn the paper over, and print on the other side. Most laser printers, however, use simple printing with manual duplex printing. Manual duplex printing is achieved by changing the print options in the printer's properties or printing one side and taking that same paper and reinserting it into the printer to print on the other side.

FPOT and warm-up time: A final consideration in purchasing a printer is FPOT (first paper out time) and warm-up time. When a laser printer receives data from the computer to print, it takes 5 to 30 seconds to prepare the printer to print a new job. This is in addition to the time it takes to actually print the document. The warm-up time is as important. When the printer is turned on, it needs time to warm up the fuser to operating temperature. If the printer has a standby mode or is turned off between printing jobs, the warm-up time becomes even more important. Large workgroup and production printers can take 5 to 15 minutes to warm up. This waiting period can hinder overall productivity.

laserdisc

Laserdisc is a technology and the physical medium used in storing and providing programmed access to a large database of text, pictures, and other objects, including motion video and full multimedia presentations.

The laserdisc itself is 12 inches in diameter and holds much more information than a CD-ROM disc can currently hold. Laserdiscs require relatively expensive players and are more

expensive to distribute than CD-ROM discs. However, for school and corporate education purposes and any presentation requiring a great deal of motion video and the ability to create scripted or programmed access to selected portions of the laserdisc, the technology can be useful.

last-mile technology

Last-mile technology is any telecommunications technology, such as **wireless** radio, that carries **signal**s from the broad telecommunication along the relatively short distance (hence, the "last mile") to and from the home or business. Or to put it another way: the infrastructure at the neighborhood level. In many communities, last-mile technology represents a major remaining challenge to high-bandwidth applications such as on-demand television, fast Internet access, and Web pages full of multimedia effects.

Today, in addition to "plain old telephone (dial-up) service," last-mile technologies to deliver voice, data, and TV can include:

- **ISDN**, a somewhat faster technology than regular phone service

- Digital Subscriber Line (**DSL**) over existing telephone **twisted pair** lines

- Cable and the **cable modem** for data, using the same installed **coaxial cable** that already is used for television

- **Wireless**, including services such as DirecTV

- Less frequently because of the installation expense, **optical fiber** and its transmission technologies

LATA

See "local access and transport area"

latency

1) In a network, latency, a synonym for *delay*, is an expression of how much time it takes for a **packet** of data to get from one designated point to another. In some usages (for example, AT&T), latency is measured by sending a packet that is returned to the sender and the round-trip time is considered the latency.

The latency assumption seems to be that data should be transmitted instantly between one point and another (that is, with no delay at all). The contributors to network latency include:

- **Propagation:** This is simply the time it takes for a packet to travel between one place and another at the speed of light.

- **Transmission:** The medium itself (whether **optical fiber**, **wireless**, or some other) introduces some delay. The size of the packet introduces delay in a round trip since a larger packet will take longer to receive and return than a short one.

- **Router and other processing:** Each **gateway node** takes time to examine and possibly change the header in a packet (for example, changing the **hop** count in the **time-to-live** field).

- **Other computer and storage delays:** Within networks at each end of the journey, a packet may be subject to storage and hard disk access delays at intermediate devices such as **switch**es and **bridge**s. (In backbone statistics, however, this kind of latency is probably not considered.)

2) In a computer system, latency is often used to mean any delay or waiting that increases real or perceived **response time** beyond the response time desired. Specific contributors to computer latency include mismatches in data speed between the **microprocessor** and input/output devices and inadequate data **buffer**s.

Within a computer, latency can be removed or "hidden" by such techniques as *prefetching* (anticipating the need for data input requests) and *multithreading*, or using parallelism across multiple execution threads.

3) In 3D simulation, in describing a helmet that provides stereoscopic vision and head tracking, latency is the time between the computer detecting head motion to the time it displays the appropriate image.

layer

See "layering"

layer 2

Layer 2 refers to the Data Link **layer** of the commonly-referenced multilayered communication model, Open Systems Interconnection (**OSI**). The Data Link layer is concerned with moving data across the physical links in the network. In a network, the **switch** is a device that redirects data messages at the layer 2 level, using the destination Media Access Control (MAC) address to determine where to direct the message.

The Data-Link layer contains two sublayers that are described in the IEEE-802 LAN standards:

- **Media Access Control** (MAC) sublayer

- **Logical Link Control** (LLC) sublayer

The Data Link layer ensures that an initial connection has been set up, divides output data into data frames, and handles the acknowledgements from a receiver that the data arrived successfully. It also ensures that incoming data has been received successfully by analyzing bit patterns at special places in the frames.

layer 3

Layer 3 refers to the **Network layer** of the commonly referenced multilayered communication model, Open Systems Interconnection (**OSI**). The Network layer is concerned with knowing the address of the neighboring nodes in the network, selecting routes and quality of service, and recognizing and forwarding to the **Transport layer** incoming messages for local host domains.

A **router** is a layer 3 device, although some newer **switches** also perform layer 3 functions. The Internet Protocol (**IP**) address is a layer 3 address.

Layer Two Tunneling Protocol

Layer Two Tunneling Protocol (L2TP) is an extension of the Point-to-Point Tunneling Protocol (**PPTP**) used by an Internet service provider (**ISP**) to enable the operation of a virtual private network (**VPN**) over the Internet. L2TP merges the best features of two other tunneling protocols: PPTP from Microsoft and L2F from Cisco Systems. The two main components that make up L2TP are the L2TP Access Concentrator (LAC), which is the device that physically terminates a call and the L2TP Network Server (LNS), which is the device that terminates and possibly authenticates the PPP stream.

PPP defines a means of encapsulation to transmit multiprotocol packets over layer two (L2) point-to-point links. Generally, a user connects to a network access server (NAS) through ISDN, ADSL, dialup POTS or other service and runs PPP over that connection. In this configuration, the L2 and PPP session endpoints are both on the same NAS.

L2TP uses packet-switched network connections to make it possible for the endpoints to be located on different machines. The user has an L2 connection to an access concentrator, which then tunnels individual PPP frames to the NAS, so that the packets can be processed separately from the location of the circuit termination. This means that the connection can terminate at a local circuit concentrator, eliminating possible long-distance charges, among other benefits. From the user's point of view, there is no difference in the operation.

layering

In computer programming, layering is the organization of programming into separate functional components that interact in some sequential and hierarchical way, with each layer usually having an interface only to the layer above it and the layer below it.

Communication programs are often layered. The reference model for communication programs, Open System Interconnection (**OSI**) is a layered set of protocols in which two multilayered programs, one at either end of a communications exchange, use an identical set of layers. In the OSI model, each multilayer program contains seven layers, each reflecting a different function that has to be performed in order for program-to-program communication to take place between computers.

TCP/IP is an example of a two-layer (**TCP** and **IP**) set of programs that provide transport and network address functions for Internet communication. A set of TCP/IP and other layered programs is sometimes referred to as a **protocol stack**.

LB film

See "Langmuir-Blodgett film"

LBA

See "logical block addressing"

LBS

See "location-based services"

LCD

LCD (liquid crystal display) is the technology used for displays in notebook and other smaller computers. Like light-emitting diode (**LED**) and gas-plasma technologies, LCDs allow displays to be much thinner than cathode ray tube (**CRT**) technology. LCDs consume much less power than LED and gas-display displays because they work on the principle of blocking light rather than emitting it.

An LCD is made with either a passive matrix or an **active matrix** display grid. The active matrix LCD is also known as a thin film transistor (**TFT**) display. The passive matrix LCD has a grid of conductors with pixels located at each intersection in the grid. A current is sent across two conductors on the grid to control the light for any **pixel**. An active matrix has a **transistor** located at each pixel intersection, requiring less current to control the luminance of a pixel. For this reason, the current in an active matrix display can be switched on and off more frequently, improving the screen refresh time (your mouse will appear to move more smoothly across the screen, for example).

Some passive matrix LCD's have dual scanning, meaning that they scan the grid twice with current in the same time that it took for one scan in the original technology. However, active matrix is still a superior technology.

LCP

See "Link Control Protocol"

LDAP

See "Lightweight Directory Access Protocol"

LDCM

See "LANDesk Client Manager"

LDIF

LDIF (Lightweight Directory Interchange Format) is an **ASCII file format** used to exchange data and enable the synchronization of that data between Lightweight Directory Access Protocol (**LDAP**) server*s* called Directory System Agents (DSAs). LDAP is a software **protocol** for enabling anyone to locate organizations, individuals, and other resources such as files and devices in a network. An LDAP directory can be distributed among many servers. LDIF is used to synchronize each LDAP directory.

The first step in synchronizing LDAP directories is extracting the full contents of or a portion of the original LDAP directory and formatting the contents into an LDIF file. The LDIF file is then mailed to a directory synchronization robot called DIRBOT. After several different steps, a final LDIF file is compared to the original LDIF file. The update instructions on what records to add, delete, or modify in the original directory are decided. These updates are then used to synchronize all LDAP directories.

leased line

A leased line is a telephone line that has been leased for private use. In some contexts, it's called a *dedicated* line. A leased line is usually contrasted with a *switched line* or *dial-up line*.

Typically, large companies rent leased lines from the telephone message carriers (such as AT&T) to interconnect different geographic locations in their company. The alternative is to buy and maintain their own private lines or, increasingly perhaps, to use the public switched lines with secure message protocols. (This is called **tunneling**.)

LEC

LEC (local exchange carrier) is the term for a public telephone company in the U.S. that provides local service. Some of the largest LECs are the Bell operating companies (**BOC**s) which were grouped into holding companies known collectively as the regional Bell operating companies (**RBOC**s) when the Bell System was broken up by a 1983 consent decree. In addition to the Bell companies, there are a number of independent LECs, such as GTE.

LEC companies are also sometimes referred to as "telcos." A "local exchange" is the local "central office" of an LEC. Lines from homes and businesses terminate at a local exchange. Local exchanges connect to other local exchanges within a local access and transport area (**LATA**) or to interexchange carriers (**IXCs**) such as long-distance carriers ATT, MCI, and Sprint.

LED

See "light-emitting diode"

legacy application

In information technology, legacy applications and data are those that have been inherited from languages, platforms, and techniques earlier than current technology. Most **enterprise**s who use computers have legacy applications and databases that serve critical business needs. Typically, the challenge is to keep the legacy application running while converting it to newer, more efficient code that makes use of new technology and programmer skills. In the past, much programming has been written for specific manufacturers' operating systems. Currently, many companies are migrating their legacy applications to new programming languages and operating systems that follow **open** or standard programming interfaces. Theoretically, this will make it easier in the future to update applications without having to rewrite them entirely and will allow a company to use its applications on any manufacturer's operating system.

In addition to moving to new languages, enterprises are redistributing the locations of applications and data. In general, legacy applications have to continue to run on the platforms they were developed for. Typically, new development environments account for the need to continue to support legacy applications and data. With many new tools, legacy databases can be accessed by newer programs.

length

See "displacement"

LEO

See "satellite"

leverage

In the physical sense, leverage is an assisted advantage. As a verb, to *leverage* means to gain an advantage through the use of a tool. For example, you can more easily lift a heavy object with a lever than you can lift it unaided. Leverage is commonly used in a metaphorical sense. For example, as a frequently used business or marketing term, leverage is any strategic or tactical advantage, and as a verb, means to exploit such an advantage, just as the use of a physical lever gives one an advantage in the physical sense.

Leverage is a very popular business term on the Web. **B2B** Web sites offer to leverage Web sites, code, interactivity, storage area networks, database technology, and many other things. In the world of finance, leverage is the use of borrowed money to make an investment and the return on an investment.

LexiBot

LexiBot is a specialized search tool developed by BrightPlanet, as a means of searching the **deep Web** (the hidden part of the Web that may contain 500 times the

content accessible to conventional search engines). LexiBot uses what BrightPlanet calls a comprehensive and intelligent search technology that enables users to conduct searches using simple text, natural language, or **Boolean** queries on hundreds of databases simultaneously, filter and analyze data, and publish the results as Web pages. LexiBot was designed to perform complex searches to identify and retrieve content from all areas of the Web, and to process the information.

Deep Web content has been accessible only to those who knew the correct **URL** for the Web site. Then, even once a user had connected to a database, its data could only be accessed by single direct queries. LexiBot acts as an automated direct **query** engine to make dozens of queries simultaneously to multiple databases. Searches are supported on close to 600 databases. Once the links are found, LexiBot downloads the links, analyzes them, removes the irrelevant ones, then downloads the text portions of the documents to the user's hard drive. The application can be used with desktop databases as well as the Internet, is customizable to user preferences, and can be set up for either simple or advanced usage.

lexical scoping

Lexical scoping (sometimes known as *static scoping*) is a convention used with many programming languages that sets the *scope* (range of functionality) of a **variable** so that it may only be *called* (referenced) from within the block of code in which it is defined. The scope is determined when the code is compiled. A variable declared in this fashion is sometimes called a *private* variable.

The opposite approach is known as *dynamic scoping*. Dynamic scoping creates variables that can be called from outside the block of code in which they are defined. A variable declared in this fashion is sometimes called a *public* variable.

light-emitting diode

Also see **laser diode**.

A light-emitting diode (LED) is a **semiconductor** device that emits visible light when an electric **current** passes through it. The light is not particularly bright, but in most LEDs it is monochromatic, occurring at a single **wavelength**. The output from an LED can range from red (at a wavelength of approximately 700 nanometers) to blue-violet (about 400 nanometers). Some LEDs emit infrared (**IR**) energy (830 nanometers or longer); such a device is known as an *infrared-emitting diode* (IRED).

An LED or IRED consists of two elements of processed material called *P-type semiconductor*s and *N-type semiconductor*s. These two elements are placed in direct contact, forming a region called the *P-N junction*. In this respect, the LED or IRED resembles most other **diode** types, but there are important differences. The LED or IRED has a

transparent package, allowing visible or IR energy to pass through. Also, the LED or IRED has a large PN-junction area whose shape is tailored to the application.

Benefits of LEDs and IREDs, compared with incandescent and fluorescent illuminating devices, include:

- **Low power requirement**: Most types can be operated with battery power supplies.
- **High efficiency:** Most of the power supplied to an LED or IRED is converted into radiation in the desired form, with minimal heat production.
- **Long life:** When properly installed, an LED or IRED can function for decades.

Typical applications include:

- **Indicator lights:** These can be two-state (i.e., on/off), bar-graph, or alphabetic-numeric readouts.
- **LCD panel backlighting:** Specialized white LEDs are used in flat-panel computer displays.
- **Fiber optic data transmission:** Ease of **modulation** allows wide communications **bandwidth** with minimal noise, resulting in high speed and accuracy.
- **Remote control:** Most home-entertainment "remotes" use IREDs to transmit data to the main unit.
- **Optoisolator:** Stages in an electronic system can be connected together without unwanted interaction.

light-emitting polymer

See "polymer LED"

Lightweight Directory Access Protocol

Lightweight Directory Access Protocol (LDAP) is a software **protocol** for enabling anyone to locate organizations, individuals, and other resources such as files and devices in a network, whether on the public **Internet** or on a corporate **intranet**. LDAP is a "lightweight" (smaller amount of code) version of Directory Access Protocol (**DAP**), which is part of **X.500**, a standard for **directory** services in a network. LDAP is lighter because in its initial version it did not include security features. LDAP originated at the University of Michigan and has been endorsed by at least 40 companies. Netscape includes it in its latest Communicator suite of products. Microsoft includes it as part of what it calls **Active Directory** in a number of products including Outlook Express. Novell's **NetWare Directory Services** interoperates with LDAP. Cisco also supports it in its networking products.

In a network, a directory tells you where in the network something is located. On **TCP/IP** networks (including the Internet), the domain name system (**DNS**) is the directory system used to relate the domain name to a specific network address (a unique location on the network). However, you may not know the domain name. LDAP allows you to search for an individual without knowing where they're located (although additional information will help with the search).

An LDAP directory is organized in a simple "tree" hierarchy consisting of the following levels:

- The **root directory** (the starting place or the source of the tree), which branches out to
- Countries, each of which branches out to
- Organizations, which branch out to
- Organizational units (divisions, departments, and so forth), which branches out to (includes an entry for)
- Individuals (which includes people, files, and shared resources such as printers)

An LDAP directory can be distributed among many servers. Each server can have a replicated version of the total directory that is synchronized periodically. An LDAP server is called a Directory System Agent (DSA). An LDAP server that receives a request from a user takes responsibility for the request, passing it to other DSAs as necessary, but ensuring a single coordinated response for the user.

Li-Ion battery

See "Lithium Ion battery"

line information database

A line information database (LIDB) is a **database** maintained by the local telephone company that contains subscriber information, such as a service profile, name and address, and credit card validation information.

line print terminal

See "LPT"

linear IC

See "linear integrated circuit"

linear integrated circuit

Also see integrated circuit (**IC**).

A linear integrated circuit (linear IC) is a solid-state **analog** device characterized by a theoretically infinite number of possible operating states. It operates over a continuous range of input levels. In contrast, a **digital** IC has a finite number of discrete input and output states.

Within a certain input range, the amplification curve of a linear IC is a straight line; the input and output voltages are directly proportional. The best known, and most common, linear IC is the operational amplifier or *op amp*, which consists of resistors, diodes, and transistors in a conventional analog circuit. There are two inputs, called inverting and non-inverting. A **signal** applied to the inverting input results in a signal of opposite **phase** at the output. A signal applied

to the non-inverting input produces a signal of identical phase at the output. A connection, through a variable **resistance**, between the output and the inverting input is used to control the **amplification factor**.

Linear ICs are employed in audio amplifiers, A/D (analog-to-digital) converters, averaging amplifiers, differentiators, DC (direct-current) amplifiers, integrators, multivibrators, oscillators, audio filters, and sweep generators. Linear ICs are available in most large electronics stores. Some devices contain several amplifiers within a single housing.

linear tape

See "Linear Tape-Open"

Linear Tape-Open

Linear Tape-Open (LTO) is an **open** standard for a **backup tape** system, providing formats for both fast data access and high storage capacity, developed jointly by Hewlett-Packard, IBM, and Seagate. IBM released the first LTO products in August 2000.

One of the tape industry's biggest problems has been a lack of standards, with each vendor providing its own technology. Standardization means that different manufacturers' tapes and tape drives will interoperate (just as audio tape cassettes work in all tape players). Like existing tape systems, LTO uses a linear multi-channel bi-directional format. LTO adds to existing technologies timing-based servo (a device that automates a process of error correction for a mechanism), hardware data **compression**, enhanced track layouts, and efficient **error correction code**.

LTO was developed in two different formats—one for fast data access and another for greater storage capacity. The Accelis format uses 8mm-wide tape on a two-reel cartridge that loads at the mid-point of the tape to provide fast data access, specifically for read-intensive applications, such as online searches and retrieval functions. The Ultrium format uses a single reel of half-inch wide tape to maximize storage capacity, specifically for write-intensive applications, such as archival and backup functions. Early products using the Accelis format offer a 25 **gigabyte** capacity for uncompressed data, while Ultrium based-products offer a 100 gigabyte capacity. Both formats provide transfer rates of 10−20 **Mbps**. While these figures are not unheard of in other technologies, LTO specifications include plans for expected increases that will double current rates with each of the next three generations of products.

linearity

Linearity is the behavior of a circuit, particularly an **amplifier**, in which the output **signal** strength varies in direct proportion to the input signal strength. In a linear device, the output-to-input signal amplitude ratio is always the same, no matter what the strength of the input signal (as long it is not too strong).

In an amplifier that exhibits linearity, the output-versus-input signal amplitude graph appears as a straight line. Two examples are shown below. The gain, or amplification factor, determines the slope of the line. The steeper the slope, the greater the gain. The amplifier depicted by the higher line has more gain than the one depicted by the lower line. Both amplifiers are linear within the input-signal strength range shown, because both lines in the graph are straight.

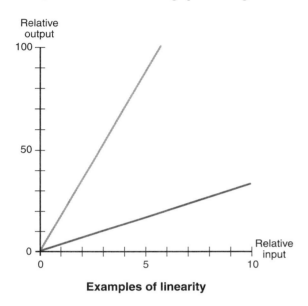

Examples of linearity

In analog applications such as amplitude-modululation (**AM**) wireless transmission and hi-fi audio, linearity is important. Nonlinearity in these applications results in signal distortion, because the fluctuation in gain affects the shape of an **analog** output **waveform** with respect to the analog input waveform.

Even if an amplifier exhibits linearity under normal conditions, it will become nonlinear if the input signal is too strong. This situation is called overdrive. The amplification curve bends towards a horizontal slope as the input-signal amplitude increases beyond the critical point, producing distortion in the output. An example is a hi-fi amplifier whose gain is set to the point where the VU (volume-unit) meter needles kick into the red range. The red zone indicates that the amplifier is not operating in a linear fashion. This can degrade the fidelity of the sound.

line-of-business application

See "LOB"

link

1) Using **hypertext**, a link is a selectable connection from one word, picture, or information object to another. In a multimedia environment such as the World Wide Web, such objects can include sound and motion video sequences. The most common form of link is the highlighted word or picture that can be selected by the user (with a mouse or in some other fashion), resulting in the immediate delivery and view of another file. The highlighted object is referred to as an **anchor**. The anchor reference and the object referred to constitute a hypertext link.

Although most links do not offer the user a choice of *types* of link, it would be possible for the user to be provided a choice of link types, such as: a definition of the object, an example of it, a picture of it, a smaller or larger picture of it, and so forth.

Links are what make the World Wide Web a web.

Also see **hypermedia** and **hyperlink**.

2) In telecommunications, a *link* is a physical (and, in some usages, a logical) connection between two points.

link checker

A link checker is a program that tests and reports on the validity of the **hypertext link**s on the pages in a **Web site**. More advanced link checkers test links to other Web sites as well as links between pages on the same site. A link checker may be a separate program that specializes in this service, part of a larger program that provides a range of Web site publishing services, or provided periodically as a service from a remote application server.

An example of a specialized link checker is NetMechanic Toolbox.

- Looks at each page in a Web site's directory of pages and tries to connect to each link it finds on a page. If a link does not work, it identifies the reason (for example, "A connection could not be established" or "This site has been permanently moved") and prepares a report on "Pages with Bad Links" that you can view with your Web **browser** or print out.

- Summarizes the number of HTML and graphic files it found, their individual size, and the average download size.

- Lets you specify whether you want individual page reports or a summary.

- Lets you run the program automatically on a daily basis at a particular time.

Link Control Protocol

In the Point-to-Point Protocol (**PPP**), the Link Control Protocol (LCP) establishes, configures, and tests data-link Internet connections. Before establishing communications over a point-to-point link, each end of the PPP link must send out LCP **packets**. The LCP packet either accepts or rejects the identity of its linked peer, agrees upon packet size limits, and looks for common misconfiguration errors. Basically, the LCP packet checks the telephone line connection to see whether the connection is good enough to sustain data transmission at the intended rate. Once the LCP packet accepts the link, traffic can be transported on the network; if the LCP packet determines the link is not functioning properly, it terminates the link.

LCP packets are divided into three classes:

1. Link configuration packets used to establish and configure a link

2. Link termination packets used to terminate a link

3. Link maintenance packets used to manage and debug a link

link encryption

Link encryption (sometimes called *link level* or *link layer encryption*) is the data security process of encrypting information at the **data link** level as it is transmitted between two points within a network. Data, which is **plaintext** in the host server, is encrypted when it leaves the host, decrypted at the next link (which may be a host or a relay point), and then reencrypted before it continues to the next link. Each link may use a different **key** or even a different **algorithm** for data encryption. The process is repeated until the data has reached the recipient.

Link encryption takes place in the lowest protocol layers (layers 1 and 2 in the **OSI** model). Because the process protects the message in transit, link encryption is very useful in situations where the security of the transmission line is not assured. However, because the message is decrypted at each host in the transmission path, vulnerability can arise at a link when the message must be transmitted between hosts that are not known to be secure.

Link encryption has been used successfully within organizations, including the military, where the security of each link can be assured. It isn't feasible over the Internet, because intermediate links are neither accessible nor secure.

link type

In **Hyper-G** and possibly other **hypertext** systems, a **link** type is the specification of the nature of the information object being linked to. A single link can have any number of defined link types. For example, for any word from which one might link to another information object, that object could be an example of that word, or a graphic illustration of it, or a definition of it, or it might be associated with one person's comments on that subject.

For example, in a page on transmission technologies, the term "ISDN" might be highlighted as a link. When the link is created, the author might choose to let the reader link to an illustration of how ISDN works, or just a brief definition of it, or a whole book about it. Or a reviewer (rather than the author) might create the link for review purposes and the link would be to a particular reviewer comment. (Later, the author or other reviewers would find the link and the linked-to comments and perhaps create additional comments.)

If link types are made generic and all links exist as separate objects apart from the files in which they are used, then different link types and links can be easily added, removed, or changed throughout a set of files.

The examples described here are hypothetical and not necessarily exactly how Hyper-G or any other hypertext system works.

linkrot

Linkrot is the tendency of **hypertext** links from one **Web site** to another site to become useless as other sites cease to exist or remove or reorganize their Web pages. A recent survey showed that almost one of every four Web pages in the survey sample contained a bad link. Observers note that the amount of linkrot that occurs can be correlated closely (and not surprisingly) with the passage of time. Links to the **home page** of large companies like IBM and Microsoft appear to be the least likely to "rot." However, links to pages within companies often generate "Not found" messages as a result of site page restructures or "old" material being removed. Links to pages created by students often no longer work after the student graduates.

A good practice followed by many sites is to leave the old pages in place with a message identifying the new page address or **Uniform Resource Locator** and specifying that an automatic refresh or redirection to the new page take place within a few seconds.

A number of Web site development and testing products provide the ability to test all the links in a Web site and report on the failing links.

Linux logo

See "Tux"

Linux

Linux (often pronounced LIH-nuhks with a short "i") is a **UNIX**-like **operating system** that was designed to provide personal computer users a free or very low-cost operating system comparable to traditional and usually more expensive UNIX systems. Linux has a reputation as a very efficient and fast-performing system. Linux's **kernel** (the central part of the operating system) was developed by Linus Torvalds at the University of Helsinki in Finland. To complete the operating system, Torvalds and other team members made use of system components developed by members of the **Free Software Foundation** for the **GNU** project.

Linux is a complete operating system, including a graphical user interface, an **X Window System**, **TCP/IP**, the **Emacs** editor, and other components usually found in a comprehensive UNIX system. Although copyrights are held by various creators of Linux's components, Linux is distributed using the Free Software Foundation's **copyleft** stipulations that mean any modified version that is redistributed must in turn be freely available.

Unlike Windows and other proprietary systems, Linux is publicly open and extendible by contributors. Because it conforms to the **Portable Operating System Interface** standard user and programming interfaces, developers can write programs that can be ported to other operating systems. Linux comes in versions for all the major microprocessor platforms including the Intel, **PowerPC**, Sparc, and **Alpha** platforms. It's also available on IBM's **S/390**. Linux is distributed commercially by a number of companies. A magazine, *Linux Journal*, is published as well as a number of books and pocket references.

Linux is sometimes suggested as a possible publicly developed alternative to the desktop predominance of Microsoft Windows. Although Linux is popular among users already familiar with UNIX, it remains far behind Windows in numbers of users.

liquid crystal display

See "LCD"

liquid

See "ice"

LISP

LISP, an acronym for *list processing*, is a programming language that was designed for easy manipulation of data strings. Developed in 1959 by John McCarthy, it is a commonly used language for artificial intelligence (**AI**) programming. It is one of the oldest programming languages still in relatively wide use.

In LISP, all computation is expressed as a function of at least one object. Objects can be other functions, data items (such as constants or variables), or data structures. LISP's ability to compute with symbolic expressions rather than numbers makes it convenient for AI applications.

list server

A list server (mailing list server) is a program that handles subscription requests for a **mailing list** and distributes new messages, newsletters, or other postings from the list's members to the entire list of subscribers as they occur or are scheduled. (A list server should not be confused with a *mail server*, which handles incoming and outgoing e-mail for Internet users.)

Two commonly used list servers are **listserv** and **Majordomo**. Lyris is a list server that is free for users maintaining very small mailing lists and scales up in price for those managing thousands of mailing list subscribers.

listserv

Listserv, like **Majordomo**, is a small program that automatically redistributes **e-mail** to names on a mailing list. Users can subscribe to a mailing list by sending an e-mail note to a mailing list they learn about; listserv will automatically add the name and distribute future e-mail postings to every subscriber. (Requests to subscribe and unsubscribe are sent to a special address so that all subscribers do not see these requests.) These programs are also known as **list servers**.

liteware

Liteware is a term for software that is distributed freely in a version having less capability than the full for-sale version. It's usually designed to provide a potential customer with a sample of the "look-and-feel" of a product and a subset of its full capability. Liteware can be considered a type of **shareware** (where shareware also includes products distributed freely, usually on a trial basis, that do have full capability).

An example of liteware is HTML Assistant Pro, an **HTML** editor. We tried their liteware version, which allows you to create HTML files (Web pages) and shows you, but doesn't let you use, table and form creation facilities. Since we liked the liteware version and needed all the capabilities, we ordered the full product.

Also see **freeware** and **postcardware**.

Lithium Ion battery

A Lithium Ion (Li-Ion) battery is a rechargeable battery with twice the energy capacity of a **Nickel-Cadmium battery** and greater stability and safety.

little-endian

See "big-endian and little-endian"

live cam

See "cam"

LMDS

LMDS (Local Multipoint Distribution System) is a system for **broadband microwave wireless** transmission direct from a local antenna to homes and businesses within a line-of-sight radius, a solution to the so-called **last-mile technology** problem of economically bringing high-**bandwidth** services to users. LMDS is an alternative to installing **optical fiber** all the way to the user or to adapting **cable TV** for broadband Internet service. Depending on the implementation, LMDS offers a bandwidth of up to 1.5 **Gbps** downstream to users and 200 **Mbps** upstream from the user. A more typical data rate is 38 Mbps downstream. Some services offer both downstream and upstream service (symmetrical service); others offer downstream only (asymmetrical service) with upstream being obtained using wire connections.

In addition to the investment by service providers for transmitters, users need to install transceivers costing about $125-225. However, the cost of installing LMDS is considered far lower than installing fiber optic cable or upgrading cable TV systems. The first markets for LMDS are seen as:

- High-speed data transmission for businesses
- Interactive television and streaming multimedia from Web sites
- Voice service (usually as a supplement to other services)

Because LMDS requires a more expensive and possibly larger transceiver than can conveniently be packaged in a handheld device, LMDS is not viewed as a replacement for or alternative to mobile wireless technologies such as cellular and **GSM**. On the other hand, LMDS offers much higher data rates because of its use of a higher range of frequencies with their wider bandwidths. In general, LMDS is for fixed locations and offers higher data rates; cellular digital such as GSM is for mobile users at lower data rates (although these will increase with technologies leading up to **UMTS**).

LMDS uses the range of **electromagnetic radiation spectrum** in the vicinity of 28 **GHz**, with the allocated range differing slightly between the U.S., Canada, and other countries. In Europe, **ETSI** sponsors an equivalent technology. In Canada, it is called Local Multipoint Communication Service (**LMCS**). Like **cellular telephone** technologies, LMDS is point-to-multipoint. It is viewed as a future component in the convergence of data and telephony services. Ericsson's LMDS system uses either **Ethernet**, **ATM**, or **T-carrier system/E-carrier system** network interfaces at the user end. ATM allows the user to select and pay for varying qualities of service.

LNP

See "Local Number Portability"

load balancing

Load balancing is dividing the amount of work that a computer has to do between two or more computers so that more work gets done in the same amount of time and, in general, all users get served faster. Load balancing can be implemented with hardware, software, or a combination of both. Typically, load balancing is the main reason for computer server *clustering*.

On the Internet, companies whose Web sites get a great deal of traffic usually use load balancing. For load balancing Web traffic, there are several approaches. For Web serving, one approach is to route each request in turn to a different server host address in a domain name system (**DNS**) table,round-robin fashion. Usually, if two servers are used to balance a work load, a third server is needed to determine which server to assign the work to. Since load balancing requires multiple servers, it is usually combined with *failover* and **backup** services. In some approaches, the servers are distributed over different geographic locations.

loader

In a computer **operating system**, a loader is a component that locates a given program (which can be an **application** or, in some cases, part of the operating system itself) in offline storage (such as a **hard disk**), loads it into **main storage** (in a personal computer, it's called **random access memory**), and gives that program control of the computer (allows it to execute its **instruction**s).

A program that is loaded may itself contain components that are not initially loaded into main storage, but can be loaded if and when their logic is needed. In a **multitasking** operating system, a program that is sometimes called a *dispatcher* juggles the computer processor's time among different tasks and calls the loader when a program associated with a task is not already in main storage. (By program here, we mean a **binary** file that is the result of a programming language compilation, linkage editing, or some other program preparation process.)

loading coil

A loading coil is an induction device placed on a **local loop** longer than 18,000 feet that carries **analog** signals. The device compensates for wire capacitance and boosts the frequencies carrying the voice information. Loading coils cause distortion at the higher frequencies used to carry digital information and so are not used on these local loops.

LOB

An LOB (line-of-business) application is one of the set of critical computer **application**s that are vital to running an enterprise, such as accounting, **supply chain management**, and resource planning applications. LOB applications are usually large progams that contain a number of integrated capabilities and tie into databases and database management systems.

Increasingly, LOB applications are being connected with network applications with user interfaces on the Web and with personal applications such as e-mail and address books.

local access and transport area

LATA (local access and transport area) is a term in the U.S. for a geographic area covered by one or more local telephone companies, which are legally referred to as local exchange carriers (**LECs**). A connection between two local exchanges within the LATA is referred to as *intraLATA*. A connection between a carrier in one LATA to a carrier in another LATA is referred to as *interLATA*. InterLATA is long-distance service. The current rules for permitting a company to provide intraLATA or interLATA service (or both) are based on the **Telecommunications Act of 1996**.

local area network

A local area network (LAN) is a group of computers and associated devices that share a common communications line and typically share the resources of a single processor or server within a small geographic area (for example, within an office building). Usually, the server has applications and data storage that are shared in common by multiple computer users. A local area network may serve as few as two or three users (for example, in a home network) or as many as thousands of users (for example, in an FDDI network).

The main local area network technologies are:

- **Ethernet**
- **Token ring**
- **ARCNET**
- **FDDI** (Fiber Distributed Data Interface)

Typically, a suite of application programs can be kept on the LAN server. Users who need an application frequently can download it once and then run it from their local hard disk. Users can order printing and other services as needed through applications run on the LAN server. A user can share files with others at the LAN server; read and write access is maintained by a LAN administrator.

A LAN server may also be used as a Web **server** if safeguards are taken to secure internal applications and data from outside access.

local exchange carrier

See "LEC"

local loop

In telephony, a local loop is the wired connection from a telephone company's **central office** in a locality to its customers' telephones at homes and businesses. This connection is usually on a pair of copper wires called **twisted pair**. The system was originally designed for voice transmission only using **analog** transmission technology on a single voice channel. Today, your computer's **modem** makes the conversion between analog signals and digital signals. With Integrated Services Digital Network (**ISDN**) or Digital Subscriber Line (**DSL**), the local loop can carry digital signals directly and at a much higher bandwidth than they do for voice only.

Local Number Portability

Local Number Portability (LNP) is the ability of a telephone customer in the U.S. to retain their local phone number if they switch to another local telephone service provider. The Telecommunications Act of 1996 required that the local exchange carriers (**LECs**) in the 100 largest metropolitan markets provide this capability by the end of 1998. The idea is that by removing the personal inconvenience of having to get a new phone number when changing service providers, competition among providers will be increased. LNP is one of the prices that local carriers must pay in order to be allowed to compete as well in the long-distance market.

LNP is made possible by the Location Routing Number (**LRN**). In the future, phone number portability may be extended so that customers can retain their phone number when they move to another locality. LNPs and LRNs are supervised by the Number Portability Administration Center, operated by Lockheed Martin under the appointment of the Federal Communications Commission (FCC). When a customer moves their local service to a competitive local exchange carrier (**CLEC**), a new LRN is assigned to the telephone number being ported. Each local exchange and long distance carrier needs to know what that new LRN is so when someone in an another area dials the number being ported, the carrier knows what LRN to route to. This is accomplished through Local Service Management System (LSMS) databases distributed among the exchange carriers. The NPAC updates all of these databases with the newly assigned LRN. Thus, when the call is made from another area, that carrier refers to its LSMS database to obtain the current LRN for the number dialed.

localization

Localization (sometimes shortened to "l10n") is the process of adapting a product or service to a particular language, culture, and desired local "look-and-feel." Ideally, a product or service is developed so that localization is relatively easy to achieve—for example, by creating technical illustrations for manuals in which the text can easily be changed to another language and allowing some expansion room for

this purpose. This enabling process is termed **internationalization**. An internationalized product or service is therefore easier to localize.

In localizing a product, in addition to idiomatic language translation, such details as time zones, money, national holidays, local color sensitivities, product or service names, gender roles, and geographic examples must all be considered. A successfully localized service or product is one that appears to have been developed within the local culture.

Language translation, which is a large part of localization, can sometimes be facilitated with **automatic language translation**. However, much additional work is usually needed.

Location Routing Number

In the U.S., a Location Routing Number (LRN) is a 10-digit number in a database called a Service Control Point (SCP) that identifies a switching port for a local telephone exchange. LRN is a technique for providing Local Number Portability (**LNP**). Using LRN, when a phone number is dialed, the local telephone exchange queries a routing database, usually the SCP, for the LRN associated with the subscriber. The LRN removes the need for the public telephone number to identify the local exchange carrier. If a subscriber changes to another telephone service provider, the current telephone number can be retained. Only the LRN needs to be changed.

In addition to supporting service provider phone number portability, an LRN also supports the possibility of two other types of number portability: service portability (for example, ordinary service to **ISDN**) and geographic portability.

LRN is an alternative to the current NPA-NXX format described in the North American Telephone Numbering System (NATNS).

LNPs and LRNs are supervised by the Number Portability Administration Center, operated by Lockheed Martin under the appointment of the Federal Communications Commission (FCC).

location-based services

Location-based services (LBS) are services that exploit knowledge about where an information device user is located. For example, the user of a wireless-connected **smartphone** could be shown ads specific to the region the user is traveling in.

Location-based services exploit any of several technologies for knowing where a network user is geographically located. One is the Global Positioning System (**GPS**), based on a collection of 24 Navstar satellites developed originally for the U.S. Department of Defense. A land-based GPS receiver uses these satellites to determine its location, within 50 meters to 100 meters. A location-based service could require

that each of its users have a mobile device that contains a GPS receiver. A second approach is E911, an initiative of the Federal Communications Commission (**FCC**) that requires wireless carriers to pinpoint a caller's telephone number to emergency dispatchers. E911 also ensures that carriers will be able to provide call locations from wireless phones. E911 is the most widely used location-based service in the U.S.

Allied Business Intelligence estimates that the LBS industry will account for more than $40 billion in revenue by 2006. Most telecommunications carriers plan to pursue either network- or handset-based location fixing technologies in their networks. Sprint Corp. recently announced it planned to incorporate GPS chips into its handsets in 2001, which could provide a boost to the nascent industry. Several other companies are wrapping up initial LBS and location-relevant wireless advertising test markets.

Another obstacle to immediate widespread adoption of LBS are concerns about privacy and unsolicited wireless advertising. The Cellular Telecommunications and Internet Association (CTIA) is asking the FCC to create specific rules about wireless location privacy. The CTIA proposal says a technical solution must include notice, consent, and security—and be technology-neutral.

log

See "access log"

logarithm

See also **exponential function** and **decibel**.

A logarithm is an **exponent** used in mathematical calculations to depict the perceived levels of variable quantities such as visible light energy, **electromagnetic field** strength, and sound intensity.

Suppose three real numbers a, x, and y are related according to the following equation:

$$x = a^y$$

Then y is defined as the base-a logarithm of x. This is written as follows:

$$\log_a x = y$$

As an example, consider the expression $100 = 10^2$. This is equivalent to saying that the base-10 logarithm of 100 is 2; that is, $\log_{10} 100 = 2$. Note also that $1000 = 10^3$; thus $\log_{10} 1000 = 3$. (With base-10 logarithms, the subscript 10 is often omitted, so we could write $\log 100 = 2$ and $\log 1000 = 3$). When the base-10 logarithm of a quantity increases by 1, the quantity itself increases by a factor of 10. A 10-to-1 change in the size of a quantity, resulting in a logarithmic increase or decrease of 1, is called an *order of magnitude*. Thus, 1000 is one order of magnitude larger than 100.

Base-10 logarithms, also called common logarithms, are used in electronics and experimental science. In theoretical science and mathematics, another logarithmic base is encountered: the transcendental number e, which is approximately equal to 2.71828. Base-*e* logarithms, written $\log_e$ or ln, are also known as natural logarithms. If $x = e^y$, then

$$\log_e x = \ln x = y$$

logic gate

A logic gate is an elementary building block of a **digital circuit**. Most logic gates have two inputs and one output. At any given moment, every terminal is in one of the two **binary** conditions *low* (0) or *high* (1), represented by different voltage levels. The logic state of a terminal can, and generally does, change often, as the circuit processes data. In most logic gates, the low state is approximately zero volts (0 V), while the high state is approximately five volts positive (+5 V).

There are seven basic logic gates: AND, OR, XOR, NOT, NAND, NOR, and XNOR.

The *AND gate* is so named because, if 0 is called "false" and 1 is called "true," the gate acts in the same way as the logical "and" operator. The following illustration and table show the circuit symbol and logic combinations for an AND gate. (In the symbol, the input terminals are at left and the output terminal is at right.) The output is "true" when both inputs are "true." Otherwise, the output is "false."

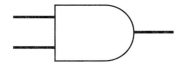

AND gate

Input 1	Input 2	Output
0	0	0
0	1	0
1	0	0
1	1	1

The *OR gate* gets its name from the fact that it behaves after the fashion of the logical inclusive "or." The output is "true" if either or both of the inputs are "true." If both inputs are "false," then the output is "false."

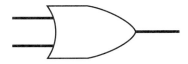

OR gate

Input 1	Input 2	Output
0	0	0
0	1	1
1	0	1
1	1	1

The *XOR (exclusive-OR) gate* acts in the same way as the logical "either/or." The output is "true" if either, but not both, of the inputs are "true." The output is "false" if both inputs are "false" or if both inputs are "true." Another way of looking at this circuit is to observe that the output is 1 if the inputs are different, but 0 if the inputs are the same.

XOR gate

Input 1	Input 2	Output
0	0	0
0	1	1
1	0	1
1	1	0

A logical *inverter*, sometimes called a *NOT gate* to differentiate it from other types of electronic inverter devices, has only one input. It reverses the logic state.

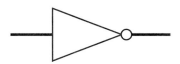

Inverter or NOT gate

Input	Output
1	0
0	1

The *NAND gate* operates as an AND gate followed by a NOT gate. It acts in the manner of the logical operation "and" followed by negation. The output is "false" if both inputs are "true." Otherwise, the output is "true."

NAND gate

Input 1	Input 2	Output
0	0	1
0	1	1
1	0	1
1	1	0

The *NOR gate* is a combination OR gate followed by an inverter. Its output is "true" if both inputs are "false." Otherwise, the output is "false."

NOR gate

Input 1	Input 2	Output
0	0	1
0	1	0
1	0	0
1	1	0

The *XNOR (exclusive-NOR) gate* is a combination XOR gate followed by an inverter. Its output is "true" if the inputs are the same, and "false" if the inputs are different.

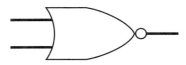

XNOR gate

Input 1	Input 2	Output
0	0	1
0	1	0
1	0	0
1	1	1

Using combinations of logic gates, complex operations can be performed. In theory, there is no limit to the number of gates that can be arrayed together in a single device. But in practice, there is a limit to the number of gates that can be packed into a given physical space. Arrays of logic gates are found in digital integrated circuits (ICs). As IC technology advances, the required physical volume for each individual logic gate decreases and digital devices of the same or smaller size become capable of performing ever-more-complicated operations at ever-increasing speeds.

logical block addressing

Logical block addressing is a technique that allows a computer to address a hard disk larger than 528 megabytes. A logical block address is a 28-**bit** value that maps to a specific cylinder-head-sector address on the disk. 28 bits allows sufficient variation to specify addresses on a hard disk up to 8.4 gigabytes in data storage capacity. Logical block addressing is one of the defining features of Enhanced IDE (**EIDE**), a hard disk interface to the computer **bus** or data paths.

Logical Link Control layer

In the Open Systems Interconnection (**OSI**) model of communication, the Logical Link Control layer is one of two sublayers of the **Data-Link layer** and is concerned with managing traffic over the physical medium. The Logical Link Control layer identifies a **line protocol**, such as **SDLC**, **NetBIOS**, or **NetWare**, and may also assign **sequence numbers** to **frame**s and track acknowledgements.

The other Data-Link sublayer is the **Media Access Control layer**.

logical partition

A logical partition (LPAR) is the division of a computer's **processor**s, **memory**, and **storage** into multiple sets of resources so that each set of resources can be operated independently with its own **operating system** instance and **application**s. The number of logical partitions that can be created depends on the system's processor model and resources available. Typically, partitions are used for different purposes such as **database** operation or **client/server** operation or to separate test and production environments. Each partition can communicate with the other partitions as if the other partition is in a separate machine. Logical partitioning was first studied by IBM in 1976 and later introduced by Amdahl and then IBM. Hitachi and Sun Microsystems also use forms of logical partitioning. Today, both IBM's **S/390** (now z/900 Series) and **AS/400** products support logical partitioning.

logical unit

In IBM's Systems Network Architecture (**SNA**), a logical unit (LU) identifies an **end user** in an SNA **network**. By end user, IBM means either a human being that is interacting with the network or an application program that is indirectly representing such an end user. Two logical units that communicate depend on physical connections being established through associated physical units (**PU**s). The network point at each end of a communication that sets up the communication session between logical units is called the *system services control point (SSCP)*. Typically, a logical unit is a unique connection to an application program. A physical unit is usually a hardware device, such as a terminal control unit. IBM's Virtual Telecommunication Access Method (**VTAM**) is used by an application program to manage session and communication requests on behalf of logical units.

In SNA, LU 6.2 is a type of logical unit used to represent end users in a **distributed** processing environment.

logical unit number

The logical unit described here is different than the **logical unit** of IBM's Systems Network Architecture (SNA).

A logical unit number (LUN) is a unique identifier used on a **SCSI bus** that enables it to differentiate between up to eight separate devices (each of which is a *logical unit*). Each LUN is a unique number that identifies a specific logical unit, which may be an **end user**, a **file**, or an **application program**.

A SCSI (Small System Computer Interface) is a **parallel** interface, that can have up to eight devices all attached through a single cable; the cable and the host (computer) **adapter** make up the SCSI bus. The bus allows the interchange of information between devices independently of the host. In the SCSI program, each device is assigned a unique number, which is either a number between 0 and 7 for an **8-bit** (narrow) bus, or between 8 and 16 for a 16-bit (wide) bus. The devices that request **input/output** (I/O) operations are *initiators* and the devices that perform these operations are *targets*. Each target has the capacity to connect up to eight additional devices through its own controller; these devices are the logical units, each of which is assigned a unique number for identification to the SCSI controller for command processing.

logon

In general computer usage, logon is the procedure used to get access to an operating system or application, usually in a remote computer. Almost always a logon requires that the user have (1) a user ID and (2) a password. Often, the user ID must conform to a limited length such as eight **characters** and the password must contain at least one digit and not match a natural language word. The user ID can be freely known and is visible when entered at a keyboard or other input device. The password must be kept secret (and is not displayed as it is entered). Some Web sites require users to register in order to use the site; registered users can then enter the site by logging on.

Logon is also used as a modifier as in "logon procedure." The verb form is two words: to log on.

In **UNIX**-based operating systems, logon is called *login*. The procedure is called "the login procedure." and the verb form is: to log in.

LOL

See "chat abbreviations"

long-distance carrier

A long-distance carrier is a telephone company that provides connections between local exchanges in different geographic areas. Referred to in the U.S. as interexchange carriers (**IXCs**), long-distance carriers provides interlocal access and transport area (interLATA) service as described in the **Telecommunications Act of 1996**. Long-distance carriers include AT&T, MCI, Sprint, and others.

loop

In computer programming, a loop is a sequence of **instruction**s that is continually repeated until a certain condition is reached. Typically, a certain process is done, such as getting an item of data and changing it, and then some condition is checked such as whether a counter has reached a prescribed number. If it hasn't, the next instruction in the sequence is an instruction to return to the first instruction in the sequence and repeat the sequence. If the condition has been reached, the next instruction "falls through" to the next sequential instruction or branches outside the loop. A loop is a fundamental programming idea that is commonly used in writing programs. An *infinite loop* is one in which the programmer assumed that some condition would eventually terminate the loop and this condition failed to happen. The result is that the loop repeats continually until the operating system senses it and terminates the program with an error or until some other event occurs (such as having the program automatically terminate after a certain duration of time).

loopback

In telephone systems, a loopback is a test signal sent to a network destination that is returned as received to the originator. The returned signal may help diagnose a problem. Sending a loopback test to each telephone system piece of equipment in succession, one at a time, is a technique for isolating a problem. (The loopback can be compared to the Internet's **ping** utility, which lets you send a message out to a host computer on the Internet. The ping echo tells you whether or not the host computer is available and the time the signal took to return.)

If you are an **ISDN** user with more than one **B-channel**, you can do a loopback test from your computer.

lossless and lossy compression

Lossless and lossy compression are terms that describe whether or not, in the **compression** of a file, all original data can be recovered when the file is uncompressed. With lossless compression, every single bit of data that was originally in the file remains after the file is uncompressed. All of the information is completely restored. This is generally the technique of choice for text or spreadsheet files,

where losing words or financial data could pose a problem. The Graphics Interchange File (**GIF**) is an image format used on the Web that provides lossless compression.

On the other hand, lossy compression reduces a file by permanently eliminating certain information, especially redundant information. When the file is uncompressed, only a part of the original information is still there (although the user may not notice it). Lossy compression is generally used for video and sound, where a certain amount of information loss will not be detected by most users. The **JPEG** image file, commonly used for photographs and other complex still images on the Web, is an image that has lossy compression. Using JPEG compression, the creator can decide how much loss to introduce and make a trade-off between file size and image quality.

Lotus iNotes Web Access

See "Shimmer"

LPAR

See "logical partition"

LPT

LPT (line print terminal) is the usual designation for a **parallel port** connection to a printer or other device on a personal computer. Most PCs come with one or two LPT connections designated as LPT1 and LPT2. Some systems support a third, LPT3. Whatever the number, LPT1 is the usual default. You can add a parallel port for a second printer or other device by buying and adding a parallel port adapter **card** to your computer. An LPT port can be used for an input device such as QuickCam, a video camera used with **CU-SeeMe**.

Parallel computer connections traditionally have used the **Centronics parallel interface** for printer communication. A newer standard called **EPP/ECP** supports the older interface while providing faster communication for a range of devices, including scanners and video cameras.

LPT1

See "LPT"

LPT2

See "LPT"

LPT3

See "LPT"

LRN

See "Location Routing Number"

LTO

See "Linear Tape-Open"

LU 6.2

See "APPC"

LUHN formula

The LUHN formula, also called modulus 10, is a simple **algorithm** used to validate the number on a credit card. It works on cards issued by all the major credit card companies, including American Express, Visa, Master Card, Discover, and Diner's Club. Originally created by a group of mathematicians in the 1960s, the LUHN formula is in the public domain, and anyone can use it.

The LUHN formula applies some simple arithemetic to a credit card number to calculate a number that must agree with the *check digit*, the last number that appears on the credit card. Here are the formula's three steps:

1. Beginning with the second digit from the end (on the right), take every other digit and multiply it by two.

2. Proceeding right to left, take each of the digits skipped in step 1 and add them to the result digits from step 1. If the result of doubling a number in step 1 resulted in a two-digit number (such as $7 \times 7 - 14$), use each of these digits (1 and 4) in adding the digits in step 2.

3. Subtract the result obtained in step 2 from the next higher number that ends in 0. The result must agree with the check digit.

The LUHN formula can be used by a business to make sure a credit card is valid before sending the number for debit authorization. In Canada, it is used to validate a person's Social Insurance Number. It does not verify any other information on a credit card, including whether the card's date is valid.

lumen

The lumen (symbolized lm) is the International Unit of luminous **flux**. It is defined in terms of **candela steradian**s (cd multiplied by sr). One lumen is the amount of light emitted in a solid angle of 1 sr, from a source that radiates to an equal extent in all directions, and whose intensity is 1 cd.

One lumen is the equivalent of 1.46 milliwatt (1.46×10^{-3} W) of radiant electromagnetic (EM) power at a frequency of 540 terahertz (540 THz or 5.40×10^{14} Hz). Reduced to SI base units, one lumen is equal to 0.00146 kilogram meter squared per second cubed (1.46×10^{-3} kg multiplied by m^2/s^3).

The lumen is a small unit. An **electromagnetic field** power level of 1.46 milliwatt is small; the radio-frequency (**RF**) output of a children's toy two-way radio is several times that much. A frequency of 540 THz corresponds to a wavelength of about 556 **nanometer**s (nm), which is in the middle of the visible-light spectrum. A steradian is the standard unit solid angle in three dimensions; a sphere encloses 4 **pi** (approximately 12.57) steradians.

Also see **candela**, **steradian**, and International System of Units (**SI**).

luminous intensity

Luminous intensity is an expression of the amount of light power emanating from a point source within a solid angle of one **steradian**. For reference, a frequency of 540 terahertz (540 **THz** or 5.40×10^{14} **Hz**) is specified. The quantities used to express luminous intensity are arcane to most non-scientists. A frequency of 540 THz corresponds to a **wavelength** of about 555 nanometers (nm), which is in the middle of the visible-light **spectrum**, and is generally accepted as the frequency and wavelength at which the average human eye is most sensitive. A steradian is the standard unit solid angle; a sphere encloses 4p (approximately 12.57) steradians.

Decades ago, luminous intensity was measured in terms of a unit called the **candle**. This expression arose from the fact that one candle represented approximately the amount of visible radiation emitted by a candle flame. This was an inexact specification, because burning candles vary in brilliance. So, for a time, a specified amount of radiation from elemental platinum at its freezing temperature was used as the standard. Late in the 20th century, the **candela** was defined and adopted as the standard unit of luminous intensity. One candela (1 cd) is the magnitude of an electromagnetic field (**EM-field**), in a specified direction, that has a power level equivalent to a visible-light field of $^1/_{683}$ **watt** (1.46×10^{-3} W) per steradian at 540 THz.

Also see **candela**, **lumen**, **steradian**, and the International System of Units (**SI**).

LUN

See "logical unit number"

lurking

Lurking is the very common practice of reading an online or e-mail discussion without taking part in the discussion. Most visitors to discussions on Web sites, **Usenet** groups, e-mail discussion groups, **Internet Relay Chat** channels, or **bulletin board system**s understandably spend much more time reading or "listening" than writing or "speaking." What this term seems to imply in its usage is that some people benefit a great deal from a discussion without ever offering to enrich it with their own information or ideas. It is well understood and accepted, however, that there will always be lurkers in any discussion. And people new to a discussion are sometimes advised to lurk until they become familiar with the discussion.

lux

The lux (symbolized lx) is the unit of illuminance in the International System of Units (**SI**). It is defined in terms of **lumen**s per meter squared (lm/m^2). Reduced to SI base units, one lux is equal to 0.00146 kilogram per second cubed (1.46×10^{-3} kg/s^3).

One lux is the equivalent of 1.46 milliwatt (1.46×10^{-3} W) of radiant electromagnetic (EM) power at a frequency of 540 terahertz (540 **THz** or 5.40×10^{14} **Hz**), impinging at a right angle on a surface whose area is one square meter. A frequency of 540 THz corresponds to a **wavelength** of about 555 **nanometer**s (nm), which is in the middle of the visible-light spectrum.

The lux is a small unit. An alternative unit is the **watt per meter squared** (W/m^2). To obtain lux when the illuminance in watts per meter squared is known, multiply by 683. To obtain watts per meter squared when the illuminance in lux is known, divide by 683 or multiply by 0.00146.

Illuminance varies inversely with the square of the distance from the source on a free-space line of sight. If the distance is doubled, the illuminance is cut to $^1/_4$; if the distance increases by a factor of 10, the illuminance becomes $^1/_{100}$ (0.01 times) as great.

Also see **candela**, **electromagnetic field**, **lumen**, **steradian**, **watt per meter squared**, and International System of Units (**SI**).

Lynx

Lynx is a keyboard-oriented text-only Web **browser** that was developed at the University of Kansas primarily for students who used **UNIX** workstations. It has also been rewritten to run on VMS operating systems for users of VT100 terminals.

If you use the UNIX **shell** interface and your access provider offers it, Lynx may be interesting for you since it has a succinct key- (not mouse-) driven user interface. Information about Lynx, including where to download it, is available at the lynx.browser.org Web site.

LZW compression

LZW compression is the **compression** of a **file** into a smaller file using a table-based lookup **algorithm** invented by Abraham Lempel, Jacob Ziv, and Terry Welch. Two commonly-used file formats in which LZV compression is used are the **GIF** image format served from Web sites and the **TIFF** image format. LZW compression is also suitable for compressing text files.

A particular LZW compression algorithm takes each input sequence of **bit**s of a given length (for example, 12 bits) and creates an entry in a table (sometimes called a "dictionary" or "codebook") for that particular bit pattern, consisting of the pattern itself and a shorter code. As input is read, any pattern that has been read before results in the substitution

of the shorter code, effectively compressing the total amount of input to something smaller. Unlike earlier approaches, known as LZ77 and LZ78, the LZW algorithm does include the look-up table of codes as part of the compressed file. The decoding program that uncompresses the file is able to build the table itself by using the algorithm as it processes the encoded input.

MAC address

On a local area network (**LAN**) or other network, the MAC (Media Access Control) address is your computer's unique hardware number. (On an **Ethernet** LAN, it's the same as your Ethernet address.) When you're connected to the Internet from your computer (or **host** as the Internet protocol thinks of it), a correspondence table relates your **IP address** to your computer's physical (MAC) address on the LAN.

The MAC address is used by the Media Access Control sublayer of the Data-Link Control (**DLC**) layer of telecommunication **protocols**. There is a different MAC sublayer for each physical device type. The other sublayer level in the DLC layer is the Logical Link Control sublayer.

Mac

See "Macintosh"

Mac OS

Mac OS is the computer **operating system** for Apple Computer's **Macintosh** line of personal computers and workstations. A popular feature of its latest version, Mac **OS X**, is a **desktop** interface with some **3-D** appearance characteristics. OS X has a modular design intended to make it easier to add new features to the operating system in the future. It runs **UNIX** applications as well as older Mac applications.

Mac OS comes with Apple Computer's **iMac** and Power Macintosh line of computers.

machine code

Machine code is the elemental language of computers, consisting of a stream of 0's and 1's. Ultimately, the output of any programming language analysis and processing is machine code. After you write a program, your source language statements are compiled or (in the case of **assembler** language) assembled into output that is machine code. This machine code is stored as an executable file until someone tells the computer's **operating system** to run it. (In personal computer operating systems, these files often have the suffix of ".exe".)

The computer's **microprocessor** reads in and handles a certain number of 0's and 1's at a time. For example, it may be designed to read 32 bits of 0's and 1's at a time. Because it is designed to know how many bits (and which bits) tell it what operation to do, it can look at the right sequence of bits and perform the next operation. Then it reads the next instruction, and so on.

In analyzing problems or debugging programs, a tool to use is a *dump* of the program. A dump is a printout that shows the program in its machine code form, but since putting it in 0's and 1's would be hard to read, each four bits (of 0's and 1's) is represented by a single **hexadecimal** numeral. (Dumps also contain other information about the computer's operation, such as the address of the instruction that was being executed at the time the dump was initiated.)

machine vision

Machine vision is the ability of a computer to "see." A machine-vision system employs one or more video cameras, analog-to-digital conversion (**ADC**), and digital signal processing (**DSP**). The resulting data goes to a computer or robot controller. Machine vision is similar in complexity to **voice recognition**.

Two important specifications in any vision system are the sensitivity and the resolution. Sensitivity is the ability of a machine to see in dim light, or to detect weak impulses at invisible wavelengths. Resolution is the extent to which a machine can differentiate between objects. In general, the better the resolution, the more confined the field of vision. Sensitivity and resolution are interdependent. All other factors held constant, increasing the sensitivity reduces the resolution, and improving the resolution reduces sensitivity.

Human eyes are sensitive to electromagnetic **wavelength**s ranging from 390 to 770 nanometers (nm). Video cameras can be sensitive to a range of wavelengths much wider than this. Some machine-vision systems function at infrared (**IR**), ultraviolet (UV), or X-ray wavelengths.

Binocular (stereo) machine vision requires a computer with an advanced processor. In addition, high-resolution cameras, a large amount of random access memory (**RAM**), and an artificial intelligence (**AI**) program are required for depth perception.

Machine vision is used in various industrial and medical applications. Examples include:

- Electronic component analysis
- Signature identification
- Optical character recognition
- Handwriting recognition
- Object recognition
- Pattern recognition
- Materials inspection
- Currency inspection
- Medical image analysis

Macintosh

The Macintosh (often called "the Mac"), introduced in 1984 by Apple Computer, was the first widely-sold personal computer with a graphical user interface (**GUI**). The Mac was designed to provide users with a natural, intuitively understandable, and, in general, "user-friendly" computer interface. Many of the user interface ideas in the Macintosh derived from experiments at the Xerox Parc laboratory in the early 1970s, including the **mouse**, the use of icons or small visual images to represent objects or actions, the point-and-click and click-and-drag actions, and a number of window operation ideas. Microsoft was successful in adapting user interface concepts first made popular by the Mac in its first **Windows** operating system.

The Macintosh has its own **operating system**, **Mac OS**. Originally built on Motorola's 68000 series **microprocessors**, Mac versions today are powered by the **PowerPC** microprocessor, which was developed jointly by Apple, Motorola, and IBM. The Mac is actually a line of personal computers, configured for individual users and businesses with different needs. A recent product, **iMac**, provides the Mac technology and interface in a low-cost package.

While Mac users represent only about 5% of the total numbers of personal computer users, Macs are highly popular and almost a cultural necessity among graphic designers and online visual artists and the companies they work for. In general, Mac users tend to be enthusiasts.

macro

1) In Microsoft Word and other programs, a macro is a saved sequence of **commands** or keyboard strokes that can be stored and then recalled with a single command or keyboard stroke.

2) In computers, a macro (for "large"; the opposite of "micro") is any programming or user interface that, when used, expands into something larger. The original use for "macro" or "macro definition" was in computer **assembler** language before higher-level, easier-to-code languages became more common. In assembler language, a macro definition defines how to expand a single language statement or computer instruction into a number of instructions. The macro statement contains the name of the macro definition and usually some variable parameter information. Macros were (and are) useful especially when a sequence of instructions is used a number of times (and possibly by different programmers working on a project). Some pre-compilers also use the macro concept. In general, however, in higher-level languages, any language statement is about as easy to write as an assembler macro statement.

Assembler macros generate **instructions** inline with the rest of a program. More elaborate sequences of instructions that are used frequently by more than one program or programmer are encoded in *subroutines* that can be branched to from or assembled into a program.

macro virus

A macro virus is a computer **virus** that "infects" a Microsoft Word or similar application and causes a sequence of actions to be performed automatically when the application is started or something else triggers it. Macro viruses tend to be surprising but relatively harmless. A typical effect is the undesired insertion of some comic text at certain points when writing a line. A macro virus is often spread as an **e-mail virus**. A well-known example in March 1999 was the **Melissa virus**.

MAE

A MAE (pronounced MAY), originally an abbreviation for Metropolitan Area Exchange and now a service mark of MCI WorldCom, is a major center in the United States for **switch** traffic between Internet service providers (**ISP**). There are two major MAEs, MAE-East in the Washington, D.C. area and MAE-West in the San Jose, California area. MAE-East interconnects all of the major ISPs and also those from Europe. MAE-West interconnects ISPs in the Silicon Valley area. These two points along with several interconnection points previously identified by the National Science Foundation as network access points (**NAPs**) form what is sometimes considered the national commercial Internet **backbone**. In addition to MAE-East and MAE-West, there are five regional "Tier-2" MAEs: in Chicago, Dallas, Houston, Los Angeles, and New York. Additional MAEs appear to be in the planning stages. The MAEs and their services, originally developed by MFS Communications, are now owned and operated by MCI WorldCom.

A MAE can be viewed as a giant local area network (**LAN**) switch. (In fact, the two major MAEs use an **Fiber Distributed-Data Interface** switch.) The only ISP device that can interconnect to a MAE switch is a **router** or a computer **host** acting as a router. The ISPs work out their own **peering** agreements and manage their own routing tables. Routers at the two major MAEs need very large routing tables. Cisco's 7xxx series routers are examples of such routers. The regional MAEs consist of an **Ethernet** switch and an FDDI concentrator. Smaller routers (such as Cisco's 4500-M) are required.

The MAEs offer **colocation** space for ISP equipment on their premises.

magnetic field

A magnetic field is generated when electric charge carriers such as **electron**s move through space or within an electrical conductor. The geometric shapes of the magnetic **flux** lines produced by moving charge carriers (electric **current**) are similar to the shapes of the flux lines in an **electrostatic field**. But there are differences in the ways electrostatic and magnetic fields interact with the environment.

Electrostatic flux is impeded or blocked by metallic objects. Magnetic flux passes through most metals with little or no effect, with certain exceptions, notably iron and nickel. These two metals, and alloys and mixtures containing them, are known as *ferromagnetic materials* because they concentrate magnetic lines of flux. An electromagnet provides a good example. An air-core coil carrying **direct current** produces a magnetic field. If an iron core is substituted for the air core in a given coil, the intensity of the magnetic field is greatly increased in the immediate vicinity of the coil. If the coil has many turns and carries a large current, and if the core material has exceptional ferromagnetic properties, the *flux density* near the ends of the core (the poles of the magnet) can be such that the electromagnet can be used to pick up and move cars.

When charge carriers are accelerated (as opposed to moving at constant velocity), a fluctuating magnetic field is produced. This generates a fluctuating electric field, which in turn produces another varying magnetic field. The result is a "leapfrog" effect, in which both fields can propagate over vast distances through space. Such a synergistic field is known as an **electromagnetic field**. This is the phenomenon that makes **wireless** communications and broadcasting possible.

magnetic permeability

See "permeability"

magneto-optical drive

The magneto-optical (MO) drive is a popular way to back up files on a personal computer. As the term implies, an MO device employs both magnetic and optical technologies to obtain ultra-high data density. A typical MO cartridge is slightly larger than a conventional 3.5-inch magnetic **diskette**, and looks similar. But while the older type of magnetic diskette can store 1.44 megabytes (MB) of data, an MO diskette can store many times that amount, ranging from 100 MB up to several gigabytes (GB).

An MO system achieves its high data density by using a laser and a magnetic read/write head in combination. Both the laser and the magnet are used to write data onto the diskette. The laser heats up the diskette surface so it can be easily magnetized, and also to allow the region of magnetization to be precisely located and confined. A less intense laser is used to read data from the diskette. Data can be erased and/or overwritten an unlimited number of times, as with a conventional 3.5-inch diskette.

Examples of magneto-optical drives are the Fujitsu DynaMO, a 230 MB drive used in the PowerPC Apple Powerbook, a note book computer, and the Pinnacle Micro Vertex, a 2.6 GB drive.

The chief assets of MO drives include convenience, modest cost, reliability, and (for some models) widespread availability approaching industry standardization. The chief

limitation of MO drives is that they are slower than **hard disk** drives, although they are usually faster than conventional 3.5-inch diskette drives.

magnetoresistive head technology

Magnetoresistive (MR) head technology is used in disk drives to allow higher storage densities than the older inductive-head technology. MR heads provide up to four times the storage densities possible with thin-film inductive heads. Almost all of the major storage vendors now sell drives based on this technology, which started to become popular in the late 1990s.

MR heads have separate read/write elements—with each optimized for its particular function. With inductive-head drives, one head performs both tasks, leading to some performance problems as it tries to read and write data simultaneously. MR drives also have less noise, meaning fewer corrective reads or writes.

magnetoresistive RAM

See "MRAM"

mail bomb

A mail bomb is the sending of a massive amount of **e-mail** to a specific person or system. A huge amount of mail may simply fill up the recipient's disk space on the server or, in some cases, may be too much for a **server** to handle and may cause the server to stop functioning. In the past, mail bombs have been used to "punish" Internet users who have been egregious violators of **netiquette** (for example, people using e-mail for undesired advertising, or **spam**).

Mail bombs not only inconvenience the intended target but they are also likely to inconvenience everybody using the server. Senders of mail bombs should be wary of exposing themselves to reciprocal mail bombs or to legal actions.

mailing list

A mailing list is a list of people who subscribe to a periodic mailing distribution on a particular topic. On the Internet, mailing lists include each person's e-mail address rather than a postal address. Mailing lists have become a popular way for Internet users to keep up with topics they're interested in. Many software producers and other vendors are now using them as a way to keep in touch with customers.

main storage

Main storage is the main area in a computer in which **data** is stored for quick access by the computer's processor. This term originated in the days of the **mainframe** computer to distinguish the more immediately accessible data storage from *auxiliary storage*. On today's computers, especially personal computers and workstations, the term **random**

access memory (RAM) is usually used instead of main storage, and the **hard disk**, **diskette**, and **CD-ROM** collectively describe auxiliary storage.

An earlier term for main storage was *core* in the days when the main data storage device contained ferrite cores.

mainframe

Mainframe is an industry term for a large computer, typically manufactured by a large company such as IBM for the commercial applications of Fortune 1000 businesses and other large-scale computing purposes. Historically, a mainframe is associated with centralized rather than distributed computing. Today, IBM refers to its larger processors as large **servers** and emphasizes that they can be used to serve distributed users and smaller servers in a computing network.

Majordomo

Like **listserv**, Majordomo (from Latin: "master of the house") is a small program that automatically redistributes **e-mail** to names on a mailing list. Users can subscribe to a mailing list by sending an e-mail note to a mailing list they learn about; Majordomo will automatically add the name and distribute future e-mail postings to every subscriber. (Requests to subscribe and unsubscribe are sent to a special address so that other subscribers do not see these requests.)

Majordomo is written in the **Perl** language. Although it originated in the **UNIX** culture, Majordomo can be run on any operating system platform with a Perl interpreter.

makefile

A makefile is used with the **UNIX make utility** to determine which portions of a program to compile. A makefile is basically a **script** that guides the make utility to choose the appropriate program files that are to be compiled and linked together.

The make utility keeps track of the last time files were updated so that it only updates the files containing changes. However, all of the files that are dependent on the updated files must be compiled as well, which can be very time-consuming. With the help of makefile, the make utility automates this compilation to ensure that all files that have been updated—and only those—are compiled and that the most recent versions of files are the ones linked to the main program, without requiring the user to perform the tasks separately.

A makefile contains three types of information for the make program: A target (the name of what the user is trying to construct); the rules (commands that tell how to construct the target from the sources) and a dependency (the reason that the target should be constructed, which is usually because it is out of date in respect to its components). To create a makefile, the user makes a file containing **shell**

commands and names it "makefile." The commands are executed according to the rules in the makefile when the user types "make" while in the directory containing the file.

MAN

See "metropolitan area network"

man in the middle

See "bucket brigade"

managed service provider

Also see **management service provider**.

A managed service provider (MSP) provides delivery and management of network-based services, applications, and equipment to enterprises, residences, or other service providers. Managed service providers can be **hosting** companies or **access providers** that offer services that can include fully outsourced network management arrangements, including advanced features like IP telephony, messaging and call center, virtual private network (**VPN**s), managed **firewall**s, and monitoring/reporting of network servers. Most of these services can be performed from outside a company's internal network with a special emphasis placed on integration and certification of Internet security for applications and content. MSPs serve as outsourcing agents for companies, especially other service providers like ISPs, that don't have the resources to constantly upgrade or maintain faster and faster computer networks.

In addition to such basic communication service as leased line wide area network (**WAN**) and **frame relay** service, an MSP can manage and integrate a range of activities associated with enterprise networks. The range of outsourcing services includes basic transport and access, managed premises, **Web hosting**, VPN, unified messaging, video networking, or other more sophisticated services. The market for managed services is forecast to grow about 20 percent annually, according to The Yankee Group, due largely to the need for enterprises to be more flexible and timely in getting to market and communicating with customers.

Nortel Networks, Lucent, and Checkpoint are three of the best-known companies that provide MSP services.

Managed service providers sometimes are referred to as management service providers, which also manage information technology services for companies. However, some industry experts say managed service providers provide a broader range of services than management service providers, which tend to limit themselves to monitoring services for servers, routers, firewalls, and other applications. Management service providers typically deliver infrastructure management services on a subscription basis, similar to the model used by application service providers (**ASP**s). They most commonly offer network- and application-monitoring services to e-businesses.

management information base

A management information base (MIB) is a formal description of a set of network **object**s that can be managed using the Simple Network Management Protocol (**SNMP**). The format of the MIB is defined as part of the SNMP. MIB-I refers to the initial MIB definition; MIB-II refers to the current definition. SNMPv2 includes MIB-II and adds some new objects.

There are MIBs (or more accurately, MIB extensions) for each set of related network entities that can be managed. For example, there are MIB definitions specified in the form of Requests for Comments (**RFC**s) for **AppleTalk**, domain name system (**DNS**), **Fiber Distributed-Data Interface**, and **RS-232C** network objects. Product developers can create and register new MIB extensions. Companies that have created MIB extensions for their sets of products include Cisco, Fore, IBM, Novell, QMS, and Onramp.

management information systems

See "MIS"

management service provider

Also see **managed service provider**.

On the Internet, a management service provider (MSP) is a company that manages information technology services for other companies. For example, a company could hire an MSP to configure and administer its business computers and related systems on a continuing basis, saving the company the need to hire, train, and pay its own administrators. Since almost all such systems today can be managed remotely using an interactive Web page as the user interface, the idea is that an administrator could just as easily be someone at an MSP as at your own company.

The MSP can be viewed as similar to an application service provider (**ASP**), a company that provides one or more computer applications that can be used by other companies using an online interface such as a page at the ASP's Web site. An ASP tends to become an MSP to the extent that it combines its application offering with additional service offerings. Another related service is the storage service provider (**SSP**), a company that provides computer storage and related services (such as automatic scheduled backup and archiving) for other companies.

Some management service providers include Candle, InteQ, and McAfee.

MAPI

MAPI (Messaging Application Program Interface) is a Microsoft Windows program interface that enables you to send **e-mail** from within a Windows application and attach the document you are working on to the e-mail note. Applications that take advantage of MAPI include word processors, spreadsheets, and graphics applications. MAPI-compatible applications typically include a **Send Mail** or **Send** in the **File** pulldown menu of the application. Selecting one of these sends a request to a MAPI **server**.

MAPI consists of a standard set of **C** language **functions** that are stored in a program library known as a dynamic link library (**DLL**). Developers who are using Microsoft's **Active Server Page** (ASP) technology access the MAPI library by using Microsoft's Collaboration Data Objects (**CDO**). The CDO library comes with Microsoft's Internet Information Server (**IIS**). MAPI functions can be accessed by **Visual Basic** developers through a Basic-to-C translation layer.

Eudora, one of the most popular e-mail programs, includes a MAPI server. To activate the Eudora MAPI server, select **Options** from the **Tools** pulldown menu and then double-click on MAPI and specify whether MAPI should always be active or whether it should be active only when Eudora is running. Microsoft Exchange and possibly some other programs may require that you turn the MAPI server off when they are in use.

maps

If you want to..	A good map site is...
Get a map of your (or someone else's) town, neighborhood, or street on "Find"	MapQuest (http://www.mapquest.com), enter your street address, and click Mapblast (http://www.mapblast.com) offers a similar service
Get detailed driving directions from one city to another in the U.S. Canada, and Mexico	MapQuest (http://www.mapquest.com) and select "TripQuest" Mapblast (http://www.mapblast.com) offers a similar service
Create a personal map for your Web site	MapQuest (http://www.mapquest.com) Mapblast (http://www.mapblast.com) offers a similar service
Find the great circle distance from one city to another	Java Online (http://www.indo.com/distance) (uses a University of Michigan database and calculator)

If you want to..	A good map site is...
Get 1990 U.S. census information; see and download a city map (which can be included in a Web site)	U. S. Gazetteer (http:// tiger.census.gov/cgi-bin/ gazetteer)
Order U.S. Geological Survey maps and other products	U. S. Geological Service (http://www.usgs.gov) Or call 1-800-USA-MAPS.

marcom

Marcom (sometimes spelled "marcomm") is an abbreviation for "marketing communications." Marcom is targeted interaction with customers and prospects using one or more media, such as direct mail, newspapers and magazines, television, radio, billboards, telemarketing, and the Internet. A marketing communications campaign may use a single approach, but more frequently combines several.

markup

Markup refers to the sequence of characters or other symbols that you insert at certain places in a text or word processing file to indicate how the file should look when it is printed or displayed or to describe the document's logical structure. The markup indicators are often called "tags." For example, this particular paragraph is preceded by a:

<p> (or paragraph tag)

so that it will be separated by an empty line from the preceding line.

There is now a standard markup definition for document structure (or really a description of how you can define markup) in the Standard Generalized Markup Language (**SGML**).

Markup can be inserted by the document creator directly by typing the symbols in, by using an editor and selecting prepackaged markup symbols (to save keystrokes), or by using a more sophisticated editor that lets you create the document as you want it to appear (this is called a **WYSIWYG** editor).

marshalling

Originally, to *marshall* was to tend horses or to arrange things in preparation for a feast. In heraldry, marshalling is the arrangement of several coats of arms to form a single composition. In the military, marshalling is the gathering and ordering of military forces in preparation for battle.

In computer programming, marshalling is the process of gathering **data** from one or more **applications** or non-contiguous sources in computer storage, putting the data pieces into a message **buffer**, and organizing or converting the data into a format that is prescribed for a particular receiver or programming interface.

Marshalling is usually required when passing the output parameters of a program written in one language as input to a program written in another language.

masquerade

In general, a masquerade is a disguise. In terms of communications security issues, a masquerade is a type of attack where the attacker pretends to be an authorized user of a system in order to gain access to it or to gain greater privileges than they are authorized for. A masquerade may be attempted through the use of stolen logon IDs and passwords, through finding security gaps in programs, or through bypassing the authentication mechanism. The attempt may come from within an organization, for example, from an employee; or from an outside user through some connection to the public network. Weak authentication provides one of the easiest points of entry for a masquerade, since it makes it much easier for an attacker to gain access. Once the attacker has been authorized for entry, they may have full access to the organization's critical data, and (depending on the privilege level they pretend to have) may be able to modify and delete software and data, and make changes to network configuration and routing information.

mass

Mass (symbolized *m*) is a dimensionless quantity representing the amount of matter in a particle or object. The standard unit of mass in the International System (SI) is the kilogram (kg).

Mass is measured by determining the extent to which a particle or object resists a change in its direction or speed when a force is applied. Isaac Newton stated: A stationary mass remains stationary, and a mass in motion at a constant speed and in a constant direction maintains that state of motion, unless acted on by an outside force. For a given applied force, large masses are accelerated to a small extent, and small masses are accelerated to a large extent. The following formula applies:

$F = ma$

where F is the applied force in **newtons**, m is the mass of the object or particle in kilograms, and a is the resulting acceleration in meters per second squared. The mass of an object can be calculated if the force and the acceleration are known.

Mass is not the same thing as weight. Weight has meaning only when an object having a specific mass is placed in an acceleration field, such as the gravitational field of the earth. At the earth's surface, a kilogram mass weighs about 2.2 pounds, for example. But on Mars, the same kilogram mass would weigh only about 0.8 pounds, and on Jupiter it would weigh roughly 5.5 pounds.

When expressing large or small masses, prefix multipliers are used. The table below shows the most common alternative mass units and their relationship to the kilogram.

Unit (and symbol)	To convert to kilograms, multiply by:	Conversely, multiply by:
metric ton (T)	1000	0.001
gram (g)	0.001	1000
milligram (mg)	10^{-6}	10^{6}
microgram (µg)	10^{-9}	10^{9}
nanogram (ng)	10^{-12}	10^{12}
picogram (pg)	10^{-15}	10^{15}

massively parallel processing

MPP (massively parallel processing) is the coordinated processing of a program by multiple processors that work on different parts of the program, using their own operating systems and memory. Typically, MPP processors communicate using some messaging interface. An "interconnect" arrangement of data paths allows messages to be sent between processors. Typically, the setup for MPP is more complicated, requiring thought about how to partition a common database among processors and how to assign work among the processors. An MPP system is also known as a "loosely coupled" or "shared nothing" system.

MPP systems are considered better than SMP systems for applications that allow a number of databases to be searched in parallel. These include **decision support system** and **data warehouse** applications.

Master Boot Record

The Master Boot Record (MBR) is the information in the first **sector** of any **hard disk** or diskette that identifies how and where an **operating system** is located so that it can be **booted** (loaded) into the computer's main storage or **random access memory**. The Master Boot Record is also sometimes called the "**partition** sector" or the "master partition table" because it includes a table that locates each partition that the hard disk has been formatted into. In addition to this table, the MBR also includes a program that reads the boot sector record of the partition containing the operating system to be booted into RAM. In turn, that record contains a program that loads the rest of the operating system into RAM.

material density

Material density, more often referred to simply as density, is a quantitative expression of the amount of **mass** contained per unit **volume**. The standard unit is the **kilogram per meter cubed** (kg/m^3 or $kg \cdot m^{-3}$).

Density is sometimes expressed in **grams per centimeter cubed** (g/cm^3 or $gm \cdot cm^{-3}$). Pure liquid water at a temperature of 4 degrees **Celsius** has a density of 1 g/cm^3, which is the equivalent of 1 kg per 1000 cm^3, or 1 kilogram

per **liter**. To convert from kg/m^3 to g/cm^3, multiply by 0.001. Conversely, to convert from g/cm^3 to kg/m^3, multiply by 1000.

Occasionally, density is expressed in unusual units such as pounds per cubic foot, pounds per cubic inch, or metric tons per cubic meter. Expressions such as this can be confusing unless reduced to standard form for comparison. Sometimes density is expressed in relative terms as the **specific gravity** (sp gr), which is the ratio of the density of a given substance to the density of pure liquid water at 4 degrees Celsius.

Also see **kilogram per meter cubed**, **specific gravity**, and **SI** (International System of Units).

MathML

MathML is an application of XML (Extensible Markup Language) designed to facilitate the use of mathematical expressions in Web pages. Historically, mathematical content has been difficult to portray because standard typographic character sets do not provide for them and because they sometimes exceed a line width in size.

On Web sites, GIF or JPG images must usually be created to portray all but the simplest mathematical expressions. This works, but it does not always look professional, and when the HTML files are saved and then viewed offline, the images do not show up unless they have been individually downloaded and their tags have been made consistent with the offline file. MathML allows the insertion of mathematical expressions within an HTML file as special data. The browser (which must support MathML) can then display the appropriate symbol or expression.

For mathematicians, engineers, and scientists familiar with TeX or LaTeX, MathML can be thought of in this way: It is to HTML as TeX or LaTeX is to plain text. In fact, conversion programs are available that can be used to generate MathML documents from TeX or LaTeX documents.

MathML is in the developmental stages. The ultimate goal is to render mathematical documents directly viewable in, and printable from, popular Web browsers such as Netscape or Microsoft Internet Explorer. Until that ideal is realized, the viewing of mathematical content in Web sites generally requires specialized plug-ins.

MathXML

See "MathML"

Matrix, The

See "matrix"

matrix

1) Apart from information technology, matrix (pronounced MAY-triks) has a number of special meanings. From the Latin word for womb (in turn from *mater* or mother), a

matrix is either the intercellular substance of a tissue, the material in which a fossil is embedded, or a mold from which a relief surface is made in printing or phonograph manufacturing.

2) In mathematics and computer science, a matrix is a set of numbers laid out in tabular form (in rows and columns). From this meaning, a less formal meaning is derived of a complex of lines intersecting at right angles.

3) In cyberculture, the Internet and other networks that flow into it are altogether sometimes called "the matrix. In William Gibson's science-fiction novel, *Neuromancer*, the "matrix" is a vast sea of computing resources that can be visualized by the user, is accessible at many levels, and is lit up more intensely in the areas of greatest activity. The hero, Case, "jacks in" to the matrix through wiring that is (perhaps, since it's not entirely clear) integrated with his brain and explores the matrix with a "deck" or computer console that provides a holographic view.

maximum transmission unit

An MTU (maximum transmission unit) is the largest size **packet** or **frame**, specified in **octets** (eight-bit bytes), that can be sent in a packet- or frame-based network (such as a network using **TCP/IP**). **Transmission Control Protocol** uses the MTU to determine the size of each packet in any transmission. Too large an MTU size may mean retransmissions if the packet encounters a **router** that can't handle that large a packet. Too small an MTU size means relatively more header overhead and more acknowledgements that have to be sent and handled. Most computer **operating system** provide a **default** MTU value that is suitable for most users. However, some users may need to change the MTU value. In general, Internet users should follow the advice of their Internet service provider (**ISP**) about whether to change the default value and what to change it to.

For Windows 95 users, the default MTU is 1500 octets (eight-bit bytes), partly because this is the **Ethernet** standard MTU. The Internet de facto standard MTU is 576, but ISPs often suggest using 1500. If you frequently access Web sites that encounter routers with an MTU size of 576, you may want to change to that size. (Apparently some users find that changing the setting to 576 improves performance and others do not find any improvement.) The minimum value that an MTU can be set to is 68.

For Windows 98 users, the operating system is able to sense whether your connection should use 1500 or 576 and select the appropriate MTU for the connection. The default is "Automatic." The user can also explicitly set the packet size to 1500, 1000, or 576.

For protocols other than TCP, different MTU sizes may apply.

MB

See "megabyte"

MBone

The MBone, now sometimes called the Multicast Internet, is an arranged use of a portion of the Internet for Internet Protocol (**IP**) **multicasting** (sending files—usually audio and video streams—to multiple users at the same time somewhat as radio and TV programs are broadcast over airwaves). Although most Internet traffic is **unicast** (one user requesting files from one source at another Internet address), the Internet's IP protocol also supports multicasting, the transmission of data **packet**s intended for multiple addresses. Since most IP servers on the Internet do not currently support the multicasting part of the protocol, the MBone was set up to form a network within the Internet that could transmit multicasts. The MBone was set up in 1994 as an outgrowth of earlier audio multicasts by the Internet Engineering Task Force (**IETF**) and has multicast a number of programs, including some well-publicized rock concerts.

The MBone consists of known servers (mostly on UNIX workstations) that are equipped to handle the multicast protocol. **Tunneling** is used to forward multicast packets through routers on the network that don't handle multicasting. An MBone router that is sending a packet to another MBone router through a non-MBone part of the network encapsulates the multicast packet as a unicast packet. The non-MBone routers simply see an ordinary packet. The destination MBone router unencapsulates the unicast packet and forwards it appropriately. The MBone consists of a **backbone** with a mesh **topology** which is used by servers that redistribute the multicast in their region in a star topology. The MBone network is intended to be global and includes nodes in Europe.

The channel **bandwidth** for MBone multicasts is 500 kilobits per second and actual traffic is from 100−300 kilobits depending on content. MBone multicasts usually consist of streaming audio and video.

Mbps

Mbps stands for *millions of bits per second* or *megabits per second* and is a measure of **bandwidth** (the total information flow over a given time) on a telecommunications medium. Depending on the medium and the transmission method, bandwidth is sometimes measured in the Kbps (thousands of bits or kilobits per second) range or the Gbps (billions of bits or gigabits per second) range.

A megabit is a million **binary** pulses, or 1,000,000 (that is, 10^6) pulses (or "bits"). For example, a U.S. phone company **T-carrier system** line is said to sustain a data rate of 1.544 megabits per second. Megabits per second is usually shortened to Mbps.

Some sources define a megabit to mean 1,048,576 (that is, 2^{20}) bits. Although the bit is a unit of the binary number system, bits in data communications are discrete signal pulses and have historically been counted using the decimal number system. For example, 28.8 kilobits per second (**Kbps**) is 28,800 bits per second. Because of computer architecture and memory address boundaries, bytes are always some multiple or exponent of two. See **kilobyte**, etc.

MBR

See "Master Boot Record"

MCA

See "Micro Channel Architecture"

MCM

See "multi-carrier modulation"

m-commerce

M-commerce (mobile commerce) is the buying and selling of goods and services through wireless handheld devices such as **cellular telephones** and personal digital assistants (**PDAs**). Known as next-generation **e-commerce**, m-commerce enables users to access the Internet without needing to find a place to plug in. The emerging technology behind m-commerce, which is based on the Wireless Application Protocol (**WAP**), has made far greater strides in Europe, where mobile devices equipped with Web-ready micro-browsers are much more common than in the U.S.

In order to exploit the m-commerce market potential, handset manufacturers such as Nokia, Ericsson, Motorola, and Qualcomm are working with carriers such as AT&T Wireless and Sprint to develop WAP-enabled smart phones, the industry's answer to the Swiss Army Knife, and ways to reach them. Using **Bluetooth** technology, smart phones offer fax, e-mail, and phone capabilities all in one, paving the way for m-commerce to be accepted by an increasingly mobile workforce.

As content delivery over wireless devices becomes faster, more secure, and scalable, there is wide speculation that m-commerce will surpass wireline e-commerce as the method of choice for digital commerce transactions. The industries affected by m-commerce include:

- Financial services, which includes mobile banking (when customers use their handheld devices to access their accounts and pay their bills) as well as brokerage services, in which stock quotes can be displayed and trading conducted from the same handheld device

- Telecommunications, in which service changes, bill payment and account reviews can all be conducted from the same handheld device

- Service/retail, as consumers are given the ability to place and pay for orders on-the-fly

- Information services, which include the delivery of financial news, sports figures and traffic updates to a single mobile device

IBM and other companies are experimenting with speech recognition software as a way to ensure security for m-commerce transactions.

MCSE

See "Microsoft Certified Systems Engineer"

MD2

MD2 is an earlier, 8-bit version of **MD5**, an **algorithm** used to verify **data integrity** through the creation of a 128-bit *message digest* from data input (which may be a message of any length) that is claimed to be as unique to that specific data as a fingerprint is to the specific individual. MD2, which was developed by Professor Ronald L. Rivest of MIT, is intended for use with **digital signature** applications, which require that large files must be compressed by a secure method before being encrypted with a **secret key**, under a **public key** cryptosystem. According to the RFC document, it is "computationally infeasible" that any two messages that have been input to the MD5 algorithm could have as the output the same message digest, or that a false message could be created through apprehension of the message digest. MD2, MD4 (a later version), and MD5, the latest version, have similar structures, but MD2 was optimized for 8-bit machines, in comparison with the two later formulas, which are optimized for 32-bit machines. The MD5 algorithm is an extension of MD4, which the critical review found to be fast, but possibly not absolutely secure. In comparison, MD5 is not quite as fast as the MD4 algorithm, but offers much more assurance of data security.

MD4

MD4 is an earlier version of **MD5**, an **algorithm** used to verify **data integrity** through the creation of a 128-bit *message digest* from data input (which may be a message of any length) that is claimed to be as unique to that specific data as a fingerprint is to the specific individual. MD4, which was developed by Professor Ronald L. Rivest of MIT, is intended for use with **digital signature** applications, which require that large files must be compressed by a secure method before being encrypted with a **secret key**, under a **public key** cryptosystem. According to the MD5 specification, it is "computationally infeasible" that any two messages that have been input to the MD5 algorithm could have as the output the same message digest, or that a false message could be created through apprehension of the message digest. MD2, an earlier 8-bit version, MD4, and MD5, the latest version, have similar structures, but MD2 was optimized for 8-bit machines, in comparison with the two

later formulas, which are optimized for 32-bit machines. The MD5 algorithm is an extension of MD4, which the critical review found to be fast, but possibly not absolutely secure. In comparison, MD5 is not quite as fast as the MD4 algorithm, but offers much more assurance of data security.

MD5

MD5 is a digital signature **algorithm** that is used to verify **data integrity** through the creation of a 128-bit *message digest* from data input (which may be a message of any length) that is claimed to be as ´unique to that specific data as a fingerprint is to the specific individual. MD5, which was developed by Professor Ronald L. Rivest of MIT, is intended for use with **digital signature** applications, which require that large files must be compressed by a secure method before being encrypted with a **secret key**, under a **public key** cryptosystem. MD5 is currently a standard, Internet Engineering Task Force (**IETF**) Request for Comments (**RFC**) 1321. According to the standard, it is "computationally infeasible" that any two messages that have been input to the MD5 algorithm could have as the output the same message digest, or that a false message could be created through apprehension of the message digest. MD5 is the third message digest algorithm created by Rivest. All three (the others are MD2 and MD4) have similar structures, but MD2 was optimized for 8-bit machines, in comparison with the two later formulas, which are optimized for 32-bit machines. The MD5 algorithm is an extension of MD4, which the critical review found to be fast, but possibly not absolutely secure. In comparison, MD5 is not quite as fast as the MD4 algorithm, but offers much more assurance of data security.

MDI

See "Multiple Document Interface"

MDRAM (Multibank Dynamic RAM)

MDRAM (Multibank Dynamic RAM) is a type of **video RAM**, developed by MoSys, that divides memory into multiple 32-**kilobyte** parts or "banks" that can be accessed individually. Traditional video RAM is monolithic; the entire frame buffer is accessed at one time. Having individual memory banks allows accesses to be interleaved concurrently, increasing overall performance. It's also cheaper since, unlike other forms of video RAM, cards can be manufactured with just the right amount of RAM for a given resolution capability instead of requiring it to be in multiples of megabytes.

meaning of life

See "42"

media

See "streaming video"

Media Access Control layer

In the Open Systems Interconnection (**OSI**) model of communication, the Media Access Control layer is one of two sublayers of the **Data Link Control layer** and is concerned with sharing the physical connection to the network among several computers. Each computer has its own unique **MAC address**. **Ethernet** is an example of a **protocol** that works at the Media Access Control layer level.

The other Data Link Control sublayer is the **Logical Link Control layer**.

media access management

In the Open Systems Interconnection (**OSI**) communication reference model, media access management is performed by the Media Access Control (**MAC**) sublayer of the Data-Link layer.

In an **Ethernet** network transmission, the function of media access management is to determine whether the transmission medium is free and available to send a **frame**. Media access management receives the frame from the Carrier Sense Multiple Access/Collision Detect (**CSMA/CD**) sublayer. It seeks to avoid collision with other traffic on the medium by monitoring the Carrier Sense Signal (CSNS) provided by the Physical Layer Signaling (PLS). Once media access management is satisfied that the transmission medium is available, transmission of the frame to the PLS can begin. If a collision does take place, media access management determines what action should be taken and when to try to send the frame again. Media access management is also responsible for checking a frame to determine its validity before passing it on to the data decapsulation function.

media attachment unit

MAU is also sometimes used as the abbreviation for the token ring network *multistation access unit* (**multistation access unit**).

In an **Ethernet** local area network (**LAN**), an MAU (media attachment unit) is a device that interconnects the **attachment unit interface port** on an attached host computer to the Ethernet network medium (such as **unshielded twisted pair** or **coaxial cable**). The MAU provides the services that correspond to the Physical layer of the Open Systems Interconnection (**OSI**) reference model. It provides an electrical connection and a transceiver that maps the digital bits between the computer and the network and detects **collision** and retries transmissions. An MAU can be built into the computer workstation or other device or it can be a separate device.

media type

On the Internet and as defined by Request for Comments (**Request for Comments**) 1521, a media type (also referred to as a *content type*) is a general category of data content, such as: application (executable program), audio content, an image, a text message, a video stream, and so forth. The media type tells the application that receives the message what kind of application is needed to process the content (for example, RealAudio or a similar program to play the audio content for a user).

Each of these media types have subtypes. For example, the "text" media type has four subtypes: plain, richtext, enriched, and tab-separated values.

E-mail users sometimes receive an attachment that describes its media type and subtype. For example, the media type and subtype of "application/octet-stream" describes an application organized in eight-bit units (**octets**). (Since this content is likely to be an executable program, it should be saved to disk so that it can be scanned by virus-scanning software before trying to run it.) Your browser may have assigned an application to handle each of several media types and subtypes or it may ask you to select an application. In the latter case, you need to know one or more applications that handle that particular media type and subtype.

medium

A medium is a third-party or element through which a message is communicated. This seems to apply to information technology as well as to seances. In information technology, a medium can be:

- A physical transmission medium such as optical fiber

- A presentation medium (and thus the terms **multimedia** and advertising media)

In his influential book, *Understanding Media*, Marshall MacLuhan said "The medium is the message." He seemed to mean that media technology itself transformed our lives more than the messages the media carried. He saw radio as a "hot medium" that imposed itself on you and television as a "cool" medium that pulled you into it. He envisioned that television would foster an electronic world community, a "global village." Although he wrote before the Internet became widely known, the Internet almost seems like his best idea.

medium earth orbit satellite

See "MEO satellite"

megabit

In data communications, a megabit is a million **binary** pulses, or 1,000,000 (that is, 10^6) pulses (or "bits"). It's commonly used for measuring the amount of data that is

transferred in a second between two telecommunication points. For example, a U.S. phone company **T-carrier system** line is said to sustain a data rate of 1.544 megabits per second. Megabits per second is usually shortened to Mbps.

Some sources define a megabit to mean 1,048,576 (that is, 2^{20}) bits. Although the bit is a unit of the binary number system, bits in data communications are discrete signal pulses and have historically been counted using the decimal number system. For example, 28.8 kilobits per second (**Kbps**) is 28,800 bits per second. Because of computer architecture and memory address boundaries, bytes are always some multiple or exponent of two. See **kilobyte**, etc.

megabyte

1) As a measure of computer processor storage and real and virtual memory, a megabyte (abbreviated MB) is 2 to the 20th power **byte**, or 1,048,576 bytes in decimal notation.

2) According to the *IBM Dictionary of Computing*, when used to describe disk storage capacity and transmission rates, a megabyte is 1,000,000 bytes in decimal notation.

According to the *Microsoft Press Computer Dictionary*, a megabyte means either 1,000,000 bytes or 1,048,576 bytes.

According to Eric S. Raymond in *The New Hacker's Dictionary*, a megabyte is always 1,048,576 bytes on the argument that bytes should naturally be computed in powers of two.

Iomega Corporation uses the decimal megabyte in calling the **Zip drive** disk a "100MB disk" when it actually holds 100,431,872 bytes. If Iomega used the powers-of-two megabyte, the disk could be said to hold only 95.8 megabytes (if you divide 100,431,872 by 1,048,576).

megaflop

A megaflop is a measure of a computer's speed and can be expressed as:

- A million floating point operations per second

- 10 to the 6th power **floating-point operations per second**

- 2 to the 20th power FLOPS

megahertz

A megahertz (MHz or sometimes Mhz) is a million cycles of electromagnetic currency alternation per second and is used as a unit of measure for the "clock speed" of computer **microprocessor**. In designing computer **bus** architectures, the microprocessor speed is considered together with the potential speed or amount of data that can come into the computer from I/O devices in order to optimize overall computer performance.

The **hertz** as a unit of measure is named after Heinrich Hertz, German physicist.

meme

A meme is an idea that is passed on from one human generation to another. It's the cultural equivalent of a *gene*, the basic element of biological inheritance. The term was coined in 1976 by Richard Dawkins in his book *The Selfish Gene*. Dawkins speculated that human beings have an adaptive mechanism that other species don't have. In addition to genetic inheritance with its possibilities and limitations, humans, said Dawkins, can pass their ideas from one generation to the next, allowing them to surmount challenges more flexibly and more quickly than through the longer process of genetic adaptation and selection.

Examples of memes might include the idea of God; the importance of the individual as opposed to group importance; the belief that the environment can to some extent be controlled; or that technologies can create an electronically interconnected world community.

Today, the word is sometimes applied ironically to ideas deemed to be of passing value. Dawkins himself described such short-lived ideas as memes that would have a short life in the meme pool.

memory

Memory is the electronic holding place for instructions and **data** that your computer's **microprocessor** can reach quickly. When your computer is in normal operation, its memory usually contains the main parts of the **operating system** and some or all of the application programs and related data that are being used. Memory is often used as a shorter synonym for random access memory (**RAM**). This kind of memory is located on one or more microchips that are physically close to the microprocessor in your computer. Most desktop and notebook computers sold today include at least 32 megabytes of RAM, and are upgradeable to include more. The more RAM you have, the less frequently the computer has to access instructions and data from the more slowly accessed hard disk form of storage.

Memory is sometimes distinguished from *storage*, or the physical medium that holds the much larger amounts of data that won't fit into RAM and may not be immediately needed there. Storage devices include hard disks, floppy disks, **CD-ROM**, and tape backup systems. The terms *auxiliary storage*, *auxiliary memory*, and *secondary memory* have also been used for this kind of data repository.

Additional kinds of integrated and quickly accessible memory are read-only memory (**ROM**), programmable ROM (**PROM**), and erasable programmable ROM (**EPROM**). These are used to keep special programs and data, such as the **basic input/output system**, that need to be in your computer all the time.

memory leak

A memory leak is the gradual loss of available computer **memory** when a program (an **application** or part of the **operating system**) repeatedly fails to return memory that it has obtained for temporary use. As a result, the available memory for that application or that part of the operating system becomes exhausted and the program can no longer function. For a program that is frequently opened or called or that runs continuously, even a very small memory leak can eventually cause the program or the system to terminate. A memory leak is the result of a program **bug**.

Some operating systems provide memory leak detection so that a problem can be detected before an application or the operating system crashes. Some program development tools also provide automatic "housekeeping" for the developer. It is always the best programming practice to return memory and any temporary file to the operating system after the program no longer needs it.

Memory Stick

Developed by Sony, the Memory Stick is a digital data storage technology with up to 10 times the storage capacity of a 3.5 **diskette**. Sony is promoting the Memory Stick as a new way to share and transfer pictures, sound, and other data between different compact electronic devices such as digital cameras and **camcorder**. About the size of a flat AA battery, Memory Sticks are available in 4mb, 8mb, 16mb, 32mb and 64mb sizes. They are smaller in size than comparable data storage devices, including smart media and compact **flash memory**.

In mid-2000, the Sony Vaio was the only laptop available with a Memory Stick slot, but any laptop with a PC card slot can use memory sticks with an adapter kit. Like its floppy disk predecessor, the Memory Stick has a lock mechanism to prevent the erasure of data. It has a 10-pin connector.

In promoting the Memory Stick as a common portable storage medium, Sony has licensed the technology to companies such as Adobe, Pioneer, Casio, and Sharp. Sony recently unveiled the Memory Stick Walkman and the Memory Stick Digital Voice Recorder.

MEMS

See "micro-electromechanical systems"

mentor

See "mentoring service"

mentoring service

A mentoring service is a company that provides professional counseling and advice for individuals and businesses for a fee. A mentoring service may provide career planning, skills training, project guidance, professional contacts, or problem-solving for an individual's career or within a company. A mentoring relationship may be for an unspecified or for a limited duration.

A typical kind of mentoring in information technology is for the management of a software development project. A professional mentor may be hired for any or all of the phases of software development including the initial planning, architecture, design, development, implementation, **debugging** and testing, and deployment and installation

Face-to-face mentoring is still the most common form of mentoring, but virtual mentoring is gaining popularity. Virtual mentoring uses videoconferencing, the Internet, and e-mail to mentor individuals or companies. This is beneficial for those who own a small business and are unable to leave their workplace and for those who live in rural or remote communities. Virtual mentoring is usually less expensive compared to face-to-face mentoring and provides an individual with more choices for mentors. Even if you choose virtual mentoring, it is recommended to meet with your mentor face-to-face at least once.

MEO satellite

A medium earth orbit (MEO) satellite is one with an orbit within the range from a few hundred miles to a few thousand miles above the earth's surface. Satellites of this type orbit higher than low earth orbit (**LEO**) satellites, but lower than geostationary satellites.

The orbital periods of MEO satellites range from about two to 12 hours. Some MEO satellites orbit in near perfect circles, and therefore have constant altitude and travel at a constant speed. Other MEO satellites revolve in elongated orbits. The **perigee** (lowest altitude) of an elliptical-orbit satellite is much less than its **apogee** (greatest altitude). The orbital speed is much greater near perigee than near apogee. As seen from a point on the surface, a satellite in an elongated orbit crosses the sky in just a few minutes when it is near perigee, as compared to several hours when it is near apogee. Elliptical-orbit satellites are easiest to access near apogee, because the earth-based antenna orientation does not have to be changed often, and the satellite is above the horizon for a fairly long time.

A fleet of several MEO satellites, with orbits properly coordinated, can provide global wireless communication coverage. Because MEO satellites are closer to the earth than geostationary satellites, earth-based transmitters with relatively low power and modest-sized antennas can access the system. Because MEO satellites orbit at higher altitudes than LEO satellites, the useful footprint (coverage area on the earth's surface) is greater for each satellite. Thus a global-coverage fleet of MEO satellites can have fewer members than a global-coverage fleet of LEO satellites.

Merced

Merced was the code name during development for the **microprocessor** that Intel markets as the **Itanium**.

message

1) Using **e-mail**, a message is an individual piece of mail.

2) In computer systems in general, a message is an information unit that the system sends back to the user or system operator with information about the status of an operation, an error, or other condition.

3) Using some telecommunication or data access methods, a message can be the unit of information or data that is transmitted from one program or user to another.

4) In **messaging**, which is the formal exchange of event notification, requests, or replies between programs through a **messaging server**, a message is data in a specified format that describes an event, a request, or a reply between programs.

5) In **object-oriented programming**, a message is the way that one program **object** requests an action from another object. A message specifies the name of the object to which the request is made, the action (or **method**) to be performed, and any parameter or value that needs to be specified for this request.

Conceptually, a message for an object that incorporates all the methods of a automatic vaccuum cleaner might look like this:

VacCleaner Chair Chair1LR

which would request the object VacCleaner to use its chair-cleaning procedure or method on "chair 1" in the living room.

message queueing

In programming, message queueing is a method by which **processes** (or program instances) can exchange or pass data using an interface to a system-managed **queue** of messages. Messages can vary in length and be assigned different types or usages. A message queue can be created by one process and used by multiple processes that read and/or write messages to the queue. For example, a **server** process can read and write messages from and to a message queue created for **client** processes. The message type can be used to associate a message with a particular client process even though all messages are on the same queue.

The message queue is managed by the **operating system** (or **kernel**). Application programs (or their processes) create message queues and send and receive messages using an application program interface (**API**). In **UNIX** systems, the **C** programming language *msgget* function is used with various parameters specifying the action requested, message queue ID, message type, and so forth.

The maximum size of a message in a queue is limited by the operating system and is typically 8,192 bytes.

Other forms of interprocess communication (IPC) include **semaphores**, **sockets**, and **shared memory**.

messages

See "Internet problems"

Messaging Application Program Interface

See "MAPI"

messaging server

A messaging server is a middleware program that handles **messages** that are sent for use by other programs using a **messaging** application program interface (**API**). A messaging server can usually queue and prioritize messages as needed and saves each of the client programs from having to perform these services.

Messaging and messaging servers usually are organized in one or both of two models: Point-to-point messaging and subscribe/publish messaging.

messaging

1) More broadly, messaging (also called *electronic messaging*) is the creation, storage, exchange, and management of text, images, voice, telex, **fax**, e-mail, paging, and Electronic Data Interchange (**EDI**) over a communications network.

You can find out more at the Web site of the Electronic Messaging Association (EMA). The EMA fosters the use of secure global electronic commerce. Its vendor members offer a wide range of telecommunications and computing services, including electronic mail, networks, directories, computer facsimile, electronic data interchange, paging, groupware, and voice mail. The EMA publishes *Messaging* magazine; back issues are available at the Web site.

2) In programming, messaging is the exchange of **messages** (specially-formatted data describing events, requests, and replies) with a **messaging server**, which acts as a message exchange program for client programs. There are two major messaging server models: the point-to-point model and the publish/subscribe model. Messaging allows programs to share common message-handling code, to isolate resources and interdependencies, and to easily handle an increase in message volume. Messaging also makes it easier for programs to communicate across different programming environments (languages, compilers, and operating systems) since the only thing that each environment needs to understand is the common messaging format and protocol.

IBM's **MQSeries** and Sun Microsystems Java Message Service (**JMS**) are examples of products that provide messaging interfaces and services.

meta

Meta is a prefix that in most information technology usages means "an underlying definition or description." Thus, *metadata* is a definition or description of data and *metalanguage* is a definition or description of language. Meta (pronounced MEH-tah in the U.S. and MEE-tah in the U.K.) derives from Greek, meaning "among, with, after, change." Whereas in some English words the prefix indicates "change" (for example, *metamorphosis*), in others, including those related to data and information, the prefix carries the meaning of "more comprehensive or fundamental."

The Standard Generalized Markup Language (**SGML**) defines rules for how a document can be described in terms of its logical structure (headings, paragraphs or idea units, and so forth). SGML is often referred to as a metalanguage because it provides a "language for how to describe a language." A specific use of SGML is called a document type definition (**DTD**). A document type definition spells out exactly what the allowable language is. A DTD is thus a metalanguage for a certain type of document. (In fact, the Hypertext Markup Language (**HTML**) is an example of a document type definition. HTML defines the set of HTML **tag**s that any Web page can contain.)

The Extensible Markup Language (**XML**), which is comparable to SGML and modelled on it, describes how to describe a collection of data. It's sometimes referred to as metadata. A specific XML definition, such as Microsoft's Channel Definition Format (**CDF**), defines a set of tags for describing a Web **channel**. XML could be considered the metadata for the more restrictive metadata of CDF (and other future data definitions based on XML).

In the case of SGML and XML, "meta" connotes "underlying definition" or set of rules. In other usages, "meta" seems to connote "description" rather than "definition." For example, the HTML tag is used to enclose descriptive language about an HTML page.

One could describe any computer programming or user interface as a metalanguage for conversing with a computer. And an English grammar and dictionary together could be said to define (and describe) the metalanguage for spoken and written English.

meta refresh

On a **Web site**, a meta refresh is coding in the Hypertext Markup Language (**HTML**) that automatically directs the visitor to a new page after a specified number of seconds. It's used when the address of a page is changed but you want visitors who know the old address to be able to find the new page. The page containing the meta refresh tag is known as a *redirect* page and the technique is known as *redirection*.

Most Web surfers are familiar with the meta refresh. A user enters a **Uniform Resource Locator** on their browser's address line and it takes them to a page that says something like: "We have moved to a new location. Please change your bookmark. In five seconds, we will transfer you to the new page." To make the transfer happen in five seconds, someone at that site has included an HTML line in the header section of the old page that looks like this:

```
<meta http-equiv="refresh'' content="5;url=http://
www.ournewsite.com''>
```

In the above example, the "5" means change to the new page in five seconds. The "url=http://www.ournewsite.com" is an example of the URL for the new page.

If you own a Web site that people have learned to use and you then change the name and location of a Web page, it's strongly recommended that you make the original page a redirect page with a meta refresh tag to the new page. Otherwise, visitors familiar with the old page will get a **404** (Page Not Found) message.

meta tag

A meta tag is a **tag** (that is, a coding statement) in the Hypertext Markup Language (**HTML**) that describes some aspect of the contents of a Web **page**. The information that you provide in a **meta** tag is used by **search engine**s to index a page so that someone searching for the kind of information the page contains will be able to find it. The meta tag is placed near the top of the HTML in a Web page as part of the heading.

There are several kinds of meta tags, but the most important for search engine indexing are the *keywords* meta tag and the *description* meta tag. The keywords meta tag lists the words or phrases that best describe the contents of the page. The description meta tag includes a brief one- or two-sentence description of the page. Both the keywords and the description are used by search engines in adding a page to their index. Some search engines also use the description to show the searcher a summary of the page's contents.

Although most search engines also use the contents of a page as a way to determine how to index it, the creator of a Web page should be sure to include meta tags with appropriate keywords and description. Well-written meta tags can help make the page rank higher in search results.

metacharacter

A metacharacter (sometimes spelled *meta character* or *meta-character*) is a special **character** in a program or data field that provides information about other characters. A metacharacter can express an idea about how to process the characters that follow the metacharacter, as the backslash character sometimes is used to indicate that the characters following it are to be treated in a special way. A common metacharacter usage is the **wildcard character**, which can represent either any one character or any string of characters. In **UNIX shell**s, metacharacters include, but are not limited to these:

```
* ; | ] [ ?
```

Each of these characters has a special meaning on the command line, and their use must be avoided for purposes other than their special meaning.

metadata

See "meta"

metafile

A metafile is a **file** containing information that describes or specifies another file.

Microsoft uses this term for its Windows Metafile (WMF) format. A WMF file contains a sequence of graphical-device-interface (GDI) function calls ("commands" to the Windows **operating system**) that results in the presentation of a graphic image. Some of the function calls are equivalent to **vector graphics** statements and others identify stored **bitmap** or literal specifications of which bits to illuminate (**raster graphics** images). Using WMF files rather than already-built bitmaps saves space when many bitmaps are used repeatedly by different components of the operating system or of an application. The WMF file assumes a 16-bit operating system. Microsoft has an enhanced metafile (EMF) format for its 32-bit operating systems. Microsoft's clipboard (CLP) file can contain a WMF file, an EMF file, or a bitmap (BMP) format file.

Another example of a metafile is the Computer Graphics Metafile (CGM). The CGM file format is a standard (**American National Standards Institute**-approved) format that can be used on any operating system that supports it (unlike the WMF format which is designed only for Windows). The CGM file is commonly used in **CAD** and presentation graphics applications.

In general, there are tools (such as HiJaak) that will convert the WMF, EMF, and CGM formats into other formats.

MetaFrame

MetaFrame is the name for a **thin client**/server software application from Citrix that is used to provide Microsoft's Windows Terminal Server product (**WTS**) with additional **server** and client functionality by allowing any **client**, no matter what operating system (**OS**) they are using, to connect to a Windows Terminal Server and run a Windows application through their browser. MetaFrame is useful for its ability to "load balance" by automatically directing a client to the server with the lightest load in a server farm, and its ability to allow publishing and application management from a single server in that farm. MetaFrame also features a secure **encryption** option through a distributed Windows presentation protocol developed by Citrix, called ICA (Independent Computing Architecture).

There is also a MetaFrame product for **UNIX** operating systems.

metal-oxide semiconductor field-effect transistor

Also see **gallium arsenide field-effect transistor**.

MOSFET (metal-oxide semiconductor field-effect transistor, pronounced MAWS-feht) is a special type of field-effect transistor (**FET**) that works by electronically varying the width of a channel along which charge carriers (**electrons** or holes) flow. The wider the channel, the better the device conducts. The charge carriers enter the channel at the *source*, and exit via the *drain*. The width of the channel is controlled by the **voltage** on an electrode called the *gate*, which is located physically between the source and the drain and is insulated from the channel by an extremely thin layer of metal oxide.

There are two ways in which a MOSFET can function. The first is known as *depletion mode*. When there is no voltage on the gate, the channel exhibits its maximum **conductance**. As the voltage on the gate increases (either positively or negatively, depending on whether the channel is made of P-type or N-type **semiconductor** material), the channel conductivity decreases. The second way in which a MOSFET can operate is called *enhancement mode*. When there is no voltage on the gate, there is in effect no channel, and the device does not conduct. A channel is produced by the application of a voltage to the gate. The greater the gate voltage, the better the device conducts.

The MOSFET has certain advantages over the conventional junction FET, or JFET. Because the gate is insulated electrically from the channel, no current flows between the gate and the channel, no matter what the gate voltage (as long as it does not become so great that it causes physical breakdown of the metallic oxide layer). Thus, the MOSFET has practically infinite **impedance**. This makes MOSFETs useful for power amplifiers. The devices are also well suited to high-speed switching applications. Some integrated circuits (**integrated circuit**) contain tiny MOSFETs and are used in computers.

Because the oxide layer is so thin, the MOSFET is susceptible to permanent damage by electrostatic charges. Even a small electrostatic buildup can destroy a MOSFET permanently. In weak-signal radio-frequency (**RF**) work, MOSFET devices do not generally perform as well as other types of FET.

metasyntactic variable

In programming, a metasyntactic (which derives from **meta** and **syntax**) variable is a **variable** (a changeable value) that is used to temporarily represent a **function**. Examples of metasyntactic variables include (but are by no means limited to) ack, **bar**, baz, blarg, wibble, **foo**, fum, and qux. Metasyntactic variables are sometimes used in developing a conceptual version of a program or examples of programming code written for illustrative purposes.

Any filename beginning with a metasyntactic variable denotes a scratch file. This means the file can be deleted at any time without affecting the program.

Also see **foo** and **bar**.

Metcalfe's Law

Metcalfe's Law is expressed in two general ways:

1. The number of possible cross-connections in a network grow as the square of the number of computers in the network increases.

2. The community value of a network grows as the square of the number of its users increase.

The original statement from Robert M. Metcalfe, inventor of **Ethernet**, was apparently (according to one source):

> "The power of the network increases exponentially by the number of computers connected to it. Therefore, every computer added to the network both uses it as a resource while adding resources in a spiral of increasing value and choice."

Metcalfe's Law is often cited as an explanation for the rapid growth of the Internet (or perhaps more especially for the World Wide Web on the Internet). Together, with **Moore's Law** about the rate at which computer power is accelerating, Metcalfe's Law can be used to explain the rising wave of information technology that we are riding into the 21st century.

meter

The meter (abbreviation, m; the British spelling is *metre*) is the International System of Units (**SI**) unit of displacement or length. One meter is the distance traveled by a ray of electromagnetic (EM) energy through a vacuum in $1/299{,}792{,}458$ ($3.33564095 \times 10^{-9}$) of a second. The meter was originally defined as one ten-millionth (0.0000001 or 10^{-7}) of the distance, as measured over the earth's surface in a great circle passing through Paris, France, from the geographic north pole to the equator.

One meter is a little more than three English feet, or about 39.37 inches. One foot is approximately 0.3048 meter. There are about 1609 meters in a statute mile. The official span was at one time formally defined as the separation between two scratches on a platinum bar in Paris. This was, of course, intended mainly for show, and not for use in the laboratory.

Power-of-10 **prefix multipliers** facilitate the derivation of other, often more convenient, distance units from the meter. One centimeter (cm) is equal to 0.01 m, one millimeter (mm) is equal to 0.001 m, and one kilometer (km) is equal to 1000 m. These units are found in nonscientific as well as scientific literature. Smaller units are the realm of the scientist and engineer. One micrometer (symbolized μm or ç), also called a **micron**, is equal to 0.000001 (10^{-6}) m. One nanometer (nm) is equal to 10^{-9} m. One Angström unit (symbolized Ä) is equal to 10^{-10} m, or 0.1 nm.

The meter and its kin are used to specify the **wavelengths** of **EM fields**. The so-called radio spectrum occupies an informally defined range of wavelengths from roughly a millimeter (microwaves) to several tens of kilometers (myriametric waves). A 3-m radio wave falls near the middle of the standard **FM** (frequency modulation) broadcast band; a 300-m radio wave is near the middle of the standard **AM** (amplitude-modulation) broadcast band. The range of visible light wavelengths is from approximately 390 nm (violet) to 770 nm (red). The speed of EM-field propagation in a vacuum, to nine significant figures, is 2.99792458×10^8 meters per second. In this sense, the meter can be derived from the second if the latter unit has been previously defined in absolute terms; one meter is the distance a ray of light travels through a vacuum in $3.33564095 \times 10^{-9}$ second.

In engineering applications, and also in an everyday sense, the term meter refers to any instrument used to measure the magnitude of a quantity. Examples include the volume-unit (VU) meter in home audio systems, the ammeter to measure electric current, and the kilowatt-hour meter to measure electrical energy consumed over a period of time.

Also see International System of Units (**SI**) and **prefix multipliers**.

meter cubed

See "cubic meter"

meter cubed per kilogram

The meter cubed per kilogram (symbolized m^3/kg) is the standard unit of **specific volume** in the International System (**SI**). It is expressed directly in base SI units, and cannot be further reduced. Specific volume is the reciprocal of **density**.

A substance with a specific volume of $1\ m^3/kg$ is extremely large for its mass. In fact, air at sea level has a specific volume less than this. Materials with high density have low specific volume; materials with low density have high specific volume.

Alternative units are often used to express specific volume. The most common of these is the centimeter cubed per gram (cm^3/g). A substance with a specific volume of $1\ cm^3/g$ has a specific volume of $0.001\ m^3/kg$. Conversely, a substance with a specific volume of $1\ m^3/kg$ has a specific volume of $1000\ cm^3/g$.

Also see **kilogram**, **meter**, **kilogram per cubic meter**, and International System of Units (**SI**).

meter per second

The meter per second (symbolized m/s or m/sec) is the International System of Units (**SI**) unit of linear speed. This quantity can be defined in either of two senses: average or instantaneous.

Average linear speed is obtained by measuring the distance in **meters** that an object travels in a certain number of **seconds**, and then dividing the distance by the time. If s_{avg} represents the average speed of an object (in meters per second) during a time interval t (in seconds), and the distance traveled in that time is equal to d (in meters), then:

$s_{avg} = d\ /\ t$

Instantaneous linear speed is more difficult to intuit, because it involves an expression of motion over an "infinitely short" interval of time. Let p represent a specific point in time. Suppose an object is in motion at about that time. The average speed can be measured over increasingly short time intervals centered at p, for example:

$[p-4, p+4]$
$[p-3, p+3]$
$[p-2 , p+2]$
$[p-1, p+1]$
$[p-0.5, p+0.5]$
$[p-0.25, p+0.25]$
.

.

$[p-x, p+x]$

.

.

where the added and subtracted numbers represent seconds. The instantaneous speed, s_{inst}, is the limit of the measured average speed as x approaches zero. This is a theoretical value, because it cannot be obtained except by inference from measurements made over progressively shorter time spans.

It is important to realize that speed is not the same thing as velocity. Speed is a **scalar** (dimensionless) quantity, while velocity is a **vector** quantity consisting of speed and direction. We might say a car is traveling at 20 m/s, and this tells us its speed. Or we might say the car is traveling at 20 m/s at a compass bearing of 25 degrees (north-by-northeast); this tells us its velocity. As with speed, we might specify either the average velocity over a period of time, or the instantaneous velocity at an exact moment in time.

Also see **meter per second squared** and International System of Units (**SI**).

meter per second squared

The meter per second squared (symbolized m/s^2 or m/sec^2) is the International System of Units (**SI**) unit of acceleration vector magnitude. This quantity can be defined in either of two senses: average or instantaneous.

For an object traveling in a straight line, the average acceleration magnitude is obtained by evaluating the object's instantaneous linear speed (in meters per second) at two different points t_1 and t_2 in time, and then dividing the distance by the span of time $t_2 - t_1$ (in seconds). Suppose the

instantaneous speed at time t_1 is equal to s_1, and the instantaneous speed at time t_2 is equal to s_2. Then the average acceleration magnitude a_{avg} (in meters per second squared) during the time interval $[t_1, t_2]$ is given by:

$$a_{avg} = (s_{2-s_1}) / (t_2 - t_1)$$

Instantaneous acceleration magnitude is more difficult to intuit, because it involves an expression of motion over an "infinitely short" interval of time. Let p represent a specific point in time. Suppose an object is in motion at about that time. The average acceleration magnitude can be determined over increasingly short time intervals centered at p, for example:

$[p-4, p+4]$
$[p-3, p+3]$
$[p-2, p+2]$
$[p-1, p+1]$
$[p-0.5, p+0.5]$
$[p-0.25, p+0.25]$
.
.
.

$[p-x, p+x]$
.
.
.

where the added and subtracted numbers represent seconds. The instantaneous acceleration magnitude, a_{inst}, is the limit of the average acceleration magnitude as x approaches zero. This is a theoretical value, because it can be obtained only by inference from instantanous speed values determined at the starting and ending points of progressively shorter time spans.

Acceleration, in its fullest sense, is a **vector** quantity, possessing direction as well as magnitude. For an object moving in a straight line and whose linear speed changes, the acceleration vector points in the same direction as the object's direction of motion. But acceleration can be the result of a change in the direction of a moving object, even if the instantaneous speed remains constant. The classic example is given by an object in circular motion, such as a revolving weight attached to the rim of a wheel. If the rotational speed of the wheel is constant, the weight's acceleration vector points directly inward toward the center of the wheel.

Also see **meter**, **second**, **meter per second**, and International System of Units (**SI**).

meter squared

See "square meter"

meter-kilogram-second system of units

See "metric system"

method

In **object-oriented programming**, a method is a programmed procedure that is defined as part of a **class** and included in any **object** of that class. A class (and thus an object) can have more than one method. A method in an object can only have access to the data known to that object, which ensures data integrity among the set of objects in an application. A method can be re-used in multiple objects.

metric

1) In software development, a metric (noun) is the measurement of a particular characteristic of a program's performance or efficiency. Similarly in network routing, a metric is a measure used in calculating the next host to route a packet to. A metric is sometimes used directly and sometimes as an element in an **algorithm**. In programming, a **benchmark** includes metrics.

2) Metric (adjective) pertains to anything based on the *meter* as a unit of spatial measurement.

metric system

The metric system, more formally called the *meter-kilogram-second* (MKS or mks) system of units, is based on three fundamental units: the **meter** (m) that quantifies **displacement**, the **kilogram** (kg) that quantifies **mass**, and the **second** (s or sec) that quantifies **time**. The metric system is formally replaced by the very similar International System of Units (**SI**).

The metric system was originally developed by scientists who were frustrated with the English (foot-pound-second) system. In theoretical and laboratory calculations, arithmetic involving English units is "messy." There are, for example, 12 inches in a foot, three feet in a yard, and 5280 feet in a statute mile; there are 16 ounces in a pound. Less common English units such as the rod, furlong, peck, and bushel seem, in modern scientific terms, to have been dreamed up ages ago without concern for common sense, although they are used by some agricultural and industrial people to this day.

In the metric or mks system, the meter and kilogram are divided into fractional units, and enlarged into multiple units, according to power-of-10 **prefix multipliers**. For example, there are 1000 millimeters (10^3 mm) in a meter, 1000 meters (10^3 m) in a kilometer, 1000 grams (10^3 g) in a kilogram, and 1000 milligrams (10^3 mg) in a gram. This makes these mks units easy to work with in scientific notation. Time, however, is denoted in the same way as in the English system. There are 60 seconds in a minute, 60 minutes in an hour, and 24 hours in a mean solar day in both systems.

The International System of Units (**SI**) provides formal definitions for the meter, the kilogram, and the second, and also specifies and defines four additional units: the **Kelvin** for temperature, the **ampere** for electric current, the **candela** for luminous intensity, and the **mole** for material quantity.

Compare centimeter-gram-second (**cgs**) or small-unit metric system, English system of units, and International System of Units (**SI**). Also see **prefix multiplier**.

metropolitan area network

A metropolitan area network (MAN) is a network that interconnects users with computer resources in a geographic area or region larger than that covered by even a large local area network (**LAN**) but smaller than the area covered by a wide area network (**WAN**). The term is applied to the interconnection of networks in a city into a single larger network (which may then also offer efficient connection to a wide area network). It is also used to mean the interconnection of several local area networks by bridging them with **backbone** lines. The latter usage is also sometimes referred to as a *campus network*.

Examples of metropolitan area networks of various sizes can be found in the metropolitan areas of London, England; Lodz, Poland; and Geneva, Switzerland. Large universities also sometimes use the term to describe their networks.

mezzanine

Mezzanine is a term used to describe the stacking of computer component **card**s into a single card that then plugs into the computer **bus** or data path. The bus itself is sometimes referred to as a mezzanine bus. The term derives from the Italian word, *mezzano*, which means middle. The more common use of this term is in architecture, where it is a low-ceilinged story between two main stories in a building. In theaters, a mezzanine is a balcony projecting partly over the ground floor below it.

A mezzanine card is a smaller form of the more familiar Peripheral Component Interconnect (**PCI**) or Industry Standard Architecture (**ISA**) card. The original and still most popular mezzanine card is the Industry Pack (IP) card. An IP card provides a 16-bit data path. The IP card is 3.9 × 1.8 inches and has two 50-pin connectors that plug into an IP-to-PCI adapter card. The IP-to-PCI adapter card usually holds up to three IP cards. Another popular mezzanine card is the PCI Mezzanine (PMC) card. This card provides 32 or 64-bit data paths and uses 64-pin connectors. Both types of mezzanine cards are widely used with **VME bus**, which is an expansion bus technology that supports up to 21 cards on a single **backplane**. VME bus is widely used in industrial, telecommunication, and military applications.

MFC

See "Microsoft Foundation Class Library"

mho

See "siemens"

MHz

The megahertz, abbreviated MHz, is a unit of alternating current (AC) or electromagnetic (EM) wave frequency equal to one million **hertz** (1,000,000 Hz). The megahertz is commonly used to express **microprocessor** clock speed. The unit is occasionally used in measurements or statements of **bandwidth** for high-speed **digital** data, **analog** and digital video signals, and **spread spectrum** signals.

An EM signal having a frequency of 1 MHz is near the center of the standard amplitude-modulation (AM) radio broadcast band, and has a wavelength of 300 meters, or about 980 feet. An EM signal of 100 MHz is near the middle of the standard frequency-modulation (FM) radio broadcast band, and has a wavelength of 3 meters, which is a little less than 10 feet. Some radio transmissions are made at frequencies up to many thousands of megahertz. Typical computer clock speeds are constantly increasing, but generally are on the order of a few hundred megahertz.

Other units of frequency are the **kHz**, equal to 1,000 Hz or 0.001 MHz, and the **gigahertz**, equal to 1,000,000,000 Hz or 1,000 MHz.

The bandwidth of a digital signal, in megahertz, is related to the data speed in **bits per second**. In general, the greater the data speed, the larger the bandwidth. Data speed is not, however, the same thing as bandwidth. A high-speed cable or fiberoptic modem operating at a speed of 5,000,000 bps has, in a certain sense, a nominal frequency of 5 MHz. But the bandwidth is generally much smaller, because it depends on variations in the individual data elements, not on the number of data bits per unit time.

MIB

See "management information base"

Micro Channel Architecture

Developed by IBM for its line of PS/2 desktop computers, Micro Channel Architecture is an interface between a computer (or multiple computers) and its expansion cards and their associated devices. MCA was a distinct break from previous **bus** architectures such as **Industry Standard Architecture**. The pin connections in MCA are smaller than other bus interfaces. For this and other reasons, MCA does not support other bus architectures. Although MCA offers a number of improvements over other bus architectures, its proprietary, nonstandard aspects did not encourage other manufacturers to adopt it. It has influenced other bus designs and it is still in use in PS/2s and in some minicomputer systems.

Also see **Extended Industry Standard Architecture** and **Peripheral Component Interconnect**.

microchip

A microchip (sometimes just called a "chip") is a unit of packaged computer circuitry (usually called an **integrated circuit**) that is manufactured from a material such as **silicon** at a very small scale. Microchips are made for program logic (logic or **microprocessor** chips) and for computer memory (memory or **RAM** chips). Microchips are also made that include both logic and memory and for special purposes such as **analog-to-digital conversion**, bit slicing, and gateways.

microchip art

Microchip art is a microscopic non-functioning drawing impressed on the surface of the design mask used in the production of **microchip**s. The art, which grew out of the tradition of having chip designers "sign" their work, is created by etching into the upper metallic layers of the chip in an unused corner of the chip mask.

Because microchip art is too small to see with the human eye, its existence was not widely known until 1998 when photographer Michal Davidson accidently stumbled on an example while photographing the geometric patterns of a microchip. Davidson, who makes his living photographing ordinary objects under a high-power Nikon optical mircroscope, was surprised to find the children's book character "Waldo" hiding among the thousands of square microns of circuitry he was looking at. (The objective of the "Where's Waldo?" books is for children to find the Waldo character who is hidden somewhere in each page's illustration.) Davidson, who at first thought the image was a fluke, began to closely examine other microchips under his microscope and found what writer Michael Stroh has described as "the Lascaux Cave of the computer industry."

Since his initial discovery, Davidson has found and photographed a wide variety of examples of microchip art, including intricate sketches of hummingbirds, locomotives, and buffalo. After posting his microphotographs on a Web site, Davidson was pleased to have many of the chip designers contact him about their work and explain the symbolism behind the chosen design. For example, a bulldozer that appears on a chip designed in 1980 by Synertek was a mystery until it was learned that the chip was used in heavy equipment electonic monitoring systems.

Microchip art is frowned upon in some corporations, notably Intel, because the software used to create chips is programmed to spot design flaws, and, as microchips become more complex, the possibility exists that poorly executed microchip art could pose production problems. Chip designers, however, compare microchip art to the

"**Easter egg**s" that programmers leave behind, and promise that somehow creative minds will continue to "make their mark" upon their work.

microcode

Microcode is programming that is ordinarily not program-addressable but, unlike hardwired logic, is capable of being modified. Microcode may sometimes be installed or modified by a device's user by altering programmable read-only memory (**PROM**) or erasable programmable read-only memory (**EPROM**).

IBM uses this term in preference to **firmware**.

microcomputer

A microcomputer is a complete **computer** on a smaller scale and is generally a synonym for the more common term, **personal computer** or **PC**, a computer designed for an individual. A microcomputer contains a **microprocessor** (a central processing unit on a **microchip**), **memory** in the form of **read-only memory** and **random access memory**, I/O ports and a **bus** or system of interconnecting wires, housed in a unit that is usually called a **motherboard**.

In an ascending hierarchy of general computer sizes, we find:

- An **embedded systems programming** computer, which is embedded in something and doesn't support direct human interaction but nevertheless meets all the other criteria of a microcomputer
- Microcomputer
- **Workstation**, as used to mean a more powerful personal computer for special applications
- **Minicomputer**, now restyled a "mid-range server"
- **Mainframe** or mainframe computer, which is now usually referred to by its manufacturers as a "large server"
- Supercomputer, formerly almost a synonym for "Cray supercomputer" but now meaning a very large server and sometimes including a system of computers using parallel processing
- A parallel processing system is a system of interconnected computers that work on the same application together, sharing tasks that can be performed concurrently

micro-electromechanical systems

Micro-electromechanical systems (MEMS) is a technology that combines computers with tiny mechanical devices such as sensors, valves, gears, mirrors, and actuators embedded in semiconductor chips. Paul Saffo of the Institute for the Future in Palo Alto, California, believes MEMS or what he calls **analog computing** will be "the foundational technology of the next decade." MEMS is also sometimes called *smart matter*.

MEMS are already used as accelerometers in automobile airbags. They've replaced a less reliable device at lower cost and show promise of being able to inflate a bag not only on the basis of sensed deceleration but also on the basis of the size of the person they are protecting. Basically, a MEMS device contains micro-circuitry on a tiny silicon chip into which some mechanical device such as a mirror or a sensor has been manufactured. Potentially, such chips can be built in large quantities at low cost, making them cost-effective for many uses.

Among the presently available uses of MEMS or those under study are:

- Global position system sensors that can be included with courier parcels for constant tracking and that can also sense parcel treatment en route

- Sensors built into the fabric of an airplane wing so that it can sense and react to air flow by changing the wing surface resistance; effectively creating a myriad of tiny wing flaps

- Optical switching devices that can switch light signals over different paths at 20-nanosecond switching speeds

- Sensor-driven heating and cooling systems that dramatically improve energy savings

- Building supports with imbedded sensors that can alter the flexibility properties of a material based on atmospheric stress sensing

Saffo distinguishes between sensor-effector type micro-computing (which he calls "MEMS") and micro-devices containing gears, mirrors, valves, and other parts (which he calls "micro-machines").

Much support for MEMS has come from **Defense Advanced Research Projects Agency** Research and Development Electronics Technology Office.

microfluidics

Microfluidics is the science of designing, manufacturing, and formulating devices and processes that deal with volumes of fluid on the order of nanoliters (symbolized nl and representing units of 10^{-9} liter) or picoliters (symbolized pl and representing units of 10^{-12} liter). The devices themselves have dimensions ranging from millimeters (mm) down to micrometers (μm), where 1 μm = 0.001 mm.

Microfluidics hardware requires construction and design that differs from macroscale hardware. It is not generally possible to scale conventional devices down and then expect them to work in microfluidics applications. When the dimensions of a device or system reach a certain size as the scale becomes smaller, the particles of fluid, or particles suspended in the fluid, become comparable in size with the apparatus itself. This dramatically alters system behavior.

Capillary action changes the way in which fluids pass through microscale-diameter tubes, as compared with macroscale channels. In addition, there are unknown factors involved, especially concerning microscale heat transfer and mass transfer, the nature of which only further research can reveal.

The volumes involved in microfluidics can be understood by visualizing the size of a one-liter container, and then imagining cubical fractions of this container. A liter is slightly more than one U.S. fluid quart. A cube measuring 100 mm (a little less than four inches) on an edge has a volume of one liter. Imagine a tiny cube whose height, width, and depth are 1/1000 (0.001) of this size, or 0.1 mm. This is the size of a small grain of table sugar; it would take a strong magnifying glass to resolve it into a recognizable cube. That cube would occupy 1 nl. A volume of 1 pl is represented by a cube whose height, width, and depth are $^1/_{10}$ (0.1) that of a 1-nl cube. It would take a powerful microscope to resolve that.

Microfluidic systems have diverse and widespread potential applications. Some examples of systems and processes that might employ this technology include inkjet printers, blood-cell-separation equipment, biochemical assays, chemical synthesis, genetic analysis, drug screening, electrochromatography, surface micromachining, laser ablation, and mechanical micromilling. Not surprisingly, the medical industry has shown keen interest in microfluidics technology.

Also see **nanotechnology**.

micron

A micron (short for *micrometer*) is one-millionth of a meter. It can also be expressed as:

- 10^{-6} meter

- One thousandth of a millimeter

- One 25-thousandth of an inch

The micron is a unit of measure for the core in a **optical fiber** cable, for which the most common diameter is 62.5 microns. It is also used to measure the line width on a **microchip**. Today's microprocessors and memory chips are typically built using 0.35 and 0.25 line widths. Recently, a 0.18 micron line width has been achieved and is being used in the latest processors from Intel and AMD.

A human hair is said to be about 50 microns wide.

micropayment

On the Web, micropayment is a business concept whose goal is to generate revenue by offering pay-per-view Web pages, Web links, or Web services for small amounts of money called "microcents." Since it is not practical for individual users to charge small amounts of money (such as a penny or a fraction of a penny) to a major charge card, a different method of payment is needed for sites that wish to go "micro." Several methods of micropayment collection are being examined, many of which involve encoding per-fee-**links** inside **HTML** pages and some kind of Internet **wallet** account where individuals would establish a cash balance with a third-party application that would monitor, collect, and distribute micropayments.

Once a common micropayment **standard** has been established, some visionaries predict that **streaming media** sites, sports access sites, and other specialized resources will pave the way for pay-per view Web use, just as they did for **cable TV**.

microprocessor

A microprocessor is a computer **processor** on a **microchip**. It's sometimes called a *logic chip*. It is the "engine" that goes into motion when you turn your computer on. A microprocessor is designed to perform arithmetic and logic operations that make use of small number-holding areas called *registers*. Typical microprocessor operations include adding, subtracting, comparing two numbers, and fetching numbers from one area to another. These operations are the result of a set of **instructions** that are part of the microprocessor design. When the computer is turned on, the microprocessor is designed to get the first instruction from the basic input/output system (**BIOS**) that comes with the computer as part of its **memory**. After that, either the BIOS, or the **operating system** that BIOS loads into computer memory, or an application progam is "driving" the microprocessor, giving it instructions to perform.

microrobot

A microrobot is a miniaturized, sophisticated machine designed to perform a specific task or tasks repeatedly and with precision. Microrobots typically have dimensions ranging from a fraction of a millimeter up to several millimeters.

A microrobot, like its larger and smaller cousins, the **robot** and the **nanorobot**, can be either autonomous or insect-like. An autonomous microrobot contains its own on-board computer, which controls the machine and allows it to operate independently. The insect scheme is more common for microrobots. In an insect-microrobot arrangement, the machine is one of a fleet of several, or many, identical units that are all controlled by a single, central computer. (The term insect comes from the fact that such robots behave like ants in an anthill or bees in a hive.)

Also see **robotics**.

microsecond

(This definition follows U.S. usage in which a billion is a thousand million and a trillion is a 1 followed by 12 zeros.)

A microsecond (us or Greek letter mu plus s) is one millionth (10^{-6}) of a second.

For comparison, a millisecond (ms or msec) is one thousandth of a second and is commonly used in measuring the time to read to or write from a **hard disk** or a **CD-ROM** player or to measure **packet** travel time on the Internet.

A nanosecond (ns or nsec) is one billionth (10^{-9}) of a second and is a common measurement of read or write access time to random access memory (**RAM**).

A picosecond is one trillionth (10^{-12}) of a second, or one millionth of a microsecond.

A femtosecond is one millionth of a nanosecond or 10^{-15} of a second and is a measurement sometimes used in laser technology.

An attosecond is one quintillionth (10^{-18}) of a second and is a term used in photon research.

microsite

As used in at least one leading Web design book, a microsite is a separately promoted part of a larger Web **site**. A microsite is designed to meet separate objectives and has a separate Web address (or **Uniform Resource Locator**) as its **home page**. Typically, a microsite resides on the same Web **server** and reflects the branding and overall visual design of the larger site with which it is associated. Occasionally, two Web sites will collaborate to produce a third, smaller site that both link to (and is probably located on one of the two main site's servers).

Minisite is also sometimes used with about the same meaning.

Microsoft Certified Solution Developer

An MCSD (Microsoft Certified Solution Developer) is someone who has passed exams that test their ability to design and develop custom business applications with Microsoft development tools, technologies, and **platform**. To prepare for the exams, you can take courses at a certified training company location, in certified courses in a high school or college, or through self-study at Microsoft's Web site or through certified training materials.

The MCSD program is part of a set of Microsoft Certified Professional (MCP) training programs. In other MCP programs, you can gain certification as a Microsoft Certified Systems Engineer (**MCSE**), a Microsoft Certified Product Specialist (MCPS), or a Microsoft Certified Trainer (MCT).

Microsoft Certified Systems Engineer

An MCSE (Microsoft Certified Systems Engineer) is someone who has passed exams about a specific Microsoft **Windows operating system**, related desktop systems, networking, and Microsoft's BackOffice server products. To prepare for the exams, you can take courses at a certified training company location, in certified courses in a high school or college, or through self-study at Microsoft's self-study Web site or through certified training materials.

The MCSE program is the most popular of a set of training programs that Microsoft calls the Microsoft Certified Professional (MCP). In other MCP programs, you can gain certification as a Microsoft Certified Solution Developer (MCSD), a Microsoft Certified Product Specialist (MCPS), or a Microsoft Certified Trainer (MCT).

Microsoft Foundation Class Library

The Microsoft Foundation Class (MFC) Library is a collection of **classes** (generalized definitions used in **object-oriented programming**) that can be used in building application programs. The classes in the MFC Library are written in the **C++** programming language. The MFC Library saves a programmer time by providing code that has already been written. It also provides an overall framework for developing the application program.

There are MFC Library classes for all graphical user interface elements (windows, frames, menus, tool bars, status bars, and so forth), for building interfaces to **databases**, for handling events such as messages from other applications, for handling keyboard and mouse input, and for creating **ActiveX control**.

Microsoft Internet Explorer

Microsoft Internet Explorer (MSIE) is the most widely used World Wide Web **browser**. It comes with the Microsoft Windows operating system and can also be downloaded from Microsoft'w Web site. The MSIE browser competes with an earlier browser, **Netscape** Navigator.

Three other browsers are **Mosaic** (the browser on which Netscape's browser was based), **Lynx**, and **Opera**.

Microsoft Management Console

The Microsoft Management Console (MMC) is an application that provides a graphical-user interface (**GUI**) and a programming framework in which consoles (collections of administrative tools) can be created, saved, and opened. MMC was originally released as part of the **Windows 98** Resource Kit, and is included on all later versions. It uses a Multiple Document Interface (**MDI**) in an environment similar to Microsoft's Windows Explorer. MMC is considered to be a **container** for the actual operations, and is known as a "tools host." It does not, itself, provide management, but rather a framework in which management tools can operate.

Consoles are used to manage Windows-based hardware, software, and networking components, and include items such as controls, wizards, tasks, documentation, and **snap-ins** which may be from Microsoft or other software vendors, or user-defined. To create a console, the administrator runs the MMC executable file to open an empty console and chooses from among a list of all the tools installed on the system (such as, for example, *certificate server manager*, *device*

manager, and *DNS manager*). Because consoles exist as files, an administrator can create them and then send them as e-mail attachments to developers responsible for specific tasks.

Microsoft Transaction Server

See "MTS"

microwave

The term microwave refers to **electromagnetic** energy having a **frequency** higher than 1 **gigahertz** (billions of cycles per second), corresponding to **wavelengths** shorter than 30 centimeters.

Microwave signals propagate in straight lines and are affected very little by the troposphere. They are not refracted or reflected by ionized regions in the upper atmosphere. Microwave beams do not readily diffract around barriers such as hills, mountains, and large human-made structures. Some **attenuation** occurs when microwave energy passes through trees and frame houses. Radio-frequency (**RF**) energy at longer wavelengths is affected to a lesser degree by such obstacles.

The microwave band is well suited for **wireless** transmission of signals having large **bandwidths**. This portion of the RF **electromagnetic radiation spectrum** encompasses many thousands of megahertz. Compare this with the so-called shortwave band that extends from 3 MHz to 30 MHz, and whose total available bandwidth is only 27 MHz. In communications, a large allowable bandwidth translates into high data speed. The short wavelengths allow the use of dish antennas having manageable diameters. These antennas produce high power gain in transmitting applications, and have excellent sensitivity and directional characteristics for reception of signals.

middleware

In the computer industry, middleware is a general term for any programming that serves to "glue together" or mediate between two separate and usually already existing programs. A common application of middleware is to allow programs written for access to a particular **database** to access other databases.

Messaging is a common service provided by middleware programs so that different applications can communicate. The systematic tying together of disparate applications is known as enterprise application integration (**EAI**).

MIDI

MIDI (Musical Instrument Digital Interface) is a protocol designed for recording and playing back music on digital synthesizers that is supported by many makes of personal computer sound cards. Originally intended to control one keyboard from another, it was quickly adopted for the personal computer. Rather than representing musical sound directly, it transmits information about how music is produced. The command set includes note-ons, note-offs, key velocity, pitch bend and other methods of controlling a synthesizer. The sound waves produced are those already stored in a **wavetable** in the receiving instrument or sound card.

Since a MIDI file only represents player information, it is far more concise than formats that the sound directly. An advantage is very small file size. A disadvantage is the lack of specific sound control.

With a program that provides this interface, you can create music using a standard keyboard or other input device. You or others can then play your MIDI-conforming creation with the same or another program and a sound card as a music synthesizer. The MIDI program may come with a graphical user interface that looks like a sound studio control room. Many sound cards come as a package with MIDI software (for example, Media Vision's Pro Audio Studio 16).

The MIDI protocol uses eight-bit serial transmission with one start bit and one stop bit, has a 31.25 Kbs data rate, and is **asynchronous**. Connection is made through a five-pin DIN plug, of which three pins are used.

midrange

In general, midrange refers to computers that are more powerful and capable than personal computers but less powerful and capable than **mainframe** computers. (Computer power is sometimes measured in terms of millions-of-instructions-per-second—**MIPS**. Capability includes, for example, how many devices can be connected to and interact with the computer at the same time.) The computer industry does not define exactly what characteristics constitute "midrange."

Historically, midrange computers have been sold to small to medium-sized businesses as their main computer and to larger enterprises for branch or department-level operations. Makers of popular midrange computer lines include Hewlett-Packard, IBM, and Sun Microsystems. Today's computers are almost universally known as **server**s to recognize that they often "serve" applications to end users at "client" computers, that they use a **client/server** computing model, and, by inference (since the client/server model developed in UNIX-based operating systems), that they support standard rather than proprietary programming interfaces.

migration

In information technology, migration is the process of moving from the use of one operating environment to another operating environment that is, in most cases, is thought to be a better one. For example, moving from Windows NT Server to Windows 2000 Server would usually be considered a migration because it involves making sure that new features are exploited, old settings do not require

changing, and taking steps to ensure that current applications continue to work in the new environment. Migration could also mean moving from Windows NT to a UNIX-based operating system (or the reverse). Migration can involve moving to new hardware, new software, or both. Migration can be small-scale, such as migrating a single system, or large-scale, involving many systems, new applications, or a redesigned network.

One can migrate data from one kind of database to another kind of database. This usually requires converting the data into some common format that can be output from the old database and input into the new database. Since the new database may be organized differently, it may be necessary to write a program that can process the migrating files.

Migration is also used to refer simply to the process of moving data from one storage device to another.

mil

"mil" is one of the top-level **domain name**s that can be used when choosing a domain name. It generally describes the entity owning the domain name as a military organization of the U.S government. Along with the second-level domain name (for example: "navy" in navy.mil), the top-level domain name is required in Web and e-mail addresses.

For more information, see **gTLD** (generic top-level domain name).

millennium

1) A millennium is a period of one thousand years. It is similar to the terms *biennium*, a period of two years, and *century*, a period of one hundred years. The term derives from the Latin *mille*, meaning thousand, and *annum*, meaning year.

2) *The millennium* is the anniversary or celebration of a 1000-year period. In the U.S., the official timekeeper at the Naval Observatory considers that the second millennium and the beginning of the third will be reached on January 1, 2001. This date is based on the **Gregorian calendar**, created in 1582 Anno Domini (A.D.) and which has since become a world standard for civil affairs. The Gregorian calendar uses the table of dates for Easter that was established by the sixth-century scholar Dionysius Exiguus who marked the modern epoch as beginning on January 1, 1 A.D. For this reason, the second millennium is not actually reached until January 1, 2001. However, because the most dramatic change in the calendar occurred on January 1, 2000, much of the world celebrated the beginning of the third millennium a year early.

3) *The millennium* is also used to refer in general to a time when great achievements finally come to pass, great happiness prevails, or some other important objective is reached. In the Book of Revelations, *the millennium* is a period of a thousand years during which Christ is to rule on Earth.

milliampere hour

A milliampere hour (mAh) is 1000th of an **ampere** hour (**Ah**). Both measures are commonly used to describe the energy charge that a **battery** will hold and how long a device will run before the battery needs recharging.

For example, an IBM Thinkpad 365 with an **Nickel-Metal Hydride** 9.6 **voltage** battery that is stated to provide a charge of 2800 mAh offers from 2.5 to 5 hours of battery use without recharge.

million instructions per second

See "MIPS"

millisecond

(This definition follows U.S. usage in which a billion is a thousand million and a trillion is a 1 followed by 12 zeros.)

A millisecond (ms or msec) is one thousandth of a second and is commonly used in measuring the time to read to or write from a **hard disk** or a **CD-ROM** player or to measure **packet** travel time on the Internet.

For comparison, a microsecond (us or Greek letter mu plus s) is one millionth (10^{-6}) of a second.

A nanosecond (ns or nsec) is one billionth (10^{-9}) of a second and is a common measurement of read or write access time to random access memory (**RAM**).

A picosecond is one trillionth (10^{-12}) of a second, or one millionth of a microsecond.

A femtosecond is one millionth of a nanosecond or 10^{-15} of a second and is a measurement sometimes used in laser technology.

An attosecond is one quintillionth (10^{-18}) of a second and is a term used in photon research.

MIM

A MIM or MME file is a **file** in the Multi-Purpose Internet Mail Extensions (**MIME**) format that is created by some **e-mail** programs, including that of America Online (AOL), to encapsulate e-mail that contains image or program attachments. The MIM or MME refers to the three-letter extension or suffix (".mim" or ".mme") at the end of the file name. AOL creates a MIM or MME file when a user sends a note with attachments to other users. Such notes sent to other than AOL users tend to be restored to their original form by the receiver's e-mail software. However, AOL recipients receive a MIM or MME file that they need to "open" so that they can get the individual files inside. AOL users with Windows can use **WinZip** (using the "Classic Winzip" mode of operation). Mac users can use a similar utility.

AOL users who enter the keyword "MIME" receive this explanation from AOL:

The Internet's e-mail system handles basic text files nicely, but doesn't reliably handle binary files – files like pictures or word processing documents. So, when you send an e-mail message with a file attachment to someone on the Internet, the AOL software automatically encodes or translates the attachment using a system called MIME. (MIME stands for Multipurpose Internet Mail Extensions.) MIME converts the binary attachment to a text format that can be handled by Internet e-mail. The message's recipient needs a program that can decode the MIME e-mail and turn it back into a binary file that the computer can work with.

When you receive MIME files...
When someone sends you a MIME-encoded file in e-mail, it needs to be translated back into a format that your computer can understand. Depending on the mail system that the sender used, the AOL software may or may not be able to automatically decode the MIME file. If it was able to decode the file, the e-mail's file attachment will be in its original, binary format: such as .GIF, or .ZIP.

If AOL was unable to decode the MIME file, the attachment will be in MIME format, with a filename extension of .MME. Download this file–it is simple to use a utility to convert the .MME file back to a binary file. Windows users can use these applications to easily decode MIME files.

* WinZip: http://www.winzip.com
* MIME Decoders: MIME Help & Software

After you've downloaded and installed these programs, please be sure to read the READ ME guide for information on how to use the decoder(s).

Macintosh users can use these applications to easily decode MIME files.

* Decoder: Harmony Software Home Page

After you've downloaded and installed any of these programs, please be sure to read the READ ME guide for information on how to use the decoder.

When you send an attachment to an Internet user...
When you attach a file to an e-mail message that you send to an Internet user, it will automatically be MIME-encoded. In order to use the attachment, your message's recipient must have a MIME-compliant e-mail program or use software that can decode MIME files–to translate it back into a format that his or her computer can understand. If the recipient has a MIME-compliant e-mail program, the MIME attachment will probably be automatically decoded for him. If not, the recipient can easily translate the file using a utility program.

MIME

MIME (Multi-Purpose Internet Mail Extensions) is an extension of the original Internet **e-mail protocol** that lets people use the protocol to exchange different kinds of data files on the Internet: Audio, video, images, application

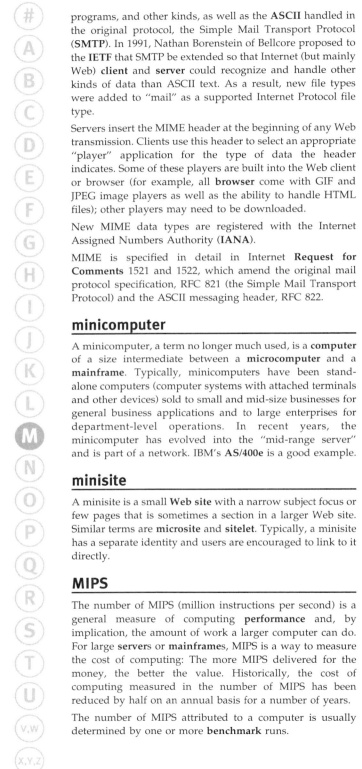

programs, and other kinds, as well as the **ASCII** handled in the original protocol, the Simple Mail Transport Protocol (**SMTP**). In 1991, Nathan Borenstein of Bellcore proposed to the **IETF** that SMTP be extended so that Internet (but mainly Web) **client** and **server** could recognize and handle other kinds of data than ASCII text. As a result, new file types were added to "mail" as a supported Internet Protocol file type.

Servers insert the MIME header at the beginning of any Web transmission. Clients use this header to select an appropriate "player" application for the type of data the header indicates. Some of these players are built into the Web client or browser (for example, all **browser** come with GIF and JPEG image players as well as the ability to handle HTML files); other players may need to be downloaded.

New MIME data types are registered with the Internet Assigned Numbers Authority (**IANA**).

MIME is specified in detail in Internet **Request for Comments** 1521 and 1522, which amend the original mail protocol specification, RFC 821 (the Simple Mail Transport Protocol) and the ASCII messaging header, RFC 822.

minicomputer

A minicomputer, a term no longer much used, is a **computer** of a size intermediate between a **microcomputer** and a **mainframe**. Typically, minicomputers have been stand-alone computers (computer systems with attached terminals and other devices) sold to small and mid-size businesses for general business applications and to large enterprises for department-level operations. In recent years, the minicomputer has evolved into the "mid-range server" and is part of a network. IBM's **AS/400e** is a good example.

minisite

A minisite is a small **Web site** with a narrow subject focus or few pages that is sometimes a section in a larger Web site. Similar terms are **microsite** and **sitelet**. Typically, a minisite has a separate identity and users are encouraged to link to it directly.

MIPS

The number of MIPS (million instructions per second) is a general measure of computing **performance** and, by implication, the amount of work a larger computer can do. For large **servers** or **mainframes**, MIPS is a way to measure the cost of computing: The more MIPS delivered for the money, the better the value. Historically, the cost of computing measured in the number of MIPS has been reduced by half on an annual basis for a number of years.

The number of MIPS attributed to a computer is usually determined by one or more **benchmark** runs.

mirror site

A mirror site is a **Web site** or set of **file** on a computer **server** that has been copied to another computer server in order to reduce network traffic, ensure better availability of the Web site or files, or make the site or downloaded files arrive more quickly for users close to the mirror site. Mirroring is the practice of creating and maintaining mirror sites.

A mirror site is an exact replica of the original site and is usually updated frequently to ensure that it reflects the content of the original site. Mirror sites are used to make access faster when the original site may be geographically distant (for example, a much-used Web site in Germany may arrange to have a mirror site in the U.S.). In some cases, the original site (for example, on a small university server) may not have a high-speed connection to the Internet and may arrange for a mirror site at a larger site with higher-speed connection and perhaps closer proximity to a large audience.

In addition to mirroring Web sites, you can also mirror files that can be downloaded from an **File Transfer Protocol** server. Netscape, Microsoft, Sun Microsystems, and other companies have mirror sites from which you can download their **browser** software.

Mirroring could be considered a static form of **content delivery**.

MIS

MIS (management information systems) is a general term for the computer systems in an **enterprise** that provide information about its business operations. It's also used to refer to the people who manage these systems. Typically, in a large corporation, "MIS" or the "MIS department" refers to a central or centrally-coordinated system of computer expertise and management, often including **mainframe** systems but also including by extension the corporation's entire network of computer resources.

In the beginning, business computers were used for the practical business of computing the payroll and keeping track of accounts payable and receivable. As applications were developed that provided managers with information about sales, inventories, and other data that would help in managing the enterprise, the term "MIS" arose to describe these kinds of applications. Today, the term is used broadly in a number of contexts and includes (but is not limited to): decision support systems, resource and people management applications, project management, and database retrieval applications.

MITOCW

See "OpenCourseWare"

mks system of units

See "metric system"

MMC

See "Microsoft Management Console"

MMDS

See "Multichannel Multipoint Distribution Service"

MME

See "MIM"

MMX

MMX is a Pentium **microprocessor** from Intel that is designed to run faster when playing multimedia applications. According to Intel, a PC with an MMX microprocessor runs a multimedia application up to 60% faster than one with a microprocessor having the same clock speed but without MMX. In addition, an MMX microprocessor runs other applications about 10% faster.

The MMX technology consists of three improvements over the non-MMX Pentium microprocessor:

1. 57 new microprocessor instructions have been added that are designed to handle video, audio, and graphical data more efficiently.

2. A new process, Single Instruction Multiple Data (**SIMD**), makes it possible for one instruction to perform the same operation on multiple data items.

3. The **memory cache** on the microprocessor has increased to 32 thousand bytes, meaning fewer accesses to memory that is off the microprocessor.

mnemonic

1) In general, a mnemonic (from Greek *mnemon* or mindful; pronounced neh-MAHN-ik) is a word, abbreviation, rhyme, or similar verbal device you learn or create in order to remember something. The technique of developing these remembering devices is called "mnemonics." Mnemonics is used to remember phone numbers, all your new department colleagues' names, or the years of the reigns of the Kings and Queens of England. A number of approaches are used. Here's a simple one for remembering a list of unrelated items in order: Start at the top of the list and make up an outlandish story connecting the first item to the next, continue by connecting the second item to the third, and so on. When your story is done and the list is removed, you'll have a mental picture of a story that, as you recall its progression, will lead you from one remembered item to the next.

2) In computer **assembler** (or assembly) language, a mnemonic is an abbreviation for an operation. It's entered in the operation code field of each assembler program instruction. For example, on an Intel microprocessor, **inc** ("increase by one") is a mnemonic. On an IBM System/370 series computer, **BAL** is a mnemonic for "branch-and-link."

MO drive

See "magneto-optical drive"

mobile satellite services

Mobile satellite services (MSS) refers to networks of communications satellites intended for use with mobile and portable **wireless** telephones. There are three major types: AMSS (aeronautical MSS), LMSS (land MSS), and MMSS (maritime MSS).

A telephone connection using MSS is similar to a **cellular telephone** link, except the repeaters are in orbit around the earth, rather than on the surface. MSS repeaters can be placed on geostationary, medium earth orbit (**MEO**), or low earth orbit (**LEO**) satellites. Provided there are enough satellites in the system, and provided they are properly spaced around the globe, an MSS can link any two wireless telephone sets at any time, no matter where in the world they are located. MSS systems are interconnected with land-based cellular networks.

As an example of how MSS can work, consider telephones in commercial airliners. These sets usually link into the standard cellular system. This allows communication as long as the aircraft is on a line of sight with at least one land-based cellular repeater. Coverage is essentially continuous over most developed countries. But coverage is spotty over less well-developed regions, and is nonexistent at most points over the oceans. Using an MSS network, the aircraft can establish a connection from any location, no matter how remote.

Mobitex

Mobitex is a **wireless** network **architecture** that specifies a framework for the fixed equipment necessary to support all the wireless terminals in a **packet-switched**, radio-based communication system. The three major components of a Mobitex network are the radio base station, the MX switch, and the network management center (NCC). Mobitex was developed in 1984 by Eritel, an Ericsson subsidiary, for the Swedish Telecommunication Administration.

In a Mobitex network, a radio base station, with one or more switches (called MX switches), serves as the **transmitter** for each single **cell** (area of coverage) of up to 30 km. The base stations, among them, provide an area of coverage and determine the network capacity. Users of wireless devices, such as mobile phones and personal digital assistants (PDAs), communicate through the base station nearest to them and can move freely from one cell to another.

The use of packet-switching technology for data transmission is less expensive than **circuit-switching**, which uses a dedicated path for each transmission. Mobitex packets (called *MPAKs*) are limited to 512 bytes of data. Each packet contains information about its origin and destination, size, type, and sequence within a transmission to ensure that it reaches its destination intact. Because packets can be sent on any route and in any order, they make more efficient use of channel capacity, supporting up to 50 times as many users per channel as a circuit-switched network. At the destination, packets are reorganized into the original transmission format.

MX switches control communication routes to and from base stations and between wireless and fixed devices. Switches may be organized hierarchically into groupings of regional and area switches, all connected by fixed links. The MX switches also act as a **gateway** to other networks. A single network management center (NCC) takes care of maintenance and operations such as configuration and subscriber administration and billing.

Currently at least twenty-eight Mobitex networks are in operation in twenty-two countries, mostly operating at either 80, 400, or 900 megahertz (**MHz**). In the US, Mobitex networks generally operate at 900 MHz, while European networks usually operate at 400 MHz. The Mobitex Operators Association (MOA) controls Mobitex specifications; Ericsson manufactures the **infrastructure** components.

mobo

Mobo is a short form for **motherboard** that is sometimes used in **Usenet** newsgroups and Web forum discussions.

model-view-controller

In **object-oriented programming** development, model-view-controller (MVC) is the name of a methodology or design **pattern** for successfully and efficiently relating the user interface to underlying data models. The MVC pattern is widely used in program development with programming languages such as Java, Smalltalk, C, and C++.

The MVC pattern has been heralded by many developers as a useful pattern for the reuse of object code and a pattern that allows them to significantly reduce the time it takes to develop applications with user interfaces.

The model-view-controller pattern proposes three main components or objects to be used in software development:

- A *Model*, which represents the underlying, logical structure of data in a software application and the high-level class associated with it. This object model does not contain any information about the user interface.

- A *View*, which is a collection of classes representing the elements in the user interface (all of the things the user can see and respond to on the screen, such as buttons, display boxes, and so forth).

- A *Controller*, which represents the classes connecting the model and the view, and is used to communicate between classes in the model and view.

modem

A modem (short for "modulator-demodulator") modulates outgoing **digital** signals from a computer or other digital device to **analog** signals on a conventional copper **twisted pair** telephone line and demodulates the incoming analog signal and converts it to a digital signal for the digital device.

In recent years, the 2400 **bits per second** modem that could carry e-mail has become obsolete. 14.4 **Kbps** and 28.8 Kbps modems were temporary landing places on the way to the much higher **bandwidth** devices and carriers of tomorrow. From early 1998, most new personal computers came with 56 Kbps modems. By comparison, using a digital **Integrated Services Digital Network** adapter instead of a conventional modem, the same telephone wire can now carry up to 128 Kbps. With Digital Subscriber Line (**DSL**) systems, now being deployed in a number of communities, bandwidth on twisted-pair can be in the megabit range.

modem bonding

See "modem doubling"

modem doubling

Modem doubling is an inexpensive way for a user who wants a fast Internet connection, but can only connect with an analog telephone line, to use two 56kbps modems to double their bandwidth. **Modem** doubling makes it possible for the user to use one of two methods, modem bonding or modem teaming, to achieve a connection speed close to 112 Kbps.

Modem bonding, which is supported by over ninety percent of Internet Service Providers (**ISPs**), takes advantage of Multilink Protocol Plus (MP+). Data packets are "inverse-multiplexed" through the two modems, meaning that each of the modems receive half of the data packets as they are sent over the Internet and then they are recombined. An advantage of modem bonding is that if either of the modems gets disconnected for some reason, the other modem will take over so that the connection isn't lost.

Modem teaming, a good alternative for users whose IPS does not support MP+, allows the modems to work as separate connections by taking advantage of the "smart download" capability that most HTTP and FTP servers use in case a download is interrupted. Modem teaming requires a software application to instruct one modem to download the first part of the file while the other modem downloads the second part. A disadvantage of modem teaming is that it is not flexible if one modem should disconnect, nor is it useful when downloading **streaming** multimedia or conducting continuous sessions such as **Telnet** or PCAnywhere.

modem error-correcting protocols

The **protocol**s that **modem**s agree on and use for checking and correcting transmission errors have evolved toward accuracy, speed, and efficiency since 1978 when the Xmodem protocol became a de facto standard. To briefly summarize: In all protocols data is chunked into "blocks" of a certain byte size and sent to the destination modem which checks each block for errors and, depending on the results and the protocol, returns a positive (ACK) or negative (NAK) acknowledgement, the latter usually resulting in a retransmission. The type of checking (**checksum** or **cyclic redundancy checking**) and the frequency at which a response is sent vary by protocol. Today, new modems use a V.42 protocol, but the earlier protocols are still in use for older modems.

modem lights

If you have an external modem, those flashing or steady lights tell you what's happening in the ongoing "handshaking" or interaction between your computer (with its Universal Asynchronous Receiver/Transmitter or **UART** microchip) and the **modem**. Or, more formally, to use the **RS-232C** serial standard terms, between the Data Terminal Equipment (**DTE**) interface and the Data Communication Equipment (**DCE**) interface.

Protocol	Block size	Frequency of response	Type of checking	Other information
Xmodem	128 bytes	Every block	Checksum	Also called MODEM 7
Xmodem CRC	128 bytes	Every block	Cyclic redundancy checking	Cyclic redundancy checks detect errors that checksum won't
Xmodem-1K	1024 bytes	Every block	Cyclic redundancy check	Better for large files
WXmodem	128 bytes	Every block but doesn't hold up the sender before accepting the next block	Checksum	More efficient than Xmodem
Ymodem	1024 bytes	Every block	Cyclic redundancy check	Includes a batch mode that allows multiple files to be sent with one command
Ymodem-g	1024 bytes	Only when an error is detected to blocks sent as a stream and all must arrive successfully	Cyclic redundancy check	Supports batch transfers
Zmodem	512 bytes	When a block with an error is detected	Cyclic redundancy check	A transmission can be interrrupted and resumed without retransmitting blocks already sent.
Kermit	Adjusts to the computer system	When a block with an error is detected	Checksum	Can resynchonrize transmissions after a line interruption
V.42 (LAPM)	128 bytes	Up to 15 blocks (frames) can be sent before a response	Cyclic redundancy check	This takes precedence over V.42 MNP4.
V.42 (MNP4)	Varies	When a packet (block) with an error is detected	Cyclic redundancy check	Used when LAPM can't be used by both modems.

Modem Light	Meaning
AA (auto answer)	The modem is ready to respond to an incoming call (assuming a communication program is also ready to handle the call). Since this light can be off even when the modem is ready, it's not useful.
CD (carrier detect)	This simply indicates that the computer and the modem have recognized each other and that a carrier connection is established. If a second call is received, carrier detect may be temporarily interrupted and, depending on a number of factors, the first connection may be dropped or lost.
HS (high speed)	If on, indicates that the modem is ready to transfer data at its highest speed. Since this is often the case, this light is also not very useful.
MR (modem ready)	If on, indicates that your modem is ready to operate.
OH (off hook)	If on, tells you that the phone line is ready for use.
RD (receive data)	When flashing on, indicates that the modem is receiving data or signals from a remote computer.
SD (send data)	When flashing on, indicates that the modem is sending data or signals to another computer.
TR (terminal ready)	When on, indicates that your computer's communications program is active. If it's not on, either the program or your computer may not be working.

modem teaming

See "modem doubling"

modem V.xx standards

See "V.xx"

modulation

Modulation is the addition of information to an electronic or optical **signal carrier**. Modulation can be applied to direct current (mainly by turning it on and off), to alternating current, and to optical signals. One can think of blanket waving as a form of modulation used in smoke signal transmission (the carrier being a steady stream of smoke). Morse code, invented for telegraphy and still used in amateur radio, uses a **binary** (two-state) **digital** code similar to the code used by modern computers. For most of radio and telecommunication today, the carrier is alternating current (**AC**) in a given range of **frequencies**. Common modulation methods include:

- **Amplitude modulation (AM)**, in which the voltage applied to the signal is varied over time
- **Frequency modulation (FM)**, in which the **frequency** of the carrier signal is transmitted is varied in small but meaningful amounts
- **Phase modulation (PM)**, in which the natural flow of the alternating current **waveform** is delayed temporarily

These are sometimes known as *continuous wave* modulation methods to distinguish them from pulse code modulation (**PCM**), which is used to encode both digital and analog information in a binary way. Radio and television **broadcast** stations typically use AM or FM. Most two-way radios use FM, although some employ a mode known as *single sideband* (SSB).

More complex forms of modulation are Phase Shift Keying (**PSK**) and Quadrature Amplitude Modulation (QAM). Optical signals are modulated by applying an electromagnetic current to vary the intensity of the laser beam.

Modem Modulation and Demodulation

Any computer with an online or Internet connection includes a **modem**. This term is derived by combining the first three letters of the words *mod*ulator and *dem*odulator. In a modem, the modulation process involves the conversion of the digital computer signals (high and low, or logic 1 and 0 states) to analog audio-frequency (AF) tones. Digital highs are converted to a tone having a certain constant pitch; digital lows are converted to a tone having a different constant pitch. These states alternate so rapidly that, if you listen to the output of a computer modem, it sounds like a hiss or roar. The demodulation process converts the audio tones back into digital signals that a computer can understand. directly.

Multiplexing

More information can be conveyed in a given amount of time by dividing the **bandwidth** of a signal carrier so that more than one modulated signal is sent on the same carrier. Known as multiplexing, the carrier is referred to as a **channel** and each separate signal carried on it is called a *subchannel*. The device that puts the separate signals on the carrier and takes them off of received transmissions is a multiplexer. Common types of multiplexing include frequency-division multiplexing (FDM) and time-division multiplexing (TDM). FDM is usually used for analog communication and divides the main frequency of the carrier into separate subchannels, each with its own frequency band within the overall bandwidth. TDM is used for digital communication and divides the main signal into time-slots, with each time-slot carrying a separate signal.

module

In computers, a module (pronounced MAHD-yewl, from Latin *modulus*, diminutive of *modus*, the measure or way of being) is, in general, a separate unit of software or hardware. The term was first used in architecture.

1) In computer programming, especially in older languages such as **PL/1**, the output of the language **compiler** was known as an *object module* to distinguish it from the set of *source* language statements, sometimes known as the *source module*. In mainframe systems such as IBM's OS/360, the object module was then linked together with other object modules to form a *load module*. The load module was the executable code that you ran in the computer.

Modular programming is the concept that similar functions should be contained within the same unit of programming code and that separate functions should be developed as separate units of code so that the code can easily be maintained and reused by different programs. **Object-oriented programming** is a newer idea that inherently encompasses modular programming.

2) In computer hardware and electronics, a module is a relatively compact unit in a larger device or arrangement that is designed to be separately installed, replaced, or serviced. For example, a single in-line memory module is a unit of random access memory (**RAM**) that you can add to a personal computer.

mole

The mole (abbreviation, mol) is the International System of Units (**SI**) unit of material quantity. One mole is the number of **atom**s in precisely 12 thousandths of a **kilogram** (0.012 kg) of C-12, the most common naturally-occurring isotope of the element carbon. This number is equal to approximately 6.022169×10^{23}, and is also called the Avogadro constant.

The mole is the only fundamental SI unit that is dimensionless. That means it represents a simple numerical quantity or value; it is a term similar in nature to "dozen" (meaning 12) or "gross" (meaning 144). But 1 mol is, unlike a dozen or a gross, an incomprehensibly large number. Written out in decimal form, it appears as 602,216,900,000,000,000,000,000. Envision a huge cubical box measuring about 84 kilometers (84 km) on each edge. Then imagine that box being neatly packed full of sand-grain-size cubes measuring a millimeter (1 mm) on an edge. If this were done, the box would contain roughly 1 mol of cubes.

The mole is of interest primarily to chemists and physicists. Sometimes, larger or smaller units are defined by attaching power-of-10 **prefix multiplier**s. For example, a kilomole (1 kmol) is 10^3 mol, or approximately 6.022169×10^{26}, and a millimole (1 mmol) is 10^{-3} mol, or approximately 6.022169×10^{20}.

Also see **amount of substance**, **prefix multiplier**, and International System of Units (**SI**).

mole per meter cubed

The mole per meter cubed (mol/m^3) is the International Unit of amount-of-substance concentration. It is an expression of the number of **atom**s of a substance per unit volume, and is of interest primarily to chemists and physicists.

One mole is equal to approximately 6.022169×10^{23}, and is also called the Avogadro constant. Thus, 1 mol/m^3 represents approximately 6.022169×10^{23} atoms of a substance in one cubic meter of space.

Sometimes, larger or smaller units are defined by attaching power-of-10 prefix multipliers. For example, a kilomole per meter cubed (1 $kmol/m^3$) is 10^3 mol/m^3, or approximately 6.022169×10^{26} atoms per cubic meter; a nanomole per meter cubed (1 $nmol/m^3$) is 10^{-9} mol/m^3, or approximately 6.022169×10^{14} atoms per cubic meter.

Also see **meter cubed**, **mole**, **prefix multiplier**s, and **SI** (International System of Units).

Molex

Molex is a company, in business since 1936, that manufactures electronic, electrical, and **optical fiber** connectors. Molex also makes a variety of **switch** and application tooling, especially crimp application tooling. Crimping is the metallurgical compression of a terminal around the conductor of a wire, which creates a common electrical path of low **resistance** and high **current**-carrying capabilities. A secondary crimp around the insulation of the wire provides support for insertion into a housing and allows the terminal to withstand shock and vibration. The crimp technology was developed as a substitute to soldering and the problems associated with it. Crimp terminations can be applied with a basic hand tool, a press and die set, a stripper crimper, or a fully automatic wire processing system.

Molex's Insulation Displacement Technology (IDT) is a wire termination technique in which an insulated wire is pressed into a terminal slot smaller than the conductor diameter, displacing the insulation and forming an electrical contact between the terminal and conductor.

Other Molex products include thermal acoustic products (noise reduction and thermal component products for quieting and cooling personal computers) and cable assemblies.

momentum

Momentum is a **vector** quantity that is the product of the **mass** and the **velocity** of an object or particle. The standard unit of momentum magnitude is the **kilogram-meter per second** (kg · m/s or kg · m · s⁻¹). Alternatively, the gram-centimeter per second (g · cm/s or g · cm · s⁻¹) can be used to express momentum magnitude. The direction of a momentum vector can be expressed in various ways, depending on the number of dimensions involved, and is the same as the direction of the velocity vector.

Momentum, like velocity, is relative. Consider a 1,000-kg car moving at 20 m/s with respect to the surface of a highway, traveling northward. If you are driving the car, the momentum of the car relative to your body is zero. If you stand by the side of the road, the momentum of the car relative to you is 20,000 kg · m/s northward.

If you are driving a 1,000-kg car at 15 m/s with respect to the road and are traveling northward, and a truck of mass 1,500 kg is moving 20 m/s with respect to the road and comes up behind you in the same direction, the truck's momentum relative to you is the product of its relative velocity (5 m/s northward) and its mass (1,500 kg), or 7,500 kg · m/s northward. Relative to the truck, the momentum of your car will be in the opposite direction, and will be smaller: 5 m/s × 1,000 kg = 5,000 kg · m/s southward. Thus, if a collision occurs, the danger is greater to the object that is less massive.

If the above mentioned truck passes you going the opposite way on the road, its momentum relative to you is 35 m/s × 1,500 kg southward, or 52,500 kg · m/s southward. Relative to it, your momentum is 35 m/s × 1,000 kg northward, or 35,000 kg m/s northward. In that situation, as with the rear-end scenario, the peril is greater to the less massive vehicle in the event of a collision.

Momentum, like velocity, can be expressed either as an average over a period of time or as an instantaneous value at a single moment in time.

Also see **mass**, **velocity**, **vector**, **SI** (International System of Units), and **Table of Physical Units**.

moniker

In general, a moniker is a name or a nickname and, in the simplest terms, that is what it is in computer terminology as well. A moniker is an **object** (or **component**) in Microsoft's Component Object Model (**COM**) that refers to a specific **instance** of another object. Monikers originated in Microsoft's Object Linking and Embedding (**OLE**) technology as a means of linking objects.

A moniker may refer to any single object, or may be a composite made of a number of separate monikers, each of which refers to a particular instantiation of an object. The moniker is sometimes referred to as an "intelligent name," because it retains information about how to create, **initialize**,

and **bind** to a single instance of an object. Once created, the moniker holds this information, as well as information about the object's states in that specific instantiation.

Since COM is not language-specific, a moniker can be used with any programming language. The programmer gives the instantiation of the object a name. By calling the moniker in code, a programmer can refer to the same object with the same states. If, for example, a moniker is created for a **query**, the programmer can reuse the query simply by calling the moniker in the code, because the moniker itself has the necessary information.

monitor

In computers, a monitor is a computer **display** and related parts packaged in a physical unit that is separate from other parts of the computer. Notebook computers don't have monitors because all the display and related parts are integrated into the same physical unit with the rest of the computer. In practice, the terms *monitor* and *display* are used interchangably.

MOO

A MOO is an **object**-oriented **MUD**. According to Canton Becker, author of "The Unofficial Moo Guide Tutorial," a MOO is:

> "...just a programming language in which you design objects. Everything is an object. Rooms are objects, exits are objects, possessions are objects, even your MOO alter-ego/**avatar** is an object. We'll be looking at how you (1) make objects, and (2) write verbs that allow you to do Interesting Things with those objects. I'm not going to talk too much about the philosophy of **object-oriented programming** (that's what the OO in MOO stands for) so let's go ahead and make your first object:"

Canton Becker's first example (of creating an object) looks like this:

```
'@create $thing called kleenex'
```

You can then go on to relate the object to other objects and define the verbs that work with the object (which is given a number by the MOO server). Effectively, you can set up how other MOO participants will be able to use or view your object.

moof monster

The moof monster is a vague and indefinable source of trouble for users of information technology. The term is used especially by people who frequent Internet Relay Chat (**IRC**) channels. If you're suddenly disconnected from your channel, it can be attributed to the moof monster. You are said to have been "moofed." The term seems reminiscent of the *gremlin* of the 1940 era.

This term is apparently unrelated to the "moof!", the sound of the **dogcow** in an Apple Macintosh.

moonbounce

Moonbounce, also called Earth-Moon-Earth (EME), is a form of **wireless** communication in which the moon is used as a passive **satellite**. To the uninitiated, this sounds a little like science fiction, but it has been done and continues to be done by experimentally-inclined **amateur radio** operators.

There are several challenges and difficulties inherent in moonbounce operation. One of the most troublesome for two-way communication is the fact that the moon's distance introduces lag time. The moon is approximately 250,000 miles away from the earth, and radio waves travel at 186,282 miles per second. A signal sent to the moon does not return until 2.7 seconds have elapsed. If two people are engaged in a conversation and one person asks a question, that person cannot expect a reply until at least 5.4 seconds later (the answer must travel to the moon and back, as must the question).

Besides propagation delay, the path loss to and from the moon is considerable. The moon is a relatively poor reflector of electromagnetic rays at any **wavelength**, including radio waves. Its surface is irregular, and it scatters, rather than focusing, reflected energy. Because of this, sophisticated equipment is necessary to successfully bounce a signal off the moon and hear it return.

Another problem with moonbounce communication is libration fading and Doppler shifting. The moon does not always present exactly the same face; it "wobbles" a few degrees back and forth. This "wobbling," called libration, produces a constant change in every component of any signal reflected from the moon. The returned signal consists of the sum total of countless rays that have bounced off mountains, boulders, crater walls, and other lunar features. The relative phase of these components rapidly fluctuates because of libration, so any signal returning from the moon is "fluttery" and distorted.

Amateur-radio moonbounce generally requires the following:

- A sensitive receiver with a narrowband filter
- A transmitter capable of operating on at least one amateur band above 144 MHz, and capable of producing 1500 watts of continuous radio-frequency output
- An **antenna** with high directivity and gain, capable of being rotated in both the azimuth and elevation planes
- A location in which the moon can be seen without obstruction for extended periods
- A location in which human-made radio noise is minimal
- Neighbors who will tolerate the presence of a large antenna and the proximity of a high-power radio transmitter
- A neighborhood without ordinances or covenants prohibiting large antennas and/or high-power radio transmitters
- Operating skill and patience

Moore's Law

Moore's Law is that the pace of **microchip** technology change is such that the amount of data storage that a microchip can hold doubles every year or at least every 18 months. In 1965 when preparing a talk, Gordon Moore noticed that up to that time microchip capacity seemed to double each year. The pace of change having slowed down a bit over the past few years, the definition has changed (with Gordon Moore's approval) to reflect that the doubling occurs only every 18 months.

Morphis

Morphis is a **Java**-based **open source** wireless **transcoding platform** from Kargo, Inc., a wireless technology company based in New York City. The new application development platform will enable delivery of customized text and graphics to users of wireless devices, such as mobile phones, personal digital assistants (**PDA**s), and **handheld** computers. Morphis provides a framework for the transformation of binary, plain text, and text markup content to suitable formats for wireless applications. It can also process images, as well as Hypertext Markup Language (**HTML**), Wireless Markup Language (**WML**), and Wireless Abstract for **XML** (**WAX**), an integral part of Morphis.

According to Kargo's Morphis product description, the platform supplies a framework that allows users to retrieve, translate, and convert any electronic document. Morphis' Extensible Markup Language (**XML**) processing framework uses Simple API for XML (**SAX**) event processing and XSL Transformations (**XSLT**). A single document may undergo multiple translations and **filters**; complex logic can be provided by writing XSLT extensions. Multiple complex transformations are performed through a pipeline SAX processing engine. Kargo claims that Morphis will allow content providers to develop both current and future wireless applications without requiring they use specific standards or technologies.

Mosaic

Mosaic was the first widely-distributed graphical **browser** or viewer for the World Wide Web. It is usually considered to have been the software that introduced the World Wide Web (and the Internet) to a wide general audience. Once Mosaic was available, the Web virtually exploded in numbers of users and content sites. (Of course, the software depended on the recent invention of the Hypertext Transport Protocol, or **Hypertext Transfer Protocol**, by Dr. Tim Berners-Lee.)

Mosaic arrived in 1993. Marc Andreessen, then in his early 20's, is credited with inventing or leading the development of Mosaic. He developed it at the National Center for Supercomputing Applications (**NCSA**) at the University of Illinois in Urbana, Illinois. Andreessen and others went on to become part of Netscape Communications, originally called Mosaic Communications, that developed what was initially the Web's most popular browser, **Netscape** (its full name is Netscape Navigator).

The original Mosaic, now in a later version, has since been licensed for commercial use and is provided to users by several Internet access providers.

Other browsers include Microsoft Internet Explorer (**MSIE**), a text-only browser, **Lynx**, and Opera.

motherboard

A motherboard is the physical arrangement in a computer that contains the computer's basic circuitry and components. On the typical motherboard, the circuitry is imprinted or affixed to the surface of a firm planar surface and usually manufactured in a single step. The most common motherboard design in desktop computers today is the AT, based on the IBM AT motherboard. A more recent motherboard specification, **ATX**, improves on the AT design. In both the AT and ATX designs, the computer components included in the motherboard are:

- The microprocessor
- (Optionally) coprocessors
- Memory
- basic input/output system (**BIOS**)
- Expansion **slot**
- Interconnecting circuitry

Additional components can be added to a motherboard through its expansion slot. The electronic interface between the motherboard and the smaller boards or cards in the expansion slots is called the **bus**.

Motif

1) Motif is a graphical user interface (**GUI**) guideline and development toolkit for the **X Window System**. As such, it defines the rules and tools for the "look-and-feel" in the graphical user interface of most **UNIX**-based operating systems and their applications. Developed in 1989 by the Open Software Foundation (now part of **The Open Group**), Motif corresponds to IBM's Common User Access (CUA) guideline for its **OS/2** Presentation Manager and to the guidelines built into the Microsoft Windows application programming interfaces, including the **Microsoft Foundation Class Library** for user interface objects (often called **widgets**).

The Motif Toolkit, also known as "Xm," ensures consistency with the Motif guideline and is used with the X Toolkit Intrinsics ("Xt"). In turn, Xt is built on the lowest-level application program level, X library ("Xlib"). The Motif Style Guide, which describes how to conform to the guideline, is published as an industry standard (IEEE 1295, orderable from the **Institute of Electrical and Electronics Engineers**). Motif is the base graphical user interface toolkit for the Open Group's Common Desktop Environment (CDE).

2) Motif is also the name of a Microsoft Windows program **object** for a sound sequence or musical *motif* (short theme or iconic sound). Motifs are also known as Microsoft Interactive Music Controls.

motion plan

A motion plan is a multi-step process that can be used by a **robot** to precisely position itself to perform a specified task.

Suppose you own an autonomous mobile personal robot. You tell it to switch on the light in a bedroom. The light switch is on the wall. The robot has a computer map of the house stored in its controller memory. This three-dimensional map includes the exact coordinates of the bedroom light switch, and/or its position relative to other objects. The robot first proceeds to the general location of the switch. The program that facilitates this is known as a gross-motion plan.

In order to find the switch, and to position its end-effector (robot hand) in the right place to toggle it, a fine-motion plan is required. **Machine vision** can facilitate this. An example is the so-called eye-in-hand system, which allows the robot to recognize the shape of the switch and guide the end effector into place, down to millimeter displacements or smaller. Another method of executing the fine-motion plan involves tactile sensing, in which the robot's end effector gropes along the wall until it finds and throws the switch, just as you could find and throw it with your eyes closed once you were in its general vicinity.

Also see **artificial intelligence**, **eye-in-hand system**, **grasping plan**, and **robotics**.

mount

In computers, to mount is to make a group of files in a file system structure accessible to a user or user group. In some usages, it means to make a device physically accessible.

Macintosh calls it mounting when a user inserts a disc into the machine. In a **UNIX** environment, the mount command attaches disks, or directories logically rather than physically.

The Unix mount command makes a directory accessible by attaching a root directory of one file system to another directory, which makes all the file systems usable as if they were subdirectories of the file system they are attached to. Unix recognizes devices by their location, as compared to Windows, which recognizes them by their names (C: drive, for example). Unix organizes directories in a tree-like structure, in which directories are attached by *mounting* them on the branches of the tree. The file system location where the device is attached is called a *mount point*.

Mounts may be local or remote. A local mount connects disc drives on one machine so that they behave as one logical system. A remote mount uses Network File System (**NFS**) to connect to directories on other machines so that they can be used as if they were all part of the user's file system.

mouse

A mouse is a small **device** that a computer user pushes across a desk surface in order to point to a place on a display screen and to select one or more actions to take from that position. The mouse first became a widely-used computer tool when Apple Computer made it a standard part of the Apple Macintosh. Today, the mouse is an integral part of the graphical user interface (**GUI**) of any personal computer. The mouse apparently got its name by being about the same size and color as a toy mouse.

A mouse consists of a metal or plastic housing or casing, a ball that sticks out of the bottom of the casing and is rolled on a flat surface, one or more buttons on the top of the casing, and a cable that connects the mouse to the computer. As the ball is moved over the surface in any direction, a sensor sends impulses to the computer that causes a mouse-responsive program to reposition a visible indicator (called a *cursor*) on the display screen. The positioning is relative to some variable starting place. Viewing the cursor's present position, the user readjusts the position by moving the mouse.

The most conventional kind of mouse has two buttons on top: the left one is used most frequently. In the Windows operating systems, it lets the user click once to send a "Select" indication that provides the user with feedback that a particular position has been selected for further action. The next click on a selected position or two quick clicks on it causes a particular action to take place on the selected object. For example, in Windows operating systems, it causes a program associated with that object to be started. The second button, on the right, usually provides some less-frequently needed capability. For example, when viewing a Web page, you can click on an image to get a popup menu that, among other things, lets you save the image on your hard disk. Some mouses have a third button for additional capabilities. Some mouse manufacturers also provide a version for left-handed people.

Windows and other operating systems let the user adjust the sensitivity of the mouse, including how fast it moves across the screen, and the amount of time that must elapse within a "double click." In some systems, the user can also choose among several different cursor appearances. Some people use a **mousepad** to improve traction for the mouse ball.

Although the mouse has become a familiar part of the personal computer, its design continues to evolve and there continue to be other approaches to pointing or positioning on a display. Notebook computers include built-in mouse devices that let you control the cursor by rolling your finger over a built-in trackball. IBM's ScrollPoint mouse adds a small "stick" between two mouse buttons that lets you scroll a Web page or other content up or down and right or left. Users of graphic design and **CAD** applications can use a stylus and a specially-sensitive pad to draw as well as move the cursor. Other display screen-positioning ideas include a video camera that tracks the user's eye movement and places the cursor accordingly.

mouse miles

Mouse miles is slang for user time at the computer (as in "I traveled a lot of mouse miles this week") and also an actual measure of how much activity a computer mouse has had over time.

At least two companies offer **shareware** you can download that will tell you how many miles your mouse has traveled. One product provides a visual warning signal when it's time to clean your mouse.

mouse potato

A mouse potato is the computer equivalent of television's *couch potato*: Someone who tends to spend a great deal of leisure time in front of the computer in much the same way the couch potato does in front of the television. Both activities tend to be accompanied by snacking. A recent survey by the American Snack Food Association found that 85% of Web surfers snack at the computer. It has been observed that this habitual nibbling and relative inactivity can lead to development of a characteristic potato-like body form.

Television networks are concerned about the new phenomenon; they want to keep their potatoes planted on the couch. The Web's main lure—and what television has been lacking—is the capacity for interaction, something that will be increasingly built into television broadcasting with the move to **digital television** and the **cable modem**. The convergence of television and the computer could perhaps be viewed as the convergence of the couch potato and the mouse potato.

mouseover

See "rollover"

mousepad

A mousepad is a small, portable surface that sometimes provides better traction for the ball on a computer **mouse** and, at the very least, provides a bounded area in which to move the mouse. On very smooth table or desktop surfaces,

the mouse ball may tend to glide instead of roll unless pressure is continually applied. Some mousepads provide a slightly rougher surface so that it's easier to get the mouse to move the screen cursor. A mousepad usually has a plastic surface and a thin rubber or plastic cushion.

Mousepads are sometimes given away at computer and Internet trade shows or with Internet or computer magazine subscriptions.

Mozilla

Mozilla was Netscape Communication's nickname for Navigator, its Web **browser**, and, more recently, the name of an **open source** public collaboration aimed at making improvements to Navigator. This public collaboration was essentially launched and is still substantially supported by Netscape (now owned by AOL); however, the Mozilla project is independent. Netscape can use its code but so can anyone else.

Mozilla originated as a name used by Navigator's developers before the product had a commercial name and in varying degrees has continued to be nurtured by the company's founders (of which the chief was Marc Andreessen, who designed **Mosaic**, the first Web browser with a graphical user interface). From time to time, Netscape has used Mozilla as the name of a kind of mascot or cartoon alterego created by illustrator Dave Titus.

MP3

MP3 (MPEG-1 Audio Layer-3) is a standard technology and format for **compressing** a sound sequence into a very small file (about one-twelfth the size of the original file) while preserving the original level of sound quality when it is played. MP3 files (identified with the file name suffix of ".mp3") are available for downloading from a number of **Web sites**. Many **Windows** users will find that they have a player built into their operating system. Otherwise, you can download a player from one of several popular MP3 sites. MP3 files are usually download-and-play files rather than **streaming sound** files that you link-and-listen-to with RealPlayer and similar products (However, streaming MP3 is possible.) Winamp (PC), MacAmp (Mac), and mpeg123 (UNIX) are popular MP3 players, but there are many others. To create an MP3 file, you use a program called a **ripper** to get a selection from a CD onto your **hard disk** and another program called an **encoder** to convert the selection to an MP3 file. Most people, however, simply download MP3s from someone else and play them.

Digital audio is typically created by taking 16 **bit** samples a second of the **analog** signal. Since this signal is typically spread out over a spectrum of 44.1 thousand cycles per second (**kHz**), this means that one second of CD quality sound requires 1.4 million bits of data. Using their knowledge of how people actually perceive sound, the developers of MP3 devised a compression **algorithm** that

reduces data about sound that most listeners can not perceive. MP3 is currently the most powerful algorithm in a series of audio encoding standards developed under the sponsorship of the Motion Picture Experts Group (**MPEG**) and formalized by the International Organization for Standardization (**ISO**).

Since it is relatively easy to create MP3 files from CD selections and make them available on Web sites for downloading, companies and sites that promote the MP3 format are sometimes accused of encouraging copyright violations. (It is illegal to copy music from a CD and redistribute it unless you have the copyright owner's permission.) On the other hand, MP3 enthusiasts claim that what CD publishers are afraid of is any kind of non-CD distribution. While there are several proposals for how to discourage such piracy, there is currently no secure distribution and copyright management standard that publishers and other parties agree upon.

MPE/iX

MPE/iX is the **operating system** for the line of **e3000 midrange** business **server**s from **Hewlett-Packard** (HP). Its latest version, MPE/iX Version 7.0, is marketed as "Web-enabled" and "Internet-ready." The operating system includes support for **Java** and HP describes it as providing "**OLTP** performance and functionality for business-critical applications." Support also is provided for **PCI** I/O devices. HP emphasizes the value of an operating system that, since its first release in 1972 has built a reputation for being stable, reliable, and **robust**.

MPE/iX provides support for applications that use standard **POSIX** C functions. In 2001, HP plans to run MPE-iX on e3000s that use the Intel **Itanium** (**IA-64**) microprocessor architecture. MPE originally stood for "Multi-Programming Executive." The "iX" suggests its new support for POSIX (UNIX-compatible) applications and interfaces and a hierarchical file system. Unlike HP's other major operating system, **HP-UX** (for the HP 9000 server line), MPE/iX supports all the **legacy application**s that have been written for HP 3000 computers over the years.

MPEG

MPEG (pronounced EHM-pehg), the Moving Picture Experts Group, develops standards for **digital video** and digital **audio compression**. It operates under the auspices of the International Organization for Standardization (**ISO**). The **MPEG standards** are an evolving series, each designed for a different purpose.

To use MPEG video files, you need a personal computer with sufficient processor speed, internal memory, and hard disk space to handle and play the typically large MPEG file (which has a file name suffix of .mpg). You also need an MPEG viewer or client software that plays MPEG files. (Note that .mp3 file suffixes indicate **MP3** (MPEG-1 audio layer-3) files, not MPEG-3 standard files.) You can download shareware or commercial MPEG players from a number of sites on the Web.

MPEG standards

The MPEG standards are an evolving set of standards for video and audio **compression** developed by the Moving Picture Experts Group (**MPEG**).

MPEG-1 was designed for coding progressive video at a transmission rate of about 1.5 million bits per second. It was designed specifically for Video-CD and CD-i media. MPEG-1 audio layer-3 (**MP3**) has also evolved from early MPEG work.

MPEG-2 was designed for coding interlaced images at transmission rates above 4 million bits per second. MPEG-2 is used for digital TV broadcast and **digital versatile discs**. An MPEG-2 player can handle MPEG-1 data as well.

A proposed MPEG-3 standard, intended for High Definition TV (**HDTV**), was merged with the MPEG-2 standard when it became apparent that the MPEG-2 standard met the HDTV requirements. An MPEG-4 standard is in the final stages of development and release. It is a much more ambitious standard and addresses speech and video synthesis, **fractal** geometry, computer **visualization**, and an artificial intelligence (**AI**) approach to reconstructing images. An MPEG-7 is being discussed.

MPEG-1 and -2 define techniques for compressing digital video by factors varying from 25:1 to 50:1. The compression is achieved using five different compression techniques:

1. The use of a frequency-based transform called Discrete Cosine Transform (DCT).

2. Quantization, a technique for losing selective information (sometimes known as *lossy compression*) that can be acceptably lost from visual information.

3. Huffman coding, a technique of lossless compression that uses code tables based on statistics about the encoded data.

4. Motion compensated predictive coding, in which the differences in what has changed between an image and its preceding image are calculated and only the differences are encoded.

5. Bi-directional prediction, in which some images are predicted from the pictures immediately preceding and following the image.

The first three techniques are also used in **JPEG** file compression.

MPLS

See "Multiprotocol Label Switching"

MPP

See "massively parallel processing"

MQSeries

MQSeries is an IBM software family whose components are used to tie together other software applications so that they can work together. This type of application is often known as *business integration software* or **middleware**.

MQSeries consists of three products:

- MQSeries Messaging, which provides the communication mechanism between applications on different platforms

- MQSeries Integrator, which centralizes and applies business operations rules

- MQSeries Workflow, which enables the capture, visualization, and automation of business processes

The point of business integration is to connect different computer systems, diverse geographical locations, and dissimilar IT infrastructures so that a seamless operation can be run. IBM's MQSeries supplies communications between applications, or between users and a set of applications on dissimilar systems. It has grown in popularity as applications are made available over the Internet because of its support of over 35 platforms and its ability to integrate disparate automation systems.

An additional helpful feature is that its messaging scheme requires the application that receives the the message to confirm receipt. If no confirmation materializes, the message is re-sent by the MQSeries.

IBM asserts that MQSeries can connect any two commercial systems that are in current business use.

MR

See "modem lights"

MRAM

MRAM (magnetoresistive random access memory) is a method of storing data bits using magnetic charges instead of the electrical charges used by **DRAM** (dynamic random access memory). Scientists define a metal as magnetoresistive if it shows a slight change in electrical resistance when placed in a **magnetic field**. By combining the high speed of **static RAM** and the high density of **DRAM**, proponents say MRAM could be used to significantly improve electronic products by storing greater amounts of data, enabling it to be accessed faster while consuming less **battery** power than existing electronic memory.

Conventional random access memory (**RAM**) computer chips store information as long as electricity flows through them. Once power is turned off, the information is lost unless it has been copied to a **hard drive** or **floppy disk**. MRAM, however, retains data after a power supply is cut off. Replacing DRAM with MRAM could prevent data loss and enable computers that start instantly, without waiting for software to boot up.

The U.S. Defense Advanced Research Projects Agency (**DARPA**) has provided funding to help private industry conduct research into the potential of MRAM. Beginning in 1995, DARPA began funding three private consortia researching the viability of making MRAM a general-purpose memory with high density, high speed, and low power usage. Leading the three consortia were IBM, Motorola, and Honeywell. Hewlett-Packard, Matsushita, NEC, Fujitsu, Toshiba, Hitachi, and Siemens also have invested in MRAM research.

Motorola Labs says its "universal memory" allows the integration of several memory options within a single chip, resulting in a chip that uses less power. The chip is a three-volt MRAM with an address **access time** of about 15 **nanosecond**s. IBM and Infineon Technologies AG are working on a proposed 256-megabit chip they say could be on the market in 2004.

Development of MRAM basically followed two scientific schools: 1) spin electronics, the science behind giant magnetoresistive heads used in disk drives and 2) tunneling magnetic resistance, or TMR, which is expected to be the basis of future MRAM.

mrouter

An mrouter, or multicast router, is a **router** program that distinguishes between **multicast** and **unicast packet**s and determines how they should be distributed along the Multicast Internet (sometimes known as the Multicast Backbone or **MBone**). Using an appropriate **algorithm**, an mrouter tells a switching device what to do with the multicast packet.

Mrouters currently make up "islands" on the MBone separated by unicast routers. Thus, an mrouter can disguise multicast packets so that they can cross unicast routers. This is done by making each multicast packet look like a unicast packet; the destination address is the next mrouter. This process is called **IP tunneling**.

There are two multicast routing protocols that mrouters use to distribute multicast packets. They are dense-mode routing and sparse-mode routing. The protocol used is determined by available **bandwidth** and the distribution of end users over the network. If the network has many end users and there is enough bandwidth, dense-mode routing is used. However, if bandwidth is limited and users are thinly distributed, sparse-mode routing is used.

MS-DOS

Also see **Disk Operating System**.

MS-DOS (Microsoft Disk Operating System) was the Microsoft-marketed version of the first widely-installed **operating system** in personal computers. It was essentially the same operating system that Bill Gates's young company developed for IBM as Personal Computer—Disk Operating System (**PC-DOS**). Most users of either DOS system simply referred to their system as **Disk Operating System**. Like PC-DOS, MS-DOS was (and still is) a non-graphical line-oriented command-driven operating system, with a relatively simple interface but not overly "friendly" user interface. Its prompt to enter a command looks like this: C:>

The first Microsoft Windows operating system was really an application that ran on top of the MS-DOS operating system. Today, Windows operating systems continue to support DOS (or a DOS-like user interface) for special purposes by emulating the operating system.

In the 1970s before the personal computer was invented, IBM had a different and unrelated DOS that ran on smaller business computers. It was replaced by IBM's VSE operating system.

MSIE

See "Microsoft Internet Explorer"

MSP

See "management service provider"

MTBF

MTBF (mean time between failures) is a measure of how reliable a hardware product or component is. For most components, the measure is typically in thousands or even tens of thousands of hours between failures. For example, a **hard disk** drive may have a mean time between failures of 300,000 hours. A desired MTBF can be used as a quantifiable objective when designing a new product. The MTBF figure can be developed as the result of intensive testing, based on actual product experience, or predicted by analyzing known factors. The manufacturer may provide it as an index of a product's or component's reliability and, in some cases, to give customers an idea of how much service to plan for.

Most sources define this term to mean *average time between failures*.

M-theory

M-theory (the "M" stands for the *mother of all theories*, *magic*, *mystery*, or *matrix*, depending on the source) is an adaptation of **superstring theory** developed by Ed Witten of Princeton and Paul Townsend of Cambridge. Townsend and Witten's version could potentially be the **unified field theory** sought by Einstein for the last 40 years of his life: A simple equation that would reconcile incompatible aspects of his **theory of relativity** and **quantum theory** to explain the nature and behavior of all matter and energy. Applications of this knowledge could, through unlocking nature's secrets, enable future technologies that currently are only spoken of within the realm of science fiction: an inexhaustible source of clean energy, and time travel, for example.

Superstring theory (sometimes just called *string theory*) has as its basic premise the belief that the four fundamental forces of nature (gravity, electromagnetism, and strong and weak nuclear forces), as well as all matter are simply different manifestations of a single essence. This essence, the material making up all energy and matter, is thought to consist of tiny (a hundred billion billion times smaller than the nucleus of an atom) vibrating strings that exist in a multi-dimensional (10 or 26 dimensions) hyperspace. The extra dimensions (beyond the ones we recognize: three spatial dimensions and time) are thought to be *compactified*, or curled up, into tiny pockets inside observable space. The particular vibrations of the strings within this multi-dimensional hyperspace are thought to correspond to particles that form the basis of everything—all matter and energy—in existence.

Mtops

Mtops (million theoretical operations per second) is a measure of **computer performance** used by the U.S. government and cooperating countries in determining whether a computer can be exported abroad to certain countries that might use it for nuclear arms development. (Mtops sometimes is written as "MTOPS" or "mtops.")

In early November 1997, the U.S. Congress included in its 1997 Defense Appropriation bill an amendment to subject any manufacturer of computers in the 2,000 to 7,000 Mtops range to licensing restrictions on sales to many countries that have not agreed to stop nuclear arms development or testing. These include China, Russia, and India. Computers in the 2,000 Mtops range include **workstation** and may soon include powerful personal computers. The computer technology industry argued that computers in this range are already widely manufactured and sold abroad, even in a number of countries on the restricted list, and that the law would make it difficult for U.S. computer manufacturers to compete with other countries. While the law, which went into effect on February 2, 1998, doesn't prohibit the shipment of computers in these classes to the designated "tier 3" countries, application for permission to ship can take up to 90 days.

The calculation of Mtops involves counting the number of operations that could be performed by the computer during a second's time, based on a specified formula. The actual number of operations that any computer performs over a given period of time depends on which operations are performed (some operations take longer than others or can be performed within the same clock cycle with other operations) and the real cycle speed.

MTS

The Microsoft Transaction Server (MTS), called "Viper" while it was being developed, is a program that runs on an Internet or other network **server** with a **Windows NT** or later system and manages application and database **transaction** requests on behalf of a **client** computer user. The Transaction Server screens the user and client computer from having to formulate requests for unfamiliar **databases** and, if necessary, forwards the requests to database servers. It also manages security, connection to other servers, and transaction integrity.

The Transaction Server is Microsoft's bid to make **distributed** applications and data in a network relatively easy to create. It's one of a category of programs sometimes known as **middleware** or *multi-tier* programming for the **enterprise** market that IBM has traditionally controlled with its CICS and similar transaction management products.

Microsoft designed the Transaction Server to fit in with its overall **object-oriented programming** strategy. Using the Transaction Server, you can use a drag-and-drop interface to create a transaction model for a single user, then allow the Transaction Server to manage the model for multiple users, including the creation and management of user and task *threads* and *processes*.

MTS runs on Windows NT Server 4.0 or higher.

MUD

A MUD or Multi-User Dungeon is an inventively structured social experience on the Internet, managed by a computer program and often involving a loosely organized context or theme, such as a rambling old castle with many rooms or a period in national history. Some MUDs are ongoing adventure games; others are educational in purpose; and others are simply social. MUDs existed prior to the World Wide Web, accessible through **Telnet** to a computer that hosted the MUD. Today, many MUDs can be accessed through a Web site and some are perhaps better known as 3-D worlds or **chatting**.

MUD participants adopt a character or **avatar** when they join or log in to a MUD. Typically, you can describe your avatar to the other participants. Each MUD has its own name, special character and ambience, and set of rules. MUDs are run by advanced participants or programmers called wizards.

Although many MUDs continue to be entirely text-based, some new MUDs use virtual reality settings and you can see the characters. However, the focus is on the exchange of text between participants who are logged in at a particular time. There are a number of variations on the MUD, including **MOO**, MUCKs, and MUSHes, each associated with a server program of that name and varied mainly by the programming language used and the capabilities offered.

multi-carrier modulation

Multi-carrier modulation (MCM) is a method of transmitting data by splitting it into several components, and sending each of these components over separate **carrier** signals. The individual carriers have narrow **bandwidth**, but the composite signal can have broad bandwidth.

The advantages of MCM include relative immunity to fading caused by transmission over more than one path at a time (multipath fading), less susceptibility than single-carrier systems to interference caused by impulse noise, and enhanced immunity to inter-symbol interference. Limitations include difficulty in synchronizing the carriers under marginal conditions, and a relatively strict requirement that amplification be linear.

MCM was first used in **analog** military communications in the 1950s. Recently, MCM has attracted attention as a means of enhancing the bandwidth of digital communications over media with physical limitations. The scheme is used in some audio broadcast services. The technology lends itself to **digital television**, and is used as a method of obtaining high data speeds in asymmetric digital subscriber line (**ADSL**) systems. MCM is also used in wireless local area networks (**WLAN**s).

Also see orthogonal frequency-division multiplexing (**OFDM**), frequency-division multiplexing (**FDM**), and time-division multiplexing (**TDM**).

Multicast Backbone

See "MBone"

Multicast Internet

See "MBone"

multicast router

See "mrouter"

multicast

Multicast is communication between a single sender and multiple receivers on a network. Typical uses include the updating of mobile personnel from a home office and the periodic issuance of online newsletters. Together with **anycast** and **unicast**, multicast is one of the packet types in the Internet Protocol Version 6 (**IPv6**).

Multicast is supported through **wireless** data networks as part of the Cellular Digital Packet Data (**CDPD**) technology.

Multicast is also used for programming on the **MBone**, a system that allows users at high-bandwidth points on the Internet to receive live video and sound programming. In addition to using a specific high-bandwidth subset of the Internet, Mbone multicast also uses a protocol that allows signals to be encapsulated as **TCP/IP packets** when passing through parts of the Internet that can not handle the multicast protocol directly.

Multichannel Multipoint Distribution Service

Multichannel Multipoint Distribution Service (MMDS) is a broadcasting and communications service that operates in the ultra-high-frequency (UHF) portion of the radio spectrum between 2.1 and 2.7 **GHz**. MMDS is also known as wireless cable. It was conceived as a substitute for conventional cable television (TV). However, it also has applications in telephone/fax and data communications.

In MMDS, a medium-power transmitter is located with an omindirectional broadcast antenna at or near the highest topographical point in the intended coverage area. The workable radius can reach up to 70 miles in flat terrain (significantly less in hilly or mountainous areas). Each subscriber is equipped with a small antenna, along with a converter that can be placed next to, or on top of, a conventional TV set. There is a monthly fee, similar to that for satellite TV service.

The MMDS frequency band has room for several dozen analog or digital video channels, along with **narrowband** channels that can be used by subscribers to transmit signals to the network. The narrowband channels were originally intended for use in an educational setting (so-called wireless classrooms). The educational application has enjoyed some success, but conventional TV viewers prefer satellite TV services, which have more channels.

Because of recent deregulation that allows cable TV companies to provide telephone and Internet services, along with the development of digital technologies that make efficient use of available bandwidth, MMDS has considerable future potential. An MMDS network can provide high-speed Internet access, telephone/fax, and TV together, without the constraints of cable connections.

Multics

Multics (Multiplexed Information and Computing Service) was a **mainframe** time-sharing **operating system** that was developed in the 1963-1969 period through the collaboration of the Massachusetts Institute of Technology (MIT), General Electric (GE), and Bell Labs. Multics was the first or one of the first operating systems that used page-segmented storage. The operating system was written in **PL/I** and ran on GE hardware. By 1970, Bell Labs had withdrawn from the project, and Honeywell, which had bought GE's computer division, continued as the hardware provider. Support from the **Advanced Research Projects Agency** helped sustain the project.

In 1973, Honeywell announced a commercial system, the 6180, consisting of two processors that ran at 1 **MIPS** each, 768 kilobytes of memory, an 8 megabyte bulk store, a 1.6

gigabyte hard disk, 8 tape drives, and two communication controllers. The price was about $7 million. Later, a multiple disk system called the New Storage System (NSS) was added. In 1977, Honeywell offered the first commercial **relational database**, the Multics Relational Data Store (MRDS).

Over time, Multics customers included General Motors, Ford, and Industrial Nucleonics (later AccuRay). By the late 1980s, efforts to migrate Multics to more strategic processor architectures such as Intel's had failed and Honeywell transferred maintenance to one of its last customers, the University of Calgary, which has passed it on to a local company, CGI Group Inc. As of September, 1998, CGI Group continued to operate the one remaining Multics system.

multidimensional database

A multidimensional database (MDB) is a type of **database** that is optimized for **data warehouse** and online analytical processing (**OLAP**) applications. Multidimensional databases are frequently created using input from existing **relational databases**. Whereas a relational database is typically accessed using a Structured Query Language (**SQL**) **query**, a multidimensional database allows a user to ask questions like "How many Aptivas have been sold in Nebraska so far this year?" and similar questions related to summarizing business operations and trends.

A multidimensional database—or a multidimensional database management system (MDDBMS)—implies the processing ability to rapidly process the data in the database so that answers can be generated quickly. A number of vendors provide products that use multidimensional databases. Approaches to how data is stored and the user interface vary somewhat.

Conceptually, a multidimensional database uses the idea of a cube to represent the dimensions of data available to a user. For example, "Sales" could be viewed in the dimensions of product, geography, time, or some additional dimension. Additionally, a database creator can define hierarchies and levels within a dimension (for example, state and city levels within a regional hierarchy).

multihomed

Multihomed describes a computer **host** that has multiple **IP addresses** to connected networks. A multihomed host is physically connected to multiple data links that can be on the same or different networks.

For example, a computer with a Windows NT 4.0 Server and multiple IP addresses can be referred to as "multihomed" and may serve as an IP **router**.

multilink bundle

A multilink bundle is a collection of simultaneously opened bandwidth channels, including video and data links, that are coherently and logically controlled by preset commands. Links can be removed or added to the bundle when one Internet service provider (**ISP**) requests another ISP to do so. This process is known as link management.

A simple example of a multilink bundle is the use of two 64 Kbps channels to effect a 128 Kbps ISDN channel. A multilink bundle enables an ISP to offer users bandwidth-on-demand services, usually for a fee. By adding or removing channels, an ISP is able to change the available bandwidth. This may be done in response to changing line conditions or changing resource conditions.

The complexity of the system can be easily understood when one thinks of it this way: One system tells another when it is capable of combining multiple physical links into a single, logical link. This coordination of multiple independent channels between a fixed pair of systems provides a virtual link that produces greater bandwidth than any of the individual physical links.

multimedia

Multimedia is more than one concurrent presentation medium (for example, on CD-ROM or a Web site). Although still images are a different medium than text, multimedia is typically used to mean the combination of text, sound, and/or motion video. Some people might say that the addition of animated images (for example, **animated GIFs** on the Web) produces multimedia, but it has typically meant one of the following:

- Text and sound
- Text, sound, and still or animated graphic images
- Text, sound, and video images
- Video and sound
- Multiple display areas, images, or presentations presented concurrently
- In live situations, the use of a speaker or actors and "props" together with sound, images, and motion video

Multimedia can arguably be distinguished from traditional motion pictures or movies both by the scale of the production (multimedia is usually smaller and less expensive) and by the possibility of audience interactivity or involvement (in which case, it is usually called *interactive multimedia*). Interactive elements can include: voice command, mouse manipulation, text entry, touch screen, video capture of the user, or live participation (in live presentations).

Multimedia tends to imply sophistication (and relatively more expense) in both production and presentation than simple text-and-images. Multimedia presentations are possible in many contexts, including the Web, CD-ROMs,

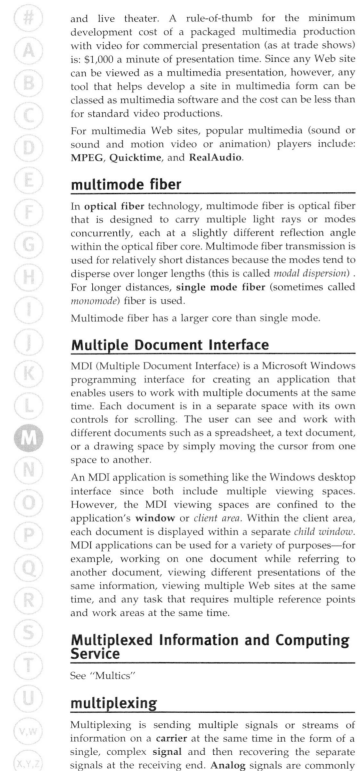

and live theater. A rule-of-thumb for the minimum development cost of a packaged multimedia production with video for commercial presentation (as at trade shows) is: $1,000 a minute of presentation time. Since any Web site can be viewed as a multimedia presentation, however, any tool that helps develop a site in multimedia form can be classed as multimedia software and the cost can be less than for standard video productions.

For multimedia Web sites, popular multimedia (sound or sound and motion video or animation) players include: **MPEG**, **Quicktime**, and **RealAudio**.

multimode fiber

In **optical fiber** technology, multimode fiber is optical fiber that is designed to carry multiple light rays or modes concurrently, each at a slightly different reflection angle within the optical fiber core. Multimode fiber transmission is used for relatively short distances because the modes tend to disperse over longer lengths (this is called *modal dispersion*) . For longer distances, **single mode fiber** (sometimes called *monomode*) fiber is used.

Multimode fiber has a larger core than single mode.

Multiple Document Interface

MDI (Multiple Document Interface) is a Microsoft Windows programming interface for creating an application that enables users to work with multiple documents at the same time. Each document is in a separate space with its own controls for scrolling. The user can see and work with different documents such as a spreadsheet, a text document, or a drawing space by simply moving the cursor from one space to another.

An MDI application is something like the Windows desktop interface since both include multiple viewing spaces. However, the MDI viewing spaces are confined to the application's **window** or *client area*. Within the client area, each document is displayed within a separate *child window*. MDI applications can be used for a variety of purposes—for example, working on one document while referring to another document, viewing different presentations of the same information, viewing multiple Web sites at the same time, and any task that requires multiple reference points and work areas at the same time.

Multiplexed Information and Computing Service

See "Multics"

multiplexing

Multiplexing is sending multiple signals or streams of information on a **carrier** at the same time in the form of a single, complex **signal** and then recovering the separate signals at the receiving end. **Analog** signals are commonly

multiplexed using frequency-division multiplexing (**FDM**), in which the carrier **bandwidth** is divided into subchannels of different frequency widths, each carrying a signal at the same time in parallel. **Digital** signals are commonly multiplexed using time-division multiplexing (**TDM**), in which the multiple signals are carried over the same channel in alternating time slots. In some optical fiber networks, multiple signals are carried together as separate wavelengths of light in a multiplexed signal using dense wavelength division multiplexing(**DWDM**).

multiprocessing

Multiprocessing is the coordinated processing of **programs** by more than one computer processor. Multiprocessing is a general term that can mean the dynamic assignment of a program to one of two or more computers working in tandem or can involve multiple computers working on the same program at the same time (in parallel).

With the advent of **parallel processing**, multiprocessing is divided into symmetric multiprocessing (**SMP**) and massively parallel processing (**MPP**).

In symmetric (or "tightly coupled") multiprocessing, the processors share memory and the I/O **bus** or data path. A single copy of the **operating system** is in charge of all the processors. SMP, also known as a "shared everything" system, does not usually exceed 16 processors.

In massively parallel (or "loosely coupled") processing, up to 200 or more processors can work on the same application. Each processor has its own operating system and memory, but an "interconnect" arrangement of data paths allows messages to be sent between processors. Typically, the setup for MPP is more complicated, requiring thought about how to partition a common database among processors and how to assign work among the processors. An MPP system is also known as a "shared nothing" system.

Multiprocessing should not be confused with **multiprogramming**, or the interleaved execution of two or more programs by a processor. Today, the term is rarely used since all but the most specialized computer operating systems support multiprogramming. Multiprocessing can also be confused with **multitasking**, the management of programs and the system services they request as tasks that can be interleaved, and with **multithreading**, the management of multiple execution paths through the computer or of multiple users sharing the same copy of a program.

multiprogramming

Multiprogramming is a rudimentary form of **parallel processing** in which several programs are run at the same time on a uniprocessor. Since there is only one **processor**, there can be no true simultaneous execution of different programs. Instead, the operating system executes part of one program, then part of another, and so on. To the user it appears that all programs are executing at the same time.

If the machine has the capability of causing an **interrupt** after a specified time interval, then the operating system will execute each program for a given length of time, regain control, and then execute another program for a given length of time, and so on. In the absence of this mechanism, the operating system has no choice but to begin to execute a program with the expectation, but not the certainty, that the program will eventually return control to the operating system.

If the machine has the capability of protecting **memory**, then a **bug** in one program is less likely to interfere with the execution of other programs. In a system without memory protection, one program can change the contents of storage assigned to other programs or even the storage assigned to the operating system. The resulting system crashes are not only disruptive, they may be very difficult to debug since it may not be obvious which of several programs is at fault.

Multiprotocol Label Switching

MPLS (Multiprotocol Label Switching) is a standards-approved technology for speeding up network traffic flow and making it easier to manage. MPLS involves setting up a specific path for a given sequence of packets, identified by a label put in each **packet**, thus saving the time needed for a **router** to look up the address to the next **node** to forward the packet to. MPLS is called *multiprotocol* because it works with the Internet Protocol (**IP**), Asynchronous Transport Mode (**ATM**), and **frame relay** network **protocol**s. With reference to the standard model for a network (the Open Systems Interconnection, or **OSI** model), MPLS allows most packets to be forwarded at the **layer 2** (**switching**) level rather than at the **layer 3** (**routing**) level. In addition to moving traffic faster overall, MPLS makes it easy to manage a network for quality of service (**QoS**). For these reasons, the technique is expected to be readily adopted as networks begin to carry more and different mixtures of traffic.

multisession CD

A multisession CD is a recordable CD format (like a **CD-R**) that allows the recording of a compact disc to be conducted in more than one recording session. If there is free space left on the CD after the first session, additional data can be written to it at a later date. Each session has its own lead in, program area, and lead out. This takes up about 20 megabytes of space, and therefore, is less efficient than recording data all at once.

Multisession CDs can be read in current CD-ROM drives, unless data is recorded *track-by-track* or *sector by sector* This process is known as **packet writing** and in this case only the newer CD-ROM drives, accompanied by appropriate software are able to read the disk.

multistation access unit

A multistation access unit is occasionally abbreviated as MAU. However, **MAU** is more frequently the abbreviation for the Ethernet *media attachment unit*.

An MSAU (multistation access unit) is a **hub** or concentrator that connects a group of computers ("nodes" in network terminology) to a **token ring** local area network. For example, eight computers might be connected to an MSAU in one office and that MSAU would be connected to an MSAU in another office that served eight other computers. In turn that MSAU could be connected to another MSAU in another office which would be connected back to the first MSAU. Such a physical configuration is called a **star topology**. However, the logical configuration is a ring topology because every message passes through every computer one at a time, each passing it on to the next in a continuing circle.

An advantage of an MSAU is that if one computer fails in the ring, the MSAU can bypass it and the ring will remain intact.

For larger networks, two additional ports on the MSAU (ring-in and ring-out) are available for connecting multiple MSAUs together. For example, using three MSAUs, the ring-out port of MSAU 1 is connected to the ring-in port of MSAU 2. The ring-out port of MSAU 2 is connected to the ring-in port of MSAU 3 and the ring-out port of MSAU 3 is connected to the ring-in port of MSAU 1, completing the ring. In such an example, up to 24 computers can be connected to the token ring network.

An MSAU is likely to be stored in a wiring closet and have cabling that extends out to a wall faceplate connection.

multitasking

It is easy to confuse multitasking with **multithreading**, a somewhat different idea.

In a computer **operating system**, multitasking is allowing a user to perform more than one computer **task** (such as the operation of an **application program**) at a time. The operating system is able to keep track of where you are in these tasks and go from one to the other without losing information. Microsoft **Windows 2000**, IBM's **OS/390**, and **Linux** are examples of operating systems that can do multitasking (almost all of today's operating systems can). When you open your Web **browser** and then open **Word** at the same time, you are causing the operating system to do multitasking.

Being able to do multitasking doesn't mean that an unlimited number of tasks can be juggled at the same time. Each task consumes system storage and other resources. As more tasks are started, the system may need to slow down or begin to run out of shared storage.

multithreading

It is easy to confuse multithreading with **multitasking** or **multiprogramming**, which are somewhat different ideas.

Multithreading is the ability of a **program** or an **operating system process** to manage its use by more than one user at a time and to even manage multiple requests by the same user without having to have multiple copies of the program running in the computer. Each user request for a program or system service (and here a user can also be another program) is kept track of as a **thread** with a separate identity. As programs work on behalf of the initial request for that thread and are interrupted by other requests, the status of work on behalf of that thread is kept track of until the work is completed.

MULTOS

MULTOS (which stands for "Multiple Operating System") is an **operating system** that allows multiple **application programs** to be installed and to reside separately and securely on a **smart card**. Each program is isolated by the operating system so that no application can interfere with another one. Whereas earlier smart card systems did not allow new applications to be installed or old ones deleted, MULTOS makes this possible. Updates or **patches** can also be installed as needed. Each application is **platform-independent** due to the implementation of a **virtual machine**. Developers write applications for MULTOS smart cards using the MULTOS Executable Language (MEL).

Before MULTOS, application developers had to write a separate version of the application for each type of smart card and the consumer needed a separate smart card for each application. With MULTOS, several applications can reside on one smart card regardless of the microchip used.

Security for MULTOS smart cards is enabled by the MULTOS Certification Authority (**CA**), which issues **cryptographic key**s for each MULTOS smart card and all MULTOS applications. These keys prevent unauthorized applications from being loaded into a card or deleted without the issuer's permission.

The MAOSCO Consortium, a group of leading international organizations, openly licenses the MULTOS specification. MasterCard, Mondex, Europay, and Discover favor MULTOS.

MUMPs

MUMPs is a program that assists companies and academic researchers with ideas for micro-electromechanical systems (**MEMS**) to manufacture prototypes. Since the manufacture of silicon chips in which MEMS are imbedded is costly, MUMPs provides special manufacturing "runs" that qualified enterprises can be part of. MUMPs is administered by the MEMS Technology Application Center (MCNC).

Murphy's Laws of Information Technology

The original Murphy's Law was "If there are two or more ways to do something, and one of those ways can result in a catastrophe, then someone will do it." The law's author was Edward A. Murphy, Jr., a U.S. Air Force engineer, who, in 1947, was involved in a rocket-sled experiment in which all 16 accelerator instruments were installed in the wrong way, resulting in Murphy's observation. Murphy's Law is commonly misstated to be "Anything that can go wrong, will," a quote invented by science-fiction writer Larry Niven as *Finagle's Law of Dynamic Negatives*.

Extrapolating from the original, we arrive at Murphy's Laws of Information Technology, a set of principles that may seem to be jokes but which events sometimes prove to be fundamental truths.

Here are a few examples of Murphy's Laws relative to hardware.

- Law of Inconvenient Malfunction: A device will fail at the least opportune possible moment.

- Law of Cable Compatibility: If you choose a cable and a connector at random, the probability that they are compatible is equal to zero.

- Law of Hardware Compatibility: The probability of a given peripheral being compatible with a PC is inversely proportional to the immediate need for that peripheral.

- Law of Bad Sectors: The probability that an untested diskette will have bad sectors is directly proportional to the importance of the data written onto the diskette.

- First Law of Selective Gravitation: When an object is dropped, it will fall in such a way as to cause the greatest possible damage to itself and/or other objects on which it lands.

- Second Law of Selective Gravitation: The tendency for an object to be dropped is directly proportional to its value.

- Law of Reality Change: Unalterable hardware specifications will change as necessary to maximize frustration for personnel affected by said specifications.

- Law of Noise: Noise bursts occur so as to cause the most, and/or most serious, errors in data communications, regardless of the actual amount of noise present.

- Law of Expectation: Consumer expectations always outpace advances in hardware technology.

- Law of the Titanic: If a device cannot malfunction, it will.

Here are a few greatly simplified examples of Murphy's Laws as they relate to programming.

- Law of Debugging: The difficulty of debugging software is directly proportional to the number of people who will ultimately use it.

- Law of Neurosis: The chances of software being neurotic (developing bugs spontaneously without apparent reason) is directly proportional to the confusion such neurosis can cause.

- Law of Available Space: If there are n bytes in a crucial software program, the available space for its convenient storage or loading is equal to n-1 bytes.

- First Law of Bad Sectors: The probability of software being mutilated by bad sectors is directly proportional to the value and/or importance of the programs.

- Second Law of Bad Sectors: When a program is mutilated by bad sectors, the damage will occur at the point(s) that result in the most frequent and/or severe errors when the program is run.

- Law of Noise: When a downloaded program is corrupted by noise, the corruption will occur at the point(s) that result in the most frequent and/or severe errors when the program is run.

- Law of Software Compatibility: If two programs are chosen at random, the probability that they are compatible is equal to zero.

- Law of Option Preferences: When two people share a computer, their software option preferences will differ in every possible way.

- Law of Expectation: Consumer expectations always outpace advances in software technology.

- Law of the Titanic: Bug-free software isn't.

mutex

In computer programming, a mutex (mutual exclusion object) is a program object that is created so that multiple program **threads** can take turns sharing the same resource, such as access to a file. Typically, when a program is started, it creates a mutex for a given resource at the beginning by requesting it from the system and the system returns a unique name or ID for it. After that, any thread needing the resource must use the mutex to lock the resource from other threads while it is using the resource. If the mutex is already locked, a thread needing the resource is typically queued by the system and then given control when the mutex becomes unlocked (when once more, the mutex is locked during the new thread's use of the resource).

mux

1) In communication transmission systems, mux (pronounce muks, sometimes spelled "MUX") is an abbreviation for **multiplexing**, a device that sends multiple signals on a carrier channel at the same time in the form of a single, complex signal to another device that recovers the separate signals at the receiving end. The receiver is sometimes called a *demux* (or "DEMUX").

2) On the Internet, a MUX is a multi-user text game played over the Internet, using the TinyMUX server. This kind of game started with the **MUD** (multi-user dungeon) movement.

MVS

MVS (Multiple Virtual Storage) is the **operating system** from IBM that is installed on most of its **mainframe** and large **server** computers. MVS has been said to be the operating system that keeps the world going. The payroll, accounts receivable, transaction processing, database management, and other programs critical to the world's largest businesses are usually run on an MVS system. Although MVS tends to be associated with a monolithic, centrally-controlled information system, IBM has in recent years repositioned it as a "large server" in a network-oriented distributed environment, using a **3-tier application** model.

The latest versions of MVS, **OS/390**, and z/OS, no longer bear the "MVS" in its name. Since MVS represents a certain epoch and culture in the history of computing and since many older MVS systems still operate, the term "MVS" will probably continue to be used for some time. Since OS/390 also comes with **UNIX** user and programming interfaces built in, it can be used as both an MVS system and a UNIX system at the same time. MVS systems run older applications developed using **COBOL** and, for transaction programs, **CICS**. Older application programs written in **PL/I** and **FORTRAN** are still running. Older applications use the **Virtual Storage Access Method** access method for file management and **Virtual Telecommunications Access Method** for telecommunication with users. The most common program environment today uses the **C** and **C++** languages. **DB2** is IBM's primary relational database management system (**RDBMS**). **Java** applications can be developed and run under OS/390's UNIX environment.

MVS is a generic name for specific products that included MVS/SP (MVS/System Product), MVS/XA (MVS/Extended Architecture), and MVS/ESA (MVS/Enterprise Systems Architecture). Historically, MVS evolved from OS/360, the operating system for the System/360, which was released in 1964. It later became the OS/370 and the System/370. OS/370 evolved into the OS/VS, OS/MFT, OS/MVT, OS/MVS, MVS/SP, MVS/XA, MVS/ESA, and finally OS/390. Throughout this evolution, application programs written for any operating system have always been able to run in any of the later operating systems. (This is called **forward compatibility**.)

An MVS system is a set of basic products and a set of optional products. This allows a customer to choose the set of functions they need and exclude the rest. In practice, most customers probably use almost all of the functions. The main user interface in MVS systems is TSO (Time Sharing Option). The Interactive System Productivity Facility (**ISPF**) is a set of menus for compiling and managing programs and for configuring the system. The main work management system

is either Job Entry Subsystem 2 or 3 (**JES2 or JES3**). Storage (**DASD**) management is performed by DFSMS (Distributed File Storage Management Subsystem). MVS is considerably more complex and requires much more education and experience to operate than smaller server and personal computer operating systems.

The *Virtual Storage* in MVS refers to the use of **virtual memory** in the operating system. Virtual storage or memory allows a program to have access to the maximum amount of **memory** in a system even though this memory is actually being shared among more than one application program. The operating system translates the program's *virtual* address into the real physical memory address where the data is actually located. The *Multiple* in MVS indicates that a separate virtual memory is maintained for each of multiple task partitions.

Other IBM operating systems for their larger computers include or have included: the Transaction Processing Facility (TPF), used in some major airline reservation systems, and **VM**, an operating system designed to serve many interactive users at the same time.

mySAP

See also **SAP**.

MySAP, a product of the German software company SAP, is an **e-business** software integration tool that delivers content to the user based on their role in the enterprise. More than 200 pre-defined role templates are available to provide the user with access to applications and resources that are task-appropriate to his or her communication needs in customer relationship management (**CRM**), supply chain management (**SCM**), e-procurement, business intelligence, product lifecycle management, human resources, or financial and marketplace channels. The user is able to work with the SAP applications they require by using a Web browser or Internet appliance to access the applications through their mySAP Web **portal**, called "Workplace." Access to the mySAP.com Workplace portal can be based on a per-user or per-number-of-transactions fee model.

mySQL

MySQL (pronounced "my ess cue el," not "my sequel") is an **open source** relational database management system (**RDBMS**) that uses Structured Query Language (**SQL**), the most popular language for adding, accessing, and processing data in a database. Because it is open source, anyone can download mySQL and tailor it to their needs in accordance with the general public license. MySQL is noted mainly for its speed, reliability, and flexibility. Most agree, however, that it works best when managing content and not executing **transaction**s.

The mySQL relational database system was first released in January 1998. It is fully multi-threaded using **kernel thread**s, provides application program interfaces (**API**s) for **C**, **C++**,

Eiffel, **Java**, **Perl**, **PHP**, **Python**, and **Tcl**, allows for many column types, and offers full operator and function support in the SELECT and WHERE parts of queries.

The development team working on future releases of mySQL plan to unveil mySQL 4.0 in mid-2001. Its features will include a new table definition file format, enhanced replication, and more functions for a full-text search. Later, mySQL developers hope to add fail-safe replication, a **port** of mySQL to **BeOS**, and an option to periodically flush key pages for tables with delayed keys. Over time, MySQL plans to be fully ANSI 92/ANSI 99-compliant.

MySQL currently runs on the **Linux**, **UNIX**, and **Windows** platforms. Many Internet startups have been especially interested in mySQL as an alternative to the proprietary database systems from Oracle, IBM, and Informix. Yahoo's news site uses mySQL.

Nagle's algorithm

Named for its creator, John Nagle, the Nagle algorithm is used to automatically **concatenate** a number of small **buffer messages**; this process (called *nagling*) increases the efficiency of a network application system by decreasing the number of **packet**s that must be sent. Nagle's **algorithm**, defined in 1984 as *Ford Aerospace and Communications Corporation Congestion Control in IP/TCP Internetworks* (**IETF RFC** 896) was originally designed to relieve congestion for a private **TCP/IP** network operated by Ford, but has since been broadly deployed.

Nagle's document specified a means of dealing with what he called *the small packet problem*, created when an application generates data one **byte** at a time, causing the network to be overloaded with packets (a situation often referred to as *send-side silly window syndrome*). A single character—one byte of data—originating from a keyboard could result in the transmission of a 41 byte packet consisting of one byte of useful information and 40 bytes of **header** data. This situation translates into 4000% overhead, which was considered to be acceptable for a lightly loaded network such as the Advanced Research Projects Agency Network (**ARPANet**—the precursor of the Internet operating at that time), but not so for a heavily loaded network such as Ford's, where it could necessitate retransmissions, cause lost packets, and hamper propagation speed through excessive congestion in switching **node**s and **gateway**s. **Throughput** could be hampered to the extent that connections were aborted. Nagle's algorithm—usually implemented through the insertion of two lines of code into a TCP program—instructs the sender to buffer (store) data if any unacknowledged data is outstanding. Any data sent subsequently is held until the outstanding data is acknowledged (**ACK**ed) or until there is a full packet's worth of data to send.

Although Nagle's algorithm addressed problems that were being experienced within Ford's network, the same problems were beginning to be experienced by ARPANet. Nagling has been broadly implemented across networks, including the Internet, and is generally performed by default—although it is sometimes considered to be undesirable in highly interactive environments, such as some **client/server** situations. In such cases, nagling may be turned off through use of the TCP_NODELAY **sockets** option.

nagling

See "Nagle's algorithm"

named pipe

In computer programming, a named pipe is a method for passing information from one computer **process** to other processes using a **pipe** or message holding place that is given a specific name. Unlike a regular pipe, a named pipe can be used by processes that do not have to share a common process origin and the message sent to the named pipe can be read by any authorized process that knows the name of the named pipe.

A named pipe is sometimes called a "FIFO" (first in, first out) because the first data written to the pipe is the first data that is read from it.

namespace

In general, a namespace uniquely identifies a set of names so that there is no ambiguity when objects having different origins but the same names are mixed together. Using the Extensible Markup Language (**XML**), an XML namespace is a collection of element type and attribute names. These element types and attribute names are uniquely identified by the name of the unique XML namespace of which they are a part. In an XML document, any element type or attribute name can thus have a two-part name consisting of the name of its namespace and then its local (functional) name.

For example, suppose the same XML document included the element type of OWNER for owners of motorcycles as well as for owners of automobiles. It might be necessary or desirable to know that an owner name was one of those who owned a motorcycle rather than an automobile. Having different motorcycle and automobile namespaces would make this possible. Effectively, it would make it possible to label motorcycle owners differently than automobile owners without having to create a different element type for each.

In XML, a namespace is commonly given the name of a Uniform Resource Identifier (**URI**)—such as a Web site's address—both because the namespace may be associated with the site or page of that URI (for example, a company name) and because a URI is conveniently likely to be a unique name. Note that the URI is not necessarily intended to be used other than as a name nor is there any namespace document or XML **schema** that must be accessed; the URI is simply used as a name (and part of the two-part name of any element type or attribute name so that the names are unique within the document).

NAND

See "logic gate"

nanite

See "nanomachine"

nanoanalysis

Nanoanalysis refers to techniques for determining the atomic structures of materials, especially crystals. The technology is similar to that used for microanalysis, except it is done on a nanometer scale. (One nanometer is 10^{-9} meter, or a millionth of a millimeter.)

With any instrument used for nanoanalysis, there is a limit to the resolution (the diameter of the smallest object that can be resolved). This is true when the instrument works directly with electromagnetic radiation such as infrared (IR), ultraviolet (UV), visible light, or X rays, and also when the instrument employs high-speed subatomic particles such as electrons or ions. There is a minimum wavelength associated with any medium of observation. Objects whose diameters are less than this wavelength defy observation. In general, as the wavelength becomes shorter, the required particle or wave energy increases. This motivates scientists involved with nanoanalysis to seek ever-more-powerful machines with which to observe samples.

The electron microscope is commonly used for nanoanalysis. There are two basic types that lend themselves to this application: the scanning electron microscope (SEM) and the high-voltage transmission analytical electron microscope. Also useful in nanoanalysis are X-ray and UV diffraction, IR microscopy, mass spectrometry, ion-beam machines, and precision optical microprobes.

nanochip

A nanochip is an integrated circuit (**IC**) that is so small, in physical terms, that individual particles of matter play major roles. Miniaturization of electronic and computer components has always been a primary goal of engineers. The smaller an electronic system can be made, the more processing power can fit into a given physical volume, the less energy is required to run it, and the faster it can work (because distances among components are reduced, minimizing charge-carrier transit time).

The earliest computers, built in the middle of the 20th century, used **vacuum tube**s for switching. These machines were so massive and bulky, and demanded so much electricity to operate, that they required buildings and power plants of their own. Today, such a computer can be placed inside a microscopic capsule. The trend toward miniaturization shows no sign of slowing until some limit is forced on the manufacturing process. The scale of this limit ultimately depends only on the structure of matter.

Traditional methods of IC manufacture involve etching unwanted **semiconductor** material from a preexisting chip, in the same way a sculptor carves a statue. Futurists suggest that, rather than etching switches and **logic gate**s into

semiconductor material, chips ought to be mechanically assembled one molecule at a time. Some scientists believe ICs can be grown from biological seeds, just as a plant reproduces cells to create a defined structure such as a tree. Both of these processes involve **nanotechnology**, and would result in the greatest possible number of switches per unit volume of material substance.

Nanochip is also the name of a nanotechnology research-and-development corporation based in San Jose, California as well as the trade name for a molecular biology workstation manufactured by Nanogen of San Diego, California.

nanocomputer

A nanocomputer is a computer whose physical dimensions are microscopic. The field of nanocomputing is part of the emerging field of **nanotechnology**. Several types of nanocomputers have been suggested or proposed by researchers and futurists.

Electronic nanocomputers would operate in a manner similar to the way present-day microcomputers work. The main difference is one of physical scale. More and more **transistor**s are squeezed into **silicon** chips with each passing year; witness the evolution of integrated circuits (**ICs**) capable of ever-increasing storage capacity and processing power. The ultimate limit to the number of transistors per unit volume is imposed by the atomic structure of matter. Most engineers agree that technology has not yet come close to pushing this limit. In the electronic sense, the term nanocomputer is relative. By 1970s standards, today's ordinary microprocessors might be called nanodevices.

Chemical and biochemical nanocomputers would store and process information in terms of chemical structures and interactions. Biochemical nanocomputers already exist in nature; they are manifest in all living things. But these systems are largely uncontrollable by humans. We cannot, for example, program a tree to calculate the digits of **pi**, or program an antibody to fight a particular disease (although medical science has come close to this ideal in the formulation of vaccines, antibiotics, and antiviral medications). The development of a true chemical nanocomputer will likely proceed along lines similar to genetic engineering. Engineers must figure out how to get individual atoms and molecules to perform controllable calculations and data storage tasks.

Mechanical nanocomputers would use tiny moving components called nanogears to encode information. Such a machine is reminiscent of **Charles Babbage**'s analytical engines of the 19th century. For this reason, mechanical nanocomputer technology has sparked controversy; some researchers consider it unworkable. All the problems inherent in Babbage's apparatus, according to the naysayers, are magnified a millionfold in a mechanical nanocomputer. Nevertheless, some futurists are optimistic about the technology, and have even proposed the evolution of nanorobots that could operate, or be controlled by, mechanical nanocomputers.

A quantum nanocomputer would work by storing data in the form of atomic quantum states or spin. Technology of this kind is already under development in the form of single-electron memory (SEM) and quantum dots. The energy state of an **electron** within an **atom**, represented by the electron energy level or shell, can theoretically represent one, two, four, eight, or even 16 bits of data. The main problem with this technology is instability. Instantaneous electron energy states are difficult to predict and even more difficult to control. An electron can easily fall to a lower energy state, emitting a **photon**; conversely, a photon striking an atom can cause one of its electrons to jump to a higher energy state.

nanofabrication

Nanofabrication is the design and manufacture of devices with dimensions measured in nanometers. One nanometer is 10^{-9} meter, or a millionth of a millimeter.

Nanofabrication is of interest to computer engineers because it opens the door to super-high-density **microprocessor**s and memory **chip**s. It has been suggested that each data bit could be stored in a single **atom**. Carrying this further, a single atom might even be able to represent a byte or word of data. Nanofabrication has also caught the attention of the medical industry, the military, and the aerospace industry.

There are several ways that nanofabrication might be done. One method involves scaling down integrated-circuit (**IC**) fabrication that has been standard since the 1970s, removing one atom at a time until the desired structure emerges. A more sophisticated hypothetical scheme involves the assembly of a chip atom-by-atom; this would resemble bricklaying. An extension of this is the notion that a chip might assemble itself atom-by-atom using programmable nanomachines. Finally, it has been suggested that a so-called **biochip** might be grown like a plant from a seed; the components would form by a process resembling cell division in living things.

Also see **nanolithography**, **nanotechnology**, and **self-assembly**.

nanolithography

Nanolithography is the art and science of etching, writing, or printing at the microscopic level, where the dimensions of characters are on the order of nanometers (units of 10^{-9} meter, or millionths of a millimeter). This includes various methods of modifying **semiconductor** chips at the **atom**ic level for the purpose of fabricating integrated circuits (**IC**s).

Instruments used in nanolithography include the scanning probe microscope (SPM) and the atomic force microscope (ATM). The SPM allows surface viewing in fine detail without necessarily modifying it. Either the SPM or the ATM can be used to etch, write, or print on a surface in single-atom dimensions.

Also see **nanomachine** and **nanotechnology**.

nanomachine

A nanomachine, also called a nanite, is a mechanical or electromechanical device whose dimensions are measured in nanometers (millionths of a millimeter, or units of 10^{-9} meter).

Nanomachines are largely in the research-and-development phase, but some primitive devices have been tested. An example is a sensor having a switch approximately 1.5 nanometers across, capable of counting specific molecules in a chemical sample. The first useful applications of nanomachines will likely be in medical technology, where they could be used to identify pathogens and toxins from samples of body fluid. Another potential application is the detection of toxic chemicals, and the measurement of their concentrations, in the environment.

The microscopic size of nanomachines translates into high operational speed. This is a result of the natural tendency of all machines and systems to work faster as their size decreases. Nanomachines could be programmed to replicate themselves, or to work synergistically to build larger machines or to construct nanochips. Specialized nanomachines called nanorobots might be designed not only to diagnose, but to treat, disease conditions, perhaps by seeking out invading bacteria and viruses and destroying them.

Another asset of nanomachines is the fact that the individual units require only a tiny amount of energy to operate. Durability is another potential asset; nanites might last for centuries before breaking down. The main challenge lies in the methods of manufacture. It has been suggested that some nanomachines might be grown in a manner similar to the way plants evolve from seeds.

Also see **nanochip**, **nanotechnology**, and **nanotube**.

nanomedicine

Nanomedicine is the application of **nanotechnology** (the engineering of tiny machines) to the prevention and treatment of disease in the human body. This discipline is in its infancy. It has the potential to change medical science dramatically in the 21st century.

The most elementary nanomedical devices will be used to diagnose illness. Chemical tests exist for this purpose; nanomachines could be employed to monitor the internal chemistry of the body. Mobile nanorobots, equipped with wireless transmitters, might circulate in the blood and lymph systems, and send out warnings when chemical

imbalances occur or worsen. Similar fixed nanomachines could be planted in the nervous system to monitor pulse, brain-wave activity, and other functions.

A more advanced use of nanotechnology might involve implanted devices to dispense drugs or hormones as needed in people with chronic imbalance or deficiency states. Heart defibrillators and pacemakers have been around for some time; nanomedicine carries this to the next level down in terms of physical dimension, with the potential to affect the behavior of individual cells. Ultimately, artificial antibodies, artificial white and red blood cells, and antiviral nanorobots might be devised.

The most advanced nanomedicine involves the use of nanorobots as miniature surgeons. Such machines might repair damaged cells, or get inside cells and replace or assist damaged intracellular structures. At the extreme, nanomachines might replicate themselves, or correct genetic deficiencies by altering or replacing DNA (deoxyribonucleic acid) molecules.

nanometer

A nanometer is a unit of spatial measurement that is 10^{-9} meter, or one millionth of a millimeter. It is commonly used in **nanotechnology**, the building of extremely small machines.

nanorobot

A nanorobot is a specialized nanomachine designed to perform a specific task or tasks repeatedly and with precision. Nanorobots have dimensions on the order of nanometers (a nanometer is a millionth of a millimeter, or 10^{-9} meter).

Nanorobots, like their larger counterparts, can be categorized into two groups, called autonomous robots and insect robots. An autonomous nanorobot contains its own on-board nanocomputer, which controls the machine and allows it to operate independently. An insect nanorobot is one of a fleet of several, or many, identical units that are all controlled by a single, central computer. (The term insect comes from the fact that such robots resemble ants in an anthill or bees in a hive.)

Nanorobots are of special interest to researchers in the medical industry. It has been suggested that a fleet of self-replicating insect nanorobots might act as a vaccine against disease. Such machines might even serve as antibodies or antiviral agents in patients with compromised immune systems, or in diseases that do not respond to more conventional measures. The nanorobots would work by seeking out and destroying specific bacteria, fungi, or viruses. Nanorobots have potential applications in the assembly of small-scale, sophisticated systems. They might function at the atomic level to build devices, machines, or circuits one particle at a time.

A major asset of nanorobots is the fact that the individual units require very little energy to operate. Durability is another potential asset; nanorobots might remain operational for years, decades, or centuries. High speed is also a significant consideration. Nanoscale systems can operate much faster than their larger counterparts because displacements are smaller; this allows mechanical and electrical events to occur in less time at a given absolute speed.

Also see **robot**, **nanotechnology**, **self-assembly**, and **self-replication**.

nanosecond

(This definition follows U.S. usage in which a billion is a thousand million and a trillion is a 1 followed by 12 zeros.)

A nanosecond (ns or nsec) is one billionth (10^{-9}) of a second and is a common measurement of read or write access time to random access memory (**RAM**).

For comparison, a millisecond (ms or msec) is one thousandth of a second and is commonly used in measuring the time to read to or write from a **hard disk** or a **CD-ROM** player or to measure **packet** travel time on the Internet.

A microsecond (μs or Greek letter mu plus s) is one millionth (10^{-6}) of a second.

A picosecond is one trillionth (10^{-12}) of a second, or one millionth of a microsecond.

A femtosecond is one millionth of a nanosecond or 10^{-15} of a second and is a measurement sometimes used in laser technology.

An attosecond is one quintillionth (10^{-18}) of a second and is a term used in photon research.

nanotechnology

Nanotechnology, or, as it is sometimes called, *molecular manufacturing*, is a branch of engineering that deals with the design and manufacture of extremely small electronic circuits and mechanical devices built at the molecular level of matter. The Institute of Nanotechnology in the U.K. expresses it as "science and technology where dimensions and tolerances in the range of 0.1 nanometer (nm) to 100 nm play a critical role." Nanotechnology is often discussed together with micro-electromechanical systems (**MEMS**), a subject that usually includes nanotechnology but may also include technologies higher than the molecular level.

There is a limit to the number of components that can be fabricated onto a **semiconductor** wafer or "chip." Traditionally, circuits have been etched onto chips by removing material in small regions. However, it is also possible in theory to build chips up, one **atom** at a time, to obtain devices much smaller than those that can be manufactured by etching. With this approach, there would be no superfluous atoms; every particle would have a purpose. Electrical conductors, called *nanowires*, would be only one atom thick. A **logic gate** would require only a few atoms. A data **bit** could be represented by the presence or absence of a single **electron**.

Nanotechnology holds promise in the quest for ever-more-powerful computers and communications devices. But the most fascinating (and potentially dangerous) applications are in medical science. So-called *nanorobots* might serve as programmable antibodies. As disease-causing bacteria and viruses mutate in their endless attempts to get around medical treatments, nanorobots could be reprogrammed to selectively seek out and destroy them. Other nanorobots might be programmed to single out and kill cancer cells.

Two concepts associated with nanotechnology are *positional assembly* and *self-replication*. Positional assembly deals with the mechanics of moving molecular pieces into their proper relational places and keeping them there. *Molecular robots* are devices that do the positional assembly. Self-replication deals with the problem of multiplying the positional arrangements in some automatic way, both in building the manufacturing device and in building the manufactured product.

nanotube

In **nanotechnology** or the building of extremely small machines and computers, a nanotube (sometimes called a *buckytube*) is a long, cylindrical carbon structure consisting of hexagonal graphite molecules attached at the edges. The nanotube developed from the so-called **Fullerene**, a structure similar to the way geodesic domes, originally conceived by R. Buckminster Fuller, are built. Because of this, nanotubes are sometimes called *buckytubes*.

Some nanotubes have a single cylinder; others have two or more concentric cylinders. Nanotubes have several characteristics: wall thickness, number of concentric cylinders, cylinder radius, and cylinder length. Some nanotubes have a property called chirality, an expression of longitudinal twisting.

Researchers have suggested several applications for nanotubes. The structures might be assembled into microscopic mechanical systems called **nanomachine**s. Because graphite can behave as a **semiconductor**, nanotubes might be used to build microscopic **resistor**s, **capacitor**s, **inductor**s, **diode**s, or **transistor**s. Concentric nanotubes might store electric charges because of capacitance among the layers, facilitating the construction of high-density memory chips.

NAP

See "network access point"

narrowband

Also see **bandwidth**.

Generally, narrowband describes telecommunication that carries voice information in a narrow **band** of frequencies. More specifically, the term has been used to describe a specific frequency range set aside by the U.S. **FCC** for mobile or radio services, including paging systems, from 50 **cps** to 64 **Kbps**.

The term is usually contrasted with **wideband** or **broadband**.

NAS

See "network-attached storage"

NAT

See "Network Address Translation"

National Computer Security Center

The National Computer Security Center (NCSC) is a U.S. government organization within the National Security Agency (**NSA**) that evaluates computing equipment for high security applications to ensure that facilities processing classified or other sensitive material are using trusted computer systems and components. NCSC was founded in 1981 as the Department of Defense Computer Security Center and changed to its current name in 1985. The organization works with industry, education, and government agency partners to promote research and standardization efforts for secure information system development. The NCSC also functions in an educational capacity to disseminate information about issues surrounding secure computing, most significantly through its annual National Information Systems Security Conference.

The NCSC's computer evaluation program is carried out by another NSA organization, the Trusted Product Evaluation Program (TPEP), which tests commercial products against a comprehensive set of security-related criteria. NCSC issued the first Department of Defense (DoD) Trusted Computer System Evaluation Criteria (TCSEC) in August, 1983. The document, more commonly referred to as the "orange book," was reissued in 1985 as a DoD standard that included the stated goals of providing manufacturers with security-related standards regarding features for inclusion in products, and providing DoD components with information about security metrics for the evaluation of trust levels to be accorded various products used for processing sensitive material.

National Institute for Standards and Technology

See "NIST"

National Security Agency

Also see **cryptography**.

The National Security Agency (NSA) is the official U.S. cryptologic (the science of cryptographic design and decryption) organization. Under a directive (revised version of the National Security Council Intelligence Directive (NSCID) No. 9) from President Truman and the National Security Council, the NSA was formed in November of 1952. The organization exists to protect national communications systems integrity, and to seek information about foreign adversaries' secret communications. The NSA works in close conjunction with the Central Security Service (CSS), which was established by Presidential Directive in 1972 to promote full partnership between the NSA and the cryptologic elements of the Armed Forces. The director of NSA/CSS, in accordance with a Department of Defense (DoD) directive, must be a high-ranking (at least 3 stars) commissioned officer of the military services.

Although the organization's number of employees (as well as its budget) falls into the category of "classified information," the NSA lists among its workforce: analysts, engineers, physicists, linguists, computer scientists, researchers, customer relations specialists, security officers, data flow experts, managers, administrative and clerical assistants; it also claims to be the largest employer of mathematicians in the U.S., and possibly worldwide. NSA/CSS mathematicians perform the Agency's two critical functions: they design cryptographic systems to protect U.S. communications and search for weaknesses in the counterpart systems of U.S. adversaries.

NSA denies rumours in circulation claiming that it has an unlimited "black budget"—undisclosed even to other government agencies. Nevertheless, the Agency admits that, if it were judged as a corporation, it would rank in the top ten percent of Fortune 500 companies.

National Television Standards Committee

The NTSC (National Television Standards Committee) was responsible for developing, in 1953, a set of standard **protocols** for television (TV) broadcast transmission and reception in the United States. Two other standards—**Phase Alternation Line** (PAL) and **Sequential Couleur avec Memoire** (SECAM)—are used in other parts of the world. The NTSC standards have not changed significantly since their inception, except for the addition of new parameters for color signals. NTSC signals are not directly compatible with computer systems.

An NTSC TV image has 525 horizontal lines per frame (complete screen image). These lines are scanned from left to right, and from top to bottom. Every other line is skipped. Thus it takes two screen scans to complete a frame: one scan for the odd-numbered horizontal lines, and another scan for the even-numbered lines. Each half-frame screen scan takes approximately $1/_{60}$ of a second; a complete frame is scanned every $1/_{30}$ second. This alternate-line scanning system is known as interlacing.

Adapters exist that can convert NTSC signals to digital video that a computer can "understand." Conversely, there are devices that can convert computer video to NTSC signals, allowing a TV receiver to be used as a computer **display**. But because a conventional TV receiver has lower **resolution** than a typical computer monitor, this does not work well for all computer applications, even if the TV screen is very large.

In recent years, there has been increasing pressure to adopt a new set of TV standards. One of the proposed protocols is known as high-definition television (**HDTV**). Ideally, the HDTV standard that is ultimately adopted will be directly compatible with computer systems. However, there are engineering problems associated with this. Some industry experts fear such compatibility could dramatically increase the cost of a conventional TV set.

native

In computer systems, *native* means "original" or "basic." Here are several usages:

1) Microsoft stresses that its Internet Information Server (**IIS**) is "a native implementation of the current Internet standards for Web servers..." Microsoft is implying that its own implementation of a Web server is likely to perform better than Netscape's (or someone else's) Web server running on a Windows NT operating system.

2) In **COBOL**, a *native character set* is the default character set that comes with the computer specified in the OBJECT-COMPUTER paragraph.

3) In IBM's Virtual Telecommunications Access Method (**VTAM**), *native mode* refers to its use directly in the VM **operating system** rather than in another operating system whose emulation is being supported by the VM operating system.

4) A computer program is **compiled** to run with a particular **processor** and its set of instructions. This is intrinsically running code in "native mode." If the same program is run on a computer with a new processor, software can be provided so that the computer emulates the old processor. In this case, the same application runs in "emulation mode" and almost certainly more slowly than in native mode on the original processor. (The application can be rewritten and recompiled so that it runs on the new processor in native mode.)

natural number

A natural number is a number that occurs commonly and obviously in nature. As such, it is a whole, non-negative number. The set of natural numbers, denoted N, can be defined in either of two ways:

$N = \{0, 1, 2, 3, ...\}$

$N = (1, 2, 3, 4, ...)$

In mathematical equations, unknown or unspecified natural numbers are represented by lower-case, italicized letters from the middle of the alphabet. The most common is n, followed by m, p, and q. In subscripts, the lower-case i is sometimes used to represent a non-specific natural number when denoting the elements in a sequence or series. However, i is more often used to represent the positive square root of -1, the unit **imaginary number**.

The set N, whether or not it includes zero, is a *denumerable* set. Denumerability refers to the fact that, even though there might be an infinite number of elements in a set, those elements can be denoted by a list that implies the identity of every element in the set. For example, it is intuitive from either the list $\{1, 2, 3, 4, ...\}$ or the list $\{0, 1, 2, 3, ...\}$ that $356,804,251$ is a natural number, but $356,804,251.5$, $^2/_3$, and -23 are not.

Both of the sets of natural numbers defined above are denumerable. They are also exactly the same size. It's not difficult to prove this; their elements can be paired off one-to-one, with no elements being left out of either set. In infinite sets, the existence of a one-to-one correspondence is the litmus test for determining *cardinality*, or size. The set of integers and the set of **rational numbers** has the same cardinality as N. However, the sets of real numbers, imaginary numbers, and complex numbers have cardinality larger than that of N.

See also: **integer, rational number, real number, imaginary number, and complex number**.

NCSA

NCSA (National Center for Supercomputing Applications) at the University of Illinois in Urbana, Illinois is the home of the first Web **browser** that had a graphical user interface. Its inventor, Marc Andreessen, then 22 years old, later lead the creation of the Netscape browser and became a founder of that company. The original browser, **Mosaic**, exists in a more advanced version.

NCSC

See "National Computer Security Center"

NDIS

NDIS (Network Driver Interface Specification) is a Windows specification for how communication **protocol** programs (such as **TCP/IP**) and network device **drivers** should communicate with each other. NDIS specifies interfaces for:

1. The program that sends and receives data by constructing or extracting it from the formatted units called **frames** (and sometimes **packets** or **datagrams**). This program, usually called a **protocol stack**, is **layered** and generally corresponds to layers 3 and 4 (the Network Addressing and Transport layers) of the Open Systems Interconnection (**OSI**) reference model. Examples are TCP/IP and **Internetwork Packet Exchange**.

2. The program, usually called a device **driver**, that interacts directly with the network interface card (**NIC**) or other adapter hardware, which sends or receives the data on the communications line in the form of electronic signals. The driver program and the NIC interact at the Media Access Control (**MAC address**) sublayer of layer-2 level of OSI, which is called Data-Link Control. (Putting the signal on the line is the layer-1 or the Physical layer of OSI.) Examples of MAC drivers are those for **Ethernet, Fiber Distributed-Data Interface**, and **token ring**.

3. A program called the Protocol Manager that assists the protocol stack program and the MAC driver program by telling each of them the computer location of the other when the **operating system** is started or, in some cases, when a new device is added to the computer. This is called **bind**. A system file called PROTOCOL.INI identifies which protocol stacks use which MAC drivers and where each is located. A protocol stack can be bound to more than one MAC driver where a computer is connected to multiple networks. And a single MAC driver can be bound to more than one protocol stack in a computer.

NDIS was developed by Microsoft and 3Com. Using NDIS, Windows software developers can develop protocol stacks that work with the MAC driver for any hardware manufacturer's communications adapter. By the same token, any adapter maker can write a MAC driver software that can communicate with any protocol stack program.

A similar interface, called Open Data-Link Interface (**ODI**), is provided by Novell for its **NetWare** local area network operating system.

NDS

See "Novell Directory Services"

near-end crosstalk

Also see **NEXT**, a computer company that developed a personal computer with an advanced user interface and operating system.

NEXT (near-end crosstalk) is an error condition that can occur when connectors are attached to **twisted pair** cabling. NEXT is usually caused by crossed or crushed wire pairs. The error condition does not require that the wires be crushed so much that the conductors inside become exposed. Two conductors only need to be close enough so that the radiating **signal** from one of the wires can interfere with the signal traveling on the other. Most medium- to high-end cable testers are capable of testing for NEXT errors.

In order to certify a cable for Category 3 (**CAT 3**), the NEXT test must be performed in 1 **MHz** steps from 1 Mhz to 16 MHz. Since the level of signal loss or interference can change with **frequency**, a range of frequencies must be used to certify that the cable is acceptable over the entire range. In order to certify a cable for Category 5 (**CAT 5**) use, the test frequency range must be extended up to 100 MHz. A 1 MHz frequency step should still be used. In both cases, you must test both ends of the cable. This is because NEXT occurs on the ends of the cable right where the connector is attached.

Simply using CAT 5 cables, connectors, and patch panels does not guarantee that a network will support 100 Mb operation. You must actually certify your network for use at this speed with a CAT 5 cable tester after the network is fully installed.

neologism

A neologism (pronounced nee-AH-low-djism) is a newly invented word or term. Neologisms would seem to occur at a greater rate in cultures with rapidly changing technologies and with greater means for information dispersal.

A *neology* is, according to our Webster's, the use of a new word or the use of an existing word but given a new meaning. A second meaning given by Webster's for *neologism* is that of "a meaningless word coined by a psychotic."

nerd

A nerd is a technically bright but socially inept person. The classic image of the nerd has been the wild-haired genius kid with thick-lensed glasses surrounded by test tubes and computers. Microsoft's Bill Gates is sometimes considered the walking embodiment of the older, successful nerd. As computer technology becomes less frightening and "nerdish" to larger numbers of people, society seems to be developing a more tolerant, even benevolent view of the nerd.

Nerd is a more general term than **geek** (which always means *computer geek*) and **weenie** and is somewhat comparable to **propellor head**.

Although the term's origin is obscure, one theory is that it derives from a children's book by Dr. Seuss, *If I Ran the Zoo*, in which this passage is found:

> And then, just to show them,
> I'll sail to Ka-Troo
> And bring back an it-kutch,
> A preep, and a proo,
> A nerkle, a nerd,
> And a seersucker, too!

Dr. Seuss's picture of the nerd looks much like the way computer nerds are portrayed today.

nested

In general, something that is nested is fully contained within something else of the same kind. In programming, nested describes code that performs a particular function and that is contained within code that performs a broader function. One well-known example is the procedure known as the *nested do-loop*. In data structures, data organizations that are separately identifiable but also part of a larger data organization are said to be nested within the larger organization. A table within a table is a nested table. A list within a list is a nested list.

A common alternative to nested is the prefix *sub*, as in subprocedure, substructure, subtransaction, and so forth.

net

1) "net" is one of the top-level **domain name**s that can be used when choosing a domain name. It generally describes the entity owning the domain name as an organization that administers or provides network connection services. Along with the second-level domain name (for example: "mhv" in mhv.net), the top-level domain name is required in Web and e-mail addresses.

For more information, see **gTLD** (generic top-level domain name).

2) Net (capitalized or not) is sometimes used as a short form for "Internet."

.Net

.Net is a business strategy from Microsoft that is aimed at a convergence of personal computing with the Web. The goal is to provide individual and business users with a seamlessly interoperable and Web-enabled interface for applications and computing devices and to make computing activities increasingly Web **browser**-oriented. Many of the details for .Net are not yet fully worked out; however, Microsoft has released information about the strategy in general and various aspects of the platform. The .Net platform will include servers; building-block services, such as Web-based data storage; and device software.

The .Net platform is expected to provide

- The ability to make the entire range of computing devices work together and to have user information automatically updated and synchronized on all of them

- Increased interactive capability for Web sites, enabled by greater use of **XML** (Extensible Markup Language) rather than **HTML**

- A premium online subscription service, that will feature customized access and delivery of products and services to the user from a central starting point for the management of various applications, such as e-mail, for example, or software, such as Office .Net

- Centralized data storage, which will increase efficiency and ease of access to information, as well as synchronization of information among users and devices

- The ability to integrate various communications media, such as e-mail, faxes, and telephones

- For developers, the ability to create reusable modules, which should increase productivity and reduce the number of programming errors

According to Bill Gates, Microsoft expects that .Net will have as significant an effect on the computing world as the introduction of Windows. One concern being voiced is that although .Net's services will be accessible through any browser, they are likely to function more fully on products designed to work with .Net code.

The full release of .Net is expected to take a year or two to complete, with intermittent releases of products such as a personal security service and new versions of Windows and Office that implement the .Net strategy coming on the market separately. A technical preview of Visual Studio.Net has been available from the Microsoft developers Web site since July of 2000. The next version of Windows, **Windows XP**, to be released later in 2001, will include certain .Net capabilities.

Net PC

The Net PC (also referred to as the Network PC) is an industry specification for a low-cost personal computer designed for businesses and their network applications. A Net PC, which is a design for what is also sometimes known as a **thin client**, is intended to be centrally managed and to lack a diskette drive, CD-ROM drive, or hardware expansion slots. It is designed to support specific business tasks and applications. Typical uses for Net PCs would be online transaction processing (**OLTP**) applications, retail point-of-sale, and banking services.

Among companies that sell or plan to sell Net PCs are Acer, Compaq, Dell, Hewlett-Packard, NEC, and Unisys. Other companies including IBM plan to accomodate their existing personal computer line to compete. Net PCs are expected to cost $1,000 or less and offer Pentium **microprocessors**, 16 to 32 megabytes of **random access memory**, and at least 1.2 gigabyte hard drives. At its inception, the Net PC was forecast to achieve about 15% of total desktop PC sales.

A concept similar to the Net PC but with different ideas about what a low-cost network PC should be built with is called the network computer (**NC**).

NetBEUI

NetBEUI (NetBIOS Extended User Interface) is an extended version of **NetBIOS**, the program that lets computers communicate within a local area network. NetBEUI (pronounced net-BOO-ee) formalizes the frame format (or arrangement of information in a data transmission) that was not specified as part of NetBIOS. NetBEUI was developed by IBM for its LAN Manager product and has been adopted by Microsoft for its Windows NT, LAN Manager, and Windows for Workgroups products. Hewlett-Packard and DEC use it in comparable products.

NetBEUI is said to be the best performance choice for communication within a single LAN. Because, like NetBIOS, it does not support the routing of messages to other networks, its interface must be adapted to other protocols such as **Internetwork Packet Exchange** or **TCP/IP**. A recommended method is to install both NetBEUI and TCP/IP in each computer and set the server up to use NetBEUI for communication within the LAN and TCP/IP for communication beyond the LAN.

NetBIOS

NetBIOS (Network Basic Input/Output System) is a program that allows applications on different computers to communicate within a local area network (**LAN**). It was created by IBM for its early PC Network, was adopted by Microsoft, and has since become a de facto industry standard. NetBIOS is used in Ethernet, token ring, and Windows NT networks. It does not in itself support a routing mechanism so applications communicating on a wide area network (WAN) must use another "transport mechanism" (such as **Transmission Control Protocol**) rather than or in addition to NetBIOS.

NetBIOS frees the application from having to understand the details of the network, including error recovery (in session mode). A NetBIOS request is provided in the form of a Network Control Block (NCB) which, among other things, specifies a message location and the name of a destination.

NetBIOS provides the session and transport services described in the Open Systems Interconnection (**OSI**) model. However, it does not provide a standard frame or data format for transmission. A standard frame format is provided in the NetBIOS Extended User Interface (**NetBEUI**).

NetBIOS provides two communication modes: session or datagram. Session mode lets two computers establish a connection for a "conversation," allows larger messages to be handled, and provides error detection and recovery. Datagram mode is "connectionless" (each message is sent independently), messages must be smaller, and the

application is responsible for error detection and recovery. Datagram mode also supports the broadcast of a message to every computer on the LAN.

Netcaster

Netcaster, a component of Netscape's Communicator (which includes the Netscape Navigator **browser**), allows a Web user to make preselected Web sites an integral part of the personal computer **desktop** and to have them automatically updated. Called **channels** and similar to the channels on Microsoft's Windows desktops, the Netcaster channels include: CNET, CNN, Gartner, and Airius News. A user can request customized news and content updates on a preset schedule. Using **push technology** (sometimes referred to as *Webcasting or netcasting*), the updating occurs in the background while other computer work is going on and is then available when you want to read the updates. (You can read the updates offline.)

Netfinity

IBM's Netfinity is an Intel-based **enterprise server** line that is based on IBM's **X-architecture**. IBM describes the X-architecture as a design blueprint that addresses the increasing need for communicating and managing huge amounts of information and the demands of business-to-consumer, business-to-business, and intra-business applications on technology platforms. Netfinity and another server line called **xSeries** are closely related. xSeries models are identified with an x preceding the model number (for example, the x430. Netfinity servers are identified without an x (for example, the Netfinity 7000).

The Netfinity server line uses copper chip wiring and Silicon On Insulator (**SOI**) **microprocessor** technologies. Netfinity also uses **64-bit** computing, which IBM began using before the introduction of Netfinity with both the **AS/400** and **RS/6000** servers. IBM also enhanced existing **memory** systems to support large amounts of memory in Netfinity servers. Currently, the Netfinity 7000 M10 supports up to 8 gigabytes (**GB**s) of memory. IBM plans to offer Netfinity servers with up to 64 GB of memory.

Netfinity servers may be **clustered** for increased reliability and decreased downtime. Netfinity servers also **interoperate** with existing servers such as the **AS/400** and the **RS/6000**. Netfinity includes the Communication Server for Windows NT that allows Netfinity applications to communicate with other applications, whether interoperable or not, using IBM's own Systems Network Architecture (**SNA**) protocols as well as Transmission Control Protocol/Internet Protocol (**TCP/IP**).

For diagnostic purposes, Netfinity includes an onboard systems management processor that allows for remote management and diagnostics of Netfinity servers even if turned off. If a server fails, it can connect to IBM's Help Center using Mobile Service Terminal (MoST) connect for diagnostic tests. RemoteConnect is another application that allows a Netfinity server to self-diagnose, issue an alert, call a service organization, and request a replacement part or a technician.

netiquette

Netiquette is etiquette on the Internet. Since the Internet changes rapidly, its netiquette does too, but it's still usually based on the Golden Rule. The need for a sense of netiquette arises mostly when sending or distributing **e-mail**, posting on **Usenet** groups, or **chatting**. To some extent, the practice of netiquette depends on understanding how e-mail, the Usenet, chatting, or other aspects of the Internet actually work or are practiced. So a little preliminary observation can help. Poor netiquette because you're new is one thing, but such practices as **spam** and **flaming** are another matter.

netizen

The word *netizen* seems to have two similar meanings.

1. A citizen who uses the Internet as a way of participating in political society (for example, exchanging views, providing information, and voting).

2. An Internet user who is trying to contribute to the Internet's use and growth. As a powerful communications medium, the Internet seems to offer great possibilities for social change. It also creates a new culture and its own special issues, such as who shall have access to it. The implication is that the Internet's users, who use and know most about it, have a responsibility to ensure that is used constructively while also fostering free speech and open access.

Cybercitizen is a synonym.

netmask

In administering Internet sites, a netmask is a string of 0's and 1's that mask or screen out the network part of an IP address (**IP**) so that only the **host** computer part of the address remains. The **binary** 1's at the beginning of the mask turn the network ID part of the IP address into 0's. The binary 0's that follow allow the host ID to remain. A frequently-used netmask is 255.255.255.0. (255 is the decimal equivalent of a binary string of eight ones.) Used for a Class C **subnet** (one with up to 255 host computers), the ".0" in the "255.255.255.0" netmask allows the specific host computer address to be visible.

NetRexx

NetRexx, a programming language designed to be easier to learn and use than **Java**, combines the **syntax** of the **Rexx** language and the **semantics** of Java. Rexx is a **script** language, developed at IBM, that is very popular among IBM's corporate mainframe system users. NetRexx, developed by Rexx's inventor, Mike Cowlishaw, superimposes Rexx's ease-of-use on the **object-oriented programming** concepts of Java—**class**, **method**, and properties. NetRexx **source code** statements are **compiled** into Java source statements, which are then compiled into Java **bytecode** that can be run in any computer **operating system** that includes a Java virtual machine (JVM). Thus, NetRexx programs can be run in Windows, OS/2, MVS, UNIX-based systems—in short, almost any operating system that supports the Java 1.1 toolkit and compiler and includes the JVM.

According to IBM, a study shows that the Java source for a typical class has about 35% more lexical tokens and requires about 20% more keystrokes than it would in NetRexx. NetRexx has equivalent classes for all Java classes.

Netscape

Netscape is one of the two most popular Web **browsers** and also the name of a company, Netscape Communications, now owned by America Online (AOL). Currently, almost all Internet users use either Netscape's browser or Microsoft's Internet Explorer (**MSIE**) browser, and many users use both. Although Netscape was initially the predominant product in terms of usability and number of users, Microsoft's browser is now considered superior by many users and has taken a lead in usage.

Netscape's browser originally was called "Navigator," and is still called that in the suite of software, Communicator, of which it is now a part. Navigator was developed in 1995 by a team led by Marc Andreessen, who created **Mosaic**, the first Web browser that had a graphical user interface, at the University of Illinois' National Center for Supercomputing Applications (**NCSA**) in 1993.

Navigator can be downloaded as part of the Communicator suite from Netscape's Web site at no charge. CD-ROM versions can also be purchased in computer stores and are sometimes distributed freely as promotions.

Netscape Server Application Programming Interface

NSAPI (Netscape Server Application Programming Interface) is an API (**application program interface**) that is provided with Netscape **Web servers** to help developers build faster and more complex Web-based applications by extending the server capabilities. NSAPI, the Common Gateway Interface (**CGI**), and the **Java** and **JavaScript**-based server API are the three components of Netscape's Internet Application Framework. NSAPI was created as a more efficient and robust replacement for the Common Gateway Interface alone. It is often used to develop applications that involve custom authorization or logging, or to change aspects of server operation.

NSAPI is used to handle **Hypertext Transfer Protocol** transactions in the Netscape Enterprise Server's *request-response* process through its built-in *Server Application*

Functions (SAF). Netscape Server's SAFs are written with the NSAPI and are functions called by the server to deal with requests received from a client. At start up, after **initialization**, the server waits for an HTTP request from the client for a resource such as an HTML file, a CGI program, or an image file, for example. The request consists of a Universal Resource Identifier (**URI**), an HTTP **method**, and, sometimes, information about the client or the request. The request-response process involves a sequence of six steps:

1) *AuthTrans*, which verifies request information (name and password, for example);

2) *NameTrans*, which translates the in the request into a local file system path;

3) *PathCheck*, which checks the validity of the path and the authorization of the user for path access;

4) *ObjectType*, which determines the **MIME** (Multi-purpose Internet Mail Encoding) type of the resource requested by the client;

5) *Service*, which is the response to the client; and finally,

6) *AddLog*, which adds related entries to the log file.

Each step may involve multiple operations, which are performed by Server Application Functions (SAF). Each SAF returns a result code to the server to indicate the success or failure of the operation. Based on the result code, the server either proceeds to the next step, carries out the next SAF in the current step, or aborts the process.

netsplit

In using an Internet Relay Chat (**IRC**) network, a netsplit is the loss of contact between two IRC **servers**. As a result, chat users at either end will see the users at the affected servers suddenly disappear.

An IRC network usually has a linear topology. That is, each server is connected in line to the next server which is connected to the next one, and so forth. When two servers lose contact, the network essentially is split into two networks. Users remain in contact with other users on their side of the network split and lose contact with the other users, who appear to have quickly departed. If a network has a mesh topology, each server can route messages to a second server when it loses a server connection.

Most netsplits are restored within a short period of time.

NetWare

NetWare, made by Novell, is the most widely-installed **network server operating system**. Initially very successful in installing its products in large and small office local area networks (**LANs**), Novell has redesigned (or at least refeatured) NetWare to work successfully as part of larger and heterogeneous networks, including the Internet. NetWare's primary competitor is the Microsoft Windows NT operating system.

The latest version of NetWare, NetWare 5, comes with support for both Novell's own **Internetwork Packet Exchange** network protocol and for the Internet's **Internet Protocol** as well as application-level support for a Web server. NetWare has integrated its own Novell Directory Services (NDS) with the industry standard Domain Name System (**DNS**) and the Dynamic Host Configuration Protocol (**DHCP**). NetWare supports **Java** applications and the Common Object Request Broker Architecture (**CORBA**) Object Request Broker (**ORB**). Its **kernel** supports **multiprocessing**. Additional features include what it calls "next generation" file system and printing services and advanced security (public-key cryptography and Secure Authentication Services—SAS).

network

In information technology, a network is a series of points or **nodes** interconnected by communication paths. Networks can interconnect with other networks and contain subnetworks.

The most common **topology** or general configurations of networks include the **bus**, star, and **token ring** topologies. Networks can also be characterized in terms of spatial distance as local area networks (**LAN**s), metropolitan area networks (**MAN**s), and wide area networks (**WAN**s).

A given network can also be characterized by the type of data transmission technology in use on it (for example, a **TCP/IP** or **Systems Network Architecture** network); by whether it carries voice, data, or both kinds of signals; by who can use the network (public or private); by the usual nature of its connections (dial-up or switched, dedicated or nonswitched, or virtual connections); and by the types of physical links (for example, **optical fiber**, **coaxial cable**, and **unshielded twisted pair**). Large telephone networks and networks using their infrastructure (such as the **Internet**) have sharing and exchange arrangements with other companies so that larger networks are created.

network access point

In the United States, a network access point (NAP) is one of several major Internet interconnection points that serve to tie all the Internet access providers together so that, for example, an AT&T user in Portland, Oregon can reach the Web site of a Bell South customer in Miami, Florida. Originally, four NAPs—in New York, Washington, D.C., Chicago, and San Francisco—were created and supported by the National Science Foundation as part of the transition from the original U.S. government-financed Internet to a commercially operated Internet. Since that time, several new NAPs have arrived, including WorldCom's "MAE West" site in San Jose, California and ICS Network Systems' "Big East."

The NAPs provide major switching facilities that serve the public in general. Using companies apply to use the NAP facilities and make their own intercompany *peering* arrangements. Much Internet traffic is handled without involving NAPs, using peering arrangements and interconnections within geographic regions. The **vBNS** network, a separate network supported by the National Science Foundation for research purposes, also makes use of the NAPs.

network access server

NAS is also the abbreviation for **network-attached storage**.

A network access server (NAS) is a computer **server** that enables an independent service provider (**ISP**) to provide connected customers with Internet **access**. A network access server has interfaces to both the local telecommunication service provider such as the phone company and to the Internet **backbone**.

The server authenticates users requesting **login**. It receives a dial-up call from each user host (such as your computer) that wants to access the Internet, performs the necessary steps to authenticate and authorize each user, usually by verifying a user name and password, and then allows requests to begin to flow between the user host and hosts (computers) elsewhere on the Internet.

The term *network access server* may refer to a server devoted entirely to managing network access or to a server that also performs other functions as well. A network access server can be configured to provide a host of services such as **VoIP**, fax-over-IP, and voicemail-over-IP as well.

One of the most well-known network access servers, the AS5800, is made by Cisco Systems. It is a workhorse product that is referred to as a carrier-class universal access server.

Network Address Translation

NAT (Network Address Translation) is the translation of an Internet Protocol address (**IP address**) used within one network to a different IP address known within another network. One network is designated the *inside* network and the other is the *outside*. Typically, a company maps its local inside network addresses to one or more global outside IP addresses and unmaps the global IP addresses on incoming packets back into local IP addresses. This helps ensure security since each outgoing or incoming request must go through a translation process that also offers the opportunity to qualify or authenticate the request or match it to a previous request. NAT also conserves on the number of global IP addresses that a company needs and it lets the company use a single IP address in its communication with the world.

NAT is included as part of a **router** and is often part of a corporate **firewall**. Network administrators create a NAT table that does the global-to-local and local-to-global IP address mapping. NAT can also be used in conjunction with *policy routing*. NAT can be statically defined or it can be set up to dynamically translate from and to a pool of IP addresses. Cisco's version of NAT lets an administrator create tables that map:

- A local IP address to one global IP address statically

- A local IP address to any of a rotating pool of global IP addresses that a company may have

- A local IP address plus a particular TCP **port** to a global IP address or one in a pool of them

- A global IP address to any of a pool of local IP addresses on a round-robin basis

NAT is described in general terms in RFC 1631. which discusses NAT's relationship to Classless Interdomain Routing (**CIDR**) as a way to reduce the IP address depletion problem. NAT reduces the need for a large amount of publicly known IP addresses by creating a separation between publicly known and privately known IP addresses. CIDR aggregates publicly known IP addresses into blocks so that fewer IP addresses are wasted. In the end, both extend the use of IPv4 IP addresses for a few more years before **IPv6** is generally supported.

network computer

A network computer (NC) is a concept from Oracle and Sun Microsystems for a low-cost personal computer for business networks that, like the **Net PC**, would be configured with only essential equipment, devoid of CD-ROM players, diskette drives, and expansion slots, and intended to be managed and maintained centrally (any new software would be downloaded). Unlike the Net PC, the network computer could be based on microprocessors other than Intel's and might include a **Java**-based operating system rather than Windows.

Along with the Net PC, the network computer is sometimes referred to as a **thin client**.

network encryption

Network encryption (sometimes called *network layer*, or *network level encryption*) is a network security process that applies **crypto** services at the network transfer layer—above the **data link** level, but below the application level. The network transfer layers are layers 3 and 4 of the Open Systems Interconnection (**OSI**) reference model, the layers responsible for connectivity and routing between two end points. Using the existing network services and application software, network encryption is invisible to the end user and operates independently of any other encryption processes used. Data is encrypted only while in transit, existing as **plaintext** on the originating and receiving hosts.

Network encryption is implemented through Internet Protocol Security (**IPSec**), a set of open Internet Engineering Task Force (**IETF**) standards that, used in conjunction, create a framework for private communication over **IP** networks.

IPSec works through the network architecture, which means that end users and applications don't need to be altered in any way. Encrypted **packet**s appear to be identical to unencrypted packets and are easily routed through any IP network.

Network encryption products and services are offered by a number of companies, including Cisco, Motorola, and Oracle.

Network File System

The Network File System (NFS) is a **client/server application** that lets a computer user view and optionally store and update **files** on a remote computer as though they were on the user's own computer. The user's system needs to have an NFS client and the other computer needs the NFS server. Both of them require that you also have **TCP/IP** installed since the NFS server and client use TCP/IP as the program that sends the files and updates back and forth. (However, the User Datagram Protocol, UDP, which comes with TCP/IP, is used instead of TCP with earlier versions of NFS.)

NFS was developed by Sun Microsystems and has been designated a file server standard. Its **protocol** uses the Remote Procedure Call (**RPC**) method of communication between computers.

Using NFS, the user or a system administrator can *mount* all or a portion of a *file system* (which is a portion of the hierarchical tree in any file directory and subdirectory, including the one you find on your PC or Mac). The portion of your file system that is mounted (designated as accessible) can be accessed with whatever privileges go with your access to each file (read-only or read-write).

NFS has been extended to the Internet with **WebNFS**, a product and proposed standard that is now part of Netscape's Communicator browser. WebNFS offers what Sun believes is a faster way to access Web pages and other Internet files.

Network Information System

See "NIS (Network Information System)"

network interface card

A network interface card (NIC) is a computer circuit board or **card** that is installed in a computer so that it can be connected to a network. Personal computers and workstations on a local area network (**LAN**) typically contain a network interface card specifically designed for the LAN transmission technology, such as **Ethernet** or **token ring**. Network interface cards provide a dedicated, full-time connection to a network. Most home and portable computers connect to the Internet through as-needed dial-up connection. The **modem** provides the connection interface to the Internet service provider.

network interface unit

A network interface unit (NIU) (sometimes called a *network interface device*) is a device that serves as a common **interface** for various other devices within a local area network (**LAN**), or as an interface to allow networked computers to connect to an outside network. The NIU enables communication between devices that use different protocols by supplying a common transmission **protocol**, which may be used instead of the devices' own protocols, or may be used to convert the specific device protocol to the common one. To enable an interface between a LAN and another network, the NIU converts protocols and associated code and acts as a **buffer** between the connected hardware. A **network interface card** (NIC) is a type of NIU.

Network layer

In the Open Systems Interconnection (**OSI**) communications model, the Network layer knows the address of the neighboring nodes in the network, packages output with the correct network address information, selects routes and **quality of service**, and recognizes and forwards to the Transport layer incoming messages for local host domains. Among existing **protocols** that generally map to the OSI network layer are the Internet Protocol (**IP**) part of TCP/IP and **NetWare IPX/SPX**. Both IP Version 4 and IP Version 6 (**IPv6**) map to the OSI network layer.

Network Node Manager

The Network Node Manager (NNM) is a program that helps a **network administrator** view and manage the conditions in a computer network. NNM is part of the **OpenView** suite of enterprise system management applications from **Hewlett-Packard** (HP). Using the Network Node Manager, an administrator can view the network in an easy-to-see graphical format. NNM "discovers" the devices that are in the network and shows their relative location and their status. When a device fails, NNM can analyze events associated with the failure and help to recommend action. BNM also provides some predictive information that helps identify potential failures before they occur.

network operating system

A network operating system (NOS) is a computer **operating system** system that is designed primarily to support **workstations**, **personal computers**, and, in some instances, older **terminals** that are connected on a local area network (**LAN**). Artisoft's LANtastic, Banyan VINES, Novell's **NetWare**, and Microsoft's LAN Manager are examples of network operating systems. In addition, some multi-purpose operating systems, such as **Windows NT** and Digital's **OpenVMS** come with capabilities that enable them to be described as a network operating system.

A network operating system provides printer sharing, common file system and database sharing, application sharing, and the ability to manage a network name directory, security, and other housekeeping aspects of a network.

network operations center

A network operations center (NOC) is a place from which a telecommunications **network** is supervised, monitored, and maintained. **Enterprises** with large networks as well as large network service providers such as GTE Internetworking typically have a network operations center, a room containing visualizations of the network or networks that are being monitored, workstations at which the detailed status of the network can be seen, and the necessary software to manage the networks. The network operations center is the focal point for network troubleshooting, software distribution and updating, **router** and **domain name** management, performance monitoring, and coordination with affiliated networks.

network PC

A network PC (sometimes called an *appliance*) is a term used to denote a new kind of relatively low-cost PC designed for Internet access and specialized business use, but without the full capabilities ot today's personal computer and software. The device is expected to cost in the $500 to $1,000 range.

IBM, Apple, Oracle, Philips, and Sony are leading companies who sell or plan to sell network PCs.

Network Service Access Point

The Network Service Access Point (NSAP) is one of two types of hierarchical addresses (the other type is the *network entity title*) used to implement Open Systems Interconnection (**OSI**) Network layer addressing. The NSAP is the logical point between the Network and Transport layers where network services are delivered to the Transport layer; the location of this point is identified to the OSI network service provider by the NSAP address. There are two NSAP address fields, Initial Domain Part (IDP) and the Domain-Specific Part (DSP).

The IDP consists of the Authority Format Identifier (AFI) and the Initial Domain Identifier (IDI). AFI serves to provide information about the makeup of IDI and DSP, indicating, for example, whether the DSP uses decimal or binary notation, or whether or not the IDI may be of variable length.

The DSP is made up of four fields: the Address Administration field, which enables further address administration tasks and task delegation; the Area field, which is used for routing and identifies the specific area within a domain; the Station field, also used for routing purposes, which specifies the station within the area; and the Selector field, also used for routing, which identifies a specific entity within the station called an *n-selector*, the last byte of the NSAP address. If an OSI end system has multiple NSAP addresses—which is frequently the case—they will typically differ only in the n-selector.

network service provider

A network service provider (NSP) is a company that provides **backbone** services to an Internet service provider (**ISP**), the company that most Web users use for access to the Internet. Typically, an ISP connects at a point called an Internet Exchange (IX) to a regional ISP that in turn connects to an NSP backbone. In the U.S., major NSPs include MCI, Sprint, UUNET, AGIS, and BBN.

An ISP can purchase a wholesale dial access service from an NSP, which provides **dialup** connectivity for their customers. Customers then dial into their ISP's network using a local access number, which in turn connects to the backbone of that Internet provider's NSP. The NSP routes all traffic and basically provides the infrastructure needed for Internet connectivity. The NSP builds, maintains, and expands their infrastructure as Internet traffic demands. The ISP is responsible for its own network, sales and marketing, and customer service. An ISP can also purchase other services from an NSP that they in turn provide their customers such as e-mail service, Web-based e-mail service, personal **Web hosting**, discussion groups, and other **end-user applications**. All these services are provided under the ISP's brand name rather than that of the NSP.

network terminating unit

See "network terminator 1"

Network Time Protocol

Network Time Protocol (NTP) is a **protocol** that is used to synchronize computer clock times in a network of computers. Developed by David Mills at the University of Delaware, NTP is now an Internet standard. In common with similar protocols, NTP uses Coordinated Universal Time (**UTC**) to synchronize computer clock times to a millisecond, and sometimes to a fraction of a millisecond.

Accurate time across a network is important for many reasons; even small fractions of a second can cause problems. For example, distributed procedures depend on coordinated times to ensure that proper sequences are followed. Security mechanisms depend on coordinated times across the network. File system updates carried out by a number of computers also depend on synchronized clock times. Air traffic control systems provide a graphic illustration of the need for coordinated times, since flight paths require very precise timing (imagine the situation if air traffic controller computer clock times were not synchronized).

UTC time is obtained using several different methods, including radio and satellite systems. Specialized receivers are available for high-level services such as the Global

Positioning System (**GPS**) and the governments of some nations. However, it is not practical or cost-effective to equip every computer with one of these receivers. Instead, computers designated as *primary time servers* are outfitted with the receivers and they use protocols such as NTP to synchronize the clock times of networked computers. Degrees of separation from the UTC source are defined as strata. A radio clock (which receives true time from a dedicated transmitter or satellite navigation system) is stratum-0; a computer that is directly linked to the radio clock is stratum-1; a computer that receives its time from a stratum-1 computer is stratum-2, and so on.

The term NTP applies to both the protocol and the client/server programs that run on computers. The programs are compiled by the user as an NTP client, NTP server, or both. In basic terms, the NTP client initiates a time request exchange with the time server. As a result of this exchange, the client is able to calculate the link delay, its local offset, and adjust its local clock to match the clock at the server's computer. As a rule, six exchanges over a period of about five to 10 minutes are required to initially set the clock. Once synchronized, the client updates the clock about once every 10 minutes, usually requiring only a single message exchange. **Redundant** servers and varied network paths are used to ensure reliability and accuracy. In addition to client/server synchronization, NTP also supports broadcast synchronization of peer computer clocks. NTP is designed to be highly **fault-tolerant** and **scalable**.

network-attached storage

Network-attached storage (NAS) is **hard disk** storage that is set up with its own network address rather than being attached to the department computer that is serving applications to a network's workstation users. By removing storage access and its management from the department server, both application programming and files can be served faster because they are not competing for the same processor resources. The network-attached storage device is attached to a local area network (typically, an **Ethernet** network) and assigned an **IP address**. File requests are mapped by the main server to the NAS file server.

Network-attached storage consists of hard disk storage, including multi-disk **RAID** systems, and software for configuring and mapping file locations to the network-attached device. Network-attached storage can be a step toward and included as part of a more sophisticated storage system known as a storage area network (**SAN**).

NAS software can usually handle a number of network **protocols**, including Microsoft's **Internetwork Packet Exchange** and **NetBEUI**, Novell's Netware **Internetwork Packet Exchange**, and Sun Microsystems' **Network File System**. Configuration, including the setting of user access priorities, is usually possible using a Web browser.

networking chip

A networking **chip** is a microprocessor that provides the logic for sending and receiving data (including voice and video) on a telecommunications network so that additional devices are not needed for these functions. Among other manufacturers, IBM reportedly will sell networking chips that support asynchronous transfer mode (**ATM**) and **token ring** communication.

networking

In information technology, networking is the construction, design, and use of **networks**, including the physical (cabling, **hubs**, **bridges**, **switches**, **routers**, and so forth), the selection and use of telecommunication **protocols** and computer software for using and managing the network, and the establishment of operation policies and procedures related to the network.

Netzip

Netzip is a **plug-in** for Web **browsers** that allows you to view the files within a **zip file** from within your browser without the need to launch an external application. Netzip lets you create a zip file **archive** (including one that spans disks). It also lets you choose a **compression algorithm** when you create an archive. You can decompress and extract from **ARJ**, Lharc (LZH, LHA, LHZ), Z, GZ, and **TAR** (TAZ, TGZ, TAR.Z, TAR.GZ) files. Netzip also lets you temporarily "check out" files within a zip file and run installation utilities.

If downloading from a site with a Netzip server and its I-ZIP technology, you can view the contents of a zip file before downloading the entire file. I-ZIP lets you download individual files within the zip file archive.

Netzip is made by Software Builders International.

neural network

In information technology, a neural network is a system of programs and data structures that approximates the operation of the human brain. A neural network usually involves a large number of processors operating in parallel, each with its own small sphere of knowledge and access to data in its local memory. Typically, a neural network is initially "trained" or fed large amounts of data and rules about data relationships (for example, "A grandfather is older than a person's father"). A program can then tell the network how to behave in response to an external stimulus (for example, to input from a computer user who is interacting with the network) or can initiate activity on its own (within the limits of its access to the external world).

In making determinations, neural networks use several principles, including gradient-based training, **fuzzy logic**, genetic algorithms, and Bayesian methods. Neural networks are sometimes described in terms of knowledge layers, with, in general, more complex networks having deeper layers. In *feedforward* systems, learned relationships about data can "feed forward" to higher layers of knowledge. Neural networks can also learn temporal concepts and have been widely used in signal processing and time series analysis.

Current applications of neural networks include: oil exploration data analysis, weather prediction, the interpretation of nucleotide sequences in biology labs, and the exploration of models of thinking and consciousness. In his novel, *Galatea 2.2*, Richard Powers envisioned a neural network (named "Helen") that could be taught to pass a comprehensive exam in English literature.

neutron

Also see **electron**.

A neutron is a subatomic particle found in the nucleus of every **atom** except that of simple hydrogen. The particle derives its name from the fact that it has no electrical charge; it is neutral. Neutrons are extremely dense. If isolated, a single neutron would have a mass of only $1.675 ? 10^{-27}$ kilogram, but if a teaspoonful of tightly packed neutrons could be scooped up, the resulting chunk of matter would weigh millions of tons at the earth's surface.

The number of **proton** in an element's nucleus is called the *atomic number*. This number gives each element its unique identity. In the atoms of any particular element, for example carbon, the number of protons in the nuclei is always the same, but the number of neutrons can vary. An atom of a given element having a specific number of neutrons in the nucleus is called an *isotope*. The isotope of an atom is denoted by writing the element's name followed by the sum of the number of protons and neutrons. The nucleus of a carbon atom always has six protons and usually has six neutrons, but some carbon nuclei contain eight neutrons. Thus, carbon-12 is the most common isotope of carbon; carbon-14 is also found, but is less common.

Neutrons need not be confined to the nuclei of atoms. They can exist all by themselves. When neutrons are found outside atomic nuclei, they acquire fascinating, bizarre, and potentially dangerous properties. When they travel at high speed, they produce deadly radiation. The so-called *neutron bomb*, known for its ability to kill people and animals while having a minimal effect on inanimate physical structures, works by producing a barrage of high-speed neutrons. The high density of these particles, combined with their speed, gives them extreme energy. As a result, they have the power to alter, or even break apart, the nuclei of atoms that they strike.

When a large star explodes, blowing off its outer layers in a brilliant fireball called a *supernova*, the remaining matter is incredibly dense, and it collapses under its own gravitation. When this stellar remnant acquires a certain critical density, virtually all of the subatomic particles become neutrons. The resulting object is a *neutron star* that might have a diameter smaller than that of the earth, yet have a mass hundreds of times that of the sun. Neutron stars can rotate at high speed, producing bursts of electromagnetic radiation that can be heard as periodic pulses in radio telescopes. These celestial objects are known as *pulsars*. If a neutron star is dense enough, it collapses into a *black hole* whose gravitation is so intense that nothing can escape, not even **photons**.

new media

New media is a catch-all term for all forms of electronic communication that have appeared or will appear since the original mainly text-and-static picture forms of online communication. New media usually includes any and all of these:

Special audiovisual effects of any kind
Larger than 17 inch displays
Streaming video and streaming audio
3-D and **virtual reality** environments and effects
Highly interactive user interfaces (possibly including mere **hypertext** or not)
Mobile presentation and computing capabilities
Any kind of communication requiring high-**bandwidth**
CD and DVD media
Telephone and digital data integration
Online communities
Microdevices with **embedded systems programming**
Live Internet broadcasting as on the **MBone**
Person-to-person visual communication (as in **CU-SeeMe**)
One-to-many visual communication as with
Applications of any of these technology in particular fields such as medicine (*telemedicine*) and other fields

Although the line is not easily drawn, users of the term often emphasize the visual and visual design aspects of the new digital technology experience. New media encompasses **multimedia**, a term originally used mainly for standalone (not online) presentations in various scales as well as **hypermedia**, which emphasizes interactivity and specifically means the ability to selectively link from one form of content to another.

newbie

A newbie (pronounced NOO-bee) is any new user of a technology. The term is commonly applied to new users of personal computers and to new users of the Internet. According to Eric Raymond's *The New Hacker's Dictionary*, the term is a variant of the English public school term, *new boy*, someone in the first year or period of school. The term predates the Web and has been used for some time in **Usenet** newsgroups. Glenn Connery reports that he used the term in 1990 as a participant in Internet **chatting** groups.

newsgroup

A newsgroup is a discussion about a particular subject consisting of notes written to a central Internet site and redistributed through **Usenet**, a worldwide network of news discussion groups. Usenet uses the Network News Transfer Protocol (**NNTP**).

Newsgroups are organized into subject hierarchies, with the first few letters of the newsgroup name indicating the major subject category and sub-categories represented by a subtopic name. Many subjects have multiple levels of subtopics. Some major subject categories are: news, rec (recreation), soc (society), sci (science), comp (computers), and so forth (there are many more). Users can post to existing newsgroups, respond to previous posts, and create new newsgroups.

Newcomers to newsgroups are requested to learn basic Usenet **netiquette** and to get familiar with a newsgroup before posting to it. A **frequently-asked questions** is provided. The rules can be found when you start to enter the Usenet through your browser or an online service. You can subscribe to the postings on a particular newsgroup.

Some newsgroups are moderated by a designated person who decides which postings to allow or to remove. Most newsgroups are unmoderated.

newsXML

See "XMLNews"

newton

The newton is the International System of Units (**SI**) unit of force. In physics and engineering documentation, the term *newton(s)* is usually abbreviated N.

One newton is the force required to cause a mass of one kilogram to accelerate at a rate of one meter per second squared in the absence of other force-producing effects. In general, force (F) in newtons, mass (m) in kilograms, and acceleration (a) in meters per second squared are related by a formula well known in physics:

$$F = ma$$

The formula also applies when **F** and **a** are vector quantities having magnitude and direction:

$$\mathbf{F} = m\mathbf{a}$$

where the direction of the force vector **F** is the same as the direction of the acceleration vector **a**.

As an example of force as a function of mass and acceleration, suppose a mass of 4 kilograms is made to accelerate at 12 meters per second squared. Then the applied force in newtons is:

$$F = ma = 4 \times 12 = 48 \text{ N}$$

NeXT computer

Also see **near-end crosstalk** (NEXT), a network wiring term.

NeXT was a computer company formed by Steven Jobs, one of the founders of Apple Computer, and also the name of the advanced personal computer or workstation that the company developed and first offered in 1988. The NeXT computer was an industrial designer's triumph, a futuristic black cube with a high-resolution display, a graphical user interface, and an **operating system** called NeXTStep.

In 1993, the computer was taken off the market. Jobs offered the **object-oriented programming** components of NeXTStep as a proposed standard for a development environment called OpenStep. In 1996, Apple Computer bought what was now NeXT Software and hired Jobs to return to Apple and help run the company. In 1998, Apple continued to offer OpenStep as a development environment for object-oriented applications that will run on multiple platforms.

Next Hop Resolution Protocol

In a computer network, NHRP (Next Hop Resolution Protocol) is a **protocol** or method that can be used so that a computer sending data to another computer can learn the most direct route (the fewest number of **hops**) to the receiving computer. If the receiving computer is in the same **subnetwork**, using NHRP will tell the sending computer and the sending computer can send subsequent data packets directly to the receiving computer using its subnetwork address rather than its global network address. If the receiving computer is not in the same subnetwork, using NHRP will tell the sending computer the computer in the subnetwork whose router provides the most direct path to the receiving computer and the sender can now forward subsequent data packets to that router.

NHRP is basically a query-and-reply protocol and all parties through which reply information passes build a "network knowledge table" that can be used for all subsequent traffic. Using this knowledge, a computer can send subsequent packets directly to the destination computer (or to an egress router) using an acquired "machine" address rather than a network address. (This kind of operation at the Media Access Control sublayer of the **Data-Link layer** communication layer level—rather than at the **Network layer**—is sometimes referred to as "operating at close to **wire speed**" because fewer program instructions are required and these can sometimes be located in a switching device.) NHRP thus provides two benefits: It reduces the number of hops a packet may have to take within a subnetwork and it allows the packets to be forwarded using the faster "machine" address.

NHRP does not currently shorten the number of hops a packet may take outside of the subnetwork. Currently, it only applies to Non-Broadcast Multi-Access (NBMA) subnetworks. That is, it applies to packet transmissions sent only to a single receiver. It is possible that in the future, NHRP may be applied to Broadcast Multi-Access (BMA) subnetworks as well.

NHRP was developed by the Internetworking Over NBMA working group of the Internet Engineering Task Force (**IETF**). It is a main component of Multiprotocol over ATM (MPOA) and is described in the IETF's RFC (Request for Comments) 2332, "NBMA Next Hop Resolution Protocol." 3Com refers to its implementation of NHRP as *Fast IP*.

NFS

See "Network File System"

Ni2

Ni2 (Net indexer 2) is the indexer for the AltaVista public search engine. According to AltaVista's parent company, Digital Equipment Corporation (DEC), Ni2 can index "an astounding one gigabyte of text per hour." Ni2 generates a link for each word that AltaVista's Web crawler, **Scooter**, brings back. It eliminates duplicates and ranks entries so that queries will produce more effective results.

In addition to AltaVista's free public search service, DEC sells AltaVista for individual use (downloaded to your computer, it can search everything on your hard disk) and for enterprise **intranets**. Ni2, Scooter, and the AltaVista product offerings are described at DEC's AltaVista Web site.

nibble

In computers and **digital** technology, a nibble (pronounced NIHB-uhl; sometimes spelled *nybble*) is four **binary digits** or half of an eight-bit **byte**. A nibble can be conveniently represented by one **hexadecimal** digit.

Like **crumb**, nibble carries on the "edible data" metaphor established with **bit** and **byte**.

In communications, a nibble is sometimes referred to as a "quadbit." or one of 16 possible four-bit combinations. A signal may be encoded in quadbits rather than one bit at a time. *Nibble interleaving or multiplexing* takes a quadbit or nibble from a lower-speed channel as input for a multiplexed signal on a higher-speed channel.

NIC

See "network interface card"

Ni-Cd battery

See "Nickel-Cadmium battery"

Nickel-Cadmium battery

The Nickel Cadmium (Ni-Cd) battery is a type of battery commonly used in portable computers, camcorders, portable drills, and other small battery-powered devices, having an effective and even power discharge. Although Nickel-Metal

Hydride and Lithium Ion batteries are becoming more popular in mobile computers, Ni-Cd batteries are still the most widely sold.

Nickel-Metal Hydride battery

The Nickel-Metal Hydride (Ni-MH) battery is a rechargeable power source that is increasingly used in portable computers and other devices. The most advanced rechargeable battery offered, the Ni-MH battery provides up to 40 percent longer service life than Nickel-Cadmium batteries as well as greater charge capacity. Ni-MH batteries are also used in cellular phones and camcorders.

Ni-MH battery

See "Nickel-Metal Hydride battery"

NIS (Network Information System)

NIS (Network Information System) is a **network** naming and administration system for smaller networks that was developed by Sun Microsystems. NIS+ is a later version that provides additional security and other facilities. Using NIS, each **host** client or server computer in the system has knowledge about the entire system. A user at any host can get access to files or applications on any host in the network with a single user identification and password. NIS is similar to the Internet's domain name system (**DNS**) but somewhat simpler and designed for a smaller network. It's intended for use on local area networks.

NIS uses the client/server model and the Remote Procedure Call (**RPC**) interface for communication between hosts. NIS consists of a server, a library of client programs, and some administrative tools. NIS is often used with the Network File System (**NFS**). NIS is a **UNIX**-based program.

Although Sun and others offer proprietary versions, most NIS code has been released into the public domain and there are **freeware** versions available. NIS was originally called *Yellow Pages* but because someone already had a trademark by that name, it was changed to Network Information System. It is still sometimes referred to by the initials: "YP".

Sun offers NIS+ together with its NFS product as a solution for Windows PC networks as well as for its own workstation networks.

NIS

See "NIS (Network Information System)"

NIS+

See "NIS (Network Information System)"

NIST

NIST is the National Institute of Standards and Technology, a unit of the US Commerce Department. Formerly known as the National Bureau of Standards, NIST promotes and maintains measurement standards. It also has active programs for encouraging and assisting industry and science to develop and use these standards.

nit

1) In information technology as elsewhere, a nit (pronounced NIHT) is a small, usually unimportant imperfection in something. People who have unusually high or unreasonable standards for the quality of a thing are sometimes referred to as *nitpickers*.

2) In lighting, the nit is a unit of visible-light intensity, commonly used to specify the brightness of a **cathode ray tube** or **liquid crystal display** computer display. One nit is equivalent to one candela per square meter. The *candela*, formerly called candlepower, is approximately the amount of light emitted by a common tallow candle; technically it is the quantity of radiation emitted by 1.667×10^{-6} square meter of a *blackbody* at the melting point of platinum. The candela is equal to one lumen per steradian (unit solid angle). (A blackbody is an object that radiates energy with 100% efficiency at all electromagnetic wavelengths. It also absorbs all electromagnetic energy that strikes it, hence the expression "black." It is a theoretical ideal of interest in physics and engineering.)

The nit is a comparatively small unit of brightness. A typical active-matrix LCD panel has an output between 200 and 300 nit, for example.

3) In digital electronics, the term nit is occasionally used to represent an amount, or increment, of data equal to 1.44 **bits**.

NLX

NLX is an industry-wide **open** specification for a space-saving computer **motherboard**. The NLX specification defines the motherboard size, hole mounting locations, riser card location, and maximum component heights on motherboard. Companies such as IBM, Hewlett-Packard, Digital Equipment, Sony, NEC, Toshiba, Gateway, and Fujitsu support NLX.

Traditionally a computer technician had to open the computer case using tools, but an NLX case is tool-free. Another feature of the NLX specification is the motherboard itself. It rests on rails and simply slides out without any screws to unscrew or **card** to remove. The motherboard plugs into a riser card that sits at a 90-degree angle from the motherboard. A riser card is an expansion card that physically extends a slot for more expansion cards. When the motherboard is removed, the riser card stays in place. This allows a technician to replace a motherboard or upgrade a component on the motherboard in about 30 minutes instead of the usual two hours, saving the customer money.

NLX motherboards support current and future processor technologies, the **Accelerated Graphics Port** (AGP), and tall memory technology. NLX is beneficial because it improves access to components, supports new technology, and lowers the cost of ownership.

NNM

See "Network Node Manager"

NNTP

NNTP (Network News Transfer Protocol) is the predominant **protocol** used by computer clients and servers for managing the notes posted on **Usenet newsgroup**s. NNTP replaced the original Usenet protocol, UNIX-to-UNIX Copy Protocol (**UUCP**) some time ago. NNTP servers manage the global network of collected Usenet newsgroups and include the server at your Internet access provider. An NNTP client is included as part of a Netscape, Internet Explorer, Opera, or other Web browser or you may use a separate client program called a newsreader.

no op

A no op (or no-op), for *no operation*, is a computer instruction that takes up a small amount of space but specifies no operation. The computer processor simply moves to the next sequential instruction. The no op is included in most **assembler** languages. It may have a label and can serve as a placeholder for a useful instruction to be inserted later during code development.

The New Hacker's Dictionary reports as a derivative meaning "A person who contributes nothing to a project, or has nothing going on upstairs, or both. As in 'He's a no-op.'"

NOC

See "network operations center"

node

In a network, a node is a connection point, either a redistribution point or an end point for data transmissions. In general, a node has programmed or engineered capability to recognize and process or forward transmissions to other nodes.

noise

Also see **audio noise**.

Noise is unwanted electrical or electromagnetic energy that degrades the quality of signals and data. Noise occurs in **digital** and **analog** systems, and can affect files and communications of all types, including text, programs, images, audio, and telemetry.

In a hard-wired circuit such as a telephone-line-based Internet hookup, *external noise* is picked up from appliances in the vicinity, from electrical transformers, from the atmosphere, and even from outer space. Normally this noise is of little or no consequence. However, during severe thunderstorms, or in locations were many electrical appliances are in use, external noise can affect communications. In an Internet hookup it slows down the data transfer rate, because the system must adjust its speed to match conditions on the line. In a voice telephone conversation, noise rarely sounds like anything other than a faint hissing or rushing.

Noise is a more significant problem in **wireless** systems than in hard-wired systems. In general, noise originating from outside the system is inversely proportional to the frequency, and directly proportional to the wavelength. At a low frequency such as 300 **kHz**, atmospheric and electrical noise are much more severe than at a high frequency like 300 **megahertz**. Noise generated inside wireless receivers, known as *internal noise*, is less dependent on frequency. Engineers are more concerned about internal noise at high frequencies than at low frequencies, because the less external noise there is, the more significant the internal noise becomes.

Communications engineers are constantly striving to develop better ways to deal with noise. The traditional method has been to minimize the signal **bandwidth** to the greatest possible extent. The less spectrum space a signal occupies, the less noise is passed through the receiving circuitry. However, reducing the bandwidth limits the maximum speed of the data that can be delivered. Another, more recently developed scheme for minimizing the effects of noise is called digital signal processing (**DSP**). Using fiber optics, a technology far less susceptible to noise, is another approach.

non-disclosure agreement

A non-disclosure agreement (NDA) is a signed formal agreement in which one party agrees to give a second party confidential information about its business or products and the second party agrees not to share this information with anyone else for a specified period of time. Non-disclosure agreements are common in technology companies where products are sometimes jointly developed. (In this case, the non-disclosure agreement is often mutual or two-way.) An NDA is also sometimes used when a company seeks venture capital from potential financial backers as a way to make sure that proprietary secrets or ideas are not stolen or leaked to someone else by the prospective investors. Today, venture capitalists for Internet startups sometimes will not consider a company that requires a non-disclosure agreement because of the time and overhead involved (they may have dozens of business plans waiting to be read!) and because of the potential for legal liability.

A number of different kinds of non-disclosure agreements can be found on the Web using popular search engines.

non-interlaced display

A non-interlaced display is a cathode-ray tube (**CRT**) display in which the lines are scanned sequentially rather than in alternating lines.

In a CRT display, there are several hundred horizontal lines in a frame (full screen). These lines are scanned from left to right, and from top to bottom. The refresh rate (number of frames scanned per second) varies, but it is normally between 60 and 100 **hertz**. Refresh rates slower than 60 Hz produce distracting screen flicker, which can cause headaches and eye fatigue.

Most CRT computer monitors scan each line in turn from top to bottom at the lowest **resolution** levels (640 × 480 and 800 × 600 **pixel**). However, at the higher resolutions, such as 1024 × 768 or 1200 × 800, the frame is sometimes scanned in interlaced fashion: First the odd-numbered lines, and then the even-numbered lines. This allows for a lower refresh rate without producing flicker. With text and fixed graphics displays, this scheme can work well. However, with animated graphics—especially images that move or change form rapidly—interlacing can produce a fluttering effect at least as irritating as screen flicker.

For serious animated-graphics work and video editing, a non- interlaced CRT display is recommended. The refresh rate should be as high as the system will allow, ideally 70 Hz or more.

nonlinearity

Nonlinearity is the behavior of a circuit, particularly an **amplifier**, in which the output **signal** strength does not vary in direct proportion to the input signal strength. In a nonlinear device, the output-to-input amplitude ratio (also called the gain) depends on the strength of the input signal.

In an amplifier that exhibits nonlinearity, the output-versus-input signal amplitude graph appears as a curved line over part or all of the input amplitude range. Two examples are shown below. The amplifier depicted by the upward-moving curve has gain that increases as the input signal strength increases; the amplifier depicted by the flattening curve has gain that decreases as the input signal strength increases.

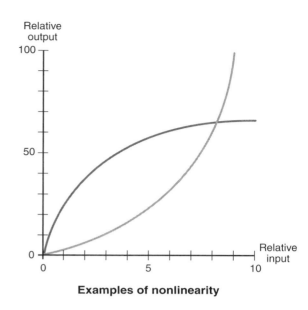

Examples of nonlinearity

Nonlinearity can be tolerated in devices and systems that use **digital modulation**, and also in frequency modulation (**FM**) **wireless** transmitters. These signals are either full-on or full-off; the amplitude **waveform**s are not **analog**, so analog distortion cannot occur. In analog devices and systems, however, linearity is important. Nonlinear circuits generally cause distortion in applications such as amplitude-modulation (**AM**) wireless transmission and hi-fi audio.

nonrepudiation

In general, nonrepudiation is the ability to ensure that a party to a contract or a communication cannot deny the authenticity of their signature on a document or the sending of a message that they originated. On the Internet, the **digital signature** is used not only to ensure that a message or document has been electronically signed by the person that purported to sign the document, but also, since a digital signature can only be created by one person, to ensure that a person cannot later deny that they furnished the signature.

Since no security technology is absolutely fool-proof, some experts warn that the digital signature alone may not always guarantee nonrepudiation. It is suggested that multiple approaches be used, such as capturing unique biometric information and other data about the sender or signer that collectively would be difficult to repudiate.

non-return-to-zero

See also **bipolar signaling**, **unipolar signaling**, and **return-to-zero**.

Non-return-to-zero (NRZ) refers to a form of **digital** data transmission in which the **binary** low and high states, represented by numerals 0 and 1, are transmitted by specific and constant **DC** (direct-current) voltages.

In positive-logic NRZ, the low state is represented by the more negative or less positive **voltage**, and the high state is represented by the less negative or more positive voltage. Examples are:

Logic 0 = +0.5 volts
Logic 1 = +5.0 volts

Logic 0 = −3.0 volts
Logic 1 = 0.0 volts

In negative-logic NRZ, the low state is represented by the more positive or less negative voltage, and the high state is represented by the less positive or more negative voltage. Examples are:

Logic 0 = +5.0 volts
Logic 1 = +0.5 volts

Logic 0 = 0.0 volts
Logic 1 = −3.0 volts

Some people wonder why the name of this mode is preceded by "non" when one of the logic states might be represented by zero voltage. The answer becomes apparent from the comparative definition of **return-to-zero** (RZ).

nonuniform rational B-spline

NURBS (nonuniform rational B-splines) are mathematical representations of 2- or 3-dimensional objects, which can be standard shapes (such as a cone) or free-form shapes (such as a car). NURBS are used in computer graphics and the CAD/CAM industry and have come to be regarded as a standard way to create and represent complex objects. In addition to curves and surfaces, NURBS can also represent hypersurfaces.

Most sophisticated graphic creation tools provide an interface for using NURBS, which are flexible enough to design a wide range of shapes—anything from points to straight lines to conic sections. NURBS are compact expressions that can be evaluated and displayed quickly. NURBS work especially well in **3-D** modeling, allowing the designer to easily manipulate control vertices, called ISO curves, and control curvature and the smoothness of contours. NURBS are defined by both control points and weights. It takes very little data to define a NURB.

A *spline* is a usually curvy pattern used to guide someone shaping something large, such as a boat hull. The B-spline is based (the B stands for "basis") on four local functions or control points that lie outside the curve itself. *Nonuniform* is the idea that some sections of a defined shape (between any two points) can be shortened or elongated relative to other sections in the overall shape. *Rational* describes the ability to give more weight to some points in the shape than to other

points in considering each positions relation to another object. (This is sometimes referred to as a 4th dimensional characteristic.)

non-virtual hosting

Also see **virtual hosting**.

Non-virtual hosting is offering to host a **Web site** for an Internet user or company within the same **domain name** as that of the service provider. Frequently, this kind of hosting provides the customer with a free Web site with the provision that the user's Web pages will contain a certain amount of advertising. Depending on how the hosting company implements their service, the user's Web site address may be a **subdomain** of the hosting site or, more typically, within a file directory name sequence that is part of the hosting site's domain name. For example, Joe Smith's Web site might be at www.thehost.com/JoeSmith/.

In addition to carrying on your pages ad banners over which you have no control, a non-virtual hosted Web site may be required to conform to an overall design pattern and to carry the logo of the hosting company.

Geocities and Tripod are two of the largest companies that provide non-virtual hosting.

nonvolatile memory

Nonvolatile memory is a general term for all forms of solid state (no moving parts) **memory** that have a continuous source of power and do not need to have their memory contents periodically refreshed. This includes all forms of read-only memory (**ROM**) such as **programmable read-only memory**, **erasable programmable read-only memory**, **electrically erasable programmable read-only memory**, and **flash memory**. It also includes random access memory (**RAM**) that is powered with a battery.

nonvolatile RAM

See "nonvolatile memory"

nonvolatile storage

See "nonvolatile memory"

NOR

See "logic gate"

norm

A norm (from *norma*, Latin for carpenter's level) is a model of what should exist or be followed, or an average of what currently does exist in some context, such as an average salary among members of a large group.

normal forms

See "normalization"

normalization

In creating a **database**, normalization is the process of organizing it into tables in such a way that the results of using the database are always unambiguous and as intended. Normalization may have the effect of duplicating data within the database and often results in the creation of additional tables. (While normalization tends to increase the duplication of data, it does not introduce redundancy, which is unnecessary duplication.) Normalization is typically a refinement process after the initial exercise of identifying the data objects that should be in the database, identifying their relationships, and defining the tables required and the columns within each table.

A simple example of normalizing data might consist of a table showing:

Customer	Item purchased	Purchase price
Thomas	Shirt	$40
Maria	Tennis shoes	$35
Evelyn	Shirt	$40
Pajaro	Trousers	$25

If this table is used for the purpose of keeping track of the price of items and you want to delete one of the customers, you will also delete a price. Normalizing the data would mean understanding this and solving the problem by dividing this table into two tables, one with information about each customer and a product they bought and the second about each product and its price. Making additions or deletions to either table would not affect the other.

Normalization degrees of relational database tables have been defined and include:

First normal form (1NF). This is the "basic" level of normalization and generally corresponds to the definition of any database, namely:

- It contains two-dimensional tables with rows and columns.

- Each column corresponds to a sub-object or an attribute of the object represented by the entire table.

- Each row represents a unique instance of that sub-object or attribute and must be different in some way from any other row (that is, no duplicate rows are possible).

- All entries in any column must be of the same kind. For example, in the column labeled "Customer," only customer names or numbers are permitted.

Second normal form (2NF). At this level of normalization, each column in a table that is not a determiner of the contents of another column must itself be a function of the other columns in the table. For example, in a table with three columns containing customer ID, product sold, and price of the product when sold, the price would be a function of the customer ID (entitled to a discount) and the specific product.

Third normal form (3NF). At the second normal form, modifications are still possible because a change to one row in a table may affect data that refers to this information from another table. For example, using the customer table just cited, removing a row describing a customer purchase (because of a return perhaps) will also remove the fact that the product has a certain price. In the third normal form, these tables would be divided into two tables so that product pricing would be tracked separately.

Domain/key normal form (DKNF). A key uniquely identifies each row in a table. A domain is the set of permissible values for an attribute. By enforcing key and domain restrictions, the database is assured of being freed from modification anomalies. DKNF is the normalization level that most designers aim to achieve.

normative

In general, normative—pertaining to a **norm**—has two related meanings: (1) a prescriptive meaning (for example, the rules specified in a standard or guideline), and (2) a descriptive meaning (for example, the median salary range in an particular occupation).

In information technology standards, normative parts of a standard are those that specify what implementors should conform to and non-normative parts consist of examples, extended explanations, and other matter not dealing directly with the specifications.

In economics, a normative statement is one that states how things ought to be and is contrasted with a positive statement, one that states factually how things are.

Northbridge

Northbridge is an Intel **chipset** that communicates with the computer **processor** and controls interaction with **memory**, the Peripheral Component Interconnect (**PCI**) bus, Level 2 **cache**, and all Accelerated Graphics Port (**AGP**) activities. Northbridge communicates with the processor using the frontside bus (**FSB**). Northbridge is one part of a two-part chipset called Northbridge/**Southbridge**. Southbridge handles the input/output (**I/O**) functions of the chipset.

The Intel Hub Architecture (IHA) has replaced the Northbridge/Southbridge chipset. The IHA chipset also has two parts: the Graphics and AGP Memory Controller Hub (GMCH) and the I/O Controller Hub (ICH). The IHA architecture is used in Intel's 800 series chipsets, which is the first chipset architecture to move away from the Northbridge/Southbridge design.

NOT

See "logic gate"

notebook computer

A notebook computer is a battery-powered personal computer generally smaller than a briefcase that can easily be transported and conveniently used in temporary spaces such as on airplanes, in libraries, temporary offices, and at meetings. A notebook computer, sometimes called a laptop computer, typically weighs less than 5 pounds and is 3 inches or less in thickness. Among the best-known makers of notebook and laptop computers are IBM, NEC, Dell, Toshiba, and Hewlett-Packard.

Notebook computers generally cost more than desktop computers with the same capabilities because they are more difficult to design and manufacture. A notebook can effectively be turned into desktop computers with a **docking station**, a hardware frame that supplies connections for peripheral input/output devices such as a printer or larger monitor. The less capable *port replicator* allows you to connect a notebook to a number of peripherals through a single plug.

Notebooks usually come with displays that use thin-screen technology. The **thin film transistor** or active matrix screen is brighter and views better at different angles than the STN or dual-scan screen. Notebooks use several different approaches for integrating a mouse into the keyboard, including the **touch pad**, the **trackball**, and the pointing stick. A serial port also allows a regular **mouse** to be attached. The **PC Card** is insertable hardware for adding a **modem** or **NIC** to a notebook. CD-ROM and **digital versatile disc** drives may be built-in or attachable.

Notes

Notes is a sophisticated **groupware application** from the Lotus Corporation, a subsidiary of IBM. Notes lets a corporation and its workers develop communications- and **database**-oriented applications so that users at different geographic locations can share files with each other, comment on them publicly or privately (to groups with special access), keep track of development schedules, work projects, guidelines and procedures, plans, white papers, and many other documents, including multimedia files. Notes keeps track of changes and makes updates to replications of all databases in use at any site. Changes are made at the field level to minimize network traffic.

Notes runs on a special server called the Lotus **Domino** Server. The servers and workstations use the **client/server** model and replicated databases are updated using Remote Procedure Call (**RPC**) requests. Notes can be coordinated with Web servers and applications on a company's **intranet**.

e-mail, calendar, and some other basic applications come with Notes. However, Notes provides facilities so that users can create their own applications. (Notes applications are generally document-oriented, not transaction-oriented.) Notes was designed with large-scale work projects in mind. Notes comes with application development tools that make it relatively easy to create applications. The Notes concepts and user interface are not intuitively understandable. Users as well as application developers usually require an assisted introduction.

Microsoft Exchange is a somewhat comparable product. It does not have the application development facilities that Notes has. It does offer an easy-to-use interface.

Novell Directory Services

NDS (Novell Directory Services) is a popular software product for managing access to computer resources and keeping track of the users of a **network**, such as a company's **intranet**, from a single point of administration. Using NDS, a network administrator can set up and control a **database** of users and manage them using a **directory** with an easy-to-use graphical user interface (**GUI**). Users of computers at remote locations can be added, updated, and managed centrally. Applications can be distributed electronically and maintained centrally.

NDS can be installed to run under **Windows NT**, (and later) Sun Microsystem's Solaris, and IBM's **OS/390** as well as under Novell's own **NetWare** so that it can be used to control a multi-platform network. NDS is generally considered an industry **benchmark** against which other products, such as Microsoft's Active Directory, must compete.

nroff

nroff and troff are UNIX commands (and the utilities that support them) for formatting text files for printing. (There are other UNIX commands for initiating printing.) nroff is designed for formatting output for line printers and letter-quality printers. troff is designed for formatting output for typesetters. troff contains some special functions that apply only to typesetters; otherwise, the commands are identical and either can be used.

In general, a text file designed for use with nroff or troff contains embedded codes for line spacing, margin settings, centering, tab stops, keeping lines together, and so forth. The command itself includes options that apply to the entire file. nroff and troff provide about the same level of formatting control as IBM's Script/VS language. In general, text formatting languages at this level have the drawback of making it difficult to reuse the text in a non-print medium (such as on the Web). This drawback led to the development of the non-output specific **markup** defined generally by **Standard Generalized Markup Language** in which a logical or functional description is applied to text elements that device-specific programs can interpret in an appropriate way.

Examples of nroff/troff formatting codes include:
.ce
Center the next lines of text.
.sp

Skip a line space.

.ps 10

Use 10-point type.

A popular UNIX replacement for nroff/troff is a formatter called TeX (pronounced "TEK"). TeX is designed to give the user a great deal of control over font choice and text arrangement and especially to support text containing mathematical symbols.

If you have inherited an nroff/troff file and need to convert it to HTML, you may be able to find a tool that will convert the file to HTML "preformatted" text (meaning that the file will look as though it has been brought in from somewhere). While this may be a temporary solution in some cases, it's likely that eventually you will have to strip the old codes and start with new formatting (using HTML tags) manually.

NSA

See "National Security Agency"

NSAP

See "Network Service Access Point"

nslookup

nslookup is the name of a program that lets an Internet server administrator or user enter a **host** name (for example, "whatis.com") and find out the corresponding **IP address**. It will also do reverse name lookup and find the host name for an IP address you specify.

For example, if you entered "whatis.com", you would receive as a response our IP address, which happens to be: 216.34.126.200

Or if you entered "216.34.126.200", it would return "whatis.com".

nslookup sends a **domain name** query **packet** to a designated (or defaulted) domain name system (**DNS**) server. Depending on the system you are using, the default may be the local DNS name server at your service provider, some intermediate name server, or the **root server system** for the entire domain name system hierarchy.

Using the **Linux** and possibly other versions of *nslookup*, you can locate other information associated with the host name or IP address, such as associated mail services. nslookup is often included with a **UNIX**-based operating system. Free versions exist that can be added to Windows operating systems. A more limited alternative to nslookup for looking up an IP address is the **ping** command.

NSP

See "network service provider"

NT

See "Windows NT"

NT1

Using the **Integrated Services Digital Network** (ISDN) Basic Rate Interchange (**BRI**) service, an NT1 (network terminating unit 1) is a device that accepts a two-wire signal from the phone company and converts it to a four-wire signal that sends and receives to and from devices within the home or business. In the U.K. and some other countries, the NT1 is located at the telephone company's central office. In the U.S., the NT1 is a separate box at the home or business or it can be integrated into one device. If it is a separate box, up to eight devices, such as telephones and computers, can be attached to it. If the NT1 is built into one device, then only that one device can be served by the line coming in from the phone company. Additional devices would require one or more additional lines.

The ISDN Basic Rate Interface is the most common service offered by ISDN providers. BRI supports two separate 64 **Kbps** B channels and one 16 Kbps D channel. The phone company replaces your conventional analog circuit with a BRI circuit. The NT1 provides the entry termination at your home or business that is required by the phone company. You must have one NT1 for each ISDN line. Some ISDN equipment such as an ISDN **terminal adapter** (the ISDN equivalent of a modem) may already have a built-in NT1. To find out if your ISDN device has a built-in NT1, check to see if it is designed to connect directly to the public ISDN network. If it is, it does not require a separate NT1. Most U.S. ISDN devices have the NT1 built-in. If you wish to have more than one ISDN device per line, consider purchasing a separate NT1 box with multiple jacks. Some NT1 boxes have built-in analog conversion so you can use both ISDN and analog equipment on the same line. Your ISDN provider may occasionally "talk" to your NT1 box to perform routine testing and maintenance.

NTFS

NTFS (NT file system) is the system that the Windows NT **operating system** uses for storing and retrieving **file** on a **hard disk**. NTFS is the Windows NT equivalent of the Windows 95 **file allocation table** (file allocation table) and the OS/2 *HPFS* (high performance file system). However, NTFS offers a number of improvements over FAT and HPFS in terms of performance, extendibility, and security.

Notable features of NTFS include:

- Use of a *b-tree* directory scheme to keep track of file clusters

- Information about a file's **cluster** and other data is stored with each cluster, not just a governing table (as FAT is)

- Support for very large files (up to 2 to the 64th power or approximately 16 billion **byte** in size)

- An access control list (**ACL**) that lets a server administrator control who can access specific files

- Integrated file **compression**

- Support for names based on **Unicode**

- Support for long file names as well as "8 by 3" names

- Data security on both removable and fixed disks

How NTFS Works

When a hard disk is formatted (initialized), it is divided into partitions or major divisions of the total physical hard disk space. Within each partition, the operating system keeps track of all the files that are stored by that operating system. Each file is actually stored on the hard disk in one or more **cluster** or disk spaces of a predefined uniform size. Using NTFS, the sizes of clusters range from 512 **byte** to 64 **kilobyte**. Windows NT provides a recommended default cluster size for any given drive size. For example, for a 4 GB (**gigabyte**) drive, the default cluster size is 4 KB (kilobytes). Note that clusters are indivisible. Even the smallest file takes up one cluster and a 4.1 KB file takes up two clusters (or 8 KB) on a 4 KB cluster system.

The selection of the cluster size is a trade-off between efficient use of disk space and the number of disk accesses required to access a file. In general, using NTFS, the larger the hard disk the larger the default cluster size, since it's assumed that a system user will prefer to increase performance (fewer disk accesses) at the expense of some amount of space inefficiency.

When a file is created using NTFS, a record about the file is created in a special file, the Master File Table (MFT). The record is used to locate a file's possibly scattered clusters. NTFS tries to find contiguous storage space that will hold the entire file (all of its clusters).

Each file contains, along with its data content, a description of its attributes (its **metadata**).

n-tier

An n-tier application program is one that is distributed among three or more separate computers in a distributed network. The most common form of n-tier (meaning 'some number of tiers') is the **3-tier application**, in which user interface programming is in the user's computer, business logic is in a more centralized computer, and needed data is in a computer that manages a **database**.

N-tier application structure implies the **client/server** program model. Where there are more than three distribution levels or tiers involved, the additional tiers in the application are usually associated with the business logic tier.

In addition to the advantages of distributing programming and data throughout a network, n-tier applications have the advantages that any one tier can run on an appropriate processor or operating system **platform** and can be updated independently of the other tiers. Communication between the program tiers uses special program interfaces such as those provided by the Common Object Request Broker Architecture (**CORBA**).

NTP

See "Network Time Protocol"

NTSC

See "National Television Standards Committee"

nuking

See "blue bomb"

null modem

A null **modem** cable allows you to connect your PC to another nearby PC or serial device using its modem protocol. A popular use of null modem cables is for setting up "head-to-head" gaming between two players at different computers in the same room. (A null modem cable is limited to 30 feet in length.)

The standard **RS-232C serial** communications interface defines a signal protocol between a Data Terminal Equipment (**DTE**)—usually your PC—and a Data Communications Equipment (**DCE**)—or your modem. The signals are transmitted on a set of lines, each of which has a function in the "talk" that the DTE and DCE do back and forth. One line each way is for data; the other lines are for different "statements" that one end of the communication sends to the other. For example, the DTE sends the DCE (usually a modem) a "Request to Send" signal on the RTS line and the DCE replies with a "Clear to Send" signal on the CTS line. After a series of similar exchanges, the DTE sends data on the line devoted to transmitting data (which for the DCE is a line for receiving data from the DTE).

Since a modem or DCE is not really needed to interconnect your PC with another local serial device, the DTE interface can be used by both your PC and the attached serial device. However, the DTE interface is designed to work with a DCE device. What a null modem cable does is to make the other end of the PC or device's DTE interface look like a DCE interface.

A null modem cable is sometimes called a **crossover cable**.

NUMA

NUMA (non-uniform memory access) is a method of configuring a cluster of **microprocessors** in a **multiprocessing** system so that they can share memory locally, improving performance and the ability of the system to be expanded. NUMA is used in a symmetric multiprocessing (**SMP**) system. An SMP system is a "tightly-coupled," "share everything" system in which multiple processors working under a single **operating system** access each other's memory over a common **bus** or "interconnect" path. Ordinarily, a limitation of SMP is that as microprocessors are added, the shared bus or data path get overloaded and becomes a performance bottleneck. NUMA adds an intermediate level of memory shared among a few microprocessors so that all data accesses don't have to travel on the main bus.

NUMA can be thought of as a "cluster in a box." The cluster typically consists of four microprocessors (for example, four **Pentium** microprocessors) interconnected on a local bus (for example, a **Peripheral Component Interconnect** bus) to a shared memory (called an "L3 **cache**") on a single **motherboard** (it could also probably be referred to as a **card**). This unit can be added to similar units to form a symmetric multiprocessing system in which a common SMP bus interconnects all of the clusters. Such a system typically contains from 16 to 256 microprocessors. To an application program running in an SMP system, all the individual processor memories look like a single memory.

When a processor looks for data at a certain memory address, it first looks in the L1 cache on the microprocessor itself, then on a somewhat larger **L1 and L2** cache chip nearby, and then on a third level of cache that the NUMA configuration provides before seeking the data in the "remote memory" located near the other microprocessors. Each of these clusters is viewed by NUMA as a "node" in the interconnection network. NUMA maintains a hierarchical view of the data on all the nodes.

Data is moved on the bus between the clusters of a NUMA SMP system using scalable coherent interface (SCI) technology. SCI coordinates what is called "cache coherence" or consistency across the nodes of the multiple clusters.

SMP and NUMA systems are typically used for applications such as **data mining** and **decision support systems** in which processing can be parceled out to a number of processors that collectively work on a common database. Sequent, Data General, and NCR are among companies that produce NUMA SMP systems.

NVRAM

See "nonvolatile storage"

NVS

See "nonvolatile storage"

NWay

NWay is a telecommunications **protocol** used with **Ethernet** networking devices (such as **routers** and **switches**) to automatically negotiate the highest possible common transmission speed between two devices. The NWay protocol (also known as *auto-negotiation* or *auto-sensing*) was developed by National Semiconductor in 1994 in response to the networking industry's need for a mechanism to handle the connections between devices with varying connection speeds.

In an Ethernet network, a device may have the capability to operate at different speeds. NWay currently supports at least the following technologies: **10BASE-T**, 10BASE-T **duplex**, **100BASE-T**, 100BASE-TX Full Duplex, and 100BASE-T4. Expanded support capability is likely in the near future.

When a connection to a network device (known as the *link partner*) has been established, the NWay protocol determines what modes that device uses, sends information about its own capabilities, and automatically configures the highest common performance mode. NWay works by taking control of the cable connected to a network device and operating like a rotary switch (an electromechanical device with a rotating shaft at one terminal that makes or breaks connections with other terminals) to change to the best mode possible, and passing control of the cable to the appropriate technology.

The benefits of NWay technology include:

- Efficient connections at the highest possible performance levels without any need for user intervention

- Protection of network integrity, because if the devices involved lack a common technology, NWay will not make the connection, thus protecting users from the potentially serious problems that can be caused by a connection that a **hub** cannot recognize or accept

- **Backward compatibility**

- An architecture that supports flexibility and extensibility.

NWay (Auto-Negotiation) is defined in Clause 28 of the D4 draft of the *ANSI/IEEE Std 802.3 MAC Parameters, Physical Layer, Medium Attachment Units and Repeater for 100 Mb/s Operation.*

nym

A nym (pronounced NIHM and a shortened form of "pseudonym,") is a name invented by or provided for an Internet user in order to conceal the user's real identity and, in some cases, to expressly create a new and separate Internet identity. Among reasons to have and use a "nym" are these:

- You want to comment or take part in controversial political or other discussions on the Internet without revealing your opinions to colleagues, friends, or employers

- You want to send **spam** (unrequested bulk e-mail) without anyone being able to trace it to you

- You are a self-declared **cracker** that wants to talk about it without being identified

- You simply feel strongly about protecting your **privacy on the Internet**

There are a number of legitimate reasons for communicating anonymously. The example of a battered spouse seeking help in a **Usenet** news group or a Web site discussion is sometimes cited.

To use a nym instead of your real e-mail name when sending and receiving e-mail, you can use the services of a **remailer**, a company with a Web server that accepts e-mail from you and forwards it to its destination with a different return address than yours. Incoming mail to your nym is forwarded to your real Internet address. Some remailing services forward mail through several remailers to make it even harder to trace the source of an e-mail note. There are free or public remailer services. Andre Bacard, author of The Anonymous Remailer FAQ and *The Computer Privacy Handbook*, divides remailers into: (1) pseudo-anonymous remailers, who know the names of the people for whom they are providing anonymity service, and (2) more serious anonymous remailers, who never know your name. Bacard believes that, for most people, the pseudo-anonymous is sufficient. It's also much easier to use. Most remailer services disallow the use of spam. Remailing is often combined with **encryption** using Pretty Good Privacy (**PGP**).

Some companies also allow you to surf the Web anonymously by first linking to an intermediary site that in turn connects you to any Web site you select without that site being able to learn anything about you from your request message.

OASIS

OASIS (Organization for Structured Information Standards) is a nonprofit, international consortium whose goal is to promote the adoption of product-independent standards for information formats such as Standard Generalized Markup Language (**SGML**), Extensible Markup Language (**XML**), and Hypertext Markup Language (**HTML**). Currently, OASIS (formerly known as SGML Open) is working to bring together competitors and industry standards groups with conflicting perspectives to discuss using XML as a common Web language that can be shared across applications and platforms.

OASIS sponsors XML.org, a non-profit XML Web portal. The goal of OASIS is not to create structured information standards for XML, but to provide a forum for discussion, to promote the adoption of interoperability standards, and to recommend ways members can provide better **interoperability** for their users. OASIS has worked with the United Nations to sponsor **ebXML**, a global initiative for electronic business data exchange. EbXML, whose goal is to make it easier for companies of all sizes and locations to conduct business on the Internet, is currently focusing on the specific needs of business-to-business (**B2B**) and Internet security as it relates to XML.

OBI

See "Open Buying on the Internet"

object

In object-oriented programming (**OOP**), objects are the things you think about first in designing a program and they are also the units of code that are eventually derived from the process. In between, each object is made into a generic **class** of object and even more generic classes are defined so that objects can share models and reuse the class definitions in their code. Each object is an instance of a particular class or subclass with the class's own **methods** or procedures and data **variables**. An object is what actually runs in the computer.

object code

Source code and object code refer to the "before" and "after" versions of a computer **program** that is compiled (see **compiler**) before it is ready to run in a computer. The source code consists of the programming statements that are created by a programmer with a **text editor** or a visual programming tool and then saved in a file. For example, a programmer using the **C** language types in a desired sequence of C language statements using a text editor and then saves them as a named file. This file is said to contain the source code. It is now ready to be compiled with a C compiler and the resulting output, the compiled file, is often referred to as object code. The object code file contains a sequence of **instruction**s that the processor can understand but that is difficult for a human to read or modify. For this reason and because even debugged programs often need some later enhancement, the source code is the most permanent form of the program.

When you purchase or receive operating system or application software, it is usually in the form of compiled object code and the source code is not included. Proprietary software vendors usually don't want you to try to improve their code since this may create additional service costs for them. Lately, there is a movement to develop software (**Linux** is an example) that is **open** to further improvement by anyone who wants to improve it, and here the source code is provided.

In large program development environments, there are often management systems that help programmers separate and keep track of different states and levels of code files. For **script** (noncompiled or interpreted) program languages, such as **JavaScript**, the terms *source code* and *object code* do not apply since there is only one form of the code.

Object Linking and Embedding

See "OLE"

Object Management Group

The OMG (Object Management Group) was formed in 1989 by a group of vendors for the purpose of creating a standard architecture for **distributed object**s (also known as "**components**") in networks. The architecture that resulted is the Common Object Request Broker Architecture (**CORBA**). A central element in CORBA is the Object Request Broker (**ORB**). An ORB makes it possible for a client object to make a server request without having to know where in a network the server object or component is located and exactly what its interfaces are.

A number of **middleware** products have begun to use CORBA and it appears to be the strategic architecture for distributed objects. The OMG now boasts of over 500 member companies.

Object Request Broker

Also see **ORBS**, a term easily confused with ORB.

In Common Object Request Broker Architecture (**CORBA**), an Object Request Broker (ORB) is the programming that acts as a "broker" between a **client** request for a service from a **distributed** object or **component** and the completion of

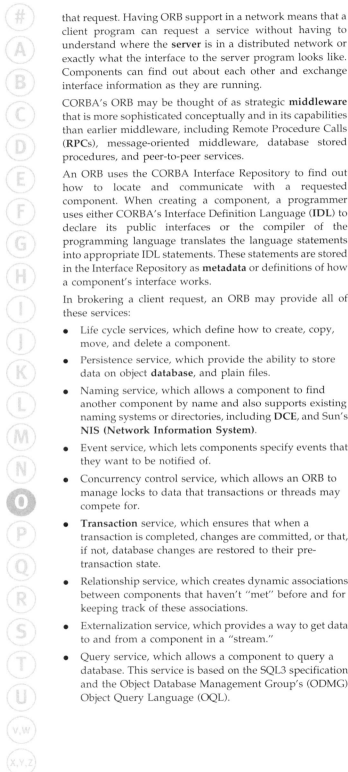

that request. Having ORB support in a network means that a client program can request a service without having to understand where the **server** is in a distributed network or exactly what the interface to the server program looks like. Components can find out about each other and exchange interface information as they are running.

CORBA's ORB may be thought of as strategic **middleware** that is more sophisticated conceptually and in its capabilities than earlier middleware, including Remote Procedure Calls (**RPC**s), message-oriented middleware, database stored procedures, and peer-to-peer services.

An ORB uses the CORBA Interface Repository to find out how to locate and communicate with a requested component. When creating a component, a programmer uses either CORBA's Interface Definition Language (**IDL**) to declare its public interfaces or the compiler of the programming language translates the language statements into appropriate IDL statements. These statements are stored in the Interface Repository as **metadata** or definitions of how a component's interface works.

In brokering a client request, an ORB may provide all of these services:

- Life cycle services, which define how to create, copy, move, and delete a component.

- Persistence service, which provide the ability to store data on object **database**, and plain files.

- Naming service, which allows a component to find another component by name and also supports existing naming systems or directories, including **DCE**, and Sun's **NIS (Network Information System)**.

- Event service, which lets components specify events that they want to be notified of.

- Concurrency control service, which allows an ORB to manage locks to data that transactions or threads may compete for.

- **Transaction** service, which ensures that when a transaction is completed, changes are committed, or that, if not, database changes are restored to their pre-transaction state.

- Relationship service, which creates dynamic associations between components that haven't "met" before and for keeping track of these associations.

- Externalization service, which provides a way to get data to and from a component in a "stream."

- Query service, which allows a component to query a database. This service is based on the SQL3 specification and the Object Database Management Group's (ODMG) Object Query Language (OQL).

- Licensing service, which allows the use of a component to be measured for purposes of compensation for use. Charging can be done by session, by node, by instance creation, and by site.

- Properties service, which lets a component contain a self-description that other components can use.

In addition, an ORB also can provide security and time services. Additional services for trading, collections, and change management are also planned. The requests and replies that originate in ORBs are expressed through the Internet Inter-ORB Protocol (**IIOP**) or other transport layer protocols.

object-oriented database management system

An object-oriented database management system (OODBMS), sometimes shortened to *ODBMS* for *object database management system*), is a database management system (**DBMS**) that supports the modelling and creation of data as **object**s. This includes some kind of support for **class**es of objects and the **inheritance** of class properties and **method**s by subclasses and their objects. There is currently no widely agreed-upon standard for what constitutes an OODBMS, and OODBMS products are considered to be still in their infancy. In the meantime, the object-relational database management system (ORDBMS), the idea that object-oriented database concepts can be superimposed on relational databases, is more commonly encountered in available products. An object-oriented database interface standard is being developed by an industry group, the Object Data Management Group (ODMG). The Object Management Group (**OMG**) has already standardized an object-oriented data brokering interface between systems in a network.

In their influential paper, *The Object-Oriented Database Manifesto*, Malcolm Atkinson and others define an OODBMS as follows:

> An object-oriented database system must satisfy two criteria: it should be a DBMS, and it should be an object-oriented system, i.e., to the extent possible, it should be consistent with the current crop of object-oriented programming languages. The first criterion translates into five features: persistence, secondary storage management, concurrency, recovery and an ad hoc query facility. The second one translates into eight features: complex objects, object identity, encapsulation, types or classes, inheritance, over-riding combined with late binding, extensibility and computational completeness.

Their paper describes each of these features in detail.

object-oriented programming

A revolutionary concept that changed the rules in computer program development, object-oriented programming (OOP) is organized around "objects" rather than "actions," data rather than logic. Historically, a program has been viewed as a logical procedure that takes input data, processes it, and produces output data. The programming challenge was seen as how to write the logic, not how to define the data. Object-oriented programming takes the view that what we really care about are the objects we want to manipulate rather than the logic required to manipulate them. Examples of objects range from human beings (described by name, address, and so forth) to buildings and floors (whose properties can be described and managed) down to the little widgets on your computer desktop (such as buttons and scroll bars).

The first step in OOP is to identify all the objects you want to manipulate and how they relate to each other, an exercise often known as **data modeling**. Once you've identified an **object**, you generalize it as a **class** of objects (think of Plato's concept of the "ideal" chair that stands for all chairs) and define the kind of data it contains and any logic sequences that can manipulate it. Each distinct logic sequence is known as a **method**. A real instance of a class is called (no surprise here) an "object" or, in some environments, an "instance of a class." The object or class instance is what you run in the computer. Its methods provide computer instructions and the class object characteristics provide relevant data. You communicate with objects—and they communicate with each other—with well-defined interfaces called *messages*.

The concepts and rules used in object-oriented programming provide these important benefits:

- The concept of a data class makes it possible to define subclasses of data objects that share some or all of the main class characteristics. Called **inheritance**, this property of OOP forces a more thorough data analysis, reduces development time, and ensures more accurate coding.

- Since a class defines only the data it needs to be concerned with, when an instance of that class (an object) is run, the code will not be able to accidentally access other program data. This characteristic of **data hiding** provides greater system security and avoids unintended data corruption.

- The definition of a class is reuseable not only by the program for which it is initially created but also by other object-oriented programs (and, for this reason, can be more easily distributed for use in networks).

- The concept of data classes allows a programmer to create any new **data type** that is not already defined in the language itself.

One of the first object-oriented computer languages was called **Smalltalk**. **C++** and **Java** are the most popular object-oriented languages today. The Java programming language is designed especially for use in distributed applications on corporate networks and the Internet.

object-oriented

See "object-oriented programming"

OC levels

See "Optical Carrier levels (OCx)"

OC-1 – OC-2 – OC-3 – OC-12 – OC-48 – OC-192 – OC-256

See "Optical Carrier levels (OCx)"

OC-768

OC-768 is currently the fastest synchronous optical network (**SONET**) standard rate for data transmission on **optical fiber** as part of the broadband ISDN (**BISDN**). OC stands for optical carrier and the number affixed is the multiple of the base rate **bandwidth** of 51.85 **Mbps**. OC-768 supports rates of 40 gigabits per second (**Gbps**) on a fiber optic carrier, a rate that translates to the equivalent of seven CD-ROM's worth of data in one second. Developed to meet ever-growing demands for bandwidth, OC-768 uses dense wavelength division multiplexing (**DWDM**) to carry multiple channels of data on a single optic fiber. New DWDM systems are now in development to run at at 10 trillion bits per second (10 Tbps) per fiber. This translates into the theoretical capability of one fiber to support, simultaneously, an active Internet connection to every household in the U.S.

Enkido was the first company to offer OC-768 service, which they currently provide for a number of clients including Deutsche Telecom.

Ockham's razor

Ockham's razor (also spelled Occam's razor, pronounced AHK-uhmz RAY-zuhr) is the idea that, in trying to understand something, getting unnecessary information out of the way is the fastest way to the truth or to the best explanation. William of Ockham (1285-1349), English theologian and philosopher, spent his life developing a philosophy that reconciled religious belief with demonstrable, generally experienced truth, mainly by separating the two. Where earlier philosophers attempted to justify God's existence with rational proof, Ockham declared religious belief to be incapable of such proof and a matter of faith. He rejected the notions preserved from Classical times of the independent existence of qualities such as truth, hardness, and durability and said these ideas had value only as descriptions of particular objects and were really characteristics of human cognition. Ockham was noted for his insistence on paying close attention to language as a tool for thinking and on observation as a tool for testing reality. His thinking and writing is considered to have laid the groundwork for modern scientific inquiry. Ockham's insistence on the use of parsimony (we might call it minimalism) in thought resulted in some later writer's invention of the term, Ockham's razor. Among his statements (translated from his Latin) are: "Plurality is not to be assumed without necessity" and "What can be done with fewer [assumptions] is done in vain with more." One consequence of this methodology is the idea that the simplest or most obvious explanation of several competing ones is the one that should be preferred until it is proven wrong.

OCR

OCR (optical character recognition) is the recognition of printed or written **text character**s by a computer. This involves photoscanning of the text character-by-character, analysis of the scanned-in image, and then translation of the character image into character codes, such as **ASCII**, commonly used in data processing.

In OCR processing, the scanned-in image or **bitmap** is analyzed for light and dark areas in order to identify each alphabetic letter or numeric digit. When a character is recognized, it is converted into an ASCII code. Special circuit boards and computer chips designed expressly for OCR are used to speed up the recognition process.

OCR is being used by libraries to digitize and preserve their holdings. OCR is also used to process checks and credit card slips and sort the mail. Billions of magazines and letters are sorted every day by OCR machines, considerably speeding up mail delivery.

octal

Octal (pronounced AHK-tuhl, from Latin *octo* or "eight") is a term that describes a base-8 number system. An octal number system consists of eight single-digit numbers: 0, 1, 2, 3, 4, 5, 6, and 7. The number after 7 is 10. The number after 17 is 20 and so forth.

In computer programming, the octal equivalent of a binary number is sometimes used to represent it because it is shorter.

octet

In computers, an octet (from the Latin *octo* or "eight") is a sequence of eight **bit**s. An octet is thus an eight-bit **byte**. Since a byte is not eight bits in all computer systems, *octet* provides a nonambiguous term.

This term should not be confused with **octal**, a term that describes a base-8 number system.

OCW

See "OpenCourseWare"

OCX

An OCX is an Object Linking and Embedding (**OLE**) custom control, a special-purpose program that can be created for use by applications running on Microsoft's Windows systems. OCXs provide such functions as handling scroll bar movement and window resizing. If you have a Windows system, you'll find a number of files in your Windows directory with the OCX file name suffix.

Object Linking and Embedding was designed to support **compound document**s (which contain multiple information types, such as text, graphic images, sound, motion video). The Windows desktop is an example of a compound document and Microsoft used OLE to build it. OLE and the **Component Object Model** (COM), a more general concept that succeeded OLE, support the development of "plug-and-play" programs that can be written in any language and used dynamically by any application in the system. These programs are known as **component**s and the application in which they are run is known as a **container**. This component-based approach to application development reduces development time and improves the program capability and quality. Windows application development programs such as **PowerBuilder** and Microsoft Access take advantage of OCXs.

Microsoft now calls an OCX an **ActiveX control**, the component object under Microsoft's set of **ActiveX** technologies, of which the fundamental concept is the Component Object Model (COM) and, in a network, the Distributed Component Object Model (**DCOM**).

An OCX or ActiveX control is actually implemented as a dynamic link library **DLL** module. (You can think of a DLL program as a "subprogram" that can be used by any number of application programs, each of which is a "container" for the DLL or OCX/ActiveX control "object.") **Visual Basic** and **C++** are commonly used to write OCX or ActiveX controls.

OC-x

See "Optical Carrier levels (OCx)"

ODBC

See "Open Database Connectivity"

ODBMS

See "object-oriented database management system"

ODI

See "Open Data-Link Interface"

ODL

1) Open and Distance Learning (ODL) is a general term for the use of telecommunication to provide or enhance learning. Around the world, the academic community is discovering and exploring the Internet, teleconferencing, and related means to achieve an extended classroom or learning experience. Students in Russia are earning degrees from a university in Australia. Primary and secondary-grade students are exchanging e-mail across continents as a supplement to their formal studies. Students and teachers at all levels are taking part in teleconferences and forming associations that would have been unlikely five years ago. A number of world conferences have been held on ODL and many experimental projects are underway.

The United States Distance Learning Association has its own formal definition of "distance learning":

> The acquisition of knowledge and skills through mediated information and instruction, encompassing all technologies and other forms of learning at a distance.

A few of the many educational organizations involved with ODL include:

- The University of Bergen in Bergen, Norway, which offers its own ODL Resource Page
- The Open University at the Institute for Educational Technology in the United Kingdom
- The Virtual Classroom at the New Jersey Institute of Technology

2) Object Description Language (ODL) is a simple language for defining data structures that is used in the United States by the National Aeronautics and Space Adinistration (NASA).

Several somewhat similar languages have been created by other organizations for defining program or data objects. These include an Object Design Language and an Object Definition Language.

ODMA

ODMA (Open Document Management API or Application Program Interface) is an industry standard **interface** for managing documents that allows users to store, retrieve, and share them with security and version control. For example, you can collaborate with someone in another city on a book in which each of you write separate chapters and occasionally work on the same chapter. Using a document management system (DMS), you can create a chapter using your favorite word processor and store it in the document management system in the "first draft library." Later, you can retrieve it from the "first draft library," edit it, and put it back. Your collaborator can also retrieve your chapter to either look at it or make further changes to it, depending on how you wish to work together. The document management system manages who has read-only or update access to the chapter, who has it "checked out," and what draft level of the book it is stored in. The Open Document Management API provides vendors of DMS products and products such as **word processor**s with a consistent interface. A word processor can integrate DMS support so that you can create, edit, and manage your documents through the word processor.

DMS is also sometimes called EDMS (Electronic Document Management System).

Oe

See "ampere per meter"

OEM

See "original equipment manufacturer"

oersted

See "ampere per meter"

OFB

See "output feedback"

OFDM

See "orthogonal frequency-division multiplexing"

offline

Offline is the condition of being currently disconnected from a computer or a telecommunications system. The term is frequently used to describe someone who has the ability to be connected to the Internet but who is not currently connected to it.

Deprecated spellings are *off-line* and *off line*. The opposite term is **online**.

OH

See "modem lights"

ohm

The ohm is the standard unit of electrical **resistance** in the International System of Units (**SI**). Ohms are also used, when multiplied by imaginary numbers, to denote **reactance** in alternating-current (**AC**) and radio-frequency (**RF**) applications. Reduced to base SI units, one ohm is the equivalent of one kilogram meter squared per second cubed per ampere squared (1 kg times $m^2 \cdot s^{-3} \cdot A^{-2}$). The ohm is also the equivalent of a **volt** per **ampere** (V/A).

In a direct-current (**DC**) circuit, a component has a resistance of one ohm when a potential difference of one volt produces a current of one ampere through the component. In AC and RF circuits, resistive ohms behave the same as they do in DC circuits, provided the root-mean-square (**rms**) AC voltage is specified. In AC and RF circuits, reactance exists only when there is a net **capacitance** or **inductance**. Capacitive reactances have negative imaginary ohmic values; inductive reactances have positive imaginary ohmic values. The reactance of a particular capacitor or inductor depends on the frequency.

Resistances and reactances are sometimes expressed in units representing power-of-10 multiples of one ohm. A kilohm is equal to one thousand (10^3) ohms. A megohm is equal to one million (10^6) ohms. Fractional **prefix multipliers** are seldom used for resistance or reactances; rarely will you hear or read about a milliohm or a microhm. Extremely small resistances and reactances are usually referred to in terms of conductance.

Also see **conductance**, **Ohm's Law**, **prefix multipliers**, **resistance**, **reactance**, **siemens**, and International System of Units (**SI**).

Ohm's Law

Ohm's Law is the mathematical relationship among electric **current**, **resistance**, and **voltage**. The principle is named after the German scientist Georg Simon Ohm.

In direct-current (DC) circuits, Ohm's Law is simple and linear. Suppose a resistance having a value of R ohms carries a current of I amperes. Then the voltage across the resistor is equal to the product IR. There are two corollaries. If a DC power source providing E volts is placed across a resistance of R ohms, then the current through the resistance is equal to E/R amperes. Also, in a DC circuit, if E volts appear across a component that carries I amperes, then the resistance of that component is equal to E/I ohms.

Mathematically, Ohm's Law for DC circuits can be stated as three equations:

$E = IR$

$I = E/R$

$R = E/I$

When making calculations, compatible units must be used. If the units are other than ohms (for resistance), amperes (for current), and volts (for voltage), then unit conversions should be made before calculations are done. For example, kilohms should be converted to ohms, and microamperes should be converted to amperes.

ohnosecond

An ohnosecond is that very short moment in time during which you realize that you have pressed the wrong key and deleted hours, days, or weeks of work.

OK

OK (pronounced oh-KAY and occasionally spelled *okay*) is a short way to say "I agree." It's sometimes encountered in computer messages that seek the user's confirmation of a request.

OLAP

See "online analytical processing"

OLE

OLE (Object Linking and Embedding) is Microsoft's framework for a **compound document** technology. Briefly, a compound document is something like a display desktop that can contain visual and information objects of all kinds: text, calendars, animations, sound, motion video, 3-D, continually updated news, controls, and so forth. Each desktop object is an independent program entity that can interact with a user and also communicate with other objects on the desktop. Part of Microsoft's **ActiveX** technologies, OLE takes advantage and is part of a larger, more general concept, the **Component Object Model** (COM) and its distributed version, **DCOM**. An OLE **object** is necessarily also a **component** (or COM object).

Some main concepts in OLE and COM are:

Microsoft terms are shown first; industry or alternative versions of those terms are shown in parentheses:

Concept	What it is
OLE	A set of APIs to create and display a (compound) document
Document (compound document)	A presentation of different items in an "animated desktop"
Item (object; also called a component)	An element in a document, such as an animated calendar, a video window, a sound player, a sound file...
Container or container application	The program entity that holds a document or a control
Server or server application	The program entity that holds an item within an OLE container
Embedding	Adding the source data for an item to a document; use the Paste command in a container application
Linking	Adding a link to the source data for an item to a document; use the Paste Link command in a container application
Visual editing	Activating an item that is embedded in a document and "editing" it
Automation	Having one container or server application drive another application

Concept	What it is
Compound files (structured storage)	A standard file format that simplifies the storing of (compound) documents; consists of *storages* (similar to directories) and *streams* (similar to files)
Uniform Data Transfer (UDT)	A single data transfer interface that accommodates drag-and-drop; clipboard; and dynamic data exchange (DDE)
Component Object Model (COM)	Provides the underlying support for OLE items (objects) and ActiveX controls to communicate with other OLE objects or ActiveX controls
ActiveX control	An item (object) that can be distributed and run on top of a COM
Microsoft Foundation Class (MCF) library	A set of ready-made classes or templates that can be used to build container and server applications

OLE contains about 660 new function calls or individual program interfaces in addition to those already in Win32. For this reason, Microsoft provides the Microsoft Foundation Class (MFC) Library, a set of ready-made classes that can be used to build container and server applications, and tools such as Visual **C++**.

In the "Introduction to OLE" on its Developer Site, Microsoft says that "OLE" no longer stands for "Object Linking and Embedding," but just for the letters "OLE."

OLE DB

OLE DB is Microsoft's strategic low-level application program interface (**API**) for access to different data sources. OLE DB includes not only the Structured Query Language (**SQL**) capabilities of the Microsoft-sponsored standard data interface Open Database Connectivity (**ODBC**) but also includes access to data other than SQL data.

As a design from Microsoft's **Component Object Model** (COM), OLE DB is a set of **method**s (in earlier days, these might have been called *routines*) for reading and writing data. The **object**s in OLE DB consist mainly of a data source object, a session object, a command object, and a rowset object. An application using OLE DB would use this request sequence:

1. Initialize OLE.
2. Connect to a data source.
3. Issue a command.
4. Process the results.
5. Release the data source object and uninitialize OLE.

OLE once stood for "Object Link Embedding" and "DB" for database. However, Microsoft no longer ascribes these meanings to the letters "OLE" and "DB."

OLTP

OLTP (online transaction processing) is a class of program that facilitates and manages transaction-oriented applications, typically for data entry and retrieval transactions in a number of industries, including banking, airlines, mailorder, supermarkets, and manufacturers. Probably the most widely installed OLTP product is IBM's **CICS** (Customer Information Control System).

Today's online transaction processing increasingly requires support for transactions that span a network and may include more than one company. For this reason, new OLTP software uses client/server processing and brokering software that allows transactions to run on different computer platforms in a network.

OMG

See "Object Management Group"

on the fly

In relation to computer technology, "on the fly" describes activities that develop or occur dynamically rather than as the result of something that is statically predefined. For example, the content of a **page** that is sent to you from a **Web site** can be developed (and varied) "on the fly" based on dynamic factors such as the time of day, what pages the user has looked at previously, and specific user input. The Web server calls an application program to produce the "on-the-fly" page that is to be returned. There are several techniques for on-the-fly page development, including the **server-side include**, the use of **cookies** (information previously stored about you that is located in a special file on your hard disk), and Microsoft's **Active Server Page**.

In general usage, the expression often connotes a degree of haste and improvisation as in "I usually grab breakfast on the fly." This usage is somewhat similar to the expression "catch as catch can." The term also can simply connote being in a mobile or fluid situation. Our *Webster's New World Dictionary* reminds us that the term probably originated with bird hunting and shooting birds on the fly (rather than on the ground). The dictionary says simply "in flight" and adds a colloquial meaning of "in a hurry."

one-armed router

A one-armed router is a **router** that routes traffic between virtual local area networks (**VLAN**s). A one-armed router operates on the 80/20 rule, which states that 80% of traffic in a network remains within a virtual local area network and doesn't need routing service. The other 20% of network traffic is between VLANs and goes through the one-armed router. Because the one-armed router takes care of the more intensive traffic between VLANs, it frees the primary data path in a network for inter-VLAN traffic.

In order for a one-armed router to be beneficial, the VLAN must be configured to the 80/20 rule. One disadvantage of using the one-armed router structure is that it represents a single point of failure in a network. Another disadvantage is it can develop into a bottleneck if there are large amounts of traffic between VLANs.

one-time pad

In cryptography, a one-time pad is a system in which a **private key** generated randomly is used only once to **encrypt** a message that is then decrypted by the receiver using a matching one-time pad and key. Messages encrypted with keys based on randomness have the advantage that there is theoretically no way to "break the code" by analyzing a succession of messages. Each **encryption** is unique and bears no relation to the next encryption so that some pattern can be detected. With a one-time pad, however, the decrypting party must have access to the same key used to encrypt the message and this raises the problem of how to get the key to the decrypting party safely or how to keep both keys secure. One-time pads have sometimes been used when the both parties started out at the same physical location and then separated, each with knowledge of the keys in the one-time pad. The key used in a one-time pad is called a secret key because if it is revealed, the messages encrypted with it can easily be deciphered. One-time pads figured prominently in secret message transmission and espionage before and during World War II and in the Cold War era. On the Internet, the difficulty of securely controlling secret keys led to the invention of **public key** cryptography.

How It Works

Typically, a one-time pad is created by generating a string of characters or numbers that will be at least as long as the longest message that may be sent. This string of values is generated in some random fashion—for example, by someone pulling numbered balls out of a lottery machine or by using a computer program with a random number generator. The values are written down on a pad (or any device that someone can read or use). The pads are given to anyone who may be likely to send or receive a message. Typically, a pad may be issued as a collection of keys, one for each day in a month, for example, with one key expiring at the end of each day or as soon as it has been used once.

When a message is to be sent, the sender uses the secret key to encrypt each character, one at a time. If a computer is used, each bit in the character (which is usually eight bits in length) is exclusively "OR'ed" with the corresponding bit in the secret key. (With a one-time pad, the encryption **algorithm** is simply the **XOR** operation. Where there is some concern about how truly random the key is, it is sometimes combined with another algorithm such as MD5.) One writer describes this kind of encryption as a "100% noise source" used to mask the message. Only the sender and receiver have the means to remove the noise. Once the one-time pad is used, it can't be reused. If it is reused, someone who intercepts multiple messages can begin to compare them for similar coding for words that may possibly occur in both messages.

one-way pager

See "pager"

online

Online is the condition of being connected to a computer or a telecommunications system. The term is frequently used to describe someone who is currently connected to the Internet.

Deprecated spellings are *on-line* and *on line*. The opposite term is **offline**.

online analytical processing

Online analytical processing (OLAP) enables a user to easily and selectively extract and view **data** from different points-of-view. For example, a user can request that data be analyzed to display a spreadsheet showing all of a company's beach ball products sold in Florida in the month of July, compare revenue figures with those for the same products in September, and then see a comparison of other product sales in Florida in the same time period. To facilitate this kind of analysis, OLAP data is stored in a **multidimensional database**. Whereas a **relational database** can be thought of as two-dimensional, a multidimensional database considers each data attribute (such as product, geographic sales region, and time period) as a separate "dimension." OLAP software can locate the intersection of dimensions (all products sold in the Eastern region above a certain price during a certain time period) and display them. Attributes such as time periods can be broken down into subattributes.

OLAP can be used for **data mining** or the discovery of previously undiscerned relationships between data items. An OLAP database does not need to be as large as a **data warehouse**, since not all transactional data is needed for trend analysis. Using Open Database Connectivity (**ODBC**), data can be imported from existing relational databases to create a multidimensional database for OLAP.

Two leading OLAP products are Arbor Software's Essbase and Oracle's Express Server. OLAP products are typically designed for multiple-user environments, with the cost of the software based on the number of users.

Online Public Access Catalog

See "OPAC"

online service provider

1) On the Internet, OSP (online service provider) has several different meanings.

- The term has had some currency in distinguishing Internet **access provider**s that have their own online independent content, such as America Online (AOL), from Internet service providers (**ISP**s) that simply connect the user directly with the Internet. In general, the companies sometimes identified as OSPs (in this usage) offer an extensive online array of services of their own apart from the rest of the Internet and sometimes their own version of a Web **browser**. Connecting to the Internet through an OSP is an alternative to connecting through one of the national Internet service providers, such as AT&T or MCI, or a regional or local ISP.

- Some Internet service providers (ISPs) describe themselves as online service providers. In this usage, ISP and OSP are synonyms.

- America Online has used the term to refer to online content providers (usually Web sites) with which AOL has a business agreement.

2) Some companies use OSP in describing themselves as *office service providers*.

online transaction processing

See "OLTP"

online voting

See "e-voting"

ontology

In its general meaning, ontology (pronounced ahn-TAH-luh-djee) is the study or concern about what kinds of things exist—what entities there are in the universe. It derives from the Greek *onto* (being) and *logia* (written or spoken discourse). It is a branch of metaphysics, the study of first principles or the essence of things.

In information technology, an ontology is the working model of entities and interactions in some particular domain of knowledge or practices, such as electronic commerce or "the activity of planning." In artificial intelligence (**AI**), an ontology is, according to Tom Gruber, an AI specialist at Stanford University, "the specification of conceptualizations, used to help programs and humans share knowledge." In this usage, an ontology is a set of concepts—such as things, events, and relations—that are specified in some way (such as specific natural language) in order to create an agreed-upon vocabulary for exchanging information.

OODBMS

See "object-oriented database management system"

OOP

See "object-oriented programming"

OPAC

An OPAC (Online Public Access Catalog) is an online bibliography of a library collection that is available to the public. OPACs developed as stand-alone online catalogs, often from VT100 terminals to a **mainframe** library catalog. With the arrival of the Internet, most libraries have made their OPAC accessible from a server to users all over the world.

User searches of an OPAC make use of the **Z39.50** protocol. This protocol can also be used to link disparate OPCS into a single "union" OPAC.

open

1) In information technology, a product or system is described as open when its workings are exposed to the public and capable of being modified or improved by anyone. The alternative is a **proprietary** product or system. Also see **open source**.

2) In programming, to open (verb) a file or unit of data is to make it accessible for reading and writing. An open file is one that is ready to be read or written to.

Open Buying on the Internet

OBI (Open Buying on the Internet) is a proposed standard for business-to-business purchasing on the Internet, aimed particularly at high-volume, low-cost-per-item transactions. OBI uses a number of security technologies such as the **digital certificate** to allow orders to be placed and filled securely. On average, 80% of company purchasing is for non-production supplies such as office supplies, cleaning products, and computer equipment. Making and fulfilling an order can cost an organization up to $150 and the seller up to $50. In the fall of 1996, the Internet Purchasing Roundtable, a group of Fortune 500 buying organizations and their suppliers met to develop an open standard for business-to-business e-commerce. The result—OBI—is intended to eliminate redundant work in purchasing, minimize errors, and reduce labor and transaction costs.

There are four entities involved in an OBI transaction: The requisitioner, the buying organization, the selling organization, and the payment authority. The requisitioner is the person who places the order and must have a digital certificate for **authentication**. The buying organization maintains an OBI **server** that receives OBI order requests and approves them. The buying organization also negotiates and maintains contracts with selling organizations. It is the responsibility of the selling organization to provide a catalog tailored to each department in each company, maintain

products and prices based on contracts with the buying organization, and authorize payments with the appropriate payment authority.

An OBI transaction is done without the user needing special knowledge of the OBI process. With OBI, a purchaser needs only a computer, an Internet connection, a Web browser, and an OBI-compliant application. The following is a typical OBI scenario:

- A janitor needs to purchase some cleaning supplies. Using the stockroom computer, the janitor connects to the organization's purchasing server using a Web browser.

- The janitor selects a merchant from a list on the purchasing department's home page and is authenticated by the merchant's server.

- The janitor views a catalog that is tailored to company needs and selects the needed cleaning supplies. The janitor clicks a button to submit the order, which is then formatted into the Electronic Data Interchange (**EDI**) format. The order is then encapsulated into an OBI **object**.

- The janitor's order is sent to the buying organization in the company for approval using Hypertext Transfer Protocol (**HTTP**) and Secure Sockets Layer (**SSL**). The buying organization decodes the OBI object and approves the order.

- The order is sent to the merchant and fulfilled.

- The merchant submits the payment to a payment authority.

- The payment authority sends the billing data to the company's billing department.

OBI architecture, technical specifications, guidelines, and compliance and implementation information is available at the OBI Consortium Web site. Future OBI versions will include international support and the use of Extensible Markup Language (**XML**) data formats.

open courseware

See "OpenCourseWare"

Open Database Connectivity

Open Database Connectivity (ODBC) is an **open** standard application programming interface (**API**) for accessing a **database**. By using ODBC statements in a program, you can access files in a number of different databases, including Access, dBase, **DB2**, Excel, and Text. In addition to the ODBC software, a separate module or **driver** is needed for each database to be accessed. The main proponent and supplier of ODBC programming support is Microsoft.

ODBC is based on and closely aligned with **The Open Group** standard Structured Query Language (**SQL**) Call-Level Interface. It allows programs to use SQL requests that

will access databases without having to know the proprietary interfaces to the databases. ODBC handles the SQL request and converts it into a request the individual database system understands.

ODBC was created by the SQL Access Group and first released in September, 1992. Although Microsoft Windows was the first to provide an ODBC product, versions now exist for UNIX, OS/2, and Macintosh platforms as well.

In the newer distributed object architecture called Common Object Request Broker Architecture (**CORBA**), the Persistent Object Service (POS) is a superset of both the Call-Level Interface and ODBC. When writing programs in the **Java** language and using the Java Database Connectivity (**JDBC**) application program interface, you can use a product that includes a JDBC-ODBC "bridge" program to reach ODBC-accessible databases.

Open Data-Link Interface

ODI (Open Data-Link Interface) is a software interface that allows different **Data-Link Layer** protocols to share the same **driver** or **adapter** in a computer. ODI was introduced by Novell. For example, using ODI, both **TCP/IP** and IPX/SPX can share the same device adapter.

The Data-Link Layer, part of the Open Systems Interconnect (**OSI**) model, provides a way to move data across a physical link.

Open Document Management API

See "ODMA"

Open eBook Forum

The Open Electronic Book Forum (OEBF) is an organization whose purpose is to develop a specification for electronic content, based on existing **HTML** and **XML** standards, that allows electronic book content to be viewed on various devices (PC display, **PDA**, or eBook reader) and all platforms. The OEB Forum brings publishers, authors, agents, distributors, hardware and software vendors, and programmers together to work towards creating this common standard in "dual-stream publishing," the simultaneous production of both electronic and print media.

Goals for the OEB Forum include:

- Providing a forum for the discussion of issues and technologies related to electronic books

- Developing, publishing, and maintaining common specifications relating to electronic books and promoting the successful adoption of these specifications

- Promoting industry-wide participation of electronic publishing through training sessions, guidelines, and demonstrations of proven technology

- Identifying, evaluating and recommending standards created by other bodies related to electronic books

- Encouraging interoperable implementations of electronic book related systems and providing a forum for resolution of interoperability issues
- Accommodating differences in language, culture, reading and learning styles, and individual abilities

Open Profiling Standard

Open Profiling Standard (OPS) is a proposed standard for how Web users can control the personal information they share with Web sites. OPS has a dual purpose: (1) to allow Web sites to personalize their pages for the individual user and (2) to allow users to control how much personal information they want to share with a Web site. OPS was proposed to the Platform for Privacy Preferences Project (**P3P**) of the World Wide Web Consortium (**W3C**) in 1997 by Netscape Communications (now part of America Online), Firefly Network, and VeriSign.

How It Works

1. A Web user uses special software (or it could be combined with a Web **browser**) to create a Personal Profile that is stored in the user's computer. (If desired, the Profile could also be placed in a corporate or global directory.)

2. When a Web user visits a Web site for the first time, the site could ask the user for information from the Personal Profile and the user could decide whether and how much information to give the site.

3. The site would store the information on its site. When the visitor returned, the Web site, after identifying the user, could use the previously-stored Profile to personalize the pages for that user (for example, provide occupation or hobby-related information on certain pages).

What the Personal Profile Contains

One could think of the Personal Profile as an elaborate, user-defined **cookie**. Cookies are files that Web sites currently place on each user's own hard disk so that they can recall some information about the user. This information is very limited and the user can control only whether cookies are permitted or not. A Personal Profile gives the user much finer control of personal information.

In general, a Personal Profile would contain:

- A unique identifier for the Profile itself
- A unique identifier for each Web site that is visited (used to control how much of the Profile the site can access)
- Basic demographic data (country, zip code, age, and gender)
- Contact information (name, address, zip or postal code, telephone number, e-mail address, and so forth). This is based on the **vCard** specification.

- Additionally, one or more sections for **e-commerce** information, such as credit card numbers
- Detailed personal preferences (hobbies, favorite activities, favorite magazines, and so forth)

The P3P Recommendations provide a formal way to implement the Personal Profile that uses the Resource Definition Framework (**RDF**) of the W3C.

Open Service Gateway Initiative

OSGi (Open Service Gateway Initiative) is an industry plan for a standard way to connect devices such as home appliances and security systems to the Internet. With such a standard, home users could, for example, install a security system and be able to change from one monitoring service to another without having to install a new system of wires and devices. The "service gateway" would be an **application server** in a computer that was a **gateway** between the Internet and a home or small business's network of device. The OSGi plans to specify the application program interface (**API**) for programmers to use to allow communication and control between service providers and the devices within the home or small business network. OSGi's API will be built on the **Java** programming language. Java programs can generally be run on any computer operating system **platform**. OSGi is an **open** standard programming interface. Changes will evolve through the "Java Community Process."

OSGi is intended to connect new **Jini** "smart appliances," **Bluetooth wireless** device groups, as well as TV **set-top** boxes, **cable modem**s, alarm systems, energy management systems, and other devices to Internet sites that can be used to manage them remotely and interactively. The service gateway (SG) is intended to manage this interconnection with "zero administration."

Among some popular device-to-Internet applications are expected to be energy measurement and load management in the home; home security systems that a home owner can monitor and control away from home; continous monitoring of critical care and home-care patients; and predictive failure reporting for home appliances. The OSGi specification will be designed to complement existing residential standards, such as those of LonWorks (see **control network**), CAL, CEBus, **HAVi**, and others.

The initial group of companies that formed the initiative were: Alcatel, Cable Wireless, Electricite de France, Enron Communications, Ericcson, IBM, Lucent Technologies, Motorola, NCI, Nortel Networks, Oracle, Philips Electronics, Sun Microsystems, Sybase, and Toshiba.

Open Shortest Path First protocol

See "OSPF"

Open Source Development Labs

Open Source Development Labs (OSDL) is a nonprofit corporation founded by IBM, Intel, and Computer Associates to support **Linux** developers and users. The goal of OSDL is to provide a place where Linux and other **Open Source** developers can work together and create standardized and compatible Linux platform **applications**. Plans for a state-of-the-art laboratory based somewhere in Oregon were announced in August 2000 by Scott McNeil, who is widely credited with the concept for OSDL.

open source

1) In general, open source refers to any program whose **source code** is made available for use or modification as users or other developers see fit. (Historically, the makers of proprietary software have generally not made source code available.) Open source software is usually developed as a public collaboration and made freely available.

2) Open Source is a certification mark owned by the Open Source Initiative (OSI). Developers of **software** that is intended to be freely shared and possibly improved and redistributed by others can use the Open Source trademark if their distribution terms conform to the OSI's Open Source Definition. To summarize, the Definition model of distribution terms require that:

- The software being distributed must be redistributed to anyone else without any restriction

- The **source code** must be made available (so that the receiving party will be able to improve or modify it)

- The license can require improved versions of the software to carry a different name or version from the original software

The idea is very similar to the **copyleft** concept of the Free Software Foundation. Open Source is the result of a long-time movement toward software that is developed and improved by a group of volunteers cooperating together on a network. Many parts of the **UNIX** operating system were developed this way, including today's most popular version, **Linux**. Linux uses applications from the **GNU** project, which was guided by Richard Stallman and the Free Software Foundation. The Open Source Definition, spearheaded by Eric Raymond (editor of *The New Hacker's Dictionary*), is an effort to provide a branded model or guideline for this kind of software distribution and redistribution. The OSI considers the existing software distribution licenses used by GNU, **BSD** (a widely-distributed version of UNIX), **X Window System**, and Artistic to be conformant with the Open Source Definition.

Prior to its acquisition by AOL, **Netscape**, in an effort to stay viable in its browser competition with Microsoft, made its browser source code (codenamed **Mozilla**) freely available, encouraging **programmers** to improve it. Possible enhancements will presumably be incorporated into future versions. The open source movement has gained momentum as commercial enterprises have begun to consider Linux as an **open** alternative to Windows operating systems.

Open Systems Interconnection

See "OSI"

OpenCourseWare

OpenCourseWare (OCW) is an educational initiative developed by the Massachusetts Institute of Technology (MIT) to make the core teaching materials for all MIT graduate and undergraduate classes available at no cost to Internet users around the world. OCW has been compared to the **open source** software movement because course materials on the OCW site will be "open and freely available worldwide for non-commerical purposes such as research and education, providing an extraordinary resource, free of charge, which others can adapt to their own needs." MIT President, Charles M. Vest, anticipates that within ten years, lecture notes, course outlines, reading lists and assignments for over 2000 MIT classes will be freely available on the OCW Web site.

President Vest has said that although OCW appears counter-intuitive in a market-driven world, it is particularly appropriate for a research university such as MIT where ideas move quickly from the laboratory to the classroom before there is even time to publish it in textbooks. OCW is not seen as a substitute for revenue-generating **distance education** (which requires interaction between teacher and student) but rather as a Web-based resource for teachers and learners around the globe. MIT anticipates that OCW will initially cost between $7.5 million and $10 million per year and is actively seeking funding partners.

MIT is known for its innovation in collaborative and distance learning projects, including long-distance education and collaborative research programs with the National University University of Singapore and Cambridge University in England. MIT faculty members will retain intellectual property ownership of most materials posted on the OCW site, following MIT's current policy on textbook authorship. MIT faculty members have expressed the hope that OCW will encourage other universities to follow their initiative and join them in this "unprecedented step in challenging the privitization of knowledge."

OpenGL

OpenGL (Open Graphics Library) is the computer industry's standard application program interface (**API**) for defining 2-D and 3-D graphic images. Prior to OpenGL, any company developing a graphical application typically had to rewrite the graphics part of it for each **operating system platform** and had to be cognizant of the graphics hardware as well.

With OpenGL, an application can create the same effects in any operating system using any OpenGL-adhering graphics adapter.

OpenGL specifies a set of "commands" or immediately executed functions. Each command directs a drawing action or causes special effects. A list of these commands can be created for repetitive effects. OpenGL is independent of the windowing characteristics of each operating system, but provides special "glue" routines for each operating system that enable OpenGL to work in that system's windowing environment. OpenGL comes with a large number of built-in capabilities requestable through the API. These include hidden surface removal, alpha blending (transparency), **antialiasing**, texture mapping, **pixel** operations, viewing and modeling transformations, and atmospheric effects (fog, smoke, and haze).

Silicon Graphics, makers of advanced graphics **workstation**s, initiated the development of OpenGL. Other companies on the industry-wide Architecture Review Board include DEC, Intel, IBM, Microsoft, and Sun Microsystems. There is no cost (other than learning) to developing an application using the OpenGL API. Microsoft offers free downloads of the OpenGL libraries for its Windows systems. Although OpenGL is not itself a development "toolkit," such toolkits are available, including Silicon Graphics **object-oriented programming** 3D graphics toolkit, Open Inventor.

OpenType

OpenType is a file format for scalable (outline) **font** files that extends the existing **TrueType** font file format used by Microsoft Windows and Apple Macintosh **operating system**s. OpenType was developed jointly by Microsoft and Adobe and allows an Adobe **PostScript** file to be part of a TrueType font file. Prior to OpenType, Adobe did not support TrueType fonts as well it did its own font format, Type 1, for printers that use PostScript. PostScript is an industry standard printer formatting language for higher-quality and more sophisticated printers. OpenType is also known as TrueType Open v. 2.0.

The main advantages of OpenType are:

- Improved cross-platform support
- Better support for the international character sets specified in the **Unicode** standard
- The ability to specify advanced typographic controls
- Smaller file sizes
- The ability to add a **digital signature** to a font set to ensure the integrity of the files

The OpenType specification includes a convention for assigning **suffix**es (file name extensions) to OpenType file names. An OpenType file contains either a TrueType outline font file, which requires a suffix of TTF, or a PostScript outline font file, with a suffix of OTF. A collection of TrueType files packaged together has the suffix TTC.

OpenView

See "HP OpenView"

OpenVMS

OpenVMS is an **operating system** from the Digital Equipment Corporation (DEC) that runs in both its **VAX** and **Alpha** computers. OpenVMS evolved from **VMS**, which originated as the operating system for the VAX in 1979. VMS exploited the concept of **virtual memory**. DEC is now part of Compaq.

OpenVMS is a multitasking and multiprocessing operating system based on VMS; it was renamed OpenVMS when it was redeveloped for the Alpha processor. (OpenVMS is also the name now used on the VAX computer.) The "Open" suggests the added support for the UNIX-like interfaces of the **POSIX** standard. Programs written to the POSIX standard, which includes a set of standard C language programming functions, can be ported to any POSIX-supporting computer platform. Formerly a 32-bit operating system, more recent versions of OpenVMS support 64-bit instructions.

Among other features, OpenVMS can be used with special software that facilitates its use with Windows servers.

Opera

Opera is a Web **browser** that provides some advantages over the two most popular browsers from Netscape and Microsoft. Much smaller in size, Opera is known for being fast and stable. Opera, which is available for BeOS, EPOC, Linux, Mac, OS/2 and Windows, offers the same capabilities of the more popular browsers including integrated searches and Instant Messaging, support for JavaScript, cascading style sheets, and mail. Because Opera is so compact, it is being promoted as the browser of choice for hand-held Internet devices.

Opera for Windows is now free; there is still a purchase fee for other platforms. The free version of Opera contains ads, which are cached weekly to insure Opera's fast speed is maintained. The other versions of Opera do not have ads, which is why Opera charges a modest one-time license fee.

The feature you notice first after installing Opera is a menu or "hotlist" that serves as both a directory to the Web and a bookmark file. The hotlist can be easily removed and you can use the full viewing space to look at multiple Web sites at the same time, either tiling or cascading the windows. You can choose to have the sites you were last looking at restored the next time you open the Opera browser. Opera offers keyboard as well as mouse control of its features. Plug-ins such as RealAudio, RealVideo, and Shockwave can be added. Opera does not support Active-X or Visual Basic.

Opera began in 1994 as a research project for the national phone company in Norway and is now considered to be the third most popular Web browser in use today.

operand

1) In computers, an operand is the part of a computer instruction that specifies **data** that is to be operating on or manipulated and, by extension, the data itself. Basically, a computer instruction describes an operation (add, subtract, and so forth) and the operand or operands on which the operation is to be performed.

2) In mathematics, an operand is the object of a mathematical operation.

operating system

An operating system (sometimes abbreviated as "OS") is the program that, after being initially loaded into the computer by a **boot** program, manages all the other programs in a computer. The other programs are called *applications* or **application program**s. The application programs make use of the operating system by making requests for services through a defined application program interface (**API**). In addition, users can interact directly with the operating system through a user interface such as a command language or a graphical user interface (**GUI**).

An operating system performs these services for applications:

- In a **multitasking** operating system where multiple programs can be running at the same time, the operating system determines which applications should run in what order and how much time should be allowed for each application before giving another application a turn.

- It manages the sharing of internal memory among multiple applications.

- It handles input and output to and from attached hardware devices, such as hard disks, printers, and dial-up ports.

- It sends messages to each application or interactive user (or to a system operator) about the status of operation and any errors that may have occurred.

- It can offload the management of what are called *batch* jobs (for example, printing) so that the initiating application is freed from this work.

- On computers that can provide parallel processing, an operating system can manage how to divide the program so that it runs on more than one processor at a time.

All major computer platforms (hardware and software) require and sometimes include an operating system. **Linux**, **Windows 2000**, **VMS**, **OS/400**, **AIX**, and **z/OS** are all examples of operating systems.

Operational Support System

An Operational Support System (OSS) is an application program that helps someone monitor, control, analyze, and manage problems with a telephone or computer network.

OPS

See "Open Profiling Standard"

optical amplifier

See "erbium amplifier"

Optical Carrier levels (OCx)

The Synchronous Optical Network (**SONET**) includes a set of signal rate multiples for transmitting digital signals on **optical fiber**. The base rate (OC-1) is 51.84 Mbps. Certain multiples of the base rate are provided as shown in the following table. Asynchronous transfer mode (**ATM**) makes use of some of the Optical Carrier levels.

Optical Carrier Level	Data Rate
OC-1	51.84 Mbps
OC-3	155.52 Mbps
OC-12	622.08 Mbps
OC-24	1.244 Gbps
OC-48	2.488 Gbps
OC-192	10 Gbps
OC-256	13.271 Gbps
OC-768	40 Gbps

optical character recognition

See "OCR"

optical computer

An optical computer is a hypothetical device that uses visible light or infrared (**IR**) beams, rather than electric current, to perform digital computations. An electric **current** flows at only about 10 percent of the speed of light. This limits the rate at which data can be exchanged over long distances, and is one of the factors that led to the evolution of **optical fiber**. By applying some of the advantages of visible and/or IR networks at the device and component scale, a computer might someday be developed that can perform operations 10 or more times faster than a conventional electronic computer.

Visible-light and IR beams, unlike electric currents, pass through each other without interacting. Several (or many) **laser** beams can be shone so their paths intersect, but there is no interference among the beams, even when they are confined essentially to two dimensions. Electric currents must be guided around each other, and this makes three-dimensional wiring necessary. Thus, an optical computer, besides being much faster than an electronic one, might also be smaller.

Some engineers think optical computing will someday be common, but most agree that transitions will occur in specialized areas one at a time. Some optical integrated circuits have been designed and manufactured. Three-dimensional, full-motion video can be transmitted along a bundle of fibers by breaking the image into voxels (see **voxel**). Some optical devices can be controlled by electronic currents, even though the impulses carrying the data are visible light or IR.

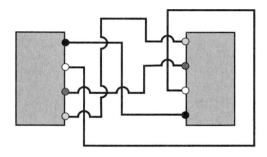

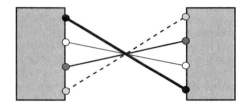

Electrical crossovers (top) require three dimensions, but optical crossovers (bottom require only two dimensions because light beams do not interact

Optical technology has made its most significant inroads in **digital** communications, where fiber optic data transmission has become commonplace. The ultimate goal is the so-called **photonic network**, which uses visible and IR energy exclusively between each source and destination. Optical technology is employed in **CD-ROM** drives and their relatives, laser printers, and most photocopiers and scanners. However, none of these devices are fully optical; all rely to some extent on conventional electronic circuits and components.

optical fiber

Optical fiber (or "fiber optic") refers to the medium and the technology associated with the transmission of information as light pulses along a glass or plastic wire or fiber. Optical fiber carries much more information than conventional copper wire and is in general not subject to electromagnetic interference and the need to retransmit signals. Most telephone company long-distance lines are now of optical fiber.

Transmission on optical fiber wire requires **repeaters** at distance intervals. The glass fiber requires more protection within an outer cable than copper. For these reasons and

because the installation of any new wiring is labor-intensive, few communities yet have optical fiber wires or cables from the phone company's branch office to local customers (known as **local loop**).

Single mode fiber is used for longer distances; **multimode fiber** fiber is used for shorter distances.

optical media

Optical media—such as the compact disc (**CD**)—are **storage** media that hold content in **digital** form and that are written and read by a **laser**; these media include all the various CD and **DVD** variations, as well as optical jukeboxes and autochangers. Optical media have a number of advantages over magnetic media such as the **floppy** disk. Optical disc capacity ranges up to 6 **gigabytes**; that's 6 billion bytes compared to the 1.44 megabytes (MB)—1,440,000 bytes—of the floppy. One optical disc holds about the equivalent of 500 floppies worth of data. Durability is another feature of optical media; they last up to seven times as long as traditional storage media.

The Optical Storage Technology Association (OSTA) is an international trade organization dedicated to the promotion of standardized writable optical technologies and related products. Incorporated in 1992, OSTA is made up of members and associates from the leading optical media manufacturers and resellers of North America, Europe, and Asia. OSTA members include Adaptec, Hewlett-Packard, Philips, and Sony.

optical mouse

An optical mouse is an advanced computer pointing device that uses a light-emitting diode (**LED**), an optical sensor, and digital signal processing (**DSP**) in place of the traditional **mouse** ball and electromechanical transducer. Movement is detected by sensing changes in reflected light, rather than by interpreting the motion of a rolling sphere.

The optical mouse takes microscopic snapshots of the working surface at a rate of more than 1,000 images per second. If the mouse is moved, the image changes. The tiniest irregularities in the surface can produce images good enough for the sensor and DSP to generate usable movement data. The best surfaces reflect but scatter light; an example is a blank sheet of white drawing paper. Some surfaces do not allow the sensor and DSP to function properly because the irregularities are too small to be detected. An example of a poor optical-mousing surface is unfrosted glass.

In practice, an optical mouse does not need cleaning, because it has no moving parts. This all-electronic feature also eliminates mechanical fatigue and failure. If the device is used with the proper surface, sensing is more precise than is possible with any pointing device using the old electromechanical design. This is an asset in graphics applications, and it makes computer operation easier in general.

opt-in e-mail

Opt-in e-mail is a Web marketing term for promotional **e-mail** that recipients have previously requested by signing up at a Web site or special ad **banner**. Typically, Web users are invited to sign up for promotional information about one or more categories of products or services. Those who sign up have thus "opted in." Anyone sending them e-mail as a result hopes that the message will not be perceived as unwanted **spam**.

Several companies gather sign-ups at their own site or through specially-designed banner ads and then sell marketers mailing lists of those who have signed up in various interest categories. The marketer sending opt-in e-mail may remind the recipient that they have previously indicated they were interested in receiving such e-mail and that this is not spam. The recipient is given an opportunity to be removed from the mailing list if they so choose. The distribution model of sending unsolicited e-mail (spam) and allowing the recipient to request removal is sometimes referred to as "opt-out."

Opt-in e-mail has been endorsed as the best practice for marketers by the Internet Direct Marketing Bureau (IDMB).

optoelectronics

Optoelectronics is a branch of electronics that overlaps with physics. The field concerns the theory, design, manufacture, and operation of hardware that converts electrical signals to visible or **infrared radiation** (infrared) energy, or vice-versa.

Examples of optoelectronic components include photocells, solar cells, **optoisolator**s (also called optical couplers or optocouplers), **LED**s (light-emitting diodes), and **laser diode**s. Applications include electric eyes, photovoltaic power supplies, various monitoring and control circuits, and **optical fiber** communications systems.

optoisolator

Also see **diode**.

An optoisolator, also known as an *optical coupler* or *optocoupler*, is a **semiconductor** device that allows signals to be transferred between circuits or systems, while keeping those circuits or systems electrically isolated from each other. Optoisolators are used in a wide variety of communications, control, and monitoring systems.

In its simplest form, an optoisolator consists of an light-emitting diode (**LED**), IRED (infrared-emitting diode), or **laser diode** for signal transmission, and a *photosensor* for signal reception. The "transmitter" takes the electrical signal and converts it into a a beam of modulated visible light or infrared (**IR**). This beam travels across a transparent gap and is picked up by the "receiver," which converts the modulated light or IR back into an electrical signal. The electrical output waveform is identical to the electrical input waveform, although the input and output amplitudes (signal strengths) often differ. The optoisolator is enclosed in a single package, and has the appearance of an integrated circuit (**IC**) or a **transistor** with extra leads.

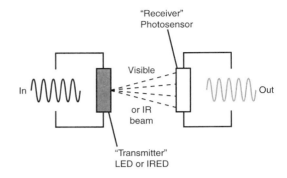

A common application of an optoisolator is in a specialized **modem** that allows a computer to be connected to a telephone line without risk of damage from electrical transients (also called "surges" or "spikes"). Two optoisolators are employed in the **analog** section of the device: one for upstream signals and the other for downstream signals. If a transient occurs on the telephone line (and these are common), the computer will be unaffected because the optical gap does not conduct electric **current**. For this reason, modems that use optoisolators provide superior protection against transients compared with modems incorporating electrical *surge suppressors* alone. (An electrical surge suppressor should be installed between the optoisolator and the telephone line for optimum protection.)

OR

See "logic gate"

Orange Book

Orange Book is the informal name for Philips and Sony's *Recordable CD Standard*. Published in 1990, the Orange Book is a follow-up to their **Red Book CD-DA** (Compact Disc—Digital Audio) specifications. The Orange Book is divided into two sections: Part I deals with **magneto-optical** (MO) drives, and Part II deals with the first recordable CD format **CD-R** (Compact Disc—Recordable). Part III, released separately, describes **CD-RW** (Compact Disc—Rewritable). In addition to specifying these CD forms, the Orange Book includes information about data organization, multisession and hybrid discs, pre-groove modulation (for motor control during writing), and recommendations for measuring reflectivity, environment, and light speed.

Orange Book specifications enabled the first desktop disc writing. Formerly, CDs had been read-only music (CD-DA), to be played in CD players, and multimedia (**CD-ROM**), to be played in computers. After the Orange Book, any user with a CD Recorder drive could create their own CDs from their desktop computers.

Magneto-optical (**CD-MO**) technology allows tracks to be erased and rewritten on 12cm CDs that are rated to allow millions of rewrites. These drives use two heads (one to write and the other to erase), in a double-pass process. System information may be permanently written in a small, premastered area, but the rest of the area is available for recording, and re-recording many times.

CD-R products can be written to only once, similarly to **WORM** (write once, read many) products. A CD-R drive records on CDs that have special recording layers and pregrooved tracks. The first tracks are a program calibration area, which is followed by the lead-in area (where the table of contents will be written), and the program area (where the user actually records), and a lead-out area. There are hybrid discs that include read-only and recordable areas.

Rewritable CD (CD-RW) was developed by Philips and Sony in 1996, as an extension to the original Orange Book. This addition specifies the use of Phase Change technology and the Universal Disc Format (**UDF**) to produce a CD that can be rewritten in one pass. CD-RW makes it possible for the user to write and rewrite the disc.

ORB

See "Object Request Broker"

ORBS

A similar but unrelated term is **ORB** (Object Request Broker).

ORBS (Open Relay Behavior-modification System) is (or possibly was—as of June 7, 2001, it was not operating) a volunteer-run New Zealand-based organization that operates an anti-**spam** screening service. The ORBS database tracks e-mail (specifically **SMTP**) servers that allow third-party relay (TPR), a practice that makes it possible for any sender to connect to the server from anywhere and forward volumes of unsolicited bulk e-mail messages. As a further precaution, ORBS also tracks networks that have set up processes to prevent verification of third-party relay permission, since administrators sometimes find it easier to block ORBS testers than to address security problems.

In the first years of the Internet's operation, third-party relaying was a necessary and accepted means of routing messages. Although technological advances have made third-party relaying no longer required, many servers continue to maintain open relays, according to ORBS, in the "Internet's spirit of cooperation." According to ORBS, however, an open relay now falls into the category of "attractive nuisance." The organization claims that since 1995, the culture of the Web has changed dramatically, with the result that open relays became vulnerable to spammers looking to make a quick profit through bulk junk mail.

ORBS maintains a blacklist of Internet service providers (**ISP**s) and other organizations found in violation of their criteria, a practice that is somewhat controversial because the targeted enterprises often believe they have been listed unfairly. In one recent instance, a New Zealand high court ruled that ORBS must remove Xtra mail servers (owned by Actrix, an New Zealand-based ISP) from their list of suspect servers. ORBS is in occasionally acrimonious competition with a similar system based in California, the Mail Abuse Prevention System (MAPS). The two organizations clashed when ORBS blacklisted Above.net (an ISP owned by Paul Vixie, who also runs MAPS) as an open relay.

order of magnitude

An order of magnitude is an exponential change of plus-or-minus 1 in the value of a quantity or unit. The term is generally used in conjunction with power-of-10 **scientific notation**.

In base 10, the most common numeration scheme worldwide, an increase of one order of magnitude is the same as multiplying a quantity by 10. An increase of two orders of magnitude is the equivalent of multiplying by 100, or 10^2. In general, an increase of n orders of magnitude is the equivalent of multiplying a quantity by 10^n. Thus, 2315 is one order of magnitude larger than 231.5, which in turn is is one order of magnitude larger than 23.15.

As values get smaller, a decrease of one order of magnitude is the same as multiplying a quantity by 0.1. A decrease of two orders of magnitude is the equivalent of multiplying by 0.01, or 10^{-2}. In general, a decrease of n orders of magnitude is the equivalent of multiplying a quantity by 10^{-n}. Thus, 23.15 is one order of magnitude smaller than 231.5, which in turn is one order of magnitude smaller than 2315.

In the International System of Units (**SI**), most quantities can be expressed in multiple or fractional terms according to the order of magnitude. For example, attaching the prefix "kilo-" to a unit increases the size of the unit by three orders of magnitude, or one thousand (10^3). Attaching the prefix "micro-" to a unit decreases the size of the unit by six orders of magnitude, the equivalent of multiplying it by one millionth (10^{-6}). Scientists and engineers have designated prefix multipliers from septillionths (10^{-24}) to septillions (10^{24}), a span of 48 orders of magnitude.

ordinal

Ordinal refers to the sequence in which something is in relation to others of its kind. Examples of ordinal numbers are first, third, 11th, and 123rd. Ordinal numbers can be contrasted to **cardinal** numbers.

org

"org" is one of the generic top-level **domain name**s that can be used when choosing a domain name. It generally describes the entity owning the domain name as one that does not fit into other categories. In general, non-profit organizations and industry standard groups tend to use this generic name. Along with the second-level domain name (for example: "moma" in moma.org), the top-level domain name is required in Web and e-mail addresses.

For more information, see **gTLD** (generic top-level domain name).

Organization for Structured Information Standards

See "OASIS"

original equipment manufacturer

An OEM (original equipment manufacturer) is a company that uses product components from one or more other companies to build a product that it sells under its own company name and **brand**. (The term is sometimes mistakenly used to refer to the company that supplies the components.) IBM is an example of a supplier to the OEM market (and IBM is also an OEM itself since it uses other companies' parts in some of its products).

Many computer hardware manufacturers that have their own brand-name products derive considerable revenue by reselling the product or key parts of it to OEM companies that seem to be competing in the same market. Arguments for selling to an OEM are that you may be able to make money from a market sector that your competitor already owns (perhaps because they have an existing customer base) and that you can be a more efficient producer because you sell and manufacture more of your product. Frequently, an OEM company differentiates itself from the company it buys parts from by adding features or using different selling concepts. Many OEM companies are selling a "solution" tailored to a particular **vertical market**.

Also see **value-added reseller** (VAR), a somewhat similar repackaging of software.

orphan file

On a computer's hard drive, an orphan file is a support file (such as a **DLL** file) that no longer serves a purpose because the "parent" application it is associated with has been moved or uninstalled. Orphan files can be deleted manually if the user is confident that the file is not being used by any other application.

orthogonal

In geometry, orthogonal means "involving right angles" (from Greek *ortho*, meaning *right*, and *gon* meaning *angled*). The term has been extended to general use, meaning the characteristic of being independent (relative to something else). It also can mean: non-redundant, non-overlapping, or irrelevant. In computer terminology, something—such as a programming language or a data **object**—is orthogonal if it can be used without consideration as to how its use will affect something else.

In itself, a programming language is orthogonal if its features can be used without thinking about how that usage will affect other features. **Pascal** is sometimes considered to be an orthogonal language, while **C++** is considered to be a non-orthogonal language.

Features of a program that is compatible with its own earlier versions—this is called **backward compatible**—have an orthogonal relationship with the features of the earlier version, because they are mutually independent; you don't have to worry about how the use of one version's features will cause an unintended effect because of an interaction with those of the other version. Both the features and the programs can be said to be mutually orthogonal.

The length of time data is kept in storage in a computer system is known as its *persistence*. *Orthogonal persistence* is the quality of a programming system that allows a programmer to treat data similarly without regard to the length of time the data is kept in storage. Data is stored for varying lengths of time; some is stored very briefly and some is stored relatively permanently. Frequently, a programmer must use different approaches and separate coding to access data depending on whether it is stored for a long time or a short time. Using a programming system with orthogonal data persistence allows the programmer to treat data the same way regardless of its persistence characteristic, saving programming time and making it easier to enforce referential integrity (a type of constraint applied to ensure correct data validity).

orthogonal frequency-division multiplexing

Orthogonal frequency-division multiplexing (OFDM) is a method of **digital modulation** in which a **signal** is split into several **narrowband channel**s at different frequencies. The technology was first conceived in the 1960s and 1970s during research into minimizing interference among channels near each other in frequency.

In some respects, OFDM is similar to conventional frequency-division multiplexing (**FDM**). The difference lies in the way in which the signals are modulated and demodulated. Priority is given to minimizing the interference, or **crosstalk**, among the channels and symbols comprising the data stream. Less importance is placed on perfecting individual channels.

OFDM is used in European digital audio broadcast services. The technology lends itself to **digital television**, and is being considered as a method of obtaining high-speed digital data transmission over conventional telephone lines. It is also used in wireless local area networks.

Also see frequency-division multiplexing (**FDM**), time-division multiplexing (**TDM**), and multi-carrier modulation (**MCM**).

OS

See "operating system"

OS 10

See "OS X"

OS X

OS X (pronounced OH-ESS-TEHN—the "X" is Roman number X) is version 10 of the Apple **Macintosh operating system** (OS). OS X is described by Apple as its first "complete revision" of the OS (the previous version is OS 9) and incorporates support for **UNIX**-based applications as well as for those written just for the Macintosh. The operating system is described as redesigned for modularity so that future changes will be easier to incorporate.

A very visible difference in OS X from earlier Mac OS versions is a **desktop** with a **3-D** appearance. OS X also includes the ability to play Quicktime movies in icon size and instant wake-from-sleep capability on portable computers. Features that Apple says will be added include support for **DVD** movies and the ability to create audio **CDs**.

OS X can be installed on an existing Mac with OS 9 and the user can choose which one to use when the computer is started.

OS/2

OS/2 is an IBM **operating system** for the personal computer that was initially intended to provide an alternative to Microsoft Windows for both enterprise and personal PC users. The latest version of OS/2 Warp, Warp 4, has a Netscape-based Web browser that exploits OS/2's existing **speech recognition** capability. IBM has also enhanced OS/2 to provide **server** functions for **e-business**.

OS/390

OS/390, recently renamed z/OS, is the IBM **operating system** most commonly installed on its S/390 line of **mainframe server**. It is an evolved version of **MVS** (Multiple Virtual Storage), IBM's long-time, **robust** mainframe operating system. By whatever name, MVS has been said to be the operating system that keeps the world going. The payroll, accounts receivable, transaction processing, database management, and other programs critical to the world's largest businesses are usually run on an MVS system. Although MVS tends to be associated with a monolithic, centrally-controlled information system, IBM has in recent years repositioned it as a "large server" in a network-oriented distributed environment that would tend to use a **3-tier application** model.

Since MVS represents a certain epoch and culture in the history of computing and since many older MVS systems still operate, the term "MVS" will probably continue to be used for some time. Since OS/390 also comes with **UNIX** user and programming interfaces built in, it can be used as both an MVS system and a UNIX system at the same time. OS/390 (and earlier MVS) systems run older applications developed using **COBOL** and, for transaction programs, **CICS**. Older application programs written in **PL/I** and **FORTRAN** are still running. Older applications use the **Virtual Storage Access Method** for file management and **Virtual Telecommunications Access Method** for telecommunication with users. The most common program environment today uses the **C** and **C++** languages. *DB2* is IBM's primary. **Java** applications can be developed and run under OS/390's UNIX environment.

For additional information about major components of OS/390, see **MVS**. Other IBM operating systems for their larger computers include or have included: the Transaction Processing Facility (TPF), used in some major airline reservation systems, and **virtual machine**, an operating system designed to serve many interactive users at the same time.

OS/400

OS/400 is IBM's **operating system** for its **AS/400** and AS/400e line of business computers. Because OS/400 is closely attuned to the AS/400 hardware design and generally comes as part of the basic package, there is no alternative operating system to compete with it. OS/400 is built to operate with the AS/400 logical partition (**LPAR**) architecture, in which multiple instances of the operating system can run concurrently in different partitions. Among other uses, LPAR is useful when migrating to a new release. The old production system can keep operating in one partition while a new system is being tested.

As the AS/400 has evolved to meet the latest trends in business and information technology, OS/400 and its related software has added support for:

- Applications written in the **Java** programming language
- The ability to run Windows 2000/NT applications (when certain other products are installed)
- The Portable Application Solutions Environment (PASE), which supports a subset of the **AIX** environment so that **UNIX** applications can be ported and run on the AS/400

- Lotus **Domino**, which provides groupware and e-mail from Lotus Notes applications or a standard Web browser

oscillator

An oscillator is an electronic device used for the purpose of generating a **signal**. Oscillators are found in computers, **wireless** receivers and transmitters, and audio-frequency equipment, particularly music synthesizers. There are many types of oscillator devices, but they all operate according to the same basic principle: an oscillator always employs a sensitive **amplifier** whose output is fed back to the input in **phase**. Thus, the signal regenerates and sustains itself. This is known as positive feedback. It is the same process that sometimes causes unwanted "howling" in public-address systems.

The **frequency** at which an oscillator works is usually determined by a quartz crystal. When a direct current is applied to such a crystal, it vibrates at a frequency that depends on its thickness, and on the manner in which it is cut from the original mineral rock. Some oscillators employ combinations of inductors, resistors, and/or capacitors to determine the frequency. However, the best stability (constancy of frequency) is obtained in oscillators that use quartz crystals.

In a computer, a specialized oscillator, called the *clock*, serves as a sort of pacemaker for the **microprocessor**. The clock frequency (or **clock speed**) is usually specified in megahertz (**MHz**), and is an important factor in determining the rate at which a computer can perform **instruction**s.

oscilloscope

An oscilloscope is a laboratory instrument commonly used to display and analyze the **waveforms** of electronic signals. In effect, the device draws a graph of the instantaneous signal **voltage** as a function of time.

A typical oscilloscope can display alternating current (**AC**) or pulsating direct current (**DC**) waveforms having a frequency as low as approximately 1 hertz (**Hz**) or as high as several megahertz (**MHz**). High-end oscilloscopes can display signals having frequencies up to several hundred gigahertz (**GHz**). The display is broken up into so-called horizontal divisions (hor div) and vertical divisions (vert div). Time is displayed from left to right on the horizontal scale. Instantaneous voltage appears on the vertical scale, with positive values going upward and negative values going downward.

The oldest form of oscilloscope, still used in some labs today, is known as the *cathode-ray oscilloscope*. It produces an image by causing a focused **electron** beam to travel, or sweep, in patterns across the face of a cathode ray tube (**CRT**). More modern oscilloscopes electronically replicate the action of the CRT using a liquid crystal display (**LCD**) similar to those found on notebook computers. The most sophisticated

oscilloscopes employ computers to process and display waveforms. These computers can use any type of display, including CRT, LCD, and gas plasma.

In any oscilloscope, the *horizontal sweep* is measured in seconds per division (s/div), milliseconds per division (ms/div), microseconds per division (s/div), or nanoseconds per division (ns/div). The *vertical deflection* is measured in volts per division (V/div), millivolts per division (mV/div), or microvolts per division (µV/div). Virtually all oscilloscopes have adjustable horizontal sweep and vertical deflection settings.

The illustration shows two common waveforms as they might appear when displayed on an oscilloscope screen. The signal on the top is a **sine wave**; the signal on the bottom is a ramp wave. It is apparent from this display that both signals have the same, or nearly the same, **frequency**. They also have approximately the same **peak-to-peak** amplitude. Suppose the horizontal sweep rate in this instance is 1 µs/div. Then these waves both complete a full cycle every 2 µs, so their frequencies are both approximately 0.5 MHz or 500 kilohertz (**kHz**). If the vertical deflection is set for, say, 0.5 mV/div, then these waves both have peak-to-peak amplitudes of approximately 2 mV.

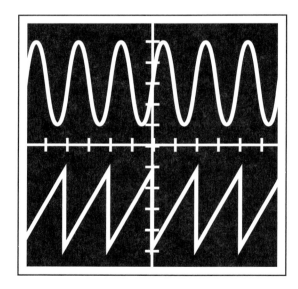

These days, typical high-end oscilloscopes are digital devices. They connect to personal computers and use their displays. Although these machines no longer employ scanning electron beams to generate images of waveforms in the manner of the old cathode-ray "scope," the basic principle is the same. Software controls the sweep rate, vertical deflection, and a host of other features which can include:

- Storage of waveforms for future reference and comparison
- Display of several waveforms simultaneously
- Spectral analysis
- Portability
- Battery power option
- Usability with all popular operating platforms
- Zoom-in and zoom-out
- Multi-color displays

OSDL

See "Open Source Development Labs"

OSGi

OSGi (Open Service Gateway Initiative) is an industry plan for a standard way to connect devices such as home appliances and security systems to the Internet. With such a standard, home users could, for example, install a security system and be able to change from one monitoring service to another without having to install a new system of wires and devices. The "service gateway" would be an **application server** in a computer that was a **gateway** between the Internet and a home or small business's network of device. The OSGi plans to specify the application program interface (**API**) for programmers to use to allow communication and control between service providers and the devices within the home or small business network. OSGi's API will be built on the **Java** programming language. Java programs can generally be run on any computer operating system **platform**. OSGi is an **open** standard programming interface. Changes will evolve through the "Java Community Process."

OSGi is intended to connect new **Jini** "smart appliances," **Bluetooth wireless** device groups, as well as TV **set-top** boxes, **cable modem**s, alarm systems, energy management systems, and other devices to Internet sites that can be used to manage them remotely and interactively. The service gateway (SG) is intended to manage this interconnection with "zero administration."

Among some popular device-to-Internet applications are expected to be energy measurement and load management in the home; home security systems that a home owner can monitor and control away from home; continous monitoring of critical care and home-care patients; and predictive failure reporting for home appliances. The OSGi specification will be designed to complement existing residential standards, such as those of LonWorks (see **control network**), CAL, CEBus, **HAVi**, and others.

The initial group of companies that formed the initiative were: Alcatel, Cable Wireless, Electricite de France, Enron Communications, Ericcson, IBM, Lucent Technologies, Motorola, NCI, Nortel Networks, Oracle, Philips Electronics, Sun Microsystems, Sybase, and Toshiba.

OSI

OSI (Open Systems Interconnection) is a standard description or "reference model" for how messages should be transmitted between any two points in a telecommunication **network**. Its purpose is to guide product implementors so that their products will consistently work with other products. The reference model defines seven layers of functions that take place at each end of a communication. Although OSI is not always strictly adhered to in terms of keeping related functions together in a well-defined layer, many if not most products involved in telecommunication make an attempt to describe themselves in relation to the OSI model. It is also valuable as a single reference view of communication that furnishes everyone a common ground for education and discussion.

Developed by representatives of major computer and telecommunication companies beginning in 1983, OSI was originally intended to be a detailed specification of interfaces. Instead, the committee decided to establish a common reference model for which others could develop detailed interfaces, that in turn could become standards. OSI was officially adopted as an international standard by the International Organization of Standards (**ISO**). Currently, it is Recommendation X.200 of the **ITU-TS**.

The main idea in OSI is that the process of communication between two end points in a telecommunication network can be divided into layers, with each layer adding its own set of special, related functions. Each communicating user or program is at a computer equipped with these seven layers of function. So, in a given message between users, there will be a flow of data through each layer at one end down through the layers in that computer and, at the other end, when the message arrives, another flow of data up through the layers in the receiving computer and ultimately to the end user or program. The actual programming and hardware that furnishes these seven layers of function is usually a combination of the computer **operating system**, applications (such as your Web browser), **TCP/IP** or alternative transport and network protocols, and the software and hardware that enable you to put a signal on one of the lines attached to your computer.

OSI divides telecommunication into seven layers. The layers are in two groups. The upper four layers are used whenever a message passes from or to a user. The lower three layers (up to the network layer) are used when any message passes through the host computer. Messages intended for this computer pass to the upper layers. Messages destined for some other host are not passed up to the upper layers but are forwarded to another host. The seven layers are:

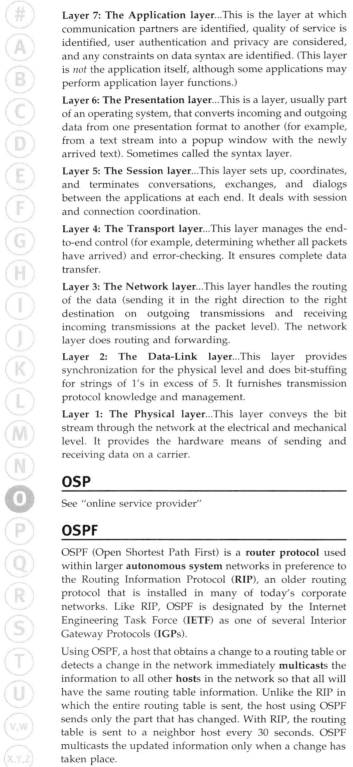

Layer 7: The Application layer...This is the layer at which communication partners are identified, quality of service is identified, user authentication and privacy are considered, and any constraints on data syntax are identified. (This layer is *not* the application itself, although some applications may perform application layer functions.)

Layer 6: The Presentation layer...This is a layer, usually part of an operating system, that converts incoming and outgoing data from one presentation format to another (for example, from a text stream into a popup window with the newly arrived text). Sometimes called the syntax layer.

Layer 5: The Session layer...This layer sets up, coordinates, and terminates conversations, exchanges, and dialogs between the applications at each end. It deals with session and connection coordination.

Layer 4: The Transport layer...This layer manages the end-to-end control (for example, determining whether all packets have arrived) and error-checking. It ensures complete data transfer.

Layer 3: The Network layer...This layer handles the routing of the data (sending it in the right direction to the right destination on outgoing transmissions and receiving incoming transmissions at the packet level). The network layer does routing and forwarding.

Layer 2: The Data-Link layer...This layer provides synchronization for the physical level and does bit-stuffing for strings of 1's in excess of 5. It furnishes transmission protocol knowledge and management.

Layer 1: The Physical layer...This layer conveys the bit stream through the network at the electrical and mechanical level. It provides the hardware means of sending and receiving data on a carrier.

OSP

See "online service provider"

OSPF

OSPF (Open Shortest Path First) is a **router protocol** used within larger **autonomous system** networks in preference to the Routing Information Protocol (**RIP**), an older routing protocol that is installed in many of today's corporate networks. Like RIP, OSPF is designated by the Internet Engineering Task Force (**IETF**) as one of several Interior Gateway Protocols (**IGP**s).

Using OSPF, a host that obtains a change to a routing table or detects a change in the network immediately **multicast**s the information to all other **host**s in the network so that all will have the same routing table information. Unlike the RIP in which the entire routing table is sent, the host using OSPF sends only the part that has changed. With RIP, the routing table is sent to a neighbor host every 30 seconds. OSPF multicasts the updated information only when a change has taken place.

Rather than simply counting the number of **hop**s, OSPF bases its path descriptions on "link states" that take into account additional network information. OSPF also lets the user assign cost **metric**s to a given host router so that some paths are given preference. OSPF supports a variable network **subnet** mask so that a network can be subdivided. RIP is supported within OSPF for router-to-end station communication. Since many networks using RIP are already in use, router manufacturers tend to include RIP support within a router designed primarily for OSPF.

out of the box

1) "Out of the box" is an expression that describes nonconformal, creative thinking. The term is used as an adverb to describe the thinking or as an adjective to describe the ideas. Although the origin of the term is unknown to us, it would seem to suggest that we tend to carry around an existing and conventional structure of thought that it is hard to escape. One also thinks of the expression "boxed-in," or having reduced choices. In the fast-paced world of information technology, employers often say they are looking for someone who "thinks out of the box." Older, related but really different terms include *blue sky*, *far out*, and *off the wall*. A variation is "outside the box."

As you might expect, the term "in the box" is sometimes used to describe conformal thinking. For example, in a recent magazine article about **MP3** and music pirating, a manager of some music groups is quoted as saying of major label recording companies who have been slow to adapt to the Internet, "They're always thinking inside of the box."

2) "Out of the box" is also used as a synonym for "off the shelf," meaning a ready-made software, hardware, or combination package that meets a need that would otherwise require an ad hoc development effort.

out-of-band signaling

Out-of-band signaling is telecommunication **signaling** (exchange of information in order to control a telephone call) that is done on a **channel** that is dedicated for the purpose and separate from the channels used for the telephone call. Out-of-band signaling is used in Signaling System 7 (**SS7**), the latest standard for the signaling that controls the world's phone calls.

output feedback

Output feedback (OFB) is a mode of operation for a **block cipher**. It has some similarities to the **ciphertext feedback** mode in that it permits encryption of differing block sizes, but has the key difference that the output of the encryption block function is the feedback (instead of the **ciphertext**). The **XOR** (exclusive OR) value of each **plaintext** block is created independently of both the plaintext and ciphertext. It is this mode that is used when there can be no tolerance for error propagation, as there are no chaining dependencies.

Like the ciphertext feedback mode, it uses an initialization vector (IV). Changing the IV in the same plaintext block results in different ciphertext.

In terms of error correction, output feedback can tolerate ciphertext bit errors, but is incapable of self-synchronization after losing ciphertext bits, as it disturbs the synchronization of the aligning keystream. A problem with output feedback is that the plaintext can be easily altered but using a **digital signature** scheme can overcome this problem.

outsourcing

Outsourcing is an arrangement in which one company provides services for another company that could also be or usually have been provided in-house. Outsourcing is a trend that is becoming more common in information technology and other industries for services that have usually been regarded as intrinsic to managing a business. In some cases, the entire information management of a company is outsourced, including planning and business analysis as well as the installation, management, and servicing of the network and workstations. Outsourcing can range from the large contract in which a company like IBM manages IT services for a company like Xerox to the practice of hiring contractors and temporary office workers on an individual basis.

overclocking

Overclocking is resetting your computer so that the **microprocessor** runs faster than the manufacturer-specified speed (for example, setting an Intel 166 **MHz** (megahertz) microprocessor to run at 200 Mhz). Somewhat surprisingly, this is possible. However, it's more likely to work with an Intel microprocessor than with those of other manufacturers because, according to Tom's Hardware Guide, Intel labels the speed of its microprocessors more conservatively.

Factors that favor your ability to successfully "upgrade by resetting" include (in addition to having an Intel microprocessor): having a well-designed **motherboard** with a fast enough **bus** and having a fan or other cooling device that will keep your system cool enough.

The procedure for "overclocking" depends on your combination of factors. The first and most commonly applicable step is to reset your computer's bus speed. The microprocessor is often able to adjust successfully to a slightly higher bus speed. Resetting the bus speed may require resetting jumpers inside your computer. In newer systems with SoftMenu **BIOS**, the bus speed can be set through your system setup interface.

P2P

See "peer-to-peer"

P4

See "Pentium 4"

PABX

See "private automatic branch exchange"

packet

A packet is the unit of data that is routed between an origin and a destination on the Internet or any other **packet-switched** network. When any file (e-mail message, **HTML** file, **Graphics Interchange Format** file, **Uniform Resource Locator** request, and so forth) is sent from one place to another on the Internet, the Transmission Control Protocol (**TCP**) layer of **TCP/IP** divides the file into "chunks" of an efficient size for routing. Each of these packets is separately numbered and includes the Internet **address** of the destination. The individual packets for a given file may travel different routes through the Internet. When they have all arrived, they are reassembled into the original file (by the TCP layer at the receiving end).

A packet-switching scheme is an efficient way to handle transmissions on a connectionless network such as the Internet. An alternative scheme, **circuit-switched**, is used for networks allocated for voice connections. In circuit-switching, lines in the network are shared among many users as with packet-switching, but each connection requires the dedication of a particular path for the duration of the connection.

"Packet" and "datagram" are similar in meaning. A protocol similar to TCP, the User Datagram Protocol(**UDP**) uses the term **datagram**.

Packet Hound

See "PacketHound"

packet monkey

On the Internet, a packet monkey is someone (see **cracker**, **hacker**, and **script kiddy**) who intentionally inundates a **Web site** or network with data **packet**s, resulting in a **denial-of-service** situation for users of the attacked site or network. Packet monkeys typically use tools created and made available on the Internet by hackers.

According to one writer's distinction, a packet monkey, unlike a script kiddy, leaves no clues as to who is making the exploit, making the identity of a packet monkey more difficult to trace. In addition, a denial-of-service attack can be launched on a wider scale than attacks performed by script kiddies, making them more difficult to investigate.

Hackers look down on packet monkeys and often describe them as "bottom feeders." Because a packet monkey uses tools created by others, the packet monkey has little understanding of the harm that may be caused. Typically, packet monkey exploits are random and without any purpose other than the thrill of making an effect.

packet writing

Packet writing is a technology that enables the writing of data to a recordable compact disc (**CD-R**) incrementally, in multiple small blocks of data, rather than in a single block (as in *disc-at-once* recording), or in blocks defined by tracks (as in *track-at-once* recording), the other two common methods. Packet writing software makes it possible for the user to save data to a CD-R or **CD-RW** in the same way as it would be saved to the hard drive or a floppy. Not all CD recorders support packet writing.

PacketHound

PacketHound is a product that aims to help an enterprise regulate traffic that might otherwise slow services down for all users of a **local area network**. PacketHound is intended to address the concern of businesses and universities about the downloading of large files, especially music files in the **MP3** format, using **Napster**, **Gnutella**, and similar approaches. PacketHound can also monitor and reduce the number of streaming media files that are downloaded by network users. Both businesses and universities are concerned not only about such traffic slowing down the network for other uses, but also about the possibility of being sued by music companies for loss of intellectual property. According to Palisade Systems, the developers of PacketHound, Napster and Gnutella traffic has had a significant effect in performance on a number of university networks.

Although Gnutella uses a known **port number** that a network **firewall** server could screen for, the port number can be changed by a sophisticated user. The makers of PacketHound claim to be the only product that can monitor and block certain traffic based on the characteristics of the request and response flow, although they do not describe their approach in detail. PacketHound customers can also use the product to monitor without blocking and to also permit or block given traffic at different times of the day. PacketHound is not installed in a firewall server but as a separate PC with an Ethernet card and running NetBSD. The machine's presence is said to be transparent to the network. When PacketHound discerns a pattern of traffic that meets the blocking criteria, it returns a reset **packet** to the requesting machine. The user sees a "Connection reset by host" message.

The company also sells PacketPup, a downloadable program that lets a company monitor **bandwidth** usage on a network. A similar product called PacketShaper (from Packeteer) analyzes and classifies applications in use on the network in terms of their bandwidth and other behavior.

Packet-Level Procedure

1) PAP (Packet-Level Procedure) is a **full-duplex** protocol for transferring **packet**s between parties in an X.25 network. PAP supports data sequencing, flow control, accountability, and error detection and recovery.

2) PAP (Password Authentication Procedure) is a procedure used by **Point-to-Point Protocol** servers to validate a connection request. PAP works as follows:

1. After the link is established, the requestor sends a password and an id to the server.

2. The server either validates the request and sends back an acknowledgement, terminates the connection, or offers the requestor another chance.

Passwords are sent without security and the originator can make repeated attempts to gain access. For these reasons, a server that supports **Challenge-Handshake Authentication Protocol** will offer to use that protocol before using PAP. PAP protocol details can be found in RFC 1334.

packet-switched

Packet-switched describes the type of network in which relatively small units of data called **packet**s are routed through a network based on the destination address contained within each packet. Breaking communication down into packets allows the same data path to be shared among many users in the network. This type of communication between sender and receiver is known as *connectionless* (rather than *dedicated*). Most traffic over the Internet uses packet switching and the Internet is basically a connectionless network.

Contrasted with packet-switched is **circuit-switched**, a type of network such as the regular voice telephone network in which the communication circuit (path) for the call is set up and dedicated to the participants in that call. For the duration of the connection, all resources on that circuit are unavailable for other users. Voice calls using the Internet's packet-switched system are possible. Each end of the conversation is broken down into packets that are reassembled at the other end.

Another type of digital network that uses packet-switching is the **X.25** network, a widely-installed commercial wide area network protocol. Internet protocol packets can be carried on an X.25 network. The X.25 network can also support a **virtual circuit** in which a logical connection is established for

two parties on a dedicated basis for some duration. A permanent virtual circuit (**PVC**) reserves the path on an ongoing basis and is an alternative for corporations to a system of **leased line**s. A permanent virtual circuit is a dedicated logical connection but the actual physical resources can be shared among multiple logical connections or users.

PACS

See "Personal Access Communications System"

page

1) On the World Wide Web, a page is a file notated with the Hypertext Markup Language (**HTML**). Usually, it contains text and specifications about where image or other multimedia files are to be placed when the page is displayed. You can think of a Web **site** as a book (albeit a hypertext kind of book rather than a sequentially arranged kind of book) that arrives a page at a time as you request each one. Each page is an individual HTML file with its own Web address (**URL**). The first page you usually request at a site is known as the **home page**. (Most home pages have a default name that doesn't have to be specified; you only need to enter the domain name for the site itself.) With **frames**, multiple pages (HTML files) can be downloaded to a browser and presented on designated sections of the display screen at the same time.

2) In a computer's random access memory (**RAM**), a page is a group of memory cells that are accessed as part of a single operation. That is, all the bits in the group of cells are changed at the same time. In some kinds of RAM, a page is all the memory cells in the same row of cells. In other kinds of RAM, a page may represent some other group of cells than all those in a row.

3) In computer systems that use **virtual memory** (also known as virtual storage), a page is a unit of data storage that is brought into real storage (on a personal computer, RAM) from auxiliary storage (on a personal computer, usually the hard disk) when a requested item of data is not already in real storage (RAM).

4) In printing, a page is what is printed on a single piece of paper.

pagefile

In storage, a pagefile is a reserved portion of a **hard disk** that is used as an extension of random access memory (**RAM**) for data in RAM that hasn't been used recently. A pagefile can be read from the hard disk as one contiguous chunk of data and thus faster than re-reading data from many different original locations. Windows administrators or users can reset the system-provided default size value of the pagefile to meet their particular needs.

In other **operating system**s, the pagefile is called a **swap file** or a *swap partition*.

pagejacking

Pagejacking is stealing the contents of a **Web site** by copying some of its pages, putting them on a site that appears to be the legitimate site, and then inviting people to the illegal site by deceptive means—for example, by having the contents indexed by major **search engine**s whose results in turn link users to the illegal site. By moving enough of a Web site's content as well as the page descriptor information (known as information) within each page, pagejackers can then submit the illegal site to major search engines for indexing. Users of the search engine sites may then receive results from both the illegitimate as well as the legitimate site and can easily be misled to link to the wrong one. Users linking to the illegitimate site may find themselves redirected to a pornographic or other unwanted site. As an additional annoyance, users subjected to pagejacking may also encounter *mousetrapping*, in which clicking the Back button with the mouse does not lead out of the illegal site but only to the viewing of additional unwanted pages. To escape, the user may need to close the browser or even restart the operating system.

Web users who enter Web page addresses (known as **URLs**) directly on their Web **browser** address line, by selecting it from a bookmark, or by clicking on a properly coded link on another site will not be subject to pagejacking. The problem most typically occurs when clicking site descriptions that result from searches at major search engine sites. Although the practice was not new at the time, the *New York Times* on September 23, 1999, carried a page one story about an Australian company that had pagejacked a number of corporate sites, adding pornographic links or ads, and then mousetrapping visitors. Australian officials were reported to be considering civil or criminal charges and a U.S. Federal judge in Virginia, where the original Internet site registration company is located, ordered the sites to lose their Web registrations.

pager

A pager is a small telecommunications device that receives (and, in some cases, transmits) alert signals and/or short messages. This type of device is convenient for people expecting telephone calls, but who are not near a telephone set to make or return calls immediately.

A typical one-way pager fits easily in a shirt pocket; some are as small as a wristwatch. A miniature, short-range **wireless** receiver captures a message, usually accompanied by a beep. (This is why the device is also known as a beeper). The simplest one-way pagers display the return-call telephone number of the person who sent the message. Alternatively, a code can be displayed that indicates which

of several designated parties is requesting a return phone call. Sophisticated one-way pagers can display short text messages.

Until recently, pagers were designed as receive-only devices. There are at least two reasons for this. First, if two-way communication is needed, cell phones are available for that purpose. Second, it is difficult to engineer an efficient wireless transmitter that can fit inside a tiny package and provide enough signal range to reach repeaters from all points within the coverage zone.

Despite the engineering challenge, a **two-way pager**, also called a two-way messaging device or two-way interactive system, has been developed. This system employs large numbers of repeaters, allowing low-power wireless transmitters with subminiature antennas to reach at least one **repeater** from any location within the coverage area. A typical unit is about the size of a pocket calculator and has a built-in, miniature keyboard and a liquid crystal display (**LCD**) screen that can display several lines of text and/or simple graphics.

PAL

See "Phase Alternation Line"

palette

A palette is both the board on which an artist puts selected colors and also the set of colors themselves. On the Web, choosing the colors you use not only involves understanding which colors work well together but also understanding the capabilities of display screens and **browser** for displaying the colors you choose. (In the case of pre-created images such as photographs someone else has taken, you don't choose the colors that were captured initially, but you can control which colors are saved for transmission.)

In computer display technology, a color is set for each individual **pixel** or addressable illumination element on the screen. Each pixel has a red, a green, and a blue (**RGB**) component. By specifying the amount of intensity for each of these components, a distinct color is given to that pixel. (A good way to remember this if you create Web **page** is to think of the way the background, text, or link colors are specified in the BODY tag as a string of eight **binary** digits, where each two-digit sequence (of eight bits, or a byte) represents one of the RGB components.)

For Web presentation, you (or the artist you're working with) will usually want to choose from a palette that is limited to the 256 colors that most computer users can display. Users with very high-quality display monitors and adapters that provides a 24-bit variation for each pixel can view up to 16,777,216 different colors. However, most of us have computers that can only handle an 8-bit variation, limiting us to a (still pretty graphic) 256 color-palette.

If you do use a larger range of colors or pallette than someone's display or browser can handle, the browser will **dithering** the colors (that is, the browser will find colors within its palette that it can substitute for any color that is outside its palette).

As a designer, you will also want to consider that Mac and Windows browsers do not have identical palettes. In the usual 256 color palette, 216 are common to both types of browsers, but 40 are different and require dithering by one of the browsers.

Palm

Palm is the trade name for a popular personal digital assistant (**PDA**), a form of handheld device that that is also known as a palmtop computer. Originally the Palm, which is used mainly for personal organization, wireless e-mail, note-taking, and electronic games, was called the **PalmPilot**. It was introduced in 1996 by Palm Computing, Inc.

The Palm is about the same size as a stenographer's tablet. Data appears on an **liquid crystal display** screen. One of the outstanding features of the Palm is its user-friendly method of data entry. The device uses an **optical character recognition** (OCR) scheme capable of converting handwriting into digital bits that the microprocessor can understand. A writing device, called a **stylus**, can be pointed at icons on the display to select items for entry. The stylus can also be used to enter alphanumeric data (words and numbers) by manually scrawling them across the face of the display. This is known as **Graffiti**.

The Palm can not only be used to originate, store, and process data on its own, but it can download data from a desktop or notebook computer or from the Internet, process it, and then upload the new data back.

Although the Palm is more convenient for some tasks than others, the pace and nature of technological evolution is likely to change and expand its role in the near future. The Palm is ideally suited for downloading data, storing it, and displaying it as electronic books and magazines. In the long term, the potential of the PDA is limited only by consumer demand, and by the skill and ingenuity of hardware and software engineers.

Palm OS

Palm OS is the computer **operating system** that provides a software platform for the PalmPilot series of **handheld** personal digital assistants made by Palm, Inc. Microsoft's **Windows CE** and Symbian's **EPOC** (originated by Psion) are also operating systems for handheld devices, but are designed to serve a broader range of devices.

Palm OS uses **multitasking**, but only one task is for applications. The user uses one application at a time, one application program must finish before the next can be selected. This constraint allows the operating system to devote full attention to the application that is open. The

space needed by the system for any application that is running is kept in dynamic, reusable random access memory (**RAM**). The application and its related database are kept in what is called permanent storage, but here the permanent storage is RAM (rather than a hard disk) that cannot be reused as the dynamic RAM can. Palm OS divides an application into runnable code and different types of data elements, such as user interface elements and icons. The data elements can be easily changed without necessarily having to rewrite code.

Palm chose not to include a keyboard in the PalmPilot in order to produce a truly palm-size device. Learning from Apple's Newton, an earlier attempt at a pen-and-notepad interface, the company also chose not to provide full handwriting recognition code. Instead, PalmPilot users learn to use a more quickly recognized but restrictive set of pen strokes. These decisions helped keep Palm OS small in size. Palm OS comes with these applications built-in: Dates, Address Book, To Do List, Memo Pad, Calculator, and Password Protection. New applications can be written and added using several facilities that accelerate development.

Palm supports Metrowerks' CodeWarrior as the official software development kit (SDK), using a **Macintosh** or Windows environment. **UNIX** platform users can use a kit called GCC, which is available through the Free Software Foundation. Programmers can use **C**, **C++**, **assembler**, or scripting. The PalmPilot user interface is emulated within a window in the desktop environment, encouraging rapid application development. Simpler applications can be developed using Palm Computing's *forms* interface.

Palm OS comes with communication interfaces to **infrared transmission** devices, **TCP/IP** (for Web connection through wireless or wireline devices), and, optionally, barcode recognition scanners.

PAN

See "personal area network"

panel

In computer program development, a panel is a representation of what information will be sent to a user's **display screen** in given circumstances. Typically, when designing a program, the user interface is specified by portraying what information (text and pictures) will be presented to the user at different stages of using the program. For example, each menu, help page, or other form of content constitutes a panel of information that is to be implemented by developers and tested by early users. Since most applications are developed against the context of an **operating system** graphical user interface (**GUI**), these elements can sometimes be assumed in describing specific panels. Generally, in a windowed user interface, a panel is designed for each **window** of information.

paradigm

A paradigm (pronounced PEHR-uh-daim, from Greek *paradeiknyai*—to show side by side) is a pattern or an example of something. The word also connotes the ideas of a mental picture and pattern of thought. Thomas Kuhn uses the word to mean the model that scientists hold about a particular area of knowledge. Kuhn's famous book, *The Structure of Scientific Revolutions*, is his view of the stages through which a science goes in getting from one paradigm to the next.

paradox

A paradox is a statement or concept that contains conflicting ideas. In logic, a paradox is a statement that contradicts itself; for example, the statement "I never tell the truth" is a paradox because if the statement is true (T), it must be false (F) and if it is false (F), it must be true (T). In everyday language, a paradox is a concept that seems absurd or contradictory, yet is true. In a Windows environment, for instance, it is a paradox that when a user wants to shut down their computer, it is necessary to click "Start."

parallel

In the context of the Internet and computing, parallel means more than one event happening at a time. It is usually contrasted with *serial*, meaning only one event happening at a time. In data transmission, the techniques of time division and space division are used, where time separates the transmission of individual bits of information sent serially and space (in multiple lines or paths) can be used to have multiple bits sent in parallel.

In the context of computer hardware and data transmission, serial connection, operation, and media usually indicate a simpler, slower operation (think of your serial mouse attachment). Parallel connection and operation (think of multiple characters being sent to your printer) indicates faster operation. This indication doesn't always hold since a serial medium (for example, fiber optic cable) can be much faster than a slower medium that carries multiple signals in parallel.

A conventional phone connection is generally thought of as a serial line since its usual transmission protocol is serial.

Conventional computers and their programs operate in a serial manner, with the computer reading a program and performing its instructions one after the other. However, some of today's computers have multiple processors that divide up the instructions and perform them in parallel.

parallel presence detect

Parallel presence detect (PPD) is a method of using **resistor**s to communicate a **memory module**'s speed and density to the basic input/output system (**BIOS**) when a computer **boots** (starts or restarts). The BIOS uses this information to configure the memory modules to run correctly or to detect if an incorrect memory module has been installed. Today, serial presence detect (**SPD**) is used on newer memory modules because SPD can store up to 400 times more information than PPD. PPD is used with 30- and 72-**pin SIMM**s.

PPD indicates the memory module's specifications using parallel pins on the module that transmit a **binary** code. If a pin has a resistor connected to it, it's a logical zero. If a pin does not have a resistor connected to it, it's a logical one. The combination of resistors connected and not connected make up the binary code that the BIOS uses.

parallel processing

In computers, parallel processing is the processing of **program** instructions by dividing them among multiple **processor**s with the objective of running a program in less time. In the earliest computers, only one program ran at a time. A computation-intensive program that took one hour to run and a tape copying program that took one hour to run would take a total of two hours to run. An early form of parallel processing allowed the interleaved execution of both programs together. The computer would start an I/O operation, and while it was waiting for the operation to complete, it would execute the processor-intensive program. The total execution time for the two jobs would be a little over one hour.

The next improvement was **multiprogramming**. In a multiprogramming system, multiple programs submitted by users were each allowed to use the processor for a short time. Then the operating system would allow the next program to use the processor for a short time, and so on. To users it appeared that all of the programs were executing at the same time. Problems of resource contention first arose in these systems. Explicit requests for resources led to the problem of **deadlock**. Competition for resources on machines with no tie-breaking instructions lead to **critical section routine**.

Vector processing was another attempt to increase performance by doing more than one thing at a time. In this case, capabilities were added to machines to allow a single instruction to add (or subtract, or multiply, or ...) two arrays of numbers. This was valuable in certain engineering applications where data naturally occurred in the form of vectors or matrices. In applications with less well-formed data, vector processing was not so valuable.

The next step in parallel processing was the introduction of **multiprocessing**. In these systems, two or more processors shared the work to be done. The earliest versions had a master/slave configuration. One processor (the master) was programmed to be responsible for all of the work in the system; the other (the slave) performed only those tasks it was assigned by the master. This arrangement was necessary because it was not then understood how to program the machines so they could cooperate in managing the resources of the system.

Solving these problems led to symmetric multiprocessing systems (**SMP**). In an SMP system, each processor is equally capable and responsible for managing the flow of work through the system. Initially, the goal was to make SMP systems appear to programmers to be exactly the same as single processor, multiprogramming systems. (This standard of behavior is known as **sequential consistency**). However, engineers found that system performance could be increased by someplace in the range of 10-20% by executing some instructions out of order and requiring programmers to deal with the increased complexity. (The problem can become visible only when two or more programs simultaneously read and write the same operands; thus the burden of dealing with the increased complexity falls on only a very few programmers and then only in very specialized circumstances.) The question of how SMP machines should behave on shared data is not yet resolved.

As the number of processors in SMP systems increases, the time it takes for data to propagate from one part of the system to all other parts grows also. When the number of processors is somewhere in the range of several dozen, the performance benefit of adding more processors to the system is too small to justify the additional expense. To get around the problem of long propagation times, message passing systems were created. In these systems, programs that share data send messages to each other to announce that particular operands have been assigned a new value. Instead of a broadcast of an operand's new value to all parts of a system, the new value is communicated only to those programs which need to know the new value. Instead of a shared memory, there is a network to support the transfer of messages between programs. This simplification allows hundreds, even thousands, of processors to work together efficiently in one system. (In the vernacular of systems architecture, these systems "**scale** well.") Hence such systems have been given the name of massively parallel processing (**MPP**) systems.

The most successful MPP applications have been for problems that can be broken down into many separate, independent operations on vast quantities of data. In **data mining**, there is a need to perform multiple searches of a static database. In **artificial intelligence**, there is the need to analyze multiple alternatives, as in a chess game. Often MPP systems are structured as clusters of processors. Within each cluster the processors interact as in a SMP system. It is only between the clusters that messages are passed. Because operands may be addressed either via messages or via memory addresses, some MPP systems are called **NUMA** machines, for Non-Uniform Memory Addressing.

SMP machines are relatively simple to program; MPP machines are not. SMP machines do well on all types of problems, providing the amount of data involved is not too large. For certain problems, such as data mining of vast data bases, only MPP systems will serve.

parallel processing software

Parallel processing software manages the execution of a program on **parallel processing hardware** with the objectives of obtaining unlimited **scalability** (being able to handle an increasing number of interactions at the same time) and reducing execution time. Applications that benefit from parallel processing divide roughly into business data processing and technical/scientific processing.

Business data processing applications are characterized by **record** processing, and the size of the data typically creates significant I/O performance issues as well as the need for fast computation. Parallel processing software assists business applications in two significant ways:

1) **Frameworks**—Dataflow frameworks provide the highest performance and simplest method for expressing record-processing applications so that they are able to achieve high scalability and total throughput. Dataflow frameworks underlie the internals of most relational database management systems (**RDBMS**s) as well as being available for direct use in construction of **data warehouse**, **business intelligence**, and **analytic CRM** (customer relationship management) applications. Frameworks hide most or all the details of inter-process and inter-processor communications from application developers, making it simpler to create these applications than it would be using low-level message passing.

2) **RDBMS**—As the most common repositories for commercial record-oriented data, RDBMS systems have evolved so that the Structured Query Language (**SQL**) that is used to access them is executed in parallel. The nature of the SQL language lends itself to faster processing using parallel techniques.

Technical and scientific applications tend to be "compute-bound" (they require much processor computation) and have tended to be associated with the **supercomputer**. There are two primary techniques used in the creation of most of these applications—**message passing** and **parallelizing compiler**s.

Message Passing—Application programs can be built using mechanisms for communication between one processor operating concurrently with others. This is the lowest-level mechanism available and can lead to the highest possible performance at the greatest implementation cost and complexity. (Note that message passing for parallel computation should not be confused with the term **messaging** which is also used to describe transactional communication systems for distributed client-to-server and inter-server business applications.)

Parallelizing Compilers—For technical and mathematical applications dominated by **matrix algebra**, there are **compilers** that can create parallel execution from seemingly sequential program source code. These compilers can decompose a program and insert the necessary message passing structures and other parallel constructs automatically.

parallel sysplex

See "sysplex and Parallel Sysplex"

parameter

In information technology, a parameter (pronounced puh-RAA-meh-tuhr, from Greek for, roughly, *through measure*) is an item of information—such as a name, a number, or a selected option—that is passed to a program by a user or another program. Parameters affect the operation of the program receiving them.

para-site

A para-site is a **Web site** that frames other Web sites or **pages** within its own site. For example, a Web site whose purpose was simply to act as a starting place for all sites about gardening-related home pages might have a framed site with a menu in the left frame. You would select a specific gardening Web site by clicking on the menu and that site would then appear in the right frame. This controversial practice has both proponents and detractors. For Web users who just want to survey all possible gardening site offerings fairly quickly, the para-site approach may be appreciated. The owner of the para-site may get more page views because users leave the site less frequently. On the other hand, it can be argued that the sites that are framed by the para-site are being "republished" within someone else's "publication." Furthermore, the framed sites are designed for full screen viewing, not for framing within a smaller space by someone else. If the framed site is itself framed (for example, as whatis.com is!), the result may be not only less than pleasing to the eye but confusing to the user.

Some observers believe that, assuming there is a valid reason to build a para-site, the para-site builder should first request and receive permission from any site it plans to frame.

parity

In computers, parity (from the Latin *paritas*: equal or equivalent) refers to a technique of checking whether data has been lost or written over when it's moved from one place in storage to another or when transmitted between computers.

Here's how it works: An additional **bit**, the *parity bit*, is added to a group of bits that are moved together. This bit is used only for the purpose of identifying whether the bits being moved arrived successfully. Before the bits are sent,

they are counted and if the total number of data bits is even, the parity bit is set to one so that the total number of bits transmitted will form an odd number. If the total number of data bits is already an odd number, the parity bit remains or is set to 0. At the receiving end, each group of incoming bits is checked to see if the group totals to an odd number. If the total is even, a transmission error has occurred and either the transmission is retried or the system halts and an error message is sent to the user.

The description above describes how parity checking works within a computer. Specifically, the **Peripheral Component Interconnect bus** and the I/O bus controller use the odd parity method of error checking. Parity bit checking is not an infallible error-checking method since it's possible that two bits could be in error in a transmission, offsetting each other. For transmissions within a personal computer, this possibility is considered extremely remote. In some large computer systems where data integrity is seen as extremely important, three bits are allocated for parity checking.

Parity checking is also used in communication between **modem**s. Here, parity checking can be selected to be even (a successful transmission will form an even number) or odd. Users may also select *no parity*, meaning that the modems will not transmit or check a parity bit. When no parity is selected (or defaulted), it's assumed that there are other forms of checking that will detect any errors in transmission. No parity also usually means that the parity bit can be used for data, speeding up transmission. In modem-to-modem communication, the type of parity is coordinated by the sending and receiving modems before the transmission takes place.

parse

To parse is to analyze something in an orderly way. In linguistics, to parse is to divide words and phrases into different parts in order to understand relationships and meaning. For example, English students are sometimes asked to parse a sentence by dividing it into subject and predicate, and then into dependent phrases, modifiers, and so forth.

In general, to parse someone's writing or speech simply means to interpret it.

In computers, to parse is to divide a computer language statement into parts that can be made useful for the computer. A **parser** in a program compiler is a program that takes each program statement that a developer has written and divides it into parts (for example, the main command, options, target objects, their attributes, and so forth) that can then be used for developing further actions or for creating the instructions that form an executable program.

parser

In computer technology, a parser is a program, usually part of a **compiler**, that receives input in the form of sequential source program instructions, interactive online commands, markup tags, or some other defined interface and breaks them up into parts (for example, the nouns (objects), verbs (methods), and their attributes or options) that can then be managed by other programming (for example, other components in a compiler). A parser may also check to see that all input has been provided that is necessary.

partition

In personal computers, a partition is a logical division of a **hard disk** created so that you can have different **operating system**s on the same hard disk or to create the appearance of having separate hard drives for file management, multiple users, or other purposes. A partition is created when you *format* the hard disk. Typically, a one-partition hard disk is labelled the "C:" drive ("A:" and "B:" are typically reserved for diskette drives). A two-partition hard drive would typically contain "C:" and "D:" drives. (**CD-ROM** drives typically are assigned the last letter in whatever sequence of letters have been used as a result of hard disk formatting, or typically with a two-partition, the "E:" drive.)

When you **boot** an operating system into your computer, a critical part of the process is to give control to the first **sector** on your hard disk. It includes a partition table that defines how many partitions the hard disk is formatted into, the size of each, and the address where each partition begins. This sector also contains a program that reads in the boot sector for the operating system and gives it control so that the rest of the operating system can be loaded into **random access memory**.

Boot **virus**es can put the wrong information in the partition sector so that your operating system can't be located. For this reason, you should have a back-up version of your partition sector on a diskette known as a **bootable floppy**.

partner relationship management

Partner relationship management (PRM) is a business strategy for improving communication between companies and their **channel** partners. Web-based PRM software applications enable companies to customize and streamline administrative tasks by making shipping schedules and other real-time information available to all the partners over the Internet. Several CRM providers have incorporated PRM features, such as Web-enabled **spreadsheet**s shared through an **extranet**, in their software applications. PRM is often compared to customer relationship management (**CRM**) and there is some argument over whether the complex relationships of channel partnerships makes it necessary for PRM to be a separate entity, or merely a component of CRM.

pascal (unit of pressure or stress)

The pascal (pronounced pass-KAL and abbreviated Pa) is the International System of Units (**SI**) unit of pressure or stress. It is named after the scientist Blaise Pascal. One pascal is equivalent to one **newton** (1 N) of force applied over an area of one **meter squared** (1 m^2). That is, 1 Pa = 1 N $^{\circ}$ m^{-2}. Reduced to base units in SI, one pascal is one kilogram per meter per second squared; that is, 1 Pa = 1 kg$^{\circ}$ m$^{-1^{\circ}}$ s^{-2}.

If a pressure p in pascals exists on an object or region whose surface area is A meters squared, then the force F, in newtons, required to produce p is given by the following formula:

$$F = pA$$

Suppose a small rocket engine produces 100,000 (10^5) Pa of pressure, and the nozzle has a cross-sectional area of $^1/_{10,000}$ of a square meter (10^{-4} m^2). Then the force F, in newtons, produced by the engine is:

$$F = pA = 10^5 \times 10^{-4} = 10$$

Imagine that this engine is used in a propellant pack for a space walker whose mass is 50 kg. How fast will the person accelerate relative to nearby objects in the weightless environment of earth orbit? The answer is found by the familiar formula stating that force is equal to mass times acceleration ($F = ma$). This can be manipulated to obtain:

$$a = F / m$$

where a is the acceleration in meters per second squared, F is the force in newtons, and m is the mass in kilograms. Plugging in the known numbers:

$$a = 10 / 50 = 0.5$$

The acceleration is 0.5 m/s^2. If the rocket engine is fired continuously by a space walker who is stationary relative to another object nearby, then after one second the space walker will be moving at a speed of 0.5 m/s with respect to that object; after two seconds, moving at 1 m/s; after three seconds, moving at 1.5 m/s; and so on. Obviously, the space walker will want to fire the engine only in short bursts!

Also see **kilogram**, **meter**, **meter per second**, **meter per second squared**, **newton**, **second**, and **SI**.

Pascal

Also see **pascal (unit of pressure or stress)**.

Pascal is a **strongly-typed** third-generation language (**3GL**) with a one-pass **compiler**. Designed for instructional purposes about 1967-68 by Nicholas Wirth, Pascal requires a programmer to define all routines and variables fully, including the nature of their use, before using them. Pascal is the language on which many programmers first learn how to write structured, compiled programs. While commercial versions of Pascal have been made available, it has had limited success in the business world. While Pascal has been extended by compiler makers to address special-purpose needs, many programmers feel that it is too restrictive in its

rules and doesn't allow a programmer to create and state new rules (for example, new **data type**s) to the compiler. While still used as an instructional language and by hobbyists, most serious programmers today are using **C**, **C++**, and **Java**.

passive FTP

Passive FTP (sometimes referred to as *PASV FTP* because it involves the FTP PASV command) is a more secure form of data transfer in which the flow of data is set up and initiated by the File Transfer Program (**FTP**) **client** rather than by the FTP **server** program. Separate FTP client programs, such as WS_FTP Pro, usually allow the user to select passive FTP. Most Web browsers (which act as FTP clients) use passive FTP by default because corporations prefer it as a safety measure. As a general rule, any corporate **firewall** server, which exists in order to protect an internal network from the outside world, recognizes input from the outside only in response to user requests that were sent out requesting the input. The use of passive FTP ensures all data flow initiation comes from inside the network rather than from the outside.

How It Works

Using normal or passive FTP, a client begins a session by sending a request to communicate through **TCP** port 21, the port that is conventionally assigned for this use at the FTP server. This communication is known as the Control Channel connection.

Using "normal" FTP communication, the client requestor also includes in the same PORT command packet on the Control Channel a second port number that is to be used when data is to be exchanged; the port-to-port exchange for data is known as the Data Channel. The FTP server then initiates the exchange from its own port 20 to whatever port was designated by the client. However, because the server-initiated communication is no longer controlled by the client and can't be correlated by a firewall to the initial request, the potential exists for uninvited data to arrive from anywhere posing as a normal FTP transfer.

Using passive FTP, a PASV command is sent instead of a PORT command. Instead of specifying a port that the server can send to, the PASV command asks the server to specify a port it wishes to use for the Data Channel connection. The server replies on the Control Channel with the port number which the client then uses to initiate an exchange on the Data Channel. The server will thus always be responding to client-initiated requests on the Data Channel and the firewall can correlate these.

passive optical network

A passive optical network (PON) is a system that brings **optical fiber** cabling and signals all or most of the way to the end user. Depending on where the PON terminates, the system can be described as fiber-to-the-curb (**FTTC**), fiber-

to-the-building (FTTB), or fiber-to-the-home (FTTH). A PON consists of an Optical Line Termination (OLT) at the communication company's office and a number of Optical Network Units (ONUs) near end users. Typically, up to 32 ONUs can be connected to an OLT. The *passive* simply describes the fact that optical transmission has no power requirements or active electronic parts once the signal is going through the network.

In a stand-alone system, a PON could deliver up to 622 **Mbps** downstream to the user and up to 155 Mbps upstream. Multiple users of a PON could be allocated portions of this **bandwidth**. A PON could also serve as a **trunk** between a larger system, such as a **CATV** system, and a neighborhood, building, or home Ethernet network on coaxial cable.

In Japan, Nippon Telephone and Telegraph (NTT) is planning to install passive optical networks throughout its system, using equipment made by Lucent Technologies.

passphrase

A passphrase is a string of **characters** longer than the usual **password** (which is typically from four to 16 characters long) that is used in creating a **digital signature** (an encoded signature that proves to someone that it was really you who sent a message) or in an **encryption** or a decryption of a message. For example, Phil Zimmermann's popular encryption program, **Pretty Good Privacy**, requires a passphrase when you sign or decrypt a message. Passphrases are often up to 100 characters in length.

password

A password is an unspaced sequence of **character**s used to determine that a computer user requesting access to a computer system is really that particular user. Typically, users of a multiuser or securely protected single-user system claim a unique name (often called a *user ID*) that can be generally known. In order to verify that someone entering that user ID really is that person, a second identification, the password, known only to that person and to the system itself, is entered by the user. A password is typically somewhere between four and 16 characters, depending on how the computer system is set up. When a password is entered, the computer system is careful not to display the characters on the display screen, in case others might see it.

Good criteria when choosing a password or setting up password guidelines include the following:

- Don't pick a password that someone can easily guess if they know who you are (for example, not your Social Security number, birthday, or maiden name)

- Don't pick a word that can be found in the dictionary (since there are programs that can rapidly try every word in the dictionary!)

- Don't pick a word that is currently newsworthy

- Don't pick a password that is similar to your previous password
- Do pick a mixture of letters and at least one number
- Do pick a word that you can easily remember

Many networks require that you change your password on some periodic basis.

password cracker

A password cracker is an application program that is used to identify an unknown or forgotten **password** to a computer or network resources. It can also be used to help a human **cracker** obtain unauthorized access to resources.

Password crackers use two primary methods to identify correct passwords: brute-force and dictionary searches. When a password cracker uses brute-force, it runs through combinations of characters within a predetermined length until it finds the combination accepted by the computer system. When conducting a dictionary search, a password cracker searches each word in the dictionary for the correct password. Password dictionaries exist for a variety of topics and combinations of topics, including politics, movies, and music groups.

Some password cracker programs search for hybrids of dictionary entries and numbers. For example, a password cracker may search for ants01; ants02; ants03, etc. This can be helpful where users have been advised to include a number in their password.

A password cracker may also be able to identify encrypted passwords. After retrieving the password from the computer's memory, the program may be able to decrypt it. Or, by using the same **algorithm** as the system program, the password cracker creates an encrypted version of the password that matches the original.

PASV FTP

See "passive FTP"

patch

A patch (sometimes called a "fix") is a quick-repair job for a piece of **program**ming. During a software product's **beta test** distribution or try-out period and later after the product is formally released, problems (called **bug**) will almost invariably be found. A patch is the immediate solution that is provided to users; it can sometimes be downloaded from the software maker's Web site. The patch is not necessarily the best solution for the problem and the product developers often find a better solution to provide when they package the product for its next release.

A patch is usually developed and distributed as a replacement for or an insertion in compiled code (that is, in a *binary file* or object module). In larger operating systems, a special program is provided to manage and keep track of the installation of patches.

patch panel

A patch panel is a mounted hardware unit containing an assembly of **port** locations in a communications or other electronic or electrical system. In a network, a patch panel serves as a sort of static switchboard, using cables to interconnect computers within the area of a local area network (**LAN**) and to the outside for connection to the Internet or other wide area network (**WAN**). A patch panel uses a sort of jumper cable called a *patch cord* to create each interconnection.

path

1) In a computer **operating system**, a path is the route through a **file system** to a particular **file**. A pathname (or *path name*) is the specification of that path. Each operating system has its own format for specifying a pathname.

In all operating systems, an *absolute pathname* (or fully qualified path name) specifies the complete path name. A *relative pathname* specifies a path relative to the directory to which the operating system is currently set.

The World Wide Web's HTTP program uses a pathname as part of a Uniform Resource Locator (**URL**).

2) In a network, a path is a route between any two points or **nodes**.

3) In a number of products or applications, a path is a route to or between points within a given organized structure.

4) In IBM's Virtual Telecommunication Access Method (VTAM), a path identifies a particular **dial-out** port.

path control

See "pathing"

path to profitability

Path to profitability (sometimes abbreviated as P2P, which also stands for **peer-to-peer**) is a term that refers to a business plan that is designed to take an enterprise from startup to turning a profit. In Internet business, the prevalent emphasis on profitability, especially in the **e-business** world, is in contrast to the attitude prevalent in recent years, when **dotcom** ventures were often encouraged to open for business, "burn" enough **venture capital** to dominate a particular business niche, and worry about profits later. Industry and stock market analysts suggest that the popularity of this term indicates a return to traditional business practices and a new, more mature stage in the evolution of the Internet.

Before the market slump of the spring of 2000, almost any entrepreneur with a concept and a PowerPoint presentation could obtain venture capital funding for a dotcom enterprise. Optimism about the future of e-business led to a suspension of traditional business principles and practices: an entrepreneur was not necessarily required to demonstrate a clear business plan—with profits in the foreseeable future—because the ultimate payoff was expected to be so large.

With the slowdown in technology stocks, there has been a return to standard business practices. Investors are much more cautious than they were in the early days of the dotcom boom. In order to obtain funding, entrepreneurs are expected to have a well-organized business plan with a clearly articulated—and hopefully short—path to profitability. Some analysts believe that the market change was, in a literal sense, a correction, since the practices employed did not lead to sustainable growth. Many are still optimistic about the future of e-business, although that must be in a world in which the old business rules—such an enterprise's need for a path to profitability—still apply.

pathing

Pathing (sometimes called *path control*) is a networking approach used to address the specific needs of storage networks (as compared to ordinary message networks) by changing the way that communication paths are managed and organized. Connection failures in message networks generally just mean that the connection must be retried; in storage networks, however, a failure is more likely to cause a system **crash**. Also, the margin for error is smaller for storage networks; whereas error recovery within minutes is acceptable for message networks, for storage networks it should be within seconds—and preferably milliseconds. Because of these differences, storage network **routing** must include redundant, well-defined paths, enable fast path changes, and have the altered **topology** information updated rapidly.

According to Marc Farley, author of *Building Storage Networks*, node routing provides more precise connection control than is afforded by **switch**es and routers. Message networks typically have a very large number of **node**s, any of which may have to connect to any other and connection requests are randomly designated. As a consequence, it is considered that routing activities would overload end nodes. In comparison, storage networks have fewer nodes and fewer connections, and connection requests are specifically assigned. In these conditions, it is possible for nodes to manage paths.

Pathing is among the most promising technologies behind the expansion of the storage market—which is projected by Adam Couture, senior analyst at Gartner Dataquest, to grow to $7 billion by 2003, up from $10 million in 1999. Storage area networks (**SAN**s) and network attached storage (**NAS**) have arisen as solutions to the rapidly increasing need for

storage of enterprise data. Originally, enterprise computers and storage devices had one-to-one relationships, not a practical arrangement for multi-user environments with complex data-sharing needs. SANs allow multiple computers to share a single storage device, with technologies like path control, mirroring, and **virtualization** used to meet the enterprise's needs for reliability and constant data availability.

pattern

In software development, a pattern (or *design pattern*) is a written document that describes a general solution to a design problem that recurs repeatedly in many projects. Software designers adapt the pattern solution to their specific project. Patterns use a formal approach to describing a design problem, its proposed solution, and any other factors that might affect the problem or the solution. A successful pattern should have established itself as leading to a good solution in three previous projects or situations.

In **object-oriented programming**, a pattern can contain the description of certain objects and object **class**es to be used, along with their attributes and dependencies, and the general approach to how to solve the problem. Often, programmers can use more than one pattern to address a specific problem. A collection of patterns is called a *pattern framework*.

The design patterns methodology has become increasingly popular among software developers since the early 1990s, due largely to some ground-breaking presentations and books on the subject released to the object-oriented world at trade shows and conventions, notably OOPSLA '94 (the Object-Oriented Programming Systems, Languages, and Applications conference). A book, "Design Patterns: Elements of Reusable Object-Oriented Software," by E. Gamma, R. Helm, R. Johnson, and J. Vlissides (known in the industry as the Gang of Four, or GOF) is generally credited with sparking the growing interest in design patterns for use in object-oriented programming. The book contains twenty-three patterns, each with a solution for a recurring problem faced in object-oriented design.

Design patterns include the following types of information:

- Name that describes the pattern
- Problem to be solved by the pattern
- Context, or settings, in which the problem occurs
- Forces that could influence the problem or its solution
- Solution proposed to the problem
- Context for the solution
- Rationale behind the solution (examples and stories of past successes or failures often go here)
- Known uses and related patterns
- Author and date information

- References and keywords used or searching
- Sample code related to the solution, if it helps

The usage of patterns also goes beyond the area of software design and development, and can be applied to any field where solutions have been derived from the experience of several projects or events.

payload

On the Internet, a payload is either:

1) The essential data that is being carried within a **packet** or other transmission unit. The payload does not include the "overhead" data required to get the packet to its destination. Note that what constitutes the payload may depend on the point-of-view. To a communications layer that needs some of the overhead data to do its job, the payload is sometimes considered to include the part of the overhead data that this layer handles. However, in more general usage, the payload is the bits that get delivered to the end user at the destination.

2) The eventual effect of a software **virus** that has been delivered to a user's computer.

pay-per-view

See "micropayment"

PBX

See "private branch exchange"

PC

1) In its more general usage, a PC (personal computer) is a computer designed for use by one person at a time. Prior to the PC, computers were designed for (and only affordable by) companies who attached terminals for multiple users to a single large computer whose resources were shared among all users. Beginning in the late 1980s, technology advances made it feasible to build a small computer that an individual could own and use.

2) The term "PC" is also commonly used to describe an "IBM-compatible" personal computer in contradistinction to an Apple Macintosh computer. The distinction is both technical and cultural. The "IBM-compatible" PC is one with an Intel microprocessor architecture and an operating system such as DOS or Windows that is written to use the Intel microprocessor. The Apple Macintosh uses a Motorola microprocessor architecture and a proprietary operating system. The "IBM-compatible" PC is associated with business (as well as home) use. The "Mac," known for its more intuitive user interface, is associated with graphic design and desktop publishing.

PC Card

A PC Card (previously known as a PCMCIA card) is a credit card-size **memory** or **I/O** device that fits into a personal computer, usually a notebook or laptop computer. Probably the most common example of a PC Card is the 28.8 Kbps **modem** for notebook computers. There are 16-**binary digit** and 32-bit (CardBus) varieties of PC Cards. Another type of PC card is the **ZV port** Card.

The PC Card is based on standards published by the Personal Computer Memory Card International Association (**PCMCIA**), an industry group organized in 1989 to promote standards for both memory and I/O integrated circuit **card**. The PCMCIA 2.1 Standard was published in 1993. As a result, PC users can be assured of standard attachments for any peripheral device that follows the standard.

A PC Card has a 68-pin connector that connects into a slot in the PC. There are three sizes (or "types") of PC Cards:

Type	Thickness (mm)	Typical use
I	3.3	Memory
II	5.0	Modems, LANs. SCSI, sound
III	10.5	ATA hard drive

The Type I and II cards work in a Type III slot and a Type I card will work in a Type II slot. (On the other hand, the thicker cards can't be fitted into the slots for the thinner cards.)

The PCMCIA standard is most commonly applied to portable PCs but it can also be used on desktop computers. The PC Card is not to be confused with another credit-size electronic card, the *smart card*.

PC demo

See "demo and demoscene"

PC100 Synchronous Dynamic Random Access Memory

PC100 SDRAM is synchronous **DRAM (dynamic random access memory)** that states that it meets the PC100 specification from Intel. Intel created the specification to enable RAM manufacturers to make chips that would work with Intel's i440BX processor chipset. The i440BX was designed to achieve a 100 MHz system bus speed. Ideally, PC100 SDRAM would work at the 100 MHz speed, using a 4-1-1-1 access cycle. It's reported that PC100 SDRAM will improve performance by 10-15% in an Intel Socket 7 system (but not in a Pentium II because its L2 cache speed runs at only half of processor speed).

PC-DOS

Also see **DOS**.

PC-DOS (Personal Computer—Disk Operating System) was the first widely-installed **operating system** used in personal computers. It was developed for IBM by Bill Gates and his fledgling Microsoft Corporation for installation in IBM's first lines of PCs. Gates marketed an almost identical version of the operating system called MS-DOS (Microsoft—Disk Operating System). Most users of either DOS system have usually referred to their system as just **DOS**. Like MS-DOS, PC-DOS was (and still is) a non-graphical line-oriented command-driven operating system, with a relatively simple interface but not overly "friendly" user interface. Its prompt to enter a command looks like this:

```
c:>
```

The first Microsoft Windows operating system was really an application that ran on top of the MS-DOS operating system. Today, Windows operating systems continue to support DOS (or a DOS-like user interface) for special purposes by emulating the operating system.

In the 1970s before the personal computer was invented, IBM had a different and unrelated DOS (Disk Operating System) that ran on smaller business computers. It was replaced by IBM's VSE operating system.

PCI

See "Peripheral Component Interconnect"

PCI-X

PCI-X (Peripheral Component Interconnect Extended) is a new computer **bus** technology (the "data pipes" between parts of a computer) that increases the speed that data can move within a computer from 66 **MHz** to 133 MHz. The technology was developed jointly by IBM, HP and Compaq. PCI-X doubles the speed and amount of data exchanged between the computer **processor** and **peripheral**s. With the current PCI design, one 64-bit bus runs at 66 MHz and additional buses move 32 bits at 66 MHz or 64 bits at 33 MHz. The maximum amount of data exchanged between the processor and peripherals using the current PCI design is 532 MB per second. With PCI-X, one 64-bit bus runs at 133 MHz with the rest running at 66 MHz, allowing for a data exchange of 1.06 GB per second. PCI-X is backwards-compatible, meaning that you can, for example, install a PCI-X card in a standard PCI slot but expect a decrease in speed to 33 MHz. You can also use both PCI and PCI-X cards on the same bus but the bus speed will run at the speed of the slowest card. PCI-X is more fault tolerant than PCI. For example, PCI-X is able to reinitialize a faulty card or take it offline before computer failure occurs.

IBM, HP and Compaq designed PCI-X for servers to increase performance for high **bandwidth** devices such as **Gigabit Ethernet** cards, **Fibre Channel**, Ultra3 **Small Computer System Interface**, and processors that are interconnected as a cluster. Compaq, IBM, and HP submitted PCI-X to the PCI Special Interest Group (**Special Interest Group of the Association for Computing Machinery**) in 1998. PCI SIG approved PCI-X, and it is now an open standard that can be adapted and used by all computer developers. PCI SIG controls technical support, training and compliance testing for PCI-X. IBM, Intel, Microelectronics and Mylex plan to develop **chipset**s to support PCI-X. 3Com and Adaptec intend to develop PCI-X peripherals.

To accelerate PCI-X adoption by the industry, Compaq offers PCI-X development tools at their Web site. The site includes a PCI-X Core Source Code, a Reference Design Guide, interface documents, PCI-X Architectural and Partitioning guidelines, and PCI-to PCI-X Enhancement guidelines. Compaq is also working with Synopsis, a leading supplier of electronic design automation solutions, to offer a structured PCI-X test environment.

PCL

See "Printer Control Language"

PCM

See "pulse code modulation"

PCMCIA card

See "PC Card"

PCMCIA

See "Personal Computer Memory Card International Association"

PCS

See "personal communications services"

PDA

See "personal digital assistant"

PDF

See "Portable Document Format"

peak

Also see **peak-to-peak**.

Peak (pk) is the maximum value, either positive (pk+) or negative (pk-), that a waveform attains. Peak values can be expressed for **voltage** (the usual case), **current**, or **power**.

Alternating current (**AC**) waveforms reach peaks in two directions of polarity or current flow. These peaks are usually of equal amplitude and opposite polarity. However, if a direct current (**DC**) component exists, pk+ differs from pk-. An example of an AC wave with a DC component, showing the pk+ and pk- values, is shown below.

For an AC sine wave without a DC component, the peak amplitude is equal to approximately 1.414 times the **root-mean-square** amplitude.

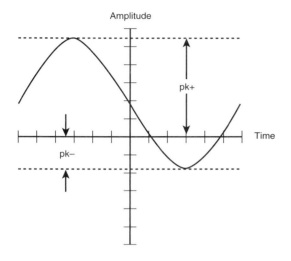

peak-to-peak

Peak-to-peak (pk-pk) is the difference between the maximum positive and the maximum negative amplitudes of a waveform, as shown below. If there is no direct current (**DC**) component in an alternating current (**AC**) wave, then the pk-pk amplitude is twice the **peak** amplitude.

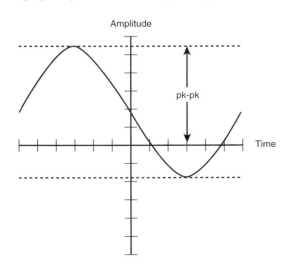

For an AC sine wave with no DC component, the peak-to-peak amplitude is equal to approximately 2.828 times the **root-mean-square** amplitude. Peak-to-peak values can be expressed for **voltage** (the usual case), **current**, or **power**.

peering

Peering is the arrangement of traffic exchange between Internet service providers (ISPs). Larger ISPs with their own **backbone** networks agree to allow traffic from other large ISPs in exchange for traffic on their backbones. They also exchange traffic with smaller ISPs so that they can reach regional end points. Essentially, this is how a number of individual network owners put the Internet together. To do this, network owners and access providers, the ISPs, work out agreements that describe the terms and conditions to which both are subject. Bilateral peering is an agreement between two parties. Multilateral peering is an agreement between more than two parties.

Peering requires the exchange and updating of **router** information between the peered ISPs, typically using the Border Gateway Protocol (**BGP**). Peering parties interconnect at network focal points such as the network access points (**NAP**) in the United States and at regional switching points. Initially, peering arrangements did not include an exchange of money. More recently, however, some larger ISPs have charged smaller ISPs for peering. Each major ISP generally develops a peering policy that states the terms and conditions under which it will peer with other networks for various types of traffic.

Private peering is peering between parties that are bypassing part of the public **backbone** network through which most Internet traffic passes. In a regional area, some ISPs exchange *local peering* arrangements instead of or in addition to peering with a backbone ISP. In some cases, peering charges include **transit** charges, or the actual line access charge to the larger network. Properly speaking, peering is simply the agreement to interconnect and exchange routing information.

peer-to-peer

1) Peer-to-peer is a communications model in which each party has the same capabilities and either party can initiate a communication session. Other models with which it might be contrasted include the **client/server** model and the *master/slave* model. In some cases, peer-to-peer communications is implemented by giving each communication node both server and client capabilities. In recent usage, peer-to-peer has come to describe applications in which users can use the Internet to exchange files with each other directly or through a mediating server.

IBM's Advanced Peer-to-Peer Networking (APPN) is an example of a product that supports the peer-to-peer communication model.

2) On the Internet, peer-to-peer (referred to as P2P) is a type of transient Internet network that allows a group of computer users with the same networking program to connect with each other and directly access files from one another's hard drives. **Napster** and **Gnutella** are examples of this kind of peer-to-peer software. Corporations are looking at the advantages of using P2P as a way for employees to share files without the expense involved in maintaining a centralized server and as a way for businesses to exchange information with each other directly.

How Does Internet P2P Work?

The user must first download and execute a peer-to-peer networking program. (Gnutellanet is currently one of the most popular of these decentralized P2P programs because it allows users to exchange all types of files.) After launching the program, the user enters the **IP address** of another computer belonging to the network. (Typically, the Web page where the user got the download will list several IP addresses as places to begin). Once the computer finds another network member on-line, it will connect to that user's connection (who has gotten their IP address from another user's connection and so on).

Users can choose how many member connections to seek at one time and determine which files they wish to share or password protect. Generally, the P2P network consists of no more than four users at any given time because each additional member slows down the transmission of data over the Internet.

penguin

See "Tux"

Pentium

Also see the Pentium **MMX** and the **Pentium 3**.

The Pentium is a widely-used personal computer **microprocessor** from the Intel Corporation. First offered in 1993, the Pentium quickly replaced Intel's 486 microprocessor as the microchip-of-choice in manufacturing a **personal computer**. The original Pentium model includes two processors on one chip that contains 3.1 million **transistor**s.

The Pentium Pro, released in 1995, was designed for PC servers and **workstation** that needed to serve multiple users or needed the speed required for graphics-intensive applications. In addition to the microprocessor, the Pentium Pro includes another microchip containing **cache memory** that, being closer to the processor than the computer's main memory (**RAM**), speeds up computer operation. The Pentium Pro contains 5.5 million transistors.

The Pentium II is a Pentium Pro with Intel's **MMX** technology included. It comes in microprocessor clock speeds of 233 **MHz** (millions of cycles per second), 266 MHz, and 300 MHz. It's suitable for applications that include

motion video and 3-D images. Among the Pentium II's features are a 512 KB (**kilobyte**) level-two (**L1 and L2**) memory cache and a 32 KB L1 and L2 cache, twice that of the Pentium Pro processor. The L2 cache can include error correcting code (**ECC**).

The latest Pentium II's are **Celeron**, a low-end Pentium without the L2 cache, and **Xeon**, a high-end Pentium that replaces the Pentium Pro for enterprise server and workstation computers.

Pentium 3

The Pentium III is a **microprocessor** designed by Intel as a successor to its **Pentium II**. The Pentium III is faster, especially for applications written to take advantage of its "Katmai New Instructions" (the code name for the Pentium III during development was "Katmai"). The 70 new computer **instruction**s make it possible to run **3-D**, **imaging**, **streaming video**, **speech recognition**, and **audio** applications more quickly. In addition, the Pentium III offers **clock speed**s up to 800 **MHz**.

The Katmai New Instructions are similar to the instructions optimized for multimedia applications called **MMX** and now included in most Pentiums. However, unlike the MMX instruction set, the Katmai instructions support **floating point unit**s as well as integer calculations, a type of calculation often required when still or video images are modified for display. The Katmai instructions also support **Single Instruction Multiple Data** instructions. These allow a single instruction to cause data to be modified in multiple memory locations simultaneously, a kind of **parallel processing**.

For 3-D applications, changing values in parallel for a given 3-D scene means that users can see smoother and more realistic effects. Application developers can create effects that the slower instructions could not support, such as scenes with subtle and complex lighting. Animated effects and streaming video should also be less choppy for the viewer. The new instructions also specifically include some that will make speech recognition faster and more accurate and allow the creation of more complex audio effects.

Pentium 4

Pentium 4 (P4) is the latest Intel **processor** (codenamed *Willamette*), released in November 2000. The P4 processor has a viable **clock speed** of 1.5 gigahertz (**GHz**)—as compared to the 1 GHz of the **Pentium 3**—and reached 2 GHz in August 2001.

P4 has the first totally new **chip architecture** since the 1995 Pentium Pro. The major difference involves structural changes that affect the way processing takes place within the chip, something Intel calls *NetBurst microarchitecture*. Aspects of the changes include: A 20-stage **pipeline**, which boosts performance by increasing processor frequency; a rapid-execution engine, which doubles the core frequency and reduces **latency** by enabling each **instruction** to be executed in a half (rather than a whole) clock cycle; a 400 MHz system **bus**, which enables transfer rates of 3.2 gigabytes per second (GBps); an *execution trace* **cache**, which optimizes cache memory efficiency and reduces latency by storing decoded sequences of micro-operations; and improved **floating point** and multimedia unit and *advanced dynamic execution*, all of which enable faster processing for especially demanding applications, such as digital video, **voice recognition**, and online gaming.

P4's main competition for processor market share is the **AMD Athlon** processor. A number of industry test results (such as those from PC Magazine Labs and Tom's Hardware Guide) have found the P4 was faster than the Athlon for **streaming video**, **3-D** graphics programs, and some similarly demanding applications, but that the Athlon processor—which is significantly less expensive—was faster for the types of tasks that make up the bulk of the typical home or business PC's workload.

Peoplesoft

PeopleSoft is a leading provider of **e-business** application software and claims to be the only software company to provide e-business solutions purely over the Internet for Fortune 1000 corporations. The company was founded in 1987 by Dave Duffield and Ken Morris, whose goal was to build **client/server** applications that empower the user, are easily adaptable in a changing marketplace, and are supported by superior customer service.

PeopleSoft originally offered human resources and finance applications. Over the years, it has developed tools and applications for general business processes such as materials management and e-business in addition to applications for specific industries, such as the automotive, communications, and higher-education fields.

In 1999, the company shifted its focus to the Internet. In 2000, the company launched PeopleSoft8, the first pure Internet software, as well as PeopleSoft e-center, its in-house application service provider (ASP). Its Web-based applications are intended to integrate systems easily so that a company can connect customers, employees, and suppliers more cost-effectively. An organization can streamline operations due to the fact that the information is readily accessible by a wide-variety of people anytime, anywhere, which includes mobile equipment such as personal digital assistants (**PDA**s) and mobile phones.

Based in Pleasanton, California, PeopleSoft in 2001 employed more than 7,000 people worldwide and had over 4,000 customers. PeopleSoft (PSFT) is publicly traded on the NASDAQ.

performance

Performance seems to have two meanings:

1) The speed at which a computer operates, either theoretically (for example, using a formula for calculating *Mtops*—millions of theoretical instructions per second) or by counting operations or instructions performed (for example, (**MIPS**)—millions of instructions per second) during a **benchmark** test. The benchmark test usually involves some combination of work that attempts to imitate the kinds of work the computer does during actual use. Sometimes performance is expressed for each of several different benchmarks.

2) The total effectiveness of a computer system, including **throughput**, individual **response time**, and availability.

perigee

When a satellite follows a non-circular orbit around the earth, the satellite's path is an ellipse with the center of the earth at one focus. Such a satellite has variable altitude and variable orbital speed. The point of lowest altitude is called perigee. The term also applies to the minimum distance in kilometers or miles between the satellite and the center of the earth. (Perigee can be measured between the satellite and the earth's surface, although this is a less precise specification because the earth is not a perfect sphere. The difference is approximately 4,000 miles or 6,400 kilometers.)

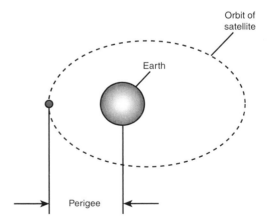

At perigee, a satellite travels faster than at any other point in its orbit. When viewed from the earth's surface, a satellite at or near perigee traverses the sky at a rapid pace. In communications, perigee is the least desirable time to access a satellite. Although its proximity means that the signal path is short, the fact that the satellite is rapidly moving means that it is accessible for only a brief time. In addition, if a directional antenna is used at a ground-based station, it is

difficult to track the satellite because the position of the antenna (azimuth and elevation) must be constantly and rapidly adjusted.

One of the principal advantages of a geostationary satellite is the fact that it follows a circular orbit, so the orbital speed is constant. In addition, the satellite's synchronization with the earth's orbit means that the antenna of an earth-based station can be pointed at a fixed spot in the sky, and no further adjustment of antenna orientation is needed.

Compare **apogee**.

peripheral

A peripheral (pronounced peh-RIHF-uh-ruhl, a noun truncation of *peripheral device*) is any computer **device** that is not part of the essential **computer** (the processor, memory, and data paths) but is situated relatively close by. A near synonym is input/output (**I/O**) device. Some peripherals are mounted in the same case with the main part of the computer as are the **hard disk drive**, **CD-ROM** drive, and **NIC**. Other peripherals are outside the computer case, such as the printer and image **scanner**, attached by a wired or **wireless** connection.

Peripheral Component Interconnect Extended

See "PCI-X"

Peripheral Component Interconnect

PCI is an interconnection system between a **microprocessor** and attached devices in which expansion **slot** are spaced closely for high speed operation. Using PCI, a computer can support both new PCI cards while continuing to support Industry Standard Architecture (**ISA**) expansion cards, currently the most common kind of expansion card. Designed by Intel, the original PCI was similar to the **VESA Local Bus**. However, PCI 2.0 is no longer a local bus and is designed to be independent of microprocessor design. PCI is designed to be synchronized with the clock speed of the microprocessor, in the range of 20 to 33 **MHz**.

PCI is now installed on most new desktop computers, not only those based on Intel's Pentium processor but also those based on the PowerPC. PCI transmits 32 bits at a time in a 124-pin connection (the extra pins are for power supply and grounding) and 64 bits in a 188-pin connection in an expanded implementation. PCI uses all active paths to transmit both address and data signals, sending the address on one clock cycle and data on the next. **Burst** data can be sent starting with an address on the first cycle and a sequence of data transmissions on a certain number of successive cycles.

Also see Extended Industry Standard Architecture (**EISA**) and Micro Channel Architecture (**MCA**).

Perl

Perl (Practical Extraction and Reporting Language) is a **script** programming language that is similar in **syntax** to the C language and that includes a number of popular **UNIX** facilities such as **sed**, **awk**, and **tr**. Perl is an **interpreted** language that can optionally be **compiled** just before execution into either C code or cross-platform **bytecode**. When compiled, a Perl program is almost (but not quite) as fast as a fully precompiled C language program. Perl is regarded as a good choice for developing common gateway interface (**CGI**) programs because it has good text manipulation facilities (although it also handles binary files). It was invented by Larry Wall.

In general, Perl is easier to learn and faster to code in than the more structured **C** and **C++** languages. Perl programs can, however, be quite sophisticated. Perl tends to have devoted adherents.

Plug-ins can be installed for some **servers** (**Apache**, for example) so that Perl is loaded permanently in memory, thus reducing compile time and resulting in faster execution of CGI Perl scripts.

permanent virtual circuit

A permanent virtual circuit (PVC) is a software-defined logical connection in a network such as a **frame relay** network. A feature of frame relay that makes it a highly flexible network technology is that users (companies or clients of network providers) can define logical connections and required **bandwidth** between end points and let the frame relay network technology worry about how the physical network is used to achieve the defined connections and manage the traffic. In frame relay, the end points and a stated bandwidth called a Committed Information Rate (**CIR**) constitute a PVC, which is defined to the frame relay network devices. The bandwidth may not exceed the possible physical bandwidth. Typically, multiple PVCs share the same physical paths at the same time. To manage the variation in bandwidth requirements expressed in the CIRs, the frame relay devices use a technique called *statistical multiplexing*.

permeability

Permeability, also called magnetic permeability, is a constant of proportionality that exists between magnetic **induction** and **magnetic field** intensity. This constant is equal to approximately 1.257×10^{-6} **henry per meter** (H/m) in free space (a vacuum). In other materials it can be much different, often substantially greater than the free-space value, which is symbolized μ_o.

Materials that cause the lines of **flux** to move farther apart, resulting in a decrease in magnetic flux density compared with a vacuum, are called diamagnetic. Materials that concentrate magnetic flux by a factor of more than 1 but less than or equal to 10 are called paramagnetic; materials that concentrate the flux by a factor of more than 10 are called ferromagnetic. The permeability factors of some substances change with rising or falling temperature, or with the intensity of the applied magnetic field.

In engineering applications, permeability is often expressed in relative, rather than in absolute, terms. If μ_o represents the permeability of free space (that is, 1.257×10^{-6} H/m) and μ represents the permeability of the substance in question (also specified in henrys per meter), then the relative permeability, μ_r, is given by:

$$\mu_r = \mu / \mu_o$$
$$= \mu \, (7.958 \times 10^5)$$

Diamagnetic materials have μ_r less than 1, but no known substance has relative permeability much less than 1. Certain ferromagnetics, especially powdered or laminated iron, steel, or nickel alloys, have μ_r that can range up to about 1,000,000. When a paramagnetic or ferromagnetic core is inserted into a coil, the inductance is multiplied by μ_r compared with the inductance of the same coil with an air core. This effect is useful in the design of **transformer**s and chokes for alternating current (**AC**), audio frequencies (AF), and radio frequencies (**RF**).

Also see **henry per meter**, **inductor**, and **magnetic field**.

permission marketing

Permission marketing is an approach to selling goods and services in which a prospect explicitly agrees in advance to receive marketing information. **Opt-in e-mail**, where Internet users sign up in advance for information about certain product categories, is a good example of permission marketing. Advocates of permission marketing argue that it is effective because the prospect is more receptive to a message that has been requested in advance and more cost-efficient because the prospect is already identified and targetted. In a world of information overload, automated telemarketing, and **spam**, most people welcome the idea of permission marketing.

permittivity

Permittivity, also called electric permittivity, is a constant of proportionality that exists between electric displacement and **electric field** intensity. This constant is equal to approximately 8.85×10^{-12} **farad per meter** (F/m) in free space (a vacuum). In other materials it can be much different, often substantially greater than the free-space value, which is symbolized e_o.

In engineering applications, permittivity is often expressed in relative, rather than in absolute, terms. If e_o represents the permittivity of free space (that is, 8.85×10^{-12} F/m) and e represents the permittivity of the substance in question (also specified in farads per meter), then the relative permittivity, also called the dielectric constant e_r, is given by:

$$e_r = e / e_o$$
$$= e \, (1.13 \times 10^{11})$$

Various substances have dielectric constants e_r greater than 1. These substances are generally called **dielectric** materials, or simply dielectrics. Commonly used dielectrics include glass, paper, mica, various ceramics, polyethylene, and certain metal oxides. Dielectrics are used in **capacitor**s and transmission lines in alternating current (**AC**), audio frequency (AF), and radio frequency (**RF**) applications.

Also see **farad per meter**, **capacitor**, and **electric field**.

Personal Access Communications System

Personal Access Communications System (PACS) is a type of **wireless** telephone network compatible with telephone sets, answering machines, fax machines, and computers. A PACS can be used like a local area network (**LAN**) with voice capability and can be part of a larger network or can be connected into the telephone system.

A typical PACS resembles a **cellular telephone** network in miniature. It contains numerous radio port control units (RCPUs), each of which is the equivalent of a cellular repeater, but with a shorter communications range, linking subscriber sets within a radius of a few hundred feet. RPCUs are located on utility poles, atop buildings, and in other unobtrusive places that offer good coverage for several hundred feet in all directions. RPCU transmitter power is limited to 800 milliwatts. The operating frequency is in the UHF (ultra-high-frequency) radio range at 1.9 GHz.

The subscriber sets in a PACS can be fixed, mobile, or portable. Voice subscriber sets use 32 **Kbps** or 64 Kbps digital speech coding. Computer modems can be supported at speeds of up to 28.8 kbps or 57.6 kbps, respectively. Transmitter output power is limited to 200 milliwatts, but is often much less, on the order of a few tens of milliwatts. This low power level minimizes the likelihood of electromagnetic interference (**EMI**) to other electronic devices that might be located near the subscriber set.

personal area network

A personal area network (PAN) is a technology that could enable **wearable computer** devices to communicate with other nearby computers and exchange digital information using the electrical conductivity of the human body as a data network. For example, two people each wearing business card-size transmitters and receivers conceivably could exchange information by shaking hands. The transference of data through intra-body contact, such as handshakes, is known as linkup. The human body's natural salinity makes it a good conductor of electricity. An electric field passes tiny currents, known as Pico amps, through the body when the two people shake hands. The handshake completes an electric circuit and each person's data, such as e-mail addresses and phone numbers, are transferred to the other

person's laptop computer or a similar device. A person's clothing also could act as a mechanism for transferring this data.

The concept of a PAN first was developed by Thomas Zimmerman and other researchers at M.I.T.'s Media Lab and later supported by IBM's Almaden research lab. In a research paper, Zimmerman explains why the concept might be useful:

> As electronic devices become smaller, lower in power requirements, and less expensive, we have begun to adorn our bodies with personal information and communication appliances. Such devices include cellular phones, personal digital assistants (PDAs), pocket video games, and pagers. Currently there is no method for these devices to share data. Networking these devices can reduce functional I/O redundancies and allow new conveniences and services.

personal communications services

PCS (personal communications services) is a **wireless** phone service somewhat similar to **cellular telephone** telephone service but emphasizing personal service and extended mobility. It's sometimes referred to as *digital cellular* (although cellular systems can also be **digital**). Like cellular, PCS is for mobile users and requires a number of antennas to blanket an area of coverage. As a user moves around, the user's phone signal is picked up by the nearest antenna and then forwarded to a base station that connects to the wired network. The phone itself is slightly smaller than a cellular phone. PCS is being introduced first in highly urban areas for large numbers of users.

The "personal" in PCS distinguishes this service from cellular by emphasizing that, unlike cellular, which was designed for car phone use with transmitters emphasing coverage of highways and roads, PCS is designed for greater user mobility. It generally requires more cell transmitters for coverage, but has the advantage of fewer blind spots. Technically, cellular systems in the U.S. operate in the 824-849 megahertz (**MHz**) **frequency** bands; PCS operates in the 1850-1990 MHz bands.

Several technologies are used for PCS in the U.S., including Cellular Digital Packet Data (**CDPD**) and Global System for Mobile (**GSM**) communication. GSM is more commonly used in Europe and elsewhere.

personal computer

See "PC"

Personal Computer—Disk Operating System

See "PC-DOS"

Personal Computer Memory Card International Association card

See "PCMCIA card"

Personal Computer Memory Card International Association

The PCMCIA (Personal Computer Memory Card International Association) is an industry group organized in 1989 to promote standards for a credit card-size **memory** or **I/O** device that would fit into a personal computer, usually a notebook or laptop computer. The PCMCIA 2.1 Standard was published in 1993. As a result, PC users can be assured of standard attachments for any peripheral device that follows the standard. The initial standard and its subsequent releases describe a standard product, the **PC Card**.

personal digital assistant

PDA (personal digital assistant) is a term for any small mobile hand-held device that provides computing and information storage and retrieval capabilities for personal or business use, often for keeping schedule calendars and address book information handy. The term **handheld** is a synonym. Many people use the name of one of the popular PDA products as a generic term. These include Hewlett-Packard's Palmtop and 3Com's PalmPilot.

Most PDAs have a small keyboard. Some PDAs have an electronically sensitive pad on which handwritng can be received. Apple's Newton, which has been withdrawn from the market, was the first widely-sold PDA that accepted handwriting. Typical uses include schedule and address book storage and retrieval and note-entering. However, many applications have been written for PDAs. Increasingly, PDAs are combined with telephones and paging systems.

Some PDAs offer a variation of the Microsoft Windows operating system called **Windows CE**. Other products have their own or another operating system.

personal firewall

A personal firewall (sometimes called a desktop firewall) is a software application used to protect a single Internet-connected computer from intruders. Personal firewall protection is especially useful for users with "always-on" connections such as **DSL** or **cable modem**. Such connections use a static **IP** address that makes them especially vulnerable to potential **hackers**. Often compared to **anti-virus applications**, personal firewalls work in the background at the device (link layer) level to protect the integrity of the system from malicious computer code by controlling Internet connections to and from a user's computer, filtering inbound and outbound traffic, and alerting the user to attempted intrusions.

Several companies have announced plans to develop personal firewall solutions that will go right in the chips used in DSL and cable modems. It is generally believed that personal firewall protection will become standard issue for new home computers in the not-too-distant future.

Personal Handyphone System

Developed by the Nippon Telegraph and Telephone Corporation, the Personal Handyphone is a lightweight portable wireless telephone that functions as a cordless phone in the home and as a mobile phone elsewhere. The Personal Handyphone also handles voice, fax, and video signals. The phone is now being marketed in other Asian countries.

Personal Home Page

In Web programming, Personal Home Page (PHP) is a **script** language and interpreter, similar to **JavaScript** and Microsoft's **VBScript**, that is freely available and used primarily on **Linux Web server**s. PHP (the initials come from the earliest version of the program, which was called "Personal Home Page Tools") is a cross-platform alternative to Microsoft's Active Server Page (**ASP**) technology (which runs only on Microsoft's **Windows NT** servers). As with ASP, the PHP script is embedded within a Web page along with its **HTML**. Before the page is sent to a user that has requested it, the Web server calls PHP to interpret and perform the operations called for in the PHP script. An HTML page that includes a PHP script is typically given a file name suffix of ".php" ".php3," or ".phtml". Like ASP, PHP can be thought of as "dynamic HTML pages," since content will vary based on the results of interpreting the script.

PHP is free and offered under an **Open Source** license.

personal portal

See "bookmark portal"

Personal Web Server

PWS (Personal Web Server) is Microsoft's version of a **Web server** program for individual PC users who want to share Web pages and other files from their hard drive. PWS is a scaled-down version of Microsoft's more robust Web server, Internet Information Server**IIS**. PWS can be used with a full-time Internet connection to serve Web pages for a Web site with limited traffic. It can also be used for testing a Web site offline or from a "staging" site before putting it on a main Web site that is exposed to larger traffic.

PWS can be used together with Microsoft's FrontPage, a Web site design product, to upload Web pages from a remote location or to the local hard drive; to check for dead links; to create directories; and to set permissions. PWS is frequently used as part of the trend toward**peer-to-peer** exchange and publishing.

The equivalent program for the Macintosh is called Personal Web Sharing.

personality profile

A personality profile is a **knowledge management** tool used to provide an evaluation of an employee's personal attributes, values and life skills in an effort to maximize his or her job performance and contribution to the company. Questions in a personality profile test, which can be taken traditionally or online, are designed to seek out information about an employee's temperament, decision-making methods, communication style and general attitude towards work and recreation. The information is used to match the right employee to the right project or task, especially when group work or **telecommuting** is involved. There are two generally accepted categories of personality profile tests, *trait* and *type*.

Trait personality profile tests, such as Orpheus, 16 PF, and OPQ, operate on the assumption that personality is made up of a number of characteristics. The goal of the test is to document the employee's characteristics and match the characteristics to appropriate roles within the company.

Type personality profile tests, such as Myers-Briggs, Insights Discovery, and the Keirsey Temperament Sorter, propose that people fall into well-defined categories. The goal of the test is to identify the category the employee belongs to, share the information, and build team skills by having team members become aware of the talents associated with each category.

Advocates of personality profiling claim that it's a valuable reality check when viewed in the context of an employee's job performance. Critics claim that the advent of sophisticated knowledge management technology could put too much emphasis on the process involved in gathering and mining employee data, especially in large companies, and recommend that face-to-face communication and evaluation be valued above all else.

personalization

On a Web site, personalization is the process of tailoring pages to individual users' characteristics or preferences. Commonly used to enhance customer service or e-commerce sales, personalization is sometimes referred to as *one-to-one marketing*, because the enterprise's Web page is tailored to specifically target each individual consumer. Personalization is a means of meeting the customer's needs more effectively and efficiently, making interactions faster and easier and, consequently, increasing customer satisfaction and the likelihood of repeat visits. There are a number of personalization software products available, including those from Broadvision, ResponseLogic, and Autonomy.

Personalization in some ways harkens back to an earlier day, by making consumer relationships more closely tailored to the individual. If you've ever bought a book from Amazon, for example, the next time you visit they will—like a friendly and helpful sales clerk—greet you by name and tell you about products in stock that they think you might like (such as more books by the same author, or books purchased by other people who also bought the book that you purchased). Many **portal** sites, such as Yahoo allow site visitors to customize the page with selected news categories, local weather reports, and other features.

In addition to use of the **cookie**, the technologies behind personalization include:

● *Ccollaborative filtering*, in which a **filter** is applied to information from different sites to select relevant data that may apply to the specific e-commerce experience of a customer or specific group of customers

● *User profiling*, using data collected from a number of different sites, which can result in the creation a personalized Web page before the user has been formally

● Data analysis tools used to predict likely future interactions

Because personalization depends on the gathering and use of personal user information, **privacy** issues are a major concern. The Personalization Consortium is an international advocacy group organized to promote and guide the development of responsible one-to-one marketing practices. Founding members include Pricewaterhouse Coopers, American Airlines, and DoubleClick. The consortium has established *ethical information and privacy management objectives*; these include, for example, the suggestion that enterprises should inform users about the information being gathered, and the purposes for which it is sought. According to a March 2000 Consortium survey of over 4,500 Web users, 73% of respondents find it helpful to have Web sites retain their personal information, while only 15% refuse to supply personal information online. 63% of respondents disliked having to reenter information that they had already supplied.

PERT chart

A PERT chart is a project management tool used to schedule, organize, and coordinate tasks within a project. PERT stands for *Program Evaluation Review Technique*, a methodology developed by the U.S. Navy in the 1950s to manage the Polaris submarine missile program. A similar methodology, the *Critical Path Method* (CPM), which was developed for project management in the private sector at about the same time, has become synonymous with PERT, so that the technique is known by any variation on the names: PERT, CPM, or PERT/CPM.

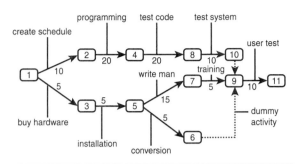

* Numbered rectangles are nodes and represent events or milestones.
* Directional arrows represent dependent tasks that must be completed sequentially.
* Diverging arrow directions (e.g. 1-2 & 1-3) indicate possibly concurrent tasks.
* Dotted lines indicate dependent tasks that do not require resources.

A PERT chart presents a graphic illustration of a project as a network diagram consisting of numbered *nodes* (either circles or rectangles) representing events, or milestones in the project linked by labelled *vectors* (directional lines) representing tasks in the project. The direction of the arrows on the lines indicates the sequence of tasks. In the diagram, for example, the tasks between nodes 1, 2, 4, 8, and 10 must be completed in sequence. These are called *dependent* or *serial* tasks. The tasks between nodes 1 and 2, and nodes 1 and 3 are not dependent on the completion of one to start the other and can be undertaken simultaneously. These tasks are called *parallel* or *concurrent* tasks. Tasks that must be completed in sequence but that don't require resources or completion time are considered to have *event dependency*. These are represented by dotted lines with arrows and are called *dummy activities*. For example, the dashed arrow linking nodes 6 and 9 indicates that the system files must be converted before the user test can take place, but that the resources and time required to prepare for the user test (writing the user manual and user training) are on another path. Numbers on the opposite sides of the vectors indicate the time allotted for the task.

The PERT chart is sometimes preferred over the **Gantt chart**, another popular project management charting method, because it clearly illustrates task dependencies. On the other hand, the PERT chart can be much more difficult to interpret, especially on complex projects. Frequently, project managers use both techniques.

PERT/CPM

See "PERT chart"

petabit

A petabit is one quadrillion (10^{15}) **bits** and is used in discussing possible volumes of data traffic per second in a large telecommunications network. A petabit is one thousand **terabit**s. Petabits per second can be shortened to Pbps.

Although the bit is a unit of the binary number system, bits in data communications have historically been counted using the decimal number system. For example, 28.8 kilobits per second (**Kbps**) is 28,800 bits per second. Because of computer architecture and memory address boundaries, bytes are always some multiple or exponent of two. See **kilobyte**, etc.

petabyte

A petabyte is a measure of memory or storage capacity and is 2 to the 50th power bytes or, in decimal, approximately a thousand **terabyte**s.

In recently announcing how many Fibre Channel storage arrays they had sold, Sun Microsystems stated that it had shipped an aggregate of two petabytes of storage or the equivalent of 40 million four-drawer filing cabinets full of text. IBM says that it has shipped four petabytes of SSA Storage.

Also see **petaflop**.

petaflop

Computer architects have begun to envision how a petaflop computer might work. A petaflop is a theoretical measure of a computer's speed and can be expressed as:

- A thousand trillion floating point operations per second
- A thousand **teraflop**s
- 10 to the 15th power **floating-point operations per second**

Today's fastest parallel computing operations are capable of teraflop speeds. The National Science Foundation, together with NASA and DARPA, has funded eight research projects for envisioning a petaflop computer. A petaflop computer would actually require a massive number of computers working in parallel on the same problem. Applications might include real-time nuclear magnetic resonance imaging during surgery, computer-based drug design, astrophysical simulation, the modeling of environmental pollution, and the study of long-term climate changes.

PGP

See "Pretty Good Privacy"

Ph

Ph is an Internet facility that lets you search for someone's **e-mail** address if their e-mail provider has a Ph **server** program. A Ph **client** program comes with Eudora, a popular e-mail program (click on "Tools," then "Directory Services"), as well as with other programs. To use Ph, you need to know at what university or other organization the person you're looking for is located. A large number of universities and research institutions maintain a directory of e-mail users. In addition, several large Web portal sites, including **AltaVista** and Bigfoot, have Ph directories. To search using Ph, you need to enter the server name for the location you're searching at and then the person's name. A number of places provide lists of servers. Several Web sites provide a forms interface that includes the server list in order to make searching easy and quick.

Some places use the Lightweight Directory Access Protocol (**LDAP**) and convert a Ph query to LDAP and return the result in Ph. Ph is somewhat similar to another Internet facility, **Finger**, which lets you search for a name if you know the e-mail address. Ph is sometimes referred to as Qi or Ph/Qi. A Ph response may include other information besides an e-mail address.

phantom dialing

1) On a computer using a dial-up connection, phantom (meaning ghost) dialing is a term used to describe what occurs when a computer's auto-connect feature has been enabled and the computer attempts to dial out and establish an Internet connection on its own.

2) In mobile wireless communication, phantom dialing is a term used to describe what occurs when a user unintentionally presses a pre-programmed auto-dial number on their **cellular telephone** keypad and unintentionally initiates a phone call. In the U.S., phantom dialing is a problem for 911 emergency centers, especially since many cell phones are configured to dial 911 (the emergency center) automatically when either a "9" or a "1" is pressed. When emergency services receives a phone call, the operator must, by law, remain on the phone long enough to determine whether or not the call is an emergency. If the operator listens and determines that the call is probably a result of phantom dialing, they may terminate the call, but must dial back the caller and verbally confirm that there is no emergency. Operators across the U.S. report thousands of such calls daily, and say that phantom dialers are almost always unaware they have made a call. Users report that they may have dropped the phone, sat on it, put it in their pocket, or otherwise jostled it, hitting auto-dial and inadvertently initiating the call. Phantom dialing can be prevented by using the cell phone's keyguard, a feature that locks the keypad, or by disabling the auto-dial feature.

phase

In electronic signaling, phase is a definition of the position of a point in time (instant) on a **waveform** cycle. A complete cycle is defined as 360 degrees of phase as shown in Illustration A below. Phase can also be an expression of relative displacement between or among waves having the same **frequency**.

Phase difference, also called *phase angle*, in degrees is conventionally defined as a number greater than -180, and less than or equal to $+180$. *Leading phase* refers to a wave that occurs "ahead" of another wave of the same frequency. *Lagging phase* refers to a wave that occurs "behind" another wave of the same frequency. When two signals differ in phase by -90 or $+90$ degrees, they are said to be in *phase quadrature*. When two waves differ in phase by 180 degrees (-180 is technically the same as $+180$), the waves are said to be in *phase opposition*. Illustration B shows two waves that are in phase quadrature. The wave depicted by the dashed line leads the wave represented by the solid line by 90 degrees.

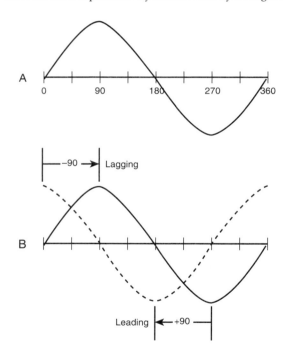

Phase is sometimes expressed in radians rather than in degrees. One radian of phase corresponds to approximately 57.3 degrees. Engineers and technicians generally use degrees; physicists more often use radians.

The time interval for one degree of phase is inversely proportional to the frequency. If the frequency of a signal (in **hertz**) is given by f, then the time t_{deg} (in seconds) corresponding to one degree of phase is:

$$t_{deg} = 1/(360f)$$

The time t_{rad} (in seconds) corresponding to one radian of phase is approximately:

$$t_{rad} = 1/(6.28f)$$

Phase Alternation Line

Phase Alternation Line (PAL) is the **analog** television display standard that is used in Europe and certain other parts of the world. PAL is one of the three major TV standards together with the American National Television Systems Committee (**NTSC**) color television system and the French Sequential Couleur avec Memoire (**SECAM**). NTSC is also used in Japan. SECAM is used in countries of the former Soviet Union.

Like SECAM, PAL scans the cathode ray tube (**CRT**) horizontally 625 times to form the video image. NTSC scans 525 lines. Color definitions between the systems vary slightly.

phase change

Phase change is a type of compact disc (**CD**) recording technology that enables the discs to be written, erased, and rewritten through the use of a layer of a special material (called the *phase change layer*) that can be changed repeatedly from an amorphous (formless) to a crystalline state, or phase-through exposure to variably-powered **laser** beams. The technology, which was developed in the late 1960s by Stanford Ovshinsky, is used in rewritable CD (**CD-RW**) and DVD (**DVD-RW**) formats. A different type of phase change technology used in CD-Magneto Optical (**CD-MO**) uses magnetic fields as well as lasers.

Like CD-Recordable (**CD-R**), CD-RW has a polycarbonate substrate, which is preformed with a spiral groove to guide the laser. The alloy phase-change recording layer, which is commonly a mix of silver, indium, antimony and tellurium, is sandwiched between two **dielectric** layers that draw excess heat from the recording layer. After heating to one particular temperature, the alloy will become crystalline when it is cooled; after heating to a higher temperature, it will become amorphous when it is cooled. By controlling the temperature of the laser, crystalline areas and non-crystalline areas are formed. The crystalline areas will reflect the laser, while the other areas will absorb it. The differences will register as binary data that can be unencoded for playback. To erase or write over recorded data, the higher temperature laser is used, which results in the amorphous form, which can then be reformed by the lower temperature laser. According to Sony, the process can be repeated up to 1000 times.

phase modulation

Also see **modulation** and **phase-shift keying**.

Phase modulation (PM) is a method of impressing data onto an alternating-current (**AC**) **waveform** by varying the instantaneous **phase** of the wave. This scheme can be used with **analog** or **digital** data.

In analog PM, the phase of the AC **signal** wave, also called the *carrier*, varies in a continuous manner. Thus, there are infinitely many possible carrier phase states. When the instantaneous data input waveform has positive polarity, the carrier phase shifts in one direction; when the instantaneous data input waveform has negative polarity, the carrier phase shifts in the opposite direction. At every instant in time, the extent of carrier-phase shift (the *phase angle*) is directly proportional to the extent to which the signal amplitude is positive or negative.

In digital PM, the carrier phase shifts abruptly, rather than continuously back and forth. The number of possible carrier phase states is usually a power of 2. If there are only two possible phase states, the mode is called *biphase modulation*. In more complex modes, there can be four, eight, or more different phase states. Each phase angle (that is, each shift from one phase state to another) represents a specific digital input data state.

Phase modulation is similar in practice to frequency modulation (**FM**). When the instantaneous phase of a carrier is varied, the instantaneous frequency changes as well. The converse also holds: When the instantaneous frequency is varied, the instantaneous phase changes. But PM and FM are not exactly equivalent, especially in analog applications. When an FM receiver is used to demodulate a PM signal, or when an FM signal is intercepted by a receiver designed for PM, the audio is distorted. This is because the relationship between phase and frequency variations is not linear; that is, phase and frequency do not vary in direct proportion.

phased antenna system

A phased antenna system consists of two or more active **antenna** elements, arranged so the electromagnetic fields effectively add in some directions and cancel in other directions. This produces enhanced transmission and reception in the directions where the fields add, and reduces the strength of radiated and received signals in the directions where the fields cancel.

Many **AM** (amplitude-modulation) broadcast stations use sets of two, three, or four phased vertical antennas. This results in a directional pattern that optimizes coverage, so the station can reach the greatest possible number of listeners in its designated area. The nulls in the pattern reduce or eliminate interference with other AM broadcast stations.

In two-way radio communications, several vertical **dipole antenna** can be placed end-to-end and fed in **phase**s. This is known as a *collinear antenna* and is a specialized type of phased array. At low elevation angles, the radiation and response are enhanced relative to a single vertical dipole. This gain occurs at the expense of radiation and response at higher elevation angles, increasing the range of communication for surface-to-surface communications.

phaser

A phaser is an electronic sound processor, that creates a sweeping effect by modulating a narrow notch signal filter. This hardware or software device is also known as a phase shifter. Its sound is similar to that of **flanging**. Phase shifting is a popular effect for keyboards and guitars. It is included in the special effects processors of a number of popular keyboards and digital effect devices.

A phase shifter works by applying a narrow signal filter to a sound source. This causes various amounts of canceling of frequency components in the original signal. The filter's output is mixed back in with the original source audio signal. To get the sweeping effect, a low frequency **oscillator** (LFO) is used to slowly move the frequency center of the notch filter. Blending the altered signal back into the signal path (called "regeneration" or "feedback") intensifies the effect.

phase-shift keying

See also frequency-shift keying (**FSK**).

Phase-shift keying (PSK) is a method of transmitting and receiving **digital** signals in which the **phase** of a transmitted **signal** is varied to convey information.

There are several schemes that can be used to accomplish PSK. The simplest method uses only two signal phases: 0 degrees and 180 degrees. The digital signal is broken up timewise into individual bits (binary digits). The state of each bit is determined according to the state of the preceding bit. If the phase of the wave does not change, then the signal state stays the same (low or high). If the phase of the wave changes by 180 degrees—that is, if the phase reverses—then the signal state changes (from low to high, or from high to low). Because there are two possible wave phases, this form of PSK is sometimes called *biphase modulation*.

More complex forms of PSK employ four or eight wave phases. This allows binary data to be transmitted at a faster rate per phase change than is possible with biphase modulation. In four-phase modulation, the possible phase angles are 0, +90, −90, and 180 degrees; each phase shift can represent two signal elements. In eight-phase modulation, the possible phase angles are 0, +45, −45, +90, −90, +135, −135, and 180 degrees; each phase shift can represent four signal elements.

phase-state low electron drive memory

See "PLEDM"

Photo CD

Photo CD is a process from Kodak that puts film images (including scanned prints and slides) on a compact disc as digitally stored images that you can view or work with at your computer. The images can also be printed out on photographic paper with a special Kodak machine.

Also see **digital camera**.

photoconductivity

See also **photosensor**.

Photoconductivity is the tendency of a substance to conduct electricity to an extent that depends on the intensity of light-radiant energy (usually **infrared transmission** or visible light) striking the surface of a sample. Most **semiconductor** materials have this property.

When there is no illumination, a photoconductive sample has a **conductance** that depends on its dimensions, on the specific material(s) from which it is made, and on the temperature. In most cases, the greater the radiant energy of a specific **wavelength** that strikes the surface, the higher the conductance of the sample becomes, up to a certain maximum. When the maximum conductance is reached for a particular sample, further increases in irradiation produce no change in the conductance.

Photoconductive materials are used in the manufacture of photoelectric devices. Typical photoconductive substances consist of germanium, gallium, selenium, or silicon with impurities, also known as *dopants*, added. Other common materials include metal oxides and sulfides.

photon

In some ways, visible light behaves like a wave phenomenon, but in other respects it acts like a stream of high-speed, submicroscopic particles. Isaac Newton was one of the first scientists to theorize that light consists of particles. Modern physicists have demonstrated that the energy in any **electromagnetic field** is made up of discrete packets. The term *photon* (meaning "visible-light particle") has been coined for these energy packets. Particle-like behavior is not restricted to the visible-light portion of the **electromagnetic radiation spectrum**, however. Radio waves, infrared rays, visible light, ultraviolet rays, X rays, and gamma rays all consist of photons, each of which contains a particular amount of energy that depends on the **wavelength**.

Photons travel through empty space at a speed of approximately 186,282 miles (299,792 kilometers) per second. This is true no matter what the electromagnetic wavelength. In media other than a vacuum, the speed is reduced. For example, visible light travels more slowly through glass than through outer space. Radio waves travel more slowly through the polyethylene in a transmission line than they do through the atmosphere. The ratio of the speed of the photons in a particular medium to their speed in a vacuum is called the *velocity factor*. This factor is always between 0 and 1 (or 0 and 100%), and it depends to some extent on the wavelength.

The shorter the wavelength of an electromagnetic disturbance, the more energy each photon contains. In fact, this relationship is so precise that a mathematical formula applies. If e represents the energy (the unit of measurement is the **joule**) contained in each photon and s represents the electromagnetic wavelength (in meters), then

$$e = hc/s$$

where h is *Planck's constant* (approximately equal to 6.626 times 10^{-34} joule-second) and c is the speed of electromagnetic-field propagation in the medium in question (approximately 2.998 times 10^8 meters per second in a vacuum). A simpler formula applies to **frequency**. If f represents the frequency of an electromagnetic field (in **hertz**), then

$$e = hf$$

The energy contained in a single photon does not depend on the intensity of the radiation. At any specific wavelength—say, the wavelength of light emitted by a helium-neon laser—every photon contains exactly the same amount of energy, whether the source appears as dim as a candle or as bright as the sun. The brilliance or intensity is a function of the number of photons striking a given surface area per unit time.

photonic network

A photonic (or optical) network is a communications network in which information is transmitted entirely in the form of optical or infrared transmission(**IR**) signals. In a true photonic network, every **switch** and every **repeater** works with IR or visible-light energy. A recent development in this field is the **erbium amplifier**. Conversion to and from electrical impulses is not done except at the source and destination (origin and end point).

Optical or IR data transmission has several advantages over electrical transmission. Perhaps most important is the greatly increased **bandwidth** provided by **photon** signals. Because the **frequency** of visible or IR energy is so high (on the order of millions of megahertz), thousands or millions of signals can be impressed onto a single beam by means of frequency division multiplexing (**FDM**). In addition, a single strand of fiber can carry IR and/or visible light at several different wavelengths, each beam having its own set of modulating signals. This is known as wave-division multiplexing (**WDM**).

A subtle, but potentially far-reaching, advantage of photonic systems over electronic media results from the fact that visible and IR energy actually moves several times faster than electricity. Electric **current** propagates at about 10 percent of the speed of light (18,000 to 19,000 miles or 30,000 kilometers per second), but the energy in fiber optic systems travels at the speed of light in the glass or plastic medium, which is a sizable fraction of the speed of light in free space (186,000 miles or 300,000 kilometers per second). This results in shorter data-transmission delay times between the end points of a network. This advantage is especially significant in systems where the individual computers or terminals continuously share data. It affects performance at all physical scales, whether components are separated by miles or by microns. It is even significant within microchips, a phenomenon of interest to research-and-development engineers in optical computer technology.

photonic switching

See "lambda switching"

photosensor

A photosensor is an electronic component that detects the presence of visible light, **infrared transmission** (IR), and/or ultraviolet (UV) energy. Most photosensors consist of **semiconductors** having a property called **photoconductivity,** in which the electrical **conductance** varies depending on the intensity of radiation striking the material.

The most common types of photosensor are the photodiode, the bipolar phototransistor, and the photoFET (photosensitive field-effect transistor). These devices are essentially the same as the ordinary **diode**, **bipolar transistor**, and **field-effect transistor**, except that the packages have transparent windows that allow radiant energy to reach the junctions between the semiconductor materials inside. Bipolar and field-effect phototransistors provide amplification in addition to their sensing capabilities.

Photosensors are used in a great variety of electronic devices, circuits, and systems, including:

- Fiber optic systems
- Optical scanners
- Wireless LAN
- Automatic lighting controls
- Machine vision systems
- Electric eyes
- Optical disk drives
- Optical memory chips
- Remote control devices

PHP

In Web programming, PHP is a **script** language and interpreter that is freely available and used primarily on **Linux** Web servers. PHP (the initials come from the earliest version of the program, which was called "Personal Home Page Tools") is an alternative to Microsoft's **Active Server Page** (ASP) technology. As with ASP, the PHP script is embedded within a Web page along with its **HTML**. Before the page is sent to a user that has requested it, the Web server calls PHP to interpret and perform the operations called for in the PHP script. An HTML page that includes a PHP script is typically given a file name suffix of ".php" ".php3," or ".phtml". Like ASP, PHP can be thought of as "dynamic HTML pages," since content will vary based on the results of interpreting the script.

PHP is free and offered under an **open source** license. The latest version is PHP4.

PHP3

See "PHP"

PHP4

See "PHP"

phreak

A phreak is someone who breaks into the telephone network illegally, typically to make free long-distance phone calls or to tap phone lines. The term is now sometimes used to include anyone who breaks or tries to break the security of any network. Recently, the phone companies have introduced new security safeguards, making phreaking more difficult.

According to Eric Raymond's *The New Hacker's Dictionary*, phreaking was originally a more innocent occupation and **hackers** would sometimes take up the challenge. The typical phreak was or is usually equipped with a specially-made "box" designed to "fool" the network in some way. Different boxes, somehow named for different colors but not necessarily painted any color, are used for different phreak approaches. A "black box" allows you to make free calls from a home phone; a "red box" to make free calls on a pay phone; and the infamous "blue box" provides complete control over the telephone system. If you look hard enough on the Web, you'll probably find directions on how to make all of these boxes. (But note that using the boxes as directed is probably illegal and any directions you find may be out-of-date.)

phreaking

See "phreak"

PHS

See "Personal Handyphone System"

PHTML and phtml suffix

A PHTML (or it's sometimes called a PHP) page is a Web **page** that includes a **script** written in **Personal Home Page**, a language comparable to **JavaScript** or Microsoft's **VBScript**. Like Microsoft's Active Server Page (**ASP**) page, a PHTML page contains programming that is executed at the Web **server** rather than at the Web **client** (which is usually your Web **browser**). You may sometimes see a Web site whose address or **URL** ends with a file with a **suffix** of ".phtml" or ".php3". Either of these suffixes indicate an **HTML** page that includes a PHP script.

Physical layer

In the Open Systems Interconnection (**OSI**) communications model, the Physical layer supports the electrical or mechanical interface to the physical medium. For example, this layer determines how to put a stream of bits from the upper (Data Link) layer on to the pins for a parallel printer interface, an optical fiber transmitter, or a radio carrier.

The Physical layer is usually a combination of software and hardware programming and may include electromechanical devices. It does not include the physical media as such.

physical unit

In IBM's Systems Network Architecture (**SNA**), a physical unit (PU) identifies a network node that supports communication sessions between **logical unit**s (LU). Logical units represent end users. Two logical units that communicate depend on physical connections being established through associated physical units. The network point at each end of a communication that sets up the communication session between logical units is called the *system services control point (SSCP)*. The SSCP sets up its own session with the PU on behalf of the LU-LU session. Typically, a logical unit is a unique connection to an application program. A physical unit is the hardware and routing aspect of a network **node**. IBM's Virtual Telecommunication Access Method (**VTAM**) is used by an application program to manage session and communication requests on behalf of logical units.

In SNA, there are different node types (formerly called physical unit types) that characterize routing, pooling, and other network capabilities.

pi

Pi is a numerical constant that represents the ratio of a circle's circumference to its diameter on a flat plane surface. The value is the same regardless of the size of the circle. The decimal expansion of pi is a nonterminating, nonrepeating

sequence of digits. For most calculations, the value can be taken as 3.14159. This means, for example, that a circle with a diameter of 10 centimeters, as measured on a flat surface, has a circumference of approximately 31.4159 centimeters.

The number pi is also the ratio of the diameter of a sphere to the length of any great circle (geodesic) on the sphere. So, for example, if the earth is considered to be a perfect sphere with a diameter of 8,000 miles, then the distance around the earth, as measured along the equator or along any great circle, is approximately $8,000 \times 3.14159$, or 25,133 miles.

Pi is an **irrational number**. It cannot be precisely defined as the ratio of any two whole numbers. Thus, its decimal expansion has no pattern and never ends. The first few hundred, thousand, million, or billion digits of pi can be calculated using a computer to add up huge initial sequences of the terms of an infinite sum known as a *Fourier series*. Mathematically, it can be shown that the following equation holds:

$$\pi = 4 - 4/3 + 4/5 - 4/7 = 4/9 - 4/11\ldots$$

The symbol to the left of the equal sign is the lowercase Greek letter used in mathematics, physics, and engineering to represent pi.

Pick

Pick is a data base management system (**DMS**) based on a business model of data and its organization and traditionally associated with **minicomputer** systems for small- to medium-size businesses. Because it lets developers view data much as a business naturally uses data, Pick is reputed to be easy to learn and use as well as cost-efficient. Originally, Pick was viewed as a data- and business-oriented **operating system** supported by an **assembler language virtual machine** for particular **minicomputer** hardware. Based on concepts from TRW's Generalized Information Retrieval Language and System, Dick Pick and Don Nelson formed the idea of a computer system that would be based on the user's data-oriented and business process perspective rather than the usual perspective of how the system itself worked. Pick's package of hardware and software was sold through value-added resellers (**VAR**s) who could adapt it for many kinds of business and hardware platforms. Today, Pick is still sold by the original company and its family of VARs as a database management system on **UNIX** and Windows systems.

Although Pick apparently missed the initial industry shift to **client/server** programming for distributed network applications, Pick Systems now offers a new version of Pick that is compliant with **Structured Query Language** and **Open Database Connectivity** for use in networks with distributed programming. Pick Systems states that over 4,000 Pick-based applications have been built and that over 2,000 are currently available. Familiarity with Pick is still a requirement in some companies, especially those with **legacy application**s built for Pick.

picosecond

(This definition follows U.S. usage in which a billion is a thousand million and a trillion is a 1 followed by 12 zeros.)

A picosecond is one trillionth (10^{-12}) of a second, or one millionth of a microsecond.

For comparison, a millisecond (ms or msec) is one thousandth of a second and is commonly used in measuring the time to read to or write from a **hard disk** or a **CD-ROM** player or to measure **packet** travel time on the Internet.

A microsecond (μs or Greek letter mu plus s) is one millionth (10^{-6}) of a second.

A nanosecond (ns or nsec) is one billionth (10^{-9}) of a second and is a common measurement of read or write access time to random access memory (**RAM**).

A femtosecond is one millionth of a nanosecond or 10^{-15} of a second and is a measurement sometimes used in laser technology.

If the term attosecond is used, it would mean one quintillionth (10^{-18}) of a second.

PICTIVE

PICTIVE (Plastic Interface for Collaborative Technology Initiatives through Video Exploration) is a paper mock-up technique that allows users to participate in the development process. A PICTIVE is a representation of a graphical user interface (**GUI**) or a **Web page** on paper. A PICTIVE prototype gives a user a sense of what a system or a piece of software will look like and how it will behave once it is finished. PICTIVE enables a non-technical person to contribute ideas to the development process.

A PICTIVE is usually made from simple office supplies like pens, paper, Post-It stickers, and paper clips. The developer uses those supplies to represent elements of the project, including drop-down boxes, menu bars, and special icons. During a design session, users manipulate the mock-up so it becomes easier for them to use. The development team takes notes and incorporates user ideas into its work. The development team also uses a video camera to record the physical changes a user might make to the PICTIVE. The team then reviews the ideas generated and incorporates them into the project. The ultimate goal of a PICTIVE is to simplify the design process enough that non-technical users are empowered to participate in it.

Developers at Bell Communications Research (Bellcore) are credited with creating PICTIVE in the early 1990s.

pie chart

See "pie graph"

pie graph

Compare with **histogram**.

A pie graph (or pie chart) is a specialized graph used in statistics. The independent variable is plotted around a circle in either a clockwise direction or a counterclockwise direction. The dependent variable (usually a percentage) is rendered as an arc whose measure is proportional to the magnitude of the quantity. Each arc is depicted by constructing radial lines from its ends to the center of the circle, creating a wedge-shaped "slice." The independent variable can attain a finite number of discrete values (for example, five). The dependent variable can attain any value from zero to 100 percent.

The illustration is a pie graph depicting the results of a final exam given to a hypothetical class of students. Each grade is denoted by a "slice." The total of the percentages is equal to 100 (this is important; if it were not, the accuracy of the graph would be suspect). The total of the arc measures is equal to 360 degrees.

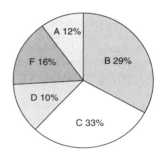

From this graph, one might gather that the professor for this course was not especially lenient nor severe. It is evident that grading was not done on a "pure curve" (in which case all the arcs would have equal measures of 72 degrees, corresponding to 20%). If this graph were compared with those of classes from other years that received the same test from the same professor, some conclusions might be drawn about intelligence changes among students over the years. If this graph were compared with those of other classes in the same semester who had received the same final exam but who had taken the course from different professors, one might draw conclusions about the relative competence and/or grading whims of the professors.

pin

A pin is a pronged contact as part of a **signal interface** in a computer or other communications device. Pins are part of a *male connector* and plug into a *female connector*. The number of pins in a connector is sometimes used in describing the

connector (for example, "a 25-way D-type connector"). The description of the signal associated with each pin is called the **pinout**.

ping

Tip: To find out the **dot address** (such as 205.245.172.72) for a given domain name, Windows users can go to their MS DOS prompt screen and enter: ping xxx.yyy where xxx is the second-level domain name like "whatis" and yyy is the top-level domain name like "com").

Ping is a basic **Internet** program that lets you verify that a particular **IP address** exists and can accept requests. The verb *ping* means the act of using the ping utility or command. Ping is used diagnostically to ensure that a **host** computer you are trying to reach is actually operating. If, for example, a user can't ping a host, then the user will be unable to use the File Transfer Protocol (**FTP**) to send files to that host. Ping can also be used with a host that is operating to see how long it takes to get a response back. Using ping, you can learn the number form of the IP address from the symbolic domain name (see "Tip").

Loosely, ping means "to get the attention of" or "to check for the presence of" another party online. Ping operates by sending a packet to a designated address and waiting for a response. The computer acronym was contrived to match the submariners' term for the sound of a returned sonar pulse.

Ping can also refer to the process of sending a message to all the members of a mailing list requesting an ACK (acknowledgement code). This is done before sending e-mail in order to confirm that all of the addresses are reachable.

ping storm

A ping storm is a condition in which the ping program is used to send a flood of **packet**s to a **server** to test its ability to handle a high amount of traffic or, maliciously, to make the server inoperable. Although the ping support in Windows operating systems does not allow someone to mount a ping storm, the ping command in at least some **UNIX**-based systems offers two options: "ping -f" which specifies to output ping packets back as fast as they are returned, and "ping -s]packetsize[", which causes the size of the outgoing packet to be padded by some specified size in order to increase the load on the receiving server.

A ping storm is one form of *packet storm*.

ping strangeness

Ping strangeness is a term used in a popular book on network design and troubleshooting to describe the incidence of an unusual pattern or frequency of **ping** messages in a network. Pings are used to determine the presence of particular Internet Protocol (**IP**) addresses on **host** computers in a network and the time it takes for the

ping packet to return. Besides being a useful diagnostic tool, pings are sometimes used by **router** program ICMP requests so that network router tables can be kept up-to-date.

The issuance of a ping request by a user or a program results in an Internet Control Message Protocol (**ICMP**) echo request. If the remote IP address is active, it responds with an ICMP echo reply. Ping can be used as an alternative to the **traceroute** utility to trace the **hop** or path that the ping echo takes through the network. Ping is faster, however, and generates less network traffic than traceroute.

Using a network monitor like LANalyzer for Windows, a network administrator can follow a **packet** exchange. If, for example, the monitor shows a consistent pattern of unexplained pings occurring in the same time period as the packet exchange, this "strange" pattern may be worth investigating. A consistent and continual pattern would suggest that the pings were not the result of someone trying to attack the network (since the attack would be made too obvious) but rather that the hosts originating the pings had been programmed to issue them for some reason. For example, Synoptic **hubs** sometimes seek a network management station, an optional facility that Synoptic offers. The hubs will look for the management station using ICMP pings at frequent time intervals. If the management station doesn't exist, the pings will continue, causing unnecessary traffic. In this example, one solution would be to disable the Internet Protocol on each hub.

pink noise

See "white noise"

pinout

A pinout is a description of the purpose of each **pin** in a multi-pin hardware connection interface. The description can be entirely in text, often in table form, or it can be an illustration.

Not all pins are used in every connection.

PIO

Programmed Input/Output (PIO) is a way of moving **data** between **device**s in a **computer** in which all data must pass through the **processor**. The **Advanced Technology Attachment/Integrated Drive Electronics** standard specifies three PIO data transfer rates (mode 0 at 3.3 MBps, mode 1 at 5.2 MBps, and mode 2 at 8.3 MBps). The newer **Advanced Technology Attachment** standard specifies two higher data transfer rates (mode 3 at 11.1 MBps and mode 4 at 16.6 MBps).

A newer alternative to PIO is Direct Memory Access (**DMA**). It's expected that PIO will be dropped from future industry standards, replaced entirely by DMA and **Ultra DMA**.

pipe

Also see **named pipe** (or FIFO).

In computer programming, especially in **UNIX** operating systems, a pipe is a technique for passing information from one program **process** to another. Unlike other forms of interprocess communication (**IC**), a pipe is one-way communication only. Basically, a pipe passes a parameter such as the output of one process to another process which accepts it as input. The system temporarily holds the piped information until it is read by the receiving process.

Using a UNIX **shell** (the UNIX interactive command interface), a pipe is specified in a command line as a simple vertical bar]|[between two command sequences. The output or result of the first command sequence is used as the input to the second command sequence. The *pipe* system call is used in a similar way within a program.

For two-way communication between processes, two pipes can be set up, one for each direction. A limitation of pipes for interprocess communication is that the processes using pipes must have a common parent process (that is, share a common open or initiation process and exist as the result of a *fork* system call from a parent process).

A pipe is fixed in size and is usually at least 4,096 bytes.

pipeline burst cache

A pipeline burst cache is a **cache** or storage area for a computer **processor** that is designed to be read from or written to in a **pipelining** succession of four data transfers (or **burst**s) in which later bursts can start to flow or transfer before the first burst has arrived at the processor. A pipeline burst cache is often used for the static RAM (**SRAM**) that serves as the **L1 and L2** cache in a computer. It was introduced in 1996 with Intel's **Pentium** series of processors. A pipeline burst cache is an alternative to an *asynchronous cache* or a *synchronous burst cache*.

In most personal computer processors, data is transferred along a path (or **bus**) that is 64 bits (8 bytes) wide. Since each line of storage in a cache is 32 bytes long, it takes four successive transfers to transfer the storage line. With a pipeline burst cache, the first transfer takes 3 of the processor's **clock speed** cycles, and the remaining three transfers take only one cycle each (since no time is required to locate the storage location for the remaining transfers). The adjectives **pipelining** and **burst** describe the idea that once the storage location has been addressed and accessed and the first read or write transfer is started, the subsequent transfers come rapidly in discrete bursts down (or up) the pipe or data path. The timing for the total transfer of a storage line using pipeline burst cache is usually shown as "3-1-1-1" or a total of 6 clock cycles.

pipelining

In computers, a pipeline is the continuous and somewhat overlapped movement of **instructions** to the **processor** or in the arithmetic steps taken by the processor to perform an instruction. Pipelining is the use of a pipeline. Without a pipeline, a computer processor gets the first instruction from memory, performs the operation it calls for, and then goes to get the next instruction from memory, and so forth. While fetching (getting) the instruction, the arithmetic part of the processor is idle. It must wait until it gets the next instruction. With pipelining, the computer architecture allows the next instructions to be fetched while the processor is performing arithmetic operations, holding them in a **buffer** close to the processor until each instruction operation can be performed. The staging of instruction fetching is continuous. The result is an increase in the number of instructions that can be performed during a given time period.

Pipelining is sometimes compared to a manufacturing assembly line in which different parts of a product are being assembled at the same time although ultimately there may be some parts that have to be assembled before others are. Even if there is some sequential dependency, the overall process can take advantage of those operations that can proceed concurrently.

Computer processor pipelining is sometimes divided into an instruction pipeline and an arithmetic pipeline. The instruction pipeline represents the stages in which an instruction is moved through the processor, including its being fetched, perhaps buffered, and then executed. The arithmetic pipeline represents the parts of an arithmetic operation that can be broken down and overlapped as they are performed.

Pipelines and pipelining also apply to computer memory controllers and moving data through various memory staging places.

piracy

Software piracy is the illegal copying, distribution, or use of software. According to one source, about 40% of all software in current use is stolen. In 1998, revenue losses from software piracy were estimated at $11 billion worldwide. North America, Asia, and Western Europe account for 80% of revenue losses with the U.S. ranking highest in dollar losses. It is such a profitable "business" that it has caught the attention of organized crime groups in a number of countries. Software piracy causes significant lost revenue for publishers, which in turn results in higher prices for the consumer. Some software publishers go out of business because of software piracy. Others are discouraged from entering markets where software piracy rates are high.

When you purchase a commercial software package, a licensing agreement is included to protect that software program from copyright infringement. Typically, the license

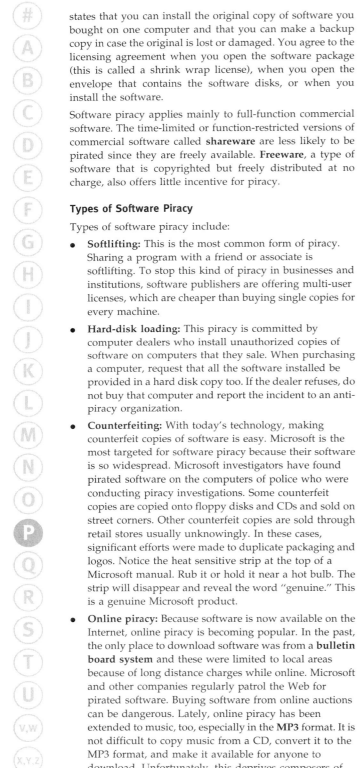

states that you can install the original copy of software you bought on one computer and that you can make a backup copy in case the original is lost or damaged. You agree to the licensing agreement when you open the software package (this is called a shrink wrap license), when you open the envelope that contains the software disks, or when you install the software.

Software piracy applies mainly to full-function commercial software. The time-limited or function-restricted versions of commercial software called **shareware** are less likely to be pirated since they are freely available. **Freeware**, a type of software that is copyrighted but freely distributed at no charge, also offers little incentive for piracy.

Types of Software Piracy

Types of software piracy include:

- **Softlifting:** This is the most common form of piracy. Sharing a program with a friend or associate is softlifting. To stop this kind of piracy in businesses and institutions, software publishers are offering multi-user licenses, which are cheaper than buying single copies for every machine.

- **Hard-disk loading:** This piracy is committed by computer dealers who install unauthorized copies of software on computers that they sale. When purchasing a computer, request that all the software installed be provided in a hard disk copy too. If the dealer refuses, do not buy that computer and report the incident to an anti-piracy organization.

- **Counterfeiting:** With today's technology, making counterfeit copies of software is easy. Microsoft is the most targeted for software piracy because their software is so widespread. Microsoft investigators have found pirated software on the computers of police who were conducting piracy investigations. Some counterfeit copies are copied onto floppy disks and CDs and sold on street corners. Other counterfeit copies are sold through retail stores usually unknowingly. In these cases, significant efforts were made to duplicate packaging and logos. Notice the heat sensitive strip at the top of a Microsoft manual. Rub it or hold it near a hot bulb. The strip will disappear and reveal the word "genuine." This is a genuine Microsoft product.

- **Online piracy:** Because software is now available on the Internet, online piracy is becoming popular. In the past, the only place to download software was from a **bulletin board system** and these were limited to local areas because of long distance charges while online. Microsoft and other companies regularly patrol the Web for pirated software. Buying software from online auctions can be dangerous. Lately, online piracy has been extended to music, too, especially in the **MP3** format. It is not difficult to copy music from a CD, convert it to the MP3 format, and make it available for anyone to download. Unfortunately, this deprives composers of

royalties that they are entitled to. Although much pirated music is available in the MP3 format, MP3.com has recently made arrangements to charge users for downloads and pay royalties to composers who make music available.

How to Fight Piracy

The first step in fighting software piracy is to make sure you don't contribute to it knowingly or unknowingly. Buy software from an authorized dealer and don't use any program offered illegally. If you discover that you might have a counterfeit copy of software, contact the dealer you bought it from, but keep in mind that they may have been fooled, too. Enterprises with networks need policies that state what is acceptable in using software, stipulating consequences for illegal use. An enterprise may want to consider purchasing an anti-piracy program. For example, KeyServer keeps track of how many copies are in use at one time on a network. Another solution certain publishers have used is the **dongle**, a device that attaches to a serial or parallel port of a desktop or into the PC-Card host of a laptop. A dongle uses codes or passwords that are embedded inside to control access to a software application. A program used with a dongle will only work when the dongle is attached to the computer. Most dongles can be daisy-chained with a printer or other dongles.

There are potentially stiff penalties for software piracy. In the U.S., software pirates can be punished with statutory damages of up to $100,000. If you are convicted of a felony charge of software piracy, you can get up to a five-year prison sentence plus fines of up to $250,000 for each work that is infringed.

pixel

A pixel (a word invented from "picture element") is the basic unit of programmable color on a computer display or in a computer image. Think of it as a logical—rather than a physical—unit. The physical size of a pixel depends on how you've set the **resolution** for the display screen. If you've set the display to its maximum resolution, the physical size of a pixel will equal the physical size of the **dot pitch** (let's just call it the dot size) of the display. If, however, you've set the resolution to something less than the maximum resolution, a pixel will be larger than the physical size of the screen's dot (that is, a pixel will use more than one dot).

The specific color that a pixel describes is some blend of three components of the color spectrum—**RGB**. Up to three bytes of data are allocated for specifying a pixel's color, one byte for each color. A **true color** or 24-bit color system uses all three bytes. However, most color display systems use only eight-bits (which provides up to 256 different colors).

A **bitmap** is a file that indicates a color for each pixel along the horizontal axis or row (called the x coordinate) and a color for each pixel along the vertical axis (called the y

coordinate). A **Graphics Interchange Format** file, for example, contains a bitmap of an image (along with other data).

Screen image sharpness is sometimes expressed as dots per inch (**dpi**). (In this usage, the term *dot* means pixel, not dot as in *dot pitch*.) Dots per inch is determined by both the physical screen size and the resolution setting. A given image will have lower resolution—fewer dots per inch—on a larger screen as the same data is spread out over a larger physical area. On the same size screen, the image will have lower resolution if the resolution setting is made lower—resetting from 800 by 600 pixels per horizontal and vertical line to 640 by 480 means fewer dots per inch on the screen and an image that is less sharp. (On the other hand, individual image elements such as text will be larger in size.)

Pixel has generally replaced an earlier contraction of picture element, *pel*.

pixels per inch

In computers, pixels per inch (ppi) is a measure of the sharpness (that is, the density of illuminated points) on a display **screen**. The **dot pitch** determines the absolute limit of the possible pixels per inch. However, the displayed **resolution** of **pixels** (picture elements) that is set up for the display is usually not as fine as the dot pitch. The pixels per inch for a given picture resolution will differ based on the overall screen size since the same number of pixels are being spread out over a different space. The term "dots per inch" (**dpi**), extended from the print medium, is sometimes used instead of pixels per inch.

pixie dust

Pixie dust is the informal name that IBM is using for its antiferromagnetically-coupled (AFC) media technology, which can increase the data capacity of **hard drives** to up to four times the density possible with current drives. AFC overcomes limits of current hard drives caused by a phenomenon called the *superparamagnet effect* (basically, alterations in magnetic orientation). The "pixie dust" used is a 3-**atom** thick magnetic coating composed of the element *ruthenium* sandwiched between two magnetic layers. The technology is expected to yield 400 GB (**gigabyte**) hard drives for desktop computers, and 200 GB hard drives for laptops by 2003.

In information technology, the term "pixie dust" is often used to refer to a technology that seemingly does the impossible. IBM's use of AFC for hard drives overcomes what was considered an insuperable problem for storage: the physical limit for data stored on hard drives. Hard drive capacities have more or less doubled in each of the last five years, and it was assumed in the storage industry that the upper limit would soon be reached. The superparamagnetic effect has long been predicted to appear when densities reached 20 to 40 gigabits per square inch—close to the data

density of current products. AFC increases possible data density, so that capacity is increased without using either more **disks** or more heads to read the data. Current hard drives can store 20 gigabits of data per square inch. IBM began shipping Travelstar hard drives in May 2001 that are capable of storing 25.7 gigabits per square inch. Drives shipped later in the year are expected to be capable of 33% greater density. Because smaller drives will be able to store more data and use less power, the new technology may also lead to smaller and quieter devices.

IBM discovered a means of adding AFC to their standard production methods so that the increased capacity costs little or nothing. The company, which plans to implement the process across their entire line of products, chose not to publicize the technology in advance. Many companies have focused research on the use of AFC in hard drives; a number of vendors, such as Seagate Technology and Fujitsu, are expected to follow IBM's lead.

pk

See "peak"

PKCS

See "Public-Key Cryptography Standards"

PKI

A PKI (public key infrastructure) enables users of a basically unsecure public network such as the Internet to securely and privately exchange data and money through the use of a public and a private cryptographic key pair that is obtained and shared through a trusted authority. The public key infrastructure provides for a **digital certificate** that can identify an individual or an organization and directory services that can store and, when necessary, revoke the certificates. Although the components of a PKI are generally understood, a number of different vendor approaches and services are emerging. Meanwhile, an Internet standard for PKI is being worked on.

The public key infrastructure assumes the use of *public key cryptography*, which is the most common method on the Internet for authenticating a message sender or encrypting a message. Traditional **cryptography** has usually involved the creation and sharing of a **secret key** for the **encryption** and decryption of messages. This secret or private key system has the significant flaw that if the key is discovered or intercepted by someone else, messages can easily be decrypted. For this reason, public key cryptography and the public key infrastructure is the preferred approach on the Internet. (The private key system is sometimes known as *symmetric cryptography* and the public key system as *asymmetric cryptography*.)

A public key infrastructure consists of:

- A certificate authority (**CA**) that issues and verifies **digital certificate**. A certificate includes the public key or information about the public key
- A registration authority (**RA**) that acts as the verifier for the certificate authority before a digital certificate is issued to a requestor
- One or more directories where the certificates (with their public keys) are held
- A certificate management system

How Public and Private Key Cryptography Works

In public key cryptography, a public and private key are created simultaneously using the same **algorithm** (a popular one is known as **RSA**) by a certificate authority (CA). The private key is given only to the requesting party and the public key is made publicly available (as part of a digital certificate) in a directory that all parties can access. The private key is never shared with anyone or sent across the Internet. You use the private key to decrypt text that has been encrypted with your public key by someone else (who can find out what your public key is from a public directory). Thus, if I send you a message, I can find out your public key (but not your private key) from a central administrator and encrypt a message to you using your public key. When you receive it, you decrypt it with your private key. In addition to encrypting messages (which ensures privacy), you can authenticate yourself to me (so I know that it is really you who sent the message) by using your private key to encrypt a **digital certificate**. When I receive it, I can use your public key to decrypt it. Here's a table that restates it:

To do this	Use whose	Kind of key
Send an encrypted message	Use the receiver's	Public key
Send an encrypted signature	Use the sender's	Private key
Decrypt an encrypted message	Use the receiver's	Private key
Decrypt an encrypted signature (and authenticate the sender)	Use the sender's	Public key

Who Provides the Infrastructure

A number of products are offered that enable a company or group of companies to implement a PKI. The acceleration of **e-commerce** and business-to-business commerce over the Internet has increased the demand for PKI solutions. Related ideas are the virtual private network (**VPN**) and the IP Security (**IPsec**) standard. Among PKI leaders are:

- RSA, which has developed the main algorithms used by PKI vendors
- Verisign, which acts as a certificate authority and sells software that allows a company to create its own certificate authorities
- GTE CyberTrust, which provides a PKI implementation methodology and consultation service that it plans to vend to other companies for a fixed price
- Check Point, which offers a product, VPN-1 Certificate Manager, that is based on the Netscape Directory Server
- Xcert, whose Web Sentry product that checks the revocation status of certificates on a server, using the Online Certificate Status Protocol (OCSP)
- Netscape, whose Directory Server product is said to support 50 million objects and process 5,000 queries a second; Secure E-Commerce, which allows a company or **extranet** manager to manage digital certificates; and Meta-Directory, which can connect all corporate directories into a single directory for security management

Pretty Good Privacy

For e-mail, the Pretty Good Privacy (**PGP**) product lets you encrypt a message to anyone who has a public key. You encrypt it with their public key and they then decrypt it with their private key. PGP users share a directory of public keys that is called a *key ring*. (If you are sending a message to someone that doesn't have access to the key ring, you can't send them an encrypted message.) As another option, PGP lets you "sign" your note with a **digital signature** using your private key. The recipient can then get your public key (if they get access to the key ring) and decrypt your signature to see whether it was really you who sent the message.

PKUNZIP

See "PKZIP"

PKZIP

PKZIP (also capitalized as PKZip) is a program, originally written for the **DOS operating system**, that gathers multiple files into a single compressed file that can be stored in less space and transmitted more quickly from one place to another. A companion program, PKUNZIP, uncompresses and restores the original files when they are needed. The compressed file archive is known as a zip file and conventionally has a .zip file name suffix. The "PK" derives from the name of the program's inventor, Phillip W. Katz. Katz is said to have developed the idea in 1986, working at his mother's kitchen table. PKZIP became one of the most popular **shareware** programs ever written and, with various platform distributions, an industry standard.

The original owner, PKWARE, still distributes the program in versions for a number of different operating system **platform**s. Several other companies also distribute cross-platform versions that enable files to be economically exchanged between locations. For example, a company with an IBM **OS/390** (**MVS**) platform can use PKZIP MVS to build an archive that can be transmitted to a Sun **Solaris** (**UNIX**) platform or to an IBM **OS/400** platform where it can be unzipped using PKUNZIP UNIX.

Windows users often use **WinZip**, another popular program that also uses the .zip file format.

PL/I

PL/I is a third-generation (**3GL**) programming language developed in the early 1960s as an alternative to **assembler** language (for low-level computer processing functions), **COBOL** (for large-scale business applications), and **FORTRAN** (for scientific and algorithmic applications). PL/I stands for "Programming Language 1." PL/I was an antecedent of the **C** programming language, which essentially replaced it as an all-purpose serious programming language.

PL/S, which IBM evolved from PL/I, was, until the advent of **C**, IBM's language of choice for its operating systems and application subsystems.

PL/S

PL/S is a language that IBM designed for use in developing system programs, especially in **mainframe operating system**s and application subsystems. It evolved from or was at least influenced by **PL/I**.

PL/SQL

In **Oracle database** management, PL/SQL is a procedural language extension to Structured Query Language (**SQL**). The purpose of PL/SQL is to combine database language and procedural programming language. The basic unit in PL/SQL is called a block, which is made up of three parts: a declarative part, an executable part, and an exception-building part.

Because PL/SQL allows you to mix SQL statements with procedural constructs, it is possible to use PL/SQL blocks and subprograms to group SQL statements before sending them to Oracle for execution. Without PL/SQL, Oracle must process SQL statements one at a time and, in a network environment, this can affect traffic flow and slow down response time. PL/SQL blocks can be compiled once and stored in **executable** form to increase response time.

A PL/SQL program that is stored in a database in compiled form and can be called by name is referred to as a **stored procedure**. A PL/SQL stored procedure that is implicitly started when an INSERT, UPDATE or DELETE statement is issued against an associated table is called a **trigger**.

plaintext

In cryptography, plaintext is ordinary readable **text** before being encrypted into **ciphertext** or after being decrypted.

planogram

A planogram is a diagram that shows how and where specific retail products should be placed on retail shelves or displays in order to increase customer purchases. Planogramming is a skill developed in the fields of merchandising and retail space planning. A person with this skill can be referred to as a planogrammer. Planograms themselves are also referred to as POGs.

Planograms can be developed for different types of retail merchandising displays (such as shelf displays, pegboards, or slatboard displays). They ar developed using other information about products, such as the amount of inventory left for the product, volume of sales per square foot of retail space, and other specific information about products (such as **stockkeeping unit** numbers, product codes, and so forth). By analyzing past and current sales patterns, a planogrammer can make successful recommendations about the number of "facings" a certain product should have on a retail display, how high or low it should be on the display, as well as which products should surround it. (Facings represent how many of the products should be facing straight out toward the customer.)

The resulting planogram can be printed out as a visual to be followed by the part-time help that is often hired to restock retail shelves and displays. This gives executive management of a retail store or chain more control over how products are displayed, and allows them to track and improve on the success of their planograms.

Planogram software is available for somewhere between $750 to well over $10,000. On the high end of the market, a planogramming component also is included with other larger space planning and retail space management software applications. Some consulting firms specialize in retail space management and planogramming.

plasma display

A plasma display is a computer video display in which each **pixel** on the screen is illuminated by a tiny bit of plasma or charged gas, somewhat like a tiny neon light. Plasma displays are thinner than cathode ray tube (**CRT**) displays and brighter than liquid crystal displays (**LCD**). Plasma displays are sometimes marketed as "thin-panel" displays and can be used to display either **analog** video signals or **display** digital computer input.

In addition to the advantage of slimness, a plasma display is flat rather than slightly curved as a CRT display is and therefore free of distortion on the edges of the screen. Unlike many LCD displays, a plasma display offers a very wide viewing angle. Plasma displays come in conventional PC displays sizes and also in sizes up to 60 inches for home theater and **high definition television**.

IBM built a monochrome plasma display in the 1980s that displayed orange letters against a black screen. Today's displays contain a grid of cells in which gas reacts with phosphors in varying degrees in red, green, or blue subpixels, making it possible to produce over 16 million different colors.

Plastic Interface for Collaborative Technology Initiatives

See "PICTIVE"

plastic pin grid array

See "PPGA"

Platform for Privacy Preferences Project

Sponsored by the World Wide Web Consortium, P3P (Platform for Privacy Preferences Project) is a framework for products and practices that will let World Wide Web users control the amount of personal information they share with **Web site**s. It's described as a "**privacy** assistant." Using a P3P **application**, a user can enter personal information once and not have to repeatedly reenter it at different Web sites. The P3P application can inform a user (or a programmed **agent** that is operating for the user) of a Web site's practices with regard to gathering and reusing its visitors' personal information. Users will be able to define the information that a specific site can be provided or not provided.

P3P is related to and encompasses the Open Profiling Standard (**OPS**) proposed by Netscape Communications (now part of America Online). It also considers Microsoft's formal proposal for privacy and profiling on the Web. P3P defines a vocabulary and a standard data format for expressing personal information within the W3C's Resource Definition Framework (RDF), which uses the **syntax** of the Extensible Markup Language (**XML**). P3P will not necessarily replace the use of **cookies** (individual files that a Web site puts on the user's own hard disk to keep track of interaction). However, it may change the way that cookies are used.

The P3P Recommendations are available at the W3C Web site. Companies that have worked on or contributed to P3P include AT&T Labs, Center for Democracy and Technology, Digital Equipment Corporation, DISA, DoubleClick, Engage Technologies, Ernst & Young LLP, Firefly Network Inc, IBM, Intermind Corporation, MatchLogic, Microsoft, MIT,

Narrowline, NEC, Netscape Communications, Open Market Inc., Open Sesame, Oracle Corporation, Sony, The DMA, TRUSTe, and VeriSign.

platform

1) In computers, a platform is an underlying computer system on which application programs can run. On personal computers, Windows 2000 and the Macintosh are examples of two different platforms. On **enterprise server**s or **mainframe**s, IBM's S/390 is an example of a platform.

A platform consists of an **operating system**, the computer system's coordinating program, which in turn is built on the instruction set for a **processor** or **microprocessor**, the hardware that performs logic operations and manages data movement in the computer. The operating system must be designed to work with the particular processor's set of instructions. As an example, Microsoft's Windows 2000 is built to work with a series of microprocessors from the Intel Corporation that share the same or similar sets of instructions. There are usually other implied parts in any computer platform such as a motherboard and a data bus, but these parts have increasingly become modularized and standardized.

Historically, most application programs have had to be written to run on a particular platform. Each platform provided a different application program interface for different system services. Thus, a PC program would have to be written to run on the Windows platform and then again to run on the Macintosh platform. Although these platform differences continue to exist and there will probably always be proprietary differences between them, new **open** or standards-conforming interfaces now allow many programs to run on different platforms or to interoperate with different platforms through mediating or "broker" programs.

2) A platform is any base of technologies on which other technologies or processes are built.

PLEDM

PLEDM (phase-state low electron drive memory) is a new **memory microchip** technology that offers vastly greater capacity than memory devices commonly used in the past. The images and sound for a full-length movie can be stored on a single PLEDM device. Because the memory is **nonvolatile memory** (data remains when power is removed), PLEDM chips, which contain no moving parts, offer the possibility of replacing the electromechanical disk drives familiar to today's PC users.

The first PLEDM chips, developed in 1999 at Hitachi's laboratory at the University of Cambridge, had a read/write time of less than 10 nanoseconds (10^{-8} seconds). In the future, these chips promise to combine the high speed currently available with **DRAM** (dynamic random-access memory) and the nonvolatility of so-called **flash memory**. It is envisioned that the chips could also be used in mobile and portable telephone sets and in digital video recorders. Ultimately, this technology might lead to single-electron memory (SEM), in which each data bit is determined by the presence or absence of one **electron** in an **atom** or at a particular energy level within an atom.

Products using PLEDM are expected to become available at the consumer level by 2005.

plenum

In building construction, a plenum (pronounced PLEH-nuhm, from Latin meaning *full*) is a separate space provided for air circulation for heating, ventilation, and air-conditioning (sometimes referred to as HVAC) and typically provided in the space between the structural ceiling and a drop-down ceiling. A plenum may also be under a raised floor. In buildings with computer installations, the plenum space is often used to house connecting communication cables. Because ordinary cable introduces a toxic hazard in the event of fire, special plenum cabling is required in plenum areas.

In the U.S., typical plenum cable sizes are **American Wire Gauge** (AWG) sizes 22 and 24. Plenum cabling is often made of Teflon and is more expensive than ordinary cabling. In the event of fire, its outer material is more resistant to flames and, when burning, produces less smoke than ordinary cabling. Both **twisted pair** and **coaxial cable** are made in plenum cable versions.

plesiochronous

Plesiochronous (pronounced plee-see-AH-krun-us, from Greek *plesos*, meaning close, and *chronos*, meaning time) is an adjective that describes operations that are almost, but not quite, in synchronization—in other words, almost synchronous. The term is used in the Plesiochronous Digital Hierarchy (**PDH**), the widely-used system in which the transmissions from one continent (such as North America) are internetworked with transmissions in other continents (such as Europe) by making small adjustments in the differing data rates between the systems.

A plesiochronous system could arise as the result of two systems having slightly different clock readings over time. In such a system, one of the systems or a third system would need to notice the mismatch and make some compensating adjustment, such as repeating or deleting a data packet or frame.

Plesiochronous can be compared with **asynchronous**, **isochronous**, and **synchronous**.

Plug and Play

Plug and Play (PnP) is a capability developed by Microsoft for its Windows 95 and later **operating system**s that gives users the ability to plug a device into a computer and have the computer recognize that the device is there. The user

doesn't have to tell the computer. In many earlier computer systems, the user was required to explicitly tell the operating system when a new device had been added. Microsoft made Plug and Play a selling point for its Windows operating systems. A similar capability had long been built into **Macintosh** computers.

With Microsoft's participation, Plug and Play has been replaced by an open, industry standard, Universal Plug and Play (**UPnP**), which uses Internet protocols for seamless device plug-in.

Also see **plug-in**.

plug-and-play

See "Plug and Play"

plug-in

Plug-in applications are programs that can easily be installed and used as part of your Web **browser**. Initially, the Netscape browser allowed you to download, install, and define supplementary programs that played sound or motion video or performed other functions. These were called helper applications. However, these applications run as a separate application and require that a second window be opened. A plug-in application is recognized automatically by the browser and its function is integrated into the main HTML file that is being presented.

Among popular plug-ins to download are Adobe's **Acrobat**, a document presentation and navigation program that lets you view documents just as they look in the print medium, RealNetworks' **streaming video** player, and Macromedia's Shockwave for DIrector, an interactive animation and sound player. There are now hundreds of possible plug-ins. Most users wait until they need a particular plug-in before they download it.

Also see **Plug and Play**.

PM

See "phase modulation"

PNG

See "Portable Network Graphics"

PnP

See "Plug and Play"

point-of-presence

A point-of-presence (POP) is an access point to the Internet. A POP necessarily has a unique Internet Protocol (**IP**) address. Your Internet service provider (**ISP**) or online service provider (such as AOL) has a point-of-presence on the Internet and probably more than one. The number of POPs that an ISP or OSP has is sometimes used as a measure of its size or growth rate.

A POP may actually reside in rented space owned by the telecommunications carrier (such as Sprint) to which the ISP is connected. A POP usually includes routers, digital/analog call aggregators, servers, and frequently **frame relay**s or **ATM** switches.

Point-to-Point Protocol

See "PPP"

Point-to-Point Tunneling Protocol

PPTP (Point-to-Point Tunneling Protocol) is a **protocol** (set of communication rules) that allows corporations to extend their own corporate network through private "tunnels" over the public Internet. Effectively, a corporation uses a wide-area network as a single large local area network. A company no longer needs to lease its own lines for wide-area communication but can securely use the public networks. This kind of interconnection is known as a virtual private network (**VPN**).

PPTP, a proposed standard sponsored by Microsoft and other companies, and Layer 2 Forwarding, proposed by Cisco Systems, are among the most likely proposals as the basis for a new Internet Engineering Task Force (**IETF**) standard. With PPTP, which is an extension of the Internet's Point-to-Point Protocol (**PPP**), any user of a PC with PPP client support is able to use an independent service provider (**ISP**) to connect securely to a server elsewhere in the user's company.

poison reverse

In a computer network that uses the Routing Information Protocol (**RIP**) or other **distance vector routing protocol**s, a poison reverse is a way in which a **gateway node** tells its neighbor gateways that one of the gateways is no longer connected. To do this, the notifying gateway sets the number of **hop**s to the unconnected gateway to a number that indicates "infinite" (meaning "You can't get there"). Since RIP allows up to 15 hops to another gateway, setting the hop count to 16 would mean "infinite."

polarity

Also see **bipolar signaling** and **unipolar signaling**.

Polarity is a term used in electricity, magnetism, and electronic signaling. Suppose there is a constant **voltage**, also called an electric potential or electromotive force (EMF), between two objects or points. In such a situation, one of the objects or points (poles) has more electrons than the other. The pole with relatively more electrons is said to have negative polarity; the other is assigned positive polarity. If the two poles are connected by a conductive path such as a wire, **electron**s flow from the negative pole toward the positive pole. This flow of charge carriers constitutes an electric **current**. In physics, the theoretical direction of current flow is considered to be from positive to negative by convention, opposite to the flow of electrons.

The movement of electric charge carriers inevitably produces a magnetic field. Conversely, any magnetic field is the result of the motion of charge carriers. In a permanent magnet, a magnetic field is produced by the composite motions of electrons in geometrically aligned **atom**s. A magnetic field is characterized by poles called north and south. Magnetic polarity refers to the orientation of these poles in space.

In **digital** communications, data is composed of short-duration pulses called **bit**s. There are two possible states for each bit: Logic 0 (also called low) and logic 1 (also called high). In a closed circuit, these logic elements are represented by **direct current** voltages. A high-speed data signal varies rapidly between the low and high states. Common values are approximately +0.5 volts for low and +5 volts for high. In some cases different values are used, for example, −3 volts for low and +3 volts for high, or −5 volts for low and −0.5 volts for high. If both voltages have the same polarity, the signal is called unipolar; if the voltages have opposite polarity, the signal is called bipolar.

policy

1) In **policy-based networking**, a policy is a formal set of statements that define how the network's resources are to be allocated among its clients. Clients can be individual users, departments, host computers, or applications. Resources can be allocated based on time of day, client authorization priorities, availability of resources, and other factors. Allocation can be static or dynamic (based on variations in traffic). Policies and policy statements are created by network managers and stored in a *policy repository*. During network operation, the policies are retrieved and used by network management software to make decisions.

Ideally, policy statements can be written in natural language like this:

```
Give voice-over-IP users the highest priority. Give
teleconference users the next highest priority.
```

In practice, most policy-based networking software today requires specific knowledge of the network configuration and the use of a more artificial language.

2) In Hierarchical Storage Management (**HSM**), a policy is a set of statements used to guide HSM software about when to backup or archive files or to migrate them from one form of backup storage to another.

policy-based management

Policy-based management is an administrative approach that is used to simplify the management of a given endeavor by establishing policies to deal with situations that are likely to occur. Policies are operating rules that can be referred to as a means of maintaining order, security, consistency, or other ways of successfully furthering a goal or mission. For example, a town council might have in place a policy against hiring the relatives of council members for civic positions. Then, each time that situation arose, council members could refer to the policy rather than deciding on the merits of individual cases. In the computing world, policy-based management is used as an administrative tool throughout an enterprise or a network, or on workstations that have multiple users. Policy-based management includes **policy-based network management**, the use of delineated policies to control access to and priorities for the use of resources. Policy-based management may be used in **systems management**, or the creation and operation of an efficient computing environment.

Policy-based management of a multi-user workstation typically includes setting individual policies for such things as access to files or applications, various levels of access (such as "read-only" permission, or permission to update or delete files), the appearance and makeup of individual users' desktops, and so on. Specific user settings are activated when that person logs in to the computer. There are a number of software packages available to automate some elements of policy-based management. In general, the way these work is as follows: business policies are input to the products, and the software communicates to network hardware how to support those policies.

policy-based networking

Policy-based networking is the management of a network so that various kinds of traffic—data, voice, and video—get the priority of availability and bandwidth needed to serve the network's users effectively. With the **convergence** of data, telephone, and video traffic in the same network, companies will be challenged to manage traffic so that one kind of service doesn't preempt another kind. Using **policy** statements, network administrators can specify which kinds of service to give priority at what times of day on what parts of their Internet Protocol (**IP**)-based network. This kind of management is often known as Quality of Service (**QoS**) and is controlled using policy-based network software. Theoretically, a policy statement could be as natural as:

"Provide the fastest forwarding for all voice traffic to Chicago between 9 am and 3pm."

In actuality, most policy-based networking software today requires a much more detailed and network-aware statement. Currently, the Internet Engineering Task Force (**IETF**) is working on a standard policy framework and related protocols. A typical policy-based network includes:

- A network management console at which policies are entered, edited, or called from a policy repository
- A **server**, referred to as the policy decision point (PDP), that retrieves policies from the policy repository and acts on the policies on behalf of Policy Enforcement Points (PEPs)
- The Policy Enforcement Points (PEPs), which are the **routers**, **switch**es, and other network devices that enforce the policies, using **access control list**, **queue** management algorithms, and so forth
- The Policy Repository, a directory server of policies that is based on the Lightweight Directory Access Protocol (**LDAP**)

Among companies that currently provide proprietary policy-based networking software are Cabletron, Cisco, Nortel, and 3Com. These companies are aware of (and perhaps contributing to) the developing standard. Their products are likely to continue to evolve in support of the standard.

polling

In electronic communication, "polling" is the continuous checking of other programs or devices by one progam or device to see what state they are in, usually to see whether they are still connected or want to communicate.

Specifically, in multipoint or multidrop communication (a controlling device with multiple devices attached that share the same line), the controlling device sends a message to each device, one at a time, asking each whether it has anything to communicate (in other words, whether it wants to use the line).

polyLED

See "polymer LED"

polymer LED

Polymer LED (**light-emitting diode**)—sometimes called *light-emitting polymer* or *polyLED*—is a technology based on the use of polymer as the **semiconductor** material in LEDs. Dow Chemical Corporation announced the discovery of light-emitting polymers at the spring meeting of the Materials Research Society in 1998. Polymers are chemical substances that consist of large molecules that are, themselves, made from many smaller and simpler molecules: Proteins and DNA are examples of naturally occuring polymers; many others, such as nylon, are artificially created. Because of their flexibility and strength, polymers are used for products such as car bumpers and bullet-proof vests.

Because polymers are lightweight and flexible, they can simply and inexpensively be used for the creation of thin film displays for future technologies such as the **electronic newspaper**. Polymer LEDs have a number of inherent qualities that are ideally suited to such applications: they enable full-spectrum color displays, high brightness at low drive voltages, glare-free viewing, and long operating lifetimes. It is currently possible to create a small text display by structuring the polymer material and electrodes. The technology also offers a great deal of promise as a basis for cheaper, simpler lighting sources. According to Edmund Woo, of Dow's Materials Researched and Development Laboratory, polymer LEDs could be used to create a brightness similiar to that of fluorescent lighting on a 5-volt power supply.

polynomial

A polynomial is a mathematical expression consisting of a sum of terms, each term including a variable or variables raised to a power and multiplied by a **coefficient**. The simplest polynomials have one variable. A one-variable (univariate) polynomial of degree n has the following form:

$$a_n x^n + a_n \text{-}1 x^n \text{-}1 + \ldots + a_2 x^2 + a_1 x^1 + a_0 x^0$$

where the a's represent the coefficients and x represents the variable. Because $x^1 = x$ and $x^0 = 1$ for all **complex numbers** x, the above expression can be simplified to:

$$a_n x^n + a_n \text{-}1 x^n \text{-}1 + \ldots + a_2 x^2 + a_1 x + a_0$$

When an nth-degree univariate polynomial is equal to zero, the result is a univariate polynomial equation of degree n:

$$a_n x^n + a_n \text{-}1 x^n \text{-}1 + \ldots + a_2 x^2 + a_1 x + a_0 = 0$$

There may be several different values of x, called roots, that satisfy a univariate polynomial equation. In general, the higher the order of the equation (that is, the larger the value of n), the more roots there are.

A univariate polynomial equation of degree 1 (n = 1) constitutes a linear equation. When n = 2, it is a quadratic equation; when n = 3, it is a cubic equation; when n = 4, it is a quartic equation; when n = 5, it is a quintic equation. The larger the value of n, the more difficult it is to find all the roots of a univariate polynomial equation.

Some polynomials have two, three, or more variables. A two-variable polynomial is called bivariate; a three-variable polynomial is called trivariate.

PON

See "passive optical network"

POP

See "point-of-presence"

POP3

POP3 (Post Office Protocol 3) is the most recent version of a standard protocol for receiving e-mail. POP3 is a client/server protocol in which e-mail is received and held for you by your Internet server. Periodically, you (or your client e-mail receiver) check your mail-box on the server and

download any mail. POP3 is built into the Netmanage suite of Internet products and one of the most popular e-mail products, Eudora. It's also built into the Netscape and Microsoft Internet Explorer browsers.

An alternative protocol is Internet Message Access Protocol (**IMAP**). With IMAP, you view your e-mail at the server as though it was on your client computer. An e-mail message deleted locally is still on the server. E-mail can be kept on and searched at the server.

POP can be thought of as a "store-and-forward" service. IMAP can be thought of as a remote file server.

POP and IMAP deal with the receiving of e-mail and are not to be confused with the Simple Mail Transfer Protocol (**SMTP**), a protocol for transferring e-mail across the Internet. You send e-mail with SMTP and a mail handler receives it on your recipient's behalf. Then the mail is read using POP or IMAP.

The conventional **port number** for POP3 is 110.

pop-up

A pop-up is a graphical user interface (**GUI**) display area, usually a small window, that suddenly appears ("pops up") in the foreground of the visual interface. Pop-ups can be initiated by a single or double mouse click or **rollover** (sometimes called a mouseover), and also possibly by voice command or can simply be timed to occur. A pop-up window must be smaller than the background window or interface; otherwise, it's a replacement interface.

On the World Wide Web, **JavaScript** (and less commonly **Java applet**s) are used to create interactive effects including pop-up and full overlay windows.

A menu or taskbar pulldown can be considered a form of pop-up. So can the little message box you get when you move your mouse over taskbars in many PC applications.

port

1) On computer and telecommunication devices, a *port* (noun) is generally a specific place for being physically connected to some other device, usually with a socket and plug of some kind. Typically, a personal computer is provided with one or more **serial** ports and usually one **parallel** port. The serial port supports sequential, one bit-at-a-time transmission to peripheral devices such as scanners and the parallel port supports multiple-bit-at-a-time transmission to devices such as printers.

2) In programming, a port (noun) is a "logical connection place" and specifically, using the Internet's protocol, **TCP/IP**, the way a client program specifies a particular server program on a computer in a network. Higher-level applications that use TCP/IP such as the Web protocol, **Hypertext Transfer Protocol**, have ports with preassigned numbers. These are known as "well-known ports" that have been assigned by the Internet Assigned Numbers Authority

(IANA). Other application processes are given port numbers dynamically for each connection. When a service (**server** program) initially is started, it is said to **bind** to its designated port number. As any **client** program wants to use that server, it also must request to bind to the designated port number.

Port numbers are from 0 to 65536. Ports 0 to 1024 are reserved for use by certain privileged services. For the HTTP service, port 80 is defined as a default and it does not have to be specified in the Uniform Resource Locator (**URL**).

3) In programming, to port (verb) is to move an application program from an operating system environment in which it was developed to another operating system environment so it can be run there. Porting implies some work, but not nearly as much as redeveloping the program in the new environment. **Open** standard programming **interfaces** (such as those specified in X/Open's **1170 C** language specification and Sun Microsystem's **Java** programming language) minimize or eliminate the work required to port a program. Also see **portability**.

port 80

On a Web server or **Hypertext Transfer Protocol daemon**, port 80 is the port that the server "listens to" or expects to receive from a Web client, assuming that the default was taken when the server was configured or set up. A port can be specified in the range from 0-65536. However, the server administrator configures the server so that only one port number can be recognized. By default, the port number for a Web server is 80. Experimental services are sometimes run at port 8080.

port mirroring

Port mirroring, also known as a roving analysis port, is a method of monitoring network traffic that forwards a copy of each incoming and outgoing **packet** from one **port** of a network **switch** to another port where the packet can be studied. A network administrator uses port mirroring as a diagnostic tool or **debugging** feature, especially when fending off an attack. It enables the administrator to keep close track of switch performance and alter it if necessary. Port mirroring can be managed locally or remotely.

An administrator configures port mirroring by assigning a port from which to copy all packets and another port where those packets will be sent. A packet bound for or heading away from the first port will be forwarded onto the second port as well. The administrator places a protocol analyzer on the port receiving the mirrored data to monitor each segment separately. The analyzer captures and evaluates the data without affecting the client on the original port.

The monitor port may be a port on the same SwitchModule with an attached **RMON** probe, a port on a different SwitchModule in the same **hub**, or the SwitchModule processor.

Port mirroring can consume significant CPU resources while active. Better choices for long-term monitoring may include a passive tap like an optical probe or an Ethernet repeater.

port number

A port number is a way to identify a specific process to which an Internet or other network message is to be forwarded when it arrives at a **server**. For the **Transmission Control Protocol** and the **User Datagram Protocol**, a port number is a 16-**bit integer** that is put in the header appended to a message unit. This port number is passed logically between **client** and server Transport layers.

For example, a request from a client (perhaps on behalf of you at your PC) to a server on the Internet may request a file be served from that host's File Transfer Protocol (**FTP**) server or process. In order to pass your request to the FTP process in the remote server, the Transmission Control Protocol (**TCP**) software layer in your computer identifies the port number of 21 (which by convention is associated with an FTP request) in the 16-bit port number integer that is appended to your request. At the server, the TCP layer will read the port number of 21 and forward your request to the FTP program at the server.

Some services or processes have conventionally assigned permanent port numbers. These are known as **well-known port numbers**. In other cases, a port number is assigned temporarily (for the duration of the request and its completion) from a range of assigned port numbers. This is called an **ephemeral port number**.

port replicator

A port replicator is an attachment for a **notebook computer** that allows a number of devices such as a printer, large monitor, and keyboard to be simultaneously connected. Each of the devices is attached to the port replicator and when the notebook user wants access to one or more of the devices, the user simply attaches the port replicator rather than having to connect one device at a time. The port replicator duplicates each of the notebook's **port**, including **parallel** and **serial** ports. In addition, it may provide some extra ports for devices such as joysticks or Musical Instrument Digital Interface (**MIDI**) devices.

A port replicator is similar to a **docking station**, but does not include expansion **slots**.

Connecting a notebook to a port replicator is a simple process:

- Attach all devices needed to the port replicator.
- Close the notebook's display panel and align the connectors of the port replicator to the notebook ports.
- Gently press the notebook down until the securing tabs lock into place.
- Open the display panel and use the computer.

The notebook computer can be on or off during the connection and disconnection process. To disconnect the computer from the port replicator, press the notebook release buttons and lift the notebook away from the replicator.

port scan

A port scan is a series of messages sent by someone attempting to break into a computer to learn which computer network services, each associated with a "well-known" **port** number, the computer provides. Port scanning, a favorite approach of computer **crackers**, gives the assailant an idea where to probe for weaknesses. Essentially, a port scan consists of sending a message to each port, one at a time. The kind of response received indicates whether the port is used and can therefore be probed for weakness.

Types of port scans include:

- **Vanilla**—An attempt to connect to all ports (there are 65,536)

- Strobe—An attempt to connect to only selected ports (typically, under 20)

- Stealth scan—Several techniques for scanning that attempt to prevent the request for connection being logged

- FTP Bounce Scan—Attempts that are directed through an **FTP server** to disguise the cracker's location

- Fragmented Packets—Scans by sending **packet** fragments that can get through simple packet filters in a **firewall**

- UDP—Scans for open **User Datagram Protocol** ports

- Sweep—Scans the same port on a number of computers

portability

Portability is a characteristic attributed to a computer program if it can be used in an **operating system**s other than the one in which it was created without requiring major rework. *Porting* is the task of doing any work necessary to make the computer program run in the new environment. In general, programs that adhere to *standard* program interfaces such as the **X/Open UNIX** 95 standard **C** language interface are portable. Ideally, such a program needs only to be **compiled** for the operating system to which it is being ported. However, programmers using standard interfaces also sometimes use operating system *extensions* or special capabilities that may not be present in the new operating system. Uses of such extensions have to be removed or replaced with comparable functions in the new operating system. In addition to language differences, porting may also require data conversion and adaptation to new system procedures for running an application.

Portability has usually meant some work when moving an application program to another operating system. Recently, the **Java** programming language and runtime environment has made it possible to have programs that run on any operating system that supports the Java standard (from Sun Microsystems) without any porting work. Java **applet**s in the form of precompiled **bytecode** can be sent from a **server** program in one operating system to a **client** program (your Web browser) in another operating system without change.

portable computer

A portable computer is a personal computer that is designed to be easily transported and relocated, but is larger and less convenient to transport than a notebook computer. The earliest PCs designed for easy transport were called portables. As the size and weight of most portables decreased, they became known as **laptop computers** and later as **notebook computers**. Today, larger transportable computers continue to be called *portable computers*. Most of these are special-purpose computers—for example, those for use in industrial environments where they need to be moved about frequently.

Portable Document Format

PDF (Portable Document Format) is a file format that has captured all the elements of a printed document as an electronic image that you can view, navigate, print, or forward to someone else. PDF files are created using Adobe **Acrobat**, Acrobat Capture, or similar products. To view and use the files, you need the free Acrobat Reader, which you can easily download. Once you've downloaded the Reader, it will start automatically whenever you want to look at a PDF file.

PDF files are especially useful for documents such as magazine articles, product brochures, or flyers in which you want to preserve the original graphic appearance online. A PDF file contains one or more page images, each of which you can zoom in on or out from. You can page forward and backward.

The Acrobat product that lets you create PDF files sells in the $200-300 range. A non-Adobe alternative is a product called Niknak from 5D, a company in the UK. (The Reader itself is free and can be used as a **plug-in** with your Web browser or can be started by itself.) Some situations in which PDF files are desirable include:

- Graphic design development in which team members are working at a distance and need to explore design ideas online

- Help desk people who need to see the printed book that users are looking at

- The online distribution of any printed document in which you want to preserve its printed appearance

Acrobat's PDF files are more than images of documents. Files can embed type fonts so that they're available at any viewing location. They can also include interactive elements such as buttons for forms entry and for triggering sound and

Quicktime or AVI movies. PDF files are optimized for the Web by rendering text before graphic images and hypertext links.

Portable Network Graphics

PNG (pronounced PEENG) is a file format for **image compression** that, in time, is expected to replace the **Graphics Interchange Format** format that is widely used on today's Internet. Owned by Unisys, the GIF format and its usage in image-handling software involves licensing or other legal considerations. (Web users can make, view, and send GIF files freely but they can't develop software that builds them without an arrangement with Unisys.) The PNG format, on the other hand, was developed by an Internet committee expressly to be patent-free. It provides a number of improvements over the GIF format.

Like a GIF, a PNG file is compressed in lossless fashion (meaning all image information is restored when the file is decompressed during viewing). A PNG file is not intended to replace the **JPEG** format, which is "lossy" but lets the creator make a trade-off between file size and image quality when the image is compressed. Typically, an image in a PNG file can be 10 to 30% more compressed than in a GIF format.

The PNG format includes these features:

- You can not only make one color transparent, but you can control the degree of transparency (this is also called "opacity").
- **Interlacing** of the image is supported and is faster in developing than in the GIF format.
- *Gamma correction* allows you to "tune" the image in terms of color brightness required by specific display manufacturers.
- Images can be saved using **true color** as well as in the **palette** and gray-scale formats provided by the GIF.

Unlike the **GIF89a**, the PNG format doesn't support animation since it can't contain multiple images. The PNG is described as "extensible," however. Software houses will be able to develop variations of PNG that can contain multiple, scriptable images.

Portable Operating System Interface

See "POSIX"

portal

1) *Portal* is a term, generally synonymous with *gateway*, for a World Wide Web site that is or proposes to be a major starting site for users when they get connected to the Web or that users tend to visit as an anchor site. There are general portals and specialized or niche portals. Some major general portals include Yahoo, Excite, Netscape, Lycos, CNET, Microsoft Network, and America Online's AOL.com.

Examples of niche portals include Garden.com (for gardeners), Fool.com (for investors), and SearchNetworking.com (for network administrators).

A number of large access providers offer portals to the Web for their own users. Most portals have adopted the Yahoo style of content categories with a text-intensive, faster loading page that visitors will find easy to use and to return to. Companies with portal sites have attracted much stock market investor interest because portals are viewed as able to command large audiences and numbers of advertising viewers.

Typical services offered by portal sites include a directory of Web sites, a facility to search for other sites, news, weather information, e-mail, stock quotes, phone and map information, and sometimes a community forum. Excite is among the first portals to offer users the ability to create a site that is personalized for individual interests.

The term *portal space* is used to mean the total number of major sites competing to be one of the portals.

2) In fantasy games, science-fiction, and some "New Age" philosophies, a portal is a gateway to another world of the past, present, or future, or to an expanded awareness.

3) In **3-D** graphics development, *portal rendering* is a technique that increases the effect of realism and speeds up presentation.

Portal Markup Language

Portal Markup Language (PML), an application of the Extensible Markup Language (**XML**), describes the characteristics of a product that is used to create a **portal** Web site (sometimes referred to as an **enterprise information portal**). PML allows manufacturers to exchange information in a standard way about "information objects, users, groups, access control subscriptions and notifications managed by the system." PML is spelled out in a formal document tag definition (**DTD**). PML does not describe **syndication** (how content from one site could be published on other sites).

portal software

Portal software is a type of development tool used to create a **portal** (starting point) on a company's **intranet** so that employees can find a centralized starting place for access to consolidated enterprise-related functions, such as **e-mail**, customer relationship management (**CRM**) tools, company information, workgroup systems, and other applications. The package may be customized to varying degrees of enterprise or individual specificity. Portal software is similar to **intranet** software, but the end product typically features more complexity, automation, organization, and interactivity. Although the end product is sometimes referred to as an *intranet portal*, it is usually called an **enterprise information portal**.

Portal software packages generally fall into one of the four following categories: Digital dashboard, pure-play, application, or infrastructure portals. A *digital dashboard* portal package creates a centralized starting point for various applications and provide a summary of information pertaining to those applications, just as a car's dashboard provides centralized access to summarized information about various aspects of the car's critical details. A *pure-play* portal package concentrates on creating a portable interface for a specific portal offering across multiple platforms. Pure-play provides more functionality than the digital dashboard in a centralized access point for various business productivity applications, such as e-mail, collaboration tools, and resource planning tools. An *application* portal package includes a wide variety of tools—such as **workgroup** software—that have been adapted to go with a portal interface. Most common applications now fall into this category, since most are built to work in a portal environment. An *infrastructure* portal package is similar to a pure-play package, but is specifically geared towards technologies developed within the company rather than towards portability; for example, Oracle's portal product is geared toward Oracle technologies.

Corechange, Epicentric, Hummingbird, and Plumtree are among the leading portal software vendors. Most major software companies have released some type of portal software. Although the current generation of portal software is oriented towards the enterprise itself, it is likely that applications will increasingly encompass enterprise-customer interactions as well.

positional assembly

Positional assembly is one of several techniques that have been developed or suggested to construct machines on an atomic scale, where dimensions are measured in nanometers. One nanometer is 10-9 meter, or a millionth of a millimeter. Two things are necessary for positional assembly to be practical.

The first requirement is that a technician be able to see, and analyze, what is taking place as the process is carried out. This is known as **nanoanalysis**, and requires the use of precision observation equipment with high magnification and excellent resolving power. Electron microscopes are commonly used; alternative devices include ultraviolet (UV) and infrared (**IR**) microscopes, ion-beam devices, and X-ray microscopes. Computer processing of the images makes it possible to get a three-dimensional view.

The second requirement for positional assembly is the ability to manipulate tiny objects at will. This sometimes involves attaching individual **atom**s to, or detaching them from, other atoms one by one. In some cases this might be done by direct manipulation with microscopic tools. It might also be accomplished with the aid of special adhesives, or by

introducing electrical charges to cause atoms to stick together or come apart. Also see **exponential assembly**, **nanoanalysis**, and **self-assembly**.

POSIX

POSIX (Portable Operating System Interface) is a set of standard **operating system** interfaces based on the **UNIX** operating system. The need for standardization arose because enterprises using computers wanted to be able to develop programs that could be moved among different manufacturer's computer systems without having to be recoded. UNIX was selected as the basis for a standard system interface partly because it was "manufacturer-neutral." However, several major versions of UNIX existed so there was a need to develop a common denominator system.

Informally, each standard in the POSIX set is defined by a decimal following the POSIX. Thus, POSIX.1 is the standard for an application program interface in the **C** language. POSIX.2 is the standard **shell** and **utility** interface (that is to say, the user's command interface with the operating system). These are the main two interfaces, but additional interfaces, such as POSIX.4 for **thread** management, have been developed or are being developed. The POSIX interfaces were developed under the auspices of the Institute of Electrical and Electronics Engineers (**IEEE**).

POSIX.1 and POSIX.2 interfaces are included in a somewhat larger interface known as the X/Open Programming Guide 4.2 (also known as the "Single UNIX Specification" and "UNIX 95"). **The Open Group**, an industry standards group, owns the UNIX trademark and can thus "brand" operating systems that conform to the interface as "UNIX" systems. IBM's **OS/390** is an example of an operating system that includes a branded UNIX interface.

POST

When power is turned on, POST (Power-On Self-Test) is the diagnostic testing sequence that a computer's **basic input/output system** (or "starting program") runs to determine if the computer keyboard, **random access memory**, disk drives, and other hardware are working correctly.

If the necessary hardware is detected and found to be operating properly, the computer begins to **boot**. If the hardware is not detected or is found not to be operating properly, the BIOS issues an error message which may be text on the display screen and/or a series of coded beeps, depending on the nature of the problem. Since POST runs before the computer's video card is activated, it may not be possible to progress to the display screen. The pattern of beeps may be a variable numbers of short beeps or a mixture of long and short beeps, depending on what type of BIOS is installed.

The patterns of beeps contain messages about the nature of the problem detected. For example, if the keyboard is not detected, a particular pattern of beeps will inform you of that fact. An error found in the POST is usually fatal (that is, it causes current program to stop running) and will halt the boot process, since the hardware checked is absolutely essential for the computer's functions.

postcardware

Postcardware is **freeware** (no-charge software that is freely shared) that requires only that the user send the software provider a postcard as a form of payment. The idea is to humanize the transaction, remind the user that someone else shared something freely, and remind the provider that someone is actually using the creation.

Postscript

Postscript is a programming language that describes the appearance of a printed page. It was developed by Adobe in 1985 and has become an industry standard for printing and imaging. All major printer manufacturers make printers that contain or can be loaded with Postscript software, which also runs on all major operating system platforms. A Postscript file can be identified by its ".ps" suffix.

Postscript describes the text and graphic elements on a page to a black-and-white or color printer or other output device, such as a slide recorder, imagesetter, or screen display. Postscript handles industry-standard, scalable **typeface** in the Type 1 and TrueType formats. Users can convert Postscript files to the Adobe Portable Document Format (**PDF**) using the Adobe **Acrobat** product. PDF files present the document's printed appearance on a display screen. (You'll find many PDF documents for downloading and viewing from Web sites; you'll need to download the Acrobat viewer as a **plug-in**.) Adobe sells a more sophisticated product called *Supra* for print-on-demand and production printing.

Note that the average home laser printer is not a Postscript printer; which is somewhat more expensive and more frequently purchased for business use. (However, they aren't that expensive and Postscript printers for home or small business use are worth considering.)

POTS

POTS (plain old telephone service) is a term sometimes used in discussion of new telephone technologies in which the question of whether and how existing voice transmission for ordinary phone communication can be accommodated. For example, **Asymmetric Digital Subscriber Line** and **Integrated Services Digital Network** connections provide some part of their channels for "plain old telephone service" while providing most of their bandwidth for digital data transmission.

power

Also see **current**, **voltage**, **resistance**, and **Ohm's Law**.

Electrical power is the rate at which electrical energy is converted to another form, such as motion, heat, or an **electromagnetic field**. The common symbol for power is the uppercase letter P. The standard unit is the watt, symbolized by W. In utility circuits, the kilowatt (kW) is often specified instead; 1 kW = 1000 W.

One watt is the power resulting from an energy dissipation, conversion, or storage process equivalent to one joule per second. When expressed in watts, power is sometimes called *wattage*. The wattage in a direct current (**DC**) circuit is equal to the product of the voltage in volts and the current in amperes. This rule also holds for low-frequency alternating current (**AC**) circuits in which energy is neither stored nor released. At high AC frequencies, in which energy is stored and released (as well as dissipated or converted), the expression for power is more complex.

In a DC circuit, a source of E volts, delivering I amperes, produces P watts according to the formula:

$$P = EI$$

When a current of I amperes passes through a resistance of R ohms, then the power in watts dissipated or converted by that component is given by:

$$P = I^2R$$

When a potential difference of E volts appears across a component having a resistance of R ohms, then the power in watts dissipated or converted by that component is given by:

$$P = E^2/R$$

In a DC circuit, power is a scalar (one-dimensional) quantity. In the general AC case, the determination of power requires two dimensions, because AC power is a vector quantity. Assuming there is no reactance (opposition to AC but not to DC) in an AC circuit, the power can be calculated according to the above formulas for DC, using **root-mean-square** values for the alternating current and voltage. If reactance exists, some power is alternately stored and released by the system. This is called **apparent power** power or reactive power. The resistance dissipates power as heat or converts it to some other tangible form; this is called **true power**. The vector combination of reactance and resistance is known as **impedance**.

PowerBuilder

PowerBuilder is a popular rapid application development (RAD) tool for building **object-oriented programming client/server** applications the parts of which can be **distributed** within a network. PowerBuilder is a product of Sybase, a company that has historically been a leader in selling products for building distributed and replicated **database** in networks. A major feature of PowerBuilder (and its competitors) is the ability to create databases using an

object-oriented interface. Applications created with Power-Builder can access other popular types of databases on other major platforms using Open Database Connectivity (**ODC**).

PowerBuilder includes:

- An extensive **class** library ("templates" or object-describing code that doesn't have to be created by the developer)
- A set of utilities (called Painters) for managing database objects. These include:
- A table utility with a graphical interface that lets you create and modify data table structures and associate business rules on individual table columns
- A utility that displays all application components
- An object browser that lists objects, functions, and attributes of objects
- A utility that lets you test **Structured Query Language** statements against the server you are building
- A transaction builder called DataWindow Painter that lets you create master-detail forms for use in transactions
- PowerScript, an object-oriented scripting language that lets you link everything together
- A **C++ compiler** that generates distributable clients and servers

PowerBuilder emphasizes its ability to provide an end-user interface through a Web browser. Data from PowerBuilder tables can be converted into **HTML** tables. With a Window plug-in, a PowerBuilder application can be run from within a Web browser. And PowerBuilder's Web.PB allows client applications to be put on servers accessible to network PC ("thin client") workstations equipped with browsers but with the clients on the local server.

power-of-10 notation

See "scientific notation"

Power-On Self-Test

See "POST"

PowerPC

PowerPC is a **microprocessor architecture**, developed jointly by Apple, IBM, and Motorola, that uses reduced instruction-set computing (**RISC**). The PowerPC chip is used principally in IBM's RS/6000 **workstation** with its **UNIX**-based operating system, **AIX**, and in Apple Computer's **Macintosh** personal computers with their **Mac OS** operating system. The three developing companies, calling themselves the PowerPC Alliance, have made the PowerPC architecture an **open** standard, inviting other companies to build the architecture further.

The PowerPC architecture provides an alternative for any computer maker to the extremely popular processor architectures from Intel, including the **Pentium** PC architecture. (Microsoft builds its Windows operating system offerings to run on Intel processors, and this widely-sold combination is sometimes known as "**Wintel**".)

Developed at IBM, reduced instruction-set computing (RISC) is based on studies showing that the simpler computer **instruction**s are the ones most frequently performed. Traditionally, processors have been designed to accommodate the more complex instructions as well. RISC performs the more complex instructions using combinations of simple instructions. The timing for the processor can then be based on simpler and faster operations, enabling the microprocessor to perform more instructions for a given **clock speed**. Typically, the PowerPC can perform one instruction for each **clock cycle**. The PowerPC architecture handles 32-bit instructions.

PPD

See "parallel presence detect"

PPGA

PPGA (plastic pin grid array) is a **microchip** design from Intel that has the **silicon** core of the microchip facing down toward the computer **motherboard**. The core is covered by a heat slug, which helps to dissipate the heat to the **heatsink**. The chip includes 370 pins that plug into a **Socket 370** connector on the motherboard. The PPGA chip is less expensive to manufacture that the slot-based chip, which is why PPGA chips are used in sub-$1000 desktop computers.

Intel has also developed another chip design called FC-PGA (**flip chip-pin grid array**). FC-PGA packages have the processor core flipped up on the back of the chip, facing away from the motherboard. In order to use either type of these microprocessors with its associated 370 socket, a computer's motherboard must support certain guidelines, known as VRM specifications. (For PPGA processors, the motherboard must support VRM 8.2 specifications. For FC-PGA processors, the motherboard must support VRM 8.4 specifications.) Both chip designs are used for the **Celeron** processor and use the Zero Insertion Force (**ZIF**) feature that helps the chip to come out of its socket easily.

ppi

See "pixels per inch"

PPP

PPP (Point-to-Point Protocol) is a **protocol** for communication between two computers using a **serial** interface, typically a personal computer connected by phone line to a server. For example, your Internet server provider may provide you with a PPP connection so that the provider's server can respond to your requests, pass them on to the Internet, and forward your requested Internet responses back to you. PPP uses the Internet protocol (**IP**) (and is designed to handle others). It is sometimes considered a member of the TCP/IP suite of protocols. Relative to the Open Systems Interconnection (**OSI**) reference model, PPP provides layer 2 (data-link layer) service. Essentially, it packages your computer's **TCP/IP** packets and forwards them to the server where they can actually be put on the Internet.

PPP is a **full-duplex** protocol that can be used on various physical media, including twisted pair or fiber optic lines or satellite transmission. It uses a variation of High Speed Data Link Control (**HDLC**) for packet encapsulation.

PPP is usually preferred over the earlier de facto standard Serial Line Internet Protocol (**SLIP**) because it can handle **synchronous** as well as **asynchronous** communication. PPP can share a line with other users and it has error detection that SLIP lacks. Where a choice is possible, PPP is preferred.

PPPoE

PPPoE (Point-to-Point Protocol over Ethernet) is a specification for connecting multiple computer users on an **Ethernet local area network** to a remote site through common **customer premises equipment**, which is the telephone company's term for a **modem** and similar devices. PPPoE can be used to have an office or building-full of users share a common Digital Subscriber Line (**DSL**), **cable modem**, or **wireless** connection to the Internet. PPPoE combines the Point-to-Point Protocol (**PPP**), commonly used in dialup connections, with the Ethernet protocol, which supports multiple users in a local area network. The PPP protocol information is encapsulated within an Ethernet **frame**.

PPPoE has the advantage that neither the telephone company nor the Internet service provider (**ISP**) needs to provide any special support. Unlike dialup connections, DSL and cable modem connections are "always on." Since a number of different users are sharing the same physical connection to the remote service provider, a way is needed to keep track of which user traffic should go to and which user should be billed. PPPoE provides for each user-remote site session to learn each other's network addresses (during an initial exchange called "discovery"). Once a session is established between an individual user and the remote site (for example, an Internet service provider), the session can be monitored for billing purposes. Many apartment houses, hotels, and corporations are now providing shared Internet access over DSL lines using Ethernet and PPPoE.

PPTP

See "Point-to-Point Tunneling Protocol"

Practical Extraction and Reporting Language

See "Perl"

PRAM

PRAM (parameter RAM or parameter random access memory) is a special battery-powered form of **random access memory** in certain **Macintosh** computers where vital system information such as the date and time are stored. PRAM also contains computer configuration information, such as what's connected to each **port** on the computer. Because PRAM is powered by an internal battery, the information isn't lost when you turn the computer off as it is with regular RAM.

PRAM occasionally gets corrupted as the result of an application failure and needs to be **zapped** or restored. The procedure of "zapping the PRAM" is easily located by searching for it on major search engines. However, be aware that it may not apply to more recent Apple computers or operating systems. We suggest contacting Apple to find out the right procedure for your particular system.

preamble

A preamble is a signal used in network communications to synchronize the transmission timing between two or more systems. Proper timing ensures that all systems are interpreting the start of the information transfer correctly. This is something like how a rock band drummer "lays down a beat" prior to beginning a song. By setting up the proper tempo, the band members are more likely to be synchronized and begin the song at the same moment.

A preamble defines a specific series of transmission pulses that is understood by communicating systems to mean "someone is about to transmit data". This ensures that systems receiving the information correctly interpret when the data transmission starts. The actual pulses used as a preamble vary depending on the network communication technology in use.

Preboot Execution Environment

The Preboot Execution Environment (PXE) is an industry standard client/server interface that allows networked computers that are not yet loaded with an operating system to be configured and **boot**ed remotely by an administrator. The PXE code is typically delivered with a new computer on a **read-only memory** chip or boot disk that allows the computer (a **client**) to communicate with the network **server** so that the client machine can be remotely configured and its operating system can be remotely booted. PXE provides three things:

1) The Dynamic Host Configuration Protocol (**DHCP**), which allows the client to receive an **IP address** to gain access to the network servers.

2) A set of application program interfaces (**API**) that are used by the client's Basic Input/Output Operating System (**BIOS**) or a downloaded Network Bootstrap Program (NBP) that automates the booting of the operating system and other configuration steps.

3) A standard method of initializing the PXE code in the PXE ROM chip or boot disk.

The PXE process consists of the client notifying the server that it uses PXE. If the server uses PXE, it sends the client a list of boot servers that contain the operating systems available. The client finds the boot server it needs and receives the name of the file to download. The client then downloads the file using Trivial File Transfer Protocol (**TFTP**) and executes it, which loads the operating system. If a client is equipped with PXE and the server is not, the server ignores the PXE code preventing disruption in the DHCP and Bootstrap Protocol (**BP**) operations.

The advantages of using PXE include:

- The client machine does not necessarily need an operating system or even a hard disk.

- The client machine can be rebooted in the event of hardware or software failure. This allows the administrator to diagnose and perhaps fix the problem.

- Since PXE is vendor-independent, new types of computers can easily be added to the network.

predication

Predication (also called *branch predication*) is a process implemented in Explicitly Parallel Instruction Computing (**EPIC**)-based **processors** and their **compilers** to increase performance by eschewing branch prediction (a common technique used in modern processors), where a wrong guess by the processor brings a performance penalty. In predication, all the possible code branches are executed in parallel before the branch condition is proved. Applications like **data mining** and **data warehousing** that depend on large **back-end database** stand to gain the most from predicative methods.

Intel's **IA-64** architecture is based on EPIC and the first processor in the IA-64 line, the **Itanium**, uses predication.

predictive dialer

A predictive dialer is a telephone control system that automatically calls a list of telephone numbers in sequence and screens out no-answers, busy signals, answering machines, and disconnected numbers while predicting at what point a human caller will be able to handle the next call. Predictive dialers are commonly used for telemarketing, surveys, appointment confirmation, payment collection, and service follow-ups. Sellers of predictive dialer systems claim that they greatly increase caller productivity. The phone calls you receive from "no one there" are often predictive dialer calls in which a manual caller isn't ready yet.

Not to be confused with an *automatic dialer,* a predictive dialer is programmed to predict when a human caller is available to pick up a call, A somewhat related system is the *lead generator,* which dials a list of telephone numbers and, when a live voice answers, delivers a recorded message.

preemptive multitasking

Preemptive multitasking is **multitasking** in which a computer **operating system** uses some criteria to decide how long to allocate to any one task before giving another task a turn to use the operating system. The act of taking control of the operating system from one task and giving it to another task is called *preempting.* A common criterion for preempting is simply elapsed time (this kind of system is sometimes called *time sharing* or *time slicing*). In some operating systems, some applications can be given higher priority than other applications, giving the higher priority programs control as soon as they are initiated and perhaps longer time slices.

presence technology

Presence technology is a type of application that makes it possible to locate and identify a computing device (including, for example, **handheld** computers as well as desktop models) wherever it might be, as soon as the user connects to the network. One application of presence technology, instant messaging (**IM**), is already very popular. Presence technology is expected to be an integral part of third generation (**3G**) wireless networks, and is likely to be employed across a wide variety of communication devices, including cellphones, **PDA**s (personal digital assistants), television sets, and pagers. A number of wireless application service providers (**WASP**s) are developing platforms for mobile presence applications, called *m-presence.*

Future applications of presence technology could take any number of forms. For example, a driver with a wireless phone enabled with **GPS** (global positioning system) could be tracked, sent messages warning about traffic delays and suggesting alternate routes. Among other possibilities, users of the technology could in the future automatically set up an impromptu **teleconference** by connecting all the parties as soon as they were detected to be available. Privacy issues will be addressed by allowing a high degree of user-defined control, allowing people to select conditions in which they would be detectable, for example.

The Internet Engineering Task Force's (**IETF**) Instant Messaging and Presence Protocol (IMPP) Working Group was formed to establish core standards that could be used to make presence technologies interoperable, a challenge that is currently slowing their development. Many of the current IM systems, for example, don't make it possible for users to exchange messages with the customers of other systems, a situation which has been compared to a long distance telephone service provider making it impossible for users to communicate with another long distance provider's customers. Lucent and Novell have joined forces to form the Presence and Availability Management Forum (PAM), a venue for collaboration within the industry.

presence

This definition is also listed under *site*, *Web site* and *Website*.

A Web presence (or Web site) is a collection of Web files on a particular subject that includes a beginning file called a **home page**. For example, most companies, organizations, or individuals that have Web sites have a single address that they give you. This is their home page address. From the home page, you can get to all the other pages on their site. For example, the Web site for IBM has the home page address of http://www.ibm.com. (In this case, the actual file name of the home page file doesn't have to be included because IBM has named this file *index.html* and told the server that this address really means http://www.ibm.com/index.html.)

Since it sounds like geography is involved, a Web site is rather easily confused with a Web **server**. A server in this context is a computer that holds the files for one or more sites. On one hand, a very large Web site may reside on a number of servers that may in different geographic locations. IBM is a good example; its Web site consists of thousands of files spread out over many servers in world-wide locations. But a more typical example is probably the site you are looking at, whatis.com. We reside on a commercial space provider's server with a number of other sites that have nothing to do with Internet glossaries.

"Web presence" seems to express the idea that a site is not tied to a specific geographic location, but is "somewhere in cyberspace." However, "Web site" seems to be used much more frequently.

Some publications have begun using the term "Website." We prefer Web site.

Presentation layer

In the Open Systems Interconnection (**OSI**) communications model, the Presentation layer ensures that the communications passing through are in the appropriate form for the recipient. For example, a Presentation layer program may format a file transfer request in binary code to ensure a successful file transfer. Programs in the presentation layer address three aspects of presentation:

- Data formats—for example, **Postscript**, **ASCII**, or **binary** formats
- Compatibility with the host **operating system**
- Encapsulation of data into message "envelopes" for transmission through the network

An example of a program that generally adheres to the Presentation layer of OSI is the program that manages the Web's Hypertext Transfer Protocol (**HTTP**). This program, sometimes called the HTTP **daemon**, usually comes

included as part of an operating system. It forwards user requests passed to the Web browser on to a Web server elsewhere in the network. It receives a message back from the Web server that includes a Multi-Purpose Internet Mail Extensions (**MIME**) header. The MIME header indicates the kind of file (text, video, audio, and so forth) that has been received so that an appropriate player utility can be used to present the file to the user.

presentation software

Presentation software (sometimes called "presentation graphics") is a category of **application** program used to create sequences of words and pictures that tell a story or help support a speech or public presentation of information. Presentation software can be divided into business presentation software and more general multimedia authoring tools, with some products having characteristics of both. Business presentation software emphasizes ease- and quickness-of-learning and use. Multimedia authoring software enables you to create a more sophisticated presentation that includes audio and video sequences. Business presentation software usually enables you to include images and sometimes audio and video developed with other tools.

Some very popular presentation software, such as Microsoft's Powerpoint and Lotus's Freelance Graphics, are sold stand-alone or can come as part of office-oriented suites or packages of software. Other popular products include Adobe Persuasion, Astound, Asymetrix Compel, Corel Presentations, and Harvard Graphics. Among the most popular multimedia authoring tools are Macromedia Director and Asymetrix's Multimedia Toolbook. These authoring tools also include presentation capability as well. Most if not all of these products come in both PC and Mac versions.

Recently, a new presentation tool has arrived: your Web browser and the tools for creating Web pages, such as Microsoft's FrontPage and Adobe's PageMill. The ubiquity of these tools and the browser as a playback device make this a popular approach, especially when a presentation can combine HTML pages on the hard disk with links to outside sites (if you have a live Internet connection).

pressure

Pressure is an expression of **force** exerted on a surface per unit area. The standard unit of pressure is the **pascal** (Pa), equivalent to one **newton** per **meter squared** (N/m^2 or N · m^{-2}). Alternatively, pressure can be measured in **dynes** per centimeter squared (dyn/cm^2 or dyn · cm^{-2}). To convert from pascals to dynes per centimeter squared, multiply by 10. Conversely, multiply by 0.1.

Consider an enclosed chamber filled with a gas and surrounded by a vacuum. The pressure exerted on the walls of the chamber by the gas depends on three factors: (1) the amount of gas in the chamber, (2) the temperature of the gas, and (3) the volume of the chamber. As the amount of gas increases, assuming the volume of the chamber and the temperature remain constant, the pressure increases. As the temperature increases, assuming the amount of gas and the size of the chamber remain constant, the pressure increases. As the volume of the chamber increases, assuming the amount of gas in the chamber and the temperature remain constant, the pressure decreases. These are idealized examples; in practical scenarios these three factors often interact.

The pressure of the Earth's atmosphere at sea level is approximately 10^5 Pa. A unit of 100 Pa is known as a **millibar** (mb); atmospheric pressure is generally about 1,000 mb at sea level.

Also see **newton**, **pascal**, **SI** (International System of Units), and **Table of Physical Units**.

pressure sensing

Pressure sensing allows a **robot** to tell when it collides with something, or when something pushes against it. Pressure sensors can be used to measure force, and in some cases, to determine the contour of an applied force.

A capacitive pressure sensor employs two metal plates separated by a layer of nonconductive foam. This forms a capacitive **transducer**. The transducer is connected in series or parallel with an **inductor**. The resulting inductance-capacitance (LC) combination determines the frequency of an **oscillator**. If an object strikes or presses against the transducer, the plate spacing decreases, causing the **capacitance** to increase. This lowers the oscillator frequency. When the pressure is removed, the foam springs back, the plates return to their original spacing, and the oscillator returns to its original frequency. A capacitive pressure sensor can be fooled by metallic objects. If a good electrical conductor comes very close to the plates, the capacitance might change even if physical contact is not made. If this occurs, the sensor will interpret this proximity as pressure.

An elastomer pressure sensor solves the proximity problem inherent in the capacitive device. The elastomer is a foam pad with resistance that varies depending on how much it is compressed. An array of electrodes is connected to the top of the pad; an identical array is connected to the bottom. Each electrode in the top matrix receives a negative voltage, and its mate in the bottom matrix receives a positive voltage. When pressure appears at some point on the pad, the material compresses at and near that point, reducing the resistance between certain electrode pairs. This causes a **current** increase in a particular region in the pad. The location of the pressure can be determined according to which electrode pairs experience the increase in current. The extent of the pressure can be determined by how much the current increases. If the electrode matrix is fine enough, the

contour of the pressure-producing object can be determined by a microprocessor that evaluates the electrode current profile.

The output of a pressure sensor is **analog**, but it can be converted to digital data using an analog-to-digital converter (**ADC**). This signal can be used by a robot controller. Pressure on a transducer in the front of a robot might cause the machine to back up; pressure on the right side might make the machine turn left. The presence of pressure might be used to actuate an alarm, or to switch a device on or off. Calibrated pressure sensors can be used to measure applied force, mass, weight, or acceleration.

Also see **back-pressure sensor**, **proximity sensing**, and **robotics**.

pressure, standard

See "standard temperature and pressure"

Pretty Good Privacy

Pretty Good Privacy (PGP) is a popular program used to **encrypt** and decrypt e-mail over the Internet. It can also be used to send an encrypted **digital signature** that lets the receiver verify the sender's identity and know that the message was not changed en route. Available both as **freeware** and in a low-cost commercial version, PGP is the most widely used privacy-ensuring program by individuals and is also used by many corporations. Developed by Philip R. Zimmermann in 1991, PGP has become a de facto standard for e-mail security. PGP can also be used to encrypt files being stored so that they are unreadable by other users or intruders.

How It Works

PGP uses a variation of the **public key** system. In this system, each user has a publicly known **encryption** key and a **private key** known only to that user. You encrypt a message you send to someone else using their public key. When they receive it, they decrypt it using their private key. Since encrypting an entire message can be time-consuming, PGP uses a faster encryption **algorithm** to encrypt the message and then uses the public key to encrypt the shorter key that was used to encrypt the entire message. Both the encrypted message and the short key are sent to the receiver who first uses the receiver's private key to decrypt the short key and then uses that key to decrypt the message.

PGP comes in two public key versions—**Rivest-Shamir-Adleman** (RSA) and **Diffie-Hellman**. The RSA version, for which PGP must pay a license fee to RSA, uses the **IDEA** algorithm to generate a short key for the entire message and RSA to encrypt the short key. The Diffie-Hellman version uses the **CAST** algorithm for the short key to encrypt the message and the Diffie-Hellman algorithm to encrypt the short key.

For sending digital signatures, PGP uses an efficient algorithm that generates a **hash** (or mathematical summary) from the user's name and other signature information. This hash code is then encrypted with the sender's private key. The receiver uses the sender's public key to decrypt the hash code. If it matches the hash code sent as the digital signature for the message, then the receiver is sure that the message has arrived securely from the stated sender. PGP's RSA version uses the **MD5** algorithm to generate the hash code. PGP's Diffie-Hellman version uses the SHA-1 algorithm to generate the hash code.

To use PGP, you download or purchase it and install it on your computer system. Typically, it contains a user interface that works with your customary e-mail program. You also need to register the public key that your PGP program gives you with a PGP public-key server so that people you exchange messages with will be able to find your public key. Network Associates maintains an LDAP/HTTP public key server that has 300,000 registered public keys. This server has **mirror site**s around the world.

Where Can You Use PGP?

Originally, the U.S. government restricted the exportation of PGP technology. Today, however, PGP encrypted e-mail can be exchanged with users outside the U.S. if you have the correct versions of PGP at both ends. Unlike most other encryption products, the international version is just as secure as the domestic version.

The freely available PGP cannot legally be used for commercial purposes—for that, one must obtain the commercial version from Network Associates (formerly PGP, Inc.). There are several versions of PGP in use. Add-ons can be purchased that allow backwards compatibility for newer RSA versions with older versions. However, the Diffie-Hellman and RSA versions of PGP do not work with each other since they use different algorithms.

PRI

See "Primary Rate Interface"

primary domain controller and backup domain controller

Primary domain controller (PDC) and backup domain controller (BDC) are roles that can be assigned to a **server** in a network of computers that use the **Windows NT operating system**. Windows NT uses the idea of a **domain** to manage access to a set of network resources (applications, printers, and so forth) for a group of users. The user need only to log in to the domain to gain access to the resources, which may be located on a number of different servers in the network. One server, known as the primary domain controller, manages the master user database for the domain. One or more other servers are designated as backup domain controllers. The primary domain controller periodically sends copies of the database to the backup domain

controllers. A backup domain controller can step in as primary domain controller if the PDC server fails and can also help balance the workload if the network is busy enough.

In Windows NT, a domain combines some of the advantages of a *workgroup* (a group of users who exchange access to each others' resources on different computers) and a **directory** (a group of users who are managed centrally by an administrator). The domain concept not only allows a user to have access to resources that may be on different servers, but it also allows one domain to be given access to another domain in a *trust relationship*. In this arrangement, the user need only log in to the first domain to also have access to the second domain's resources as well.

In a Windows NT network, not all servers need to be a PDC or BDC. A server can be designated as a *member server* whose resources become part of a domain without having a role in the logon process.

Setting up and maintaining PDCs and BDCs and domain information is a major activity for the administrator of a Windows NT network. In Windows 2000, the domain controller concept is retained but the PDC and BDC server roles are generally replaced by the *Active Directory*.

Primary Rate Interface

In the Integrated Services Digital Network (**ISDN**), there are two levels of service: The **Basic Rate Interface** (BRI), intended for the home and small enterprise, and the Primary Rate Interface (PRI), for larger users. Both rates include a number of B-channels and a D-channel. Each **B-channel** carries data, voice, and other services. The **D-channel** carries control and signaling information.

The Basic Rate Interface consists of two 64 **Kbps** B-channels and one 16 Kbps D-channel. Thus, a Basic Rate Interface user can have up to 128 Kbps service. The Primary Rate Interface consists of 23 B-channels and one 64 Kpbs D-channel using a **T-1** line or 30 B-channels and 1 D-channel using an **E1** line. Thus, a Primary Rate Interface user on a T-1 line can have up to 1.544 **Mbps** service or up to 2.048 Mbps service on an E1 line. PRI uses the Q.931 protocol over the D-channel.

The Primary Rate Interface channels are carried on a **T-carrier system** line (in the U.S., Canada, and Japan) or an **E-carrier** line (in other countries) and are typically used by medium to large enterprises. The 23 (or 30) B-channels can be used flexibly and reassigned when necessary to meet special needs such as videoconferences. The Primary Rate user is hooked up directly to the telephone company central office.

For more information, see **ISDN**.

prime number

A prime number is a whole number greater than 1, whose only two whole-number factors are 1 and itself. The first few prime numbers are 2, 3, 5, 7, 11, 13, 17, 19, 23, and 29. As we proceed in the set of natural numbers $N = \{1, 2, 3, \ldots\}$, the primes become less and less frequent in general. However, there is no largest prime number. For every prime number p, there exists a prime number p' such that p' is greater than p. This was demonstrated in ancient times by the Greek mathematician Euclid.

Suppose n is a whole number, and we want to test it to see if it is prime. First, we take the square root (or the $^1/_2$ power) of n; then we round this number up to the next highest whole number. Call the result m. We must find all of the following quotients:

$q_m = n \,/\, m$

$q_{(m-1)} = n \,/\, (m-1)$

$q_{(m-2)} = n \,/\, (m-2)$

$q_{(m-3)} = n \,/\, (m-3)$

$\ldots$

$q_3 = n \,/\, 3$

$q_2 = n \,/\, 2$

The number n is prime if and only if none of the q's, as derived above, are whole numbers.

A computer can be used to test extremely large numbers to see if they are prime. But, because there is no limit to how large a natural number can be, there is always a point where testing in this manner becomes too great a task even for the most powerful supercomputers. Various algorithms have been formulated in an attempt to generate ever-larger prime numbers. These schemes all have limitations.

primitive

1) In computer programming, a primitive (pronounced PRIH-muh-teev) is a basic interface or segment of code that can be used to build more sophisticated program elements or interfaces.

2) In computer graphics, a primitive is an image element, such as an arc, a square, or a cone, from which more complicated images can be constructed.

printer

In computers, a printer is a device that accepts text and graphic output from a computer and transfers the information to paper, usually to standard size sheets of paper. Printers are sometimes sold with computers, but more frequently are purchased separately. Printers vary in size, speed, sophistication, and cost. In general, more expensive printers are used for higher-resolution color printing.

Personal computer printers can be distinguished as *impact* or *non-impact* printers. Early impact printers worked something like an automatic typewriter, with a key striking an inked impression on paper for each printed **character**. The *dot-matrix* printer was a popular low-cost personal computer printer. It's an impact printer that strikes the paper a line at a time. The best-known non-impact printers are the *inkjet* printer, of which several makes of low-cost color printers are an example, and the laser printer. The inkjet sprays ink from an ink cartridge at very close range to the paper as it rolls by. The laser printer uses a laser beam reflected from a mirror to attract ink (called *toner*) to selected paper areas as a sheet rolls over a drum.

The four printer qualities of most interest to most users are:

- **Color:** Color is important for users who need to print pages for presentations or maps and other pages where color is part of the information. Color printers can also be set to print only in black-and-white. Color printers are more expensive to operate since they use two ink cartridges (one color and one black ink) that need to be replaced after a certain number of pages. Users who don't have a specific need for color and who print a lot of pages will find a black-and-white printer cheaper to operate.

- **Resolution:** Printer resolution (the sharpness of text and images on paper) is usually measured in dots per inch (**dpi**). Most inexpensive printers provide sufficient resolution for most purposes at 600 dpi.

- **Speed:** If you do much printing, the speed of the printer becomes important. Inexpensive printers print only about 3 to 6 sheets per minute. Color printing is slower. More expensive printers are much faster.

- **Memory:** Most printers come with a small amount of memory (for example, one **megabyte**) that can be expanded by the user. Having more than the minimum amount of memory is helpful and faster when printing out pages with large images or tables with lines around them (which the printer treats as a large image).

Printer I/O Interfaces

The most common **I/O** interface for printers has been the **parallel** Centronics interface with a 36-pin plug. In the future, however, new printers and computers are likely to use a **serial** interface, especially **Universal Serial Bus** or **FireWire** with a smaller and less cumbersome plug.

Printer Languages

Printer languages are commands from the computer to the printer to tell the printer how to format the document being printed. These commands manage font size, graphics, compression of data sent to the printer, color, etc. The two most popular printer languages are **Postscript** and **Printer Control Language**.

Postscript is a printer language that uses English phrases and programmatic constructions to describe the appearance of a printed page to the printer. This printer language was developed by Adobe in 1985. It introduced new features such as outline fonts and **vector graphics**. Printers now come from the factory with or can be loaded with Postscript support. Postscript is not restricted to printers. It can be used with any device that creates an image using dots such as screen displays, slide recorders, and image setters.

PCL (Printer Command Language) is an escape code language used to send commands to the printer for printing documents. Escape code language is so-called because the escape key begins the command sequence followed by a series of code numbers. Hewlett Packard originally devised PCL for dot matrix and inkjet printers. Since its introduction, it has become an industry standard. Other manufacturers who sell HP clones have copied it. Some of these clones are very good, but there are small differences in the way they print a page compared to real HP printers. In 1984, the original HP Laserjet printer was introduced using PCL. PCL helped change the appearance of low-cost printer documents from poor to exceptional quality.

Fonts

Fonts are characters of a specific style and size within an overall **typeface** design. Printers use resident fonts and soft fonts to print documents. Resident fonts are built into the hardware of a printer. They are also called internal fonts or built-in fonts. All printers come with one or more resident fonts. Additional fonts can be added by inserting a font cartridge into the printer or installing soft fonts to the hard drive. Resident fonts cannot be erased unlike soft fonts. Soft fonts are installed onto the hard drive and then sent to the computer's memory when a document is printed that uses the particular soft font. Soft fonts can be purchased in stores or downloaded from the Internet.

There are two types of fonts used by the printer and screen display, **bitmap** fonts and outline fonts. Bitmap fonts are digital representations of fonts that are not scalable. This means they have a set size or a limited set of sizes. For example, if a document using a bitmap font sized to 24 point is sent to the printer and there is not a bitmap font of that size, the computer will try to guess the right size. This results in the text looking stretched-out or squashed. Jagged edges are also a problem with bitmap fonts. Outline fonts are mathematical descriptions of the font that are sent to the printer. The printer then rasterizes (see **raster graphics**) or converts them to the dots that are printed on the paper. Because they are mathematical, they are scalable. This means the size of the font can be changed without losing the sharpness or **resolution** of the printed text. TrueType and Type 1 fonts are outline fonts. Outline fonts are used with Postscript and PCL printer languages.

Printer Control Language

Printer Control Language (PCL) is a language (a set of command codes) that enable **application**s to control Hewlett-Packard DeskJet, LaserJet, and other HP printers. Many personal computer users find themselves in need of PCL **driver**s after purchasing a new HP or HP-compatible printer and attaching it to their existing PC and operating system. These drivers (which are small programs that work between the **operating system** and the printer) are available for downloading from Hewlett-Packard's Web site.

privacy

On the Internet, privacy, a major concern of users, can be divided into these concerns:

- What personal information can be shared with whom
- Whether messages can be exchanged without anyone else seeing them
- Whether and how one can send messages anonymously

Personal Information Privacy

Most Web users want to understand that personal information they share will not be shared with anyone else without their permission. An annual survey conducted by the Graphics, Visualization and Usability Center of the Georgia Institute of Technology showed that 70% of the Web users surveyed cited concerns about privacy as the main reason for not registering information with Web sites. 86% indicated that they wanted to be able to control their personal information. A study by TRUSTe revealed that 78% of users surveyed would be more likely to provide information to sites that offered privacy assurance.

The World Wide Web Consortium's Platform for Personal Privacy Project (**P3P**) offers specific recommendations for practices that will let users define and share personal information with Web sites that they agree to share it with. The P3P incorporates a number of industry proposals, including the Open Profiling Standard (**OPS**). Using software that adheres to the P3P recommendations, users will be able to create a personal profile, all or parts of which can be made accessible to a Web site as the user directs. A tool that will help a user decide whether to trust a given Web site with personal information is a Statement of Privacy Policy that a Web site can post.

Message Privacy

In an open network such as the Internet, message privacy, particularly for e-commerce transactions, requires **encryption**. The most common approach on the Web is through a public key infrastructure (**PKI**). For e-mail, many people use Pretty Good Privacy (**PGP**), which lets an individual encrypt a message or simply send a digital signature that can be used to verify that the message was not tampered with en route.

Anonymity

Although this form of privacy is not usually needed or wanted, there are occasions when a user may want anonymity (for example, to report a crime). The need is sometimes met through the use of a site—called a **remailer**—that reposts a message from its own address, thus disguising the originator of the message. (Unfortunately, many **spam** distributors also take advantage of remailers.)

private automatic branch exchange

A private automatic branch exchange (PABX) is an automatic telephone switching system within a private enterprise. Originally, such systems—called private branch exchanges (**PBX**)—required the use of a live operator. Since almost all private branch exchanges today are automatic, the abbreviation "PBX" usually implies a "PABX."

Some manufacturers of PABX (PBX) systems distinguish their products from others by creating new kinds of private branch exchanges. Rolm offers a Computerized Branch Exchange (CABX) and Usha Informatics offers an Electronic Private Automatic Branch Exchange (EPABX).

For additional information, see **private branch exchange**.

private branch exchange

A PBX (private branch exchange) is a telephone system within an **enterprise** that switches calls between enterprise users on local lines while allowing all users to share a certain number of external phone lines. The main purpose of a PBX is to save the cost of requiring a line for each user to the telephone company's central office.

The PBX is owned and operated by the enterprise rather than the telephone company (which may be a supplier or service provider, however). Private branch exchanges used **analog** technology originally. Today, PBXs use **digital** technology (digital signals are converted to analog for outside calls on the local loop using **plain old telephone service**).

A PBX includes:

- Telephone trunk (multiple phone) lines that terminate at the PBX

- A computer with memory that manages the switching of the calls within the PBX and in and out of it

- The network of lines within the PBX

- Usually a console or switchboard for a human operator

In some situations, alternatives to a PBX include **centrex** service (in which a pool of lines are rented at the phone company's central office), *key telephone systems*, and, for very small enterprises, primary rate **Integrated Services Digital Network**.

Among the larger manufacturers of PBXs are Lucent Technologies, Northern Telecom (NORTEL), Rolm/Siemens, NEC, GTE, Intecom, Fujitsu, Hitachi, and Mitel.

private key

In cryptography, a private or secret key is an encryption/decryption **key** known only to the party or parties that exchange secret messages. In traditional secret key **cryptography**, a key would be shared by the communicators so that each could **encrypt** and decrypt messages. The risk in this system is that if either party loses the key or it is stolen, the system is broken. A more recent alternative is to use a combination of public and private keys. In this system, a **public key** is used together with a private key. See public key infrastructure (**PKI**) for more information.

private port numbers

See "dynamic port numbers"

PRM

See "partner relationship management"

probability

Probability is a branch of mathematics that deals with calculating the likelihood of a given event's occurrence, which is expressed as a number between 1 and 0. An event with a probability of 1 can be considered a certainty: For example, the probability of a coin toss resulting in either "heads" or "tails" is 1, because there are no other options, assuming the coin lands flat. An event with a probability of .5 can be considered to have equal odds of occurring or not occurring: For example, the probability of a coin toss resulting in "heads" is .5, because the toss is equally as likely to result in "tails." An event with a probability of 0 can be considered an impossibility: For example, the probability that the coin will land (flat) without either side facing up is 0, because either "heads" or "tails" must be facing up. A little paradoxical, probability theory applies precise calculations to quantify uncertain measures of random events.

In its simplest form, probability can be expressed mathematically as: The number of occurrences of a targeted event divided by the number of occurrences *plus* the number of failures of occurrences (this adds up to the total of possible outcomes):

$$p(a) = p(a)/p(a) + p(b)$$

Calculating probabilities in a situation like a coin toss is straightforward, because the outcomes are mutually exclusive: Either one event or the other must occur. Each coin toss is an *independent* event; the outcome of one trial has no effect on subsequent ones. No matter how many consecutive times one side lands facing up, the probability that it will do so at the next toss is always .5 (50-50). The mistaken idea that a number of consecutive results (six "heads" for example) makes it more likely that the next toss will result in a "tails" is known as the *gambler's fallacy*, one that has led to the downfall of many a bettor.

Probability theory had its start in the 17th century, when two French mathematicians, Blaise Pascal and Pierre de Fermat carried on a correspondence discussing mathematical problems dealing with games of chance. Contemporary applications of probability theory run the gamut of human inquiry, and include aspects of computer programming, astrophysics, music, weather prediction, and medicine.

probe

1) In telecommunications, a probe is an action taken or an object used for the purpose of learning something about the state of the network. For example, an empty message can be sent simply to see whether the destination actually exists. **ping** is a common utility for sending such a probe. A probe is also something inserted by a hardware device or software program at a key juncture in a network for the purpose of monitoring or collecting data about network activity.

2) In semiconductor testing, a *probe card* is a microchip placed in a circuit in order to test its signals.

problem program

Now seldom used, the term *problem program* is used to distinguish a computer **program** that directly supports a user application from an **operating system**, a **utility**, or any other underlying support programming. This term has generally been replaced by the term **application program**.

problems

See "Internet problems"

process

A process is an instance of a program running in a computer. In **UNIX** and some other operating systems, a process is started when a program is initiated (either by a user entering a **shell** command or by another program). A process is a running program with which a particular set of data is associated so that the process can be kept track of. An **application** that is being shared by multiple users will generally have one process at some stage of execution for each user.

A process can initiate a subprocess, which is a called a *child* process (and the initiating process is sometimes referred to as its *parent*). A child process is a replica of the parent process and shares some of its resources, but cannot exist if the parent is terminated.

Processes can exchange information or synchronize their operation through several methods of interprocess communication (**IC**).

processor

A processor is the logic circuitry that responds to and processes the basic **instructions** that drive a computer.

The term processor has generally replaced the term central processing unit (**CPU**). The processor in a personal computer or that is embedded in small devices is often called a **microprocessor**.

processor serial number

A PSN (processor serial number) is a software-readable unique serial number that Intel has stamped into its **Pentium 3 microprocessor**. Intel offers this as a feature that can be optionally used to provide certain network management and **e-commerce** benefits. Basically, it lets a program identify individual PCs.

Pentiums are not the the first processors to be shipped with software-readable serial numbers. Sun **RISC** chips have, for many years, shipped with serial numbers, and it is a commonplace for software keys for applications software to be generated with reference to the processor ID, to provide a mechanism for copyright protection. However, Intel's PSN has caused concern to privacy advocates, on grounds that it may undercut individual user efforts to maintain their anonymity, especially when using the Internet. There is a concern that Web pages could covertly acquire PSNs which, if matched with user identities disclosed through a registration process, would facilitate detailed monitoring of the use of the Internet by the individual. For example, chat rooms could use PSNs to prevent unwelcome users from posting.

Reacting to the objections, Intel announced that they would ship Pentium IIIs with the PSN function turned off. However, since the function appears to be software-configurable without need for a reboot, this assurance seems to be of little comfort.

program layer

See "layer"

program temporary fix

In IBM, a program temporary fix (PTF) is a temporary solution to a **bug** in an IBM software product that is made available for customers to install. A PTF is developed after a customer or someone at IBM encounters the problem and an authorized program analyis report (**APAR**) is written. The PTF effectively "closes" the APAR and then is made available for delivery to customers. PTFs can be applied individually but are usually made available as part of a fix package that includes a number of PTFs. A fix package can be distributed as one or more downloadable compressed files or on a CD-ROM.

Meanwhile, the PTFs are provided to the development group that is working on the next product release. The developers may or may not use the PTFs (since these are temporary fixes), but will determine and design the correct problem solution to incorporate in the next product release.

program

In computing, a program is a specific set of ordered operations for a **computer** to perform. In the modern computer that John von Neumann outlined in 1945, the program contains a one-at-a-time sequence of instructions that the computer follows. Typically, the program is put into a storage area accessible to the computer. The computer gets one instruction and performs it and then gets the next instruction. The storage area or **memory** can also contain the data that the instruction operates on. (Note that a program is also a special kind of "data" that tells how to operate on "application or user data.")

Programs can be characterized as interactive or batch in terms of what drives them and how continuously they run. An interactive program receives data from an interactive user (or possibly from another program that simulates an interactive user). A batch program runs and does its work, and then stops. Batch programs can be started by interactive users who request their interactive program to run the batch program. A command interpreter or a Web **browser** is an example of an interactive program. A program that computes and prints out a company payroll is an example of a batch program. Print jobs are also batch programs.

When you create a program, you write it using some kind of computer language. Your language statements are the *source program*. You then "compile" the source program (with a special program called a language compiler) and the result is called an *object program* (not to be confused with object-oriented programming). There are several synonyms for object program, including *object module* and *compiled program*. The object program contains the string of 0s and 1s called *machine language* that the logic processor works with.

The machine language of the computer is constructed by the language compiler with an understanding of the computer's logic architecture, including the set of possible computer instructions and the length (number of bits) in an instruction.

programmable read-only memory

Programmable read-only memory (PROM) is read-only memory (**ROM**) that can be modified once by a user. PROM is a way of allowing a user to tailor a microcode program using a special machine called a *PROM programmer*. This machine supplies an electrical current to specific cells in the ROM that effectively blows a fuse in them. The process is known as *burning the PROM*. Since this process leaves no margin for error, most ROM chips designed to be modified

by users use erasable programmable read-only memory (**EPROM**) or electrically erasable programmable read-only memory (**EEPROM**).

Programmed Input/Output

See "PIO"

programming language generations

In the computer industry, these abbreviations are widely used to represent major steps or "generations" in the evolution of programming languages.

1GL or first-generation language was (and still is) *machine language* or the level of instructions and data that the processor is actually given to work on (which in conventional computers is a string of 0s and 1s).

2GL or second-generation language is **assembler** (sometimes called "assembly") language. A typical 2GL instruction looks like this:

```
ADD 12,8
```

An assembler converts the assembler language statements into machine language.

3GL or third-generation language is a "high-level" programming language, such as **PL/I**, **C**, or **Java**. Java language statements look like this:

```
public boolean handleEvent (Event evt) {
    switch (evt.id) {
        case Event.ACTION_EVENT: {
            if (''Try me'' .equald(evt.arg)) {
```

A **compiler** converts the statements of a specific high-level programming language into machine language. (In the case of Java, the output is called **bytecode**, which is converted into appropriate machine language by a Java **virtual machine** that runs as part of an operating system platform.) A 3GL language requires a considerable amount of programming knowledge.

4GL or fourth-generation language is designed to be closer to natural language than a 3GL language. Languages for accessing databases are often described as 4GLs. A 4GL language statement might look like this:

```
EXTRACT ALL CUSTOMERS WHERE ''PREVIOUS PURCHASES''
TOTAL MORE THAN $1000
```

5GL or fifth-generation language is programming that uses a visual or graphical development interface to create source language that is usually compiled with a 3GL or 4GL language compiler. Microsoft, Borland, IBM, and other companies make 5GL visual programming products for developing applications in Java, for example. Visual programming allows you to easily envision **object-oriented programming class** hierarchies and drag icons to assemble program components.

Programming Language/System

PL/S is a language that IBM designed for use in developing system programs, especially in **mainframe operating system** and application subsystems. It evolved from or was at least influenced by **PL/I**.

progressive JPEG

A progressive **JPEG** is the JPEG equivalent of the **interlaced GIF (Graphics Interchange Format)**. It's an image created using the JPEG suite of compression algorithms that will "fade in" in successive waves of lines until the entire image has completely arrived. Like the interlaced GIF, a progressive JPEG is a more appealing way to deliver an image at **modem** connection speeds. Users with faster connections are not likely to notice the difference.

ProLiant

ProLiant, an "industry standard" computer **server** from Compaq, typifies the popularly-priced server that is designed to satisfy general computing needs at various levels in an **enterprise**. Servers like the ProLiant are sometimes purchased in large orders when an enterprise is upgrading its servers, creating a new building installation, or simply becoming larger. Based on several versions of Intel's **Pentium III microprocessor**, the ProLiant can be ordered with enterprise versions of **Windows 2000**, **Linux**, or several other **UNIX**-based **operating system**s. The ProLiant can also be ordered in configurations containing up to eight Intel microprocessors.

Like other servers designed for industry, the ProLiant comes in models that can be **rack-mounted**. The ProLiant with the least amount of storage comes with 73 **gigabyte**s. A server can also be equipped with connections for **Fibre Channel** and similar fast-connect technologies that enable **clustering** and **storage area network**s.

PROM

See "programmable read-only memory"

promiscuous mode

In a local area network (**LAN**), promiscuous mode is a mode of operation in which every **data packet** transmitted is received and read by every network **adapter**. Promiscuous mode must be supported by each network adapter as well as by the input/output **driver** in the host operating system. Promiscuous mode is often used to monitor network activity.

Promiscuous mode is the opposite of non-promiscuous mode. When a data packet is transmitted in non-promiscuous mode, all the LAN devices "hear" the data to determine if the network **address** included in the data packet is theirs. If it isn't, the data packet is passed onto the next LAN device until the device with the correct network address is reached. That device then receives and reads the data.

Promiscuous mode is often used by **hackers** because sensitive data such as user names, passwords, and corporate information are transmitted in the data packets and is open to all LAN devices allowing the data to be easily intercepted. Promiscuous mode also allows a hacker access to the **mainframe**. It is recommended to **encrypt** sensitive data before sending over a LAN especially when in promiscuous mode.

propeller head

A propeller head (also spelled *propellor head*, and sometimes shortened to *prop head* or *prophead*) is jargon for someone who is exceptionally, perhaps weirdly bright or knowledgeable, especially in some technical field. In computers, according to **The New Hacker's Dictionary**, it's a synonym for computer **geek**. The term refers to the child's beanie cap that comes with a spinning propeller sticking out of the top.

The New Hacker's Dictionary says that the propeller cap somehow became a self-parody symbol of the out-of-this-worldness of science fiction fans. It attributes the idea to science fiction writer Ray Faraday Nelson. We like this tongue-in-cheek definition from *The Web Developer's Journal*:

> "The term 'prophead' is a holdover from the days when the **nerd** kids on the block wore caps with little propellers on top. This fashion gave way to the pencil pocket protector. Here at the WDJ, 'propheads' refers to programmers, developers and other technically-oriented types. A **weenie** doesn't even use a regular keyboard, just a little one with two keys: 1 and 0. Weenies talk among themselves in continuous data streams, which sound to mortal ears like a modem logging on."

proprietary

Also see **open** and **Open Source**.

In information technology, proprietary describes a technology or product that is owned exclusively by a single company that carefully guards knowledge about the technology or the product's inner workings. Some proprietary products can only function properly if at all when used with other products owned by the same company. An example of a proprietary product is Adobe **Acrobat**, whose Portable Document Format (**PDF**) files can only be read with the Acrobat Reader. Microsoft is often held up as the best example of a company that takes the proprietary approach. It should be observed that the proprietary approach is a traditional approach. Throughout history, the knowledge of how an enterprise makes its

products has usually been guarded as a valuable secret and such legal devices as the patent, trademark, and copyright were invented to protect a company's intellectual property.

A prime motivation behind development of products using proprietary technology is straightforward—buyers are compelled to use other products marketed by the same company. Microsoft is often held up as the exemplary company in terms of proprietary sophistication. Nevertheless, the strongest reason in favor of using proprietary standards leads to the strongest reason against: Customers may be disinclined to buy one product that limits their choice of others. The IT world is increasingly moving toward open standardization.

Criteria for open standard products include: Absence of specificity to a particular vendor, wide distribution of standards, and easy and free or low-cost accessibility. One of the best known examples of an open standard product is the **Linux operating system**. (There are free versions of Linux and for-cost versions. The latter come with accessability to service and updating.)

protected mode

Protected mode is a mode of program operation in a computer with an Intel-based microprocessor in which the program is restricted to addressing a specific contiguous area of 640 kilobytes. Intel's original PC microprocessor, the 8088, provided a one megabyte (1 Mbyte) random access memory (**RAM**). The memory was divided into several areas for **basic input/output system** data, signals from your display, and other system information. The remainder or 640 kilobytes of contiguous space was left for the operating system and application programs. The 8088 ensured that any instruction issued by a program running in protected mode would not be able to address space outside of this contiguous 640 kilobytes. Typically, much operating system code and almost all application programs run in protected mode to ensure that essential data is not unintentionally overwritten.

Real mode is program operation in which an instruction can address any space within the 1 megabyte of RAM. Typically, a program running in real mode is one that needs to get to and use or update system data and can be trusted to know how to do this. Such a program is usually part of the operating system or a special application subsystem.

As new microprocessors (such as the 80386) with larger RAM followed the 8088, DOS continued to preserve the 640 kilobyte addressing limitation so that newly-written application programs could continue to run on both the old as well as new microprocessors. Several companies developed DOS "extenders" that allowed DOS applications to be freed from the 640K constraint by inserting memory management code into the application. Microsoft developed the DOS Protected Mode Interface to go with a DOS

extender included with Windows 3.0 (which was itself a DOS application). Microsoft later gave the standard to an industry organization, the DPMI Committee.

Today's personal computers, using microprocessors that succeeded the 8088, typically contain eight or more megabytes of RAM. Today's operating systems (including the latest DOS versions) come with extended memory management that frees the programmer from the original addressing constraints.

Besides the DPMI standard interface, two other standard extended memory management interfaces exist. Extended Memory Specification (XMS) is a program added to more recent versions of DOS and Windows when the system is loaded. It's called HIMEM.SYS. Another extended memory manager is the Virtual Control Program Interface (VCPI). A copy of the DPMI Specification is viewable at the Tenberry Web site.

protocol

In information technology, a protocol (pronounced PROH-tuh-cahl, from the Greek *protocollon*, which was a leaf of paper glued to a manuscript volume, describing its contents) is the special set of rules that end points in a telecommunication connection use when they communicate. Protocols exist at several levels in a telecommunication connection. There are hardware telephone protocols. There are protocols between each of several functional layers and the corresponding layers at the other end of a communication. Both end points must recognize and observe a protocol. Protocols are often described in an industry or international standard.

On the Internet, there are the **TCP/IP** protocols, consisting of:

- **Transmission Control Protocol** (TCP), which uses a set of rules to exchange messages with other Internet points at the information packet level.

- **Internet Protocol** (IP), which uses a set of rules to send and receive messages at the Internet address level.

- Additional protocols that are usually packaged with a TCP/IP suite, including the **Hypertext Transfer Protocol** (HTTP) and **File Transfer Protocol** (FTP), each with defined sets of rules to use with corresponding programs elsewhere on the Internet.

proton

A proton is a subatomic particle found in the nucleus of every **atom**. The particle has a positive electrical charge, equal and opposite to that of the **electron**. If isolated, a single proton would have a mass of only 1.673×10^{-27} kilogram, just slightly less than the mass of a **neutron**.

The number of protons in an element's nucleus is called the *atomic number*. This number gives each element its unique identity. In the atoms of any particular element, the number of protons in the nuclei is always the same. An atom of simple hydrogen has a nucleus consisting of a single proton all by itself. The nuclei of all other elements nearly always contain neutrons in addition to protons.

Protons need not be confined to the nuclei of atoms. When protons are found outside atomic nuclei, they acquire fascinating, bizarre, and potentially dangerous properties, similar to those of neutrons in similar circumstances. But protons have an additional property. Because they carry an electric charge, they can be accelerated by electric and/or magnetic fields. High-speed protons, and atomic nuclei containing them, are emitted in large numbers during solar flares. The particles are accelerated by the earth's magnetic field, causing ionospheric disturbances known as *geomagnetic storms*.

prototyping model

The prototyping model is a systems development method (SDM) in which a prototype (an early approximation of a final system or product) is built, tested, and then reworked as necessary until an acceptable prototype is finally achieved from which the complete system or product can now be developed. This model works best in scenarios where not all of the project requirements are known in detail ahead of time. It is an iterative, trial-and-error process that takes place between the developers and the users.

There are several steps in the Prototyping Model:

1. The new system requirements are defined in as much detail as possible. This usually involves interviewing a number of users representing all the departments or aspects of the existing system.

2. A preliminary design is created for the new system.

3. A first prototype of the new system is constructed from the preliminary design. This is usually a scaled-down system, and represents an approximation of the characteristics of the final product.

4. The users thoroughly evaluate the first prototype, noting its strengths and weaknesses, what needs to be added, and what should to be removed. The developer collects and analyzes the remarks from the users.

5. The first prototype is modified, based on the comments supplied by the users, and a second prototype of the new system is constructed.

6. The second prototype is evaulated in the same manner as was the first prototype.

7. The preceding steps are iterated as many times as necessary, until the users are satisfied that the prototype represents the final product desired.

8. The final system is constructed, based on the final prototype.

9. The final system is thoroughly evaluated and tested. Routine maintenance is carried out on a continuing basis to prevent large-scale failures and to minimize downtime.

Also see systems development method (**SDM**).

provisioning

In general, provisioning means "providing." In telecommunications terminology, provisioning means providing a product or service, such as wiring or bandwidth. The term has a number of varied meanings when used in telecommunications:

1) Providing telecommunications service to a user, including everything necessary to set up the service, such as equipment, wiring, and transmission.

2) Used as a synonym for *configuring*, as in "Telecommunications lines must be correctly provisioned to work with the customer's equipment and enabled for various options the customer has chosen."

3) In a traditional telecommunications environment, there are three separate types of provisioning: **Circuit** provisioning, service provisioning, and **switch** provisioning.

4) In a **wireless** environment, provisioning refers to service activation and involves programming various network databases with the customer's information.

5) In a slightly different sense, network provisioning systems are intermediary systems that are used to provide customer services, log transactions, carry out requests, and update files.

6) Provisioning is the fourth step of the telecommunications sequence called OAM&P: Operations, Administration, Maintenance, and Provisioning.

proximity sensing

Proximity sensing is the ability of a **robot** to tell when it is near an object, or when something is near it. This sense keeps a robot from running into things. It can also be used to measure the distance from a robot to some object.

The simplest proximity sensors do not measure distance. A bumper can be passive, simply making the robot bounce away from things it hits. More often, a bumper has a switch that closes when it makes contact, sending a signal to the controller causing the robot to back away. When whiskers hit something, they vibrate. This can be detected, and a signal sent to the robot controller.

A photoelectric proximity sensor uses a light-beam generator, a photodetector, a special amplifier, and a microprocessor. The light beam reflects from an object and is picked up by the photodetector. The light beam is modulated at a specific frequency, and the detector has a frequency-sensitive amplifier that responds only to light modulated at that frequency. This prevents false imaging that might otherwise be caused by lamps or sunlight. If the robot is approaching a light-reflecting object, its microprocessor senses that the reflected beam is getting stronger. The robot can then steer clear of the object. This method of proximity sensing won't work for black objects, or for things like windows or mirrors approached at a sharp angle.

An acoustic proximity sensor works on the same principle as sonar. A pulsed signal, having a frequency somewhat above the range of human hearing, is generated by an **oscillator**. This signal is fed to a **transducer** that emits ultrasound pulses at various frequencies in a coded sequence. These pulses reflect from nearby objects and are returned to another transducer, which converts the ultrasound back into high-frequency pulses. The return pulses are amplified and sent to the robot controller. The delay between the transmitted and received pulses is timed, and this will give an indication of the distance to the obstruction. The pulse coding prevents errors that might otherwise occur because of confusion between adjacent pulses.

A capacitive proximity sensor uses a radio-frequency (**RF**) oscillator, a frequency detector, and a metal plate connected into the oscillator circuit. The oscillator is designed so that a change in the capacitance of the plate, with respect to the environment, causes the frequency to change. This change is sensed by the frequency detector, which sends a signal to the apparatus that controls the robot. In this way, a robot can avoid bumping into things. Objects that conduct electricity to some extent, such as house wiring, animals, cars, or refrigerators, are sensed more easily by capacitive transducers than are things that do not conduct, like wood-frame beds and dry masonry walls.

Also see **robotics**, **pressure sensing**, and **texture sensing**.

proxy

See "proxy server"

proxy server

In an enterprise that uses the Internet, a proxy server is a **server** that acts as an intermediary between a workstation user and the Internet so that the enterprise can ensure security, administrative control, and caching service. A proxy server is associated with or part of a **gateway** server that separates the enterprise network from the outside network and a **firewall** server that protects the enterprise network from outside intrusion.

A proxy server receives a request for an Internet service (such as a Web page request) from a user. If it passes filtering requirements, the proxy server, assuming it is also a **cache server**, looks in its local **cache** of previously downloaded Web pages. If it finds the page, it returns it to the user without needing to forward the request to the Internet. If the page is not in the cache, the proxy server, acting as a client on behalf of the user, uses one of its own IP addresses to request the page from the server out on the Internet. When the page is returned, the proxy server relates it to the original request and forwards it on to the user.

To the user, the proxy server is invisible; all Internet requests and returned responses appear to be directly with the addressed Internet server. (The proxy is not quite invisible; its IP address has to be specified as a configuration option to the browser or other protocol program.)

An advantage of a proxy server is that its cache can serve all users. If one or more Internet sites are frequently requested, these are likely to be in the proxy's cache, which will improve user response time. In fact, there are special servers called cache servers. A proxy can also do logging.

The functions of proxy, firewall, and caching can be in separate server programs or combined in a single package. Different server programs can be in different computers. For example, a proxy server may in the same machine with a firewall server or it may be on a separate server and forward requests through the firewall.

pseudocode

Pseudocode (pronounced SOO-doh-kohd) is a detailed yet readable description of what a computer program or algorithm must do, expressed in a formally-styled natural language rather than in a programming language. Pseudocode is sometimes used as a detailed step in the process of developing a program. It allows designers or lead programmers to express the design in great detail and provides programmers a detailed **template** for the next step of writing code in a specific programming language.

Because pseudocode is detailed yet readable, it can be inspected by the team of designers and programmers as a way to ensure that actual programming is likely to match design specifications. Catching errors at the pseudocode stage is less costly than catching them later in the development process. Once the pseudocode is accepted, it is rewritten using the vocabulary and **syntax** of a programming language. Pseudocode is sometimes used in conjunction with **computer-aided software engineering**-based methodologies.

It is possible to write programs that will convert a given pseudocode language into a given programming language.

PSK

See "phase-shift keying"

PSTN

PSTN (public switched telephone network) is the world's collection of interconnected voice-oriented public telephone networks, both commercial and government-owned. It's also referred to as the "plain old telephone service" (**POTS**). It's the aggregation of circuit-switching telephone networks that has evolved from the days of Alexander Graham Bell ("Doctor Watson, come here!"). Today, it is almost entirely digital in technology except for the final link from the central (local) telephone office to the user.

In relation to the Internet, the PSTN actually furnishes much of the Internet's long-distance **infrastructure**. Because Internet service providers **ISP**s pay the long-distance providers for access to their infrastructure and share the circuits among many users through **packet**-switching, Internet users avoid having to pay usage tolls to anyone other than their ISPs.

PTF

See "program temporary fix"

PU

See "physical unit"

public domain software

Programs that are uncopyrighted because their authors intended to share them with everyone else are in the public domain. The UNIX community has developed a number of such programs over the years. Programs in the public domain can be used without restriction as components of other programs. When reusing such code, it is good to understand its history so that you can be sure it really is in the public domain.

Also see **shareware**, which is programming that is "free" but more or less on a trial basis, and **freeware**.

public key

A public key is a value provided by some designated authority as a **key** that, combined with a private key derived from the public key, can be used to effectively **encrypt** messages and **digital signatures**.

The use of combined public and private keys is known as *asymmetric* cryptography. A system for using public keys is called a public key infrastructure (**PKI**).

public key certificate

A public key certificate is a digitally signed document that serves to validate the sender's authorization and name. The document consists of a specially formatted block of data that contains the name of the certificate holder (which may be either a user or a system name) and the holder's **public key**, as well as the **digital signature** of a certification authority for authentication. The certification authority attests that the sender's name is the one associated with the public key in the document. A user ID packet, containing the sender's unique identifier, is sent after the certificate packet. There are different types of public key certificates for different functions, such as authorization for a specific action or delegation of authority. Public key certificates are part of a **public key infrastructure** that deals with digitally signed documents. The other components are public key **encryption**, trusted third parties (such as the certification authority), and mechanisms for certificate publication and issuing.

public key infrastructure

See "PKI"

public switched telephone network

See "PSTN"

Public-Key Cryptography Standards

The Public-Key Cryptography Standards (PKCS) are a set of intervendor standard protocols for making possible secure information exchange on the Internet using a public key infrastructure (**PKI**). The standards include RSA **encryption**, password-based encryption, extended **certificate syntax**, and cryptographic message syntax for **S/MIME**, RSA's proposed standard for secure e-mail. The standards were developed by **RSA** Laboratories in cooperation with a consortium that included Apple, Microsoft, DEC, Lotus, Sun, and MIT.

pulse code modulation

PCM (pulse code modulation) is a **digital** scheme for transmitting **analog** data. The signals in PCM are binary; that is, there are only two possible states, represented by logic 1 (high) and logic 0 (low). This is true no matter how complex the analog waveform happens to be. Using PCM, it is possible to digitize all forms of analog data, including full-motion video, voices, music, telemetry, and virtual reality (VR).

To obtain PCM from an analog waveform at the source (transmitter end) of a communications circuit, the analog signal amplitude is sampled (measured) at regular time intervals. The sampling rate, or number of samples per second, is several times the maximum frequency of the analog waveform in cycles per second or **hertz**. The instantaneous amplitude of the analog signal at each sampling is rounded off to the nearest of several specific, predetermined levels. This process is called quantization. The number of levels is always a power of 2—for example, 8, 16, 32, or 64. These numbers can be represented by three,

four, five, or six binary digits (bits) respectively. The output of a pulse code modulator is thus a series of binary numbers, each represented by some power of 2 bits.

At the destination (receiver end) of the communications circuit, a pulse code demodulator converts the binary numbers back into pulses having the same quantum levels as those in the modulator. These pulses are further processed to restore the original analog waveform.

Also see **modulation**.

pulsing zombie

A pulsing zombie is a computer whose security has been compromised without its owner's knowledge by a **cracker** so that it intermittently carries out a **denial-of-service** attack on target computers in a network. Unlike a regular **zombie**, the pulsing zombie doesn't completely paralyze its targets, but merely weakens them, in what some call *degradation-of-service* attacks.

Whereas the usual zombie attack consists of a steady (and therefore more easily traced) stream of attack **traffic** intended to overwhelm one or more target computers, the pulsing zombie attack consists of irregular bursts of traffic intended to hamper service. It is more difficult to locate the source of an attack from a pulsing zombie, or even to know that an attack has taken place. Pulsing zombie attacks have been known to go on for months before they are detected; in one case, a victim received six times its normal traffic volume for several months, according to Asta Networks CEO Joe Devich.

pure-play

Pure-play, a term used in stock trading (especially on the Internet), refers to ownership in companies that focus on and specialize in a particular product or service area to the exclusion of other market opportunities in order to obtain a large market share and brand identity in one area. Examples of such companies are said to include **SAP** for corporate **back-office** applications; Siebel Systems in customer relationship management (**CRM**) applications; i2 Technologies in supply chain management (**SCM**); and Ariba in **e-procurement**.

A *conglomerate* is usually considered to be the opposite of a pure-play company.

Purple Book

The Purple Book is the informal name for Philips and Sony's specification document for the double-density compact disc (**DDCD**) format. By narrowing the track pitch (to 1.1 **micron** from 1.6 micron), and shortening the minimum pit length (to 0.623 micron from 0.833 micron), the Purple Book enables a **CD** to hold 1.3 **gigabytes**, roughly twice the capacity of a standard CD. Other Purple Book specifications include a

new type of error correction (known as *CIRC7*), an adaptation of the **ISO 9660** file format, and a scanning velocity of 0.9 meters per second.

The Purple Book-defined products are expected to be released in recordable and rewritable formats, rather than read-only. Because of the specific requirements for reading DDCD, they cannot be read by other drives currently on the market. Sony has plans to manufacture DDCD-R/RW drives that can read any type of CD, record **CD-R**, rewrite **CD-RW**, and perform all three tasks on DDCD. Some upcoming CD-R and CD-RW drives, such as Adaptec's new version of Easy CD Creator, are being designed to be DDCD-compatible.

push

Push (or "server-push") is the delivery of information on the Web that is initiated by the information **server** rather than by the information user or **client**, as it usually is. An early Web service that specialized in "pushing" information rather than having it "pulled" as the result of requests for Web pages was Pointcast, a site that provided up-to-date news and other information tailored to a previously defined user profile. Marimba was a somewhat similar site (and product) that pushed information to the user on a predefined schedule.

In fact, the information pushed from a server to a user actually comes as the result of a programmed request from the client in your computer. That is, any information pusher on the Web requires that you download a client program. This program captures your profile and then periodically initiates requests for information on your behalf from the server.

A truer form of push is *broadcast* information. In this case, the information is pushed to everyone that has access to a particular channel or frequency. Broadcast usually (but not always) involves a continuous flow of information.

Another form of "pushed" information is e-mail. Although the e-mail client in your computer has to occasionally go to your local e-mail server to "pick up" the e-mail, the e-mail arrived because someone sent it (pushed) it to you without a one-for-one request having been made.

push technology

Also see **Webcasting**, another usage. In both usages, *netcasting* is a synonym.

Push technology (Webcasting) is the prearranged updating of news, weather, or other selected information on a computer user's desktop interface through periodic and generally unobtrusive transmission over the World Wide Web (including the use of the Web protocol on **intranet**). Webcasting is a feature of the Microsoft Internet Explorer browser and Netscape's Netcaster, part of its Communicator suite. Webcasting is also available through separate applications such as Pointcast and Backweb that run on current **browser**s.

Webcasting uses so-called *push technology* in which the Web server ostensibly "pushes" information to the user rather than waiting until the user specifically requests it. (In actuality, most of the push is triggered by user or administrator preselection and arrives only as the result of client requests.) In addition to changing the Web for the home user, new Webcasting products offer corporations an organized way to manage information for their intranet users.

PVC

See "permanent virtual circuit"

PWS

See "Personal Web Server"

Python

Python is an **interpreted**, **object-oriented programming** language similar to **PERL**, that has gained popularity because of its clear **syntax** and readability. Python is said to be relatively easy to learn and portable, meaning its statements can be interpreted in a number of **operating system**s, including **UNIX**-based systems, **Mac OS**, **MS-DOS**, **OS/2**, and various versions of Microsoft **Windows 98**. Python was created by Guido van Rossum, a former resident of the Netherlands, whose favorite comedy group at the time was Monty Python's Flying Circus. The **source code** is freely available and **open** for modification and reuse. Python has a significant number of users.

A notable feature of Python is its indenting of source statements to make the code easier to read. Python offers dynamic **data type**, ready-made **class**, and interfaces to many system calls and libraries. It can be extended, using the **C** or **C++** language.

Python can be used as the script in Microsoft's Active Server Page (**ASP**) technology. The scoreboard system for the Melbourne (Australia) Cricket Ground is written in Python. **Zope**, a popular Web **application server**, is also written in the Python language.

QAM

QAM (quadrature amplitude modulation) is a method of combining two amplitude-modulated (**AM**) signals into a single channel, thereby doubling the effective bandwidth. QAM is used with pulse amplitude modulation (**PAM**) in digital systems, especially in **wireless** applications.

In a QAM signal, there are two carriers, each having the same frequency but differing in phase by 90 degrees (one quarter of a cycle, from which the term quadrature arises). One signal is called the I signal, and the other is called the Q signal. Mathematically, one of the signals can be represented by a **sine wave**, and the other by a cosine wave. The two modulated carriers are combined at the source for transmission. At the destination, the carriers are separated, the data is extracted from each, and then the data is combined into the original modulating information.

Also see **bandwidth**, **modulation**, and **wireless**.

QDOS

QDOS was the forerunner of **DOS** (Disk Operating System), the first widely-used personal computer operating system. In 1980, when IBM was making plans to enter the personal computer market, it asked Bill Gates, the young owner of a small company called Microsoft, if they could locate an operating system for the new PC that IBM was developing. Microsoft, which had previously furnished IBM with a **BASIC** language product for the IBM PC, looked around and found an operating system called 86-DOS at a small company called Seattle Computer Products.

86-DOS—often referred to as QDOS, or Quick and Dirty Operating System—was written in six weeks by Tim Paterson, based on ideas in CP/M (Control Program for Microcomputers), an operating system popular with early personal computer users. 86-DOS was designed for use with Seattle Computer's Intel 8086-based computers. It contained about 4,000 lines of **assembler** language code. Microsoft bought 86-DOS from Seattle Computer Products for $50,000, revised it, renaming it **MS-DOS**, and then delivered it to IBM for its new PC.

IBM rewrote MS-DOS after finding 300 **bug**s in it and renamed it **PC-DOS**, which is why both IBM and Microsoft hold a copyright for it. Bill Gates saw the potential for MS-DOS and persuaded IBM to let Microsoft sell it separately from IBM's PC projects. The initial IBM PC actually offered the user a choice of one of three operating systems: PC-DOS, CP/M 86, and UCSD p-System, a **Pascal**-based system. PC-DOS, which was cheaper, proved the most popular and began to come bundled with the IBM PC in its second product release. The IBM PC brought personal computing to the business world for the first time and was successful

beyond IBM's imaginings. In 18 months, IBM introduced the PC-XT, which included a hard drive loaded with a newer version of DOS. Microsoft promised a **multitasking** DOS, but that never happened. Instead, Microsoft developed Windows with multitasking features.

QFE

See "Quick Fix Engineering"

QoS

On the Internet and in other networks, QoS (Quality of Service) is the idea that transmission rates, error rates, and other characteristics can be measured, improved, and, to some extent, guaranteed in advance. QoS is of particular concern for the continuous transmission of high-**bandwidth** video and multimedia information. Transmitting this kind of content dependably is difficult in public networks using ordinary "best effort" protocols.

Using the Internet's Resource Reservation Protocol (**RSVP**), **packet**s passing through a **gateway host** can be expedited based on policy and reservation criteria arranged in advance. Using **ATM**, which also lets a company or user preselect a level of quality in terms of service, QoS can be measured and guaranteed in terms of the average delay at a gateway, the variation in delay in a group of cells (cells are 53-byte transmission units), cell losses, and the transmission error rate.

The Common Open Policy Service (**COPS**) is a relatively new protocol that allows **routers** and layer 3 switches to get QoS **policy** information from the network policy server.

quad

A quad (pronounced KWAHD) is a unit in a set of something that comes in four units. The term is sometimes used to describe each of the four numbers that constitute an Internet Protocol (**IP**) address. Thus, an Internet address in its numeric form (which is also sometimes called a **dot address**) consists of four quads separated by "dots" (periods). For example:
192.68.00.21
192, 68, 00, and 21 are each quads of the entire address.

A quad also means "a quarter" in some usages.

Quad FastEthernet

Quad FastEthernet (QFE) is a network interface card (**NIC**) manufactured by Sun Microsystems that is designed to enhance the **bandwidth** of a Peripheral Component Interconnect (**PCI**)-based **server** using Sun Microsystem's Solaris 8 or later operating environment. Speeds of up to 100 megabits per second (**Mbps**) are provided by converting PCI data streams into **Fast Ethernet** traffic. QFE cards are **hot-swap**pable, minimizing downtime, and comply with the IEEE 802/3U Ethernet standard. A single card can work with up to four network interfaces at a time and provide support for **multihoming**.

quad tree

A quad tree is a method of placing and locating files (called records or keys) in a **database**. The **algorithm** finds data by repeatedly dividing the number of ultimately accessible records in four parts until only one remains.

In a tree, records are stored in locations called leaves. This name derives from the fact that records always exist at end points; there is nothing beyond them. Branch points are called nodes. The order of a tree is the number of branches (called children) per node. In a quad tree, there are always four children per node, so the order is 4. The number of leaves in a quad tree is always a power of 4. The number of access operations required to reach the desired record is called the depth of the tree. The image below shows a quad tree of depth 3.

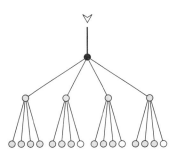

In a practical tree, there can be thousands, millions, or billions of records. Not all leaves necessarily contain a record, but more than half do. A leaf that does not contain a record is called a null. In the example shown here, the eighth, twelfth, and sixteenth leaves are nulls, indicated by open circles.

The quad tree is uniquely suited as an algorithm to locate pixels in a two-dimensional image. The reason for this is that, in two dimensions (the usual way in which graphics are depicted), square pixels can be divided into four square parts repeatedly. The depth of such a tree depends on the image **resolution**, the computer memory, and the complexity of the image.

Also see **binary tree**, **B-tree**, **splay tree**, and **tree structure**.

quadbit

A quadbit, sometimes called a **nibble**, is one of 16 possible four-bit combinations used in some communication signals. A signal may be encoded in quadbit (nibble) units rather than one bit at a time. According to Harry Newton, *nibble interleaving or multiplexing* takes a quadbit or nibble from a lower-speed channel as input for a multiplexed signal on a higher-speed channel. In the IEEE 1284 Parallel Port Interface standard, data can be sent in nibbles (a sequence of two four-bit units) across the line.

quadrature amplitude modulation

See "QAM"

Quality of Service

See "QoS"

quantum

Quantum is the Latin word for *amount* and, in modern understanding, means *the smallest possible discrete unit of any physical property, such as energy or matter*. Quantum came into the latter usage in 1900, when the physicist Max Planck used it in a presentation to the German Physical Society. Planck had sought to discover the reason that radiation from a glowing body changes in color from red, to orange, and, finally, to blue as its temperature rises. He found that by making the assumption that radiation existed in discrete units in the same way that matter does, rather than just as a constant electromagnetic wave, as had been formerly assumed, and was therefore quantifiable, he could find the answer to his question.

Planck wrote a mathematical equation involving a figure to represent individual units of energy. He called the units *quanta*. Planck assumed there was a theory yet to emerge from the discovery of quanta, but in fact, their very existence defined a completely new and fundamental law of nature. **Quantum theory** and Einstein's theory of relativity, together, explain the nature and behavior of all matter and energy on earth and form the basis for modern physics.

Quantum is sometimes used loosely, in an adjective form, to mean *on such an infinitessimal level as to be infinite,* as, for example, you might say "Waiting for pages to load is quantumly boring."

quantum computer

A quantum computer is a machine, as-yet hypothetical, that performs calculations based on the behavior of particles at the sub-atomic level. Such a computer will be, if it is ever developed, capable of executing far more millions of instructions per second (**MIPS**) than any previous computer. Such an exponential advance in processing capability would be due to the fact that the data units in a quantum computer, unlike those in a **binary** computer, can exist in more than one state at a time. In a sense, the machine "thinks" several "thoughts" simultaneously, each "thought" being independent of the others even though they all arise from the same set of particles.

Engineers have coined the term **qubit** (pronounced KYEW-bit) to denote the fundamental data unit in a quantum computer. A qubit is essentially a **bit** (binary digit) that can take on several, or many, values simultaneously. The theory behind this is as bizarre as the theory of quantum mechanics, in which individual particles appear to exist in multiple locations. One way to think of how a qubit can exist in multiple states is to imagine it as having two or more aspects or dimensions, each of which can be high (logic 1) or low (logic 0). Thus if a qubit has two aspects, it can have four simultaneous, independent states (00, 01, 10, and 11); if it has three aspects, there are eight possible states, binary 000 through 111, and so on.

Quantum computers might prove especially useful in the following applications:

- Breaking ciphers
- Statistical analysis
- Factoring large numbers
- Solving problems in theoretical physics
- Solving optimization problems in many variables

The main difficulty that the research-and-development engineers have encountered is the fact that it is extremely difficult to get particles to behave in the proper way for a significant length of time. The slightest disturbance will cause the machine to cease working in quantum fashion and revert to "single-thought" mode like a conventional computer. Stray electromagnetic fields, physical movement, or a tiny electrical discharge can disrupt the process.

quantum computing

Quantum computing is the area of study focused on developing computer technology based on the principles of **quantum theory**, which explains the nature and behavior of energy and matter on the **quantum** (atomic and subatomic) level. Development of a **quantum computer**, if practical, would mark a leap forward in computing capability far greater than that from the **abacus** to a modern day **supercomputer**, with performance gains in the billion-fold realm and beyond. The quantum computer, following the laws of quantum physics, would gain enormous processing power through the ability to be in multiple states, and to perform tasks using all possible permutations simultaneously. Current centers of research in quantum computing include MIT, IBM, Oxford University, and the Los Alamos National Laboratory.

The essential elements of quantum computing originated with Paul Benioff, working at Argonne National Labs, in 1981. He theorized a classical computer operating with some quantum mechanical principles. But it is generally accepted that David Deutsch of Oxford University provided the critical impetus for quantum computing research. In 1984, he was at a computation theory conference and began to wonder about the possibility of designing a computer that

was based exclusively on quantum rules, then published his breakthrough paper a few months later. With this, the race began to exploit his ideas. However, before we delve into what he started, it is beneficial to have a look at the background of the quantum world.

Quantum Theory

Quantum theory's development began in 1900 with a presentation by Max Planck to the German Physical Society, in which he introduced the idea that energy exists in individual units (which he called "quanta"), as does matter. Further developments by a number of scientists over the following thirty years led to the modern understanding of quantum theory.

The Essential Elements of Quantum Theory:

- Energy, like matter, consists of discrete units, rather than solely as a continuous wave.
- Elementary particles of both energy and matter, depending on the conditions, may behave like either particles or waves.
- The movement of elementary particles is inherently random, and, thus, unpredictable.
- The simultaneous measurement of two complementary values, such as the position and momentum of an elementary particle, is inescapably flawed; the more precisely one value is measured, the more flawed will be the measurement of the other value.

Further Developments of Quantum Theory

Niels Bohr proposed the Copenhagen interpretation of quantum theory, which asserts that a particle is whatever it is measured to be (for example, a wave or a particle) but that it cannot be assumed to have specific properties, or even to exist, until it is measured. In short, Bohr was saying that objective reality does not exist. This translates to a principle called superposition that claims that while we do not know what the state of any object is, it is actually in all possible states simultaneously, as long as we don't look to check.

To illustrate this theory, we can use the famous and somewhat cruel analogy of Schrodinger's Cat. First, we have a living cat and place it in a thick lead box. At this stage, there is no question that the cat is alive. We then throw in a vial of cyanide and seal the box. We do not know if the cat is alive or if it has broken the cyanide capsule and died. Since we do not know, the cat is both dead and alive, according to quantum law—in a superposition of states. It is only when we break open the box and see what condition the cat is in that the superposition is lost, and the cat must be either alive or dead.

The second interpretation of quantum theory is the *multiverse* or *many-worlds* theory. It holds that as soon as a potential exists for any object to be in any state, the universe of that object transmutes into a series of parallel universes equal to the number of possible states in which the object can exist, with each universe containing a unique single possible state of that object. Furthermore, there is a mechanism for interaction between these universes that somehow permits all states to be accessible in some way and for all possible states to be affected in some manner. Stephen Hawking and the late Richard Feynman are among the scientists who have expressed a preference for the many-worlds theory.

Whichever argument one chooses, the principle that, in some way, one particle can exist in numerous states opens up profound implications for computing.

A Comparison of Classical and Quantum Computing

Classical computing relies, at its ultimate level, on principles expressed by Boolean algebra, operating with a (usually) 7-mode **logic gate** principle, though it is possible to exist with only three modes (which are AND, NOT, and COPY). Data must be processed in an exclusive binary state at any point in time—that is, either 0 (off/false) or 1 (on/true). These values are binary digits, or bits. The millions of transistors and capacitors at the heart of computers can only be in one state at any point. While the time that the each transistor or capacitor need be either in 0 or 1 before switching states is now measurable in billionths of a second, there is still a limit as to how quickly these devices can be made to switch state. As we progress to smaller and faster circuits, we begin to reach the physical limits of materials and the threshold for classical laws of physics to apply. Beyond this, the quantum world takes over, which opens a potential as great as the challenges that are presented.

The Quantum computer, by contrast, can work with a two-mode logic gate: **XOR** and a mode we'll call QO1 (the ability to change 0 into a superposition of 0 and 1, a logic gate which cannot exist in classical computing). In a quantum computer, a number of elemental particles such as electrons or photons can be used (in practice, success has also been achieved with ions), with either their charge or polarization acting as a representation of 0 and/or 1. Each of these particles is known as a quantum bit, or qubit, the nature and behavior of these particles form the basis of quantum computing. The two most relevant aspects of quantum physics are the principles of superposition and *entanglement*.

Superposition

Think of a qubit as an electron in a magnetic field. The electron's spin may be either in alignment with the field, which is known as a *spin-up* state, or opposite to the field, which is known as a *spin-down* state. Changing the electron's spin from one state to another is achieved by using a pulse of energy, such as from a **laser**—let's say that we use 1 unit of laser energy. But what if we only use half a unit of laser energy and completely isolate the particle from all external influences? According to quantum law, the particle then enters a superposition of states, in which it behaves as if it were in both states simultaneously. Each qubit utilized could take a superposition of both 0 and 1. Thus, the number of

computations that a quantum computer could undertake is 2^n, where n is the number of qubits used. A quantum computer comprised of 500 qubits would have a potential to do 2^{500} calculations in a single step. This is an awesome number—2^{500} is infinitely more atoms than there are in the known universe (this is true parallel processing—classical computers today, even so called parallel processors, still only truly do one thing at a time: There are just two or more of them doing it). But how will these particles interact with each other? They would do so via quantum entanglement.

Entanglement

Particles (such as photons, electrons, or qubits) that have interacted at some point retain a type of connection and can be entangled with each other in pairs, in a process known as *correlation*. Knowing the spin state of one entangled particle—up or down—allows one to know that the spin of its mate is in the opposite direction. Even more amazing is the knowledge that, due to the phenomenon of superpostition, the measured particle has no single spin direction before being measured, but is simultaneously in both a spin-up and spin-down state. The spin state of the particle being measured is decided at the time of measurement and communicated to the correlated particle, which simultaneously assumes the opposite spin direction to that of the measured particle. This is a real phenomenon (Einstein called it "spooky action at a distance"), the mechanism of which cannot, as yet, be explained by any theory—it simply must be taken as given. Quantum entanglement allows qubits that are separated by incredible distances to interact with each other instantaneously (not limited to the speed of light). No matter how great the distance between the correlated particles, they will remain entangled as long as they are isolated.

Taken together, quantum superposition and entanglement create an enormously enhanced computing power. Where a 2-bit register in an ordinary computer can store only one of four binary configurations (00, 01, 10, or 11) at any given time, a 2-qubit register in a quantum computer can store all four numbers simultaneously, because each qubit represents two values. If more qubits are added, the increased capacity is expanded exponentially.

Quantum Programming

Perhaps even more intriguing than the sheer power of quantum computing is the ability that it offers to write programs in a completely new way. For example, a quantum computer could incorporate a programming sequence that would be along the lines of "take all the superpositions of all the prior computations"—something which is meaningless with a classical computer—which would permit extremely fast ways of solving certain mathematical problems, such as factorization of large numbers, one example of which we discuss below.

There have been two notable successes thus far with quantum programming. The first occurred in 1994 by Peter Shor, (now at AT&T Labs) who developed a quantum algorithm that could efficiently factorize large numbers. It centers on a system that uses number theory to estimate the periodicity of a large number sequence. The other major breakthrough happened with Lov Grover of Bell Labs in 1996, with a very fast algorithm that is proven to be the fastest possible for searching through unstructured databases. The algorithm is so efficient that it requires only, on average, roughly N square root (where N is the total number of elements) searches to find the desired result, as opposed to a search in classical computing, which on average needs N/2 searches.

The Problems—And Some Solutions

The above sounds promising, but there are tremendous obstacles still to be overcome. Some of the problems with quantum computing are as follows:

- Interference—During the computation phase of a quantum calculation, the slightest disturbance in a quantum system (say a stray photon or wave of EM radiation) causes the quantum computation to collapse, a process known as de-coherence. A quantum computer must be totally isolated from all external interference during the computation phase. Some success has been achieved with the use of qubits in intense magnetic fields, with the use of ions.

- Error correction—Because truly isolating a quantum system has proven so difficult, error correction systems for quantum computations have been developed. Qubits are not digital bits of data, thus they cannot use conventional (and very effective) error correction, such as the triple redundant method. Given the nature of quantum computing, error correction is ultra critical—even a single error in a calculation can cause the validity of the entire computation to collapse. There has been considerable progress in this area, with an error correction algorithm developed that utilizes 9 qubits (1 computational and 8 correctional). More recently, there was a breakthrough by IBM that makes do with a total of 5 qubits (1 computational and 4 correctional).

- Output observance—Closely related to the above two, retrieving output data after a quantum calculation is complete risks corrupting the data. In an example of a quantum computer with 500 qubits, we have a 1 in 2^{500} chance of observing the right output if we quantify the output. Thus, what is needed is a method to ensure that, as soon as all calculations are made and the act of observation takes place, the observed value will correspond to the correct answer. How can this be done? It has been achieved by Grover with his database search algorithm, that relies on the special "wave" shape of the probability curve inherent in quantum computers, that

ensures, once all calculations are done, the act of measurement will see the quantum state decohere into the correct answer.

Even though there are many problems to overcome, the breakthroughs in the last 15 years, and especially in the last 3, have made some form of practical quantum computing not unfeasible, but there is much debate as to whether this is less than a decade away or a hundred years into the future. However, the potential that this technology offers is attracting tremendous interest from both the government and the private sector. Military applications include the ability to break encryptions keys via brute force searches, while civilian applications range from DNA modeling to complex material science analysis. It is this potential that is rapidly breaking down the barriers to this technology, but whether all barriers can be broken, and when, is very much an open question.

quantum cryptography

Quantum cryptography uses our current knowledge of physics to develop a cryptosystem that is not able to be defeated—that is, one that is completely secure against being compromised without knowledge of the sender or the receiver of the messages. The word *quantum* itself refers to the most fundamental behavior of the smallest particles of matter and energy: quantum theory explains everything that exists and nothing can be in violation of it.

Quantum cryptography is different from traditional cryptographic systems in that it relies more on physics, rather than mathematics, as a key aspect of its security model.

Essentially, quantum cryptography is based on the usage of individual particles/waves of light (**photon**) and their intrinsic quantum properties to develop an unbreakable cryptosystem—essentially because it is impossible to measure the quantum state of any system without disturbing that system. It is theoretically possible that other particles could be used, but photons offer all the necessary qualities needed, their behavior is comparatively well-understood, and they are the information carriers in **optical fiber** cables, the most promising medium for extremely high-bandwidth communications.

How It Works in Theory

In theory, quantum cryptography works in the following manner (this view is the "classical" model developed by Bennett and Brassard in 1984—some other models do exist):

Assume that two people wish to exchange a message securely, traditionally named Alice and Bob. Alice initiates the message by sending Bob a **key**, which will be the mode for encrypting the message data. This is a random sequence of bits, sent using a certain type of scheme, which can see two different initial values represent one particular binary value (0 or 1).

Let us assume that this key is a stream of photons travelling in one direction, with each of these photon particles representing a single bit of data (either a 0 or 1). However, in addition to their linear travel, all of these photons are oscillating (vibrating) in a certain manner. These oscillations can occur in any 360-degree range across any conceivable axis, but for the purpose of simplicity (at least as far as it is possible to simplify things in quantum cryptography), let us assume that their oscillations can be grouped into 4 particular states: We'll define these as UP/DOWN, LEFT/RIGHT, UPLEFT/RIGHTDOWN and UPRIGHT/LEFT-DOWN. The angle of this vibration is known as the polarization of the photon. Now, let us introduce a polarizer into the equation. A polarizer is simply a filter that permits certain photons to pass through it with the same oscillation as before and lets others pass through in a changed state of oscillation (it can also block some photons completely, but let's ignore that property for this exercise). Alice has a polarizer that can transmit the photons in any one of the four states mentioned—in effect, she can choose either rectilinear (UP/DOWN and LEFT/RIGHT) or diagonal (UPLEFT/RIGHTDOWN and UPRIGHT/LEFTDOWN) polarization filters.

Alice swaps her polarization scheme between rectilinear and diagonal filters for the transmission of each single photon bit in a random manner. In doing so, the transmission can have one of two polarizations represent a single bit, either 1 or 0, in either scheme she uses.

When receiving the photon key, Bob must choose to measure each photon bit using either his rectilinear or diagonal polarizer: Sometimes he will choose the correct polarizer and at other times he will choose the wrong one. Like Alice, he selects each polarizer in a random manner. So what happens with the photons when the wrong polarizer is chosen?

The Heisenberg Uncertainty Principle states that we do not know exactly what will happen to each individual photon, for in the act of measuring its behavior, we alter its properties (in addition to the fact that if there are two properties of a system that we wish to measure, measuring one precludes us from quantifying the other). However, we can make a guess as to what happens with them as a group. Suppose Bob uses a rectilinear polarizer to measure UPLEFT/RIGHTDOWN and UPRIGHT/LEFTDOWN (diagonal) photons. If he does this, then the photons will pass through in a changed state—that is, half will be transformed to UP/DOWN and the other half to LEFT/RIGHT. But we cannot know which individual photons will be transformed into which state (it is also a reality that some photons may be blocked from passing altogether in a real world application, but this is not relevant to the theory).

Bob measures some photons correctly and others incorrectly. At this point, Alice and Bob establish a channel of communication that can be insecure—that is, other people can listen in. Alice then proceeds to advise Bob as to which polarizer she used to send each photon bit—but not how she

polarized each photon. So she could say that photon number 8597 (theoretically) was sent using the rectilinear scheme, but she will not say whether she sent an UP/DOWN or LEFT/RIGHT. Bob then confirms if he used the correct polarizer to receive each particular photon. Alice and Bob then discard all the photon measurements that he used the wrong polarizer to check. What they have, is, on average, a sequence of 0s and 1s that is half the length of the original transmission...but it will form the basis for a **one-time pad**, the only cryptosystem that, if properly implemented, is proven to be completely random and secure.

Now, suppose we have an eavesdropper, Eve, who attempts to listen in, has the same polarizers that Bob does and must also randomly choose whether to use the rectilinear or diagonal one for each photon. However, she also faces the same problem that Bob does, in that half the time she will choose the wrong polarizer. But Bob has the advantage of speaking to Alice to confirm which polarizer type was used for each photon. This is useless to Eve, as half the time she used the wrong detector and will misinterpret some of the photons that will form that final key, rendering it useless.

Furthermore, there is another level of security inherent in quantum cryptography—that of intrusion detection. Alice and Bob would know if Eve was eavesdropping on them. The fact that Eve is on the "photon highway" can become obvious because of the following.

Let's say that Alice transmits photon number 349 as an UPRIGHT/LEFTDOWN to Bob, but for that one, Eve uses the rectilinear polarizer, which can only measure UP/DOWN or LEFT/RIGHT photons accurately. What Eve will do is transform that photon into either UP/DOWN or LEFT/RIGHT, as that is the only way the photon can pass. If Bob uses his rectilinear polarizer, then it will not matter what he measures as the polarizer check Alice and Bob go through above will discard that photon from the final key. But if he uses the diagonal polarizer, a problem arises when he measures its polarization; he may measure it correctly as UPRIGHT/LEFTDOWN, but he stands an equal chance, according to the Heisenberg Uncertainty Principle, of measuring it incorrectly as UPLEFT/RIGHTDOWN. Eve's use of the wrong polarizer will warp that photon and will cause Bob to make errors even when he is using the correct polarizer.

To discover Eve's nefarious doings, they must perform the above procedures, with which they will arrive at an identical key sequence of 0s and 1s—unless someone has been eavesdropping, whereupon there will be some discrepancies. They must then undertake further measures to check the validity of their key. It would be foolish to compare all the binary digits of the final key over the unsecured channel discussed above, and also unnecessary.

Let us assume that the final key comprises 4,000 binary digits. What needs to be done is that a subset of these digits be selected randomly by Alice and Bob, say 200 digits, in terms of both position (that is, digit sequence number 2, 34,

65, 911 etc) and digit state (0 or 1). Alice and Bob compare these—if they match, then there is virtually no chance that Eve was listening. However, if she was listening in, then her chances of being undiscovered are one in countless trillions, that is, no chance in the real world. Alice and Bob would know someone was listening in and then would not use the key—they would need to start the key exchange again over a secure channel inaccessible to Eve, even though the comparisons between Alice and Bob discussed above can still be done over an insecure channel. However, even if Alice and Bob have concluded that the their key is secure, since they have communicated 200 digits over an un-secure channel, these 200 digits should be discarded from the final key, turning it from a 4,000 into a 3,800 bit key).

Thus, quantum cryptography is a way to combine the relative ease and convenience of key exchange in public key cryptography with the ultimate security of a onetime pad.

How It Works in Practice

In practice, quantum cryptography has been demonstrated in the laboratory by IBM and others, but over relatively short distances. Recently, over longer distances, fiber optic cables with incredibly pure optic properties have successfully transmitted **photon** bits up to 60 kilometers. Beyond that, BERs (bit error rates) caused by a combination of the Heisenberg Uncertainty Principle and microscopic impurities in the fiber make the system unworkable. Some research has seen successful transmission through the air, but this has been over short distances in ideal weather conditions. It remains to be seen how much further technology can push forward the distances at which quantum cryptography is practical.

quantum dot

A quantum dot is a particle of matter so small that the addition or removal of an **electron** changes its properties in some useful way. All **atom**s are, of course, quantum dots, but multi-molecular combinations can have this characteristic. In biochemistry, quantum dots are called redox groups. In **nanotechnology**, they are called quantum bits or **qubit**s. Quantum dots typically have dimensions measured in nanometers, where one nanometer is 10^{-9} meter or a millionth of a millimeter.

The fields of biology, chemistry, computer science, and electronics are all of interest to researchers in nanotechnology. An example of the overlapping of these disciplines is a hypothetical **biochip**, which might contain a sophisticated computer and be grown in a manner similar to the way a tree evolves from a seed. In this scenario, the terms redox group and qubit are equally applicable; it is hard to classify such a chip as either animate or inanimate. The quantum dots in a biochip would each account for at least one data bit, and possibly several.

In the extreme, the position of a single electron in a quantum dot might attain several states, so that a quantum dot could represent a **byte** of data. Alternatively, a quantum dot might be used in more than one computational instruction at a time. Other applications of quantum dots include **nanomachines**, neural networks, and high-density memory or storage media.

quantum mirage

The term quantum mirage refers to a phenomenon that may make it possible to transfer data without conventional electrical wiring. Instead of forcing charge carriers through solid conductors, a process impractical on a microscopic scale, electron wave phenomena are made to produce effective currents. Leading the research are physicists Donald Eigler, Hari Manoharan, and Christopher Lutz of the IBM facility in San Jose, California.

All moving particles have a wavelike nature. This is rarely significant on an everyday scale. But in atomic dimensions, where distances are measured in **nanometer**s (nm), moving particles behave like waves. This phenomenon is what makes the **electron microscope** workable. It is of interest to researchers in **nanotechnology**, who are looking for ways to deliver electric currents through circuits too small for conventional wiring.

A quantum mirage is a spot where electron waves are focused so they reinforce each other. The result is an energy hot zone, similar to the acoustical hot zones observed in concrete enclosures, or the electromagnetic wave focus of a **dish antenna**. In the case of electron waves, the enclosure is called a quantum corral. An elliptical corral produces mirages at the foci of the ellipse. A typical quantum corral measures approximately 20 nm long by 10 nm wide. By comparison, the range of visible wavelengths is approximately 390 nm (violet light) to 750 nm (red light). One nanometer is 10^{-9} meter, or a millionth of a millimeter.

quantum theory

Quantum theory is the theoretical basis of modern physics that explains the nature and behavior of matter and energy on the atomic and subatomic level. **Quantum** theory dates to 1900, with physicist Max Planck's presentation to the German Physical Society. Planck had sought to discover the reason that radiation from a glowing body changes in color from red, to orange, and, finally, to blue as its temperature rises. He found that by making the assumption that energy existed in individual units in the same way that matter does, rather than just as a constant electromagnetic wave—as had been formerly assumed—and was therefore *quantifiable*, he could find the answer to his question. The existence of these units became the first assumption of quantum theory.

Planck wrote a mathematical equation involving a figure to represent these individual units of energy, which he called *quanta*. The equation explained the phenomenon very well;

Planck found that at certain discrete temperature levels (exact multiples of a basic minimum value), energy from a glowing body will occupy different areas of the color spectrum. Planck assumed there was a theory yet to emerge from the discovery of quanta, but, in fact, their very existence implied a completely new and fundamental understanding of the laws of nature. Planck won the Nobel Prize in Physics for his theory in 1918, but developments by various scientists over a thirty-year period all contributed to the modern understanding of quantum theory.

The Development of Quantum Theory

- In 1900, Planck made the assumption that energy was made of individual units, or quanta.

- In 1905, Albert Einstein theorized that not just the energy, but the radiation itself was *quantized* in the same manner.

- In 1924, Louis de Broglie proposed that there is no fundamental difference in the makeup and behavior of energy and matter; on the atomic and subatomic level either may behave as if made of either particles or waves. This theory became known as the *principle of wave-particle duality*: Elementary particles of both energy and matter behave, depending on the conditions, like either particles or waves.

- In 1927, Werner Heisenberg proposed that precise, simultaneous measurement of two complementary values—such as the position and momentum of a subatomic particle—is impossible. Contrary to the principles of classical physics, their simultaneous measurement is inescapably flawed; the more precisely one value is measured, the more flawed will be the measurement of the other value. This theory became known as the *uncertainty principle*, which prompted Albert Einstein's famous comment, "God does not play dice."

The Copenhagen Interpretation and the Many-Worlds Theory

The two major interpretations of quantum theory's implications for the nature of reality are the Copenhagen interpretation and the many-worlds theory. Niels Bohr proposed the Copenhagen interpretation of quantum theory, which asserts that a particle is whatever it is measured to be (for example, a wave or a particle), but that it cannot be assumed to have specific properties, or even to exist, until it is measured. In short, Bohr was saying that objective reality does not exist. This translates to a principle called *superposition* that claims that while we do not know what the state of any object is, it is actually in all possible states simultaneously, as long as we don't look to check.

To illustrate this theory, we can use the famous and somewhat cruel analogy of Schrodinger's Cat. First, we have a living cat and place it in a thick lead box. At this stage, there is no question that the cat is alive. We then throw in a vial of cyanide and seal the box. We do not know if the cat is alive or if it has broken the cyanide capsule and died. Since we do not know, the cat is both dead and alive, according to quantum law—in a superposition of states. It is only when we break open the box and see what condition the cat is that the superposition is lost, and the cat must be either alive or dead.

The second interpretation of quantum theory is the *many-worlds* (or *multiverse* theory. It holds that as soon as a potential exists for any object to be in any state, the universe of that object transmutes into a series of parallel universes equal to the number of possible states in which that the object can exist, with each universe containing a unique single possible state of that object. Furthermore, there is a mechanism for interaction between these universes that somehow permits all states to be accessible in some way and for all possible states to be affected in some manner. Stephen Hawking and the late Richard Feynman are among the scientists who have expressed a preference for the many-worlds theory.

Quantum Theory's Influence

Although scientists throughout the past century have balked at the implications of quantum theory—Planck and Einstein among them—the theory's principles have repeatedly been supported by experimentation, even when the scientists were trying to disprove them. Quantum theory and Einstein's theory of relativity form the basis for modern physics. The principles of quantum physics are being applied in an increasing number of areas, including quantum optics, quantum chemistry, **quantum computing**, and **quantum cryptography**.

qubit

A qubit is a **quantum bit**, the counterpart in **quantum computing** to the binary digit or **bit** of classical computing. Just as a bit is the basic unit of information in a classical computer, a qubit is the basic unit of information in a **quantum computer**.

In a quantum computer, a number of elemental particles such as electrons or photons can be used (in practice, success has also been achieved with ions), with either their charge or polarization acting as a representation of 0 and/or 1. Each of these particles is known as a qubit; the nature and behavior of these particles (as expressed in **quantum theory**) form the basis of quantum computing. The two most relevant aspects of quantum physics are the principles of **superposition** and **entanglement**.

Superposition

Think of a qubit as an electron in a magnetic field. The electron's spin may be either in alignment with the field, which is known as a *spin-up* state, or opposite to the field, which is known as a *spin-down* state. Changing the electron's

spin from one state to another is achieved by using a pulse of energy, such as from a **laser**—let's say that we use 1 unit of laser energy. But what if we only use half a unit of laser energy and completely isolate the particle from all external influences? According to quantum law, the particle then enters a superposition of states, in which it behaves as if it were in both states simultaneously. Each qubit utilized could take a superposition of both 0 and 1. Thus, the number of computations that a quantum computer could undertake is 2^n, where n is the number of qubits used. A quantum computer comprised of 500 qubits would have a potential to do 2^{500} calculations in a single step. This is an awesome number—2^{500} is infinitely more atoms than there are in the known universe (this is true parallel processing—classical computers today, even so called parallel processors, still only truly do one thing at a time: there are just two or more of them doing it). But how will these particles interact with each other? They would do so via quantum entanglement.

Entanglement

Particles that have interacted at some point retain a type of connection and can be entangled with each other in pairs, in a process known as *correlation*. Knowing the spin state of one entangled particle—up or down—allows one to know that the spin of its mate is in the opposite direction. Even more amazing is the knowledge that, due to the phenomenon of superposition, the measured particle has no single spin direction before being measured, but is simultaneously in both a spin-up and spin-down state. The spin state of the particle being measured is decided at the time of measurement and communicated to the correlated particle, which simultaneously assumes the opposite spin direction to that of the measured particle. This is a real phenomenon (Einstein called it "spooky action at a distance"), the mechanism of which cannot, as yet, be explained by any theory—it simply must be taken as given. Quantum entanglement allows qubits that are separated by incredible distances to interact with each other instantaneously (not limited to the speed of light). No matter how great the distance between the correlated particles, they will remain entangled as long as they are isolated.

Taken together, quantum superposition and entanglement create an enormously enhanced computing power. Where a 2-bit register in an ordinary computer can store only one of four binary configurations (00, 01, 10, or 11) at any given time, a 2-qubit register in a quantum computer can store all four numbers simultaneously, because each qubit represents two values. If more qubits are added, the increased capacity is expanded exponentially.

query

In general, a query (noun) is a question, often required to be expressed in a formal way. The word derives from the Latin *quaere* (the imperative form of *quaerere*, meaning to ask or

seek). In computers, what a user of a search engine or database enters is sometimes called the query. To query (verb) means to submit a query (noun).

A database query can be either a *select query* or an *action query*. A select query is simply a data retrieval query. An action query can ask for additional operations on the data, such as insertion, updating, or deletion.

Languages used to interact with databases are called *query languages*, of which the Structured Query Language (**SQL**) is the well-known standard.

Query by Example

Query by Example (QBE) is a method of **query** creation that allows the user to search for documents based on an example in the form of a selected text string or in the form of a document name or a list of documents. Because the QBE system formulates the actual query, QBE is easier to learn than formal query languages, such as the standard Structured Query Language (**SQL**), while still enabling powerful searches.

To conduct a search for similar documents based on matching text, the user enters or copies selected text into the form search field. This is then passed to the QBE **parser** for processing. A query is created using the relevant words (common words such as "and," "is" and "the" are ignored by default) and a search is carried out for documents containing them. Because the meaning of the selected text is less precise than a formal query, results may be more variable than those in a formal query entry.

To conduct a search for similar documents based on full document text, the user submits documents or lists of documents to the QBE results template. The QBE parser performs an analysis of these and formulates a query to submit to the **search engine**, which in turn conducts a search for similar material.

In terms of **database management system**, QBE can be thought of as a "fill-in the blanks" method of query creation. The Microsoft Access Query Design Grid is an example. To conduct a search for field data matching particular conditions, the user enters criteria into the form, creating search conditions for as many fields as desired. A query is automatically generated to search the database for matching data.

queue

In general, a queue is a line of people or things waiting to be handled, usually in sequential order starting at the beginning or top of the line or sequence. In computer technology, a queue is a sequence of work objects that are waiting to be processed. The possible factors, arrangements, and processes related to queues is known as **queueing theory**.

queueing theory

In computer science, queueing theory is the study of **queue**s as a technique for managing processes and objects in a computer. A queue can be studied in terms of: The source of each queued item, how frequently items arrive on the queue, how long they can or should wait, whether some items should jump ahead in the queue, how multiple queues might be formed and managed, and the rules by which items are enqueued and dequeued.

The queues that a computer manages are sometimes viewed as being in **stack**s. In most systems, an item is always added to the top of a stack. A process that handles queued items from the bottom of the stack first is known as a first-in first-out (**FIFO**) process. A process that handles the item at the top of the stack first is known as a last-in first-out (**LIFO**) process.

Quick Fix Engineering

Quick Fix Engineering (QFE) is a Microsoft term for the delivery of individual service updates to its **operating system**s and **application program**s such as Word. Formerly called a hotfix, "QFE" can be used to describe both the method of delivering and applying a **patch** or fix, and also to refer to any individual fix. Because of the complexity and sheer number of lines of code in most application programs and operating systems, the delivery of temporary fixes to users has long been provided by major software manufacturers. Typically, not all fixes are necessarily applied by an enterprise since they can occasionally introduce new problems. All of the fixes in any given system are usually incorporated (so they don't have to be reapplied) whenever a new version of a program or operating system comes out.

Periodically, all current QFEs (or hotfixes) are delivered together as a **service pack**, which can be applied more efficiently than applying fixes one at a time.

Quicktime

Quicktime is a multimedia development, storage, and playback technology from Apple. Quicktime files combine sound, text, animation, and video in a single file. Using a Quicktime player that either comes with a Web **browser** or can be downloaded from Apple or the browser company, you can view and control brief multimedia sequences.

Quicktime files can be recognized by their file name extensions: qt, mov, and moov.

quiesce

To quiesce is to put a computer, a program, a **thread**, or some other computer resource into a temporarily inactive or inhibited state. A resource that is in a quiesced state can be reactivated more quickly than one that has been completely removed from the system. Typically, any descriptive information about a resource that has been built by the system remains where it is during the quiescence. The reverse of *quiesce* is usually *unquiesce*, but *reset* and other terms are also used.

QWERTY keyboard

The QWERTY (pronounced KWEHR-tee) keyboard is the standard typewriter and computer keyboard in countries that use a Latin-based alphabet. QWERTY refers to the first six letters on the upper row of the keyboard. The key arrangement was devised by Christopher Latham Sholes whose "Type-Writer," as it was then called, was first mass-produced in 1874. Since that time, it has become what may be the most ubiquitous machine-user interface of all time.

The QWERTY arrangement was intended to reduce the jamming of typebars as they moved to strike ink on paper. Separating certain letters from each other on the keyboard reduced the amount of jamming. In 1932, August Dvorak developed what was intended to be a faster keyboard, putting the vowels and the five most common consonants in the middle row, with the idea that an alternating rhythm would be established between left and right hands. Although the Dvorak keyboard has many adherents, it has never overcome the culture of learning to type on a QWERTY.

R/3

R/3 is the comprehensive set of integrated business applications from **SAP**, the German company that states it is the market and technology leader in business application software. R/3 replaced an earlier system, R/2, which is still in use. R/3 uses the client-server model and provides the ability to store, retrieve, analyze, and process in many ways corporate data for financial analysis, production operation, human resource management, and most other business processes.

A recent release, R/3 3.1, makes it possible to get to the R/3 database and applications through Internet access and Web browsers. A sales representative can initiate the workflow for a sales order by filling out an electronic form on a laptop that will be "translated" into input for the R/3 system. Other interfaces such as Lotus Notes can also be used. The Web implementation adheres to the Workflow Client API standard of the Workflow Management Coalition (WfMC).

A more recent version of R/3 adds features designed to speed product delivery by helping to manage the supply chain.

RA

See "registration authority"

RACF

See "Resource Access Control Facility"

RAD

See "rapid application development"

radar

Radar is an **acronym** for "radio detection and ranging." A radar system usually operates in the ultra-high-frequency (UHF) or microwave part of the radio-frequency (**RF**) spectrum, and is used to detect the position and/or movement of objects. Radar can track storm systems, because precipitation reflects **electromagnetic fields** at certain frequencies. Radar can also render precise maps. Radar systems are widely used in air-traffic control, aircraft navigation, and marine navigation.

High-power radar, using large dish antennas, has been used to measure distances to the moon, other planets, asteroids, and artificial satellites. From unmanned space probes, radar has been used to map Venus, whose surface is obscured at visible wavelengths by a thick layer of clouds. Radar has been employed by NASA (the U.S. National Aeronautics and Space Administration) to make highly detailed topographical maps of the earth's surface as well.

Most radar systems determine position in two dimensions: Azimuth (compass bearing) and radius (distance). The display is in polar coordinates. A rotating antenna transmits RF pulses at defined intervals. The delay between a transmitted pulse and the echo, or return pulse, determines the radial position of the plotted point(s) for each azimuth direction on the display. The greater the echo delay from a particular object in space, the farther from the display center its point appears. The maximum range of a UHF or microwave radar system depends on the height of the antenna above average terrain, the topography of the surface in the region, the atmospheric conditions in the region, and in some cases the level of radio background noise.

Radar is known to the general public for its use by law enforcement in determining the speeds of motor vehicles. This type of radar does not display the exact position of an object, but determines its radial speed vector from the *Doppler effect*. A radar detector, which consists of a simple UHF/microwave broadband receiver, can be used in a car or truck to warn drivers of the presence of police radar. Radar detectors are illegal in some states.

The Weather Service uses so-called Doppler radar to determine not only the positions and extent of storm systems, but wind patterns and velocities aloft. Doppler radar employs a combination of position-sensing and speed-sensing radar, making it possible to ascertain the locations and intensity of severe thunderstorms, hurricanes, and tornadoes.

Radar has been used on the high-frequency (HF) radio bands, between approximately 5 MHz and 20 MHz, in an attempt to obtain early warning in the event of a nuclear assault via ballistic missiles. The ionosphere refracts HF waves, allowing much greater system range than is possible with radar at UHF or microwave frequencies. During the 1970s and early 1980s, the signals from these systems became infamous because of the interference they caused. Radio amateurs coined the term *woodpecker* to describe the sound of HF over-the-horizon radar pulses in communications receivers.

radian

The radian is the International System of Units (**SI**) unit of plane angular measure. There are 2 **pi**, or approximately 6.28318, radians in a complete circle. Thus, one radian is about 57.296 angular degrees.

The term radian arises from the fact that the length of a circular arc, corresponding to an angle of one radian, is equal to the radius of the arc. This is shown in the illustration. Point *P* represents the center of the circle. The angle q, representing one radian, is such that the length of the subtended circular arc is equal to the radius, r, of the circle.

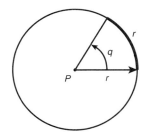

The radian is used by mathematicians, physicists, and engineers. It arises in natural phenomena and in equations which, unlike the angular degree, were invented for human convenience.

Also see International System of Units (**SI**).

radian per second squared

The **radian** per second squared (symbolized rad/s^2 or rad/sec^2) is the International System of Units (**SI**) unit of angular (rotational) acceleration, which is the rate of change of angular speed or velocity. This quantity can be defined in either of two senses: Average or instantaneous.

The average angular acceleration magnitude can be obtained by evaluating an object's instantaneous angular speed (in radians per second) at two different points t_1 and t_2 in time, and then dividing the distance by the span of time $t_2 - t_1$ (in seconds). Suppose the instantaneous angular speed at time t_1 is equal to u_1, and the instantaneous angular speed at time t_2 is equal to u_2. Then the average angular acceleration magnitude b_{avg} (in meters per second squared) during the time interval $[t_1, t_2]$ is given by:

$$b_{avg} = (u_2 - u_1) / (t_2 - t_1)$$

Instantaneous angular acceleration magnitude is more difficult to intuit, because it involves an expression of rotational motion over an "infinitely short" interval of time. Let p represent a specific point in time. Suppose an object is in rotational motion at about that time. The average angular acceleration magnitude can be determined over increasingly short time intervals centered at p, for example:

[p-4, p+4]
[p-3, p+3]
[p-2, p+2]
[p-1, p+1]
[p-0.5, p+0.5]
[p-0.25, p+0.25]
.
.
.
[p-x, p+x]
.
.
.

where the added and subtracted numbers represent seconds. The instantaneous angular acceleration magnitude, b_{inst}, is the limit of the average angular acceleration magnitude as x approaches zero. This is a theoretical value, because it can be obtained only by inference from instantanous speed values determined at the starting and ending points of progressively shorter time spans.

In the complete sense, angular acceleration is a **vector** quantity having direction as well as magnitude, and representing the rate of change of angular velocity. Suppose, for example, that a wheel's rate of rotation is increasing at 0.5 rad/s^2 in the counterclockwise sense; this might be the case for a car or truck moving from right to left (relative to the viewer) with increasing speed. This would produce an angular acceleration vector with a magnitude of 0.5 rad/s^2, pointing toward the viewer in line with the wheel's axle. But if rate of rotation were decreasing at 0.5 rad/s^2 in the counterclockwise sense (the same car or truck slowing down while moving from right to left), the angular acceleration vector would have a magnitude of 0.5 rad/s^2 in the opposite direction, that is, away from the viewer in line with the wheel's axle.

radian per second

The radian per second (symbolized rad/s or rad/sec) is the International System of Units (**SI**) unit of angular (rotational) speed. This quantity can be defined in either of two senses: average or instantaneous.

Average angular speed is obtained by measuring the angle in **radians** through which an object rotates in a certain number of seconds, and then dividing the total angle by the time. If u_{avg} represents the average angular speed of an object (in radians per second) during a time interval t (in seconds), and the angle through which the object rotates in that time is equal to q (in radians), then:

$$u_{avg} = q / t$$

Instantaneous angular speed is more difficult to intuit, because it involves an expression of motion over an "infinitely short" interval of time. Let p represent a specific point in time. Suppose an object is in rotational motion at about that time. The average angular speed can be measured over increasingly short time intervals centered at p, for example:

$[p-4, p+4]$
$[p-3, p+3]$
$[p-2, p+2]$
$[p-1, p+1]$
$[p-0.5, p+0.5]$
$[p-0.25, p+0.25]$
.
.
.
$[p-x, p+x]$
.
.
.

where the added and subtracted numbers represent seconds. The instantaneous angular speed, u_{inst}, is the limit of the measured average speed as x approaches zero. This is a theoretical value, because it cannot be obtained except by inference from measurements made over progressively shorter time spans.

It is important to realize that angular speed is not the same thing as angular velocity. Angular speed is a **scalar** (dimensionless) quantity, while angular velocity is a **vector** quantity consisting of angular speed and direction in the form of a rotational sense (clockwise or counterclockwise). We might say the earth rotates at at 7.272×10^{-5} rad/s, and this tells us its angular speed. Or we might say the earth rotates at at 0.00007272 (7.272×10^{-5}) rad/s counter-clockwise relative to the sun as viewed from above the north geographic pole; this tells us the earth's angular velocity. As with angular speed, we might specify either the average angular velocity over a period of time, or the instantaneous angular velocity at an exact moment in time.

In the case of the earth, the instantaneous angular velocity is essentially constant, and it can be said that $u_{inst} = u_{avg}$. In the case of a moving car or truck, the angular speeds of the wheels, axles, and drive shaft often change, and the statement $u_{inst} = u_{avg}$ is, in general, not true.

Also see **radian**, **second**, **radian per second squared**, and International System of Units (**SI**).

radiation shield

In mobile phones, a radiation shield is an accessory that serves to decrease the amount of radio frequency (**RF**) energy being absorbed by a mobile phone user. Mobile phones are **wireless** communications devices that use frequencies in the **microwave** band. Microwave energy can be absorbed by water and converted to heat energy.

There is growing concern, especially in Europe, about the potential for harm arising out of the effects of the absorbtion of mobile phone microwave radiation in the brain of the user. In particular, both the use of unidirectional aerials and their very close proximity with the cranium have been identified as special risks. It is suggested that a significant proportion (perhaps 40%) of the output of unidirectional aerials is absorbed by the head of the user; and that energy is concentrated around the aerial, which tends to be bare millimeters from the brain.

Mobile phones have been linked with a number of phenomena including short-term and long-term memory loss, increased blood pressure, and brain tumors.

Radiation shields, designed to clip around the body and aerial of mobile phones, absorb and/or reflect microwave energy. Manufacturers claim that the action of placing the user in what amounts to a radiation shadow, can diminish the quantity of radiation absorbed to perhaps 2% of the level of an unshielded phone.

Radio frequency energy limits for mobile phones are specified in international standards EN55022b & IEC1000-4-3. However, some current research suggests these standards may be inadequate and incomplete.

radio detection and ranging

See "radar"

radio frequency

See also **audio frequency** (AF).

Radio frequency (abbreviated RF, rf, or r.f.) is a term that refers to alternating current (**AC**) having characteristics such that, if the current is input to an **antenna**, an **electromagnetic (EM) field** is generated suitable for **wireless** broadcasting and/or communications. These frequencies cover a significant portion of the **electromagnetic radiation spectrum**, extending from nine kilohertz (9 **kHz**), the lowest allocated wireless communications frequency (it's within the range of human hearing), to thousands of gigahertz (**GHz**).

Designation	Abbreviation	Frequencies	Free-space Wavelengths
Very Low Frequency	VLF	9 kHz—30 kHz	33 km – 10 km
Low Frequency	LF	30 kHz—300 kHz	10 km – 1 km
Medium Frequency	MF	300 kHz—3 MHz	1 km – 100 m
High Frequency	HF	3 MHz—30 MHz	100 m – 10 m
Very High Frequency	VHF	30 MHz—300 MHz	10 m – 1 m
Ultra High Frequency	UHF	300 MHz—3 GHz	1 m – 100 mm
Super High Frequency	SHF	3 GHz—30 GHz	100 mm – 10 mm
Extremely High Frequency	EHF	30 GHz—300 GHz	10 mm – 1 mm

When an RF current is supplied to an antenna, it gives rise to an electromagnetic field that propagates through space. This field is sometimes called an RF field; in less technical jargon it is a "radio wave." Any RF field has a **wavelength** that is inversely proportional to the frequency. In the atmosphere or in outer space, if f is the frequency in megahertz and s is the wavelength in meters, then

$$s = 300/f$$

The **frequency** of an RF signal is inversely proportional to the wavelength of the EM field to which it corresponds. At 9 kHz, the free-space wavelength is approximately 33 kilometers (km) or 21 miles (mi). At the highest radio frequencies, the EM wavelengths measure approximately one millimeter (1 mm). As the frequency is increased beyond that of the RF spectrum, EM energy takes the form of infrared (IR), visible, ultraviolet (UV), X rays, and gamma rays.

Many types of **wireless** devices make use of RF fields. Cordless and **cellular telephone**, radio and television broadcast stations, **satellite** communications systems, and two-way radio services all operate in the RF spectrum. Some wireless devices operate at IR or visible-light frequencies, whose electromagnetic wavelengths are shorter than those of RF fields. Examples include most television-set remote-control boxes, some cordless computer keyboards and mice, and a few wireless hi-fi stereo headsets.

The RF spectrum is divided into several ranges, or bands. With the exception of the lowest-frequency segment, each band represents an increase of frequency corresponding to an order of magnitude (power of 10). The table depicts the eight bands in the RF spectrum, showing frequency and bandwidth ranges. The SHF and EHF bands are often referred to as the *microwave spectrum*.

radio paper

See "e-paper"

RADIUS

See "Remote Authentication Dial-In User Service"

RAID

RAID (redundant array of independent disks; originally *redundant array of inexpensive disks*) is a way of storing the same data in different places (thus, redundantly) on multiple **hard disk**s. By placing data on multiple disks, I/O operations can overlap in a balanced way, improving performance. Since multiple disks increases the mean time between failure (MTBF), storing data redundantly also increases fault-tolerance.

A RAID appears to the **operating system** to be a single logical hard disk. RAID employs the technique of *striping*, which involves partitioning each drive's storage space into units ranging from a sector (512 bytes) up to several megabytes. The stripes of all the disks are interleaved and addressed in order.

In a single-user system where large records, such as medical or other scientific images, are stored, the stripes are typically set up to be small (perhaps 512 bytes) so that a single record spans all disks and can be accessed quickly by reading all disks at the same time.

In a multi-user system, better performance requires establishing a stripe wide enough to hold the typical or maximum size record. This allows overlapped disk I/O across drives.

There are at least nine types of RAID plus a non-redundant array (RAID-0):

- RAID-0. This technique has striping but no redundancy of data. It offers the best performance but no fault-tolerance.

- RAID-1. This type is also known as *disk mirroring* and consists of at least two drives that duplicate the storage of data. There is no striping. Read performance is improved since either disk can be read at the same time. Write performance is the same as for single disk storage. RAID-1 provides the best performance and the best fault-tolerance in a multi-user system.

- RAID-2. This type uses striping across disks with some disks storing error checking and correcting (**ECC**) information. It has no advantage over RAID-3.

- RAID-3. This type uses striping and dedicates one drive to storing **parity** information. The embedded error checking (ECC) information is used to detect errors. Data recovery is accomplished by calculating the exclusive OR (XOR) of the information recorded on the other drives. Since an I/O operation addresses all drives at the same time, RAID-3 cannot overlap I/O. For this reason, RAID-3 is best for single-user systems with long record applications.

- RAID-4. This type uses large stripes, which means you can read records from any single drive. This allows you to take advantage of overlapped I/O for read operations. Since all write operations have to update the parity drive, no I/O overlapping is possible. RAID-4 offers no advantage over RAID-5.

- RAID-5. This type includes a rotating parity array, thus addressing the write limitation in RAID-4. Thus, all read and write operations can be overlapped. RAID-5 stores parity information but not redundant data (but parity information can be used to reconstruct data). RAID-5 requires at least three and usually five disks for the array. It's best for multi-user systems in which performance is not critical or which do few write operations.

- RAID-6. This type is similar to RAID-5 but includes a second parity scheme that is distributed across different drives and thus offers extremely high fault- and drive-failure tolerance. There are few or no commercial examples currently.

- RAID-7. This type includes a real-time embedded operating system as a controller, caching via a high-speed bus, and other characteristics of a stand-alone computer. One vendor offers this system.

- RAID-10. This type offers an array of stripes in which each stripe is a RAID-1 array of drives. This offers higher performance than RAID-1 but at much higher cost.

- RAID-53. This type offers an array of stripes in which each stripe is a RAID-3 array of disks. This offers higher performance than RAID-3 but at much higher cost.

rain fade

Rain fade is an interruption of **wireless** communication signals as a result of rain or snow droplets whose separation approximates the signal **wavelength**s. The phenomenon can affect **satellite Internet connection**s as well as satellite television and other systems.

Most **satellite** communication takes place in the **microwave** portion of the **electromagnetic radiation spectrum**. Signals at these **wavelength**s, typically on the order of a few inches, are affected by heavy concentrations of water droplets or ice crystals in the atmosphere. When the mean distance between water droplets or crystals is comparable to the wavelength of the electromagnetic signals, severe attenuation can occur. The observed effect is a degradation or loss of communications during heavy downpours, snow squalls, and blizzards.

Rain fade usually does not last long. Once a heavy shower or squall has passed, normal communications returns. However, during tropical storms or severe winter storms at northern latitudes, fadeouts can persist for hours at a time. The phenomenon occurs with all types of satellite systems, including geostationary (GEO), low-earth-orbit (LEO), and medium-earth-orbit (MEO). It can also affect the Global Positioning System (**GPS**).

Compare **solar fade**.

RAM

RAM (random access memory) is the place in a computer where the **operating system**, application programs, and data in current use are kept so that they can be quickly reached by the computer's **processor**. RAM is much faster to read from and write to than the other kinds of storage in a computer, the hard disk, floppy disk, and CD-ROM. However, the data in RAM stays there only as long as your computer is running. When you turn the computer off, RAM loses its data. When you turn your computer on again, your operating system and other files are once again loaded into RAM, usually from your **hard disk**.

RAM can be compared to a person's short-term memory and the hard disk to the long-term memory. The short-term memory focuses on work at hand, but can only keep so many facts in view at one time. If short-term memory fills up, your brain sometimes is able to refresh it from facts stored in long-term memory. A computer also works this way. If RAM fills up, the processor needs to continually go to the hard disk to overlay old data in RAM with new, slowing down the computer's operation. Unlike the hard disk which can become completely full of data so that it won't accept any more, RAM never runs out of memory. It keeps operating, but much more slowly than you may want it to.

How Big is RAM?

RAM is small, both in physical size (it's stored in **microchip**s) and in the amount of data it can hold. It's much smaller than your hard disk. A typical computer may come with 32 million bytes of RAM and a hard disk that can hold 4 billion bytes. RAM comes in the form of "discrete" (meaning separate) **microchip**s and also in the form of **module**s that plug into holes in the computer's **motherboard**. These holes connect through a **bus** or set of electrical paths to the **processor**. The hard drive, on the other hand, stores data on a magnetized surface that looks like a phonograph record.

Today's personal computers come with 16 or more **megabyte**s of RAM, usually increasing in multiples of 8 megabytes. Users of graphic applications usually need 32 or 64 megabytes of memory. Most personal computers are designed to allow you to add additional RAM modules up to a certain limit (for example, up to 64 or 128 megabytes). Having more RAM in your computer reduces the number of times that the computer processor has to read data in from your **hard disk**, an operation that takes much longer than reading data from RAM. (RAM access time is in **nanoseconds**; hard disk access time is in **milliseconds**.)

Why Random Access?

RAM is called "random access" because any storage location can be accessed directly. Originally, the term distinguished regular core memory from offline memory, usually on magnetic tape in which an item of data could only be accessed by starting from the beginning of the tape and finding an address sequentially. Perhaps it should have been called "nonsequential memory" because RAM access is hardly random. RAM is organized and controlled in a way that enables data to be stored and retrieved directly to specific locations. A term IBM has preferred is *direct access* storage or memory. Note that other forms of storage such as the hard disk and CD-ROM are also accessed directly (or "randomly") but the term *random access* is not applied to these forms of storage.

In addition to disk, floppy disk, and CD-ROM storage, another important form of storage is read-only memory (**ROM**), a more expensive kind of memory that retains data even when the computer is turned off. Every computer comes with a small amount of ROM that holds just enough programming so that the operating system can be loaded into RAM each time the computer is turned on.

RAMAC

(IBM had an earlier system called RAMAC. See **RAMAC (original)**.)

RAMAC (pronounced RAY-mac; IBM does not spell out the initials) is a multiple-disk storage subsystem from IBM that emphasizes fault-tolerance and is intended for large **enterprise**s. IBM claims that its RAMAC product family "provides the highest data availability of any **DASD**

subsytem." The RAMAC product family uses redundant array of independent disks technology (**RAID**)—in particular, the RAID-5 storage technique. RAMAC also includes redundant (backup) power and cooling subsystems. RAMAC also uses multilevel **caching** to improve performance and it uses predictive failure analysis to identify potential disk failures.

The RAMAC subsystem can be addressed by any **operating system** (such as IBM's **OS/390**) that currently works with IBM's main storage controller products. RAMAC is **scalable** from nine **gigabyte**s up to 90 gigabytes of storage.

RAMAC (original)

(Also see **RAMAC**, a current line of storage products from IBM.)

RAMAC (which stood for *random access method of accounting and control*) was the world's first computer **disk** storage system, developed by **IBM** engineers in San Jose and introduced in 1957. Prior to this, computer storage was largely reliant on **magnetic tape**. The disk-based method introduced moveable read/write heads, which enabled a semi-random access capability; this ability was a momentous achievement, both for IBM and for the computing world in general, because fast random access to large volumes of data now made it practical to have interactive computer systems. RAMAC's development also led to IBM opening its first storage manufacturing plant.

As part of the IBM 350, RAMAC was a system that used fifty metallic disks, each two feet in diameter, arranged on a rotating spindle. Data was recorded on both sides of the disks, each holding a hundred concentric tracks, for a storage capacity of 5 **megabyte**s. An access arm under servo control moved two read/write heads to access to any of the tracks. Originally, RAMAC's purchase price worked out to about $10,000 per megabyte of storage capacity; by 1997 the price per megabyte had dropped to about ten cents.

Rambus

Rambus Dynamic Random Access Memory (RDRAM) is a **memory** subsystem that promises to transfer up to 1.6 billion bytes per second. The subsystem consists of the **random access memory**, the RAM controller, and the **bus** (path) connecting RAM to the **microprocessor** and devices in the computer that use it. High-speed RAM is expected to accelerate the growth of visually intensive interfaces such as **3-D**, interactive games, and streaming multimedia. Rambus is intended to replace the current main memory technology of dynamic random access memory (**DRAM**). Much faster data transfer rates from attached devices such as videocams using **FireWire** and the Accelerated Graphics Port (**AGP**) make it important to reduce the bottleneck in getting data into the computer, staging it in RAM, and moving it throught the microprocessor and to the display or other output devices.

Direct Rambus (DRDRAM) provides a two-byte (16 bit) bus rather than DRAM's 8-bit bus. At a RAM speed of 800 megahertz (800 million cycles per second), the peak data transfer rate is 1.6 billion bytes per second. Direct Rambus uses **pipelining** to move data from RAM to **cache** memory levels that are closer to the microprocessor or display. Up to eight operations may be underway at the same time. Rambus is designed to fit into existing **motherboard** standards. The components that are inserted into motherboard connections are called Rambus in-line memory modules (RIMMs). They can replace conventional **dual in-line memory modules**.

The latest version of RDRAM is Direct RDRAM (DRDRAM). A proposed alternative to DRDRAM is SyncLink DRAM (**SDRAM**).

Rambus DRAM

See "DRDRAM"

RAMDAC

RAMDAC (random access memory digital-to-analog converter) is a **microchip** that converts **digital** image data into the **analog** data needed by a computer display. A RAMDAC microchip is built into the video adapter in a computer. It combines a small static RAM (**SRAM**) containing a color table with three digital-to-analog converters that change digital image data into analog signals that are sent to the display's color generators, one for each primary color—red, green, and blue. In a cathode ray tube (**CRT**) display, an analog signal is sent to each of three electron guns. With displays using other technologies, the signals are sent to a corresponding mechanism.

How It Works

The SRAM part of the RAMDAC contains a color **palette** table. A logical color number in the digital data input to SRAM is used to generate three separate values obtained from the table—one for each of red, green, and blue—that are output to one of three digital-to-analog converters. The analog signal output from the converter is input directly to the display electron guns or other image projecting mechanisms.

For displays with **true color**, the digital color data is fed directly to the DACs, bypassing the SRAM table, which is not needed.

random access memory

See "RAM"

rapid application development

RAD (rapid application development) is a concept that products can be developed faster and of higher quality through:

- Gathering requirements using workshops or focus groups
- Prototyping and early, reiterative user testing of designs
- The re-use of software components
- A rigidly paced schedule that defers design improvements to the next product version
- Less formality in reviews and other team communication

Some companies offer products that provide some or all of the tools for RAD software development. (The concept can be applied to hardware development as well.) These products include requirements gathering tools, prototyping tools, **computer-aided software engineering** tools, language development environments such as those for the **Java** platform, **groupware** for communication among development members, and testing tools. RAD usually embraces **object-oriented programming** methodology, which inherently fosters software re-use. The most popular object-oriented programming languages, **C++** and **Java**, are offered in visual programming packages often described as providing rapid application development.

RARP

See "Reverse Address Resolution Protocol"

RAS

In computer **memory** technology, RAS (row address strobe) is a signal sent to a dynamic random access memory (**DRAM**) that tells it that an associated address is a row address. A data bit in DRAM is stored in a cell located by the intersection of a column address and a row address. A **column address strobe** (CAS) signal is used to validate the column address.

raster

Also see **frame**, **raster graphics**, and **raster image processor**.

The term *raster* refers to the region of a cathode ray tube (**CRT**) or liquid crystal display (**LCD**) monitor that is capable of **rendering** images.

In a CRT, the raster is a sequence of horizontal lines that are scanned rapidly with an electron beam from left to right and top to bottom, in much the same way as a TV picture tube is scanned. However, there are certain differences. In general, the **resolution** is better in a computer CRT than in a TV picture tube. Also, a TV raster scan is **interlaced**, while the raster scan in a computer CRT is almost always **non-interlaced**. In a CRT, the raster is slightly smaller than the full screen size of the monitor. The height and width of the raster can be adjusted, as can the horizontal and vertical position. Other parameters such as pincushioning, horizontal linearity, and vertical linearity can be adjusted in some CRT monitors.

In an LCD, the raster (usually called a *grid*) is scanned differently than in a CRT; image elements are displayed individually. The raster normally matches the screen monitor in size. But if low resolution is used (for example, 640 × 480 **pixel**s on an LCD intended for 800 × 600), the displayed image may fill only part of the screen. If high resolution is used (such as 1024 × 768 pixels on an LCD intended for 800 × 600), the displayed image may exceed the area of the screen, and scrolling will be necessary to view all portions of the raster.

raster graphics

Raster graphics are digital images created or captured (for example, by **scanner** in a photo) as a set of samples of a given space. A *raster* is a grid of **x and y coordinates** on a display space. (And for three-dimensional images, a **z coordinate**.) A raster image file identifies which of these coordinates to illuminate in monochrome or color values. The raster file is sometimes referred to as a **bitmap** because it contains information that is directly mapped to the display grid.

A raster file is usually larger than a **vector graphics** image file. A raster file is usually difficult to modify without loss of information, although there are software tools that can convert a raster file into a vector file for refinement and changes. Examples of raster image file types are: BMP, TIFF, **GIF**, and **JPEG** files.

raster image processor

Also see **Routing Information Protocol** (RIP).

A raster image processor (RIP) is a hardware or combination hardware/software product that converts images described in the form of **vector graphics** statements into **raster graphics** images or **bitmap**s. For example, laser printers use RIPs to convert images that arrive in vector form (for example, text in a specified **font**) into rasterized and therefore printable form.

RIPs are also used to enlarge images for printing. They use special **algorithm**s (such as *error diffusion* and *schochastic*) to provide large blow-ups without loss of clarity.

rational number

A rational number is a number determined by the ratio of some **integer** p to some nonzero **natural number** q. The **set** of rational numbers is denoted **Q**, and represents the set of all possible integer-to-natural-number ratios p/q. In mathematical expressions, unknown or unspecified rational numbers are represented by lowercase, italicized letters from the late middle or end of the alphabet, especially r, s, and t, and occasionally u through z. Rational numbers are primarily of interest to theoreticians. Theoretical mathematics has potentially far-reaching applications in communications and computer science, especially in data **encryption** and security.

If r and t are rational numbers such that r t, then there exists a rational number s such that r s t. This is true no matter how small the difference between r and t, as long as the two are not equal. In this sense, the set **Q** is "dense." Nevertheless, Q is a *denumerable* set. Denumerability refers to the fact that, even though a set might contain an infinite number of elements, and even though those elements might be "densely packed," the elements can be defined by a list that assigns them each a unique number in a sequence corresponding to the set of natural numbers **N** = {1, 2, 3, ...}..

For the set of natural numbers **N** and the set of integers **Z**, neither of which are "dense," denumeration lists are straightforward. For **Q**, it is less obvious how such a list might be constructed. An example appears below. The matrix includes all possible numbers of the form p/q, where p is an integer and q is a nonzero natural number. Every possible rational number is represented in the array. Following the line with the arrow, think of 0 as the "first stop," 1/1 as the "second stop," -1/1 as the "third stop," 1/2 as the "fourth stop," and so on. This defines a sequential (although redundant) list of the rational numbers. There is a one-to-one correspondence between the elements of the array and the set of natural numbers **N**.

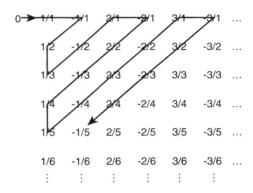

To demonstrate a true one-to-one correspondence between **Q** and **N**, a modification must be added to the algorithm shown in the illustration. Some of the elements in the matrix are repetitions of previous numerical values. For example, 2/4 = 3/6 = 4/8 = 5/10, and so on. These redundancies can be eliminated by imposing the constraint, "If a number represents a value previously encountered, skip over it." In this manner, it can be rigorously proven that the set **Q** has exactly the same number of elements as the set **N**. Some people find this hard to believe, but the logic is sound.

In contrast to the natural numbers, integers, and rational numbers, the sets of **irrational numbers**, **real numbers**, **imaginary numbers**, and **complex numbers** are *non-denumerable*. They have **cardinality** greater than that of the set **N**. This leads to the conclusion that some "infinities" are larger than others!

Rational Rose

Rational Rose is an **object-oriented** Unified Modeling Language (**UML**) software design tool intended for visual modeling and **component** construction of enterprise-level software applications. In much the same way a theatrical director blocks out a play, a software designer uses Rational Rose to visually create (model) the framework for an application by blocking out classes with actors (stick figures), **use case** elements (ovals), objects (rectangles) and messages/relationships (arrows) in a sequence diagram using drag-and-drop symbols. Rational Rose documents the diagram as it is being constructed and then generates code in the designer's choice of **C++**, **Visual Basic**, **Java**, **Oracle8**, **Corba** or **Data Definition Language**.

Two popular features of Rational Rose are its ability to provide iterative development and round-trip engineering. Rational Rose allows designers to take advantage of iterative development (sometimes called evolutionary development) because the new application can be created in stages with the output of one iteration becoming the input to the next. (This is in contrast to waterfall development where the whole project is completed from start to finish before a user gets to try it out.) Then, as the developer begins to understand how the components interact and makes modifications in the design, Rational Rose can perform what is called "round-trip engineering" by going back and updating the rest of the model to ensure the **code** remains consistent.

Rational Rose is **extensible**, with downloadable add-ins and third-party partner applications. It supports COM/DCOM (**ActiveX**), **JavaBeans**, and CORBA component standards.

raw spool files

See "EMF"

RBOC

See "regional Bell operating company"

RD

See "modem lights"

RDBMS

See "relational database management system"

RDF

See "Resource Description Framework"

RDO

See "Remote Data Objects"

RDRAM

See "DRDRAM"

reach

In Internet marketing, *reach* is how many different people visit a **Web site** to see an ad and also what percentage of these people fall into the audience to which an ad is targeted. A common measure of reach for a Web site is its "unique visitors per month." For example, assume an advertising **banner** campaign was targeted to car owners. On a Web site visited by 100,000 unique visitors a month where 90% of the audience owned a car, an ad running on such the site would reach 90,000 different car owners in a one-month run. The term is used in other advertising media as well as on the Web.

reactance

Reactance, denoted X, is a form of opposition that electronic components exhibit to the passage of **AC** (alternating current) because of capacitance or inductance. In some respects, reactance is like an AC counterpart of DC (direct current) **resistance**. But the two phenomena are different in important ways, and they can vary independently of each other. Resistance and reactance combine to form **impedance**, which is defined in terms of two-dimensional quantities known as **complex number**.

When alternating current passes through a component that contains reactance, energy is alternately stored in, and released from, a magnetic field or an electric field. In the case of a magnetic field, the reactance is inductive. In the case of an electric field, the reactance is capacitive. Inductive reactance is assigned positive **imaginary number** values. Capacitive reactance is assigned negative imaginary-number values.

As the inductance of a component increases, its inductive reactance becomes larger in imaginary terms, assuming the frequency is held constant. As the frequency increases for a given value of inductance, the inductive reactance increases in imaginary terms. If L is the inductance in henries (H) and f is the **frequency** in **hertz** (Hz), then the inductive reactance $+jX_L$, in imaginary-number ohms, is given by:

$$+jX_L = +j(6.2832fL)$$

where 6.2832 is approximately equal to 2 times **pi**, a constant representing the number of radians in a full AC cycle, and j represents the unit imaginary number (the positive square root of -1). The formula also holds for inductance in microhenries (μH) and frequency in **megahertz** (MHz).

As a real-world example of inductive reactance, consider a coil with an inductance of 10.000 μH at a frequency of 2.0000 MHz. Using the above formula, $+jX_L$ is found to be $+j125.66$ ohms. If the frequency is doubled to 4.000 MHz, then $+jX_L$ is doubled, to $+j251.33$ ohms. If the frequency is halved to 1.000 MHz, then $+jX_L$ is cut in half, to $+j62.832$ ohms.

As the capacitance of a component increases, its capacitive reactance becomes smaller negatively (closer to zero) in imaginary terms, assuming the frequency is held constant. As the frequency increases for a given value of capacitance, the capacitive reactance becomes smaller negatively (closer to zero) in imaginary terms. If C is the capacitance in farads (F) and f is the frequency in Hz, then the capacitive reactance $-jX_C$, in imaginary-number ohms, is given by:

$$-jX_C = -j\,(6.2832fC)^{-1}$$

This formula also holds for capacitance in microfarads (μF) and frequency in megahertz (MHz).

As a real-world example of capacitive reactance, consider a capacitor with a value of 0.0010000 μF at a frequency of 2.0000 MHz. Using the above formula, $-jX_C$ is found to be $-j79.577$ ohms. If the frequency is doubled to 4.0000 MHz, then $-jX_C$ is cut in half, to $-j39.789$ ohms. If the frequency is cut in half to 1.0000 MHz, then $-jX_C$ is doubled, to $-j159.15$ ohms.

reactive power

In a direct current (**DC**) circuit, or in an alternating current (**AC**) circuit whose **impedance** is a pure **resistance**, the voltage and current are in phase, and the following formula holds:

$$P = E_{rms}I_{rms}$$

where P is the power in watts, E_{rms} is the root-mean-square (**rms**) voltage in volts, and I_{rms} is the rms current in amperes. But in an AC circuit whose impedance consists of reactance as well as resistance, the voltage and current are not in phase. This complicates the determination of **power**.

In the absence of reactance, the product $E_{rms}I_{rms}$ represents **true power** because it is manifested in tangible form (radiation, dissipation, and/or mechanical motion). But when there is reactance in an AC circuit, the product $E_{rms}I_{rms}$ is greater than the true power. The excess is called reactive power, and represents energy alternately stored and released by inductors and/or capacitors. The vector sum of the true and reactive power is known as **apparent power**.

read-only memory

ROM is "built-in" computer memory containing data that normally can only be read, not written to. ROM contains the programming that allows your computer to be "booted up" or regenerated each time you turn it on. Unlike a computer's random access memory (**RAM**), the data in ROM is not lost when the computer power is turned off. The ROM is sustained by a small long-life battery in your computer.

If you ever do the hardware setup procedure with your computer, you effectively will be writing to ROM.

real life

Real life is a term used to describe what happens outside the **Internet** and implies that somehow the Internet furnishes us with a *virtual life*. Depending on the context, usage of the term may imply one or more of the following:

- The Internet is an artificial reflection or weak imitation of life that, in spite of its ability to let us quickly be in contact with knowledge and people at great distance, lacks the ability to engage the full range of our emotions and powers. In this sense, real life is seen as superior to virtual life.

- Increasing numbers of us spend time working on or using the Internet and somehow our work life on or frequent preoccupation with the Internet is seen as an intrusion into our lives. In this sense, real life is seen as a welcome respite from the keyboard and display.

- For those who become happily and fully engaged with the Internet – for example, **gamer**s and those who get involved with **3-D** environments or chatting—real life can be seen as a letdown, meaning back to the mundane.

- For anyone who communicates with others on the Internet, there is an air of the virtual or "made-up" in one's e-mail or chat voice or persona (often exemplified by the e-mail address or the chat name that one adopts). In chat environments, there is even the possibility of using a mask or **avatar** to represent you. In the aspect of personal identity, real life means returning to your "real" name and place in the world.

Paradoxically, perhaps especially for those who work on it every day, Internet activity can come to seem more like one's real life and feeding the cat can come to seem surreal or virtual.

real number

A real number is any element of the set **R**, which is the union of the set of **rational number** and the set of **irrational number**. In mathematical expressions, unknown or unspecified real numbers are usually represented by lowercase italic letters u through z. The set **R** gives rise to other sets such as the set of **imaginary number**s and the set of **complex number**s. The idea of a real number (and what

makes it "real") is primarily of interest to theoreticians. Abstract mathematics has potentially far-reaching applications in communications and computer science, especially in data encryption and security.

If x and z are real numbers such that $x < z$, then there always exists a real number y such that $x < y < z$. The set of reals is "dense" in the same sense as the set of irrationals. Both sets are *nondenumerable*. There are more real numbers than is possible to list, even by implication.

The set **R** is sometimes called the *continuum* because it is intuitive to think of the elements of **R** as corresponding one-to-one with the points on a geometric line. This notion, first proposed by Georg Cantor who also noted the difference between the cardinalities (sizes) of the sets of rational and irrational numbers, is called the *Continuum Hypothesis*. This hypothesis can be either affirmed or denied without causing contradictions in theoretical mathematics.

real time

Also see **real-time clock** and **real-time operating system**.

Real time is a level of computer responsiveness that a user senses as sufficiently immediate or that enables the computer to keep up with some external process (for example, to present visualizations of the weather as it constantly changes). *Real-time* is an adjective pertaining to computers or processes that operate in real time. Real time describes a human rather than a machine sense of time.

In the days when **mainframe batch** computers were predominant, an expression for a mainframe that interacted immediately with users working from connected terminals was *online in real time*.

RealAudio

RealAudio is a continous or **streaming sound** technology from Progressive Networks' RealAudio. A RealAudio player or **client** program may come included with a Web **browser** or can be downloaded from the RealAudio or other Web sites. To deliver RealAudio sound from your own Web site, you (or your space provider) need to have a RealAudio **server**.

A RealAudio file can be recognized by its file name extensions of: ra, ram.

real-time clock

A real-time clock (RTC) is a battery-powered clock that is included as part of a **microchip** in a computer **motherboard**. This microchip is usually separate from the microprocessor and other chips and is often referred to simply as "the **CMOS**." A small **memory** on this microchip stores system description or setup values—including current time values stored by the real-time clock. The time values are for the year, month, date, hours, minutes, and seconds. When the computer is turned on, the basic input-output operating

system (**BIOS**) that is stored in the computer's read-only memory (**ROM**) microchip reads the current time from the memory in the chip with the real-time clock.

real-time operating system

A real-time operating system (RTOS) is an **operating system** that guarantees a certain capability within a specified time constraint. For example, an operating system might be designed to ensure that a certain object was available for a robot on an assembly line. In what is usually called a "hard" real-time operating system, if the calculation could not be performed for making the object available at the designated time, the operating system would terminate with a failure. In a "soft" real-time operating system, the assembly line would continue to function but the production output might be lower as objects failed to appear at their designated time, causing the robot to be temporarily unproductive. Some real-time operating systems are created for a special application and others are more general purpose. Some existing general purpose operating systems claim to be a real-time operating systems. To some extent, almost any general purpose operating system such as Microsoft's **Windows 2000** or IBM's **OS/390** can be evaluated for its real-time operating system qualities. That is, even if an operating system doesn't qualify, it may have characteristics that enable it to be considered as a solution to a particular real-time application problem.

In general, real-time operating systems are said to require:

- **Multitasking**
- Process **thread**s that can be prioritized
- A sufficient number of **interrupt** levels

Real-time operating systems are often required in small embedded operating systems that are packaged as part of microdevices. Some **kernel**s can be considered to meet the requirements of a real-time operating system. However, since other components, such as **device driver**s, are also usually needed for a particular solution, a real-time operating system is usually larger than just the kernel.

recency, frequency, monetary analysis

See "RFM analysis"

reciprocal meter

The reciprocal meter is the standard unit of wave number for **electromagnetic field**s (EM fields). In terms of International Units (**SI**), the reciprocal **meter** is equal to m^{-1}. The wave number is the number of complete wave cycles that exist in a linear span of 1 meter (m).

At the speed of light in free space, 2.99792×10^8 m/s, the frequency f in hertz (**Hz**) is related to the wave number y in reciprocal meters (m^{-1}) according to the following formula:

$$y = f / (2.99792 \times 10^8)$$

To cite a few examples, an EM wave at 300 megahertz (MHz) in free space has a wave number of almost exactly 1 m⁻¹. If the frequency is doubled to 600 MHz, the wave number also doubles, to 2 m⁻¹. If the frequency becomes 1/10 as great, that is, it is decreased to 30 MHz, then the wave number is reduced to 0.1 m⁻¹. As a point of reference, it is easy to remember that the wave number of a 300-MHz signal in free space is very close to 1 m⁻¹.

In general, if the speed of propagation in meters per second for a specific medium is given by c, then:

$$y = f / c$$

where y is in reciprocal meters, and f is in hertz.

In radio-frequency (**RF**) transmission lines such as **coaxial cable**s and **waveguide**s, the speed of propagation is less than 2.99792×10^8 m/s. This increases the wave number, although it has no effect on the frequency.

Also see **frequency**, **electromagnetic field**, **meter**, **wavelength**, and International System of Units (**SI**).

record

1) In computer data processing, a record is a collection of **data** items arranged for processing by a **program**. Multiple records are contained in a **file** or data set. The organization of data in the record is usually prescribed by the programming language that defines the record's organization and/or by the application that processes it. Typically, records can be of fixed-length or be of variable length with the length information contained within the record.

2) In **Virtual Telecommunications Access Method**, IBM's proprietary telecommunications access method for mainframes and part of its Systems Network Architecture (**SNA**), a record is the unit of data that is transmitted from sender to receiver.

recursion

In computer programming, a recursion (noun, pronounced ree-KUHR-zhion) is programming that is recursive (adjective), and recursive has two related meanings:

1) A recursive procedure or *routine* is one that has the ability to call itself. This usually means that it has the capability to save the condition it was in or the particular process it is serving when it calls itself (otherwise, any variable values that have been developed in executing the code are overlaid by the next iteration or go-through). Typically, this is done by saving values in **register**s or data area **stack**s before calling itself or at the beginning of the sequence where it has just been reentered.

2) A recursive expression is a **function**, **algorithm**, or sequence of instructions (typically, an IF, THEN, ELSE sequence) that **loop**s back to the beginning of itself until it

detects that some condition has been satisified. Here is a simple example (using a made-up computer source language):

```
CODELINE1  N=0;
CODELINE2  IF N=<10 THEN DO WRITE LETTER;
CODELINE3  ELSE GOTO CODELINE6;
CODELINE4  N=N+1;
CODELINE5  GOTO CODELINE2;
CODELINE6  ...some other instruction
```

Here, the instructions labeled CODELINE2 through CODELINE5 are recursive until the condition of N having the value of 10. "IF N=<10" means "If N has a value less than 10." "N=N+1" means "Add 1 to the current value of N."

In mathematics, recursion has similar but more complicated meanings than it does when used in programming.

Red Book

The Red Book is the 1980 document that provides the specifications for the standard compact disc (**CD**) developed by Sony and Philips. According to legend, the document was in a binder with red covers, originating the tradition for subsequent adaptations of CD specifications to be referred to as variously colored books. The Red Book described the CD's physical specifications, such as the tracks, sector and block layout, coding, and sampling. Sony and Philips referred to the discs as CD-DA (digital audio), defined as a content medium for audio data digitized at 44,100 samples per second (44.1KHz) and in a range of 65,536 possible values (16 bits).

The CD Format

According to Red Book specifications, a standard CD is 120 mm (4.75 inches) in diameter and 1.2 mm (0.05 inches) thick and is composed of a polycarbonate plastic substrate (underlayer—this is the main body of the disc), one or more thin reflective metal (usually aluminum) layers, and a lacquer coating. CDs are divided into a *lead-in* area, which contains the table of contents (TOC), a *program* area, which contains the audio data, and a *lead-out* area, which contains no data. An audio CD can hold up to 74 minutes of recorded sound, and up to 99 separate tracks. Data on a CD-DA is organized into sectors (the smallest possible separately addressable block) of information. The audio information is stored in frames of $^1/_{75}$ second length. 44,100 16-bit samples per second are stored, and there are two channels (left and right). This gives a sector size of 2,352 bytes per frame, which is the total size of a physical block on a CD.

CD data is not arranged in distinct physical units; data is organized into frames (consisting of 24 bytes of user data, plus synchronization, error correction, and control and display bits) which are intricately interleaved so that damage to the disc will not destroy any single frame, but only small parts of many frames.

The Red Book specifications form the basis for all later CD technologies.

Red Hat

Red Hat is a leading software company in the business of assembling **open source** components for the **Linux** operating system and related programs into a distribution package that can easily be ordered. Red Hat provides over 400 different software packages, including the C language **compiler** from Cygnus, a **Web server** from **Apache**, and the **X Window System** from X Consortium. The advantages to buying the distribution from Red Hat rather than assembling it at no cost yourself from various sources is that you get it as a single assembled package. Red Hat also offers service that isn't provided as quickly by the individual component developers, including members of the **Free Software Foundation**. Like all free software, Red Hat's packages allow the buyer to modify and even resell modified versions of code as long as they do not restrict anyone else from further modification.

Red Hat was one of the first companies to realize that "free" software could be sold as a product. After examining the successful marketing campaign of Evian water, Red Hat concluded that to achieve success, the company had to create more Linux users and brand Red Hat as the Linux name that customers preferred. Today, the "Red Hat Plan" is discussed as a model in business schools.

redirection

On a **Web site**, redirection is a technique for moving visitors to a Web page when its address has been changed and visitors are familiar with the old address. Web users often encounter redirection when they visit the Web site of a company whose name has been changed or which has been acquired by another company. In either case, the Web site probably will include a new **domain name** and it will have a new **Uniform Resource Locator**. To make sure that visitors familiar with the old company get to the new site, the company will turn the original Web site home page into a redirect page, containing a message that says something like: "We have moved to a new location. Please change your bookmark. In five seconds, we will transfer you to the new page."

In addition to replacing the content of the old page with the redirect text, the company adds a **meta refresh** line in the header section of the page that looks something like this:

```
<meta http-equiv="refresh" content="5;url=http://
www.ournewsite.com">
```

In the above example, the "5" means change to the new page in five seconds. The "url=http://www.ournewsite.com" is an example of the URL for the new page.

If you own a Web site that people have learned to use and you then change the name and location of a Web page, it's strongly recommended that you make the original page a

redirect page with a meta refresh tag to the new page. Otherwise, visitors familiar with the old page will get a **404** (Page Not Found) message.

reduced instruction set computer

See "RISC"

redundant

In information technology, the term redundant has several usages:

1) Redundant describes computer or network system components, such as fans, hard disk drives, servers, operating systems, switches, and telecommunication links that are installed to back up primary resources in case they fail. A well-known example of a redundant system is the redundant array of independent disks (RAID).

2) Redundant information is unneeded or duplicated information.

3) Redundant bits are extra **bits** that are generated and transferred along with a data transfer to ensure that no bits were lost during the data transfer.

Redundancy is the quality of a system, an item of information, or a bit that is redundant.

redundant array of independent disks

See "RAID"

redundant array of inexpensive disks

See "RAID"

reentrant

Reentrant is an adjective that describes a computer program or *routine* that is written so that the same copy in **memory** can be shared by multiple users. Reentrant code is commonly required in **operating system**s and in **application**s intended to be shared in multi-use systems. A programmer writes a reentrant program by making sure that no **instruction**s modify the contents of variable values in other instructions within the program. Each time the program is entered for a user, a data area is obtained in which to keep all the variable values for that user. The data area is in another part of memory from the program itself. When the program is interrupted to give another user a turn to use the program, information about the data area associated with that user is saved. When the interrupted user of the program is once again given control of the program, information in the saved data area is recovered and the program can be reentered without concern that the previous user has changed some instruction within the program.

refresh rate

The refresh rate is the amount of times a display's image is repainted or refreshed per second. The refresh rate is expressed in **hertz** so a refresh rate of 75 means the image is refreshed 75 times in a second. The refresh rate for each display depends on the video card used. You can change the refresh rate in the display properties. However, if you change the refresh rate to a setting that the display or video card cannot support, the display goes blank or the image becomes distorted. It is recommended to consult the display and video card manuals before changing the settings to determine the supported refresh rates.

An older refresh rate standard, developed by the Video Electronics Standards Association (**VESA Local Bus**), was only 60 Hz. This refresh rate caused the display's image to flicker causing eye fatigue and headaches in users. A new standard set the refresh rate to 75 Hz. It is believed that 70 Hz or higher eliminates the flicker. When purchasing a monitor, look for a refresh rate of 75 to 85 Hz.

Dynamic random access memory (**DRAM**) memory **modules** also have a refresh rate. A DRAM module is made up of electrical cells. These cells must be recharged or refreshed thousands of times per second or they lose their data. The refresh cycles depend on the number of rows that must be refreshed. For example, a DRAM module that has 4 rows of cells has a refresh cycle of 4K. Some DRAM modules are able to refresh themselves independently of the **processor** or external refresh circuits. Since this reduces power consumption, this kind of DRAM is commonly used in notebook computers.

refurbished

Refurbish, in everyday language, is "to renew or to restore to a new condition and/or appearance." In the computer world, refurbished equipment is not necessarily defective in any way; it may just be "old" (a relative term in the world of computers). When **hardware** is refurbished, the **components** are examined and non-working parts are replaced.

Companies that lease computers may use refurbishing as a means of dealing with units that are returning from long-term leases; after the computers are refurbished, they may be sold at a reduced price or donated to charity—either of which is good for business. Corporations may buy refurbished computers and hardware for a number of reasons. Refurbished hardware costs less than new hardware, which makes it possible for small businesses to make the move to computerized operations for the first time or for businesses with limited means to buy higher quality computers for less money. Another reason for a corporation to buy refurbished equipment is to maintain corporate standards by ensuring that all employees have the same equipment, even when the model being used is not being sold any longer.

There are additional reasons for choosing refurbished hardware if a company is already computerized. For example, there may be a corporate plan to use desktop computers for three years before upgrading to newer ones. In the latter part of the three-year period, equipment purchases may be needed for new staff or to replace a **component** that no longer works. Since the corporation intends to replace *all* desktop computers in the near future, the purchasing department may not want to pay full price for any new equipment at the end of this three-year period. Refurbished computers provide a cost-effective alternative.

A number of organizations, such as StRUT (Students Recycling Used Technology), the National Cristina Foundation, and the Resource Area for Teachers (RAFT) collect and refurbish donated computer equipment for redistribution to schools and charities around the world.

regional Bell operating company

Regional Bell operating company (RBOC) is a term describing one of the U.S. regional telephone companies (or their successors) that were created as a result of the breakup of American Telephone and Telegraph Company (AT&T, known also as the Bell System or "Ma Bell") by a U.S. Federal Court consent decree on December 31, 1983. The seven original regional Bell operating companies were Ameritech, Bell Atlantic, BellSouth, NYNEX, Pacific Bell, Southwestern Bell, and US WEST. Each of these companies owned at least two Bell operating companies (**BOCs**). The BOCs were given the right to provide local phone service while AT&T was allowed to retain its long-distance service. The RBOCs and their constituent BOCs are part of the class of local exchange carriers (**LECs**).

In addition to the RBOCs, there are more than 100 other franchised local telephone companies classed as local exchange carriers. Competitive local exchange carriers (CLECs) are additional companies allowed to compete with the LECs. These include AT&T in some localities and power companies. An interexchange carrier (**IC**) is a long-distance carrier that carries traffic between LECs.

Under the **Telecommunications Act of 1996**, RBOCs and LECs are allowed to compete for long-distance telephone traffic under certain circumstances. RBOCs are generally in competition for digital data and Internet traffic with **wireless** service providers and **cable TV** companies. RBOCs are gradually making available new telephone carrier technologies such as **ISDN** and **DSL**.

register

In a computer, a register is one of a small set of data holding places that are part of a computer **microprocessor** and that provide a place for passing data from one **instruction** to the next sequential instruction or to another program that the operating system has just given control to. A register must be large enough to hold an instruction—for example, in a

32-bit instruction computer, a register must be 32 bits in length. In some computer designs, there are smaller registers—for example, *half-registers*—for shorter instructions. Depending on the processor design and language rules, registers may be numbered or have arbitrary names.

registered port numbers

The registered port numbers are the **port numbers** that companies and other users register with the Internet Corporation for Assigned Names and Numbers (**ICANN**) for use by the applications that communicate using the Internet's Transmission Control Protocol (**TCP**) or the User Datagram Protocol (**UDP**). In most cases, these applications run as ordinary programs that can be started by nonprivileged users. The registered port numbers are in the range from 1024 through 49151. They follow in sequence the **well-known port numbers**, which are, in most cases, applications that can only be started by privileged users, such as the Hypertext Transfer Protocol (**HTTP**) and Post Office Protocol Version 3 (**POP3**) applications. When one application communicates with another application at another **host** computer on the Internet, it specifies that application in each data transmission by using its port number.

Examples of applications with registered port numbers include Sun's NEO Object Request Broker (port numbers 1047 and 1048) and Shockwave (port number 1626). Besides the well-known port numbers and the registered port numbers, the remaining ports in the port number spectrum are referred to as **dynamic port**s or **private port**s and are numbered from 49152 through 65535.

Before the arrival of ICANN, the port numbers were administered by the Internet Internet Assigned Numbers Authority (**IANA**).

registration authority

A registration authority (RA) is an authority in a network that verifies user requests for a **digital certificate** and tells the certificate authority (**CA**) to issue it. RAs are part of a public key infrastructure (**PKI**), a networked system that enables companies and users to exchange information and money safely and securely. The digital certificate contains a **public key** that is used to encrypt and decrypt messages and **digital signature**s.

registry

In the Microsoft Windows 95, **Windows 98**, **Windows NT**, and **Windows 2000 operating system**s, the registry is a single place for keeping such information as what hardware is attached, what system options have been selected, how computer **memory** is set up, and what application programs are to be present when the operating system is started. The registry is somewhat similar to and a replacement for the simpler INI (initialization) and configuration files used in

earlier Windows (**DOS**-based) systems. INI files are still supported, however, for compatibility with the 16-bit applications written for earlier systems.

In general, the user updates the registry indirectly using Control Panel tools, such as **TweakUI**. When you install or uninstall application programs, they also update the registry. In a network environment, registry information can be kept on a **server** so that system policies for individuals and workgroups can be managed centrally.

regression testing

Regression testing is the process of testing changes to computer programs to make sure that the older programming still works with the new changes. Regression testing is a normal part of the program development process and, in larger companies, is done by code testing specialists. Test department coders develop code test scenarios and exercises that will test new units of code after they have been written. These test cases form what becomes the *test bucket*. Before a new version of a software product is released, the old test cases are run against the new version to make sure that all the old capabilities still work. The reason they might not work is because changing or adding new code to a program can easily introduce errors into code that is not intended to be changed.

relational database management system

A relational database management system (RDBMS) is a program that lets you create, update, and administer a **relational database**. An RDBMS takes Structured Query Language (**SQL**) statements entered by a user or contained in an application program and creates, updates, or provides access to the database. Some of the best-known RDBMS's include **Oracle**'s database product line, Computer Associates' CA-OpenIngres, and IBM's **DB2**.

The majority of new corporate, small business, and personal databases are being created for use with an RDBMS. Meanwhile, the idea of object-orientation has begun to contend with the RDBMS as the database management system of the future, sometimes in hybrid implementations.

relational database

A relational **database** is a collection of **data** items organized as a set of formally-described tables from which data can be accessed or reassembled in many different ways without having to reorganize the database tables. The relational database was invented by E. F. Codd at IBM in 1970.

The standard user and application program interface to a relational database is the Structured Query Language (**SQL**). SQL statements are used both for interactive queries for information from a relational database and for gathering data for reports.

In addition to being relatively easy to create and access, a relational database has the important advantage of being easy to extend. After the original database creation, a new data category can be added without requiring that all existing applications be modified.

A relational database is a set of tables containing data fitted into predefined categories. Each table (which is sometimes called a *relation*) contains one or more data categories in columns. Each row contains a unique instance of data for the categories defined by the columns. For example, a typical business order entry database would include a table that described a customer with columns for name, address, phone number, and so forth. Another table would describe an order: product, customer, date, sales price, and so forth. A user of the database could obtain a *view* of the database that fitted the user's needs. For example, a branch office manager might like a view or report on all customers that had bought products after a certain date. A financial services manager in the same company could, from the same tables, obtain a report on accounts that needed to be paid.

When creating a relational database, you can define the *domain* of possible values in a data column and further *constraints* that may apply to that data value. For example, a domain of possible customers could allow up to ten possible customer names but be constrained in one table to allowing only three of these customer names to be specifiable.

The definition of a relational database results in a table of **metadata** or formal descriptions of the tables, columns, domains, and constraints.

relational online analytical processing

Relational online analytical processing (ROLAP) is a form of online analytical processing (**OLAP**) that performs dynamic multidimensional analysis of data stored in a **relational database** rather than in a **multidimensional database** (which is usually considered the OLAP standard).

Data processing may take place within the database system, a mid-tier **server**, or the **client**. In a two-tiered architecture, the user submits a Structure Query Language (**SQL**) query to the database and receives back the requested data. In a three-tiered architecture, the user submits a request for multidimensional analysis and the ROLAP engine converts the request to SQL for submission to the database. Then the operation is performed in reverse: the engine converts the resulting data from SQL to a multidimensional format before it is returned to the client for viewing. As is typical of relational databases, some queries are created and stored in advance. If the desired information is available, then that query will be used, which saves time. Otherwise, the query is created **on the fly** from the user request. Microsoft Access's PivotTable is an example of a three-tiered architecture.

Since ROLAP uses a relational database, it requires more processing time and/or disk space to perform some of the tasks that multidimensional databases are designed for. However, ROLAP supports larger user groups and greater amounts of data and is often used when these capacities are crucial, such as in a large and complex department of an enterprise.

reliability

Reliability is an attribute of any computer-related component (software, or hardware, or a network, for example) that consistently performs according to its specifications. It has long been considered one of three related attributes that must be considered when making, buying, or using a computer product or component. Reliability, availability, and serviceability—RAS, for short—are considered to be important aspects to design into any system. In theory, a reliable product is totally free of technical errors; in practice, however, vendors frequently express a product's reliability quotient as a percentage. Evolutionary products (those that have evolved through numerous versions over a significant period of time) are usually considered to become increasingly reliable, since it is assumed that **bugs** have been eliminated in earlier releases. For example, IBM's **z/OS** (an operating system for their **S/390** server series), has a reputation for reliability because it evolved from a long line of earlier **MVS** and **OS/390** operating system versions.

The Institute of Electrical and Electronics Engineers (**IEEE**) sponsors an organization devoted to reliability in engineering, the IEEE Reliability Society (IEEE RS). The Reliability Society promotes industry-wide acceptance of a systematic approach to design that will help to ensure reliable products. To that end, they promote reliability not just in engineering, but in maintenance and analysis as well. The Society encourages collaborative effort and information sharing among its membership, which encompasses organizations and individuals involved in all areas of engineering, including aerospace, transportation systems, medical electronics, computers, and communications.

remailer

A remailer is an Internet site to which you can send e-mail for forwarding to an intended destination while concealing your own e-mail address. E-mail sent through a remailer is sometimes known as **anonymous e-mail**. There may be valid reasons for wanting to conceal your e-mail address (and personal identity) from an e-mail recipient. There are, of course, unworthy reasons, too. However, advocates of anonymous e-mail and remailer services remind us that having the right to conceal your identity in a note can, on occasion, be socially useful and the practice should be possible.

A small number of Web sites provide remailer services. Until it was recently closed, the best-known remailer was the Finland-based anon.penet.fi. It reportedly handled about 10,000 messages a day and had almost 700,000 registered users.

Remote Access Server Application Program Interface

RAS API (Remote Access Server Application Program Interface) is an application program interface (**API**) in Microsoft Windows 95/98/NT systems that supports **remote access** for users with **dial-up** connections. The Windows program component with which a program must interface is called rasapi32.dll.

remote access server

See "remote access"

remote access

Remote access is the ability to get access to a computer or a network from a remote distance. In corporations, people at branch offices, telecommuters, and people who are travelling may need access to the corporation's network. Home users get access to the Internet through remote access to an Internet service provider (**ISP**). Dial-up connection through desktop, notebook, or handheld computer **modem** over regular telephone lines is a common method of remote access. Remote access is also possible using a dedicated line between a computer or a remote local area network and the "central" or main corporate local area network. A dedicated line is more expensive and less flexible but offers faster data rates. Integrated Services Digital Network (**ISDN**) is a common method of remote access from branch offices since it combines dial-up with faster data rates. **Wireless**, **cable modem**, and Digital Subscriber Line (**DSL**) technologies offer other possibilities for remote access.

A remote access server is the computer and associated software that is set up to handle users seeking access to network remotely. Sometimes called a *communication server*, a remote access server usually includes or is associated with a **firewall** server to ensure security and a **router** that can forward the remote access request to another part of the corporate network. A remote access server may include or work with a modem pool manager so that a small group of modems can be shared among a large number of intermittently present remote access users.

A remote access server may also be used as part of a virtual private network (**VPN**).

Remote Authentication Dial-In User Service

RADIUS (Remote Authentication Dial-In User Service) is a **client/server protocol** and software that enables remote access servers to communicate with a central server to authenticate dial-in users and authorize their access to the requested system or service. RADIUS allows a company to maintain user profiles in a central **database** that all remote servers can share. It provides better security, allowing a company to set up a policy that can be applied at a single administered network point. Having a central service also means that it's easier to track usage for billing and for keeping network statistics. Created by Livingston (now owned by Lucent), RADIUS is a de facto industry standard used by Ascend and other network product companies and is a proposed **IETF** standard.

Remote Data Objects

RDO (Remote Data Objects) is an application program interface (**API**) from Microsoft that lets programmers writing Windows applications get access to and from both Microsoft and other database providers. In turn, RDO statements in a program use Microsoft's lower-layer Data Access Objects (**DAO**) for actual access to the database. Database providers write to the DAO interface.

RDO has evolved into ActiveX Data Objects (**ADO**) which is now the program interface Microsoft recommends for new programs. ADO also provides access to nonrelational databases and is somewhat easier to use.

Remote Function Call

RFC is also an abbreviation for **Request for Comments**.

A Remote Function Call (RFC) is an **application program interface** to **R/3** applications from **SAP**, the German company that sells a coordinated set of applications and databases to Fortune 1000 companies. SAP customers who wish to write other applications that communicate with R/3 applications and databases can use the RFC interface to do so.

Remote Installation Service

Remote Installation Service (RIS) is a feature included in Microsoft's **Windows 2000 server** that allows network administrators to install the Windows 2000 Professional **operating system** and its upgrades to any number of **client** computers at one time from a centralized location. If the client computer is connected to the server through a local area network (**LAN**), the computer's hardware will find the RIS server and request a copy of the operating system. The **network administrator** can use the RISrep imaging option to copy several versions, or images, of a company's desktop configuration to the server so that if a request is made, the server can issue an "image" for a particular computer or user. Microsoft promotes the use of RIS as a way to **configure** new computers right out of the box and to restore the operating system on a computer that has failed.

Remote Method Invocation

RMI (Remote Method Invocation) is a way that a programmer, using the **Java** programming language and development environment, can write **object-oriented programming** in which **object**s on different computers can interact in a distributed network. RMI is the Java version of what is generally known as a remote procedure call (**RPC**), but with the ability to pass one or more **object**s along with the request. The object can include information that will change the service that is performed in the remote computer. Sun Microsystems, the inventors of Java, calls this "moving behavior." For example, when a user at a remote computer fills out an expense account, the Java program interacting with the user could communicate, using RMI, with a Java program in another computer that always had the latest policy about expense reporting. In reply, that program would send back an object and associated **method** information that would enable the remote computer program to screen the user's expense account data in a way that was consistent with the latest policy. The user and the company both would save time by catching mistakes early. Whenever the company policy changed, it would require a change to a program in only one computer.

Sun calls its object parameter-passing mechanism *object serialization*. An RMI request is a request to invoke the method of a remote object. The request has the same **syntax** as a request to invoke an object method in the same (local) computer. In general, RMI is designed to preserve the object model and its advantages across a network.

RMI is implemented as three layers:

- A **stub** program in the **client** side of the **client/server** relationship, and a corresponding skeleton at the server end. The stub appears to the calling program to be the program being called for a service. (Sun uses the term *proxy* as a synonym for stub.)

- A Remote Reference Layer that can behave differently depending on the parameters passed by the calling program. For example, this layer can determine whether the request is to call a single remote service or multiple remote programs as in a multicast.

- A Transport Connection Layer, which sets up and manages the request. A single request travels down through the layers on one computer and up through the layers at the other end.

RMI is supplied as part of Sun Microsystem's Java Development Kit (JDK).

Remote Network Access Application

RNAAPP (Remote Network Access Application) is one of those occasionally visible yet mysterious little programs that come with the Microsoft Windows 95/98 **operating system**. It is part of Windows' Dial Up Networking capability. Users can see it in Windows Explorer as rnaapp.exe. (The *exe* stands for **executable**, meaning it's a file that is a program.) RNAAPP can be the source of a problem when trying to get Internet access. It sometimes remains in **memory** from a previous connection, making the system believe that a connection is already established.

One approach if you get the message that "Dial-up Networking could not establish a compatible set of network protocols" or a message similar to it is to simply press **ctrl-alt-delete**, find RNAAPP in the task list, select it, and then click on the End Task button. There may also be other approaches, too.

Remote Network Monitoring

See "RMON"

Remote Procedure Call

Remote Procedure Call (RPC) is a **protocol** that one program can use to request a service from a program located in another computer in a network without having to understand network details. (A *procedure call* is also sometimes known as a *function call* or a *subroutine call*.) RPC uses the **client/server** model. The requesting program is a client and the service-providing program is the server. Like a regular or local procedure call, an RPC is a **synchronous** operation requiring the requesting program to be suspended until the results of the remote procedure are returned. However, the use of *lightweight processes* or **thread**s that share the same address space allows multiple RPCs to be performed concurrently.

When program statements that use RPC are **compiled** into an executable program, a **stub** is included in the compiled code that acts as the representative of the remote procedure code. When the program is run and the procedure call is issued, the stub receives the request and forwards it to a client **runtime** program in the local computer. The client runtime program has the knowledge of how to address the remote computer and server application and sends the message across the network that requests the remote procedure. Similarly, the server includes a runtime program and stub that interface with the remote procedure itself. Results are returned the same way.

There are several RPC models and implementations. A popular model and implementation is the Distributed Computing Environment (**DCE**). The **IEEE** defines RPC in its *ISO Remote Procedure Call Specification*, ISO/IEC CD 11578 N6561, ISO/IEC, November 1991.

RPC spans the **Transport layer** and the **Application layer** in the Open Systems Interconnection (**OSI**) model of network communication. RPC makes it easier to develop an application that includes multiple programs distributed in a network.

Alternative methods for client/server communication include **message queueing** and IBM's Advanced Program-to-Program Communication (**APPC**).

remote-control software

Remote-control software is programming in a central or server computer that is used to control other computers (or their users) at a distance, either under the control of an administrator or at the request of the user. Although remote-control software existed before the World Wide Web (for remote diagnosis of computer problems and other purposes), the Web has essentially built a platform on which anyone can build a new remote-control application that can reach millions of computers and their users. Remote-control software can be viewed as one class of application furnished by **application service provider**s.

Remote-control software can be divided into applications for use within a private network (such as an **intranet**) or for use on the public network. In a private network, remote-control software can be used to configure and administer all computers from a central point. On the public network, users can request such services as name lookup or arrange to have their files backed up automatically once a day. Remote-control software can also be used in a classroom system where one PC becomes the "master" of student computers, automatically reconfiguring them or turning them off at night.

render

To render (a verb, pronounced REHN-dir, from the medieval French *rendre* meaning "to give back or yield") has a number of usages along the lines of forming something out of something else originally given. A jury renders a verdict given evidence and the rules of law. Animal fat can be rendered into lard. Out of loyalty to the king, a service is rendered. An artist can render an idea in the mind into a drawing on paper. A translator renders one language into another.

In computer graphics technology, computer software can be used to render special 3-D effects given the right programming statements. A computer display system renders an image that is sent to it in the form of a **bitmap** or streaming image.

A rendering (noun) is a term sometimes used to describe a drawing, sketch, plan, or other artistic or engineered effort to depict or portray something on paper or in another medium.

repeater

1) In telecommunication networks, a repeater is a device that receives a **signal** on an electromagnetic or optical transmission medium, amplifies the signal, and then retransmits it along the next leg of the medium. Repeaters overcome the **attenuation** caused by free-space electromagnetic-field divergence or cable loss. A series of repeaters make possible the extension of a signal over a distance. Repeaters are used to interconnect segments in a local area network (**LAN**). They're also used to amplify and extend wide area network transmission on wire and wireless media.

Because digital signals depend on the presence or absence of voltage, they tend to dissipate more quickly than analog signals and need more frequent repeating. Whereas analog signal amplifiers are spaced at 18,000 meter intervals, digital signal repeaters are typically placed at 2,000 to 6,000 meter intervals.

In a cable system, a repeater can be simple, consisting of an amplifier circuit and a couple of signal transformers. The impedance of the cable must be matched to the input and output of the amplifier to optimize the efficiency of the amplifier. Impedance matching also minimizes reflection of signals along the cable. Such reflection can produce undesirable echo effects.

In a **wireless** communications system, a repeater consists of a radio receiver, an amplifier, a transmitter, an isolator, and two antennas. The transmitter produces a signal on a frequency that differs from the received signal. This so-called **frequency** offset is necessary to prevent the strong transmitted signal from disabling the receiver. The isolator provides additional protection in this respect. A repeater, when strategically located on top of a high building or a mountain, can greatly enhance the performance of a wireless network by allowing communications over distances much greater than would be possible without it.

In a fiber optic network, a repeater consists of a photocell, an amplifier, and a light-emitting diode (LED) or infrared-emitting diode (IRED) for each light or IR signal that requires amplification. Fiber optic repeaters operate at power levels much lower than wireless repeaters, and are also much simpler and cheaper. However, their design requires careful attention to ensure that internal circuit **noise** is minimized.

2) A *bus repeater* links one computer **bus** to a bus in another computer chassis, essentially chaining one computer to another.

3) Repeaters are commonly used by amateur and commercial radio operators to extend signals in the radio frequency range from one receiver to another. These consist of *drop repeaters*, similar to the cells in cellular radio, and *hub repeaters*, which receive and retransmit signals from and to a number of directions.

replication

Replication (pronounced rehp-lih-KA-shun) is the process of making a replica (a copy) of something. A replication (noun) is a copy. The term is used in fields as varied as microbiology (cell replication), knitwear (replication of knitting patterns), and information distribution (CD-ROM replication).

On the Internet, a **Web site** that has been replicated in its entirety and put on another site is called a **mirror site**.

Using the **groupware** product, Lotus **Notes**, replication is the periodic electronic refreshing (copying) of a **database** from one computer server to another so that all users in the Notes network constantly share the same level of information.

Report Program Generator

RPG also stands for **role-playing game**.

RPG (Report Program Generator) is a programming language that originated as a report-building program used in DEC and IBM **minicomputer** operating systems and evolved into a fully procedural programming language. Its latest version, RPG IV, is supported by IBM's leading minicomputer system, the **AS/400**. Historically, RPG has probably been the second most used programming language, after **COBOL**, for commercial applications on mid-range computers.

repository

In information technology, a repository (pronounced ree-PAHZ-ih-tor-i) is a central place in which an aggregation of **data** is kept and maintained in an organized way, usually in computer storage. The term is from the Latin *repositorium*, a vessel or chamber in which things can be placed, and it can mean a place where things are collected. Depending on how the term is used, a repository may be directly accessible to users or may be a place from which specific databases, files, or documents are obtained for further relocation or distribution in a network. A repository may be just the aggregation of data itself into some accessible place of storage or it may also imply some ability to selectively extract data. Related terms are **data warehouse** and **data mining**.

Request for Comments

RFC is also an abbreviation for **Remote Function Call**.

A Request for Comments (RFC) is a formal document from the Internet Engineering Task Force (**IETF**) that is the result of committee drafting and subsequent review by interested parties. Some RFCs are informational in nature. Of those that are intended to become Internet standards, the final version of the RFC becomes the standard and no further comments

or changes are permitted. Change can occur, however, through subsequent RFCs that supersede or elaborate on all or parts of previous RFCs.

Reseau Numerique a Integration de Services

See "RNIS"

reseller

In information technology, a reseller, also sometimes known as a value-added reseller (**VAR**), is a company that typically buys products such as computers in bulk from a manufacturer and then "adds value" to the original equipment by including specific software applications or other components. The reseller then markets and sells the customized product under its own name. For example, a VAR might take an operating system such as IBM's **OS/390** with **UNIX** services and, adding its own proprietary UNIX application designed for architects, resell the package to architectural firms. Depending on sales and installation requirements, the reseller could choose whether or not to identify OS/390 as part of the package.

reseller hosting

Reseller hosting is the provision of **Web hosting** services to companies that in turn act as Web hosts for other companies, typically providing **Web site** design and management services as well as acting as host for the site and serving its pages to users. For example, a hypothetical Sports Site Server Inc. could provide a package for professional or amateur sports teams that included an easy-to-use approach to creating a Web site as well as the space for the Web site's pages and an easy-to-use interface for keeping the site up-to-date. Sports Site Server would actually use the computer and storage facilities of Giant Host, Inc., a hosting company that offered similar reselling capabilities to many companies like Sports Site Server. A large hosting company that allowed reselling (like Giant Host) might actually host hundreds of Web sites.

In general, a **reseller** is a company that buys a product or service from another company and repackages it, usually adding something to it, to other companies under its own company or brand name.

Resilient Packet Ring

Resilient Packet Ring (RPR) is a network **topology** being developed as a new standard for **fiber optic ring**s. The Institute of Electrical and Electronic Engineers (**IETF**) began the RPR standards (IETF 802.17) development project in December 2000 with the intention of creating a new **Media Access Control layer** for RPR. The IETF working group is part of the IETF's Local Area Network (**LAN**) and Metropolitan Area Network (**MAN**) Committee. Fiber optic rings are widely deployed in both MANs and wide area

networks (**WANs**); however, these topologies are dependent on **protocols** that aren't optimized or scalable to meet the demands of **packet-switched** networks. The working group intends to actively promote RPR as a technology for the networking market as a whole, and as a technology to enable connectivity among various computing and telecommunications devices. The working group will specify an RPR access protocol and **physical layer** interfaces to enable high-speed data transmission in a fiber optic ring topology. Among the issues the RPR working group is addressing are **bandwidth** allocation and **throughput**, speed of deployment, and equipment and operational costs.

resistance

Also see **current**, **voltage**, and **Ohm's Law**.

Resistance is the opposition that a substance offers to the flow of electric **current**. It is represented by the uppercase letter R. The standard unit of resistance is the ohm, sometimes written out as a word, and sometimes symbolized by the uppercase Greek letter omega. When an electric current of one ampere passes through a component across which a potential difference (**voltage**) of one volt exists, then the resistance of that component is one ohm.

In general, when the applied voltage is held constant, the current in a direct-current (DC) electrical circuit is inversely proportional to the resistance. If the resistance is doubled, the current is cut in half; if the resistance is halved, the current is doubled. This rule also holds true for most low-frequency alternating-current (AC) systems, such as household utility circuits. In some AC circuits, especially at high frequencies, the situation is more complex, because some components in these systems can store and release energy, as well as dissipating or converting it.

The electrical resistance per unit length, area, or volume of a substance is known as resistivity. Resistivity figures are often specified for copper and aluminum wire, in ohms per kilometer.

Opposition to AC, but not to DC, is a property known as reactance. In an AC circuit, the resistance and reactance combine vectorially to yield impedance.

resistor

A resistor is an electrical component that limits or regulates the flow of electrical **current** in an electronic circuit. Resistors can also be used to provide a specific **voltage** for an active device such as a **transistor**.

All other factors being equal, in a direct-current (**DC**) circuit, the current through a resistor is inversely proportional to its **resistance**, and directly proportional to the voltage across it. This is the well-known **Ohm's Law**. In alternating-current (**AC**) circuits, this rule also applies as long as the resistor does not contain inductance or capacitance.

Resistors can be fabricated in a variety of ways. The most common type in electronic devices and systems is the *carbon-composition resistor*. Fine granulated carbon (graphite) is mixed with clay and hardened. The resistance depends on the proportion of carbon to clay; the higher this ratio, the lower the resistance.

Another type of resistor is made from winding Nichrome or similar wire on an insulating form. This component, called a *wirewound resistor*, is able to handle higher currents than a carbon-composition resistor of the same physical size. However, because the wire is wound into a coil, the component acts as an **inductors** as well as exhibiting resistance. This does not affect performance in DC circuits, but can have an adverse effect in AC circuits because inductance renders the device sensitive to changes in **frequency**.

resolution

Resolution is the number of **pixels** (individual points of color) contained on a display monitor, expressed in terms of the number of pixels on the horizontal axis and the number on the vertical axis. The sharpness of the image on a display depends on the resolution and the size of the monitor. The same pixel resolution will be sharper on a smaller monitor and gradually lose sharpness on larger monitors because the same number of pixels are being spread out over a larger number of inches.

A given computer display system will have a maximum resolution that depends on its physical ability to focus light (in which case the physical dot size—the **dot pitch**—matches the pixel size) and usually several lesser resolutions. For example, a display system that supports a maximum resolution of 1280 by 1023 pixels may also support 1024 by 768, 800 by 600, and 640 by 480 resolutions. Note that on a given size monitor, the maximum resolution may offer a sharper image but be spread across a space too small to read well.

Display resolution is not measured in dots per inch as it usually is with printers. However, the resolution and the physical monitor size together do let you determine the pixels per inch. Typically, PC monitors have somewhere between 50 and 100 pixels per inch. For example, a 15-inch **VGA** monitor has a resolution of 640 pixels along a 12-inch horizontal line or about 53 pixels per inch. A smaller VGA display would have more pixels per inch.

Resource Access Control Facility

RACF (Resource Access Control Facility) is the IBM security management product for its **mainframe** (large server) **operating system**, OS/390 (**MVS**) as well as for its **VM** operating system. RACF allows an enterprise to manage the biggest security threat in most enterprises: destruction of computing resources by its own employees. Since its first release in 1976, RACF has screened millions of mainframe users who are familiar with their **logon** identification as their "RACF userid."

RACF gives access to a computer system only to users who have the **authorization** to use a requested resource (such as a file, a printer queue, space to run a program, and so forth). To do this, RACF identifies and authenticates a user, determines the resources to which the user is authorized, and logs and reports attempts to get access to protected resources by unauthorized users.

In OS/390, RACF is part of the Security Server.

Resource Description Framework

The Resource Description Framework (RDF) is a general framework for how to describe any Internet resource such as a Web site and its content. An RDF description (such descriptions are often referred to as **metadata**, or "data about data") can include the authors of the resource, date of creation or updating, the organization of the pages on a site (the sitemap), information that describes content in terms of audience or content rating, key words for search engine data collection, subject categories, and so forth. The Resource Description Framework will make it possible for everyone to share Web site and other descriptions more easily and for software developers to build products that can use the metadata to provide better search engines and directories, to act as intelligent **agents**, and to give Web users more control of what they're viewing. The RDF is an application of another technology, the Extensible Markup Language (**XML**), and is being developed under the auspices of the World Wide Consortium (**W3C**).

A certain amount of metadata is already provided for Web site resources using the Hypertext Markup Language (**HTML**). For example, when we wrote this page, we added HTML statements containing key words that describe the content of this definition and that are used by search engines for indexing. We also added a one-sentence description that can be shown by search engines. (These statements, called META tag statements, are invisible to you unless you click on this page and then right-click on "View source"). Less formally, the "Created on" or "Updated on" date at the bottom of this definition is also metadata—that is, data that tells you something about the data or content on this page. These are simply a few examples of many possible existing and future resource descriptions needed about a Web resource.

Originally conceived as an extension of the content rating PICS Recommendation, the RDF will in time subsume it, with the idea that it can express any data that a PICS-1.1 label can express. However, both RDF and the equivalent PICS expression are expected to be in use for a while.

Benefits

Here are some of the likely benefits:

- By providing a consistent framework, RDF will encourage the providing of metadata about Internet resources.

- Because RDF will include a standard **syntax** for describing and querying data, software that exploits metadata will be easier and faster to produce.

- The standard syntax and query capability will allow applications to exchange information more easily.

- Searchers will get more precise results from searching, based on metadata rather than on indexes derived from full text gathering.

- Intelligent software agents will have more precise data to work with.

How RDF Works

An Internet resource is defined as any resource with a Uniform Resource Identifier (**URI**). This includes the Uniform Resource Locators (**URL**) that identify entire Web sites as well as specific Web pages. As with today's HTML META tags, the RDF description statements, encased as part of an Extensible Markup Language (XML) section, could be included within a Web page (that is, a Hypertext Markup Language—HTML—file) or could be in separate files.

RDF is now a formal W3C Recommendation, meaning that it is ready for general use. Currently, a second W3C recommendation, still at the Proposal stage, proposes a system in which the descriptions related to a particular purpose (for example, all descriptions related to security and privacy) would constitute a **class** of such like descriptions (using *class* here much as it is used in **object-oriented programming** data modeling and programming). Such classes could fit into a *schema* or hierarchy of classes, with subclasses of a class able to inherit the descriptions of the entire class. The schema of classes proposal would save having to repeat descriptions since a single reference to the class of which a particular RDF description was a part would suffice. The scheme or description of the collection of classes could itself be written in RDF language.

Resource Reservation Protocol

See "RSVP"

response time

According to the *IBM Dictionary of Computing* (which cites **International Organization for Standardization** *Information Technology Vocabulary* as the source), response time is:

The elapsed time between the end of an inquiry or demand on a computer system and the beginning of a response; for example, the length of the time between an indication of the end of an inquiry and the display of the first character of the response at a user terminal.

Since user input and system response can now be in terms other than text, the examples in the ISO definition could be expanded. There is also the concept of *perceived* response time, which is the time a user senses as the beginning of input and the end of the response.

Latency is any characteristic of a computer system that increases response time beyond the time desired for an operation.

return merchandise authorization

An RMA (return merchandise authorization) is a numbered authorization provided by a mail-order merchant to permit the return of a product. Most mail-order businesses have a policy concerning returns. Some companies allow only defective products to be returned; others allow any software to be returned if it is unopened. To return a defective product, a typical process is:

- First, the customer must call the technical support office and speak with a technician. The technician helps to determine whether the product is indeed defective. This usually involves the customer answering several questions and following the technician's directions for testing the product in question. If the technician feels that the product is defective, the technician issues an RMA. This process is especially important concerning software. Most merchants do not allow the return of software unless the packaging is unopened. This policy prevents software **piracy**. Some merchants allow the customer to send an e-mail message requesting an RMA instead of having to call.

- Secondly, the customer must write the RMA number on the outside of the box that the product is being shipped in. It is important to mail all the original boxes, manuals, and any other items along with the product. If a return is sent without an RMA number, the merchant can return the product to the customer or charge a restocking fee.

- Finally, the customer mails the product. Most merchants recommend using a shipping company that can track packages. RMA numbers are important to both the merchant and customer. An RMA number tells the merchant that a return is being made and offers protection against fraudulent returns. The customer can use the RMA number to inquire on the progress of a return. For example, if the customer hasn't received any information about the return, the customer can call the merchant and use the RMA number as a reference.

return on investment

For a given use of money in an **enterprise**, the ROI (return on investment) is how much "return," usually profit or cost saving, results. An ROI calculation is sometimes used along with other approaches to develop a business case for a given proposal. The overall ROI for an enterprise is sometimes used as a way to grade how well a company is managed.

If an enterprise has immediate objectives of getting market revenue share, building infrastructure, positioning itself for sale, or other objectives, a return on investment might be measured in terms of meeting one or more of these objectives rather than in immediate profit or cost saving.

return-to-zero

See also **bipolar signaling**, **unipolar signaling**, and **non-return-to-zero**.

Return-to-zero (RZ) refers to a form of **digital** data transmission in which the **binary** low and high states, represented by numerals 0 and 1, are transmitted by voltage pulses having certain characteristics. The signal state is determined by the **voltage** during the first half of each data **binary digit**. The signal returns to a resting state (called zero) during the second half of each bit. The resting state is usually zero volts, although it does not have to be.

In positive-logic RZ, the low state is represented by the more negative or less positive voltage, and the high state is represented by the less negative or more positive voltage. Examples are:

Logic 0 = 0 volts for 1 bit
Logic 1 = +5 volts for $^1/_2$ bit, then 0 volts for $^1/_2$ bit

Logic 0 = -4 volts for $^1/_2$ bit, then 0 volts for $^1/_2$ bit
Logic 1 = 0 volts for 1 bit

In negative-logic RZ, the low state is represented by the more positive or less negative voltage, and the high state is represented by the less positive or more negative voltage. Examples are:

Logic 0 = +5 volts for $^1/_2$ bit, then 0 volts for $^1/_2$ bit
Logic 1 = 0 volts for 1 bit

Logic 0 = 0 volts for 1 bit
Logic 1 = -4 volts for $^1/_2$ bit, then 0 volts for $^1/_2$ bit

reverb

Reverb (short for reverberation) is the acoustic environment that surrounds a sound. Natural reverb exists everywhere. Whether the space being described is a bathroom or a gymnasium, the essential characteristics remain the same.

Reverb is composed of a series of tightly-spaced echoes. The number of echoes and the way that they decay play a major role in shaping the sound that you hear. Many other factors influence the sound of a reverberant space. These include the dimensions of the actual space (length, width, and height),

the construction of the space (such as whether the walls are hard or soft and whether the floor is carpeted), and diffusion (what the sound bounces off of).

In addition to natural reverb, software synthesis of reverberation is also possible. Many audio cards, synthesizers, dedicated effects processors, and digital audio applications can create reverb, simulating both natural and supernatural environments. For example, one could create the reverb for a room fifty feet long, five feet wide, with a four-foot ceiling, lined with carpet.

The synthesis of reverb by a digital signal processing **algorithm** usually attempts to mimic the way a real acoustic space works. The algorithm designers simulate the early reflections, the compounding of echoes, and the decay of high versus low frequencies when designing their product. Of course, the more processing power and speed available, the more complex and potentially realistic a reverb signal can be created.

Reverse Address Resolution Protocol

RARP (Reverse Address Resolution Protocol) is a **protocol** by which a physical machine in a local area network can request to learn its **IP address** from a **gateway** server's Address Resolution Protocol (**ARP**) table or cache. A network administrator creates a table in a local area network's gateway **router** that maps the physical machine (or Media Access Control—**MAC address**) addresses to corresponding Internet Protocol addresses. When a new machine is set up, its RARP **client** program requests from the RARP **server** on the router to be sent its IP address. Assuming that an entry has been set up in the router table, the RARP server will return the IP address to the machine which can store it for future use.

RARP is available for **Ethernet**, **Fiber Distributed-Data Interface**, and **token ring** LANs.

reverse engineering

Reverse engineering is taking apart an object to see how it works in order to duplicate or enhance the object. It's a practice taken from older industries that is now frequently used on computer hardware and software. In the automobile industry, for example, a manufacturer may purchase a competitor's vehicle, disassemble it, and examine the welds, seals, and other components of the vehicle for the purpose of enhancing their vehicles with similar components.

Software reverse engineering involves reversing a program's **machine code** (the string of 0s and 1s that are sent to the logic processor) back into the **source code** that it was written in, using program language statements. Software reverse engineering is done to retrieve the source code of a program because the source code was lost, to study how the program performs certain operations, to improve the performance of a program, to fix a **bug** (correct an error in the program when the source code is not available), to identify malicious

content in a program such as a **virus**, or to adapt a program written for use with one **microprocessor** for use with a differently-designed microprocessor. Reverse engineering for the sole purpose of copying or duplicating programs constitutes a copyright violation and is illegal. In some cases, the licensed use of software specifically prohibits reverse engineering.

Someone doing reverse engineering on software may use several tools to disassemble a program. One tool is a hexadecimal dumper, which prints or displays the binary numbers of a program in **hexadecimal** format (which is easier to read than a binary format). By knowing the bit patterns that represent the processor instructions as well as the **instruction** lengths, the reverse engineer can identify certain portions of a program to see how they work. Another common tool is the disassembler. The disassembler reads the binary code and then displays each executable instruction in text form. A disassembler cannot tell the difference between an executable instruction and the data used by the program so a **debugger** is used, which allows the disassembler to avoid disassembling the data portions of a program. These tools might be used by a **cracker** to modify code and gain entry to a computer system or cause other harm.

Hardware reverse engineering involves taking apart a device to see how it works. For example, if a processor manufacturer wants to see how a competitor's processor works, they can purchase a competitor's processor, disassemble it, and then make a processor similar to it. However, this process is illegal in many countries. In general, hardware reverse engineering requires a great deal of expertise and is quite expensive.

Another type of reverse engineering involves producing **3-D** images of manufactured parts when a blueprint is not available in order to remanufacture the part. To reverse engineer a part, the part is measured by a coordinate measuring machine (CMM). As it is measured, a 3-D wire frame image is generated and displayed on a monitor. After the measuring is complete, the wire frame image is dimensioned. Any part can be reverse engineered using these methods.

The term *forward engineering* is sometimes used in contrast to reverse engineering.

reverse Telnet

Reverse Telnet (sometimes called *direct Telnet*) is the initiation of a **Telnet** session from a computer system to one of its remote users. Usually, a Telnet session is initiated by a user who wishes to access and share resources on a remote computer system. The user must have permission and is prompted to provide a user name and password. Reverse Telnet is when the host computer initiates a Telnet session instead of accepting one.

Reverse Telnet is typically used by a **system administrator** to configure or to troubleshoot a remote computer.

REXX

REXX is an **interpreted** *script* language developed by IBM originally for use by personal users of large operating systems. It was designed for ease of learning and use and to make programming accessible to non-programmers. It offers powerful character-manipulation, automatic data typing, manipulation of words, numbers, and names, and debugging capabilities.

REXX can be compared with these interpreted script languages:

Visual Basic
Netscape's **JavaScript**
Sun Microsystem Tool Command Language
Larry Wall's **Perl**

In general, script languages are easier and faster to code in than the more structured, compiled languages such as **C** and **C++** and are ideal for programs of very limited capability or that can reuse and tie together existing compiled programs.

RF

See "radio frequency"

RFC

See "Request for Comments"

RFM

See "RFM analysis"

RFM analysis

RFM (recency, frequency, monetary) analysis is a marketing technique used to determine quantitatively which customers are the best ones by examining how recently a customer has purchased (recency), how often they purchase (frequency), and how much the customer spends (monetary). RFM analysis is based on the marketing axiom that "80% of your business comes from 20% of your customers."

For more than 30 years, direct mailing marketers for non-profit organizations have used an informal RFM analysis to target their mailings to customers most likely to make donations. The reasoning behind RFM was simple: People who donated once were more likely to donate again. With the advent of e-mail marketing campaigns and customer relationship management software, RFM ratings have become an important tool. Using RFM analysis, customers are assigned a ranking number of 1,2,3,4, or 5 (with 5 being highest) for each RFM parameter. The three scores together are referred to as an RFM "cell." The database is sorted to determine which customers were "the best customers" in the past, with a cell ranking of "555" being ideal.

Although RFM analysis is a useful tool, it does have its limitations. A company must be careful not to oversolicit customers with the highest rankings. Experts also caution marketers to remember that customers with low cell rankings should not be neglected, but instead should be cultivated to become better customers.

RGB

Also see **palette**.

RGB (red, green, and blue) refers to a system for representing the colors to be used on a computer display. Red, green, and blue can be combined in various proportions to obtain any color in the visible spectrum. Levels of R, G, and B can each range from 0 to 100 percent of full intensity. Each level is represented by the range of decimal numbers from 0 to 255 (256 levels for each color), equivalent to the range of binary numbers from 00000000 to 11111111, or **hexadecimal** 00 to FF. The total number of available colors is 256 × 256 × 256, or 16,777,216 possible colors.

In the Hypertext Markup Language (**HTML**), the color for a page background or text font is specified by an RGB value, expressed with six digits in hexadecimal format. The first and second digits represent the red level; the third and fourth digits represent the green level; the fifth and sixth digits represent the blue level. In order to actually display the colors for all possible values, the computer display system must have 24 bits to describe the color in each **pixel**. In display systems or modes that have fewer bits for displaying colors, an approximation of the specified color will be displayed.

In creating Web pages, the number of RGB values that are recommended for use is considerably reduced—first, by the fact that many displays can handle only 256 colors and, secondly, because PC and Mac Web browsers handle 40 of these 256 colors slightly differently. In order to ensure that your colors will be consistent on both browsers, a palette of the 216 colors common to both PC and Web browsers is recommended. Any color outside of these will be **dithered** (approximated).

rich media

Rich media is an Internet advertising term for a Web page ad that uses advanced technology such as **streaming video**, downloaded **applet**s (programs) that interact instantly with the user, and ads that change when the user's mouse passes over it. For example:

- An ad for a Hollywood movie that inclues a streaming video sample of a scene from the movie
- A mouse cursor that is changed to an image on a particular Web site if the user requests it (for example, a cursor that changes to a tiny red question mark on a site like whatis.com)
- A standard-size **banner** ad that includes an inquiry form about ISDN installation, capturing the user's filled-in personal information, and telling the user they will be contacted by a company representative—all simply by interacting with an ad on an online publisher's Web page

Advertiser servers of rich media ads that use **Java** applets or components may also serve regular **GIF** images to people whose browsers don't support Java well.

Rich Text Format

RTF (Rich Text Format) is a file format that lets you exchange **text file** between different **word processor**s in different **operating system**s. For example, you can create a file using Microsoft Word 97 in Windows 95, save it as an RTF file (it will have a ".rtf" file name suffix), and send it to someone who uses WordPerfect 6.0 on Windows 3.1 and they will be able to open the file and read it. (In some cases, the RTF capability may be built into the word processor. In others, a separate reader or writer may be required.)

The RTF Specification uses the ANSI, PC-8, Macintosh, and IBM PC character sets. It defines control words and symbols that serve as "common denominator" formatting commands. When saving a file in the Rich Text Format, the file is processed by an RTF writer which converts the word processor's markup to the RTF language. When being read, the control words and symbols are processed by an RTF reader that converts the RTF language into formatting for the word processor that will display the document. The Specification, a copy of which is located in the archives at the World Wide Web Consortium, is used to create an RTF reader or writer.

Rijndael

Rijndael (pronounced rain-dahl) is the **algorithm** that has been selected by the U.S. National Institute of Standards and Technology (**NIST**) as the new Advanced Encryption Standard (**AES**). It was selected from a list of five finalists, that were themselves selected from an original list of more than 15 submissions. Rijndael will begin to supplant the Data Encryption Standard (**DES**)—and later **Triple DES**—over the next few years in many **cryptography** applications. The algorithm was designed by two Belgian cryptologists, Vincent Rijmen and Joan Daemen, whose surnames are reflected in the cipher's name. Rijndael has its origins in Square, an earlier collaboration between the two cryptologists.

The Rijndael algorithm is a new generation symmetric **block cipher** that supports **key** sizes of 128, 192 and 256 bits, with data handled in 128-bit blocks—however, in excess of AES design criteria, the block sizes can mirror those of the keys. Rijndael uses a variable number of rounds, depending on key/block sizes, as follows:

9 rounds if the key/block size is 128 bits

11 rounds if the key/block size is 192 bits

13 rounds if the key/block size is 256 bits

Rijndael is a substitution linear transformation cipher, not requiring a **Feistel network**. It use triple discreet invertible uniform transformations (layers). Specifically, these are: Linear Mix Transform; Non-linear Transform and Key Addition Transform. Even before the first round, a simple key addition layer is performed, which adds to security. Thereafter, there are Nr-1 rounds and then the final round. The transformations form a State when started but before completion of the entire process.

The State can be thought of as an **array**, structured with 4 rows and the column number being the block length divided by bit length (for example, divided by 32). The **cipher key** similarly is an array with 4 rows, but the key length divided by 32 to give the number of columns. The blocks can be interpreted as unidimensional arrays of 4-byte vectors.

The exact transformations occur as follows: The byte subtransformation is nonlinear and operates on each of the State bytes independently—the invertible S-box (substitution table) is made up of 2 transformations. The shiftrow transformation sees the State shifted over variable offsets. The shift offset values are dependent on the block length of the State. The mixcolumn transformation sees the State columns take on **polynomial** characteristics over a Galois Field values (28), multiplied x4 + 1 (modulo) with a fixed polynomial. Finally, the roundkey transform is **XOR**ed to the State. The key schedule helps the cipher key determine the round keys through key expansion and round selection.

Overall, the structure of Rijndael displays a high degree of modular design, which should make modification to counter any attack developed in the future much simpler than with past algorithm designs.

RIMM

In a computer, a RIMM is a **memory module** developed by Kingston Technology Corp. that takes up less space inside the computer than the older **DIMM** module and has different **pin** characteristics. A RIMM has a 184-pin connector and an SO-RIMM module has a 160-pin connector. An SO-RIMM is smaller and is used in systems that require smaller **form factor**s. While RIMM is commonly believed to stand for "Rambus inline memory module," Kingston Technology has trademarked "RIMM" and uses only that term.

A RIMM module consists of **RDRAM chips** that are attached using a thin layer of solder, a metal alloy that, when melted, fuses metals to each other. Solder balls on each chip create a metal pathway used to conduct electricity.

ring

Also see **Web ring**.

A ring is a network topology or circuit arrangement in which each device is attached along the same signal path to two other devices, forming a path in the shape of a ring. Each device in the ring has a unique address. Information flow is unidirectional and a controlling device intercepts and manages the flow to and from the ring. The **token ring** is the most prevalent form of ring network.

RIP

See "raster image processor"

ripper

In digital audio technology, a ripper is a program that moves a sound sequence from a compact disk onto a computer hard drive as a **Wave file**, often as a step toward converting it to an **MP3**-encoded file. The program that converts the WAV file to an MP3 file is known as an **encoder**. The program that plays the MP3 file is called a *player*. Some audio products provide all three programs together as a package.

RIS

See "Remote Installation Service"

RISC

A RISC (reduced instruction set computer) is a **microprocessor** that is designed to perform a smaller number of types of computer **instruction** so that it can operate at a higher speed (perform more **million instructions per second**, or millions of instructions per second). Since each instruction type that a computer must perform requires additional transistors and circuitry, a larger list or set of computer instructions tends to make the microprocessor more complicated and slower in operation.

John Cocke of IBM Research in Yorktown, New York, originated the RISC concept in 1974 by proving that about 20% of the instructions in a computer did 80% of the work. The first computer to benefit from this discovery was IBM's PC/XT in 1980. Later, IBM's RISC System/6000, made use of the idea. The term itself (RISC) is credited to David Patterson, a teacher at the University of California in Berkeley. The concept was used in Sun Microsystems' SPARC microprocessors and led to the founding of what is now MIPS Technologies, part of Silicon Graphics. DEC's **Alpha** microchip also uses RISC technology.

The RISC concept has led to a more thoughtful design of the microprocessor. Among design considerations are how well an instruction can be mapped to the clock speed of the microprocessor (ideally, an instruction can be performed in one clock cycle); how "simple" an architecture is required; and how much work can be done by the microchip itself without resorting to software help.

Besides performance improvement, some advantages of RISC and related design improvements are:

- A new microprocessor can be developed and tested more quickly if one of its aims is to be less complicated.
- Operating system and application programmers who use the microprocessor's instructions will find it easier to develop code with a smaller instruction set.
- The simplicity of RISC allows more freedom to choose how to use the space on a microprocessor.
- Higher-level language compilers produce more efficient code than formerly because they have always tended to use the smaller set of instructions to be found in a RISC computer.

Rivest-Shamir-Adleman

RSA is an Internet **encryption** and authentication system that uses an **algorithm** developed in 1977 by Ron Rivest, Adi Shamir, and Leonard Adleman. The RSA algorithm is the most commonly used encryption and authentication algorithm and is included as part of the Web **browser** from Netscape and Microsoft. It's also part of Lotus Notes, Intuit's Quicken, and many other products. The encryption system is owned by RSA Security. The company licenses the algorithm technologies and also sells development kits. The technologies are part of existing or proposed Web, Internet, and computing standards.

How the RSA System Works

The mathematical details of the algorithm used in obtaining the public and private keys are available at the RSA Web site. Briefly, the algorithm involves multiplying two large prime numbers (a prime number is a number divisible only by that number and 1) and through additional operations deriving a set of two numbers that constitutes the public key and another set that is the private key. Once the keys have been developed, the original prime numbers are no longer important and can be discarded. Both the public and the private keys are needed for encryption/decryption but only the owner of a private key ever needs to know it. Using the RSA system, the private key never needs to be sent across the Internet.

The private key is used to decrypt text that has been encrypted with the public key. Thus, if I send you a message, I can find out your public key (but not your private key) from a central administrator and encrypt a message to you using your public key. When you receive it, you decrypt it with your private key. In addition to encrypting messages (which ensures privacy), you can authenticate yourself to me (so I know that it is really you who sent the message) by using your private key to encrypt a digital certificate. When I receive it, I can use your public key to decrypt it. A table might help us remember this.

To do this	Use whose	Kind of key
Send an encrypted message	Use the receiver's	Public key
Send an encrypted signature	Use the sender's	Private key
Decrypt an encrypted message	Use the receiver's	Private key
Decrypt an encrypted signature (and authenticate the sender)	Use the sender's	Public key

RJ-11 – RJ-14 – RJ-45 – RJ-XX

See "telephone jacks"

rlogin

Rlogin (remote login) is a **UNIX** command that allows an authorized user to login to other UNIX machines (**host**s) on a network and to interact as if the user were physically at the host computer. Once logged in to the host, the user can do anything that the host has given permission for, such as read, edit, or delete files.

Rlogin is similar to the better known **Telnet** command. Rlogin is considered useful for simple logins that don't require a lot of control over the client/host interaction, but is thought to be less useful than Telnet where a lot of customization is desired, for multiple sessions, for connections between very distant terminals or to terminals that are not running UNIX, for that matter, since rlogin can only connect to UNIX hosts. A benefit of rlogin is the ability to use a file called .rhosts that resides on the host machine and maintains a list of terminals allowed to login without a password.

A secure version of rlogin (slogin) was combined with two other UNIX **utility**, ssh and scp, in the **Secure Shell** suite, an interface and **protocol** created to replace the earlier utilities.

RMI

See "Remote Method Invocation"

RMON

RMON (Remote Network Monitoring) provides standard information that a network administrator can use to monitor, analyze, and troubleshoot a group of **distributed** local area networks (**LAN**s) and interconnecting **T-1/E-1 and T-2/E-3 lines** from a central site. RMON specifically defines the information that any network monitoring system will be able to provide. It's specified as part of the Management Information Base (**MIB**) in **Request for Comments** 1757 as an extension of the Simple Network Management Protocol (**SNMP**). The latest level is RMON Version 2 (sometimes referred to as "RMON 2" or "RMON2").

RMON can be supported by hardware monitoring devices (known as "probes") or through software or some combination. For example, Cisco's line of LAN **switch**es includes software in each switch that can trap information as traffic flows through and record it in its MIB. A software **agent** can gather the information for presentation to the network administrator with a graphical user interface. A number of vendors provide products with various kinds of RMON support.

RMON collects nine kinds of information, including packets sent, bytes sent, packets dropped, statistics by host, by conversations between two sets of addresses, and certain kinds of events that have occurred. A network administrator can find out how much **bandwidth** or traffic each user is imposing on the network and what Web sites are being accessed. Alarms can be set in order to be aware of impending problems.

rms

See "root-mean-square"

RNIS

RNIS (Reseau Numerique a Integration de Services) is the European name for Integrated Services Digital Network (ISDN).

roaming service

Roaming service is the ability to get **access** to the Internet when away from home at the price of a local call or at a charge considerably less than the regular long-distance charges. For example, if you normally get access to the Internet from an **access provider** in Brooklyn, New York and are travelling to Hong Kong, you can call a designated access provider in Hong Kong. Instead of paying long distance charges to your local provider in Brooklyn, you pay the local phone connection charge in Hong Kong and possibly a modest additional charge for the service.

Roaming service is made possible through Internet service providers (**ISPs**) who have cooperative agreements to grant each others' customers local access to the Internet. Special software allows cooperating ISPs to keep track of and calculate prearranged payments for usage differences. Here's how it works for the user:

1. The Internet user must already subscribe to an ISP that offers roaming service arrangements.

2. Assuming the ISP does, the user can determine a cooperating ISP in a city to which the user is travelling.

3. In the travel location, the user can call the local ISP's designated phone number through the computer modem, entering information during login that will identify the user's home ISP.

4. The "foreign" ISP will contact the ISP and determine that the user is a valid user.

5. The "foreign" ISP will grant the user access to the Internet. The user will be able to access e-mail from the home mail server.

6. The user will be charged at local phone rates. In addition, depending on the particular service arrangement, the home ISP may levy an additional hourly usage charge of several dollars an hour or a monthly charge in case the service is used during that month.

A similar roaming service is provided by some cooperating **cellular telephone** telephone or personal digital assistant (**PDA**) service providers.

If you are travelling and simply need to be able to exchange **e-mail**, you can consider getting a **freemail** membership (usually free) from HotMail, Rocketmail, or other freemail providers. Hotmail also offers **POP3** server accounts for access to up to four e-mail accounts you may already have, assuming you remember the POP3 server name and your user IDs and passwords.

If you subscribe to a somewhat global service such as AT&T's WorldNet or the IBM Global Network, you may already be able to access your account in certain cities through your provider's local point-of-presence (**POP**) on the Internet without having to pay for a long-distance call.

roaming

See "roaming service"

robot

A robot is a machine designed to execute one or more tasks repeatedly, with speed and precision. There are as many different types of robots as there are tasks for them to perform.

A robot can be controlled by a human operator, sometimes from a great distance. But most robots are controlled by computer, and fall into either of two categories: Autonomous robots and insect robots. An autonomous

robot acts as a stand-alone system, complete with its own computer (called the controller). Insect robots work in fleets ranging in number from a few to thousands, with all fleet members under the supervision of a single controller. The term insect arises from the similarity of the system to a colony of insects, where the individuals are simple but the fleet as a whole can be sophisticated.

Robots are sometimes grouped according to the time frame in which they were first widely used. First-generation robots date from the 1970s and consist of stationary, nonprogrammable, electromechanical devices without sensors. Second-generation robots were developed in the 1980s and can contain sensors and programmable controllers. Third-generation robots were developed between approximately 1990 and the present. These machines can be stationary or mobile, autonomous or insect type, with sophisticated programming, speech recognition and/or synthesis, and other advanced features. Fourth-generation robots are in the research-and-development phase, and include features such as **artificial intelligence**, **self-replication**, **self assembly**, and nanoscale size (physical dimensions on the order of nanometers, or units of 10^{-9} meter).

Some advanced robots are called androids because of their superficial resemblance to human beings. Androids are mobile, usually moving around on wheels or a track drive (robots legs are unstable and difficult to engineer). The android is not necessarily the end point of robot evolution. Some of the most esoteric and powerful robots do not look or behave anything like humans. The ultimate in robotic intelligence and sophistication might take on forms yet to be imagined.

Also see **artificial intelligence**, **nanotechnology**, and **robotics**.

robotics

Robotics is a branch of engineering that involves the conception, design, manufacture, and operation of **robot**s. This field overlaps with electronics, computer science, **artificial intelligence**, mechatronics, **nanotechnology**, and bioengineering.

Science-fiction author Isaac Asimov is often given credit for being the first person to use the term robotics in a short story composed in the 1940s. In the story, Asimov suggested three principles to guide the behavior of robots and smart machines. Asimov's Three Laws of Robotics, as they are called, have survived to the present:

1. Robots must never harm human beings.

2. Robots must follow instructions from humans without violating rule 1.

3. Robots must protect themselves without violating the other rules.

robust

Robust (pronounced RO-buhst) is an adjective commonly applied in marketing literature to information technology products in several ways. It derives from the Latin *robustus*, meaning "strength."

1) A robust product can be one that doesn't break easily. Thus, an **operating system** in which any individual **application** can fail without disturbing the operating system or other applications can be said to be robust.

2) Robust is also sometimes used to mean a product or system of products designed with a full complement of capabilities. Thus, in the context of the business world, early **UNIX** systems were not considered as robust as IBM's **mainframe** operating systems, such as *MVS*, which were designed for continuous operation with a very low failure rate and features such as automatic backup of file systems.

Roentgen

Roentgen is IBM's development name for a liquid crystal display (**LCD**) that has 2560 × 2048 pixels and is described as providing an image "as precise as the original paper document." Roentgen can provide an image **resolution** of up to 200 pixels per inch.

The Roentgen display is a form of active matrix LCD (AMLCD). Aluminum and copper are used, instead of the traditional molybdenum and tungsten. Aluminum and copper are better conductors, and make possible a higher resolution at moderate cost. Display sizes vary from approximately 16 inches to 22 inches diagonal measure. The images are more than four times as sharp as those in a high-end high-definition television (**HDTV**) display.

AMLCD displays such as Roentgen are used mainly in high-end graphics applications. However, this type of display also has advantages in text applications. Because it renders text more cleanly than displays having lower resolution, Roentgen allows some people to read online text faster and with less fatigue than is possible with older technologies. In addition, the expanded effective screen area makes it possible to **render** a large amount of information on a single screen.

A typical Roentgen display contains more than 8600 feet of thin-film wiring. The backlight consumes 44 watts of power, about the same as a conventional cathode-ray tube (**CRT**). The entire unit weighs about 20 pounds and is housed in a box measuring less than 10 inches deep.

The development name apparently is derived from Wilhelm Röntgen, the physicist who discovered X-rays.

ROI

See "return on investment"

ROLAP

See "relational online analytical processing"

role-playing game

RPG also stands for **Report Program Generator**.

A role-playing game (RPG) is a game in which each participant assumes the role of a character (such as an ogre or a futuristic spaceship captain) that can interact within the game's imaginary world. More popular games include Dungeons and Dragons, one of the early online games, Battletech, and Star Wars. The online environments known as **MUD** and **MOO** include software for playing and developing role-playing games.

A different but somewhat related idea is the "world" in which a participant defines an appearance or **avatar** and interacts with others in the chat world using that avatar.

rollback

A rollback is the undoing of partly completed **database** changes when a database **transaction** is determined to have failed.

rollout

A rollout is a staged series of activities that often accumulate meaning as they occur. Computer product makers and marketers use the term to describe a series of related product announcements that are staged over time. Public relations campaigns use the term to describe the revelation of a major company theme, event, or other message over a period of time calculated to lead to ideal results. When a company installs new equipment, the installation staging is sometimes called a rollout.

rollover

In creating **page** for a Web **site**, a rollover (some people call it a "mouseover") is a technique using **JavaScript** that lets you change a page element (usuallly a graphic image) when the user rolls the mouse over something on the page (like a line of text or a graphic image). The term *rollover* recognizes that there is a little ball in your mouse that you roll on a surface.

Some common uses of the rollover include:

- Inviting user interaction by causing text elements in a menu to "pop up" or otherwise become lively as you roll the mouse over each line. This is done by creating a small graphic image for each text line and a second graphic image for each line that is substituted when a given text line is rolled over with a mouse. The effect invites users to click on one of the rolled over lines.

- Causing a previously invisible graphic image or other element to suddenly appear when the user rolls the mouse over a particular page element. Raymond Pirouz's home page site for his book, *click here*, uses this technique. Try it.

- Have one element on a page change color as you roll the mouse over other elements. It's a way to reinforce the user's recognition that certain page elements are "alive" and clickable.

ROM

See "read-only memory"

root directory

In a computer **file system** that is organized as a hierarchy or tree, the root directory is the directory that includes all other directories. (Unlike a real tree, a tree file system has only one root!) In **UNIX**-based as well as in other **operating system**, the root directory has no name. It is simply represented by the special character that separates directories in a file system .

In UNIX-based systems, the root directory is represented simply as:

/

In Windows systems, the root directory is represented as:

\

Only a few special users of a shared operating system will be given the authority to access all file directories and files under the root directory.

root server system

On the Internet, the root server system is the way that an authoritative master list of all top-level **domain name** (such as **com**, **net**, **org**, and individual country codes) is maintained and made available. The system consists of 13 file servers. The central or "A" server is operated by Network Solutions, Inc., the company that currently manages domain name registration, and the master list of top-level domain (TLD) names is kept on the A server. On a daily basis, this list is replicated to 12 other geographically dispersed file servers that are maintained by an assortment of agencies. The Internet routing system uses the nearest root server list to update routing tables.

rootkit

A rootkit is a collection of tools (programs) that a **hacker** uses to mask intrusion and obtain administrator-level access to a computer or computer network. The intruder installs a rootkit on a computer after first obtaining user-level access, either by exploiting a known vulnerability or cracking a password. The rootkit then collects userids and passwords to other machines on the network, thus giving the hacker **root** or privileged access.

A rootkit may consist of utilities that also: Monitor traffic and keystrokes; create a "backdoor" into the system for the hacker's use; alter log files; attack other machines on the network; and alter existing system tools to circumvent detection.

The presence of a rootkit on a network was first documented in the early 90s. At that time Sun and Linux operating systems were the primary targets for a hacker looking to install a rootkit. Today, rootkits are available for a number of operating systems and are increasingly difficult to detect on any network.

root-mean-square

Also see **peak** and **peak-to-peak**.

In a direct current (**DC**) circuit, voltage or current is simple to define, but in an alternating current (**AC**) circuit, the definition is more complicated, and can be done in several ways. *Root-mean-square (rms)* refers to the most common mathematical method of defining the effective voltage or current of an AC wave.

To determine rms value, three mathematical operations are carried out on the function representing the AC waveform:

(1) The square of the waveform function (usually a sine wave) is determined.

(2) The function resulting from step (1) is averaged over time.

(3) The square root of the function resulting from step (2) is found.

In a circuit whose **impedance** consists of a pure **resistance**, the rms value of an AC wave is often called the *effective value* or *DC-equivalent* value. For example, if an AC source of 100 volts rms is connected across a resistor, and the resulting current causes 50 watts of heat to be dissipated by the resistor, then 50 watts of heat will also be dissipated if a 100-volt DC source is connected to the resistor.

For a sine wave, the rms value is 0.707 times the **peak** value, or 0.354 times the **peak-to-peak** value. Household utility voltages are expressed in rms terms. A so-called "117-volt" AC circuit carries about 165 volts peak (pk), or 330 volts peak-to-peak (pk-pk).

RosettaNet

RosettaNet is an organization set up by leading information technology companies to define and implement a common set of standards for **e-business**. RosettaNet is defining a common parts dictionary so that different companies can define the same product the same way. It is also defining up to 100 e-business transaction processes and standardizing them. Because RosettaNet is supported by all or most of the major companies in the IT industry, its standards are expected to be widely adopted.

RosettaNet has developed a structured four-part approach for creating what it calls Partner Interface Processes (PIPs).

- **Business Process Modeling** examines common business procedures and defines the components of the processes.

- **Business Process Analysis** analyzes the processes and defines a target list of desireable changes to the processes.

- **PIP Development** establishes guidelines and documentation for the changes.

- **Dictionaries** consist of two **data dictionary**: a technical properties dictionary and a business properties dictionary. Along with the RosettaNet Implementation Framework (which defines an exchange protocol for PIP implementation), the dictionaries form the basis for PIP development.

RosettaNet's more than 40 members include Microsoft, Netscape, 3Com, Toshiba America, Compaq, CompUSA, Hewlett-Packard, IBM, and Intel. Its name refers to the Rosetta Stone, a stone on which Egyptian hieroglyphics were also written in other languages, making it possible to decipher the hieroglyphics. *Rosetta stone* has the more general meaning of "something that provides a key to understanding." The organization's slogan is "lingua franca for eBusiness." (A *lingua franca* is a common second language, such as English for countries in the industrialized world whose first language is not English.)

ROT-13

ROT-13 is the encrypting of a message by exchanging each of the letters on the first half of the alphabet with the corresponding letter in the second half of the alphabet (that is, swapping positions by 13 characters). Thus, A becomes N, B becomes O, and so forth, and conversely, N becomes A, O becomes B, and so forth. Numbers, spaces and punctuation are not changed. ROT-13 is sometimes used to encrypt messages that may be offensive or of questionable taste, or messages that contain spoilers (like movie endings or punch lines). The purpose of the code is not to guarantee security, but simply to make it difficult for anyone to read.

ROT-13 is sometimes used on the Internet to encrypt e-mail addresses to discourage spamming. Some browsers or Word editors offer users the ability to convert back and forth between regular text and ROT-13. Typically, you highlight text you want to encrypt or decrypt and then select the ROT-13 encode/decode button.

Here's an example of some regular text:

> This is a sample of a message encoded using ROT-13 encoding. Because of the simple nature of the encryption, its purpose is not security but to prevent accidental reading.

that would look like this in ROT-13:

> Guvf vf n fnzcyr bs n zrffntr rapbqrq hfvat EBG-13 rapbqvat. Orpnhfr bs gur fvzcyr angher bs gur rapelcgvba, vgf checbfr vf abg frphevgl ohg gb cerirag nppvqragny ernqvat.

ROT-13 is sometimes known as *Caesar's code* because the Roman General is said to have used it during the Pelloponesian Wars.

ROTFL

See "chat abbreviations"

rotoscoping

For either broadcast video or Internet **streaming video**, rotoscoping is the rotated projection of a sequence of usually photographed action image frames so that the artist can trace from the frame or create an image to superimpose on it. It can be thought of as "painting on movies" efficiently. Prior to computers, an animation stand called a Rotoscope was used to project a sequence of action frames against a surface so that a set of animation frames could be traced or created. The same work can now be done with digital images and special computer software. Tools that provide efficient ways to rotoscope include Digital Magic and Elastic Reality. Rotoscoping is frequently used as a technique for combining (*compositing*) cartoon figures with realistic settings in television commercials and is also used for special effects in feature-length films.

A *rotoscoping texture* (sometimes called a *sequence map*) is the use of video within an animation, something like an animation within an animation. For example, in a cartoon animation, the television set could show a program containing another animation. Or in a background to an animation in the foreground, you could include some clouds that slowly changed during the foreground animation. The frame rate for both the main animation and the "animation within the animation" must be the same.

round robin

A round robin is an arrangement of choosing all elements in a group equally in some rational order, usually from the top to the bottom of a list and then starting again at the top of the list and so on. A simple way to think of round robin is that it is about "taking turns." Used as an adjective, round robin becomes "round-robin."

In computer operation, one method of having different program **processes** take turns using the resources of the computer is to limit each process to a certain short time period, then suspending that process to give another process a turn (or "time-slice"). This is often described as round-robin process scheduling.

In sports tournaments and other games, round-robin scheduling arranges to have all teams or players take turns playing each other, with the winner emerging from the succession of events.

A round-robin story is one that is started by one person and then continued sucessively by others in turn. Whether an author can get additional turns, how many lines each person can contribute, and how the story can be ended depend on the rules. Some Web sites have been created for the telling of round robin stories by each person posting the next part of the story as part of an online conference **thread**.

roundtripping

In information processing, roundtripping is the conversion (or, in some usages, the repeated conversion back and forth) of a document in one format such as Microsoft Word to a document in another format such as WordPerfect or **HTML** and then back again. Since conversion from one format to another sometimes introduces compromises in the appearance or content of the original, conversion back and forth tends to compound the problem. The problem can become a concern for enterprises such as law offices that often exchange documents back and forth a number of times.

router

Also see **bridge**, **gateway**, **hub**, and **switch**.

On the Internet, a router is a device or, in some cases, software in a computer, that determines the next network point to which a **packet** should be forwarded toward its destination. The router is connected to at least two networks and decides which way to send each information packet based on its current understanding of the state of the networks it is connected to. A router is located at any **gateway** (where one network meets another), including each Internet **point-of-presence**. A router is often included as part of a network **switch**.

A router may create or maintain a table of the available routes and their conditions and use this information along with distance and cost algorithms to determine the best route for a given packet. Typically, a packet may travel through a number of network points with routers before arriving at its destination. Routing is a function associated with the **Network layer (layer 3)** in the standard model of network programming, the Open Systems Interconnection (**OSI**) model. A layer-3 switch is a switch that can perform routing functions.

An **edge router** is a router that interfaces with an asynchronous transfer mode (**ATM**) network. A **brouter** is a network **bridge** combined with a router.

routine

In computer programming, routine and subroutine are general and nearly synonymous terms for any sequence of code that is intended to be called and used repeatedly during the **execution** of a program. This makes the program shorter and easier to write (and also to read when necessary). The main sequence of logic in a program can branch off to a common routine when necessary. When finished, the routine branches back to the next sequential instruction following the instruction that branched to it. A routine may also be useful in more than one program and save other programmers from having to write code than can be shared.

Typically, in **assembler** languages, a routine that requires some variable input can be encoded into a *macro definition* with a specified interface called a *macro instruction*. The programmer can then use a macro instruction instead of having to include and manage the branching to a routine. Macro definitions and instructions also tend to be shared among programmers for use in multiple programs, especially in software development projects.

In higher-level computer languages, many commonly-needed routines are prepackaged as **functions**, which are routines with specified programming interfaces. Some functions can be compiled in line with other code. Other functions are compiled in as **stub** that make dynamic calls for system services during program execution. Functions are sometimes called *library routines.* The compiler and a set of library routines usually come as part of a related software development package.

In Windows and some other personal computer operating systems, the system routines for handling specific tasks such as interacting with specific I/O devices are called dynamic link library (**DLL**) routines. These routines are dynamic because their files are not actually loaded into memory until the first time they are called.

A more recent term, *procedure,* is similar in meaning.

Routing Information Protocol

Also see **raster image processor** (RIP).

RIP (Routing Information Protocol) is a widely-used protocol for managing **router** information within a self-contained network such as a corporate local area network () or an interconnected group of such LANs. RIP is classified by the Internet Engineering Task Force (**IETF**) as one of several internal gateway protocols (**Interior Gateway Protocol**).

Using RIP, a **gateway host** (with a router) sends its entire routing table (which lists all the other hosts it knows about) to its closest neighbor host every 30 seconds. The neighbor host in turn will pass the information on to its next neighbor and so on until all hosts within the network have the same knowledge of routing paths, a state known as *network convergence*. RIP uses a **hop** count as a way to determine network distance. (Other protocols use more sophisticated algorithms that include timing as well.) Each host with a router in the network uses the routing table information to determine the next host to route a **packet** to for a specified destination.

RIP is considered an effective solution for small homogeneous networks. For larger, more complicated networks, RIP's transmission of the entire routing table every 30 seconds may put a heavy amount of extra traffic in the network.

The major alternative to RIP is the Open Shortest Path First Protocol (**OSPF**).

routing switch

In a network, a routing switch is a device that combines the functions of a switch, which forwards data by looking at a physical device address, and a router, which forwards packets by locating a next hop address.

routing

See "router"

roving analysis port

See "port mirroring"

row address strobe

See "RAS"

RPC

See "Remote Procedure Call"

RPG

See "Report Program Generator"

RPR

See "Resilient Packet Ring"

RS-232C

RS-232C is a long-established standard ("C" is the current version) that describes the physical interface and **protocol** for relatively low-speed **serial** data communication between computers and related devices. It was defined by an industry trade group, the Electronic Industries Association (EIA), originally for **teletypewriter** devices.

RS-232C is the interface that your computer uses to talk to and exchange data with your modem and other serial devices. Somewhere in your PC, typically on a **Universal Asynchronous Receiver/Transmitter** chip on your motherboard, the data from your computer is transmitted to an internal or external modem (or other serial device) from its Data Terminal Equipment (**Data Terminal Equipment**) interface. Since data in your computer flows along parallel circuits and serial devices can handle only one bit at a time, the UART chip converts the groups of bits in parallel to a serial stream of bits. As your PC's DTE agent, it also communicates with the modem or other serial device, which, in accordance with the RS-232C standard, has a complementary interface called the Data Communications Equipment (**DCE**) interface.

RSA

See "Rivest-Shamir-Adleman"

RSVP

RSVP (Resource Reservation Protocol) is a set of communication rules that allows channels or paths on the Internet to be reserved for the **multicast** (one source to many receivers) transmission of video and other high-**bandwidth** messages. RSVP is part of the Internet Integrated Service (IIS) model, which ensures best-effort service, real-time service, and controlled link-sharing.

The basic routing philosophy on the Internet is "best effort," which serves most users well enough but isn't adequate for the continuous stream transmission required for video and audio programs over the Internet. With RSVP, people who want to receive a particular Internet "program" (think of a television program broadcast over the Internet) can reserve bandwidth through the Internet in advance of the program and be able to receive it at a higher data rate and in a more dependable data flow than usual. When the program starts, it will be **multicast** to those specific users who have reserved routing priority in advance. RSVP also supports **unicast** (one source to one destination) and multi-source to one destination transmissions.

How It Works

Let's assume that a particular video program is to be multicast at a certain time on Monday evening. Expecting to receive it, you send an RSVP request before the broadcast (you'll need a special client program or perhaps your browser includes one) to allocate sufficient bandwidth and priority of **packet** scheduling for the program. This request will go to your nearest Internet gateway with an RSVP server. It will determine whether you are eligible to have such a reservation set up and, if so, whether sufficient bandwidth remains to be reserved to you without affecting earlier reservations. Assuming you can make the reservation and it is entered, the gateway then forwards your reservation to the next gateway toward the destination (or source of multicast). In this manner, your reservation is ensured all the way to the destination. (If the reservation can't be made all the way to the destination, all reservations are removed.)

When the multicast begins, packets from the source speed through the Internet on a high-priority basis. As packets arrive at a gateway host, they are classified and scheduled out using a set of **queue**s and, in some cases, timers. An RSVP packet is very flexible; it can vary in size and in the number of data types and objects. Where packets need to travel through gateways that don't support RSVP, they can be "tunneled" through as ordinary packets. RSVP works with both Internet Protocol version 4 and **IPv6**.

RTC

See "real-time clock"

RTF

See "Rich Text Format"

RTOS

See "real-time operating system"

Ruby

Ruby is an open source, **interpreted**, **object-oriented** programming language created by Yukihiro Matsumoto, who chose the gemstone's name to suggest "a jewel of a language." Ruby is designed to be simple, complete, extensible, and **portable**. Developed mostly on **Linux**, Ruby works across most platforms, such as most **UNIX**-based platforms, **DOS**, **Windows**, **Macintosh**, **BeOS**, and **OS/2**, for example. According to proponents, Ruby's simple **syntax** (partially inspired by **Ada** and **Eiffel**), makes it readable by anyone who is familiar with any modern programming language.

Ruby is considered similar to **Smalltalk** and **Perl**. The authors of the book *Programming Ruby: The Pragmatic Programmer's Guide*, David Thomas and Andrew Hunt say that it is fully object-oriented, like Smalltalk, although more conventional to use, and as convenient as Perl, but fully object-oriented, which leads to better structured and easier-to-maintain programs. To be compliant with the principles of **extreme programming** (XP), Ruby allows portions of projects to be written in other languages if they are better suited.

Ruby has become extremely popular in Japan; it is sometimes said that, at the moment, although there are a huge number of Ruby programmers, most of them don't speak English. That situation is expected to change, however: Hunt and Thomas predict that Ruby will undergo explosive growth between 2001 and 2002, and overtake **Python** within four years.

rule base

In the context of a computer server acting as a **firewall**, a rule base is a set of rules that govern what is and what is not allowed through the firewall. A rule base can work in one of two ways: it can either explicitly assume that all traffic is allowed unless there is a rule to prevent it, or, more typically, it can assume that no traffic may flow through it unless there is an explicit rule to allow it. Rule bases usually work on a top-down principle in which the first rule in the list is acted upon first, so that traffic allowed by the first rule, will never be judged by the remainder of the rules. Rule bases typically have the format of SOURCE/DESTINATION/SERVICE/ACTION.

run book

In a computer system or network, a run book is a written set of procedures for the routine and exceptional operation of the system or network by an administrator or operator. Typically, a run book will contain procedures for starting, stopping, and monitoring the system or network; for handling special requests such as the mounting of a storage device containing archived material; and for handling problems that may arise.

runbook

See "run book"

runt

In networks, a runt is a **packet** that is too small. For example, the **Ethernet** protocol requires that each packet be at least 64 bytes long. In Ethernet, which operates on the idea that two parties can attempt to get use of the line at the same time and sometimes do, runts are usually the fragments of packet collisions. Runts can also be the result of bad wiring or electrical interference. Runts are recorded by programs that use the Remote Network Monitoring (**RNM**) standard information base for network adminstration. RMON calls them "undersize packets."

As you might expect, a **giant** is a packet that's oversize.

runtime

Runtime is when a program is running (or being **executable**). That is, when you start a program running in a computer, it is runtime for that program. In some programming languages, certain reusable programs or "routines" are built and packaged as a "runtime library." These routines can be linked to and used by any program when it is running.

Programmers sometimes distinguish between what gets embedded in a program when it is **compiler** and what gets embedded or used at runtime. The former is sometimes called "compile time."

For a number of years, technical writers resisted "runtime" as a term, insisting that something like "when a program is run" would obviate the need for a special term. Gradually, the term crept into general usage.

S interface

In Integrated Services Digital Network (**ISDN**) service, an S interface is the electrical interface between a network terminating unit 1 (**NT1**) and up to eight addressable devices such as a computer or a telephone. Like the **T interface** (which usually connects the signal from the NT1 to a PBX), the S interface has four wires, allowing up to eight devices to be addressed. In Basic Rate Interface ISDN, the bits that flow from the central office through the NT1 are divided into two 64 Kbps **channels** (known as B, or bearer, channels) and one 16 Kbps channel (the D, for data or delta, channel) for control signals. The control signals allow a specific device to be addressed. The wires to the devices from the NT-1 are sometimes referred to as the *S-bus*.

The following table summarizes the various ISDN electrical interfaces at different demarcation points or places in the traffic flow:

Electrical interface	Between what two points
U interface	Central office and NT1
T interface	NT1 and NT2 devices (such as a PBX)
S interface	NT1 or NT2 and ISDN devices (such as a telephone or terminal adapter)
R interface	Terminal adapter and non-ISDN devices (such as a computer)
V interface	Within the ISDN node at the central office; separates line termination equipment from exchange termination equipment

S/390

S/390, recently renamed zSeries 900, is IBM's large **server** (or **mainframe**) line of computer systems, which are marketed to the world's Fortune 1000 and many mid-size companies as a "tried-and-true" system with a history that stretches back to the System/360 of the early 1960s. The S/390 combines a hardware design based on the use of multiple microprocessor packaging with the **OS/390 operating system**, whose multitasking architecture and long evolution (most of the bugs have already been found) results in a system that seldom crashes. IBM's **VM** operating system also runs on the S/390.

S/MIME

S/MIME (Secure Multi-Purpose Internet Mail Extensions) is a secure method of sending **e-mail** that uses the **Rivest-Shamir-Adleman** (RSA) **encryption** system. S/MIME is included in the latest versions of the Web browsers from Microsoft and Netscape and has also been endorsed by other vendors that make **messaging** products. RSA has proposed S/MIME as a standard to the Internet Engineering Task Force (**IETF**). An alternative to S/MIME is PGP/MIME, which has also been proposed as a standard.

MIME itself, described in the IETF standard called **Request for Comments** 1521, spells out how an electronic message will be organized. S/MIME describes how encryption information and a digital certificate can be included as part of the message body. S/MIME follows the **syntax** provided in the Public-Key Cryptography Standard format #7.

S/N

See "signal-to-noise ratio"

S/PDIF

S/PDIF (Sony/Philips Digital Interface) is a standard audio transfer file format. It is usually found on digital audio equipment such as a DAT machine or audio processing device. It allows the transfer of audio from one file to another without the conversion to and from an **analog** format, which could degrade the signal quality.

The most common connector used with an S/PDIF interface is the RCA connector, the same one used for consumer audio products. An optical connector is also sometimes used.

SAA

Systems Application Architecture (SAA) was IBM's strategy for **enterprise** computing in the late 1980s and early 1990s. It was replaced and considerably expanded by IBM's **Open Blueprint**, an enterprise strategy for network computing. Both of these are structured views of the types of computing services that an enterprise may need, the relationships between these services, and specification of the standards and products that are envisioned as providing these services.

SAA defined three layers of service:

- Common User Access
- Common Programming Interface
- Common Communications Support

By using or creating applications and data that conformed to these three layers (provided by strategic IBM products), an enterprise could be assured of consistency and some amount of program portability among IBM's range of computer systems. As IBM, along with the rest of the computer industry, discovered the value of industry-wide standardization and **open** computing, the company revised its strategy. Its new strategy, the Open Blueprint, would recognize that customers wanted consistency and portability of programs and data across different manufacturers' systems, not just within IBM's systems. Two other trends not current when SAA was developed have influenced IBM's Open Blueprint: the **client/server** model of distributing computing and the concept and implementation of **object-oriented programming**. The Open Blueprint seems well positioned to absorb another new trend: Network computing, including use of the Internet.

Since most of IBM's large customers have a large investment in **legacy application**s and data developed during the era of SAA and prior, IBM's Open Blueprint recognizes the need to support them. Notably, IBM's Systems Network Architecture (**SNA**), the keystone of the SAA Common Communications Support, is retained in the Open Blueprint as an alternative to **TCP/IP**. Other companies have also made investments in SAA, recognizing that IBM customers' legacy applications will not be going away soon and that in some cases these applications may represent the current best solution. Novell's Netware for SAA is an example of a widely-installed product that retains the SAA identity.

SACD

See "Super Audio CD"

Safe Harbor

Safe Harbor is the name of a policy agreement established between the United States Department of Commerce and the European Union (E.U.) in November 2000 to regulate the way that U.S. companies export and handle the personal data (such as names and addresses) of European citizens. The agreement is a policy compromise set up in response to a European directive that differed from traditional business procedures for U.S. companies dealing with the E.U. In 1998, the E.U. established the *European Commission Directive on Data Protection*, which prohibited data transfer to non-European countries that did not adhere to stringent criteria. In effect, because the guidelines were very strict, they made it illegal to transfer most citizens' personal data outside of Europe.

Safe Harbor stipulations require that: Companies collecting personal data must inform people that the data is being gathered, and tell them what will be done with it; they must obtain permission to pass on the information to a third party; they must allow people access to the data gathered; **data integrity** and security must be assured; and a means of enforcing compliance must be guaranteed.

The agreement establishes a framework for a compromise solution between U.S. and E.U. privacy procedures. All 15 member countries are subject to the agreement, which means that data transfers can proceed without requiring individual authorization. U.S. companies that don't join Safe Harbor must obtain authorization separately from each European country. E.U. organizations can check a list of U.S. companies that have joined the collective to ensure that the *Safe Harbor Privacy Principles* will be adhered to.

safe mode

Safe mode is an alternate **boot** method for Windows 95/98 that makes it easier to diagnose problems. The only startup programs loaded are the **operating system** and **driver**s for the **mouse**, keyboard, and display.

To find out how to boot Windows 95/98 in safe mode, click Start, then Help, and then type in "safe mode". The procedure varies slightly depending on whether your computer contains a network interface card or not.

If a normal startup fails (for example, because the Registry is missing an important key parameter such as SYSTEM), Windows 95/98 will initiate a safe mode boot for you.

sales automation software

Sales automation software is a type of program that automates business tasks such as inventory control, sales processing, and tracking of customer interactions, as well as analyzing sales forecasts and performance. Businesses may have a custom version developed specifically for their needs, or choose from among the increasing number of sales automation software products, such as Interact Commerce's ACT! and GoldMine Software's GoldMine. Sales automation software is sometimes called *sales force automation* (SFA) software, and sometimes called customer relations management (**CRM**) software.

Sales automation packages typically include a Web-ready database, an e-mail package, and customizable **template**s. A **three-tiered** architecture is typically used to separate the database, server, and application to reduce programming demands on clients. A module-based design is generally used, to allow users to customize the package to suit their needs.

In August 2000, Oracle released a free CRM software package, OracleSalesOnline.com which makes information—such as contacts, schedules, and performance tracking—available online through the included database program. The package is designed for medium-to-large enterprises with mobile work forces. All data and storage are based at an Oracle facility, similar to the application service provider (**ASP**) model, which means that data can be accessed from any Internet connection and that the client doesn't need special hardware or software. The Oracle package also includes online staff training.

sales force automation software

See "sales automation software"

Samba

Samba is a popular freeware program that allows end users to access and use files, printers, and other commonly shared resources on a company's **intranet** or on the **Internet**. Samba is often referred to as a **network file system** and can be installed on a variety of **operating system platform**s, including: **Linux**, most common **UNIX** platforms, **OpenVMS**, and **OS/2**.

Samba is based on the common client/server **protocol** of Server Message Block (**SMBP**) and Common Internet File System (**CIFS**). Using client software that also supports SMB/CIFS (for example, most Microsoft Windows products), an end user sends a series of client requests to the Samba server on another computer in order to open that computer's files, access a shared printer, or access other resources. The Samba server on the other computer responds to each client request, either granting or denying access to its shared files and resources.

The Samba SMB/CIFS client is called smbclient.

sample rate

In developing an audio sound for computers or telecommunication, the sample rate is the number of samples of a sound that are taken per second to represent the event digitally.

The more samples taken per second, the more accurate the digital representation of the sound can be. For example, the current sample rate for CD-quality audio is 44,100 samples per second. This sample rate can accurately reproduce the audio frequencies up to 20,500 **hertz**, covering the full range of human hearing.

SAN

See "storage area network"

sandbox

Using the **Java** programming language and development environment, the sandbox is the program area and set of rules that programmers need to use when creating Java code (called an **applet**) that is sent as part of a **page**. Since a Java applet is sent automatically as part of the page and can be executed as soon as it arrives, the applet can easily do harm, either accidentally or as the result of someone with malicious intent, if it is allowed unlimited access to memory and operating system services. The sandbox restrictions provide strict limitations on what system resources the applet can request or access. Essentially, the programmer must write code that "plays" only within the sandbox, much as children are allowed to make anything they want to within the confined limits of a real sandbox. The sandbox can be conceived as a small area within your computer where an applet's code can play freely—but it's not allowed to play anywhere else.

The sandbox is implemented not only by requiring programmers to conform to certain rules but also by providing code checkers. The Java language itself provides features such as automatic memory management, **garbage** collection, and the checking of address ranges in strings and arrays that inherently help to guarantee safe code. In addition, Java includes a compiled code (Java's compiled code is known as **bytecode**) verifier that guarantees adherence to certain limitations. Java also provides for a *local name space* within which code may be restricted. The Java **virtual machine** (the layer that interprets the Java bytecode for a given computer platform) also mediates access to system resources and ensures that sandbox code is restricted.

In the original sandbox security model, the sandbox code is generally known as *untrusted code*. In later versions of the Java Development Kit (JDK)—the programmer's development environment—the sandbox has been made more sophisticated by introducing several levels of trust that the user can specify for sandbox code. The more trust the user allows, the more capability the code has to "play" outside of the sandbox. In the Java Development Kit 1.1 version, the concept of a *signed applet* was introduced. An applet accompanied by a **digital signature** can contain trusted code that will be allowed to execute if the signature is recognized by the client browser.

In JDK 2.0, Java provides for assigning different levels of trust to all application code, whether loaded locally or arriving from the Internet. A mechanism exists to define a security policy that will be used to screen all code—whether signed or not—as it executes.

SAP

SAP, started in 1972 by five former IBM employees in Mannheim, Germany, states that it is the world's largest inter-enterprise software company and the world's fourth-largest independent software supplier overall. The original SAP idea was to provide customers with the ability to interact with a common corporate database for a comprehensive range of applications. Gradually, the applications have been assembled and today many corporations, including IBM and Microsoft, are using SAP products to run their own businesses.

SAP applications, built around their latest **R/3** system, provide the capability to manage financial, asset, and cost accounting, production operations and materials, personnel, plants, and archived documents. The R/3 system runs on a number of platforms including **Windows 2000** and uses the **client/server** model. The latest version of R/3 includes a comprehensive Internet-enabled package.

SAP has recently recast its product offerings under a comprehensive Web interface, called mySAP.com, and added new **e-business** applications, including customer relationship management (**CRM**) and supply chain management (**SCM**).

In early 2001, SAP, a publicly traded company, had 21,500 employees in over 50 countries, and more than 30,000 installations. SAP is turning its attention to small- and-medium sized businesses. A recent R/3 version was provided for IBM's **AS/400** platform.

SASID

See "Self-scanned Amorphous Silicon Integrated Display"

satellite

A satellite is a specialized **wireless** receiver/transmitter that is launched by a rocket and placed in orbit around the earth. There are hundreds of satellites currently in operation. They are used for such diverse purposes as weather forecasting, television broadcast, amateur radio communications, Internet communications, and the Global Positioning System, (**GPS**).

The first artificial satellite, launched by Russia (then known as the Soviet Union) in the late 1950s, was about the size of a basketball. It did nothing but transmit a simple Morse code signal over and over. In contrast, modern satellites can receive and re-transmit thousands of signals simultaneously, from simple digital data to the most complex television programming.

There are three types of communications satellite systems. They are categorized according to the type of orbit they follow.

A geostationary satellite orbits the earth directly over the equator, approximately 22,000 miles up. At this altitude, one complete trip around the earth (relative to the sun) takes 24 hours. Thus, the satellite remains over the same spot on the earth's surface at all times, and stays fixed in the sky from any point on the surface from which it can be "seen." So-called weather satellites are usually of this type. You can view images from some of these satellites on the Internet via the Purdue Weather Processor. A single geostationary satellite can "see" approximately 40 percent of the earth's surface. Three such satellites, spaced at equal intervals (120 angular degrees apart), can provide coverage of the entire civilized world. A geostationary satellite can be accessed using a dish antenna aimed at the spot in the sky where the satellite hovers.

A low-earth-orbit (LEO) satellite system employs a large fleet of "birds," each in a circular orbit at a constant altitude of a few hundred miles. The orbits take the satellites over, or nearly over, the geographic poles. Each revolution takes approximately 90 minutes to a few hours. The fleet is arranged in such a way that, from any point on the surface at any time, at least one satellite is on a line of sight. The entire system operates in a manner similar to the way a **cellular telephone** functions. The main difference is that the transponders, or wireless receiver/transmitters, are moving rather than fixed, and are in space rather than on the earth. A well-designed LEO system makes it possible for anyone to access the Internet via wireless from any point on the planet, using an antenna no more sophisticated than old-fashioned television "rabbit ears."

Some satellites revolve around the earth in elliptical orbits. These satellites move rapidly when they are near perigee, or their lowest altitude; they move slowly when they are near apogee, or their highest altitude. Such "birds" are used by amateur radio operators, and by some commercial and government services. They require directional antennas whose orientation must be constantly adjusted to follow the satellite's path across the sky.

satellite Internet connection

A satellite Internet connection is an arrangement in which the upstream (outgoing) and the downstream (incoming) data are sent from, and arrive at, a computer through a **satellite**. Each subscriber's hardware includes a satellite dish **antenna** and a transceiver (transmitter/receiver) that operates in the **microwave** portion of the radio spectrum.

In a two-way satellite Internet connection, the upstream data is usually sent at a slower speed than the downstream data arrives. Thus, the connection is asymmetric. A **dish antenna**, measuring about two feet high by three feet wide by three feet deep, transmits and receives signals. Uplink speeds are nominally 50 to 150 **Kbps** for a subscriber using a single computer. The downlink occurs at speeds ranging from about 150 Kbps to more than 1200 Kbps, depending on factors such as Internet traffic, the capacity of the server, and the sizes of downloaded files.

Satellite Internet systems are an excellent, although rather pricey, option for people in rural areas where Digital Subscriber Line (**DSL**) and **cable modem** connections are not available. A satellite installation can be used even where the most basic utilities are lacking, if there is a generator or battery power supply that can produce enough electricity to run a desktop computer system. The two-way satellite Internet option offers an always-on connection that bypasses the dial-up process. In this respect, the satellite system resembles a cable modem Internet connection. But this asset can also be a liability, unless a **firewall** is used to protect the computer against hack attempts.

The nature of the satellite connection is good for Web browsing and for downloading of files. Because of long latency compared with purely land-based systems, interactive applications such as online gaming are not compatible with satellite networks. In a two-way geostationary-satellite Internet connection, a transaction requires two round trips between the earth's surface and transponders orbiting 22,300 miles above the equator. This occurs in addition to land-based data transfer between the earthbound satellite system hub and the accessed Internet sites. The speed in such a connection is theoretically at least 0.48 second (the time it takes an electromagnetic signal to make two round trips at 186,000 miles per second to and from a geostationary satellite), and in practice is somewhat longer. Satellite systems are also prone to rain fade (degradation during heavy precipitation) and occasional brief periods of solar interference in mid-March and late September, when the sun lines up with the satellite for a few minutes each day. Rain fade and solar interference affect all satellite links from time to time, not just Internet systems.

The author of this topic recently had StarBand, a two-way satellite Internet service, installed at his rural home office. Bandwidth tests were conducted with the new system compared with a conventional telephone modem. The telephone connection provided actual bandwidth ranging from 10 to 15 Kbps. StarBand worked at 200 to 1350 Kbps; throughput seemed to depend mainly on the download file size. The fastest speeds were obtained with files of 50 KB (kilobytes) or less, typical of images and text contained in Web sites. Surprisingly, fast downloads were obtained even during times of maximum Internet traffic.

Compare **satellite return Internet connection**.

satellite return Internet connection

A satellite return Internet connection is an arrangement in which incoming data arrives at your computer from a **satellite downlink** and outgoing data (such as your request for the next Web page) is sent over a regular telephone line.

Because most of the traffic on the Internet is toward the user (in the form of text, graphic images, **streaming video**, and so forth), the kind of high-speed channel that a satellite can provide (direct to the user using wireless radio) is desirable. On the other hand, the user's outgoing requests, typically for a Web page, are relatively small bursts of text, easily and more economically handled by slower telephone transmission.

In a typical satellite return connection, the outgoing data speed for "plain old telephone service" (**POTS**) is typically 28.8 or 57.6 **Kbps** (depending on the user's modem), but in practice is often slower. Incoming data from the satellite to the user's system arrives at a much higher speed. Thus, the satellite return connection is asymmetric. A medium-sized, elongated dish **antenna**, measuring about two feet high by three feet wide by three feet deep, receives the signals. When the Internet is heavily used, the downlink occurs at 200 to 300 Kbps. During periods of light usage, the downlink speed can be 400 to 500 Kbps, and sometimes exceeds 700 Kbps.

The author of this topic recently had AOL (America Online) Plus, a satellite return Internet service offered jointly by AOL and DirectPC, installed at his rural home office. **Bandwidth** tests were conducted with the new system compared with

POTS. The telephone connection provided actual bandwidth ranging from 10 to 15 Kbps; the AOL Plus link worked at 250 to 770 Kbps.

SAX

SAX (Simple API for XML) is an application program interface (**API**) that allows a programmer to interpret a Web file that uses the Extensible Markup Language (**XML**)—that is, a Web file that describes a collection of data. SAX is an alternative to using the Document Object Model (**DOM**) to interpret the XML file. As its name suggests, it's a simpler interface than DOM and is appropriate where many or very large files are to be processed, but it contains fewer capabilities for manipulating the data content.

SAX is an *event-driven* interface. The programmer specifies an event that may happen and, if it does, SAX gets control and handles the situation. SAX works directly with an XML **parser**.

SCADA

SCADA (supervisory control and data acquisition) is a category of software application program for **process control**, the gathering of data in **real time** from remote locations in order to control equipment and conditions. SCADA is used in power plants as well as in oil and gas refining, telecommunications, transportation, and water and waste control.

SCADA systems include hardware and software components. The hardware gathers and feeds data into a computer that has SCADA software installed. The computer then processes this data and presents it in a timely manner. SCADA also records and logs all events into a file stored on a hard disk or sends them to a printer. SCADA warns when conditions become hazardous by sounding alarms.

scalability

In information technology, scalability (frequently spelled *scaleability*) seems to have two usages:

1) It is the ability of a computer application or product (hardware or software) to continue to function well as it (or its context) is changed in size or volume in order to meet a user need. Typically, the rescaling is to a larger size or volume. The rescaling can be of the product itself (for example, a line of computer systems of different sizes in terms of storage, RAM, and so forth) or in the scalable object's movement to a new context (for example, a new operating system).

An example: John Young in his book *Exploring IBM's New-Age Mainframes* describes the RS/6000 SP operating system as one that delivers scalability ("the ability to retain performance levels when adding additional processors").

Another example: In printing, scalable fonts that can be resized smaller or larger using software without losing quality.

2) It is the ability not only to function well in the rescaled situation, but to actually take full advantage of it. For example, an application program would be scalable if it could be moved from a smaller to a larger operating system and take full advantage of the larger operating system in terms of **performance** (user response time and so forth) and the larger number of users that could be handled.

It is usually easier to have scalability upward rather than downward since developers often must make full use of a system's resources (for example, the amount of disk storage available) when an application is initially coded. Scaling a product downward may mean having to achieve the same results in a more constrained environment.

scalable font

A scalable font is a type **font** that can be resized (enlarged or reduced) without introducing distortion. The outline of each character is stored as a mathematical formula. The set of all such formulas for a complete set of characters is called an *outline font*. The outline font remains essentially the same regardless of the size of the characters. This eliminates the necessity for storing a gigantic set of characters to encompass all the possible sizes for a particular font.

Once the size of the characters has been selected (for example, 12-point), the outlines are filled in with a **bitmap** for each character. Usually (but not always), the same bitmap is used for all the characters in the font. The bitmap can itself have mathematical formulas incorporated into it. For example, the characters might be italicized and shaded solid blue; rendered as normal and solid black; or a special **typeface** might be used with shading from blue at the top to red at the bottom.

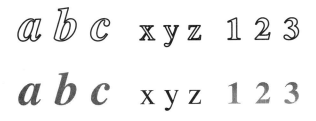

Some outline-font characters are shown in the first line of the illustration. The same characters, filled in with various bitmaps, are shown in the second line. They have been scaled to different sizes. The mathematical formulas for the bitmaps, as well as for the outline fonts, are pre-determined. So, for example, if the numerals 1 2 3 at lower right were enlarged or reduced, the outline-font formulas could simply be multiplied by a constant. In all other respects, the appearance of the characters would remain the same.

Scalable Processor Architecture

See "SPARC"

Scalable Vector Graphics

Scalable Vector Graphics (SVG) is the description of an image as an application of the Extensible Markup Language (**XML**). Any program such as a Web **browser** that recognizes XML can display the image using the information provided in the SVG format. **Vector graphics** is the expression of an image using mathematical statements rather than bit-pattern description. **Scalable** emphasizes that vector graphic images can easily be made scalable (whereas an image specified in **raster graphics** is a fixed-size bitmap). Thus, the SVG format enables the viewing of an image on a computer display of any size and resolution, whether a tiny **LCD** screen in a cell phone or a large **CRT** display in a workstation. In addition to ease of size reduction and enlargement, SVG allows text within images to be recognized as such, so that the text can be located by a search engine and easily translated into other languages.

Vector graphics images also have the potential advantage over the standard Web image formats, the **GIF** and the **JPEG**, of size. Compared with a bitmap image, an SVG image may be much smaller and arrive more quickly.

GIF and JPG images (and a newer format, the **PNG**) are expected to continue to predominate. While the bitmaps of these image formats can be resized, dimensional reduction does not necessarily save memory, storage, or bandwidth, and significant enlargement produces irregular edges ("the jaggies"). It is expected, however, that bitmaps are, and will likely continue to be, favored for digital transmission of photographs, especially scenes containing complex objects not readily translatable into the formulas used by vector graphics programs.

scalar

1) In mathematics, scalar (noun) and scalar (adjective) refer to a quantity consisting of a single real number used to measured magnitude (size). Voltage, mass, and temperature measurements can be described as scalar quantities.

2) In **Perl** programming, a scalar is a variable used to represent a block of information. A scalar can refer to an integer, a float, a string, an object, binary information, or just about anything else. It's a versatile variable that has no length limit and is easily recognizable when looking at Perl code because it is preceded by the symbol "$".

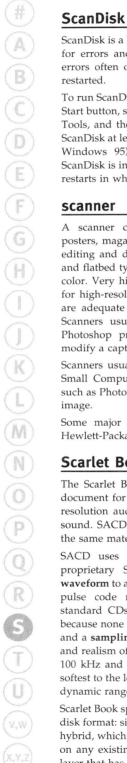

ScanDisk

ScanDisk is a Windows **utility** used to check your **hard disk** for errors and to correct problems that are found. These errors often occur when Windows locks up and must be restarted.

To run ScanDisk in Windows 95 and later versions, click the Start button, select Programs, then Accessories, then System Tools, and then Scandisk. It is recommended that you run ScanDisk at least once per month. In **OSR2** (a later release of Windows 95) and in **Windows 98** and later versions, ScanDisk is initiated for you automatically following system restarts in which shutdown was not complete.

scanner

A scanner captures images from photographic prints, posters, magazine pages, and similar sources for computer editing and display. Scanners come in hand-held, feed-in, and flatbed types and for scanning black-and-white only or color. Very high resolution scanners are used for scanning for high-resolution printing, but lower resolution scanners are adequate for capturing images for computer display. Scanners usually come with software, such as Adobe's Photoshop product, that lets you resize and otherwise modify a captured image.

Scanners usually attach to your personal computer with a Small Computer System Interface (**SCSI**). An application such as PhotoShop uses the **TWAIN** program to read in the image.

Some major manufacturers of scanners include: Epson, Hewlett-Packard, Microtek, and Relisys.

Scarlet Book

The Scarlet Book is Philips and Sony's 1999 specification document for Super Audio Compact Disc (**SACD**), a high-resolution audio format that features complex six-channel sound. SACD discs can contain three different versions of the same material.

SACD uses Direct Stream Digital (DSD) recording, a proprietary Sony technology that converts an **analog waveform** to a 1-bit signal for direct recording, instead of the pulse code modulation (**PCM**) and filtering used by standard CDs. DSD uses **lossless compression** (so-called because none of the data is lost in the compression process) and a **sampling rate** of 2.8 **MHz** to improve the complexity and realism of sound. DSD enables a **frequency** response of 100 kHz and a **dynamic range** of 120 **dB** (the ratio of the softest to the loudest sound—120 db is also the approximate dynamic range of human hearing) on all channels.

Scarlet Book specifications include three separate options for disk format: single-layer DSD, dual-layer DSD, or dual-layer hybrid, which includes a **Red Book** layer that can be played on any existing CD player in addition to the high-density layer that has the capacity to deliver eight channels of DSD.

In addition to DSD and the hybrid disk technology, Scarlet Book specifications include: *Super Bit Mapping Direct*, a proprietary downconversion method that enables improved audio when the disks are played on an ordinary CD player; Direct Stream Transfer, a type of coding that increases data capacity; and a digital **watermark** to protect against piracy.

According to some, SACD is a hybrid CD/DVD format, since Scarlet Book specifications are identical to those for DVD disks for the file system, sector size, error correction, and **modulation**. SACD is in competition with a similar product, **DVD-Audio**, as the format that will replace standard audio CD.

SCART connector

A SCART connector is a physical and electrical interconnection between two pieces of audio-visual equipment, such as a television set and a video cassette recorder (VCR). Each device has a female 21-pin connector interface. A cable with a male plug at each end is used to connect the devices. (The 21st pin is actually not a pin but a ground shield contact.) Stereo **audio**, composite video, and control signals are provided in both directions. RGB video signals are input only. The interface is an industry standard originated by the French company, Peritel. Today, most new television sets and VCRs in the European market and other countries that use the PAL video standard come equipped with a SCART connector. SCART stands for Syndicat francais des Constructeurs d'Appareils Radio et Television. The connector is also known as a Euro-connector.

Although it is possible to build your own connecting cable, knowledgable people recommend buying a commercial cable because of the detailed pin-crossovers and close pin connections. Differeent cables serve different purposes. A cable for connecting a VCR or a TV set to a high-fidelity audio system needs to use only three of the 21 pins.

It is more difficult to use the SCART connector to interconnect a VCR to a computer monitor because of the difficulty of synchronizing the composite video signal (which is companded into red, green, and blue) from the VCR with the **RGB** signals needed by the monitor.

A user reports that the torsional load of the cable can in time lead to difficulty getting all the connections to align properly.

Schrodinger's cat

Schrodinger's cat is a famous illustration of the principle in **quantum theory** of **superposition**, proposed by Erwin Schrodinger in 1935. Schrodinger's cat serves to demonstrate the apparent conflict between what quantum theory tells us is true about the nature and behavior of matter on the microscopic level and what we observe to be true about the nature and behavior of matter on the macroscopic level.

First, we have a living cat and place it in a thick lead box. At this stage, there is no question that the cat is alive. We then throw in a vial of cyanide and seal the box. We do not know if the cat is alive or if it has broken the cyanide capsule and died. Since we do not know, the cat is both dead and alive, according to **quantum** law, in a superposition of states. It is only when we break open the box and learn the condition of the cat that the superposition is lost, and the cat becomes one or the other (dead or alive).

We know that superposition actually occurs at the subatomic level, because there are observable effects of interference, in which a single particle is demonstrated to be in multiple locations simultaneously. What that fact implies about the nature of reality on the observable level (cats, for example, as opposed to electrons) is one of the stickiest areas of quantum physics. Schrodinger himself said, later in life, that he wished he had never met that cat.

scientific notation

Scientific notation, also called power-of-10 notation, is a method of writing extremely large and small numbers. There are two forms of this scheme; one is by far more common.

In common scientific notation, any nonzero quantity can be expressed in two parts: a coefficient whose absolute value is greater than or equal to 1 but less than 10, and a power of 10 by which the coefficient is multiplied. In some writings, the coefficients are closer to zero by one order of magnitude. In this scheme, any nonzero quantity is expressed in two parts: a coefficient whose absolute value is greater than or equal to 0.1 but less than 1, and a power of 10 by which the coefficient is multiplied. The quantity zero is denoted as 0 unless precision is demanded, in which case the requisite number of signficant digits are written out—for example, 0.00000.

For numbers of reasonable magnitude, conventional decimal notation is often used, even in scientific writings. Let s be a number rounded or truncated to a few significant figures. If the absolute value of s is at least 0.001 (10^{-3}) but less than 10,000 (10^4), then s is usually written out in full. Examples are 21.3389 and -0.002355. However, if the absolute value of s is smaller than 0.001 or if it is 10,000 or larger, scientific notation is usually preferred, because writing such numbers out in decimal form can be confusing and messy. This is especially true when the absolute value of s is very close to zero or is exceedingly large. It is inconvenient, for example, to write out either of the expressions 6.0205×10^{74} or -0.64453×10^{-45} in decimal form.

The table shows several examples of numbers written in standard decimal notation (left-hand column) and in scientific notation (right-hand column). For negative numbers, the values are simply mirror-image positive numbers; a minus sign is placed in front of the values. The number of digits in the coefficient is the number of

significant figures. Note that an expression can have various degrees of precision; the greater the number of significant figures, the greater the precision.

Number in decimal form	Examples in scientific notation
1,222,000.00	1.222×10^6
	1.22200000×10^6
	0.1222×10^7
	0.122200000×10^7
0.00003450000	3.45×10^{-5}
	3.450000×10^{-5}
	0.345×10^{-4}
	0.3450000×10^{-4}
$-9,876,543,210$	-9.87654×10^9 (approximately)
	-9.876543210×10^9 (exactly)
	-0.987654×10^{10} (approximately)
	$-0.9876543210 \times 10^{10}$ (exactly)
-0.0000000100	-10^{-8}
	-1.00×10^{-8}
	-0.1×10^{-7}
	-0.100×10^{-7}

Scientific notation makes it easy to multiply and divide gigantic and/or minuscule numbers, when the use of decimal notation would give rise to frustration. Consider, for example, the following product:

$2.56 \times 10^{67} \times -8.33 \times 10^{-54}$

To obtain the product of these two numbers, the coefficients are multiplied, and the powers of 10 are added. This produces the following result:

$2.56 \times (-8.33) \times 10^{67+(-54)}$
$= 2.56 \times (-8.33) \times 10^{67-54}$
$= -21.3248 \times 10^{13}$

The proper form of common scientific notation requires that the absolute value of the coefficient be larger than 1 and less than 10. Thus, the coefficient in the above expression should be divided by 10 and the power of 10 increased by one, giving:

-2.13248×10^{14}

Because both multiplicands in the original product are specified to only three significant figures, a scientist might see fit to round off the final expression to three significant figures as well, yielding:

-2.13×10^{14}

as the product.

Now consider the quotient of the two numbers multiplied in the previous example:

$(2.56 \times 10^{67}) / (-8.33 \times 10^{-54})$

To obtain the quotient, the coefficients are divided, and the powers of 10 are subtracted. This gives the following:

$(2.56 \ / \ (-8.33)) \times 10^{67-(-54)}$
$= (2.56 \ / \ (-8.33)) \times 10^{67+54}$
$= -0.30732 \times 10^{121}$

The proper form of common scientific notation requires that the absolute value of the coefficient be larger than 1 and less than 10. Thus, the coefficient in the above expression should be multiplied by 10 and the power of 10 decreased by one, giving:

-3.0732×10^{120}

Because both numbers in the original quotient are specified to only three significant figures, a scientist might see fit to round off the final expression to three significant figures as well, yielding:

-3.07×10^{120}

as the quotient.

Also see **order of magnitude** and **significant figures**.

SCM

See "supply chain management"

screen

In a computer **display**, the screen is the physical surface on which visual information is presented. This surface is usually made of glass. The screen size is measured from one corner to the opposite corner diagonally. Common screen sizes for desktop display screens are 12, 14, 17, 19, and 21 inches.

This term is not to be confused with **panel**, which is a representation of what information will appear on the screen in given circumstances.

screen capture

See "screen shot"

screen saver

A screen saver is an animated image that is activated on a personal computer display when no user activity has been sensed for a certain time. The original purpose of a screen saver was to prevent burn-in (the burning of an image into the phosphor inside the **cathode ray tube** after hours of the same image being rescanned). In fact, today's CRT display technology makes burn-in unlikely except under extreme conditions. (On larger displays used for room presentations, burn-in is still a possibility.)

Windows comes with built-in screen savers that you can select. If you purchase your computer with the operating system already installed, a screen saver may have been selected for you. You can set the screen saver using the task bar by selecting Start, then Settings, then Control Panel, then Display, and then Screen Saver, which lets you select one of the provided screen savers or one you have added to the Windows screen saver directory. The Mac also lets you set up a screen saver.

screen scraping

Screen scraping is programming that translates between **legacy application** programs (written to communicate with now generally obsolete input/output devices and user interfaces) and new user interfaces so that the logic and data associated with the legacy programs can continue to be used. Screen scraping is sometimes called *advanced terminal emulation*. A program that does screen scraping must take the data coming from the legacy program that is formatted for the **screen** of an older type of terminal such as an IBM **3270** display or a **Digital Equipment Corporation** VT100 and reformat it for a **Windows 2000** user or someone using a Web **browser**. The program must also reformat user input from the newer user interfaces (such as a Windows graphical user interface or a Web browser) so that the request can be handled by the legacy application as if it came from the user of the older device and user interface.

screen shot

A screen shot (sometimes called a screen capture) is a copy of the screen's contents that can be saved as a graphics file or copied into a document or graphics editor. Various programs are available for creating screen shots, but it is easy to do without any special program.

To take a screen shot on a Windows **platform**, you press the Print Screen button (usually on the top row of the keyboard) to get a shot of the entire screen. To get a shot of the active window only, you press the Alt key and the Print Screen key at the same time. The screen shot is copied to the clipboard (the memory area that temporarily stores information to be copied to another location) and can then be pasted into a document in a word processing program such as Word or WordPerfect, or into an image editor, such as Adobe Photo Shop, Paint Shop Pro, or Microsoft Paint if you want to alter the image.

On a Macintosh platform, you press the Command, Shift, and 3 keys to create an image file (called a PICT file). If you press 4 instead of 3, the cursor changes to allow you to select an area of the screen to save. Command, Shift, and 4 with the Caps Lock pressed allows you to create a circular image. Any of the commands with the Control key pressed copies the image to the clipboard.

On a UNIX, there are different methods for the various interfaces. A common one is the command xwd -out filename.xwd, which allows you to click a screen to make an image file.

script

1) In computer programming, a script is a **program** or sequence of instructions that is interpreted or carried out by another program rather than by the computer **processor** (as a **compiler** program is).

Some languages have been conceived expressly as script languages. Among the most popular are **Perl**, **Rexx** (on IBM mainframes), **JavaScript**, and **Tcl/Tk**. In the context of the World Wide Web, Perl, VBScript, and similar script languages are often written to handle forms input or other services for a Web site and are processed on the Web **server**. A JavaScript script in a Web page runs "client-side" on the Web **browser**.

In general, script languages are easier and faster to code in than the more structured and compiled languages such as **C** and **C++** and are ideal for programs of very limited capability or that can reuse and tie together existing compiled programs. However, a script takes longer to run than a compiled program since each instruction is being handled by another program first (requiring additional instructions) rather than directly by the basic instruction processor.

2) A script is sometimes used to mean a list of **operating system** commands that are prestored in a file and performed sequentially by the operating system's command interpreter whenever the list name is entered as a single command.

3) Multimedia development programs use "script" to mean the sequence of instructions that you enter to indicate how a multimedia sequence of files will be presented (the sequence of images and sounds, their timing, and the possible results of user interaction).

script kiddie

See "script kiddy"

script kiddy

Script kiddy (sometimes spelled kiddie) is a derogative term, originated by the more sophisticated **cracker**s of computer security systems, for the more immature, but unfortunately often just as dangerous exploiter of security lapses on the Internet. The typical script kiddy uses existing and frequently well-known and easy-to-find techniques and programs or **script**s to search for and exploit weaknesses in other computers on the Internet—often randomly and with little regard or perhaps even understanding of the potentially harmful consequences. Hackers view script kiddies with alarm and contempt since they do nothing to advance the "art" of hacking while sometimes unleashing the wrath of authority on the entire hacker community.

While a hacker will take pride in the quality of an attack—leaving no trace of an intrusion, for example—a script kiddy may aim at quantity, seeing the number of attacks that can be mounted as a way to obtain attention and notoriety. Script kiddies are sometimes portrayed in media as bored, lonely teenagers seeking recognition from their peers.

SCSI

SCSI (pronounced SKUH-zee and sometimes colloquially known as "scuzzy"), the Small Computer System Interface, is a set of evolving **ANSI** standard electronic interfaces that allow personal computers to communicate with peripheral hardware such as disk drives, tape drives, CD-ROM drives, printers, and scanners faster and more flexibly than previous interfaces. Developed at Apple Computer and still used in the Macintosh, the present set of SCSIs are **parallel** interfaces. SCSI ports are built into most personal computers today and are supported by all major operating systems.

In addition to faster data rates, SCSI is more flexible than earlier parallel data transfer interfaces. The latest SCSI standard, Ultra-2 SCSI for a 16-bit **bus** can transfer data at up to 80 **megabytes** per second (MBps). SCSI allows up to 7 or 15 devices (depending on the bus width) to be connected to a single SCSI port in daisy-chain fashion. This allows one circuit board or card to accommodate all the peripherals, rather than having a separate card for each device, making it an ideal interface for use with portable and notebook computers. A single host adapter, in the form of a **PC Card**, can serve as a SCSI interface for a "laptop," freeing up the parallel and serial ports for use with an external modem and printer while allowing other devices to be used in addition.

Although not all devices support all levels of SCSI, the evolving SCSI standards are generally backwards-compatible. That is, if you attach an older device to a newer computer with support for a later standard, the older device will work at the older and slower data rate.

The original SCSI, now known as SCSI-1, evolved into SCSI-2, known as "plain SCSI." as it became widely supported. SCSI-3 consists of a set of primary commands and additional specialized command sets to meet the needs of specific device types. The collection of SCSI-3 command sets is used not only for the SCSI-3 parallel interface but for additional parallel and serial protocols, including **Fibre Channels**, Serial Bus Protocol (used with the IEEE 1394 **Firewire** physical protocol), and the Serial Storage Protocol (SSP).

A widely implemented SCSI standard is Ultra-2 (sometimes spelled "Ultra2") which uses a 40 **MHz** clock rate to get maximum data transfer rates up to 80 MBps. It provides a longer possible cabling distance (up to 12 meters) by using Low Voltage Differential (LVD) signaling. Earlier forms of SCSIs use a single wire that ends in a terminator with a ground. Ultra-2 SCSI sends the signal over two wires with the data represented as the difference in voltage between the two wires. This allows support for longer cables. A low voltage differential reduces power requirements and manufacturing costs.

The latest SCSI standard is Ultra-3 (sometimes spelled "Ultra3")which increases the maximum burst rate from 80 Mbps to 160 Mbps by being able to operate at the full clock rate rather than the half-clock rate of Ultra-2. The standard is also sometimes referred to as Ultra160/m. New disk drives supporting Ultra160/m will offer much faster data transfer rates. Ultra160/m also includes cyclical redundancy checking (**CRC**) for ensuring the integrity of transferred data and domain validation for testing the SCSI network.

Currently existing SCSI standards are summarized in the table below.

Technology Name	Maximum Cable Length (meters)	Maximum Speed (MBps)	Maximum Number of Devices
SCSI-1	6	5	8
SCSI-2	6	5–10	8 or 16
Fast SCSI-2	3	10–20	8
Wide SCSI-2	3	20	16
Fast Wide SCSI-2	3	20	16
Ultra SCSI-3, 8-bit	1.52	0	8
Ultra SCSI-3, 16-bit	1.5	40	16
Ultra-2 SCSI	12	40	8
Wide Ultra-2 SCSI	12	80	16
Ultra-3 (Ultra160/m) SCSI	12	160	16

scuzzy

See "SCSI"

SD

See "modem lights"

SD2

SDII (Sound Designer II, sometimes seen abbreviated as SD2) is a monophonic/stereophonic **audio** file format, originally developed by Digidesign for their **Macintosh**-based recording/editing products. It is the successor to the original monophonic Sound Designer I audio file format.

An SDII file can be monophonic or stereophonic. When stereo is used, the tracks are interleaved (sample-001-left, sample-001-right, sample-002-left, sample-002-right, etc.) Files also store **sample rate** and bit depth information.

The SDII file has become a widely accepted standard for transferring audio files between editing applications. Most Mac CD-ROM writer software, for example, specifies SDII or **Audio Interchange File Format** as the file format needed when making audio CDs.

The SDII file has also become accepted among **personal computer** audio application developers. This makes transferring audio from Mac to PC platforms much easier. When used on a PC, the file must use the extension of ".sd2".

SDH

SDH (Synchronous Digital Hierarchy) is a standard technology for synchronous data transmission on optical media. It is the international equivalent of **Synchronous Optical Network**. Both technologies provide faster and less expensive network interconnection than traditional PDH (Plesiochronous Digital Hierarchy) equipment.

In digital telephone transmission, "synchronous" means the bits from one call are carried within one transmission frame. "Plesiochronous" means "almost (but not) synchronous," or a call that must be extracted from more than one transmission frame.

SDH uses the following Synchronous Transport Modules (STM) and rates: STM-1 (155 megabits per second), STM-4 (622 Mbps), STM-16 (2.5 gigabits per second), and STM-64 (10 Gbps).

SDK

See "software developer's kit"

SDLC

SDLC (Synchronous Data Link Control) is a transmission **protocol** developed by IBM in the 1970s as a replacement for its binary synchronous (BSC) protocol. SDLC is equivalent to layer 2 of the **OSI** (Open Systems Interconnection) model of network communication. This level of protocol makes sure that data units arrive successfully from one network point to the next and flow at the right pace.

SDLC uses the primary station-secondary station model of communication. Typically in IBM **mainframe** networks, the host mainframe is the primary station and workstations and other devices are secondary stations. Each secondary station has its own address. Typically, multiple devices or secondary stations are attached to a common line in what is known as a *multipoint* or *multidrop* arrangement. SDLC can also be used for *point-to-point* communication. SDLC is primarily for *remote* communication on corporate wide-area networks (**WAN**s).

SDLC was a basis for the **International Organization for Standardization** standard data link protocol, **HLDLC** (High-Level Data Link Control). SDLC essentially became one of several variations of HDLC, the *normal response mode (NRM)*. While SDLC (and normal response mode) are efficient protocols for closed private networks with dedicated lines, other modes of HDLC serve **X.25** and **frame relay** protocols that manage **packet**s on shared-line switched networks like those used by the Internet.

SDLC became part of IBM's Systems Network Architecture (**SNA**) and the more comprehensive Systems Application Architecture (**SAA**) and its more recent **Open Blueprint**. SDLC is still a commonly encountered and prevalent data link protocol in today's mainframe environment.

SDM

See "systems development method"

SDMA

See "spatial division multiple access"

SDR

See "software-defined radio"

SDRAM

SDRAM (synchronous DRAM) is a generic name for various kinds of dynamic random access memory (**DRAM**) that are synchronized with the **clock speed** that the **microprocessor** is optimized for. This tends to increase the number of instructions that the processor can perform in a given time. The speed of SDRAM is rated in **MHz** rather than in nanoseconds (ns). This makes it easier to compare the **bus** speed and the RAM chip speed. You can convert the RAM clock speed to nanoseconds by dividing the chip speed into 1 billion ns (which is one second). For example, an 83 MHz RAM would be equivalent to 12 ns.

SDTV

See "standard definition television"

SDWT

See "self-directed work team"

seamless interface

A seamless interface is the joining of two computer programs so that they appear to be one program with a single user **interface**. In sewing and other crafts, a seam is the place where two pieces of material are joined together. Often, the seam is visible; you often see the thread where two pieces of cloth are sewn together. In computer program development as in sewing, concealing the seam is often desirable so that the finished work looks like one object rather than two joined together. In programming, a seamless user interface often involves developing a **back-end** program that presents a single user interface that conceals the fact that what is behind the interface are a number of different programs written in different languages, at different times, and by different developers. With programming **distributed** among different computers in a network, it becomes important to screen the user from the location of the logic and the data behind the user interface. A common objective of any methodology for **application integration** and *systems integration* is a seamless user interface. The term is sometimes used loosely to mean that one program works with another one and the user can use both of them.

Seamless is somewhat similar to the term *transparent*. Both mean that the user of something is unburdened by having to see what went into making it.

search engine

On the Internet, a search engine has three parts:

- A **spider** (also called a "crawler" or a "bot") that goes to every page or representative pages on every Web site that wants to be searchable and reads it, using hypertext links on each page to discover and read a site's other pages

- A program that creates a huge index (sometimes called a "catalog") from the pages that have been read

- A program that receives your search request, compares it to the entries in the index, and returns results to you

An alternative to using a search engine is to explore a structured **directory** of topics. Yahoo, which also lets you use its search engine, is the most widely-used directory on the Web. A number of Web **portal** sites offer both the search engine and directory approaches to finding information.

Different Search Engine Approaches

- Major search engines such as Google, Yahoo, AltaVista, and Lycos index the content of a large portion of the Web and provide results that can run for pages—and consequently overwhelm the user.

- Specialized content search engines are selective about what part of the Web is crawled and indexed. For example, TechTarget sites for products such as the AS/400 (http://www.search400.com) and CRM applications (http://www.searchCRM.com) selectively index only the best sites about these products and provide a shorter but more focused list of results.

- Ask Jeeves (http://www.askjeeves.com) provides a general search of the Web but allows you to enter a search request in natural language, such as "What's the weather in Seattle today?"

- Special tools and some sites such as Yahoo let you use a number of search engines at the same time and compile results for you in a single list.

- Individual Web sites, especially larger corporate sites, may use a search engine to index and retrieve the content of just their own site. Some of the major search engine companies license or sell their search engines for use on individual sites.

Where to Search First

The last time we looked, the Open Directory Project listed 370 search engines available for Internet users. There are about ten major search engines, each with its own anchor Web site (although some have an arrangement to use another site's search engine or license their own search engine for use by other Web sites). Some sites, such as Yahoo, search not only using their search engine but also give you the results from simultaneous searches of other search indexes. Sites that let you search multiple indexes simultaneously include:

- Yahoo (http://www.yahoo.com)

- search.com (http://search.com)

- EasySearcher (http://www.easysearcher.com)

Yahoo first searches its own hierarchically-structured subject directory and gives you those entries. Then, it provides a few entries from the AltaVista search engine. It also launches a concurrent search for entries matching your search argument with six or seven other major search engines. You can link to each of them from Yahoo (at the bottom of the search result page) to see what the results were from each of these search engines.

A significant advantage of a Yahoo search is that if you locate an entry in Yahoo, it's likely to lead you to a Web site or entire categories of sites related to your search argument.

A search.com search primarily searches the Infoseek index first but also lets you search the other major search engines as well.

EasySearcher lets you choose from either the popular search engines or a very comprehensive list of specialized search engine/databases in a number of fields.

Yahoo, search.com, and EasySearcher all provide help with entering your search phrase. Most Web **portal** sites offer a quickly-located search entry box that connects you to the major search engines.

How to Search

For "tips" on entering your search argument, see each search engine, including Google's . It's good to read the information at least once.

By "How to Search," we mean a general approach to searching: what to try first, how many search engines to try, whether to search USENET newsgroups, when to quit. It's difficult to generalize, but this is the general approach we use at whatis.com:

1. If you know of a specialized search engine such as SearchNetworking that matches your subject (for example, Networking), you'll save time by using that search engine. You'll find some specialized databases accessible from Easy Searcher 2.

2. If there isn't a specialized search engine, try Yahoo. Sometimes you'll find a matching subject category or two and that's all you'll need.

3. If Yahoo doesn't turn up anything, try AltaVista, Google, Hotbot, Lycos, and perhaps other search engines for their results. Depending on how important the search is, you usually don't need to go below the first 20 entries on each.

4. For efficiency, consider using a **ferret** that will use a number of search engines simultaneously for you. We use WebFerret (from a company called SoftFerret).

5. At this point, if you haven't found what you need, consider using the subject directory approach to searching. Look at Yahoo or someone else's structured organization of subject categories and see if you can narrow down a category your term or phrase is likely to be in. If nothing else, this may give you ideas for new search phrases.

6. If you feel it's necessary, also search the **Usenet** newsgroups as well as the Web.

7. As you continue to search, keep rethinking your search arguments. What new approaches could you use? What are some related subjects to search for that might lead you to the one you really want?

8. Finally, consider whether your subject is so new that not much is available on it yet. If so, you may want to go out and check the very latest computer and Internet magazines or locate companies that you think may be involved in research or development related to the subject.

Search for Extraterrestrial Intelligence

SETI (the Search for Extraterrestrial Intelligence) is a scientific effort to discover intelligent life elsewhere in the universe, primarily by attempting to discover radio signals that indicate intelligence. Cornell astronomer Frank Drake is credited with being the first to "listen" for intelligent signals with a radio telescope in 1960. Although NASA has funded some study in the past, current efforts are privately funded, in part by Arthur C. Clarke, Microsoft co-founder Paul Allen, Intel founder Gordon Moore, and Hewlett-Packard cofounders David Packard and William Hewlett.

The SETI Institute's Project Phoenix is using computers to search about 1,000 stars within 200 light-years of our solar system for radio signals beamed toward us or any other location. Project Phoenix's 140-foot radio telescope in Green Bank, West Virginia aims at one star at a time while astronomer-monitored computers search each 1,000 band from 1,000 to 3,000 **MHz** for a signal limited to a **narrowband** range. Scientists believe that a signal focused within a narrow frequency band would suggest an intelligent source.

About two-thirds of the first 1,000 stars have been searched with no success yet reported. There are, however, over 400 billion stars in our own galaxy so the study may last quite a long time. The directors of the project are soliciting volunteers to help analyze the radio telescope data at their home computers.

search-and-replace

Search-and-replace is a capability that allows a computer user to find a given sequence of **character**s in one or more **text file**s and, if desired, replace the sequence with another sequence of characters. A *global* search-and-replace means that the replace is to take effect in all files within the context of the search.

In **UNIX** and some other operating systems, a **grep** command or utility can be used to do search-and-replace. In Windows operating systems, a popular product that provides a graphical user interface is called Search and Replace for Windows 95/NT.

second

The second (abbreviation, s or sec) is the International System of Units (**SI**) unit of time. One second is the time that elapses during 9,192,631,770 (9.192631770×10^9) cycles of the radiation produced by the transition between two levels of the cesium 133 atom.

There are other expressions for the second. It is the time required for an **electromagnetic field** to propagate 299,792,458 meters (2.99792458×10^8 m) through a vacuum. This figure is sometimes rounded to 3.00×10^8 m, or 300,000 kilometers (3.00×10^5 km). One second is equal to 1/86,400 of a mean solar day. This is easy to derive from the fact that there are 60 seconds in a minute, 60 minutes in an hour, and 24 hours in a mean solar day. This definition is, however, subject to limited accuracy because of irregularities in the earth's orbit around the sun.

Engineers and scientists often use smaller units than the second by attaching power-of-10 **prefix multiplier**s. One millisecond is 10^{-3} s; one microsecond is 10^{-6} s; one nanosecond is 10^{-9} s; one picosecond is 10^{-12} s. During these spans of time, respectively, an EM field propagates through a vacuum over distances of approximately 300 kilometers, 300 meters, 300 millimeters, and 300 micrometers.

The second is sometimes specified as a unit of angular measure, especially in astronomy and global positioning. In these contexts, it is also known as an arc second or a second of arc, and is equal to exactly 1/3600 of an angular degree or 1/1,296,000 of a circle. Sixty arc seconds comprise an arc minute; 60 arc minutes comprise an angular degree. One arc second of latitude at the earth's surface corresponds to a north-south distance of only about 31 m.

Also see International System of Units (**SI**) and **prefix multiplier**s.

second generation RISC

See "superscalar"

secondary storage

Secondary storage is all magnetic data **storage** that is not currently in the computer's **main storage** or **memory**. Synonyms are **external storage** and **auxiliary storage**.

second-hand

See "refurbished"

second-level domain

A second-level domain (SLD) is the portion of a Uniform Resource Locator (**URL**) that identifies the specific and unique administative owner associated with an Internet Protocol address (**IP address**). The second-level domain name includes the top-level domain (**top-level domain**) name. For example, in:

whatis.com

"whatis" is a second-level domain. "whatis.com" is a second-level domain name (and includes the top-level domain name of "com"). Second-level domains can be divided into further domain levels. These subdomains sometimes represent different computer servers within different departments.

More than one second-level domain name can be used for the same IP address.

secret key

See "private key"

secret key algorithm

Also see **cryptography**.

A secret key algorithm (sometimes called a *symmetric* algorithm) is a cryptographic **algorithm** that uses the same **key** to encrypt and decrypt data. The best known algorithm is the U.S. Department of Defense's Data Encryption Standard (**DES**). DES, which was developed at IBM in 1977, was thought to be so difficult to break that the U.S. government restricted its exportation.

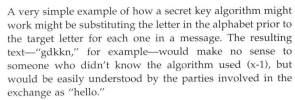

A very simple example of how a secret key algorithm might work might be substituting the letter in the alphabet prior to the target letter for each one in a message. The resulting text—"gdkkn," for example—would make no sense to someone who didn't know the algorithm used (x-1), but would be easily understood by the parties involved in the exchange as "hello."

The problem with secret or symmetric keys is how to securely get the secret keys to each end of the exchange and keep them secure after that. For this reason, an asymmetric key system is now often used that is known as the public key infrastructure (**PKI**).

sector

On a computer diskette or **hard disk**, a sector is one of the "pies slices" the diskette or disk is divided into. Dividing the circular medium into pie slices is a way to organize it so that data can be located by the read/write heads of the drive. The diskette or disk is also divided into a number of concentric circles. Data can be located by knowing the number of the sector and the concentric track that passes through that sector. Each track is divided into a number of *clusters* that represent the smallest unit of storage that is addressable (can be written to or read). Typically, a cluster is 256 or 512 bytes in length.

Sector 0 of the diskette or disk contains a special file, the file allocation table (FAT). The FAT tells where the directory to the files on the medium is located and information about how clusters are used. You can't look at sector 0 directly.

On hard disks, the first sector is called variously the *master boot record*, the *partition sector*, or the *partition table*. This record or table tells how and whether the disk has been divided into logical *partitions* (for example, you can divide your hard drive into two logical partitions or drives so that you can load different operating systems on to the disk and switch back of forth). When your operating system is being booted or loaded into RAM, a program in this partition sector briefly gets control, determines how your disk is partitioned, and then reads the operating system **boot** sector and gives that boot sector program control so that the rest of the operating system can be loaded into RAM. The partition sector is the sector that can be "infected" when you leave a diskette in drive A that contains a boot **virus**.

The sectors as well as the rest of the organization of the diskette or disk are set up as a result of the process called *formatting*. Most diskettes you buy today are already formatted. However, if you're using an old one, you may need to reformat it. You can do this using a common utility that comes with your operating system.

Secure Electronic Transaction

SET (Secure Electronic Transaction) is a system for ensuring the security of financial transactions on the Internet. It was supported initially by Mastercard, Visa, Microsoft, Netscape, and others. With SET, a user is given an *electronic wallet* (**digital certificate**) and a transaction is conducted and verified using a combination of digital certificates and digital signatures among the purchaser, a merchant, and the purchaser's bank in a way that ensures privacy and confidentiality. SET makes use of Netscape's Secure Sockets Layer (**SSL**), Microsoft's Secure Transaction Technology (**STT**), and Terisa System's Secure Hypertext Transfer Protocol (**S-HTTP**). SET uses some but not all aspects of a public key infrastructure (**PKI**).

Here's how SET works:

Assume that a customer has a SET-enabled browser such as Netscape or Microsoft's Internet Explorer and that the transaction provider (bank, store, etc.) has a SET-enabled server.

1. The customer opens a Mastercard or Visa bank account. Any issuer of a credit card is some kind of bank.

2. The customer receives a **digital certificate**. This electronic file functions as a credit card for online purchases or other transactions. It includes a *public key* with an expiration date. It has been through a **digital switch** to the bank to ensure its validity.

3. Third-party merchants also receive certificates from the bank. These certificates include the merchant's public key and the bank's public key.

4. The customer places an order over a Web page, by phone, or some other means.

5. The customer's browser receives and confirms from the merchant's certificate that the merchant is valid.

6. The browser sends the order information. This message is encrypted with the merchant's public key, the payment information, which is encrypted with the bank's public key (which can't be read by the merchant), and information that ensures the payment can only be used with this particular order.

7. The merchant verifies the customer by checking the digital signature on the customer's certificate. This may be done by referring the certificate to the bank or to a third-party verifier.

8. The merchant sends the order message along to the bank. This includes the bank's public key, the customer's payment information (which the merchant can't decode), and the merchant's certificate.

9. The bank verifies the merchant and the message. The bank uses the digital signature on the certificate with the message and verifies the payment part of the message.

10. The bank digitally signs and sends authorization to the merchant, who can then fill the order.

Secure Hypertext Transfer Protocol

See "HTTPS"

Secure Shell

Secure Shell (SSH), sometimes known as Secure Socket Shell, is a **UNIX**-based command interface and **protocol** for securely getting access to a remote computer. It is widely used by network administrators to control Web and other kinds of servers remotely. SSH is actually a suite of three utilities—slogin, ssh, and scp—that are secure versions of the earlier UNIX utilities, **rlogin**, rsh, and rcp. SSH commands are encrypted and secure in several ways. Both ends of the **client/server** connection are authenticated using a **digital certificate**, and passwords are protected by being encrypted.

SSH uses **RSA public key** cryptography for both connection and authentication. Encryption algorithms include **Blowfish**, **DES**, and **IDEA**. IDEA is the default.

SSH2, the latest version, is a proposed set of standards from the Internet Engineering Task Force (**IETF**).

Secure Socket Shell

See "Secure Shell"

Secure Sockets Layer

The Secure Sockets Layer (SSL) is a commonly used **protocol** for managing the security of a message transmission on the Internet. SSL has recently been succeeded by Transport Layer Security (**TLS**), which is based on SSL. SSL uses a program **layer** located between the Internet's Hypertext Transfer Protocol (**HTTP**) and Transport Control Protocol (**TCP**) layers. SSL is included as part of both the Microsoft and Netscape browsers and most Web server products. Developed by Netscape, SSL also gained the support of Microsoft and other Internet **client/server** developers as well and became the de facto standard until evolving into Transport Layer Security. The "sockets" part of the term refers to the **sockets** method of passing data back and forth between a client and a server program in a network or between program layers in the same computer. SSL uses the public-and-private key **encryption** system from **RSA**, which also includes the use of a **digital certificate**.

TLS and SSL are an integral part of most Web browsers (clients) and Web servers. If a **Web site** is on a server that supports SSL, SSL can be enabled and specific Web pages can be identified as requiring SSL access. Any Web server can be enabled by using Netscape's SSLRef program library which can be downloaded for noncommercial use or licensed for commercial use.

TLS and SSL are not interoperable. However, a message sent with TLS can be handled by a client that handles SSL but not TLS.

Security Identifier

In Windows NT and 2000 operating systems, the Security Identifier (SID) is a unique alphanumeric character string that identifies each operating system and each user in a network of NT/2000 systems.

security policy

In business, a security policy is a document that states in writing how a company plans to protect the company's physical and information technology (**IT**) assets. A security policy is often considered to be a "living document", meaning that the document is never finished, but is continuously updated as technology and employee requirements change. A company's security policy may include an **acceptable use policy**, a description of how the company plans to educate its employees about protecting the company's assets, an explanation of how security measurements will be carried out and enforced, and a procedure for evaluating the effectiveness of the security policy to ensure that necessary corrections will be made.

self-assembly

Self-assembly is a method of constructing devices and machines whose dimensions are measured in nanometers (units of 10^{-9} meter or millionths of a millimeter). The technique works by simulating the way biological systems build molecules, viruses, cells, plants, and animals.

Self-assembly involves a process known as convergent synthesis. This has been taking place for eons in life forms of all kinds. The technology is largely unexploited, but researchers have succeeded in initiating convergent synthesis to produce some primitive nanodevices. Self assembly is of special interest to the manufacturers of integrated circuits (**ICs**), especially microprocessors. A device called a **biochip** might be grown like a plant from a seed, giving rise to computers with high-level artificial intelligence (**AI**).

Self-assembly should not be confused with positional assembly. In the latter process, the engineer has a relatively high degree of control over where each individual **atom** or molecule is placed. In self-assembly, although the positioning and arrangement of atoms or molecules might be just as critical as in positional assembly, the process is carried out largely by nature once the engineer has initiated it. In that sense, self-assembly is a sophisticated chemical reaction. Some nanotechnology researchers are, however, exploring ways to add positional control to chemical synthesis.

Also see **dendrimer**, **exponential assembly**, **nanotechnology**, **positional assembly**, and **self-replication**.

#
A
B
C
D
E
F
G
H
I
J
K
L
M
N
O
P
Q
R
S
T
U
V,W
X,Y,Z

self-directed work team

A self-directed work team (SDWT) is a group of people, usually employees in a company, who combine different skills and talents to work without the usual managerial supervision toward a common purpose or goal. Typically, an SDWT has somewhere between two and 25 members. An optimal SDWT is said to be between five and nine members. An SDWT is similar to a **skunkworks** except that an SDWT is not temporary and is not limited to a single project.

SDWT members use their company's mission statement to develop their purpose, which must be meaningful and beneficial to the company. Purposes might include problem solving, increasing sales and productivity, career training, and product improvement.

SDWT members must decide how they want to work together. Because a manager or boss does not lead, they must agree on the rules and deadlines for accomplishing their purpose. Some teams create a charter or set of rules that describe what is expected of each member. If a problem arises during the course of a project, the team members work together to provide a solution.

In order for an SDWT to succeed, the company or organization must provide a meaningful mission statement to the team, empower the team to do what it needs to do including making important decisions, support the team, establish and provide the boundaries, rules, and company policies, and train the members with the skills and knowledge needed to accomplish their purpose. But, in the end, the team is held accountable for the success or failure of a project.

Saturn and Federal Express are examples of companies that use self-directed work teams.

Self-Monitoring Analysis & Reporting Technology

Self-Monitoring Analysis and Reporting Technology (S.M.A.R.T.) is an interface between a computer's start-up program or **basic input/output system** and the computer **hard disk**. It is a feature of the Enhanced Integrated Drive Electronics (**EIDE**) technology that controls access to the hard drive. If S.M.A.R.T is enabled when a computer is set up, the BIOS can receive analytical information from the hard drive and determine whether to send the user a warning message about possible future failure of the hard drive.

self-replication

In **nanotechnology**, self-replication is a process in which devices whose diameters are of atomic scale, on the order of nanometers, create copies of themselves. A nanometer is 10^{-9} meter or a millionth of a millimeter. In order for self-replication to take place in a constructive manner, three conditions must be met.

The first requirement is that each unit be a specialized machine called a nanorobot, one of whose functions is to construct at least one copy of itself during its operational life. (Each unit should also have some other function, unless the intended purpose of the aggregate is to cause havoc by generating the mechanical equivalent of a cancerous tumor.) A hypothetical example of a constructively self-replicating nanorobot is an artificial antibody. In addition to reproducing itself, it seeks and destroys disease-causing organisms.

The second requirement is the existence of all the energy and ingredients necessary to build a certain minimum number of complete copies of the nanorobot in question. Ideally, the quantities of each ingredient should be such that they are consumed in the correct proportion. If the process is intended to be finite, then when the desired number of nanorobots has been constructed, there should be no unused quantities of any ingredient remaining.

The third requirement is that the environment be controlled so that the replication process can proceed efficiently and without malfunctions. Excessive turbulence, temperature extremes, intense radiation, or other adverse circumstances might prevent the proper functioning of the nanorobots and cause the process to falter or fail. Science-fiction writers have suggested that mutations might occur in a sophisticated self-replicating nanorobotic community, giving rise to the machine equivalent of natural selection. Such a process might be used to create a self-sustaining, evolving colony of robots on an extraterrestrial planet.

Also see **exponential assembly**, **nanotechnology**, **positional assembly**, and **self-assembly**.

Self-scanned Amorphous Silicon Integrated Display

Self-scanned Amorphous Silicon Integrated Display (SASID) is the trade name for an active-matrix **liquid crystal display** (AMLCD) technology developed by Sarnoff Corporation. The technology is intended primarily for flat-panel displays in notebook and portable computers, and for projection panels.

The hallmarks of the SASID are the amorphous **silicon** (aSi or a-Si) manufacturing process and the self-scanning feature. The horizontal and vertical scanning circuitry, rather than being external to the display, is incorporated directly on the glass substrate of the panel. This reduces the cost of manufacture by up to 35 percent, and enhances reliability by minimizing the number of interconnects.

The average useful life of preliminary SASID designs is more than 10,000 hours at 70 degrees centigrade, and the random failure rate is approximately half that of most other AMLCDs. In addition, SASIDs are brighter than most other AMLCDs, offer an image **resolution** of more than 200 pixels per inch, provide excellent contrast, and consume minimal power (typically less than 200 milliwatts). The SASID is compatible with existing **pixel** designs, and offers equivalent system interaction to other AMLCDs.

Semantic Web Agreement Group

The Semantic Web Agreement Group (SWAG) is an organization of interested parties working together to further the development of the **Semantic Web** (SW), a concept that might lead to a Web that was self-described in a way that would make it easier for programs to work with it. (**Semantic** refers to the meaning of something.) **Tim Berners-Lee**, whose Hypertext Transfer Protocol (**HTTP**) virtually created the World Wide Web, is also the man behind the Semantic Web. Berners-Lee describes the Semantic Web as "a web of data that can be processed directly or indirectly by machines". SW is a new vision of the Web in which document components describe and comprehend relationships between various aspects of Web content, enabling machines to process data in a more intelligent and autonomous way. Because the Semantic Web would be dependent upon effective data sharing, SWAG is working towards building the support system, such as a standardized glossary to ensure that terms will be processed identically by all computer systems.

Computer systems already rely on a standardized vocabulary to communicate; this ensures that instructions (such as *load*, for example) are interpreted consistently. The Semantic Web would make Web documents and document components much more meaningful to the machines that process them. Markup languages have steadily progressed towards more intelligent versions. Extensible Markup Language (**XML**), for example, has much more ability to perform tasks autonomously than HTML. New adaptations, such as DARPA Agent Markup Language (**DAML**) are being developed as potential vehicles that could make it possible for the Semantic Web to function as a comprehensive universal database.

Semantic Web

The Semantic Web is an idea of World Wide Web inventor **Tim Berners-Lee** that the Web as a whole can be made more intelligent and perhaps even intuitive about how to serve a user's needs. Berners-Lee observes that although search engines index much of the Web's content, they have little ability to select the pages that a user really wants or needs. He foresees a number of ways in which developers and authors, singly or in collaborations, can use self-descriptions and other techniques so that context-understanding programs can selectively find what users want.

semantics

Semantics (pronounced seh-MANT-iks, from Greek *semantikos* or significant and *sema* or sign) is the branch of *semiotics*, the philosophy or study of signs, that deals with meaning. The other two branches of semiotics are syntactics (the arrangement of signs) and pragmatics (the relationship between the speaker and the signs). In discussing natural and computer languages, the distinction is sometimes made between **syntax** (for example, the word order in a sentence or the exact computer command notation) and semantics (what the words really say or what functions are requested in the command).

semaphore

In programming, especially in **UNIX** systems, semaphores are a technique for coordinating or synchronizing activities in which multiple processes compete for the same operating system resources. A semaphore is a value in a designated place in operating system (or **kernel**) storage that each process can check and then change. Depending on the value that is found, the process can use the resource or will find that it is already in use and must wait for some period before trying again. Semaphones can be **binary** (0 or 1) or can have additional values. Typically, a process using semaphores checks the value and then, if it using the resource, changes the value to reflect this so that subsequent semaphore users will know to wait.

Semaphores are commonly use for two purposes: to share a common memory space and to share access to files. Semaphores are one of the techniques for interprocess communication (**IPC**). The **C** programming language provides a set of interfaces or "functions" for managing semaphores.

semiconductor

See also **atom**, **transistor**, **bipolar transistor**, and **field-effect transistor**.

A semiconductor is a substance, usually a solid chemical element or compound, that can conduct electricity under some conditions but not others, making it a good medium for the control of electrical current. Its conductance varies depending on the **current** or **voltage** applied to a control electrode, or on the intensity of irradiation by infrared (**IR**), visible light, ultraviolet (UV), or X rays.

The specific properties of a semiconductor depend on the impurities, or *dopants*, added to it. An *N-type* semiconductor carries current mainly in the form of negatively-charged **electron**s, in a manner similar to the conduction of current in a wire. A *P-type* semiconductor carries current predominantly as electron deficiencies called **hole**s. A hole has a positive electric charge, equal and opposite to the charge on an electron. In a semiconductor material, the flow of holes occurs in a direction opposite to the flow of electrons.

Elemental semiconductors include antimony, arsenic, boron, carbon, germanium, selenium, silicon, sulfur, and tellurium. **Silicon** is the best-known of these, forming the basis of most integrated circuits (ICs). Common semiconductor com-

pounds include gallium arsenide, indium antimonide, and the oxides of most metals. Of these, gallium arsenide (**GaAs**) is widely used in low-noise, high-gain, weak-signal amplifying devices.

A semiconductor device can perform the function of a vacuum tube having hundreds of times its volume. A single integrated circuit (**IC**), such as a microprocessor **chip**, can do the work of a set of vacuum tubes that would fill a large building and require its own electric generating plant.

sendmail

On the Internet, sendmail is the most popular **UNIX**-based implementation of the Simple Mail Transfer Protocol (**SMTP**) for transmitting **e-mail**. When a sendmail **server** receives e-mail, it attempts to deliver the mail to the intended recipient immediately and, if the recipient is not present, it queues messages for later delivery. However, because it does not provide a mailbox facility and for other reasons, other software such as a **POP3** or **Internet Message Access Protocol** server are also needed. Most Internet service providers (**ISPs**) provide both an SMTP server (such as sendmail) and a POP or IMAP server.

A commercial version of sendmail, called Sendmail, includes a **POP3** server and other enhancements to the basic open source sendmail. It also comes in a version that can be installed on a **Windows NT** operating systems platform.

Sequenced Packet Exchange

SPX (Sequenced Packet Exchange) is the **protocol** for handling **packet** sequencing in a Novell **NetWare** network. SPX prepares the sequence of packets that a message is divided into and manages the reassembly of received packets, confirming that all have been received and requesting retransmission when they haven't. SPX works directly with the Internetwork Packet Exchange (**IPX**), which manages the forwarding of packets in the network.

IPX/SPX are comparable to the basic Internet protocols, **Internet Protocol** and **Transmission Control Protocol**.

sequencer

In digital audio recording, a sequencer is a program in a computer or stand-alone keyboard unit that puts together a sound sequence from a series (or sequence) of Musical Instrument Digital Interface (**MIDI**) *events* (operations). The MIDI sequencer allows the user to record and edit a musical performance without using an audio-based input source. The performance is recorded as a series of events that would ordinarily be played in from a keyboard instrument. The MIDI sequencer does not record the actual audio, but rather the events related to the performance—what note was played at what time, how hard the key was pressed, when did the sustain pedal get depressed, and so forth. This data is then played back into a MIDI instrument or sound module. Using this method, the performer can select a piano

sound for a musical passage and later decide that the passage would work better as an organ sound. The editor can simply change the sound program on the MIDI keyboard to alter the sound without needing to rerecord the entire performance.

Using sound modules and keyboards that can respond on different MIDI channels, the player can layer the sounds of different instruments to create the illusion of an entire band or orchestra. There is sequencing software available in a range from that which would suit a beginner all the way to the most advanced film composer.

sequential consistency

In computers, sequential consistency is best defined by its inventor, Leslie Lamport, who declared that a **multiprocessing** system had sequential consistency if:

> "...the results of any execution is the same as if the operations of all the processors were executed in some sequential order, and the operations of each individual processor appear in this sequence in the order specified by its program."

This definition was one of the first statements on what constituted "correct" behavior for a symmetric multiprocessing (**SMP**) system. It has been restated in various forms, among them the following:

> Sequential consistency requires that a shared memory multiprocessor appear to be a **multiprogramming** uniprocessor system to any program running on it.

Sequential consistency requires that:

1. All instructions are executed in order.
2. Every write operation becomes instantaneously visible throughout the system.

Implicit in the definition of sequential consistency was the acknowledgement that SMP systems could fail to be sequentially consistent. Should machines be sequentially consistent? From the vantage point of almost twenty years later, the answers are mixed. Some say "yes," that machines should conceal implementation complexities in order to make the machines as easy to use as possible. Others say "no," that violating SC allows machines to increase performance considerably while at the same time inconveniencing only a vanishingly small number of programmers.

Sequential Couleur avec Memoire

SECAM (Sequential Couleur avec Memoire) is the television display technology that is standard in France, the countries of the former Soviet Union, and certain other countries. It is one of the three world TV standards together with **National Television Standards Committee** (United States) and **Phase Alternation Line** (Europe other than France).

Like PAL, SECAM scans the cathode ray tube (**CRT**) horizontally 625 times to form the video image.

serendipity

In general, serendipity is the act of finding something valuable or delightful when you are not looking for it. In information technology, serendipity often plays a part in the recognition of a new product need or in solving a design problem. Web surfing can be an occasion for serendipity since you sometimes come across a valuable or interesting site when you are looking for something else.

The term was coined by English writer Horace Walpole on January 28, 1754, in a letter written to Horace Mann. He credited it to a "silly fairy tale" he once read called *The Three Princes of Serendip*.

According to the fairy tale, three Persian princes sailed off to make their fortunes in the "land of silk", an island called *Serendip*. (Today, the island is known as Sri Lanka.) Along the way, the princes made all types of wondrous and delightful discoveries about the island, and learned things they never expected. One such learning was purported to be the discovery that a mule blind in its right eye had recently traveled the same road. This was discovered when they noticed that the grass had been eaten only on the left side of the road.

The term is also sometimes used to mean "the randomness of fate," as in "whatever happens to cross my desk today."

serial

Serial means one event at a time. It is usually contrasted with *parallel*, meaning more than one event happening at a time. In data transmission, the techniques of time division and space division are used, where time separates the transmission of individual bits of information sent serially and space (on multiple lines or paths) can be used to have multiple bits sent in parallel.

In the context of computer hardware and data transmission: serial connection, operation, and media usually indicate a simpler, slower operation and parallel indicates a faster operation. This indication doesn't always hold since a serial medium (for example, fiber optic cable) can be much faster than a slower medium that carries multiple signals in parallel.

On your PC, the printer is usually attached through a parallel interface and cable so that it will print faster. Your keyboard and mouse are one-way devices that only require a serial interface and line. Inside your computer, much of its circuitry supports bits being moved around in parallel.

Your computer modem uses one of your PC's serial connections or COM ports. Serial communication between your PC and the modem and other serial devices adheres to the **RS-232C** standard.

Conventional computers and their programs operate in a serial manner, with the computer reading a program and performing its instructions one after the other. However, some of today's computers have multiple processors and can perform instructions in parallel.

Serial Line Internet Protocol

SLIP (Serial Line Internet Protocol) is a protocol used for communication between two machines that are previously configured for communication with each other. For example, your Internet server provider may provide you with a SLIP connection so that the provider's server can respond to your requests, pass them on to the Internet, and forward your requested Internet responses back to you. Your dial-up connection to the server is typically on a slower serial line rather than on the **parallel** or multiplex lines such as a line of the network you are hooking up to.

A better service is provided by the Point-to-Point Protocol (**PPP**).

serial presence detect

When a computer is **boot**ed (started), serial presence detect (SPD) is information stored in an electrically erasable programmable read-only memory (**EEPROM**) chip on a synchronous dynamic random access memory (**SDRAM**) **memory module** that tells the basic input/output system (**BIOS**) the module's size, data width, speed, and voltage. The BIOS uses this information to configure the memory properly for maximum reliability and performance. If a memory module does not have SPD, the BIOS assumes the memory module's information. With some memory, this does not cause problems. But SDRAM memory has to have SPD or the computer may not boot at all. If it does boot, the assumed information may cause **fatal exception** errors

Before SPD, memory chips were identified with parallel presence detect (PPD). PPD used a separate **pin** for each bit of information, which meant that only the speed and density of the memory module could be stored because of the limited space for pins. The EEPROM chip on an SPD memory module only requires two pins so more information can be stored.

server

1) In general, a server is a computer **program** that provides services to other computer programs in the same or other computers.

2) The computer that a server program runs in is also frequently referred to as a server (though it may contain a number of server and **client** programs).

3) In the **client/server** programming model, a server is a program that awaits and fulfills requests from **client** programs in the same or other computers. A given

application in a computer may function as a *client* with requests for services from other programs and also as a *server* of requests from other programs.

Specific to the Web, a **Web server** is the computer program (housed in a computer) that serves requested **HTML** pages or files. A Web *client* is the requesting program associated with the user. The Web **browser** in your computer is a client that requests HTML files from Web servers.

server accelerator card

A server accelerator card (also known as an *SSL card*) is a Peripheral Component Interconnect (**PCI**) **card** used to generate **encryption keys** for secure transactions on e-commerce Web sites. When a secure transaction is initiated, the Web site's **server** sends its **certificate**, which has been provided by a certifying authority, to the **client** machine to verify the Web site's authenticity. After this exchange, a **secret key** is used to encrypt all data transferred between sender and receiver so that all personal and credit card information is protected. This process can severely overload a server resulting in fewer transactions processed per second, which means fewer sales. The server accelerator card takes over this process, thus reducing the load on the server. Server accelerator cards support a number of security **protocol**s including Secure Sockets Layer (**SSL**) and Secure Electronic Transaction (**SET**).

The server accelerator card is installed into the PCI **slot** of the server. A software **driver** is loaded, and the server is ready to receive orders. This is much easier and more cost-effective than buying additional servers. Additional cards can be installed as the server's secure transactions increase.

There are also SSL acceleration appliances. These are external units that have server accelerator cards installed inside them. The unit is then plugged into the server. When a secure transaction is detected, the transaction is routed to the SSL acceleration unit for processing. SSL accelerator appliances can be added as needed by clustering them together.

server farm

A server farm is a group of computers acting as **server** and housed together in a single location. A server farm is sometimes called a server *cluster*. A Web server farm is either (1) a Web site that has more than one server, or (2) an Internet service provider (**ISP**) that provides Web hosting services using multiple servers.

In a business network, a server farm or cluster might perform such services as providing centralized access control, file access, printer sharing, and backup for workstation users. The servers may have individual operating systems or a shared operating system and may also be set up to provide load balancing when there are many server requests. In a server farm, if one server fails, another can act as backup.

On the Internet, a Web server farm, or simply *Web farm*, may refer to a Web site that uses two or more servers to handle user requests. Typically, serving user requests for the files (pages) of a Web site can be handled by a single server. However, larger Web sites may require multiple servers.

Web farm is a term that is also simply used to mean a business that performs Web site hosting on multiple servers. Some Web farms allow you to put your own server on their site, a service known as **colocation**.

Server Message Block Protocol

The Server Message Block Protocol (SMB protocol) provides a method for **client** applications in a computer to read and write to files on and to request services from **server** programs in a computer network. The SMB **protocol** can be used over the Internet on top of its **TCP/IP** protocol or on top of other network protocols such as **Internetwork Packet Exchange** and **NetBEUI**. Using the SMB protocol, an application (or the user of an application) can access files at a remote server as well as other resources, including printers, mailslots, and **named pipe**s. Thus, a client application can read, create, and update files on the remote server. It can also communicate with any server program that is set up to receive an SMB client request.

Microsoft Windows operating systems since Windows 95 include client and server SMB protocol support. For **UNIX** systems, a shareware program, Samba, is available. The SMB protocol originated at Microsoft and has gone through a number of developments. A given client and server may implement different sets of protocol variations which they negotiate before starting a session.

Microsoft has offered a public or **open source** version of SMB for the Internet to the Internet Engineering Task Force (**IETF**). Called the Common Internet File System (**CIFS**), this new protocol provides more flexibility than existing Internet applications such as the File Transfer Protocol (**FTP**). CIFS is envisioned as a complement to the Internet's **Hypertext Transfer Protocol** for Web browsing.

server space provider

A server space provider is an individual, company, or organization that provides storage space on a **server** for Web pages, usually for a charge. Some independent access providers and online services provide a limited amount of free space for Web pages (for example, one megabytes of hard disk storage).

Note that not all **access providers** offer server space. And many server space providers do not provide access. Server space and access are two different services.

Relative to other costs of developing a Web site, the cost of server space is usually small. A new trend on some sites, however, is to charge for the amount of traffic your pages get rather than the space they use. This is because server space is relatively cheap compared to the administrative costs of managing a busy site for someone.

serverless backup

Serverless backup is a method of offloading **backup** procedures from a **server** so that the time ordinarily devoted to backup functions can be used to carry out other server tasks. Ordinarily, the amount of time that a server can devote to processing requests from applications is limited by the *backup window*—the amount of time that must be reserved for data backup. Serverless backup is a storage area network (**SAN**) solution that is designed to lead to lower hardware costs and improved time-effectiveness, scalability, and fault tolerance. A number of companies, including Legato, Veritas, EMC, and Computer Associates offer or are developing serverless backup products.

Serverless backup enables disk-to-tape or disk-to-disk backup without depending on server resources or network bandwidth. The Legato, Veritas, and CA products are based on a process known as *disk imaging*. These applications use an **intelligent agent**, which makes a *snapshot copy* of pointers to the data. The snapshot copy consists of an image of the pointers, which indicate the location of the data. The intelligent agent and backup procedures communicate through the Network Data Management Protocol (NDMP). The EMC version is based on something called a Fastrax *data movement platform* and Hewlett Packard's OpenView OmniBak II backup application. Proprietary software within the hardware platform is used, first, to mark logical backup objects, and then to back up data on the list.

server-push

See "push"

servers

See "server"

server-side include

A server-side include (SSI) is a variable value (for example, a file "Last modified" date) that a **server** can include in an HTML file before it sends it to the requestor. If you're creating a Web page, you can insert an include statement in the HTML file that looks like this:

```
<!-#echo var="LAST_MODIFIED"->
```

and the server will obtain the last-modified date for the file and insert it before the HTML file is sent to requestors.

LAST_MODIFIED is one of several *environment variables* that an operating system can keep track of and that can be accessible to a server program. The server administrator can make these environment variables usable when the system is set up.

A Web file that contains server-side include statements (such as the "echo" statement above) is usually defined by the administrator to be a file with an "." suffix. You can think of a server-side include as a limited form of **common gateway interface** application. In fact, the CGI is not used. The server simply searches the server-side include file for CGI environment variables, and inserts the variable information in the places in the file where the "include" statements have been inserted.

When creating a Web site, a good idea is to ask your server administrator which environment variables can be used and whether the administrator can arrange to set the server up so that these can be handled. The administrator may be able to help you add the appropriate "include" statements to your HTML file.

service contact port numbers

See "well-known port numbers"

Service Level Agreement

A Service Level Agreement (SLA) is a contract between a network service provider and a customer that specifies, usually in measurable terms, what services the network service provider will furnish. Many Internet service providers (**ISP**)s provide their customers with an SLA. More recently, **IS** departments in major enterprises have adopted the idea of writing a Service Level Agreement so that services for their customers (users in other departments within the enterprise) can be measured, justified, and perhaps compared with those of **outsourcing** network providers.

Some **metric**s that SLAs may specify include:

- What percentage of the time services will be available
- The number of users that can be served simultaneously
- Specific performance **benchmark**s to which actual performance will be periodically compared
- The schedule for notification in advance of network changes that may affect users
- Help desk response time for various classes of problems
- Dial-in access availability
- Usage statistics that will be provided

service pack

A service pack is an orderable or downloadable update to a customer's software that fixes existing problems and, in some cases, delivers product enhancements. IBM and Microsoft are examples of companies that use this term to describe their periodic product updates.

When a new product version comes out, it usually incorporates the fixes from the service packs that have been shipped to update the previous product version.

Service Profile Identifier

See "SPID"

servlet

A servlet is a small program that runs on a **server**. The term was coined in the context of the **Java applet**, a small program that is sent as a separate file along with a Web (**HTML**) page. Java applets, usually intended for running on a **client**, can result in such services as performing a calculation for a user or positioning an image based on user interaction.

Some programs, often those that access databases based on user input, need to be on the server. Typically, these have been implemented using a Common Gateway Interface (**CGI**) application. However, with a Java **virtual machine** running in the server, such programs can be implemented with the Java programming language. The advantage of a Java servlet on servers with lots of traffic is that they can execute more quickly than CGI applications. Rather than causing a separate program **process** to be created, each user request is invoked as a **thread** in a single **daemon** process, meaning that the amount of system overhead for each request is slight.

Instead of a URL that designates the name of a CGI application (in a "cgi-bin" subdirectory), a request in a form on a Web HTML page that results in a Java servlet getting called would call a URL that looks like this:

```
http://www.whatis.com:8080/servlet/gotoUrl?http://
www.someplace.com
```

The "8080" port number in the URL means the request is intended directly for the Web server itself. The "servlet" would indicate to the Web server that a servlet was being requested.

Add-on modules allow Java servlets to run in Netscape Enterprise, Microsoft Internet Information Server (**IIS**), and **Apache** servers.

session

Also see **user session**.

In telecommunication, a session is a series of interactions between two communication end points that occur during the span of a single connection. Typically, one end point requests a connection with another specified end point and if that end point replies agreeing to the connection, the end points take turns exchanging commands and data ("talking to each other"). The session begins when the connection is established at both ends and terminates when the connection is ended.

In the standard industry communications reference model, Open Systems Interconnection (**OSI**), the **Session layer** (sometimes called the "port layer") manages the setting up and taking down of the association between two communicating end points that is called a connection. A connection is maintained while the two end points are communicating back and forth in a conversation or session of some duration. Some connections and sessions last only long enough to send a message in one direction. However, other sessions may last longer, usually with one or both of the communicating parties able to terminate it. For Internet applications, each session is related to a particular **port**, a number that is associated with a particular upper layer application. For example, the **HTTP** program or daemon always has port number 80. The port numbers associated with the main Internet applications are referred to as **well-known port numbers**. Most port numbers, however, are available for dynamic assignment to other applications.

session cookie

See "transient cookie"

Session Initiation Protocol

The Session Initiation Protocol (SIP) is an Internet Engineering Task Force (**IETF**) standard **protocol** for initiating an interactive **user session** that involves **multimedia** elements such as video, voice, chat, gaming, and virtual reality.

Like **HTTP** or **SMTP**, SIP works in the **Application layer** of the Open Systems Interconnection (**OSI**) communications model. The Application layer is the level responsible for ensuring that communication is possible. SIP can establish multimedia sessions or **Internet telephony** calls, and modify, or terminate them. The protocol can also invite participants to **unicast** or **multicast** sessions that do not necessarily involve the initiator. Because the SIP supports name mapping and **redirection** services, it makes it possible for users to initiate and receive communications and services from any location, and for networks to identify the users whereever they are.

SIP is a request-response protocol, dealing with requests from clients and responses from servers. Participants are identified by *SIP URLs*. Requests can be sent through any transport protocol, such as **UDP**, SCTP, or **TCP**. SIP determines the end system to be used for the session, the communication media and media parameters, and the called party's desire to engage in the communication. Once these are assured, SIP establishes call parameters at either end of the communication, and handles call transfer and termination.

The Session Initiation Protocol is specified in IETF Request for Comments [**RFC**] 2543.

Session layer

In the Open Systems Interconnection (**OSI**) communications model, the Session layer (sometimes called the "port layer") manages the setting up and taking down of the association between two communicating end points that is called a *connection*. A connection is maintained while the two end points are communicating back and forth in a conversation or *session* of some duration. Some connections and sessions last only long enough to send a message in one direction. However, other sessions may last longer, usually with one or both of the communicating parties able to terminate it.

For Internet applications, each session is related to a particular **port**, a number that is associated with a particular upper layer application. For example, the HTTP program or daemon always has port number 80. The port numbers associated with the main Internet applications are referred to as *well-known port numbers*. Most port numbers, however, are available for dynamic assignment to other applications.

set

A set is a group or collection of objects or numbers, considered as an entity unto itself. Sets are usually symbolized by uppercase, italicized, boldface letters such as A, B, S, or Z. Each object or number in a set is called a member or element of the set. Examples include the set of all computers in the world, the set of all apples on a tree, and the set of all irrational numbers between 0 and 1.

When the elements of a set can be listed or denumerated, it is customary to enclose the list in curly brackets. Thus, for example, we might speak of the set (call it K) of all natural numbers between, and including, 5 and 10 as:

K = {5, 6, 7, 8, 9, 10}

A set can have any non-negative quantity of elements, ranging from none (the empty set or null set) to infinitely many. The number of elements in a set is called the cardinality, and can range from zero to denumerably infinite (for the sets of natural numbers, integers, or rational numbers) to non-denumerably infinite for the sets of irrational numbers, real numbers, imaginary numbers, or complex numbers).

The most basic relations in set theory can be summarized as follows.

- A set S_1 is a subset of set S if and only if every element of S_1 is also an element of S.

- A set S_1 is a proper subset of set S if and only if every element of S_1 is also an element of S, but there are some elements in S that are not elements of S_1.

- The intersection of two sets S and T is the set X of all elements x such that x is in S and x is in T.

- The union of two sets S and T is the set Y of all elements y such that y is in S or y is in T, or both.

Relationships between and among sets can be illustrated by means of a special type of drawing called a **Venn diagram**. The table below denotes common set symbology.

Set theory is fundamental to all of mathematics. In its "pure" form, set theory can be esoteric and even bizarre, and is primarily of interest to academics. However, set theory is closely connected with symbolic logic, and these fields are becoming increasingly relevant in software engineering, especially in the fields of **artificial intelligence** and communications security.

SYMBOL	MEANING	EXAMPLE
{}	is a set	S = {4, 5}
∈	is an element of	$S \in S$
∉	is not an element of	$S \notin T$
⊆	is a subset of	$S \subseteq T$
⊂	is a proper subset of	$S \subset T$
∪	union	$S \cup T$
∩	intersection	$S \cap T$
∅	the empty set	{2, 3, 4}∩ {5, 6, 7} =∅

set theory

See "set"

SETI

See "Search for Extraterrestrial Intelligence"

set-top box

A set-top box is a device that enables a television set to become a user interface to the Internet and also enables a television set to receive and decode digital television (**DTV**) broadcasts. DTV set-top boxes are sometimes called receivers. A set-top box is necessary to television viewers who wish to use their current analog television sets to receive digital broadcasts. It is estimated that 35 million homes will use digital set-top boxes by the end of 2006, the estimated year ending the transition to DTV.

In the Internet realm, a set-top box is really a specialized computer that can "talk to" the Internet—that is, it contains a Web **browser** (which is really a Hypertext Transfer Protocol client) and the Internet's main program, TCP/IP. The service to which the set-top box is attached may be through a telephone line as, for example, with **WebTV**, or through a **cable TV** company like TCI.

In the DTV realm, a typical digital set-top box contains one or more microprocessors for running the operating system, possibly **Linux** or **Windows CE**, and for **parsing** the **MPEG** transport stream. A set-top box also includes **random access memory**, an MPEG decoder chip, and more chips for audio decoding and processing. The contents of a set-top box depend on the DTV standard used. European

DVB-compliant set-top boxes contain parts to decode COFDM transmissions while ATSC-compliant set-top boxes contain parts to decode VSB transmissions. More sophisticated set-top boxes contain a hard drive for storing recorded television broadcasts, for downloaded software, and for other applications provided by your DTV service provider.

Digital television set-top boxes are used for satellite, cable, and terrestrial DTV services. They are especially important for terrestrial services because they guarantee viewers free television broadcasting. A set-top box price ranges from $100 for basic features to over $1,000 for a more sophisticated box. It is often leased as part of signing up for a service.

SFA

See "sales automation software"

SFF

See "small form factor"

SFP

See "small form-factor pluggable"

SFT III

SFT III is a feature providing fault-tolerance in Intel-based PC network **server** running Novell's **NetWare** operating system. SFT III allows two servers to mirror each other so that one server is always available in case the other one fails. (Novell doesn't say whether SFT is an abbreviation for something. However, "servers with fault-tolerance" seems to fit.) With SFT III, two servers, which can be in different geographical locations up to 40 kilometers apart, are connected by a high-speed data link through network interface cards (**NIC**). The relationship is one of peers. Either server can be taken offline for maintenance and upgrading while the other continues to run. Up to 1,000 users can be served.

Another fault-tolerant feature is that a redundant backup data link can be added. Novell calls the data link a Mirrored Server Link (MSL). A group of administrator can be notified if any system element fails. The NetWare Management System (NMS) provides a graphical map showing the SFT III servers and sends alert messages to a system console in the event of a failure.

SGF

See "Structured Graph Format"

SGFXML

See "Structured Graph Format"

SGML

SGML (Standard Generalized Markup Language) is a standard for how to specify a document **markup** language or tag set. Such a specification is itself a document type definition (**DTD**). SGML is not in itself a document language, but a description of how to specify one. It is **metadata**.

SGML is based on the idea that documents have structural and other semantic elements that can be described without reference to how such elements should be displayed. The actual display of such a document may vary, depending on the output medium and style preferences. Some advantages of documents based on SGML are:

- They can be created by thinking in terms of document structure rather than appearance characteristics (which may change over time).

- They will be more portable because an SGML compiler can interpret any document by reference to its document type definition (DTD).

- Documents originally intended for the print medium can easily be re-adapted for other media, such as the computer display screen.

The language that a Web browser uses, Hypertext Markup Language (**HTML**), is an example of an SGML-based language. There is a document type definition for HTML (and reading the HTML specification is effectively reading an expanded version of the document type definition).

SGML is based somewhat on earlier generalized markup languages developed at IBM, including General Markup Language (GML) and ISIL.

SGRAM

See "Synchronous Graphics RAM"

shadow password file

In the **Linux operating system**, a shadow password file is a system file in which **encryption** user **passwords** are stored so that they aren't available to people who try to break into the system. Ordinarily, user information, including passwords, is kept in a system file called /etc/passwd. The password for each user is stored in an encrypted form (some would call it an *encoded* form since it isn't really encrypted by the usual **algorithm**) that is created and used as follows:

1. The original password is encrypted (or encoded) by using a randomly-generated value or encryption **key** between 1 and 4096 and a one-way **hashing** function to arrive at the encoded password that is actually stored. Note that the stored result is not something that you can enter as a password itself.

2. The key (referred to as the *salt*) is stored with the encoded password. Note the key itself can't be used to decode the encrypted/encoded password because the encoding is one-way. You can't decode the result back into the original password by using the key.

3. When someone enters a password, their password is then rehashed with the salt value and compared with the encoded password value. If they match, the user is given access to the system.

In spite of encoding the password with a randomly-generated one-way hash function, a **cracker** could still break the system if they got access to the /etc/passwd file. Using an approach known as the *dictionary attack*, a cracker could methodically test each encoded password in the file against their dictionary of commonly-used passwords, each encoded 4096 different ways (to cover all the hash possibilities). Assuming that the system was lax in its password creation requirements and some user used one of the many commonly-used passwords, at least one password could be discovered. In Linux, this possibility can be foreclosed by simply moving the passwords in the /etc/passwd file to another file, usually named /etc/shadow and making this file readable only by those who have access to the system **root directory**. Using a shadow password file requires that the Linux system installer also install the optional Shadow Suite, which, like Linux, is open source software and available from a number of sites on the Web.

shadow RAM

Shadow RAM is a copy of basic input/output operating system (**BIOS**) routines from read-only memory (**ROM**) into a special area of random access memory (**RAM**) so that they can be accessed more quickly. Access in shadow RAM is typically in the 60-100 nanosecond range whereas ROM access is in the 125-250 ns range. In some operating systems such as **DOS**, certain BIOS routines are not only used during the **boot** or startup of the system, but also during normal operation, especially to drive the **video display terminal**. In Windows and OS/2, however, these routines are not used and the use of shadow RAM is not necessary. In some systems, the user can turn the use of shadow RAM off or on.

Shannon, Claude

See "Claude Shannon"

shared hosting

Shared hosting is **Web hosting** in which the service provider serves pages for multiple **Web site**s, each having its own Internet **domain name**, from a single **Web server**. Most Web hosting companies provide shared hosting. Although shared hosting is a less expensive way for businesses to create a Web presence, it is usually not sufficient for Web sites with high traffic. These sites need a dedicated Web server, either provided by a Web hosting service or maintained in-house.

shared memory

In computer programming, shared memory is a method by which program **processes** can exchange data more quickly than by reading and writing using the regular operating system services. For example, a **client** process may have data to pass to a **server** process that the server process is to modify and return to the client. Ordinarily, this would require the client writing to an output file (using the **buffer** of the operating system) and the server then reading that file as input from the buffer to its own work space. Using a designated area of shared memory, the data can be made directly accessible to both processes without having to use the system services. To put the data in shared memory, the client gets access to shared memory after checking a **semaphore** value, writes the data, and then resets the semaphore to signal to the server (which periodically checks shared memory for possible input) that data is waiting. In turn, the server process writes data back to the shared memory area, using the semaphore to indicate that data is ready to be read.

Other forms of interprocess communication (**IPC**) include **message queueing**, **semaphore**, and **sockets**.

shareware

Shareware is software that is distributed free on a trial basis with the understanding that the user may need or want to pay for it later. Some software developers offer a shareware version of their program with a built-in expiration date (after 30 days, the user can no longer get access to the program). Other shareware (sometimes called **liteware**) is offered with certain capabilities disabled as an enticement to buy the complete version of the program.

Freeware is programming that is offered at no cost. However, it is copyrighted so that you can't incorporate its programming into anything you may be developing. The least restrictive "no-cost" programs are uncopyrighted programs in the **public domain software**. These include a number of small UNIX programs. When reusing public domain software in your own programs, it's good to know the history of the program so that you can be sure it really is in the public domain.

Also see **Free Software Foundation** and **postcardware**.

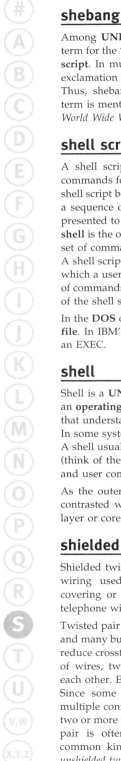

shebang

Among **UNIX shell** (user interface) users, a shebang is a term for the "#!" characters that must begin the first line of a **script**. In musical notation, a "#" is called a sharp and an exclamation point—"!"—is sometimes referred to as a bang. Thus, shebang becomes a shortening of sharp-bang. The term is mentioned in Elizabeth Castro's *Perl and CGI for the World Wide Web*.

shell script

A shell script is a text **file** that contains a sequence of commands for a **UNIX**-based **operating system**. It's called a shell script because it combines into a "script" in a single file a sequence of commands that would otherwise have to be presented to the system from a keyboard one at a time. The **shell** is the operating system's command interpreter and the set of commands you use to communicate with the system. A shell script is usually created for command sequences for which a user has a repeated need. You initiate the sequence of commands in the shell script by simply entering the name of the shell script on a command line.

In the **DOS** operating system, a shell script is called a **batch file**. In IBM's mainframe VM operating systems, it's called an EXEC.

shell

Shell is a **UNIX** term for the interactive user interface with an **operating system**. The shell is the layer of programming that understands and executes the commands a user enters. In some systems, the shell is called a **command interpreter**. A shell usually implies an interface with a command syntax (think of the DOS operating system and its "C:>" prompts and user commands such as "dir" and "edit").

As the outer layer of an operating system, a shell can be contrasted with the **kernel**, the operating system's inmost layer or core of services.

shielded twisted pair

Shielded twisted pair is a special kind of copper telephone wiring used in some business installations. An outer covering or shield is added to the ordinary twisted pair telephone wires; the shield functions as a ground.

Twisted pair is the ordinary copper wire that connects home and many business computers to the telephone company. To reduce crosstalk or electromagnetic induction between pairs of wires, two insulated copper wires are twisted around each other. Each signal on twisted pair requires both wires. Since some telephone sets or desktop locations require multiple connections, twisted pair is sometimes installed in two or more pairs, all within a single cable. Shielded twisted pair is often used in business installations. The more common kind of wire that is installed to your home is *unshielded twisted pair*.

Twisted pair is now frequently installed with two pairs to the home, with the extra pair making it possible for you to add another line (perhaps for modem use) when you need it.

Twisted pair comes with each pair uniquely color-coded when it is packaged in multiple pairs. Different uses such as **analog**, **digital**, and **Ethernet** require different pair multiples.

Although twisted pair is often associated with home use, a higher grade of twisted pair is often used for horizontal wiring in LAN installations because it is less expensive than **coaxial cable**.

The wire you buy at a local hardware store for extensions from your phone or computer modem to a wall jack is not twisted pair. It is a side-by-side wire known as *silver satin*. The wall jack can have as many five kinds of hole arrangements or **pinout**s, depending on the kinds of wire the installation expects will be plugged in (for example, digital, analog, or LAN). (That's why you may sometimes find when you carry your notebook computer to another location that the wall jack connections won't match your plug.)

Shimmer

Shimmer is the code name for the **beta test** version of the Lotus iNotes Web Access **client**. Shimmer is designed to allow users to access their **Domino**-based mail, calendar, schedule, to-do lists, contact lists, and notebooks from any computer, at any location, as long as they have an Internet connection. Shimmer is being promoted for its ability to allow users to interact with Web-enabled Domino applications by using a feature called "quicklinks," as well as for its ability to perform "data islanding," a feature that allows users to **download** "islands" (segments) of data at one time and minimize server contacts. Lotus iNotes Web Access is integrated with Sametime, Lotus's **instant messaging**, and offers offline support through Domino Off-Line Services (DOLS).

Shockwave

Shockwave, developed by Macromedia, is a family of **multimedia** players. Web users with Windows and Mac platforms can download the Shockwave players from the Macromedia site and use it to display and hear Shockwave files. Shockwave is especially popular for interactive games. However, Macromedia has identified over 2,000 sites that offer Shockwave files, including sites for General Motors, Nissan, Kodak, Microsoft, Intel and Apple. To create Shockwave files, you use Macromedia Director and several related programs.

shopping cart software

See "shopping cart"

shopping cart

On a Web site that sells products or services online, the shopping cart is a common metaphor (from the original grocery store shopping cart) for the catalog or other pages where a user reads and makes selections. Typically, the user checks off any products or services that are being ordered and then, when finished ordering, indicates that and proceeds to a page where the total order is placed and confirmed. The programming that provides a Web site with the ability to build a catalog and its associated **database** and to integrate pages into its site that provide users the ability to shop is known as *shopping cart software.*

A primary consideration when choosing shopping cart software is whether it will continue to serve a Web site's needs as its catalog and volume of orders grow.

Short Message Service

SMS (Short Message Service) is a service for sending messages of up to 160 characters to mobile phones that use Global System for Mobile (**GSM**) communication. GSM and SMS service is primarily available in Europe. SMS is similar to *paging.* However, SMS messages do not require the mobile phone to be active and within range and will be held for a number of days until the phone is active and within range. SMS messages are transmitted within the same **cell** or to anyone with **roaming service** capability. They can also be sent to digital phones from a Web site equipped with PC Link or from one digital phone to another. Typical uses of SMS include:

- Notifying a mobile phone owner of a voicemail message

- Notifying a salesperson of an inquiry and contact to call

- Notifying a doctor of a patient with an emergency problem

- Notifying a service person of the time and place of their next call

- Notifying a driver of the address of the next pickup

An *SMS gateway* is a Web site that lets you enter an SMS message to someone within the cell served by that gateway or that acts as an international gateway for users with roaming capability.

shortcut

In general, a shortcut is a path that is shorter than the usual or formal path to something or a method of operation that saves time over the regular operation. In Windows 95 and later **operating system**s, a shortcut is a computer **desktop icon** that enables a user to easily see and select a particular program or data object. The operating system comes with some shortcuts already visible on the desktop. A user can remove these or add new ones.

To create a shortcut in Windows 95 or 98, click on My Computer, then click on your "C" drive (or other drive where your files may be). Find the folder or file that you want to put on your desktop, click on it with the right mouse button, and select Create Shortcut from the pop-up menu. A new icon will now appear in My Computer. Hold the left mouse button down and drag the new icon to your desktop (you may need to minimize the My Computer window to do this). Now your new file or program will always be visible for quick selection on your desktop without having to go through Start menus or the Windows file manager.

In the Macintosh operating system, a shortcut is called an "alias."

shovelware

Shovelware is content taken from any source and put on the Web as fast as possible with little regard for appearance and usability.

.shtml

A Web file with the suffix of ".shtml" (rather than the usual ".htm") indicates a file that includes some information that will be added "on the fly" by the server before it is sent to you. A typical use is to include a "Last modified" date at the bottom of the page.

This **Hypertext Transfer Protocol** facility is referred to as a **server-side include**. (Although rarely done, the server administrator can identify some other file name suffix than ".shtml" as a server-side include file.) You can think of a server-side include as a limited form of **common gateway interface** application. In fact, the CGI is not used. The server simply searches the server-side include file for CGI environment variables, and inserts the variable information in the places in the file where the "include" statements have been inserted.

When creating a Web site, a good idea is to ask your server administrator which environment variables can be used and whether the administrator can arrange to set the server up so that these can be handled. Your server administrator should usually be able to help you insert the necessary include statements in an HTML file.

S-HTTP

Secure HTTP (S-HTTP) is an extension to the Hypertext Transfer Protocol (**Hypertext Transfer Protocol**) that allows the secure exchange of files on the World Wide Web. Each S-HTTP file is **encrypted** and/or contains a **digital certificate**. For a given document, S-HTTP is an option that is additional to another well-known security protocol, Secure Sockets Layer (**SSL**). A major difference is that S-HTTP allows the client to send a certificate to authenticate the user whereas, using SSL, only the server can be authenticated. S-HTTP is

more likely to be used in situations where the server represents a bank and requires authentication from the user that is more secure than a userid and password.

S-HTTP does not use any single encryption system, but it does support the **Rivest-Shamir-Adleman** public-and-private **key** encryption system. SSL works at a program layer slightly higher than the Transmission Control Protocol (**TCP**) level. S-HTTP works at the higher level of the HTTP application. Both security protocols can be used by a browser user, but only one can be used with a given document. Terisa Systems includes both SSL and S-HTTP in their Internet security tool kits.

S-HTTP has been submitted to the Internet Engineering Task Force (**IETF**) for consideration as a standard. Request for Comments (**Request for Comments**) Internet draft 2660 describes S-HTTP in detail.

SI

See "International System of Units"

sideband

In electronic **signal** transmission, a sideband is the portion of a modulated **carrier** wave that is either above or below the basic (**baseband**) signal. The portion above the baseband signal is the *upper sideband*; the portion below is the *lower sideband*. In regular amplitude modulation (**AM**) transmission, both sidebands are used to carry a message. In some forms of tranmission, one sideband is removed (*single-sideband transmission*) or a portion of one sideband is removed.

siemens

(Siemens AG is a German company engaged in electrical engineering and electronics.)

The siemens (symbolized S) is the International System of Units (**SI**) unit of electrical **conductance**. The archaic term for this unit is the mho (**ohm** spelled backwards). Siemens are also used, when multiplied by **imaginary number**s, to denote **susceptance** in alternating current (**AC**) and radio frequency (**RF**) applications. Reduced to base SI units, 1 S is the equivalent of one second cubed **ampere** squared per kilogram per meter squared ($1 \ s^3 \cdot A^2 \cdot kg^{-1} \cdot m^{-2}$). The siemens is also the equivalent of an ampere per **volt** (A/V).

In a direct current (**DC**) circuit, a component has a conductance of 1 S when a potential difference of one volt (1 V) produces a current of one ampere (1 A) through the component. Thus, one siemens is the equivalent of one ohm. But mathematically, **resistance** and **conductance** are reciprocals of each other. If R is the resistance of a component in ohms and G is the conductance in siemens,

$$R = 1 / G$$

and

$$G = 1 / R$$

In AC and RF circuits, conductive siemens behave the same as they do in DC circuits, provided the root-mean-square (**rms**) AC voltage is specified. In AC and RF circuits, susceptance exists only when there is a net capacitance or inductance. Capacitive susceptances have positive imaginary number values; inductive susceptances have negative imaginary-number values. The susceptance of a particular capacitor or inductor depends on the frequency.

Conductances and susceptances are sometimes expressed in units representing power-of-10 multiples or fractions of 1 S. A kilosiemens (1 kS) is equal to one thousand (10^3) siemens. A megasiemens (1 MS) is equal to one million (10^6) siemens. A millisiemens (1 mS) is equal to one-thousandth (10^{-3}) of a siemens. A microsiemens (1 µS) is equal to one-millionth (10^{-6}) of a siemens.

Also see **conductance**, **Ohm's Law**, **prefix multipliers**, **resistance**, **reactance**, **ohm**, and International System of Units (**SI**).

Signal Computing System Architecture

Signal Computing System Architecture (SCSA) is an industry standard architectural framework for the hardware and software components in a **computer-telephony integration** system. The framework has three layers:

- Applications, which control the media portion of a call (play, record, **voice recognition**, and other applications) and the call flow.

- The Software Model, which provides programming interfaces for manipulating the media portion of a call. This portion of the framework includes the SCSA Telephony Applications Objects (TAO) Framework. It also includes the call control framework and possible interfaces such as **Telephony Application Program Interface**, TSAPI, and JTAPI.

- The Hardware Model, consisting of one of two **bus** protocols, ANSI/VITA SCBus or ECTF H.100 CT Bus.

Both the Hardware Model and the Software Model layers can interface with intelligent **switch**, such as those used in the Advanced Intelligent Network (**AIN**), and with the Public Switched Telephone Network (**PSTN**) or the Internet.

shrinkwrapped software

Shrinkwrapped software is **software** that is packaged with a terms-and-conditions statement, ready for installation by the purchaser. Shrinkwrapped software may be sold on retail shelves, through the mail, or by direct selling; the significant point is that (1) it is generic rather than custom software you need to develop yourself or have someone develop for you, and (2) it is designed so that the purchaser can install it with relative ease rather than is depending on on-site assistance or extensive phone communication. The term refers to the plastic covering in which the box and the electronic storage media are enclosed and sealed.

The term is sometimes used metaphorically—that is, the software may not actually be shrinkwrapped, but it is sold as an independent, separate product and is designed for purchaser installation. Much of this kind of software is sold over the Web and received by downloading it electronically. Some shrinkwrapped software is usually preinstalled when you buy a computer. Almost all personal computer software and most small-business software is shrinkwrapped software. Shrinkwrapped software is often licensed so that multiple copies can be made and redistributed in enterprises.

signal

1) In electronics, a signal is an electric current or **electromagnetic field** used to convey data from one place to another. The simplest form of signal is a direct current (DC) that is switched on and off; this is the principle by which the early telegraph worked. More complex signals consist of an alternating-current (AC) or electromagnetic carrier that contains one or more data streams.

Data is superimposed on a carrier current or wave by means of a process called **modulation**. Signal modulation can be done in either of two main ways: **analog** and **digital**. In recent years, digital modulation has been getting more common, while analog modulation methods have been used less and less. There are still plenty of analog signals around, however, and they will probably never become totally extinct.

Except for DC signals such as telegraph and baseband, all signal carriers have a definable **frequency** or frequencies. Signals also have a property called **wavelength**, which is inversely proportional to the frequency.

2) In some information technology contexts, a signal is simply "that which is sent or received," thus including both the carrier (see 1) and the data together.

3) In telephony, a signal is special data that is used to set up or control communication. See **signaling**.

signaling

In telephony, signaling is the exchange of information between involved points in the network that sets up, controls, and terminates each telephone call. In **in-band signaling**, the signaling is on the same **channel** as the telephone call. In **out-of-band signaling**, signaling is on separate channels dedicated for the purpose.

Signaling System 7

On the public switched telephone network (**PSTN**), Signaling System 7 (SS7) is a system that puts the information required to set up and manage telephone calls in a separate network rather than within the same network that the telephone call is made on. Signaling information is in the form of **digital packet**s. SS7 uses what is called **out-of-**band signaling, meaning that **signaling** (control) information travels on a separate, dedicated 56 or 64 **Kbps** channel rather than within the same channel as the telephone call. Historically, the signaling for a telephone call has used the same voice circuit that the telephone call traveled on (this is known as **in-band signaling**). Using SS7, telephone calls can be set up more efficiently and with greater security. Special services such as call forwarding and **wireless roaming service** are easier to add and manage. SS7 is now an international telecommunications standard.

SS7 is used for these and other services:

- Setting up and managing the connection for a call
- Tearing down the connection when the call is complete
- Billing
- Managing call forwarding, calling party name and number display, three-way calling, and other Intelligent Network (**IN**) services
- Toll-free (800 and 888) and toll (900) calls
- Wireless as well as wireline call service including mobile telephone subscriber authentication, personal communication service (**PCS**), and roaming

SS7 messages contain such information as:

How should I route a call to 914 331-4985?

The route to network point 587 is crowded. Use this route only for calls of priority 2 or higher.

Subscriber so-and-so is a valid wireless subscriber. Continue with setting up the call.

Because control signals travel in a separate network from the call itself, it is more difficult for anyone to violate the security of the system. (See **2600** and **phreak** for cracking techniques that are defeated by SS7.)

The Integrated Services Digital Network (**ISDN**) also uses out-of-band signaling, extending it all the way to the end user on the ISDN **D-channel** while voice and data flow on B channels.

Briefly How It Works

SS7 consists of a set of reserved or dedicated **channels** known as *signaling links* and the network points that they interconnect. There are three kinds of network points (which are called *signaling points*): Service Switching Points (SSPs), Signal Transfer Points (STPs), and Service Control Points (SCPs). SSPs originate or terminate a call and communicate on the SS7 network with SCPs to determine how to route a call or set up and manage some special feature. Traffic on the SS7 network is routed by packet switches called STPs. SCPs and STPs are usually mated so that service can continue if one network point fails.

signal-to-noise ratio

In **analog** and **digital** communications, signal-to-noise ratio, often written S/N or SNR, is a measure of **signal** strength relative to background **noise**. The ratio is usually measured in decibels (dB).

If the incoming signal strength in microvolts is V_s, and the noise level, also in microvolts, is V_n, then the signal-to-noise ratio, S/N, in decibels is given by the formula

$$S/N = 20 \log_{10}(V_s/V_n)$$

If $V_s = V_n$, then S/N = 0. In this situation, the signal borders on unreadable, because the noise level severely competes with it. In digital communications, this will probably cause a reduction in data speed because of frequent errors that require the source (transmitting) computer or terminal to resend some packets of data.

Ideally, V_s is greater than V_n, so S/N is positive. As an example, suppose that V_s = 10.0 microvolts and V_n = 1.00 microvolt. Then

$$S/N = 20 \log_{10}(10.0) = 20.0 \text{ dB}$$

which results in the signal being clearly readable. If the signal is much weaker but still above the noise—say 1.30 microvolts—then

$$S/N = 20 \log_{10}(1.30) = 2.28 \text{ dB}$$

which is a marginal situation. There might be some reduction in data speed under these conditions.

If V_s is less than V_n, then S/N is negative. In this type of situation, reliable communication is generally not possible unless steps are taken to increase the signal level and/or decrease the noise level at the destination (receiving) computer or terminal.

Communications engineers always strive to maximize the S/N ratio. Traditionally, this has been done by using the narrowest possible receiving-system **bandwidth** consistent with the data speed desired. However, there are other methods. In some cases, **spread spectrum** techniques can improve system performance. The S/N ratio can be increased by providing the source with a higher level of signal output power if necessary. In some high-level systems such as radio telescopes, internal noise is minimized by lowering the temperature of the receiving circuitry to near absolute zero (-273 degrees Celsius or -459 degrees Fahrenheit). In **wireless** systems, it is always important to optimize the performance of the transmitting and receiving antennas.

signature file

A signature file is a short text file you create for use as a standard appendage at the end of your **e-mail** notes or **Usenet** messages. For example, you might include your full name, occupation or position, phone number, fax number, e-mail address, and the address of your Web site if you have one. Many people also include a favorite quote, company motto, or short personal statement.

Most e-mail and Usenet news facilities make it possible for you to either create the signature file as part of the application or to specify another file you've created with a word processor. Then, you tell the facility (usually in an "Options" menu) the name of your signature file and it automatically adds it to the note or message template it provides you.

significant figures

The term *significant figures* refers to the number of important single digits (0 through 9 inclusive) in the coefficient of an expression in **scientific notation**. The number of significant figures in an expression indicates the confidence or precision with which an engineer or scientist states a quantity.

The table shows several examples of numbers written in standard decimal notation (first column) and in scientific notation (second column). The third column shows the number of signficant figures in the corresponding expression in the second column.

Decimal expression	Scientific notation	Sig. figs.
1,222,000.00	1.222×10^6	4
	1.22200000×10^6	9
0.00003450000	3.45×10^{-5}	3
	3.450000×10^{-5}	7
$-9,876,543,210$	-9.87654×10^9	6
	-9.876543210×10^9	10
-0.0000000100	-1×10^{-8}	1
	-1.00×10^{-8}	3

Significant figures are arrived at by rounding off an expression after a calculation is executed. In any calculation, the number of significant figures in the solution must be equal to, or less than, the number of significant figures in the least precise expression or element. Consider the following product:

$$2.56 \times 10^{67} \times -8.33 \times 10^{-54}$$

To obtain the product of these two numbers, the coefficients are multiplied, and the powers of 10 are added. This produces the following result:

$$2.56 \times (-8.33) \times 10^{67+(-54)}$$
$$= 2.56 \times (-8.33) \times 10^{67-54}$$
$$= -21.3248 \times 10^{13}$$

The proper form of common scientific notation requires that the absolute value of the coefficient be larger than 1 and less than 10. Thus, the coefficient in the above expression should be divided by 10 and the power of 10 increased by one, giving:

$$-2.13248 \times 10^{14}$$

Because both multiplicands in the original product are specified to only three significant figures, a scientist or engineer will round off the final expression to three significant figures as well, yielding:

$$-2.13 \times 10^{14}$$

as the product.

Also see **order of magnitude** and **scientific notation**.

silence suppression

See "voice activation detection"

silicon

Silicon is a chemical element (its symbol in chemical formula expressions is "Si") that is present in sand and glass and which is the best known **semiconductor** material in electronic components. Its atomic number is 14. The most common isotope has atomic weight 28. In its pure state, silicon is a metal-like substance with an appearance and heft somewhat resembling aluminum. In its natural state, silicon appears bound up with other elements in the form of compounds. It is abundant in the crust of the earth.

Silicon conducts electricity to an extent that depends on the extent to which impurities are added. The addition of impurities to silicon, or to any semiconductor material, is called *doping*. Some impurities produce N-type silicon, in which the majority charge carriers are negatively charged **electron**s. Other impurities result in the production of P-type silicon, in which the majority charge carriers are positively charged **hole**s. Most silicon devices contain both N-type and P-type material.

Silicon is used in a wide variety of electronic and computer components, including:

- **Diode**s
- Light-emitting diodes(**LED**)
- Power-control devices
- Power supplies
- Switching systems
- Photodetectors
- **Bipolar transistor**s
- **Field-effect transistor**s
- **Integrated circuit**s

silicon cockroach

Silicon cockroach is a term invented by networking expert John Sidgmore to describe the tiny portable electronic devices that are expected to become popular in the next few years, creating new behavior patterns while putting new demands on network **bandwidth** capacity. Sidgmore's pervasive cockroaches are expected to multiply and become a significant driver of Internet growth with the average person carrying as many as five separate devices at a time

within a few years. Examples include not only smart phones, personal digital assistants (PDAs), and other handheld devices but also "smart" home appliances, computerized clothing, and other less visible sensors. Such devices may communicate locally with **Bluetooth RF** or with **infrared** wireless, or at some point be plugged into longer-range wireless or wired networks.

Silicon-on-Insulator

Silicon-On-Insulator (SOI) is a **semiconductor** fabrication technique developed by IBM that uses pure crystal **silicon** and silicon oxide for integrated circuits (**IC**s) and **microchips**. An SOI microchip processing speed is often 30% faster than today's complementary metal-oxide semiconductor (**CMOS**)-based chips and power consumption is reduced 80%, which makes them ideal for mobile devices. SOI chips also reduce the soft error rate, which is data corruption caused by cosmic rays and natural radioactive background signals.

A CMOS-based chip has impurities added to it, a process called "doping," that allows the chip to store an electrical charge called **capacitance**. In order to control the electrical currents needed, the capacitance must be discharged and recharged, which takes time and causes the **transistor**s on the chip to heat up. This production of heat limits the speed at which microchips can operate. For this reason, microchips have poor yield rates above 1 **GHz** and are not expected to attain future speeds above 5 GHz. SOI microchips are not doped with impurities, which eliminates much of the capacitance and allows an SOI microchip to operate faster and cooler.

When IBM began developing SOI chips, they found it difficult to bond the insulator layer of the chip, which was a non-crystal substance, to the pure crystal silicon layer. The SOI technology team tried using several different insulating materials, and found the most promising was sapphire; however, sapphire deteriorated easily. Then they discovered Separation by Implantation of Oxygen (SIMOX). SIMOX involves the direct injection of purified oxygen into the silicon wafer at an extremely high temperature. The oxygen bonds with the silicon and forms thin layers of silicon oxide. This layer of silicon oxide film is perfect enough that it bonds with the pure crystal silicon layer.

Currently, SOI chips are used in IBM's **AS/400** iSeries servers. The production of SOI chips requires minor restructuring of current fabrication methods and facilities allowing microchip manufacturers such as Intel or AMD to produce SOI chips with little extra cost. IBM expects SOI chips to replace current CMOS-based chips in consumer-oriented devices beginning in 2002.

SIMD

See "single instruction multiple data"

Simple API for XML

See "SAX"

Simple Mail Transfer Protocol

See "SMTP"

Simple Network Management Protocol

Simple Network Management Protocol (SNMP) is the **protocol** governing **network management** and the monitoring of network devices and their functions. It is not necessarily limited to **TCP/IP** networks.

SNMP is described formally in the Internet Engineering Task Force (**IETF**) Request for Comment (**RFC**) 1157 and in a number of other related RFCs.

Simple Object Access Protocol

Simple Object Access Protocol (SOAP) is a way for a program running in one kind of **operating system** (such as **Windows 2000**) to communicate with a progam in the same or another kind of an operating system (such as **Linux**) by using the World Wide Web's Hypertext Transfer Protocol (**HTTP**) and its Extensible Markup Language (**XML**) as the mechanisms for information exchange. Since Web **protocol**s are installed and available for use by all major operating system platforms, HTTP and XML provide an already at-hand solution to the problem of how programs running under different operating systems in a network can communicate with each other. SOAP specifies exactly how to encode an HTTP header and an XML file so that a program in one computer can call a program in another computer and pass it information. It also specifies how the called program can return a response.

SOAP was developed by Microsoft, DevelopMentor, and Userland Software and has been proposed as a standard interface to the Internet Engineering Task Force (**IETF**). It is somewhat similar to the Internet Inter-ORB Protocol (**IIOP**), a protocol that is part of the Common Object Request Broker Architecture (**CORBA**). Sun Microsystems' Remote Method Invocation (**RMI**) is a similar **client/server** interprogram protocol between programs written in **Java**.

An advantage of SOAP is that program calls are much more likely to get through **firewall** servers that screen out requests other than those for known applications (through the designated **port** mechanism). Since HTTP requests are usually allowed through firewalls, programs using SOAP to communicate can be sure that they can communicate with programs anywhere.

simplex

See "duplex"

simplicity

In information technology, simplicity is a quality that is frequently sought by both users and technologists, although, as users frequently attest, it is not always found. In programming, an **elegant** solution is sometimes one that addresses a need with surprising simplicity and efficiency. In the creation of the **user interface** to information technology, simplicity is usually one of several important objectives.

The desirability of simplicity is sometimes expressed as the **KISS Principle**.

Simula

Simula, short for "simulation language," was the first **object-oriented programming** language. In the late 1960s, the Norwegian developers of Simula, O. J. Dahl and Kristen Nygaard, were looking for a way for programs to simulate or model the world as computer users see it. They conceived the idea that programmers should model programs around **object**s rather than procedures. They also invented the idea of **class**es so that objects could be developed that shared similar characteristics. So that objects could communicate and make requests of each other, they conceived the simple notion of the **message**.

Simula led in turn to **Smalltalk**, **C++**, and **Java**.

simultaneous peripheral operations online

See "spool"

sine wave

See "waveform"

single in-line memory module

A SIMM is a module containing one or several random access **memory** (**RAM**) chips on a small circuit board with pins that connect to the computer **motherboard**. Since the more RAM your computer has, the less frequently it will need to access your secondary storage (for example, hard disk or CD-ROM), PC owners sometimes expand RAM by installing additional SIMMs. SIMMs typically come with a 32 data bit (36 bits counting **parity** bits) path to the computer that requires a 72-pin connector. SIMMs usually come in memory chip multiples of four megabytes.

The memory chips on a SIMM are typically dynamic RAM (**DRAM**) chips. An improved form of RAM called Synchronous DRAM (**SDRAM**) can also be used. Since SDRAM provides a 64 data bit path, it requires at least two SIMMs or a dual in-line memory module (**DIMM**).

single instruction multiple data

As one of the three performance enhancements of **MMX**, single instruction multiple data (**SIMD**) lets one microinstruction operate at the same time on multiple data items. This is especially productive for applications in which visual images or audio files are processed. What usually requires a repeated succession of instructions (a loop) can now be performed in one instruction. Intel offers the analogy of a drill sergeant issuing the order "About face" to an entire platoon rather than to each soldier, one at a time.

single mode fiber

In **optical fiber** technology, single mode fiber is optical fiber that is designed for the transmission of a single ray or mode of light as a carrier and is used for long-distance signal transmission. For short distances, **multimode fiber** is used.

Single mode fiber has a much smaller core than multimode fiber.

single signon

1) In any **client/server** relationship, single signon (pronounced SING-uhl SAIN-awn) is a session/user **authentication** process that permits a user to enter one name and password in order to access multiple applications. The single signon, which is requested at the initiation of the session, authenticates the user to access all the applications they have been given the rights to on the server, and eliminates future authentication prompts when the user switches applications during that particular session.

2) In e-commerce, the single signon (sometimes referred to as SSO) is designed to centralize consumer financial information on one **server**—not only for the consumer's convenience, but also to offer increased security by limiting the number of times the consumer enters credit card numbers or other sensitive information used in billing. Microsoft's "Passport" single signon service (averaging over 40 million consumers and more than 400 authentications per second) is an example of a growing trend towards the use of Web-based single signons that allow users to register financial information once, shop at multiple Web sites, and feel more confident about security on the Web.

single-electron memory

See also **phase-state low electron drive memory**.

Single-electron memory (SEM) refers to experimental hardware technologies in which the position or presence of a single charge carrier, usually an **electron**, makes the difference between the logical low (0) and high (1) states in a **digital** system. Primitive forms of SEM have been explored, and some engineers believe it is only a matter of time before it is put into use at the consumer level. When this happens, computer **memory** chips will have far greater capacity than

anything known today. There are various ways in which SEM might work. Two hypothetical schemes are outlined here:

SEM might be used to detect the presence or absence of electrical charges in individual **atom**s. If the number of electrons in an atom is the same as the number of protons (the normal or usual case), that atom has no electrical charge. If there are fewer electrons than protons, the atom acquires a positive charge; if there are more electrons than protons, the atom acquires a negative charge. Charged atoms are known as ions. The charge (or absence thereof) can be detected, and electronic circuits designed to act in different ways depending on whether a given atom is negative, neutral, or positive. In binary logic, a neutral or negative ion might represent a 0 (low) bit, and a positive ion might represent 1 (high). Ions can also represent the states of *trinary* logic. A negative ion can represent logic −1; a neutral ion can represent logic 0; a positive ion can represent logic +1. The contents of an ionic SEM chip could be changed by means of precisely directed electrical currents.

Another way in which SEM might operate involves the relative energy states of atoms depending on the positions, or orbits, of electrons within. Every atom has several different energy levels, called shells, at which electrons can exist. The shells resemble spheres surrounding the nucleus. The larger the diameter of the shell, the greater the energy contained in an electron orbiting in that shell. Low-energy shells in each atom of a given element might be assigned logic 0; high-energy shells could be assigned logic 1. An electron changes shells when a photon of a certain energy level (represented by a pulse of energy at a specific **wavelength**) is emitted or absorbed by the atom. When a photon having the correct wavelength is absorbed by the atom, the electron rises to a higher energy state; when the electron falls to a lower energy state, a photon of the same wavelength is emitted by the atom. The contents of such a memory could be changed using tiny electromagnetic pulses directed at specific atoms in a chip.

SIP

See "Session Initiation Protocol"

site

A Web site is a collection of Web files on a particular subject that includes a beginning file called a **home page**. For example, most companies, organizations, or individuals that have Web sites have a single address that they give you. This is their home page address. From the home page, you can get to all the other pages on their site. For example, the Web site for IBM has the home page address of http://www.ibm.com. (In this case, the actual file name of the home page file doesn't have to be included because IBM has named this file *index.html* and told the server that this address really means http://www.ibm.com/index.html.)

Since it sounds like geography is involved, a Web site is rather easily confused with a Web **server**. A server is a computer that holds the files for one or more sites. A very large Web site may reside on a number of servers that may be in different geographic locations. IBM is a good example; its Web site consists of thousands of files spread out over many servers in world-wide locations.

A synonym and less frequently used term for Web site is "Web presence." That term seems to better express the idea that a site is not tied to specific geographic location, but is "somewhere in cyberspace." However, "Web site" seems to be used much more frequently.

site map

A site map is a visual model of a Web site's content that allows the users to navigate through the site to find the information they are looking for, just as a traditional geographical map helps people find places they are looking for in the real world. An example of *information modeling technology*, a site map can be considered like an interactive table of contents, in which the listed items link directly to their counterpart sections of the Web site. Site maps perform the same service that the layout maps in large shopping malls perform: Without them, it is possible to explore a complex site by trial and error, but if you want to be sure to find what you're looking for, the most efficient way to do that is to consult a model of the resources available. If a Web site is small and uncomplicated, a site map may be unnecessary, just as a layout map may not be required for shoppers to find their way through small shopping malls.

Typically, site maps are organized hierarchically, breaking down the Web site's information into increasingly specific subject areas. There are a number of different types of site maps: *organizational chart* site maps are quite similar in appearance to a traditional table of contents; others, based on a perspective view of the site, are like a three dimensional model with individual pages upright, like index cards, arranged in sections and linked by lines. Structured Graph Format (SGF) site maps use an **XML** format language to describe Web site content, and a **Java** SGF viewer to interact with the data. There are a number of companies making site mapping products; generally, these don't require Web design skills—such as HTML or XML ability—on the part of the user. Popular site mapping products include TheBrain's SiteBrain, Inxight Software's Tree Studio, IBM's Java-based **Mappuccino**, and Dynamic Diagram's eponymous product. Site maps can also be created using more general Web site management tools, such as Visual Web, or Microsoft's Site Analyst.

sitelet

A sitelet is a small section of a **Web site** that has a special purpose and identity. In some cases, users are encouraged to link to a sitelet directly (rather than to come through the main Web site). A related term is **minisite**.

In Web advertising campaigns, a sitelet can be created for the duration of a campaign as the page that is linked to from a banner ad. The sitelet page can develop the campaign message more fully and immediately than if the user were linked to the main corporate or product site.

The term is also sometimes used for the temporary Web sites that are created for conventions, award presentations, or other events.

skin

On the Internet, a skin is a graphic or audio file used to change the appearance of the user interface to a program or for a game character. Skins can usually be downloaded at no charge from sites that provide them. The skin concept can be compared to the Xpress-On covers that snap to the front of the Nokia 3210 cell phone. These come in various colors and graphic designs such as Cyber Fish and Tribal Sign. The covers alter the appearance of the phone but not the phone itself. When using a skin, the appearance of the user interface changes, but not the functions available with the program.

Here are some examples:

- Macintosh enthusiasts can change the skin on their PC at work to make it look and sound like a Mac.

- Neoplanet changes the appearance of Microsoft's Internet Explorer browser.

- WindowBlinds from StarDock Systems changes the titlebar, the border, the buttons, the taskbar, and other aspects of the Windows 95/98/NT desktop interface.

- Winamp is a media player for Windows 95, 98 and NT for which you can select from over 3,000 skins. A Winamp skin changes the appearance of the cover, the antenna, the display, the fonts, the number pad, the beeping tones, and other aspects.

- Games such as Quake, Hexen, and Heretic use skins to change the appearance of game characters. Using a skin in a game gives you an edge because you are not easily recognized.

- Skins are available for the popular chat program **ICQ**.

You can download skins from a number of sites that specialize in skins. They come in high-color (for systems that support more than 256 colors) and low-color (256 colors or less). Most skin sites offer **template**s and instructions for creating your own skin. You need a good graphics editor such as Photoshop or Paint Shop Pro and a **render**ing program such as Macromedia's Extreme 3D to create 3-dimensional models. If you create a skin, you can share it by uploading it to a skin site.

skin effect

Skin effect is a tendency for alternating current (**AC**) to flow mostly near the outer surface of a solid electrical conductor, such as metal wire, at frequencies above the audio range. The effect becomes more and more apparent as the frequency increases.

The main problem with skin effect is that it increases the effective **resistance** of a wire for AC at moderate to high frequencies, compared with the resistance of the same wire at direct current (**DC**) and low AC frequencies. The effect is most pronounced in radio-frequency (**RF**) systems, especially **antenna**s and transmission lines. But it can also affect the performance of high-fidelity sound equipment by causing attenuation in the treble range (the highest-pitched components of the audio).

Skin effect can be reduced by using stranded rather than solid wire. This increases the effective surface area of the wire for a given **wire gauge**. Tinned wire should be avoided because tin has higher resistance than copper. In large RF antenna arrays, hollow tubing can be used in place of solid rods with little or no loss of efficiency; in this respect, skin effect is an asset. It also works in favor of the use of copper-clad steel wire for more modest antennas. Such wire is mechanically stronger than solid or stranded copper, because steel has a higher tensile strength than copper. The skin effect causes most of the current to flow through the copper cladding, which is a better electrical conductor than steel.

Skin effect occurs with brief pulses of **current**, for the same reasons it occurs at high AC frequencies. This can save lives. If you are caught in a thundershower, you can take refuge in a car or other metal vehicle and be relatively safe even if you suffer a direct hit. The skin effect causes virtually all of the current to flow on the outside of the vehicle as it passes from cloud to ground.

SKU

SKU (stockkeeping unit, sometimes spelled "Sku") is an identification, usually alphanumeric, of a particular product that allows it to be tracked for inventory purposes. Typically, an SKU (pronounced with the individual letters or as SKYEW) is associated with any purchasable item in a store or catalog. For example, a woman's blouse of a particular style and size might have an SKU of "3726-8," meaning "Style 3726, size 8." The SKU identification for a product may or may not be made visible to a customer. SKU numbers can sometimes be seen in online **e-commerce** sites.

An SKU is not the same as a product model number from a manufacturer, although the model number could form all or part of the SKU. The SKU is established by the merchant.

skunkworks

A skunkworks is a group of people who, in order to achieve unusual results, work on a project in a way that is outside the usual rules. A skunkworks is often a small team that assumes or is given responsibility for developing something in a short time with minimal management constraints. Typically, a skunkworks has a small number of members in order to reduce communications overhead. A skunkworks is sometimes used to spearhead a product design that thereafter will be developed according to the usual process. A skunkworks project may be secret.

As for the term's origin, we like what Harry Newton says in *Newton's Telecom Dictionary*:

"Term for usually-secret high-pressure/high-tech research group in a company or government, often populated by people who don't see much sunlight or soap. Hence the name, skunkworks."

The name of the animal itself was derived by early American settlers from the Algonquin Indian *seganku*.

skuzzy

See "SCSI"

SLA

See "Service Level Agreement"

slamming

Slamming is the practice by some U.S. long-distance phone carriers of switching users to their service without the user's knowledge or authorization. Southwestern Bell, a local carrier, reports that they received calls about slamming from 558,000 customers in 1997. Slamming methods include "free trials" and offers for credit cards that offer prize or give-away points for each dollar of charges from a given carrier. Phone solicitors often get "approval" from children, baby-sitters, and domestic employees. Occasionally, your carrier may be switched if your current carrier has been sold to another company. If your carrier is switched, there may be a $5-6 switching charge on your bill. Unless you agreed to the switch, you do not have to pay the charge.

You can find out who your current long-distance carrier is by calling 700-555-4141, toll-free.

Slashdot Effect

The Slashdot Effect is the sudden, relatively temporary surge in traffic to a **Web site** that occurs when a high-traffic Web site or other source posts a story that refers visitors to another Web site. The effect gets its name from the Slashdot Web site, which provides content about **Linux** and related software, and sometimes features news about other related but less-traveled sites. However, the effect can be perceived when any large Web site posts a high-interest, widely-

publicized story, about another site. The effect is obviously much more noticeable on smaller sites and the surge in traffic sometimes will slow a site down or make it impossible to reach.

Slashdot, the Web site, is named, according to Slashdot originator Jeff "Hemos" Bates, as "a play on how terrible it is to say domain names out loud." In this case: h-t-t-p-colon-slash-slash-slash-dot-dot-o-r-g

SLD

See "second-level domain"

slice and dice

To slice and dice is to break a body of information down into smaller parts or to examine it from different viewpoints so that you can understand it better. In cooking, you can slice a vegetable or other food or you can dice it (which means to break it down into small cubes). One approach to dicing is to first slice and then cut the slices up into dices. In data analysis, the term generally implies a systematic reduction of a body of data into smaller parts or views that will yield more information. The term is also used to mean the presentation of information in a variety of different and useful ways.

This term can be compared to **drilldown**, which is the process of dividing an information area up into finer and finer layers in a hierarchy, but with the purpose of narrowing in to one small area or item.

sliding windows

Sliding windows, a technique also known as *windowing*, is used by the Internet's Transmission Control Protocol (**TCP**) as a method of controlling the flow of **packet**s between two computers or network hosts. TCP requires that all transmitted data be acknowledged by the receiving host. Sliding windows is a method by which multiple packets of data can be affirmed with a single acknowledgment.

TCP includes a memory **buffer** that sits between the upper application **layer** (for example, **Hypertext Transfer Protocol** or **File Transfer Protocol**) and the lower layer that receives data (the **Data Link layer** in the **OSI** reference model). The buffer allows TCP to receive and process data independently of the upper application. In other words, TCP can use this buffer space to "read ahead" while the upper application processes the data at its own pace.

Window "announcements" are sent by the receiving system to the transmitting system in order to acknowledge data receipt as well as to inform the transmitting system of the current buffer size. For example, if a window size of zero is reported, the transmitting system must wait for an acknowledgment before sending the next chunk of data. If the receiving system reports that the buffer size is larger than the size of a single data packet, the transmitting system

knows that it can send multiple chunks of data before waiting for an acknowledgment. Transmitting multiple data packets between acknowledgments allows the data to be transferred faster and more efficiently than if an acknowledgment must be received prior to each transmission.

You can find out more about TCP by reading Request for Comment (**RFC**) 793 and 1180.

SLIP

See "Serial Line Internet Protocol"

slot

In computers, a slot, or *expansion slot*, is an engineered technique for adding capability to a computer in the form of connection pinholes (typically, in the range of 16 to 64 closely-spaced holes) and a place to fit an expansion **card** containing the circuitry that provides some specialized capability, such as video acceleration, sound, or disk drive control.

Almost all desktop computers come with a set of expansion slots. These help ensure that you'll be able to add new hardware capabilities in the future.

Slot 1

Slot 1 and Slot 2 are names for the way Intel P6-based **microprocessor**s connect to a computer **motherboard** so that it makes contact with the built-in paths called the data **bus**. Slot 1 and Slot 2 were developed by Intel as a replacement for its Zero Insertion Force (**ZIF**) sockets, the most familiar of which is Socket 7 for Intel's **Pentium** processors. For the Pentium II, which is based on Intel's P6 micro architecture, Intel switched to the Slot 1 configuration. With the slot approach, the microprocessor is packaged in a cartridge, known as a Single Edge Cartridge, that is easily inserted into a slot designed into the motherboard. The new approach will make connection to the faster and larger number of data paths in future processors more feasible.

Officially, Intel now refers to Slot 1 as the 242-contact slot connector and Slot 2 as the 330-contact slot connector. Besides the Pentium II, Intel's **Celeron** processor also uses the Slot 1 configuration. Intel's high-end Pentium II **Xeon** processor uses the Slot 2 configuration. Intel is said to be developing a Slot M.

Since the motherboards are different, computer owners with Socket 7 Pentiums will not be able to upgrade to the newer P6 Pentiums with Slot 1 and Slot 2 configurations. and **Cyrix**, which offer processors that compete with the Pentium II, say they plan to continue using the Socket 7 motherboard.

slot time

In **Ethernet** and its Carrier Sense Multiple Access/Collision Detect (**CSMA/CD**) approach to managing which device can use the communication link next, slot time is the amount of time a device waits after a **collision** before retransmitting. The transmitting device determines the appropriate amount of slot time by adding the amount of time it took for another device to detect a collision, the amount of time it took for the device to notify the original transmitting device of the collision, and the amount of time it took to transmit a **jam** sequence. Should a second collision occur, the device doubles the slot time in an effort to avoid future collisions; this process is called "backoff." In **half-duplex** Ethernet, where data can only travel in one direction at once, slot time becomes an important parameter in determining the how many devices can share a network.

Small Business Extensible Markup Language (SMBXML)

SMBXML (Small Business Extensible Markup Language) is an **open**, **XML**-based standard, designed especially for use by small and medium-sized businesses, that describes a data exchange format for use in common business applications.

The SMBXML package includes elements intended primarily for transactions and recordkeeping. Examples include sales records, purchasing records, payroll, tax records, and general banking. Currency exchange rates can be calculated, and conversions can be made, allowing SMBXML to be used in international business operations. The standard can also be applied to general databases, such as employee shift scheduling, vacation scheduling, sick time, and so forth.

SMBXML is compatible with most Internet transport and security protocols. Data can be exchanged between consenting parties provided integration agreements are signed.

Small Computer System Interface

See "SCSI"

small form factor

Small form factor (SFF) refers to any of several physically compact **connector** designs that have been developed for use in **fiber optic** systems. They are about half the size of conventional connectors. Currently there are at least three designs: the LC by Lucent, the VF-45 by 3M, and the MT-RJ by Tyco.

The main motivator for the development of SFF connectors is an ongoing demand for smaller components in network systems. Using SFF connectors, it is possible to get many more interfaces on a single **card**. In addition, the use of connectors, rather than direct soldering, increases the flexibility and versatility of network systems, and makes it easier and less expensive to maintain them.

The fact that there are several SFF connector configurations allows the use of products from multiple sources. An argument has been made for standardization, but individual connector makers have so far resisted this idea, preferring instead to develop and promote their own connector designs.

SFF connectors are used with **transceiver**s called small-form-factor pluggable (**SFP**) modules. This design has been called a miniature gigabit interface converter (**GBIC**).

Also see small-form-factor pluggable (**SFP**) and gigabit interface converter (**GBIC**).

small form-factor pluggable

Small form-factor pluggable (SFP) is a specification for a new generation of optical modular **transceiver**s. The devices are designed for use with small form factor (**SFF**) connectors, and offer high speed and physical compactness. They are **hot-swap**pable.

SFP transceivers are expected to perform at data speeds of up to five gigabits per second (5 **Gbps**), and possibly higher. Because SFP modules can be easily interchanged, electro-optical or **fiber optic** networks can be upgraded and maintained more conveniently than has been the case with traditional soldered-in modules. Rather than replacing an entire circuit board containing several soldered-in modules, a single module can be removed and replaced for repair or upgrading. This can result in a substantial cost savings, both in maintenance and in upgrading efforts.

Several companies have formed a consortium supporting the use of SFP transceivers to meet their common objectives of broad **bandwidth**, small physical size and mass, and ease of removal and replacement.

Also see small form factor (**SFF**) and gigabit interface converter (**GBIC**).

Small Office Home Office

See "SOHO"

small to medium enterprise

1) SME (small-to-medium enterprise) is a convenient term for segmenting businesses and other organizations that are somewhere between the "small office-home office" (**SOHO**) size and the larger **enterprise**. The European Union has defined an SME as a legally independent company with no more than 500 employees.

2) SME also stands for the Society of Manufacturing Engineers.

Smalltalk

Smalltalk is a programming language that was designed expressly to support the concepts of **object-oriented programming**. In the early 1970s, Alan Kay led a team of researchers at Xerox to invent a language that let programmers envision the data objects they intended to manipulate. Unlike **C++**, Smalltalk was not built on the syntax of a procedural language; it is a "pure" object-oriented language with more rigorously enforced rules than C++, which permits some of the procedural constructs of the **C** language.

Although Smalltalk may continue to attract a loyal following, **Java**, a derivative of C++ designed for distributed systems, has become the most prevalent object-oriented language on the Web.

small-unit metric system

The small-unit metric system (or more formally, the *centimeter-gram-second (cgs) system of units*) is based on three fundamental units: The **centimeter** (cm), which quantifies **displacement**, the **gram** (g), which quantifies **mass**, and the **second** (s or sec), which quantifies **time**.

The small-unit metric system is so-called because one centimeter is equal to 0.01 meter (10^{-2} m), and one gram is equal to 0.001 kilogram (10^{-3} kg). The cgs system, like the **metric system**, was originally developed by scientists who were frustrated with the English (foot-pound-second) system. The cgs and metric system units of displacement and mass lend themselves neatly to calculations in scientific notation, while English units generally do not. Time remains somewhat messy in all systems; there are 60 seconds in a minute, 60 minutes in an hour, and 24 hours in a mean solar day.

The International System of Units (**SI**) has officially supplanted the small-unit metric system (as well as the metric system). But it is good to have passing familiarity with the small-unit metric system, because that scheme is still used by some astronomers and physicists, and many older scientific books and papers were written with a preference for it. Today's SI system provides formal definitions for the **meter**, the **kilogram**, and the **second**, and also specifies and defines four additional units: The **kelvin** for temperature, the **ampere** for electric current, the **candela** for luminous intensity, and the **mole** for material quantity.

Compare **metric system**, **English system of units**, and International System of Units (**SI**). Also see **prefix multipliers**.

smart building

See "smart home or building"

smart card

A smart card is a plastic card about the size of a credit card, with an embedded **microchip** that can be loaded with data, used for telephone calling, electronic cash payments, and other applications, and then periodically refreshed for additional use. Currently or soon, you may be able to use a smart card to:

- Dial a connection on a mobile telephone and be charged on a per-call basis
- Establish your identity when logging on to an Internet access provider or to an online bank
- Pay for parking at parking meters or to get on subways, trains, or buses
- Give hospitals or doctors personal data without filling out a form
- Make small purchases at electronic stores on the Web (a kind of cybercash)
- Buy gasoline at a gasoline station

Over a billion smart cards are already in use. Currently, Europe is the region where they are most used. Ovum, a research firm, predicts that 2.7 billion smart cards will be shipped annually by 2003. Another study forecasts a $26.5 billion market for recharging smart cards by 2005. Compaq and Hewlett-Packard are reportedly working on keyboards that include smart card slots that can be read like bank credit cards. The hardware for making the cards and the devices that can read them is currently made principally by Bull, Gemplus, and Schlumberger.

How Smart Cards Work

A smart card contains more information than a magnetic stripe card and it can be programmed for different applications. Some cards can contain programming and data to support multiple applications and some can be updated to add new applications after they are issued. Smart cards can be designed to be inserted into a slot and read by a special reader or to be read at a distance, such as at a toll booth. Cards can be disposable (as at a trade-show) or reloadable (for most applications).

An industry standard interface between programming and PC hardware in a smart card has been defined by the PC/SC Working Group, representing Microsoft, IBM, Bull, Schlumberger, and other interested companies. Another standard is called OpenCard. There are two leading smart card operating systems: JavaCard and **MULTOS**.

smart frame

See "digital photo album"

smart home or building

A smart home or building is a home or building, usually a new one, that is equipped with special structured wiring to enable occupants to remotely control or program an array of automated home electronic devices by entering a single command. For example, a homeowner on vacation can use a Touchtone phone to arm a home security system, control temperature gauges, switch appliances on or off, control lighting, program a home theater or entertainment system, and perform many other tasks.

The field of home automation is expanding rapidly as electronic technologies converge. The home network encompasses communications, entertainment, security, convenience, and information systems.

A technology known as Powerline Carrier Systems (PCS) is used to send coded signals along a home's existing electric wiring to programmable switches, or outlets. These signals convey commands that correspond to "addresses" or locations of specific devices, and that control how and when those devices operate. A PCS transmitter, for instance, can send a signal along a home's wiring, and a receiver plugged into any electric outlet in the home could receive that signal and operate the appliance to which it is attached.

One common protocol for PCS is known as **X10**, a signaling technique for remotely controlling any device plugged into an electrical power line. X10 signals, which involve short radio frequency (**RF**) bursts that represent digital information, enable communication between transmitters and receivers.

In Europe, technology to equip homes with smart devices centers on development of the European Installation Bus, or **Instabus**. This embedded control protocol for digital communication between smart devices consists of a two-wire **bus** line that is installed along with normal electrical wiring. The Instabus line links all appliances to a decentralized communication system and functions like a telephone line over which appliances can be controlled. The European Installation Bus Association is part of Konnex, an association that aims to standardize home and building networks in Europe.

Echelon Corp., the creator of the LonWorks system, is helping drive adoption of an open interoperability standard among vendors in the control networks industry. LonWorks is an open standard for network automation and control for the building, transportation, industrial and home markets. The American National Standards Institute (**ANSI**) has adopted the protocol underlying LonWorks control networks as an industry standard. The LonMark Interoperability Association is made up of more than 200 controls companies mission working on standard to integrate multi-vendor systems based on LonWorks networks.

smart matter

Smart matter is another term for micro-electromechanical systems (MEMS), a technology that combines computers with tiny mechanical devices such as sensors, valves, gears, mirrors, and actuators imbedded in semiconductor chips. Paul Saffo of the Institute for the Future in Palo Alto, California, believes MEMS or what he calls **analog computing** will be "the foundational technology of the next decade."

MEMS are already used as accelerometers in automobile airbags. They've replaced a less reliable device at lower cost and show promise of being able to inflate a bag not only on the basis of sensed deceleration but also on the basis of the size of the person they are protecting. Basically, a MEMS device contains micro-circuitry on a tiny silicon chip into which some mechanical device such as a mirror or a sensor has been manufactured. Potentially, such chips can be built in large quantities at low cost, making them cost-effective for many uses.

Among the presently available uses of MEMS or those under study are:

- Global position system sensors that can be included with courier parcels for constant tracking and that can also sense parcel treatment en route

- Sensors built into the fabric of an airplane wing so that it can sense and react to air flow by changing the wing surface resistance; effectively creating a myriad of tiny wing flaps

- Optical switching devices that can switch light signals over different paths at 20-nanosecond switching speeds

- Sensor-driven heating and cooling systems that dramatically improve energy savings

- Building supports with imbedded sensors that can alter the flexibility properties of a material based on atmospheric stress sensing

Saffo distinguishes between sensor-effector type micro-computing (which he calls "MEMS") and micro-devices containing gears, mirrors, valves, and other parts (which he calls "micro-machines").

Much support for MEMS has come from **Defense Advanced Research Projects Agency** Research and Development Electronics Technology Office.

smart tag

See "Smart Tags"

Smart Tags

Microsoft's Smart Tags were a proposed feature of **Windows XP** that would allow Microsoft and its partners to insert their own **links** into any Web page viewed through its **Internet Explorer browser**. These links (which appear as purple dashed underlining, to differentiate them from original

content links) are similar to traditional **hyperlinks**, but more complex and interactive: when the **cursor** hovers over a Smart Tagged word, a drop-down list appears with a selection of links related to the word. A number of companies are developing industry or application-specific Smart Tag libraries—for example, for the insurance industry or for medical applications. A Microsoft partner, Keylogix, has an application called *ActiveDocs* Smart Tags that allows end users to create their own Smart Tags from within Microsoft Word.

Although Microsoft may not include Smart Tags as part of XP, they have a version of them available for free download, *Smart Tags for the Everyday Web*. This Smart Tags application is compatible with Internet Explorer 6 and requires 200 KB of free disk space.

How Smart Tags work: Someone reading a sports article moves their cursor over a Smart Tag on the name of a particular baseball team. A drop-down list appears with a selection of links—such as current standings, official web site, and related news, for example; when the user clicks a link in the list they are taken to that Web page. A button on the toolbar turns the Smart Tag option on and off.

Although Smart Tag technology has a lot of potential for helping the Web develop its interactive potential, the corporate background has made many Web site developers leery of less benign possibilities. Because the tagged words and associated links are selected by Microsoft, many Web content creators and site owners are very concerned about Smart Tag implementation, which they fear would allow Microsoft to have editorial control of their work. As an example, an anti-Microsoft rant on a Web page might have a lot less impact if links took the reader to pro-Microsoft pages. In response to the outcry against Smart Tags, Microsoft has made them available to Internet Explorer users who want them—but not an integral part of their new operating systems—and created a **meta tag** that allows developers to disable Internet Explorer-added Smart Tags for their Web pages.

SmartDownload

Netscape's SmartDownload is a free software program that allows a user to pause, stop, and resume a file **download** without losing any data. If the user choses to stop the download or if a dial-up connection terminates unexpectedly, the SmartDownload client takes advantage of the Multichannel Protocol Plus (MP+) capability of most Web servers to determine that the "resume call" should be added to the existing session.

AOL, the owner of **Netscape**, whose SmartDownload application is compatible with other browsers including **Internet Explorer**, has been criticized for using the application to gather data and create a **user profile** without the user's knowledge. It is speculated that disputes over the legality of these user profiles could have ramifications for

other disputes, including those involving the music industry, whose copyright lawyers would like to be able to locate individual users who are violating the law.

smartphone

The term smartphone is sometimes used to characterize a wireless telephone set with special computer-enabled features not previously associated with telephones.

In addition to functioning as an ordinary telephone, a smartphone's features may include:

- Wireless e-mail, Internet, Web browsing, and fax
- Intercom function
- Personal information management
- Online banking
- LAN connectivity
- Graffiti style data entry
- Local data transfer between phone set and computers
- Remote data transfer between phone set and computers
- Remote control of computers
- Remote control of home or business electronic systems
- Interactivity with **unified messaging**

SMB protocol

See "Server Message Block Protocol"

SMBXML

See "Small Business Extensible Markup Language (SMBXML)"

SMDS

SMDS (Switched Multimegabit Data Service) is a public, **packet**-switched service aimed at enterprises that need to exchange large amounts of data with other enterprises over the wide-area network on a nonconstant or "bursty" basis. SMDS provides an architecture for this kind of data exchange and a set of services. In general, SMDS extends the performance and efficiencies of a company's local area network (LANs) over a wide area on a switched, as-needed basis.

SMDS is connectionless, meaning that there is no need to set up a connection through the network before sending data. This provides bandwidth on demand for the "bursty" data transmission typically found on LANs.

SMDS packets contain up to 7168 bytes of data, which is large enough to accept the most common LAN packets. Each packet includes the source address and the destination address and is sent separately from other packets.

Each enterprise using SMDS is assigned from one to sixteen unique SMDS addresses, depending on needs. An address is a ten digit number that looks like an ordinary telephone number.

SMDS also provides for broadcasting packets to multiple SMDS addresses. Each SMDS company is assigned one or more group addresses that can be used to define destination groups. Group addressing is similar to LAN multicasting. It lets routing protocols, such as TCP/IP, use dynamic address resolution and routing updates.

Since SMDS is a public service, any SMDS customer can exchange data with any other customer. The SMDS Interest Group, an association of service providers, equipment manufacturers, and users, develops technical specifications, promotes awareness of SMDS, stimulates new applications, and ensures worldwide service interoperability, working with its international affiliates. Their home page provides a list of companies providing SMDS services.

SME

See "small to medium enterprise"

SMF

The SMF (Standard MIDI File) was developed to allow musicians and audio file developers to transfer their sequenced **MIDI** data from one software application to another. This file format lets users exchange music and data without regard to computer **operating system** platform. Today, there are many Web sites devoted to the sale and exchange of music data in the Standard MIDI File format.

There are two variations of the Standard MIDI File format, called Type 0 and Type 1. Both variations contain the same data, but the arrangement of the data within the file is different. Type 0 is a single track of data; Type 1 is multi-track. Many of the popular sequencing software packages available can import and export either type of file.

In the Type 0 Standard MIDI File, all data is saved to a single track without regard to its MIDI channel reference. The file plays normally, but accessing the individual components is a bit more difficult. If editing is needed, the user can open the Standard MIDI File in the application of choice and copy/paste individual channels of information manually as needed.

A Type 1 Standard MIDI File outputs a separate track for each MIDI channel in the original sequence. This format greatly simplifies editing once the sequence has been transferred from one sequencer to another.

SMIL

SMIL (Synchronized Multimedia Integration Language), is a language that allows Web site creators to be able to easily define and synchronize multimedia elements (video, sound, still images) for Web presentation and interaction. On today's Web, although you can send moving and still images and sound to a Web user, each element is separate from the others and can't be coordinated with other elements without elaborate programming. SMIL (pronounced "smile") lets site creators send multiple movies, still images, and sound separately but coordinate their timing. Each media object is accessed with a unique Uniform Resource Locator (**URL**) which means that presentations can be made of objects arriving from more than one place and that objects can easily be reused in multiple presentations.

SMIL also lets the "producer" store a media object in multiple versions, each with a different **bandwidth** so that a lower-bandwidth version of a Web page can be sent to users who need it. SMIL also accommodates multiple language versions of soundtracks.

SMIL statements are simple and can be entered with a text editor similar to those used to create Hypertext Markup Language (**HTML**) pages. A presentation can be described using only three Extensible Markup Language (**XML**) elements. It's intended that SMIL will be usable by anyone who can use HTML.

SMIL was developed by a group coordinated by the World Wide Web Consortium (**W3C**) and included representatives from the CD-ROM, interactive television, Web, and audio/video streaming industries. The first public draft of SMIL was released in November, 1997.

smiley

See "emoticon"

SMP

SMP (symmetric multiprocessing) is the processing of **program**s by multiple **processor**s that share a common **operating system** and **memory**. In symmetric (or "tightly coupled") multiprocessing, the processors share memory and the I/O **bus** or data path. A single copy of the **operating system** is in charge of all the processors. SMP, also known as a "shared everything" system, does not usually exceed 16 processors.

SMP systems are considered better than MPP systems for online transaction processing (**OTP**) in which many users access the same database in a relatively simple set of transactions. An advantage of SMP for this purpose is the ability to dynamically balance the workload among computers (and as a result serve more users faster).

SMR

See "Specialized Mobile Radio"

SMS

See "Short Message Service"

SMTP

SMTP (Simple Mail Transfer Protocol) is a **TCP/IP protocol** used in sending and receiving e-mail. However, since it's limited in its ability to **queue** messages at the receiving end, it's usually used with one of two other protocols, **POP3** or **Internet Message Access Protocol**, that let the user save messages in a server mailbox and download them periodically from the server. In other words, users typically use a program that uses SMTP for sending e-mail and either POP3 or IMAP for receiving messages that have been received for them at their local server. Most mail programs such as Eudora let you specify both an SMTP server and a POP server. On **UNIX**-based systems, **sendmail** is the most widely-used SMTP server for e-mail. A commercial package, Sendmail, includes a POP3 server and also comes in a version for **Windows NT**.

SMTP usually is implemented to operate over **Transmission Control Protocol port** 25. The details of SMTP are in **Request for Comments** 821 of the Internet Engineering Task Force (**IETF**). An alternative to SMTP that is widely used in Europe is **X.400**.

smurfing

Smurfing is the attacking of a network by exploiting Internet Protocol (**IP**) broadcast addressing and certain other aspects of Internet operation. Smurfing uses a program called Smurf and similar programs to cause the attacked part of a network to become inoperable. The exploit of smurfing, as it has come to be known, takes advantage of certain known characteristics of the Internet Protocol (IP) and the Internet Control Message Protocol (**ICMP**). The ICMP is used by network nodes and their administrators to exchange information about the state of the network. ICMP can be used to **ping** other nodes to see if they are operational. An operational node returns an echo message in response to a ping message.

A smurf program builds a network packet that appears to originate from another address (this is known as **spoofing** an IP address). The packet contains an ICMP ping message that is addressed to an IP broadcast address, meaning all IP addresses in a given network. The echo responses to the ping message are sent back to the "victim" address. Enough pings and resultant echoes can flood the network making it unusable for real traffic.

One way to defeat smurfing is to disable IP broadcast addressing at each network **router** since it is seldom used. This is one of several suggestions provided by the **CERT** Coordination Center.

SNA

See "Systems Network Architecture"

snail mail

Snail mail is a slang term for the regular postal service (for example, the U.S. Postal Service) with the implication that it is a lot slower than **e-mail**. It's worth noting, perhaps, that in the early days of the Internet, it was proposed that the U.S. Post Office manage e-mail. Electronic messages would come to your local post office and then be delivered to you along with the regular mail. The proposal was not considered for very long.

Snail mail or not, one must acknowledge that regular postal services offer a number of valuable services not likely to be available soon on the World Wide Web.

snake oil

In security, snake oil is a name for the exaggerated claims made by vendors. **Cryptography** experts have compared the exaggerated claims made by some vendors to the claims made by medicine show pitchmen in mid-19th century America, who bragged of secret ingredients much as today's marketers brag of secret proprietary **algorithm**s.

Commentators note that both the snake oil pitchman and the snake oil cryptographer may actually have a legitimate product worthy of purchase if the product's capabilities were not overstated. In mid-19th century America, snake oil was an alternative medicine used by Chinese immigrants working on the trans-continental railroad. The oil seemed to be effective in treating the aches and pains encurred from hard manual labor. European railroad workers learned of snake oil's healing properties first-hand and began to tell others. Entrepreneurs saw there was a market for snake oil and began to promise consumers that the magic Chinese elixir could cure just about anything that was wrong with them. "Snake oil" rapidly became a synonym for "fraudulent" or "bogus" and people forgot that it had once had a valuable, though limited, use.

Matt Curtin, who is credited with applying the term to computer security products, advises buyers to beware of top-secret products that promise unbreakable algorithms and to avoid any vendor who has a "trust us, we know what we're doing" approach to questions. According to Curtin, public scrutiny of an algorithm by mathematicians and other cryptographers is the best way to ensure an algorithm cannot be broken within a reasonable time frame.

snap-in

Snap-in, in general, refers to an object that can be attached to another object and that will then function as part of the whole. Hardware snap-ins usually fit this description. In reference to software applications, a snap-in is a **program** designed to function as a modular component of another application. Examples of snap-ins include Shym Technology's *PKEnable* snap-in security system for use in e-mail and Web applications, and Novell's *ZENworks for*

Desktops 3 Cluster Snap-in, which contains the program to support workstation inventory in a **cluster** environment. iMaximize claims that their snap-in products make it possible for any user who can operate a word processing program to create a feature-rich **Web site** in an hour.

Snap-ins are the basic components of Microsoft's Management Console (**MMC**). The MMC snap-ins are the actual management tools; the console—sometimes referred to as a "tools host"—is simply a framework into which the snap-ins are added. Within the MMC environment—which is similar to Windows explorer—the user selects from a list of all installed snap-ins; these might include, for example, *DNS manager* or *device manager*. Multiple copies of a particular snap-in can be added to apply to separate workstations. Snap-ins for MMC can include those from other vendors as well as Microsoft. Many companies, including IBM, Hewlett-Packard, NetIQ, Seagate, Symantec and Compuware, are also making MMC snap-ins; users can develop snap-ins to administer their own systems and custom applications.

sneakernet

Sneakernet is a jargon term for the method of transmitting electronic information by personally carrying it from one place to another on floppy disk or other removable medium. The idea is that someone is using their shoes (possibly sneakers) to move data around rather than using the telecommunications network.

sniffer

A sniffer is a program that monitors and analyzes network traffic, detecting bottlenecks and problems. Using this information, a network manager can keep traffic flowing efficiently.

A sniffer can also be used legitimately or illegitimately to capture data being transmitted on a network. A network **router** reads every **packet** of data passed to it, determining whether it is intended for a destination within the router's own network or whether it should be passed further along the Internet. A router with a sniffer, however, may be able to read the data in the packet as well as the source and destination addresses. Sniffers are often used on academic networks to prevent traffic bottlenecks caused by file-sharing applications such as Napster or Gnutella.

The term "sniffer" is occasionally used for a program that analyzes data other than network traffic. For example, a database could be analyzed for certain kinds of duplication.

A number of companies offer products that include "Sniffer" as part of their name.

SNMP

See "Simple Network Management Protocol"

SNR

See "signal-to-noise ratio"

SOAP

See "Simple Object Access Protocol"

social engineering

In computer security, social engineering is a term that describes a non-technical kind of intrusion that relies heavily on human interaction and often involves tricking other people to break normal security procedures. A social engineer runs what used to be called a "con game." For example, a person using social engineering to break into a computer network would try to gain the confidence of someone who is authorized to access the network in order to get them to reveal information that compromises the network's security. They might call the authorized employee with some kind of urgent problem; social engineers often rely on the natural helpfulness of people as well as on their weaknesses. Appeal to vanity, appeal to authority, and old-fashioned eavesdropping are typical social engineering techniques.

Another aspect of social engineering relies on people's inability to keep up with a culture that relies heavily on information technology. Social engineers rely on the fact that people are not aware of the value of the information they possess and are careless about protecting it. Frequently, social engineers will search dumpsters for valuable information, memorize access codes by looking over someone's shoulder (shoulder surfing), or take advantage of people's natural inclination to choose passwords that are meaningful to them but can be easily guessed. Security experts propose that as our culture becomes more dependent on information, social engineering will remain the greatest threat to any security system. Prevention includes educating people about the value of information, training them to protect it, and increasing people's awareness of how social engineers operate.

Socket 370

Socket 370 is the descriptive term for the way certain Intel **microprocessor**s plug into a computer **motherboard** so that it makes contact with the motherboard's built-in wires or data **bus**. The Socket 370 chip is less expensive to manufacture than **Slot 1 Pentium II** chips. A Socket 370 chip is the same size as a **Socket 7** chip but has a different number of **pin**s and a different **voltage**. Socket 370 is commonly used with **Celeron** processors

Socket 370 uses the Zero Insertion Force (**ZIF**) socket. As its name implies, the ZIF socket is designed for ease of manufacture and so that the average computer owner will be able to upgrade the microprocessor. The ZIF socket contains

a lever that opens and closes, securing the microprocessor in place. Different sockets have differing numbers of pins and pin layout arrangements.

Socket 7

Socket 7 is the descriptive term for the way certain Intel **Pentium** microprocessors plug into a computer **motherboard** so that it makes contact with the motherboard's built-in wires or data **bus**. Socket 7 is the best-known of eight connection variations that use the Zero Insertion Force (**ZIF**) socket. As its name implies, the ZIF socket is designed for ease of manufacture and so that the average computer owner will be able to upgrade the microprocessor. The ZIF socket contains a lever that opens and closes, securing the microprocessor in place. Various sockets have a differing number of pins and pin layout arrangements.

For its Pentium II processor, Intel has moved from the socket configuration to an approach in which the processor is packaged in a cartridge and fits into a slot in the motherboard.

The following table summarizes the socket characteristics for different Intel processors.

Socket	Pins	Layout	Processor(s)	Voltage
0	168	Inline	486DX5 V	
1	169	Inline	486DX,SX	5 V
2	238	Inline	486DX, SX,DX2	5 V
3	237	Inline	486DX,SX, DX2,DX4	3V or 5 V
4	273	Inline	60 or 66 MHz Pentium	5 V
5	320	Staggered	Pentium	3 V
6	235	Inline	486DX4	3 V
7	321	Staggered	Pentium	3 V
8	387	Staggered	Pentium Pro	3 V

sockets

Sockets is a method for communication between a **client** program and a **server** program in a network. A socket is defined as "the endpoint in a connection." Sockets are created and used with a set of programming requests or "function calls" sometimes called the sockets application programming interface (**API**). The most common sockets API is the Berkeley **UNIX C** interface for sockets. Sockets can also be used for communication between processes within the same computer.

This is the typical sequence of sockets requests from a server application in the "connectionless" context of the Internet in which a server handles many client requests and does not maintain a connection longer than the serving of the immediate request:

```
socket()
  |
bind()
  |
recvfrom()
  |
(wait for a sendto request from some client)
  |
(process the sendto request)
  |
 sendto (in reply to the request from the
client...for example, send an HTML file)
```

A corresponding client sequence of sockets requests would be:

```
socket()
  |
bind()
  |
sendto()
  |
recvfrom()
```

Sockets can also be used for "connection-oriented" transactions with a somewhat different sequence of C language system calls or functions.

socks

Socks (or "SOCKS") is a protocol that a **proxy server** can use to accept requests from client users in a company's network so that it can forward them across the Internet. Socks uses **sockets** to represent and keep track of individual connections. The client side of Socks is built into certain Web browsers and the server side can be added to a proxy server.

A socks server handles requests from clients inside a company's **firewall** and either allows or rejects connection requests, based on the requested Internet destination or user identification. Once a connection and a subsequent "bind" request have been set up, the flow of information exchange follows the usual protocol (for example, the Web's **Hypertext Transfer Protocol**).

soft handoff

In **cellular telephone** communication, soft handoff refers to the overlapping of repeater coverage zones, so that every cell phone set is always well within range of at least one **repeater** (also called a base station). In some cases, mobile sets transmit signals to, and receive signals from, more than one repeater at a time.

Soft handoff technology is used by code-division multiple access (**CDMA**) systems. Older networks use frequency division multiplex (**FDM**) or time division multiplex (**TDM**). In CDMA, all repeaters use the same frequency channel for each mobile phone set, no matter where the set is located. Each set has an identity based on a code, rather than on a frequency (as in FDM) or sequence of time slots (as in TDM).

Because no change in frequency or timing occurs as a mobile set passes from one base station to another, there are practically no dead zones. As a result, connections are almost never interrupted or dropped.

softswitch

Softswitch (software switch) is a generic term for any open application program interface (**API**) software used to bridge a public switched telephone network (**PSTN**) and voice over Internet protocol (**VOiP**) by separating the call control functions of a phone call from the media gateway (transport layer).

software

Software is a general term for the various kinds of **programs** used to operate **computers** and related devices. (The term **hardware** describes the physical aspects of computers and related devices.)

Software can be thought of as the variable part of a computer and hardware the invariable part. Software is often divided into **application** software (programs that do work users are directly interested in) and **system** software (which includes **operating system**s and any program that supports application software). The term **middleware** is sometimes used to describe programming that mediates between application and system software or between two different kinds of application software (for example, sending a remote work request from an application in a computer that has one kind of operating system to an application in a computer with a different operating system).

An additional and difficult-to-classify category of software is the *utility*, which is a small useful program with limited capability. Some utilities come with operating systems. Like applications, utilities tend to be separately installable and capable of being used independently from the rest of the operating system.

Applets are small applications that sometimes come with the operating system as "accessories." They can also be created independently using the **Java** or other programming languages.

Software can be purchased or acquired as **shareware** (usually intended for sale after a trial period), **liteware** (shareware with some capabilities disabled), **freeware** (free software but with copyright restrictions), **public domain software** (free with no restrictions), and **open source** (software where the **source code** is furnished and users agree not to limit the distribution of improvements).

Software is often packaged on **CD-ROM**s and *diskettes*. Today, much purchased software, shareware, and freeware is **downloaded** over the Internet. A new trend is software that is made available for use at another site known as an **application service provider**.

Some general kinds of application software include:

- Productivity software, which includes **word processor**s, **spreadsheet**s, and tools for use by most computer users
- Presentation software
- Graphics software for graphic designers
- **CAD/CAM** software
- Specialized scientific applications
- **Vertical market** or industry-specific software (for example, for banking, insurance, retail, and manufacturing environments)

Firmware or *microcode* is programming that is loaded into a special area on a **microprocessor** or **read-only memory** on a one-time or infrequent basis so that thereafter it seems to be part of the hardware.

software developer's kit

A software developer's kit (SDK) is a set of programs used by a computer programmer to write **application** programs. Typically, an SDK includes a visual screen builder, an editor, a **compiler**, a linker, and sometimes other facilities. The term is used by Microsoft, Sun Microsystems, and a number of other companies.

This term is sometimes seen as *software development kit*.

software-defined radio

Software-defined radio (SDR), sometimes shortened to software radio (SR), refers to wireless communication in which the transmitter modulation is generated or defined by a computer, and the receiver uses a computer to recover the signal intelligence. To select the desired modulation type, the proper programs must be run by microcomputers that control the transmitter and receiver.

A typical voice SDR transmitter, such as might be used in mobile two-way radio or cellular telephone communication, consists of the following stages. Items with asterisks represent computer-controlled circuits whose parameters are determined by the programming (software).

- Microphone
- Audio amplifier
- Analog-to-digital converter (**ADC**) that converts the voice audio to **ASCII** data *
- Modulator that impresses the ASCII intelligence onto a radio-frequency (**RF**) carrier *
- Series of amplifiers that boosts the RF carrier to the power level necessary for transmission
- Transmitting antenna

A typical receiver designed to intercept the above-described voice SDR signal would employ the following stages, essentially reversing the transmitter's action. Again, items followed by asterisks represent programmable circuits.

- Receiving antenna
- **Superheterodyne** system that boosts incoming RF signal strength and converts it to a constant frequency
- Demodulator that separates the ASCII intelligence from the RF carrier *
- Digital-to-analog converter (**DAC**) that generates a voice waveform from the ASCII data *
- Audio amplifier
- Speaker, earphone, or headset

The most significant asset of SDR is versatility. Wireless systems employ protocols that vary from one service to another. Even in the same type of service, for example wireless fax, the protocol often differs from country to country. A single SDR set with an all-inclusive software repertoire can be used in any mode, anywhere in the world. Changing the service type, the mode, and/or the modulation protocol involves simply selecting and launching the requisite computer program, and making sure the batteries are adequately charged if portable operation is contemplated.

The ultimate goal of SDR engineers is to provide a single radio transceiver capable of playing the roles of cordless telephone, cell phone, wireless fax, wireless e-mail system, pager, wireless videoconferencing unit, wireless Web browser, Global Positioning System (**GPS**) unit, and other functions still in the realm of science fiction, operable from any location on the surface of the earth, and perhaps in space as well.

SOHO

In information technology, SOHO (small office home office) is a term for the small office or home office environment and business culture. A number of organizations, businesses, and publications now exist to support people who work or have businesses in this environment. The term "virtual office" is sometimes used as a synonym.

SOI

See "Silicon-on-Insulator"

solar fade

Solar fade, also called sun interference, is a phenomenon that occurs in **satellite** communications on certain occasions when the downlink signal is aligned with the sun's position and it is overcome by signal noise from the sun. The term is used mainly in reference to geostationary (GEO) satellite systems.

The sun is a powerful emitter of electromagnetic energy at all **wavelengths**, including those in the **microwave** portion of the radio-frequency (**RF**) spectrum, where most satellite communication is carried out. Normally, the sun does not affect the reception of microwave signals, because microwave-receiving antennas are rarely pointed right at the sun. But once in awhile, a signal source and the sun line up, and then they compete.

At the equinoxes, around March 21 and September 21 of every year, the sun is directly over the earth's equator. GEO satellites orbit over the equator. Thus, for about a week before and after the equinoxes, the sun lines up almost exactly with any given GEO satellite once a day for users living at the equator. For subscribers in the northern hemisphere, the same thing happens for a couple of weeks before March 21 and after September 21. In the southern hemisphere, the effect is observed just after March 21 and before September 21. Unless the satellite **downlink** satellite signal is exceptionally strong, RF noise from the sun overpowers it, and reception is degraded or interrupted. After a few minutes, the sun's course across the sky takes it past the satellite, and normal reception resumes.

Solar fade never occurs more than once a day for any GEO satellite, and presents a problem for only a few days out of the year. Nevertheless, it can be frustrating to satellite system users. It is important to realize that solar fade is not caused by a malfunction in system hardware or programming.

Compare with **rain fade**.

Solaris

Solaris is the computer **operating system** that Sun Microsystems provides for its family of **SPARC**-based processors as well as for Intel-based processors. Sun has historically dominated the large **UNIX** workstation market. As the Internet grew in the early 1990s, Sun's SPARC/Solaris systems became the most widely installed servers for Web sites. Sun emphasizes the system's availability (meaning it seldom crashes), its large number of features, and its Internet-oriented design. Sun advertises that its latest version, the Solaris 8 Operating Environment, is "the leading UNIX environment" today.

Sun emphasizes these features of Solaris:

- Its availability. Special features make it easy to add new capability or to fix problems without having to restart the system. Because it has evolved through a number of versions, it is "stable"—that is, like IBM's well-known mainframe operating system, **MVS**, Solaris has exercised and fixed almost any code path that might break. It can be upgraded, monitored, and controlled from a remote console.
- Its **scalability**. If you move to a larger processor, your applications should not only run, but run faster.

- It is built for network computing. As part of the first and most successful Web server system in history, the latest Solaris systems are built on the company's experience with early Web sites and network demands.

- It includes security features. These include support for **IPSec**, **Kerberos**, AMI, and smart cards. Sun provides three extensions for its Solaris operating system:

- The Easy Access Server, which is designed to run in a network that also has Windows NT systems

- The Enterprise Server, which is aimed at the "business-critical" environment, and includes support for *clustering*

- The Internet Service Provider (**ISP**) Server

Since Sun originated the platform-independent **Java** programming language and runtime environment, Solaris systems come with a Java **virtual machine** and the Java Development Kit (**JDK**).

Solaris replaced **SunOS**, a system still in use on many Sun machines today.

solenoid

Also see **toroid**.

A solenoid is a coil of insulated or enameled wire wound on a rod-shaped form made of solid iron, solid steel, or powdered iron. Devices of this kind can be used as electromagnets, as inductors in electronic circuits, and as miniature **wireless** receiving antennas.

In a solenoid, the core material is ferromagnetic, meaning that it concentrates magnetic lines of flux. This increases the inductance of the coil far beyond the inductance obtainable with an air-core coil of the same dimensions and the same number of turns. When **current** flows in the coil, most of the resulting magnetic flux exists within the core material. Some flux appears outside the coil near the ends of the core; a small amount of flux also appears outside the coil and off to the side.

A *solenoid chime* is wound on a cylindrical, hollow, plastic or phenolic form with a movable, solid iron or steel core. The core can travel in and out of the coil along its axis. The coil is oriented vertically; the core normally rests somewhat below the coil center. When a current pulse is applied to the coil, the magnetic field pulls the core forcefully upward. Inertia carries the core above the center of the coil, where the core strikes a piece of metal similar to a xylophone bell, causing a loud "ding."

solid-state

Solid-state refers to electronic components, devices, and systems based entirely on the **semiconductor**. The expression was especially prevalent in the late 1950s and early 1960s, during the transition from **vacuum tube** technology to the semiconductor diode and **transistor**. More

recently, the integrated circuit (**IC**), the light-emitting diode (**LED**), and the liquid-crystal display (**LCD**) have evolved as further examples of solid-state devices.

In a solid-state component, the **current** is confined to solid elements and compounds engineered specifically to switch and amplify it. Current flows in two forms: As negatively charged electrons, and as positively charged electron deficiencies called holes. In some semiconductors, the current consists mostly of electrons; in other semiconductors, it consists mostly of holes. Both the **electron** and the **hole** are called charge carriers.

An example of a non-solid-state component is a cathode-ray tube (**CRT**). In this device, electrons flow freely through a vacuum from an electron gun, through deflecting and focusing fields, and finally to a phosphorescent screen.

soliton

A soliton is a special form of light pulse that can be transmitted over a **fiber optic** channel. Potentially, a soliton retains its shape or wavelength over a longer distance than ordinary light pulses, permitting a higher rate of information bits to be transmitted.

SONET

See "Synchronous Optical Network"

Sony/Philips Digital Interface

S/PDIF (Sony/Philips Digital Interface) is a standard audio transfer file format. It is usually found on digital audio equipment such as a DAT machine or audio processing device. It allows the transfer of audio from one file to another without the conversion to and from an **analog** format, which could degrade the signal quality.

The most common connector used with an S/PDIF interface is the RCA connector, the same one used for consumer audio products. An optical connector is also sometimes used.

sosofo

A sosofo (specification of a sequence of flow objects), a term used in the Document Style Semantics and Specification Language (**DSSL**), is a set of statements that describe how a sequence of document elements (such as a paragraph and headings) fit into a document and how they are to be formatted (for example, in what type **font** and with what spacing).

Using a sosofo in DSSSL, a document element can contain other elements (a paragraph can contain "notes" or "emphasized text" in different font sizes).

In DSSSL, sosofo's are the main way in which you describe the presentation of language elements. The inventors of DSSSL feel that "sosofo" takes a lot less time to read and say than "specification of a sequence of flow objects."

sound card

A sound card (also referred to as an *audio card*) is a **peripheral** device that attaches to the **ISA** or **PCI slot** on a **motherboard** to enable the computer to input, process, and deliver sound.

The sound card's four main functions are: as a synthesizer (generating sounds), as a **MIDI** interface, **analog-to-digital conversion** (used, for example, in recording sound from a microphone), and **digital-to-analog conversion** (used, for example, to reproduce sound for a speaker). The three methods of sound synthesis are through frequency modulation (**FM**) technology, **wavetable**, and physical modeling.

FM synthesis is the least expensive and least effective method. Sounds are simulated by using **algorithm**s to create **sine wave**s that are as close to the sound as possible. For example, the sound of a guitar can be simulated, although the result does not really sound very much like a guitar. Wavetable uses actual, digitally recorded sound samples stored on the card for the highest performance. Physical modeling is a new type of synthesizing, in which sounds are simulated through a complex programming procedure. Some sound cards can also have sounds downloaded to them.

Creative Lab's Sound Blaster is the de facto standard sound card, to the extent that some people use the name as a generic term. Most sound cards in the past have been Sound Blaster-compatible, because most programs that use the sound card have been designed that way. Sound cards were once all connected to the ISA slot. However, because connection to the PCI **bus** offers advantages such as improved **signal-to-noise ratio** and decreased demand on the **CPU**, sound cards being produced today are intended for use with a PCI bus.

Some sound cards, such as Diamond MX300 and SoundBlaster Live!, have 3-D capabilities enabled by processors on the card that use mathematical formulas to create greater depth, complexity, and realism of sound. High quality audio can be produced through a system that uses the Universal Serial Bus (**USB**) and does not require a sound card. Processing is left to the CPU, and digital-to-audio conversion to the speakers.

Sound Designer II

SDII (Sound Designer II, sometimes seen abbreviated as SD2) is a monophonic/stereophonic **audio** file format, originally developed by Digidesign for their **Macintosh**-based recording/editing products. It is the successor to the original monophonic Sound Designer I audio file format.

An SDII file can be monophonic or stereophonic. When stereo is used, the tracks are interleaved (sample-001-left, sample-001-right, sample-002-left, sample-002-right, etc.) Files also store **sample rate** and bit depth information.

The SDII file has become a widely accepted standard for transferring audio files between editing applications. Most Mac CD-ROM writer software, for example, specifies SDII or **Audio Interchange File Format** as the file format needed when making audio CDs.

The SDII file has also become accepted among **personal computer** audio application developers. This makes transferring audio from Mac to PC platforms much easier. When used on a PC, the file must use the extension of ".sd2".

source code

Source code and object code refer to the "before" and "after" versions of a computer **program** that is compiled (see **compiler**) before it is ready to run in a computer. The source code consists of the programming statements that are created by a programmer with a **text editor** or a visual programming tool and then saved in a file. For example, a programmer using the **C** language types in a desired sequence of C language statements using a text editor and then saves them as a named file. This file is said to contain the source code. It is now ready to be compiled with a C compiler and the resulting output, the compiled file, is often referred to as object code. The object code file contains a sequence of **instruction**s that the processor can understand but that is difficult for a human to read or modify. For this reason and because even debugged programs often need some later enhancement, the source code is the most permanent form of the program.

When you purchase or receive operating system or application software, it is usually in the form of compiled object code and the source code is not included. Proprietary software vendors usually don't want you to try to improve their code since this may created additional service costs for them. Lately, there is a movement to develop software (**Linux** is an example) that is **open** to further improvement and here the source code is provided.

In large program development environments, there are often management systems that help programmers separate and keep track of different states and levels of code files. For **script** (noncompiled or interpreted) program languages, such as **JavaScript**, the terms *source code* and *object code* do not apply since there is only one form of the code.

source quench

Using the Internet Control Message Protocol (**ICMP**), a source quench is a message from one **host** computer to another telling it to reduce the pace at which it is sending **packets** to that host. The source quench is one of several ways to manage the flow of packets on the Internet.

Ideally, a receiving host would detect when packets were stacking up too fast and send a source quench in time to slow the pace down so that no packets were lost. Note that the Internet Protocol (**IP**) of which ICMP is a part does not itself guarantee the delivery of packets. Higher-level protocols, such as the Transport Control Protocol (**TCP**), have responsibility for ensuring successful end-to-end communication. IP and ICMP simply report errors or situations as they are detected so that packets can be resent or sent at a different pace. Source quench is not the only way to control flow in a network and not necessarily the most efficient way. In IP Version 4, the most commonly-used IP version, **router**s are not allowed to originate a source quench and are not obligated to act on a received source quench. Because the source quench message may itself increase network traffic, other approaches to network flow control are preferred.

Source Quench Introduced Delay

Also see **SQUID**, a UNIX-based program for caching Web pages and other Internet content closer to the user.

Source Quench Introduced Delay (SQuID) is the use of some **algorithm**s by a computer that is sending messages too fast to a destination computer that will allow the source computer to slow the timing of its transmissions down to a level acceptable to the destination. On the Internet, when **packet**s arrive at a destination **host** (computer) faster than the host can handle them, they are discarded and a reply may be sent back indicating that they should be resent. Although a destination host may have a message **buffer**, the buffer may become full before new packets can be read by a higher-layer application. Having a way to slow down the pace at which packets are sent would not only make work more efficient for both sender and receiver but would reduce unnecessary network traffic. SQuID describes a kind of packet that is returned as a source quench message. The source host would use an algorithm to react to one or a sequence of source quench messages.

SQuID is described in a **Request for Comments** paper of the Internet Engineering Task Force (**IETF**).

source-route transparent bridging

Source-route transparent (SRT) bridging is a bridging scheme developed by IBM that combines source-route bridging (**SRB**) and **transparent bridging** in the same **network**. SRT is commonly used with **token ring** networks.

Transparent bridging was first developed by Digital Equipment Corporation in the early 1980s and has become **IEEE** standard 802.1. A transparent bridge learns the network's **topology** from the source **address** of each incoming **frame**. It then uses this information to create a table of the paths used by the **host**s so that it can use the same paths to forward network traffic. Network hosts do not detect the presence or operation of transparent bridges.

When an SRT bridge receives a frame, it immediately checks the frame's routing information indicator (RII) bit to see if the frame is a transparent bridging frame or an SRB frame. Once it determines the frame's type, it processes it accordingly.

Southbridge

Southbridge is an Intel **chipset** that manages the basic forms of input/output (**I/O**) such as Universal Serial Bus (**USB**), **serial**, audio, Integrated Drive Electronics (**IDE**), and Industry Standard Architecture (**ISA**) I/O in a computer. Southbridge is one of two chipsets that are collectively called **Northbridge**/Southbridge. Northbridge controls the **processor**, **memory**, Peripheral Component Interconnect (**PCI**) **bus**, Level 2 **cache**, and all Accelerated Graphics Port (**AGP**) activities. Unlike Northbridge, Southbridge consists of one chip, which sits on Northbridge's PCI bus.

The Intel Hub Architecture (IHA) has replaced the Northbridge/Southbridge chipset. The IHA chipset has two parts also, the Graphics and AGP Memory Controller Hub (GMCH) and the I/O Controller Hub (ICH). The IHA architecture is used in Intel's 800 series chipsets, which is the first chipset architecture to move away from the Northbridge/Southbridge design.

SP

See "service pack"

space

See "swap file"

spacer GIF

See "transparent GIF"

spam

Spam is unsolicited e-mail on the Internet. From the sender's point-of-view, it's a form of bulk mail, often to a list culled from subscribers to a **Usenet** discussion group or obtained by companies that specialize in creating e-mail distribution lists. To the receiver, it usually seems like junk e-mail. In general, it's not considered good **netiquette** to send spam. It's generally equivalent to unsolicited phone marketing calls except that the user pays for part of the message since everyone shares the cost of maintaining the Internet.

Some apparently unsolicited e-mail is, in fact, e-mail people agreed to receive when they registered with a site and checked a box agreeing to receive postings about particular products or interests. This is known as both **opt-in e-mail** and permission-based e-mail.

A first-hand report indicates that the term is derived from a famous Monty Python sketch ("Well, we have Spam, tomato & Spam, egg & Spam, Egg, bacon & Spam...") that was current when spam first began arriving on the Internet. Spam is a trademarked Hormel meat product that was well-known in the U.S. Armed Forces during World War II.

spanning tree protocol

Where two bridges are used to interconnect the same two computer network segments, spanning tree is a protocol that allows the **bridge**s to exchange information so that only one of them will handle a given message that is being sent between two computers within the network. The spanning tree protocol prevents the condition known as a *bridge loop*.

In a local area network (**LAN**) such as an **Ethernet** or **token ring** network, computers compete for the ability to use the shared telecommunications path at any given time. If too many computers try to send at the same time, the overall performance of the network can be affected, even to the point of bringing all traffic to a near halt. To make this possibility less likely, the local area network can be divided into two or more *network segments* with a device called a bridge connecting any two segments. Each message (called a **frame**) goes through the bridge before being sent to the intended destination. The bridge determines whether the message is for a destination within the same segment as the sender's or for the other segment, and forwards it accordingly. A bridge does nothing more than look at the destination address and, based on its understanding of the two segments (which computers are on which segments), forwards it on the right path (which means to the correct outgoing **port**). The benefit of network segmentation (and the bridge) is that the amount of competition for use of the network path is reduced by half (assuming each segment has the same number of computers) and the possibility of the network coming to a halt is significantly reduced.

Each bridge learns which computers are on which segment by sending any first-time message to both segments (this is known as *flooding*) and then noticing and recording the segment from which a computer replied to the message. Gradually, the bridge builds a picture for itself of which computers are in which segments. When a second and subsequent messages are sent, the bridge can use its table to determine which segment to forward it to. The approach of allowing the bridge to learn the network through experience is known as *transparent bridging* (meaning that bridging does not require setup by an administrator).

In order to build into a network, it is typical to add a second bridge between two segments as a backup in case the primary bridge fails. Both bridges need to continually understand the topography of the network, even though only one is actually forwarding messages. And both bridges need to have some way to understand which bridge is the primary one. To do this, they have a separate path connection just between the bridges in which they exchange information, using bridge protocol data units (BPDUs).

The program in each bridge that allows it to determine how to use the protocol is known as the *spanning tree algorithm*. The **algorithm** is specifically constructed to avoid bridge loops (multiple paths linking one segment to another, resulting in an infinite loop situation). The algorithm is responsible for a bridge using only the most efficient path when faced with multiple paths. If the best path fails, the algorithm recalculates the network and finds the next best route.

The spanning tree algorithm determines the network (which computer hosts are in which segment) and this data is exchanged using Bridge Protocol Data Units (BPDUs). It is broken down into two steps:

Step 1: The algorithm determines the best message a bridge can send by evaluating the configuration messages it has received and choosing the best option.

Step 2: Once it selects the top message for a particular bridge to send, it compares its choice with possible configuration messages from the non-root-connections it has. If the best option from step 1 isn't better than what it receives from the non-root-connections, it will prune that port.

The spanning tree protocol and algorithm were developed by a committe of the IEEE. Currently, the IEEE is attempting to institute enhancements to the spanning tree algorithm that will reduce network recovery time. The goal is to go from 30 to 60 seconds after a failure or change in link status to less than 10 seconds. The enhancement, called Rapid Reconfiguration or Fast Spanning Tree, would cut down on data loss and session timeouts when large, Ethernet networks recover after a topology change or a device failure.

SPARC

SPARC (Scalable Processor Architecture) is a 32- and **64-bit microprocessor architecture** from Sun Microsystems that is based on reduced instruction set computing (**RISC**). SPARC has become a widely-used architecture for hardware used with **UNIX**-based operating systems, including Sun's own **Solaris** systems. Sun has made SPARC an **open** architecture that is available for licensing to microprocessor manufacturers. In its most recent brand name, UltraSPARC, microprocessors can be built for PC boards (using either **Peripheral Component Interconnect** or **ATX**) as well as for SPARC's original **workstation** market. As evidence of SPARC's **scalability**, Sun says that its UltraSPARC III will be designed to allow up to 1,000 processors to work together.

Although the idea of RISC is sometimes attributed to IBM's John Cocke, Sun Microsystems was the first to provide a microprocessor that exploited it for the **workstation** market and it's possible to say that, together with **UNIX**, SPARC created the workstation market. (IBM has since used it in its successful RISC System/6000 line of workstations.) Since its inception in 1987, the SPARC architecture has included these ideas:

- Reduce the number of instructions that the processor has to perform to a minimal number (one idea of RISC is that a complex instruction in a conventional computer can be reduced to a series of simpler operations, requiring a simpler architecture and a more compact microprocessor)

- Reduce the number of types of memory addresses that the processor needs to handle

- Put as little processor operation as possible in **microcode**, which requires **clock speed**-consuming time to access

- Provide language **compilers** that compile programs that are optimized for a SPARC microprocessor by being arranged in an order that the processor can handle more efficiently

spatial division multiple access

Also see frequency division multiple access (**FDMA**) and time division multiple access (**TDMA**).

Spatial division multiple access (SDMA) is a **satellite** communications mode that optimizes the use of radio spectrum and minimizes system cost by taking advantage of the directional properties of dish antennas. In SDMA, also known as SDM (spatial-division multiplex), satellite dish antennas transmit signals to numerous zones on the earth's surface. The antennas are highly directional, allowing duplicate frequencies to be used for multiple surface zones.

Consider a scenario in which signals must be transmitted simultaneously by one satellite to mobile or portable **wireless** receivers in 20 different surface zones. In a conventional system, 20 channels and 20 antennas would be necessary to maintain channel separation. In SDMA, there can be far fewer channels than zones. If duplicate-channel zones are sufficiently separated, the 20 signals can be transmitted to earth using four or five channels. The narrow signal beams from the satellite antennas ensure that interference will not occur between zones using the same frequency.

SDMA requires careful choice of zones for each transmitter, and also requires precise antenna alignment. A small error can result in failure of one or more channels, interference among channels, and/or confusion between surface coverage zones.

SPD

See "serial presence detect"

Specialized Mobile Radio

Also see Enhanced Specialized Mobile Radio (**ESMR**).

Specialized Mobile Radio (SMR) is any two-way radio system in which two or more mobile/portable **wireless** transceivers are linked by a single **repeater**. The repeater is elevated above average terrain; this maximizes the area of

coverage. Operating frequencies are in the VHF (very-high-frequency) or UHF (ultra-high-frequency) range, that is, between approximately 30 MHz and 3 GHz.

In some ways, an SMR system is like a **cellular telephone** network. But there are important differences. An SMR system is simpler than a cellular telephone network. There is only one repeater in a SMR system, and it links only the mobile/portable units for that system, not to other repeaters. In SMR, the range of each individual mobile/portable transceiver is greater than the range of a cell phone set. But total system coverage is usually far more limited than that of a cellular network, because there is no linking among repeaters.

SMR systems use channel pairs. Each transceiver has a transmit frequency and a receive frequency. These frequencies differ by a fixed amount, called the offset. The transmit and receive frequencies are in the same band, that is, relatively close to each other in the radio spectrum. The transmit and receive frequencies of each mobile or portable transceiver in a system are all identical.

An SMR system uses **half-duplex** communication and a PTT (push-to-talk) mode. Neither party can hear the other while transmitting. An example of half-duplex operation is a radio conversation between two people using simple walkie-talkies. SMR is used by taxi dispatchers, parcel delivery companies, fire departments, paramedic squads, police departments, and amateur radio operators.

specific gravity

The term specific gravity, symbolized sp gr, refers to the ratio of the density of a solid or liquid to the density of water at 4 degrees Celsius. The term can also refer to the ratio of the density of a gas to the density of dry air at **standard temperature and pressure**, although this specification is less often used. Specific gravity is a dimensionless quantity; that is, it is not expressed in units.

To find the sp gr of a solid or liquid, you must know its density in kilograms per meter cubed (kg/m^3) or in grams per centimeter cubed (g/cm^3). Then, divide this density by the density of pure water in the same units. If you use kg/m^3, divide by 1000. If you use g/cm^3, divide by 1 (that is, leave the number alone). It is important to use the same units in the numerator and denominator.

Water has a specific gravity equal to 1. Materials with a specific gravity less than 1 are less dense than water, and will float on the pure liquid; substances with a specific gravity more than 1 are more dense than water, and will sink. An object with a density of 85 kg/m^3 has a specific gravity of 0.085, and will float high on the surface of a body of water. An object with a density of 85 g/cm^3 has a specific gravity of 85, and will sink rapidly.

To find the specific gravity of a gas, you must know its density in kilograms per meter cubed (kg/m^3). Then, divide this density by the density of dry air at standard temperature and pressure. This value is approximately 1.29 kg/m³. Gases with a specific gravity less than 1 will rise in the atmosphere at sea level; gases with a specific gravity greater than 1 will sink and seek regions of low elevation at the earth's surface.

Also see **kilogram**, **meter**, **kilogram per meter cubed**, **SI** (International System of Units), and **standard temperature and pressure**.

specific volume

Specific volume is a property of materials, defined as the number of cubic meters occupied by one kilogram of a particular substance. The standard unit is the **meter cubed per kilogram** (m^3/kg or $m^3 \cdot kg^{-1}$).

Sometimes specific volume is expressed in terms of the number of cubic centimeters occupied by one gram of a substance. In this case, the unit is the centimeter cubed per gram (cm^3/g or $cm^3 \cdot g^{-1}$). To convert m^3/kg to cm^3/g, multiply by 1000; conversely, multiply by 0.001.

Specific volume is inversely proportional to **density**. If the density of a substance doubles, its specific volume, as expressed in the same base units, is cut in half. If the density drops to 1/10 its former value, the specific volume, as expressed in the same base units, increases by a factor of 10.

Imagine a variable-volume, airtight chamber containing a certain number of atoms of oxygen gas. Consider the following four examples:

- If the chamber is made smaller without allowing gas in or out, the density increases and the specific volume decreases

- If the chamber expands without letting gas in or out, the density decreases and the specific volume increases

- If the size of the chamber remains constant and new atoms of gas are injected, the density increases and the specific volume decreases

- If the size of the chamber remains constant and some atoms are removed, the density decreases and the specific volume increases

Also see **density**, **kilogram**, **meter cubed**, **volume**, and **SI** (International System of Units).

specification of a sequence of flow objects

See "sosofo"

spectrum

See "electromagnetic radiation spectrum"

speculation

Speculation (also known as *speculative loading*), is a process implemented in Explicitly Parallel Instruction Computing (**EPIC**) processors and their **compilers** to reduce processor-

memory exchanging bottlenecks or **latency** by putting all the data into memory in advance of an actual load instruction. Invalid changes or exceptions to the load are delayed and cross-checked until the processor finally resolves them.

Intel's **IA-64** architecture is based on EPIC and the first processor in the IA-64 line, the **Itanium**, uses speculation.

Speech Application Program Interface

SAPI (Speech Application Program Interface) is an application program interface (**API**) provided with the Microsoft Windows **operating system** that allows programmers to write programs that offer text-to-speech and **speech recognition** capabilities. Interfaces are provided for the **C**, **C++**, and **Visual Basic** programming languages. Using Microsoft's **COM** (Component Object Model) architecture, SAPI is the most widely used speech application program interface used today. In the future, Microsoft plans to embed speech technology using SAPI into their **operating system**.

SAPI has seven main components:

- **Voice Command:** Voice Command is a high-level interface that provides command and control speech recognition for applications. Voice Command allows a developer to create a Voice Command menu that contains voice commands, such as "new file" or "send mail to someone@anywhere.net" that a user speaks into a microphone or other audio device. The user can control the computer without needing a keyboard or mouse.

- **Voice Dictation:** Voice Dictation allows the user to dictate into any application that supports speech recognition. An invisible or virtual edit box receives the text the user dictates and displays the text in an application window. Voice Dictation allows text formatting such as capitalization, translation of punctuation words into punctuation symbols, built-in glossary entries, and correction of the last word spoken or a selected word. Applications that use Voice Dictation classify speech by topics that use different language styles. Topics include e-mail speech, formal writing, or programming speech. Voice Dictation stores the information for each topic on your hard drive.

- **Voice Text:** Voice Text converts text into speech that is played over computer speakers or sent over a telephone line. The speech played has several different modes, each with a different voice.

- **Voice Telephony:** Voice Telephony uses **telephony** controls that are similar to Windows controls. Windows controls include buttons, list boxes, sliders and other objects that can be manipulated by a mouse or keyboard. Telephony controls are codes that recognize spoken responses such as Yes or No, your phone number, the date, and the time. Telephony controls create a dialogue between the user and the computer. For example, a user calls a vendor to order an item. The user then answers several questions by speaking into the telephone receiver. The telephony controls recognize these responses and sends them to the application that processes responses. Telephony controls also handle error conditions (these are common with spoken numbers or when the caller does not respond) and variations of answers such as "January 4th" or "tomorrow."

- **DirectSpeechRecognition:** This is a low-level interface similar to Voice Command. The main difference is DirectSpeechRecognition speaks directly to the speech **engine**. This gives the application more control and speed.

- **DirectTextToSpeech:** This is a low-level interface similar to Voice Text that also speaks directly to the speech engine.

- **Audio Objects:** An Audio Object tells the speech engine where to get its audio.

The future of speech technology will include products that allow you to do such things as surfing the Internet using speech and asking your television what is showing tonight. Software developers are developing applications that understand concepts. For example, if you tell your computer to print a certain document, your application will know whether to print it on your printer or the network's printer. Speech technology is important for medical professionals, law enforcement personnel, the physically handicapped, as well as many business and home users.

speech recognition

Speech or voice recognition is the ability of a machine or program to recognize and carry out voice commands or take dictation. In general, speech recognition involves the ability to match a voice pattern against a provided or acquired vocabulary. Usually, a limited vocabulary is provided with a product and the user can record additional words. More sophisticated software has the ability to accept *natural speech* (meaning speech as we usually speak it rather than carefully-spoken speech).

Dragon Systems and IBM are two companies that have led in the research and development of products that support speech recognition.

speeds

See "The speed of…"

SPID

A SPID (Service Profile Identifier) is a number assigned by a phone company to a terminal on an **Integrated Services Digital Network B-channel**. A SPID tells equipment at the phone company's central office about the capabilities of each terminal (computer or phone) on the B-channels. A Basic Rate home or business user may divide service into two B-

channels with one used for normal phone service and the other for computer data. The SPID tells the phone company whether the terminal accepts voice or data information.

Technically, the SPID is a numeric string from 3 to 20 digits in length. A SPID (or more than one, if necessary) is assigned when you order the ISDN Basic Rate Interface (BRI) from the phone company. Beginning in 1998, most phone companies began to use a generic SPID format. In this format, the SPID is a 14-digit number that includes your 10-digit telephone number (which includes your 3-digit Numbering Plan Area]NPA[or area code), a 2-digit Sharing Terminal Identifier, and a 2-digit Terminal Identifier (TID). The generic SPID format makes it easier to tell users what to specify when installing an ISDN line and simplifies corporate installation procedures.

Beginning in 1998, some ISDN manufacturers began to provide *non-initializing terminals* (NITs) that do not require the entering of a SPID. Manufacturers also are delivering terminals with *automated SPID selection* in which the correct SPID is downloaded to the terminal rather than having to be specified by the user.

spider

A spider is a program that visits Web sites and reads their pages and other information in order to create entries for a **search engine** index. The major search engines on the Web all have such a program, which is also known as a "crawler" or a "bot." Spiders are typically programmed to visit sites that have been submitted by their owners as new or updated. Entire sites or specific pages can be selectively visited and indexed. Spiders are called spiders because they usually visit many sites in parallel at the same time, their "legs" spanning a large area of the "web." Spiders can crawl through a site's pages in several ways. One way is to follow all the hypertext links in each page until all the pages have been read.

The spider for the **AltaVista** search engine and its Web site is called **Scooter**. Scooter adheres to the rules of politeness for Web spiders that are specified in the Standard for Robot Exclusion (SRE). It asks each server which files should be excluded from being indexed. It does not (or can not) go through **firewalls**. And it uses a special **algorithm** for waiting between successive server requests so that it doesn't affect response time for other users.

spiral model

The spiral model, also known as the spiral lifecycle model, is a systems development method (**SDM**) used in information technology (IT). This model of development combines the features of the **prototyping model** and the **systems development life cycle model** (SDLC) or **waterfall model**. The spiral model is favored for large, expensive, and complicated projects.

The steps in the spiral model can be generalized as follows:

1. The new system requirements are defined in as much detail as possible. This usually involves interviewing a number of users representing all the external or internal users and other aspects of the existing system.

2. A preliminary design is created for the new system.

3. A first prototype of the new system is constructed from the preliminary design. This is usually a scaled-down system, and represents an approximation of the characteristics of the final product.

4. A second prototype is evolved by a fourfold procedure: (1) evaluating the first prototype in terms of its strengths, weaknesses, and risks; (2) defining the requirements of the second prototype; (3) planning and designing the second prototype; (4) constructing and testing the second prototype.

5. At the customer's option, the entire project can be aborted if the risk is deemed too great. Risk factors might involve development cost overruns, operating-cost miscalculation, or any other factor that could, in the customer's judgment, result in a less-than-satisfactory final product.

6. The existing prototype is evauated in the same manner as was the previous prototype, and, if necessary, another prototype is developed from it according to the fourfold procedure outlined above.

7. The preceding steps are iterated until the customer is satisfied that the refined prototype represents the final product desired.

8. The final system is constructed, based on the refined prototype.

9. The final system is thoroughly evaluated and tested. Routine maintenance is carried out   on a continuing basis to prevent large-scale failures and to minimize downtime.

Also see **systems development life cycle** (SDLC), and **systems development method** (SDM).

splash page

A splash page (or splash screen) is:

1) An initial **Web site** page used to capture the user's attention for a short time as a promotion or lead-in to the site **home page** or to tell the user what kind of **browser** and other software they need to view the site.

To have the splash page automatically move to the home page after a specified delay, include the HTML tag in the splash page as in this example with a 10-second delay:

```
META http-equiv="refresh" content="10; URL=http://
www.somesitename.com/home.html" >
```

The advantage of a splash page is that you can create effects or provide information that is only needed once a visit. For example, a user can keep coming back to the home page without having to be bothered with browser requirements.

2) Some sites use "splash page" to mean the home page itself, especially where it contains attention-capturing visual or multimedia effects (creating a "splash").

splay tree

A splay tree is a self-adjusting search **algorithm** for placing and locating files (called records or keys) in a **database**. The algorithm finds data by repeatedly making choices at decision points called nodes.

In a splay tree, as in a **binary tree**, a node has two branches (also called children). Records are stored in locations called leaves. This name derives from the fact that records always exist at end points; there is nothing beyond them. The starting point is called the root. The number of access operations required to reach the desired record is called the depth. In a practical tree, there can be thousands, millions, or billions of nodes, children, leaves, and records. Not every leaf necessarily contains a record, but more than half do. A leaf that does not contain data is called a null.

The splay tree scheme is unique because the tree organization varies depending on which nodes are most frequently accessed. This structural change takes place by means of so-called splaying operations, also called rotations. (In general, to splay is to spread or extend out or apart.) There are several ways in which splaying can be done. It always involves interchanging the root with the node in question. One or more other nodes might change position as well. The purpose of splaying is to minimize the number of access operations required to recover desired data records over a period of time.

Also see **binary tree**, **B-tree**, and **tree structure**.

spline

In computer graphics, a spline is a curve that connects two or more specific points, or that is defined by two or more points. The term can also refer to the mathematical equation that defines such a curve.

Consider the set of points in the illustration below. It is easy to envision a curve that approximately connects the four points. In the old days of mechanical drafting, a flexible metal or wooden strip (called a *spline*, and the term from which the present term derives) was used to construct approximate graphs such as this.

A computer can be used to test various curves, having known formulas, for an optimal "fit" for any finite set of points. In the example shown here, a near-perfect fit exists, and the curve has a relatively simple formula. Not all splines are this straightforward. But in theory, at least one spline curve can be found that approximates a continuous graph for any finite set of points.

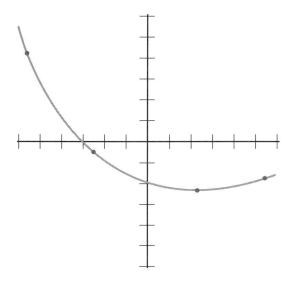

split

Among Internet Relay Chat (**IRC**) users, a split is a condition where two or more IRC **server**s are temporarily unable to communicate. When a split occurs between two computers on IRC, each seems to have gone offline to the other. The condition is usually temporary. It can be caused by a **packet** route timing out, a server rebooting, or a similar circumstance.

splitter

In telephony, a splitter, sometimes called a "**plain old telephone service** splitter," is a device that divides a telephone **signal** into two or more signals, each carrying a selected frequency range, and can also reassemble signals from multiple signal sources into a single signal. Users getting connected to the Internet with Asymmetric Digital Subscriber Line (**ADSL**) service may, in some cases, have a splitter installed at their home or business. Users elsewhere may be able to get **splitterless** service (which means that a splitter doesn't need to be installed). For ADSL, the splitter divides the incoming signal into low frequencies to send to voice devices and high frequencies for data to the computer. The telephone company's central office also uses a POTS splitter to send low-frequency voice signals on to the voice telephone network and to send high-frequency data to a Digital Subscriber Line Access Multiplexor (**DSLAM**) for transmission to the Internet.

splitterless

Splitterless refers to a type of Digital Subscriber Line (**DSL**) telephone service that does not require the installation of a **plain old telephone service splitter** at the customer location. Splitterless installation means that installation does not require "a truck roll" (that is, the cost of a visit from an installer).

spontaneous area network

See "ad-hoc network"

spoof

"Spoof" was a game involving trickery and nonsense that was invented by an English comedian, Arthur Roberts, prior to 1884, when it is recorded as having been "revived." Webster's defines the verb to mean (1) to deceive or hoax, and (2) to make good-natured fun of.

On the Internet, "to spoof" can mean:

1) To deceive for the purpose of gaining access to someone else's resources (for example, to fake an Internet address so that one looks like a certain kind of Internet user)

2) To simulate a communications protocol by a program that is interjected into a normal sequence of processes for the purpose of adding some useful function

3) To playfully satirize a Web site.

spool

To spool (which stands for "simultaneous peripheral operations online") a computer document or task list (or "job") is to read it in and store it, usually on a **hard disk** or larger storage medium so that it can be printed or otherwise processed at a more convenient time (for example, when a printer is finished printing its current document). One can envision spooling as reeling a document or task list onto a spool of thread so that it can be unreeled at a more convenient time.

The idea of spooling originated in early computer days when input was read in on punched cards for immediate printing (or processing and then immediately printing of the results). Since the computer operates at a much faster rate than input/output devices such as printers, it was more effective to store the read-in lines on a magnetic disk until they could be conveniently printed when the printer was free and the computer was less busy working on other tasks. Actually, a printer has a **buffer** but frequently the buffer isn't large enough to hold the entire document, requiring multiple **I/O** operations with the printer.

The spooling of documents for printing and **batch** job requests still goes on in mainframe computers where many users share a pool of resources. On personal computers, your print jobs (for example, a Web page you want to print) are spooled to an output file on hard disk if your printer is already printing another file.

spread spectrum

Spread spectrum is a form of **wireless** communications in which the frequency of the transmitted signal is deliberately varied. This results in a much greater **bandwidth** than the signal would have if its frequency were not varied.

A conventional wireless signal has a frequency, usually specified in megahertz (**MHz**) or gigahertz (**GHz**), that does not change with time (except for small, rapid fluctuations that occur as a result of modulation). When you listen to a signal at 103.1 MHz on an FM stereo receiver, for example, the signal stays at 103.1 MHz. It does not go up to 105.1 MHz or down to 99.1 MHz. The digits on the radio's frequency dial stay the same at all times. The frequency of a conventional wireless signal is kept as constant as the state of the art will permit, so the bandwidth can be kept within certain limits, and so the signal can be easily located by someone who wants to retrieve the information.

There are at least two problems with conventional wireless communications that can occur under certain circumstances. First, a signal whose frequency is constant is subject to catastrophic interference. This occurs when another signal is transmitted on, or very near, the frequency of the desired signal. Catastrophic interference can be accidental (as in amateur-radio communications) or it can be deliberate (as in wartime). Second, a constant-frequency signal is easy to intercept, and is therefore not well suited to applications in which information must be kept confidential between the source (transmitting party) and destination (receiving party).

To minimize troubles that can arise from the above mentioned vulnerabilities of conventional communications circuits, the frequency of the transmitted signal can be deliberately varied over a comparatively large segment of the **electromagnetic radiation spectrum**. This variation is done according to a specific, but complicated mathematical function. In order to intercept the signal, a receiver must be tuned to frequencies that vary precisely according to this function. The receiver must "know" the frequency-versus-time function employed by the transmitter, and must also "know" the starting-time point at which the function begins. If someone wants to jam a spread-spectrum signal, that person must have a transmitter that "knows" the function and its starting-time point. The spread-spectrum function must be kept out of the hands of unauthorized people or entities.

Most spread-spectrum signals use a **digital** scheme called frequency hopping. The transmitter frequency changes abruptly, many times each second. Between "hops," the transmitter frequency is stable. The length of time that the transmitter remains on a given frequency between "hops" is

known as the dwell time. A few spread-spectrum circuits employ continuous frequency variation, which is an **analog** scheme.

spreadsheet

A spreadsheet is a sheet of paper that shows accounting or other data in rows and columns; a spreadsheet is also a computer **application program** that simulates a physical spreadsheet by capturing, displaying, and manipulating **data** arranged in rows and columns. The spreadsheet is one of the most popular uses of the personal computer.

In a spreadsheet, spaces that hold items of data are called cells. Each cell is labeled according to its placement (for example, A1, A2, A3...) and may have an absolute or relative reference to the cells around it. A spreadsheet is generally designed to hold numerical data and short text strings. Spreadsheets usually provide the ability to portray data relationships graphically. Spreadsheets generally do not offer the ability to structure and label data items as fully as a database and usually do not offer the ability to query the database. In general, a spreadsheet is a much simpler program than a database program.

Daniel Bricklin and Bob Frankston created the first spreadsheet application, VisiCalc (for "visible calculator"). Lotus 1-2-3 came next, followed by Microsoft Excel. While Lotus 1-2-3 was the first to introduce cell names and macros, Microsoft Excel implemented a graphical user interface and the ability to point and click using a mouse. There are many other spreadsheet applications on the market today; however, Lotus 1-2-3 and Microsoft Excel continue to be the most popular.

spyware

In general, spyware is any technology that aids in gathering information about a person or organization without their knowledge. On the Internet, spyware is programming that is put in someone's computer to secretly gather information about the user and relay it to advertisers or other interested parties. Spyware can get in a computer as a software **virus** or as the result of installing a new program. Data collecting programs that are installed with the user's knowledge are not, properly speaking, spyware, if the user fully understands what data is being collected and with whom it is being shared.

The **cookie** is a well-known mechanism for storing information about an Internet user on their own computer. However, the existence of cookies and their use is generally not concealed from users, who can also disallow access to cookie information. Nevertheless, to the extent that a Web site stores information about you in a cookie that you don't know about, the cookie mechanism could be considered a form of spyware. DoubleClick, a leading banner ad serving company, changed its plans to combine cookie information with database information from other sources to target ad campaigns directly to individuals without their permission. DoubleClick's current policy is not to collect "personally-identifiable" information about a user without their explicit permission or "opt-in."

Aureate Media, which distributes free software on the Web in exchange for the right to gather user information, is another company that has been criticized for not plainly indicating what data it gathers and for making it difficult to remove its programming.

Spyware is part of an overall public concern about **privacy on the Internet**.

SQL

SQL (Structured Query Language) is a standard interactive and programming language for getting information from and updating a **database**. Although SQL is both an **ANSI** and an **ISO** standard, many database products support SQL with proprietary extensions to the standard language. Queries take the form of a command language that lets you select, insert, update, find out the location of data, and so forth. There is also a programming interface.

SQLJ Java

See "SQLJ"

SQLJ

SQLJ is a set of programming extensions that allow a programmer using the **Java** programming language to embed statements that provide **SQL** (Structured Query Language) database requests. SQLJ is similar to existing extensions for SQL that are provided for **C**, **Formula Translation**, and other programming languages. IBM, Oracle, and several other companies are proposed SQLJ as a standard and as a simpler and easier-to-use alternative to **Java Database Connectivity**.

The SQLJ specifications are in several parts:

- SQLJ: Embedded SQL...Specifications for embedding SQL statements in Java **method**s.

- SQLJ: SQL Routines...Specifications for calling Java static methods as SQL stored procedures and user-defined **function**s.

- SQLJ: SQL Types...Specifications for using Java **class**es as SQL user-defined **data type**s.

square meter

The square meter, also called the meter squared, is the International System of Units (**SI**) unit of area. The symbol for square meter is m^2. Less formally, square meter is sometimes abbreviated sq m.

When calculating area, it is important to realize that area is proportional to the square of the linear dimension. Thus, if all linear dimensions are doubled, the area becomes four

times (2^2) as great; if all linear dimensions are cut to 1/3, the area becomes 1/9 ($1/3^2$) as great. An area of 1 m^2 is equal to 10,000 centimeters squared (10^4 cm^2) or 1,000,000 millimeters squared (10^6 mm^2). In the opposite sense, 1 m^2 is equal to 0.000001 kilometer squared (10^{-6} km^2).

When converting between square meters and non-SI units of area such as square inches (sq in) or square miles (sq mi), the linear-unit conversion factor must be squared. For example, one meter is approximately 39.37 inches (39.37 in); therefore 1 m^2 = 39.37^2 = 1550 sq in (approximately). As another example, 1 meter is about 0.0006215 mile (6.215 × 10^{-4} mi); therefore 1 m^2 = (6.215 × 10^{-4})^2 = 3.863 × 10^{-7} sq mi (approximately).

Also see **meter**, **cubic meter**, and International System of Units (**SI**).

Squeak

Squeak is an implementation of the **Smalltalk** programming environment that is designed to allow code to be run on any major **operating system**, including Windows 95/98/NT, **Windows CE**, and **UNIX**. Squeak includes a Smalltalk-80 compiler and a caching **just-in-time compiler** (JIT) compiler and a large **class** library. The environment supports real-time sound and music synthesis, Musical Instrument Digital Interface (**MIDI**) performance and scheduling, text-to-speech synthesis, 2- and 3-D graphics, and Web serving and interaction.

Squeak's easy-to-use graphical interface and its object-oriented approach make it an appealing development environment for educators. A pointer device such as a mouse is required as with all Smalltalk programming environments. The original mouse used with Smalltalk required three buttons each labeled yellow, red, and blue, which is still required today. If a three-button mouse is not available, it must be simulated using another method. For example, the Macintosh-based Squeak environment uses a single-button mouse so the functions are determined by context. This means that if the mouse is placed over a certain area of the screen or another key is pushed at the same time, a menu is activated.

The Squeak programming environment is not the same as the Squeak language developed by Rob Pike and Luca Cardelli in 1985.

SQUID

Also see **SQUID** (Source Quench Introduced Delay).

SQUID is a program that **cache**s Web and other Internet content in a **UNIX**-based **proxy server** closer to the user than the content-originating site. SQUID is provided as open source software and can be used under the **GNU** license for **Free Software Foundation**.

SRAM

SRAM (static RAM) is random access memory (**RAM**) that retains data bits in its memory as long as power is being supplied. Unlike dynamic RAM (**DRAM**), which stores bits in cells consisting of a **capacitor** and a **transistor**, SRAM does not have to be periodically refreshed. Static RAM provides faster access to data and is more expensive than DRAM. SRAM is used for a computer's **cache memory** and as part of the **random access memory digital-to-analog converter** on a video card.

SS7

See "Signaling System 7"

SSADM

SSADM (Structured Systems Analysis & Design Method) is a widely-used computer application development method in the UK, where its use is often specified as a requirement for government computing projects. It is increasingly being adopted by the public sector in Europe. SSADM is in the public domain, and is formally specified in British Standard BS7738.

SSADM divides an application development project into modules, stages, steps, and tasks, and provides a framework for describing projects in a fashion suited to managing the project. SSADM's objectives are to:

- Improve project management & control
- Make more effective use of experienced and inexperienced development staff
- Develop better quality systems
- Make projects resilient to the loss of staff
- Enable projects to be supported by computer-based tools such as **computer-aided software engineering** systems
- Establish a framework for good communications between participants in a project

SSADM covers those aspects of the life-cycle of a system from the feasibility study stage to the production of a physical design; it is generally used in conjunction with other methods, such as PRINCE, which is concerned with the broader aspects of project management.

In detail, SSADM sets out a cascade or waterfall view of systems development, in which there are a series of steps, each of which leads to the next step. This might be contrasted with the rapid application development (**RAD**) method, which pre-supposes a need to conduct steps in parallel. SSADM's steps, or stages, are:

- Feasibility
- Investigation of the current environment
- Business systems options
- Definition of requirements

- Technical system options
- Logical design
- Physical design

For each stage, SSADM sets out a series of techniques and procedures, and conventions for recording and communicating information pertaining to these—both in textual and diagramatic form. SSADM is a very comprehensive model, and a characteristic of the method is that projects may use only those elements of SSADM appropriate to the project. SSADM is supported by a number of CASE tool providers.

SSH

See "Secure Shell"

SSI

See "Server-side include"

SSL card

See "server accelerator card"

SSL

See "Secure Sockets Layer"

SSO

See "single signon"

SSP

See "storage service provider"

stack

(1) **TCP/IP** is frequently referred to as a "stack." This refers to the layers (TCP, IP, and sometimes others) through which all data passes at both client and server ends of a data exchange. A clear picture of layers similar to those of TCP/IP is provided in our description of **OSI**, the reference model of the layers involved in any network communication.

The term "stack" is sometimes used to include utilities that support the layers of TCP/IP. The Netscape Handbook says (and we quote): "To make a successful connection to the Internet, your PC needs application software such as Netscape plus a TCP/IP stack consisting of TCP/IP software, **sockets** software (**Winsock.dynamic link library**), and hardware driver software (**packet** drivers). Several popular TCP/IP stacks are available for Windows, including **shareware** stacks."

(2) In programming, a stack is a data area or buffer used for storing requests that need to be handled. The *IBM Dictionary of Computing* says that a stack is always a push-down list, meaning that as new requests come in, they push down the old ones. Another way of looking at a push-down list—or

stack—is that the program always takes its next item to handle from the top of the stack. (This is unlike other arrangements such as "FIFO" or "first-in first-out.")

stackable hub

A stackable hub is a **hub** designed to be connected and stacked or positioned on top of another hub, forming an expanding stack. Since a hub is basically a concentrator of device connections, a set of stackable hubs is just a bigger concentrator. The stackable approach allows equipment to be easily and economically expanded as a grows in size. The stacking feature also reduces clutter.

Typically, devices with network interface cards (**NICs**) are connected to each hub with shielded twisted pair (**STP**) or unshielded twisted pair (**UTP**) cable. The set of stackable hubs is interconnected with a very short "cascading" cable in the rear of the stack. A special port, such as an **Ethernet** Attachment Unit Interface (**AUI**) port, may be provided to connect the set of stackable hubs to a **backbone** cable that connects to other sets of stackable hubs or other network devices.

Typical stackable hub options include:

- The ability to mix hubs, **routers**, and other devices in the same stack
- Fault tolerance so that if one hub fails, the other hubs in the stack can continue to operate
- **port** redundancy so that if one port fails, a backup port can be automatically substituted
- Hardware and software to let you manage the stackable hubs using the Simple Network Management Protocol (**SNMP**)

stale data

In computer processing, if a **processor** changes the value of an **operand** and then, at a subsequent time, fetches the operand and obtains the old rather than the new value of the operand, then it is said to have seen stale data.

On a uniprocessor, stale data cannot be tolerated. It would mean that the processor violated fundamental expectations about its own behavior. On shared memory multiprocessors, however, it is considered acceptable for machines to generate stale data on operands shared between processes. For such operands, the expectation is that programs will take precautions (**atomic** instructions or **critical section routines**) to prevent stale data from being seen.

stamped multisession CD standard

See "Blue Book"

standalone dump

A standalone dump is the copying of the contents of computer main storage (**RAM**) to another storage device, usually for the purpose of debugging a programming problem. (An earlier, now out-of-date term is **core dump**.) The term is primarily used in the **mainframe** environment. When an IBM mainframe stops operating because of a "hard wait state" or a "machine check" condition, an operator or system programmer can perform a "Store Status" operation that saves the program status word (PSW) and the 16 general purpose registers (GPRs), which tell exactly what the computer was doing when it stopped operating, and then performs a standalone dump to copy real and **virtual memory** to tape or **direct access storage device** (disk storage). These operations are performed from a system master console. After an initial program load (**IPL**) to restart the **operating system**, the standalone dump can be formatted by a special utility program and printed or displayed. Diagnostic techniques can be used to isolate the failing **component** so that ultimately the customer can get a fix from IBM or report a new problem.

When a mainframe operator encounters "hard stop" errors in the middle of the night and calls the system programmer, the advice is often to "Take a standalone dump and call me in the morning."

standard definition television

Standard definition television (SDTV) is a digital television (**DTV**) format that provides a picture quality similar to digital versatile disc (**DVD**). SDTV and high definition television (**HDTV**) are the two categories of display formats for digital television (DTV) transmissions, which are becoming the standard.

HDTV provides a higher quality display, with a vertical **resolution** display from 720p to 1080i and higher and an aspect ratio (the width to height ratio of the screen) of 16:9, for a viewing experience similar to watching a movie. In comparison, SDTV has a range of lower resolutions and no defined aspect ratio. New television sets will be either HDTV-capable or SDTV-capable, with receivers that can convert the signal to their native display format. SDTV, in common with HDTV, uses the **MPEG-2** file compression method.

Because a compressed SDTV digital signal is smaller than a compressed HDTV signal, broadcasters can transmit up to five SDTV programs simultaneously instead of just one HDTV program. This is **multicasting**. Multicasting is an attractive feature because television stations can receive additional revenue from the additional advertising these extra programs provide. With today's analog television system, only one program at a time can be transmitted.

When the U.S. decided to make the transition from analog television to DTV, the Federal Communications Commission decided to let broadcasters decide whether to broadcast SDTV or HDTV programs. Most have decided to broadcast SDTV programs in the daytime and to broadcast HDTV programs during prime time broadcasting. Both SDTV and HDTV are supported by the Digital Video Broadcasting (**DTV**) and Advanced Television Systems Committee (ATSC) set of standards.

Standard Generalized Markup Language

See "SGML"

Standard MIDI File

The SMF (Standard MIDI File) was developed to allow musicians and audio file developers to transfer their sequenced **MIDI** data from one software application to another. This file format lets users exchange music and data without regard to computer **operating system** platform. Today, there are many Web sites devoted to the sale and exchange of music data in the Standard MIDI File format.

There are two variations of the Standard MIDI File format, called Type 0 and Type 1. Both variations contain the same data, but the arrangement of the data within the file is different. Type 0 is a single track of data; Type 1 is multi-track. Many of the popular sequencing software packages available can import and export either type of file.

In the Type 0 Standard MIDI File, all data is saved to a single track without regard to its MIDI channel reference. The file plays normally, but accessing the individual components is a bit more difficult. If editing is needed, the user can open the Standard MIDI File in the application of choice and copy/paste individual channels of information manually as needed.

A Type 1 Standard MIDI File outputs a separate track for each MIDI channel in the original sequence. This format greatly simplifies editing once the sequence has been transferred from one sequencer to another.

standard temperature and pressure

Standard temperature and pressure, abbreviated STP, refers to nominal conditions in the atmosphere at sea level. This value is important to physicists, chemists, engineers, and pilots and navigators.

Standard temperature is defined as zero degrees Celsius (0°C), which translates to 32 degrees Fahrenheit (32°F) or 273.15 degrees kelvin (273.15°K). This is essentially the freezing point of pure water at sea level, in air at standard pressure.

Standard pressure supports 760 millimeters in a mercurial barometer (760 mmHg). This is about 29.9 inches of mercury, and represents approximately 14.7 pounds per inch (14.7 lb/in^2). Imagine a column of air measuring one inch square, extending straight up into space beyond the atmosphere. The air in such a column would weigh about 14.7 pounds.

The density of air at STP is approximately 1.29 **kilogram per meter cubed** (1.29 kg/m^3). This fact comes as a surprise to many people; a cubic meter of air weighs nearly three pounds!

Also see **kilogram**, **meter**, **kilogram per meter cubed**, **SI** (International System of Units), and **specific gravity**.

Star processor

IBM's Star processor is a reduced instruction set computer (**RISC**) **processor** that is available in several series versions for IBM's **AS/400** and RS/6000 systems. The three processors in the Star Series are the Northstar, the Pulsar, and the Silicon-On-Insulator (**SOI**) processor.

The first in the Star Series, the Northstar processor, is **superscalar**, which means it can execute multiple instructions per **clock cycle**, and includes two 64 **Kbps** on-chip level-one (**L1**) **cache**s. Its operating frequency is 262 **MHz**, and it has a 162 mm2 die size. It uses 27 watts of power. The Northstar processor is based on traditional complementary metal-oxide semiconductor (**CMOS**) fabrication technology. It is often called the A50 processor in AS/400 systems and the RS64-II processor in RS/6000 systems.

The Pulsar is the second Star Series processor. It is based on a combined copper and **silicon** fabrication technology, which affords more operating speed using less power. Its operating frequency is 450 MHz, and it has a 140 mm2 die size. It includes two 128 Kbps on-chip L1 caches and operates on 24 watts of power. The Northstar processor was the basis for the Pulsar. The Pulsar powers the RS/6000 S80 system. It is often called the RS64-III processor.

The final Star Series processor is the Silicon-on-Insulator-based processor used in the AS/400 iSeries server. SOI-based processors are manufactured using pure silicon and silicon oxide. The operating frequency is 550 MHz, and it has a 140 mm2 die size. It includes two 128 Kbps on-chip L1 caches and uses 22 watts of power.

StarBand

StarBand is a broadband Internet service provider (**ISP**) that uses geostationary **satellite**s to provide always-on connection independent of other media. Established in late 2000, StarBand was the first widely-available service for the general public that made use of satellite links for both upstream and downstream data.

StarBand connection requires a Universal Serial Bus (**USB**) port or an **Ethernet** card, a special **modem**, a **dish antenna** measuring approximately 2 feet high by 3 feet wide by 3 feet deep, and two **coaxial cable**s that run between the dish and the modem. Professional installation is recommended.

Upstream data speeds, at the time of writing, were reported by users as 30 to 100 kilobits per second (**Kbps**), with 50 Kbps being typical. **Downstream** data speeds depend on the Web site visited, the complexity of downloaded pages, and the time of day. Normal downloads range from 150 Kbps to 500 Kbps.

Because StarBand uses a satellite for both the upstream and the downstream links, the **latency** is considerable. A geostationary satellite orbits 22,300 miles above the Earth's equator. For a user at a temperate latitude, signals must make four trips through space, each of approximately 23,000 miles, between a mouse click and the appearance of Web site data on the display. This introduces a delay of 0.5 second, because the speed of electromagnetic (EM) radiation is finite. But that is the mathematical minimum. In reality, the latency is usually longer. The upstream data must travel from the user's dish to the satellite, and then back down to the StarBand hub, where it is transmitted over land-based media. The downstream data must travel from the Web site under observation to the StarBand hub over land-based media, then up to the satellite, and back down to the user. The result is latency that sometimes exceeds 1 second. This is not a system defect, but technical reality.

StarBand is not recommended for highly interactive applications such as gaming. But for people in remote regions with no other option, StarBand can provide good broadband Internet service. The author of this definition has had the service since March of 2001, and it has proven invaluable. The only alternative is **dial-up** through antiquated telephone lines, resulting in real-world browsing speeds averaging 10 Kbps or somewhat higher. StarBand cannot compete with a well-installed **DSL** or **cable modem** connection, but it has provided the author with a browsing speed increase of over 1,000 percent, even taking latency into account.

StarOffice

StarOffice is a free productivity **application** suite from Sun Microsystems that includes a word processor (Writer), spreadsheet (Calc), database (Base), presentation maker (Impress), illustrator (Draw), schedule managment (Schedule), e-mail (Mail) and newsgroup (Discussion) component. StarOffice is compatible with Microsoft Office components (for example, you can open and save in Microsoft's Word, Excel, and PowerPoint file formats) and is available in 11 languages.

Fans of StarOffice appreciate its cross-platform capabilities and feel it offers low-budget users a good alternative to Microsoft's Office. Critics acknowledge that StarOffice is intuitive to use, but find the desktop interface floating palettes awkward. A common complaint about StarOffice is that you must open the entire suite of applications even if you only want to work with an individual component.

Sun Microsystems released an open-source version of StarOffice under the **GNU** general public license in October of 2000. Sun appointed Openoffice.org to manage the open-source version, using a development model similar to that of Netscape's **Mozilla**. Users of the open-source version of StarOffice must not only agree to the GNU general public license terms, they must also agree to Sun Industry Standard Source License (SISSL) which includes control over programming interfaces and compatibility tests. Sun plans to replace their proprietary default file format with Extensible Markup Language (**XML**), and is promoting the development of a Web-based version of StarOffice.

StarOffice is compatible with Sun Solaris SPARC, Sun Solaris Intel, Windows 95/98/NT, Linux, and OS/2. At present, there is no Mac version.

statampere

The statampere (abbreviated statA or A-esu) is the unit of electric **current** in the **cgs** (centimeter/gram/second) system of electrostatic units (esu). It is the equivalent of one **statcoulomb** (1 statC), also called one electrostatic unit (1 esu), of charge carriers moving past a specific point in one second.

The statampere is a small unit of current, equivalent to approximately 3.3356×10^{-10} **ampere** (A) or 0.33356 nanoampere (nA). In most applications, the ampere, which is the unit of current in the International System of Units (**SI**), is preferred.

Also see **current**, **cgs** or **small-unit metric system**, and International System of Units (**SI**).

statcoulomb

The statcoulomb (abbreviated statC) is the unit of electric charge quantity in the **cgs** (centimeter/gram/second) system. It is approximately equal to the charge contained in 2.082×10^9 **electrons**. When two objects, carrying like electrical charges of 1 statC each, are placed so their charge centers are one centimeter (1 cm) apart, the objects repel each other with a force of one **dyne** (1 dyn).

The statcoulomb is the basis for the system of electrostatic units (esu). It is a comparatively small unit in practical terms, equivalent to approximately 3.3356×10^{-10} **coulomb** (C). In most applications, the coulomb, which is the standard unit of charge quantity in the International System of Units (**SI**), is preferred.

Also see **charge quantity**, **small-unit metric system** or **cgs** system of units, and International System of Units (**SI**).

state machine

In general, a state machine is any device that stores the status of something at a given time and can operate on input to change the status and/or cause an action or output to take place for any given change. A **computer** is basically a state

machine and each machine **instruction** is input that changes one or more states and may cause other actions to take place. Each computer's data register stores a state. The **read-only memory** from which a **boot** program is loaded stores a state (the boot program itself is an initial state). The **operating system** is itself a state and each **application** that runs begins with some initial state that may change as it begins to handle input. Thus, at any moment in time, a computer system can be seen as a very complex set of states and each program in it as a state machine. In practice, however, state machines are used to develop and describe specific device or program interactions.

To summarize it, a state machine can be described as:

- An initial state or record of something stored someplace
- A set of possible input events
- A set of new states that may result from the input
- A set of possible actions or output events that result from a new state

In their book *Real-time Object-oriented Modeling*, Bran Selic & Garth Gullekson view a state machine as:

- A set of input events
- A set of output events
- A set of states
- A function that maps states and input to output
- A function that maps states and inputs to states (which is called a state transition function)
- A description of the initial state

A finite state machine is one that has a limited or finite number of possible states. (An infinite state machine can be conceived but is not practical.) A finite state machine can be used both as a development tool for approaching and solving problems and as a formal way of describing the solution for later developers and system maintainers. There are a number of ways to show state machines, from simple tables through graphically animated illustrations.

stateless

Also see **finite state machine**.

Stateful and stateless are adjectives that describe whether a computer or computer program is designed to note and remember one or more preceding events in a given sequence of interactions with a user, another computer or program, a device, or other outside element. Stateful means the computer or program keeps track of the state of interaction, usually by setting values in a storage field designated for that purpose. Stateless means there is no record of previous interactions and each interaction request has to be handled based entirely on information that comes with it. Stateful and stateless are derived from the usage of *state* as a set of conditions at a moment in time. (Computers are inherently

stateful in operation, so these terms are used in the context of a particular set of interactions, not of how computers work in general.)

The Internet's basic protocol, the Internet Protocol (**IP**), is an example of a stateless interaction. Each **packet** travels entirely on its own without reference to any other packet. When you request a Web page from a Web site, the request travels in one or more packets, each independent of the other as far as the Internet Protocol program itself is concerned. (The upper layer Transmission Control Protocol—TCP—does relate packets to each other, but uses the information within the packet rather than some external information to do this.) The term *connectionless* is also used to describe communication in which a connection is made and terminated for each message that is sent. IP is connectionless as well as stateless.

The Web's Hypertext Transfer Protocol (**HTTP**), an application layer above TCP/IP, is also stateless. Each request from a user for a Web page or URL results in the requested pages being served, but without the Web (HTTP) server remembering the request later. In other words, there is no recorded continuity. Each communication is discrete and unrelated to those that precede or follow. In order to have stateful communication, a site developer must furnish a special program that the server can call that can record and retrieve state information. Web browsers such as Netscape Explorer and Microsoft Internet Explorer provide an area in their subdirectories where state information can be stored and accessed. The area and the information that Web browsers and server applications put in this area is called a **cookie**.

In formal protocol specifications, a **finite state machine** is an abstract desciption of how a stateful system works that describes the action that follows each possible state.

The Internet (including the World Wide Web) can be thought of as a stateless system or machine. Most computers and human beings are stateful.

statfarad

The statfarad (abbreviated statF) is the unit of **capacitance** in the **cgs** (centimeter/gram/second) or **small-unit metric system**. It is equivalent to 1.1126×10^{-12} farads. The **farad** (F) is the standard unit of capacitance in the International System of Units (**SI**).

A capacitance as large as 1 F is almost unknown in the real world, but a 1-statF capacitance is common. In fact, two wires only a few centimeters long, placed in the vicinity of and parallel to each other, display a mutual capacitance on the order of 1 statF.

In practical applications, the microfarad (μF) and the picofarad (pF) are most often used to quantify capacitance; the statfarad is rarely seen in literature. For comparison, 1 μF $= 10^{-6}$ F and 1 pF $= 10^{-12}$ F. Thus, 1 statF $= 1.1126 \times 10^{-6}$ μF = 1.1126 pF.

Also see **capacitance**, **farad**, **cgs** or **small-unit metric system**, and International System of Units (**SI**).

stathenry

The stathenry (abbreviated statH) is the unit of **inductance** in the **cgs** (centimeter/gram/second) or **small-unit metric system**. It is equivalent to 8.9876×10^{11} henrys. The **henry** (H) is the standard unit of inductance in the International System of Units (**SI**).

It is rare to see an inductance as large as 1 H, but a 1-statH inductance is unknown in the real world. To produce an inductance that large, an impossibly long span of wire would have to be coiled into a tiny volume around a ferromagnetic core having a permeability higher than that of any known substance. (It might someday be possible, however, to produce inductances of that magnitude by supercooling.)

In practical applications, the microhenry (μH) and the nanohenry (nH) are most often used to quantify inductance. For comparison, 1 μH = 10^{-6} H and 1 nH = 10^{-9} H. Thus, 1 statH = 8.9876×10^{17} μH = 8.9876×10^{20} nH.

Also see **inductance**, **henry**, **cgs** or **small-unit metric system**, and International System of Units (**SI**).

static IP address/dynamic IP address

Also see **IP address**.

A static IP is a number (in the form of a **dotted quad**) that is assigned to a computer by an Internet Service Provider (**ISP**) to be its permanent address on the Internet. Computers use IP addresses to locate and talk to each other on the Internet, much the same way people use phone numbers to locate and talk to one another on the telephone. When you want to visit whatis.com, your computer asks a domain name system (**DNS**) server (think telephone information operator) for the correct dotted quad number (think phone number) for whatis.com and your computer uses the answer it receives to connect to the whatis.com **server**.

It would be simple if every computer that connects to the Internet could have its own static IP number, but when the Internet was first conceived, the architects didn't foresee the need for an unlimited number of IP addresses. Consequently, there are not enough IP numbers to go around. To get around that problem, many Internet service providers limit the number of static IP addresses they allocate, and economize on the remaining number of IP addresses they possess by temporarily assigning an IP address to a requesting Dynamic Host Configuration Protocol (**DHCP**) computer from a pool of IP addresses. The temporary IP address is called a **dynamic** IP address.

Requesting DHCP computers receive a dynamic IP address (think temporary phone number) for the duration of that Internet session or for some other specified amount of time. Once the user disconnects from the Internet, their dynamic

IP address goes back into the IP address pool so it can be assigned to another user. Even if the user reconnects immediately, odds are they will not be assigned the same IP address from the pool. To keep our telephone telephone analogy going, using a dynamic IP address is similar to using a pay phone. Unless there is a reason to receive a call, the user does not care what number he or she is calling from.

There are times, however, when users who connect to the Internet using dynamic IP wish to allow other computers to locate them. Perhaps they want to use **CU-SeeMe** or use a **VoIP** application to make long distance phone calls using their IP connection. In that case, they would need a static IP address. The user has two choices; they can contact their ISP and request a static IP address, or they can use a dynamic DNS service. Either choice will probably involve an additional monthly fee.

Using a dynamic DNS service works as if there was an old-fashioned telephone message service at your computer's disposal. When a user registers with a DNS service and connects to the Internet with a dynamic IP address, the user's computer contacts the DNS service and lets them know what IP address it has been assigned from the pool; the service works with the DNS server to forward the correct address to the requesting DHCP computer. (Think of calling the message service and saying "Hi. I can be reached at 435.44.32.111 right now. Please tell anyone who tries to reach me to call that number.) Using a dynamic DNS service to arrange for computers to find you even though you are using a dynamic IP address is the next-best thing to having a static IP.

IPv6, which has also been called "IPng" (IP Next Generation) will lengthen IP addresses from 32 bits to 128 bits and increase the number of available IP addressess significantly, making static IP addresses easier and less expensive to obtain and maintain.

static random access memory

See "SRAM"

static

See "dynamic and static"

statistical time-division multiplexing

See "STDM"

statohm

The statohm (symbolized statΩ) is the unit of **resistance** in the **cgs** (centimeter/gram/second) electrostatic system of units. It is equivalent to approximately 8.9876×10^{11} ohms. The **ohm** (Ω) is the standard unit of resistance in the International System of Units (**SI**).

The statohm is an extremely large unit of resistance. In fact, an object with a resistance of 1 statΩ would make an excellent insulator or **dielectric**. In practical applications, the ohm, the kilohm (kΩ) and the megohm (MΩ or M) are most often used to quantify resistance. For comparison, 1 statΩ = 8.9876×10^5 MΩ = 8.9876×10^8 kΩ.

Also see **resistance**, **ohm**, **cgs** or **small-unit metric system**, and International System of Units (**SI**).

statsiemens

The statsiemens (symbolized statS) is the unit of **conductance** in the **cgs** (centimeter/gram/second) electrostatic system of units. It is equivalent to approximately 1.11265×10^{-12} siemens (S) or 1.11265 picosiemens (pS). The siemens is the standard unit of conductance in the International System of Units (**SI**).

The statsiemens is an extremely small unit of conductance. In fact, an object with a conductance of 1 statS would make an excellent insulator or **dielectric**. In practical applications, the siemens, the millisiemens (mS) and the microsiemens (μS)are most often used to quantify conductance. For comparison, 1 statS = 1.11265×10^{-6} μS = 1.11265×10^{-9} mS.

Also see **conductance**, **siemens**, **cgs** or **small-unit metric system**, and International System of Units (**SI**).

statvolt

The statvolt (symbolized statV) is the unit of electromotive force (EMF) or potential difference in the **cgs** (centimeter/gram/second) electrostatic system. When an EMF of 1 statV exists between two points, then one **erg** of energy is needed to move one **statcoulomb** (1 statC) of charge carriers between those two points.

A potential difference of 1 statV will drive a **current** of one **statampere** (1 statA) through a resistance of one **statohm** (statΩ). **Ohm's Law** applies for the electrostatic units, just as it does for the units in the International System (**SI**). That is:

$$E = IR$$

where E is the EMF in statvolts, I is the current in statamperes, and R is the resistance in statohms.

The statvolt is a fairly large unit of EMF, equal to approximately 299.79 volts (V). In most practical applications, the **volt**, which is the unit of potential difference in SI, is preferred.

Also see **voltage**, **cgs** or **small-unit metric system**, and International System of Units (**SI**).

statwatt

The statwatt (symbolized statW) is the unit of power in the **cgs** (centimeter/gram/second) electrostatic system. In a direct current (**DC**) circuit, 1 statW is the **power** dissipated,

radiated, or expended when one statvolt (1 statV) of potential difference drives a **current** of one **statampere** (1 statA) through a component.

In a DC circuit, or in an alternating current (**AC**) circuit in which there is no **reactance**, the following formula holds:

$$P = EI$$

where P is the power in statwatts, E is the potential difference in statvolts, and I is the current in statamperes.

The statwatt is a small unit of power, equivalent to 10^{-7} watt (W) or 0.1 microwatt (μW). In most applications, the **watt**, which is the unit of power in the International System (**SI**), is preferred.

Also see **power**, **watt**, **cgs** or **small-unit metric system**, and International System of Units (**SI**).

STDM

STDM, or statistical time division multiplexing, is one method for transmitting several types of data simultaneously across a single transmission cable or line (such as a T1 or T3 line). STDM is often used for managing data being transmitted via a local area network (LAN) or a wide area network (WAN). In these situations, the data is often simultaneously transmitted from any number of input devices attached to the network, including computers, printers, or fax machines.

STDM can also be used in telephone switchboard settings to manage the simultaneous calls going to or coming from multiple, internal telephone lines.

The concept behind STDM is similar to TDM, or time division multiplexing. TDM allows multiple users or input devices to transmit or receive data simultaneously by assigning each device the same, fixed amount of time on one of many "channels" available on the cable or line. The TDM method works well in many cases, but does not always account for the varying data transmission needs of different devices or users.

For example, a busy laser printer shared by many users might need to receive or transmit data 80-90% of the time at a much higher transmission rate than a seldom-used, data-entry computer attached to the same T-1 line. With TDM, even though the printer's transmission needs are greater, both devices would still be allocated the same duration of time to transmit or receive data.

In comparison to TDM, the STDM method analyzes statistics related to the typical workload of each input device (printer, fax, computer) and determines on-the-fly how much time each device should be allocated for data transmission on the cable or line. In the above example, STDM would allocate more time to the group printer, based on its past and current transmission needs and less time to the data-entry computer. Many believe the STDM method is a more efficient use of total bandwidth available than the TDM method.

The main statistics used in STDM are: each input device's peak data rates (in kbps, or kilobytes per second), and each device's duty factors (which is the percentage of time the device typically spends either transmitting or receiving data).

Besides TDM and STDM, other methods for simultaneously transmitting data on the same channel include Wavelength Division Multiplexing (WDM) and Frequency Division Multiplexing (FDM).

stealth

In computing, stealth refers to an event, object, or file that evades methodical attempts to find it. In particular, the term applies to certain computer **virus**es, and to a state of affairs in which a computer or port is rendered invisible to hacking programs.

A stealth virus can pass through an **antivirus program** unless and until the program is updated to include the virus in its database. Such a virus can infect the **boot sector** of a diskette, removable disk, or hard drive, thereby copying itself onto other media when files or folders are opened or transferred. If such a virus is written and distributed with malicious intent, it can cause great damage to computers and networks. The problem is especially serious if the virus does its dirty work insidiously, so it is not even discovered until it has spread to thousands of computers and corrupted millions of files.

Hackers are constantly scanning the Internet for computers or networks to exploit. An effective **firewall** can keep hackers out of computers, and is considered a must for computers equipped with broadband, always-on Internet connections. The best firewalls keep hacking programs from detecting the existence of a computer or network port. When a port-scanning program encounters a stealth (invisible) port, no reply is received in response to requests for connection. The hacking program then passes on to the next potential victim.

steganography

Steganography (pronounced STEHG-uh-NAH-gruhf-ee, from Greek *steganos*, or "covered," and *graphie*, or "writing") is the hiding of a secret message within an ordinary message and the extraction of it at its destination. Steganography takes **cryptography** a step farther by hiding an **encrypted** message so that no one suspects it exists. Ideally, anyone scanning your data will fail to know it contains encrypted data.

In modern digital steganography, data is first encrypted by the usual means and then inserted, using a special **algorithm**, into redundant (that is, provided but unneeded) data that is part of a particular file format such as a **JPEG** image. Think of all the bits that represent the same color **pixel**s repeated in a row. By applying the encrypted data to this redundant data in some random or nonconspicuous

way, the result will be data that appears to have the "noise" patterns of regular, nonencrypted data. A trademark or other identifying symbol hidden in software code is sometimes known as a *watermark*.

Recently revived, this formerly obsolete term gained currency in its day (1500) from a work by Johannes Trithemius, *Steganographia*, ostensibly a system of angel magic but also claiming to include a synthesis of how to learn and know things contained within a system of cryptography. The book was privately circulated but never published by the author because those who read it found it rather fearsome.

steradian

The steradian (symbolized sr) is the International System of Units (**SI**) unit of solid angular measure. There are 4 **pi**, or approximately 12.5664, steradians in a complete sphere.

A steradian is defined as conical in shape, as shown in the illustration. Point P represents the center of the sphere. The solid (conical) angle q, representing one steradian, is such that the area A of the subtended portion of the sphere is equal to r^2, where r is the radius of the sphere.

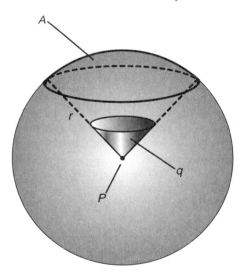

A general sense of the steradian can be envisioned by considering a sphere whose radius is one **meter** ($r = 1m$). Imagine a cone with its apex P at the center of the sphere, and that intersects the surface in a circle (shown as an ellipse, the upper half of which is dashed). Suppose the flare angle q of the cone is such that the area A of the spherical segment within the circle is equal to one meter squared ($A = 1$ m^2). Then the flare angle of the cone is equal to 1 steradian ($q = 1$ sr). The total surface area of the sphere is, in this case, 12.5664 square meters (4 pi times the square of the radius).

Based on the foregoing example, the geometry of which is independent of scale, it can be said that a solid angle of 1 sr encompasses about 1/12.5664, or 7.9577 percent, of the space surrounding a point.

Also see **radian** and International System of Units (**SI**).

stickiness

Stickiness is anything about a Web site that encourages a visitor to stay longer. A Web site is sticky if a visitor tends to stay for a long time and to return.

The two most important measurements of what a Web site has to offer advertisers are ad views and the average time each visitor spends on the site. If you can make your visitor spend more time at your site, they will view more ads and they can be considered more loyal to the site and presumably somewhat more likely to click on the ads and patronize advertisers. **Portal** sites like Yahoo achieve stickiness by having a great deal of content, and also by finding ways to involve the user with the site.

The most common stickiness approaches are:

- Providing content that the user really wants

- Allowing the user to personalize the site (Yahoo, Excite, and MSN Network, for example)

- Building online communities in which users post information or form discussion groups (Yahoo, Geocities)

- Inviting user feedback in response to columnists (ZDNet)

- Adding games to the site (Yahoo)

- Using extensive hypertext cross-references to other parts of the site (whatis.com and many others)

Stickiness may also be said to apply to a set of related sites such as those of CNET and TechTarget, which have a common design and navigation interface and sell ads across the sites as well as on individual sites.

stochastic

1) Generally, stochastic (pronounced stow-KAS-tik, from the Greek *stochastikos*, or "skilled at aiming," since *stochos* is a target) describes an approach to anything that is based on probability.

2) In mathematics, a stochastic approach is one in which values are obtained from a corresponding sequence of jointly distributed random variables. Classic examples of the stochastic process are guessing the length of a queue at a stated time given the random distribution over time of a number of people or objects entering and leaving the queue and guessing the amount of water in a reservoir based on the random distribution of rainfall and water usage.

stockkeeping unit

See "SKU"

storage

Computer storage is the holding of data in an electromagnetic form for access by a computer processor. Primary storage is data in random access memory (**RAM**) and other "built-in" devices. Secondary storage is data on **hard disk**s, tapes, and other external devices.

Primary storage is much faster to access than secondary storage because of the proximity of the storage to the processor or because of the nature of the storage devices. On the other hand, secondary storage can hold much more data than primary storage.

In addition to RAM, primary storage includes read-only memory (**ROM**) and **L1 and L2 cache** memory. In addition to hard disks, secondary storage includes a range of device types and technologies, including **diskette**s, **Zip drive**s, **RAID** systems, and **holographic storage**.

Devices that hold storage are collectively known as *storage media*.

storage area network

A storage area network (SAN) is a high-speed special-purpose **network** (or subnetwork) that interconnects different kinds of data storage devices with associated data **server**s on behalf of a larger network of users. Typically, a storage area network is part of the overall network of computing resources for an **enterprise**. A storage area network is usually clustered in close proximity to other computing resources such as IBM S/390 **mainframe**s but may also extend to remote locations for **backup** and archival storage, using wide area network carrier technologies such as **asynchronous transfer mode** or **Synchronous Optical Network**s.

A storage area network can use existing communication technology such as IBM's **optical fiber ESCON** or it may use the newer **Fibre Channel** technology. Some SAN system integrators liken it to the common storage **bus** (flow of data) in a personal computer that is shared by different kinds of storage devices such as a hard disk or a CD-ROM player.

SANs support disk mirroring, backup and restore, archival and retrieval of archived data, data migration from one storage device to another, and the sharing of data among different servers in a network. SANs can incorporate subnetworks with network-attached storage (**NAS**) systems.

storage media

See "storage medium"

storage medium

In computers, a storage medium is any technology (including devices and materials) used to place, keep, and retrieve **data** on a long-term basis. A **medium** is an element used in communicating a message; on a storage medium, the "messages"—in the form of data—are suspended for use when needed. The plural form of this term is *storage media.* **Storage** is sometimes used to mean "all forms of storage media." Storage is usually distinguished from **memory**, which is the place in a computer where data is kept on a short-term basis for faster access.

Examples of storage media include:

- The **diskette**
- The **hard disk**
- The **compact disk**

Storage media can be arranged for access in many ways. Some well-known arrangements include:

- A redundant array of independent disks (**RAID**)
- **Network-attached storage**
- A **storage area network**

storage service provider

Also see two related terms, **application service provider** and **management service provider**.

On the Internet, a storage service provider (SSP) is a company that provides computer **storage** space and related management to other companies. In addition to the storage itself, SSPs typically offer periodic backup and archiving and some offer the ability to consolidate data from multiple company locations so that all locations can share the data effectively. Customers may be billed a monthly rate and for each managed **terabyte** of storage. Two leading SSP companies are StorageNetworks and Managed Storage International.

Some companies specialize in providing limited storage service, such as periodic remote backup, to individual computer users and small businesses.

storage-over-IP

See "iSCSI"

stored procedure

In a database management system (**DBMS**), a stored procedure is a set of Structured Query Language (**SQL**) statements with an assigned name that's stored in the database in compiled form so that it can be shared by a number of programs. The use of stored procedures can be helpful in controlling access to data (end-users may enter or change data but do not write procedures), preserving data integrity (information is entered in a consistent manner), and improving productivity (statements in a stored procedure only need to be written one time).

STP

See "shielded twisted pair"

stream cipher

A stream **cipher** is a method of encrypting text (to produce **ciphertext**) in which a cryptographic key and **algorithm** are applied to each **binary digit** in a data stream, one bit at a time. This method is not much used in modern cryptography. The main alternative method is the **block cipher** in which a key and algorithm are applied to blocks of data rather than individual bits in a stream.

See also: **encryption**

streaming

See "streaming video"

streaming media

Streaming media is sound (**audio**) and pictures (**video**) that are transmitted on the Internet in a **streaming** or continuous fashion, using data **packet**s. The most effective reception of streaming **media** requires some form of **broadband** technology such as **cable modem** or **DSL**.

Also see **streaming sound** and **streaming video**.

streaming sound

Streaming sound is sound that is played as it arrives. The alternative is a sound recording (such as a WAV file) that doesn't start playing until the entire file has arrived. Support for streaming sound may require a **plug-in** player or come with the **browser**. Leading providers of streaming sound include Progressive Networks' RealAudio and Macromedia's Shockwave for Director (which includes an animation player as well).

streaming video

Streaming video is a sequence of "moving images" that are sent in compressed form over the Internet and displayed by the viewer as they arrive. Streaming media is streaming video with sound. With streaming video or streaming media, a Web user does not have to wait to download a large file before seeing the video or hearing the sound. Instead, the media is sent in a continuous stream and is played as it arrives. The user needs a *player*, which is a special program that uncompresses and sends video data to the display and audio data to speakers. A player can be either an integral part of a browser or downloaded from the software maker's Web site.

Major streaming video and streaming media technologies include RealSystem G2 from RealNetwork, Microsoft Windows Media Technologies (including its NetShow Services and Theater Server), and VDO. Microsoft's approach uses the standard **MPEG** compression **algorithm** for video. The other approaches use proprietary algorithms. (The program that does the compression and decompression is sometimes called the **codec**.) Microsoft's technology offers streaming audio at up to 96 **Kbps** and streaming video at up to 8 **Mbps** (for the NetShow Theater Server). However, for most Web users, the streaming video will be limited to the data rates of the connection (for example, up to 128 Kbps with an ISDN connection). Microsoft's streaming media files are in its Advanced Streaming Format (ASF).

Streaming video is usually sent from prerecorded video files, but can be distributed as part of a live broadcast "feed." In a live broadcast, the video signal is converted into a compressed digital signal and transmitted from a special Web server that is able to do **multicasting**, sending the same file to multiple users at the same time.

string

In programming, a string is a contiguous (see **contiguity**) sequence of symbols or values, such as a **character** string (a sequence of characters) or a **bit** string (a sequence of binary values).

strobe

In computer or memory technology, a strobe is a **signal** that is sent that validates data or other signals on adjacent parallel lines. In memory technology, the **CAS** (column address strobe) and RAS (**row address strobe**) signals are used to tell a dynamic RAM that an address is a column or row address.

strongly-typed

A strongly-typed programming language is one in which each type of **data** (such as integer, character, hexadecimal, packed decimal, and so forth) is predefined as part of the programming language and all constants or variables defined for a given program must be described with one of the data types. Certain operations may be allowable only with certain data types. The language **compiler** enforces the data typing and use compliance. An advantage of strong data typing is that it imposes a rigorous set of rules on a programmer and thus guarantees a certain consistency of results. A disadvantage is that it prevents the programmer from inventing a data type not anticipated by the developers of the programming language and it limits how "creative" one can be in using a given data type.

Structured Graph Format

Structured Graph Format (SGF), an application of the Extensible Markup Language (**XML**), is used to describe a Web site so that its pages and content can be displayed and accessed in a structured, usually tabular form. Using SGF, a Web site is rendered as a structured graph, which is a set of nodes and links that enable a browser to conveniently interact with the site. A typical use of an SGF file is to describe a site to a browser in the form of a site map, which is created dynamically when requested by the user. If the structure of the site changes, the site map seen by a browser will change accordingly, without a human programmer having to intervene and write new HTML code. Typically, the user can also search by keywords, phrases, or topics.

For SGF to be effectively used, the browser must use another **client** application, such as SFViewer and SGMapper. The client application creates the graphical interface that allows the user to navigate the site according to selected criteria.

Structured Query Language

See "SQL"

Structured Systems Analysis & Design Method

See "SSADM"

stub

A stub is a small program routine that substitutes for a longer program, possibly to be loaded later or that is located remotely. For example, a program that uses Remote Procedure Calls (**RPCs**) is compiled with stubs that substitute for the program that provides a requested procedure. The stub accepts the request and then forwards it (through another program) to the remote procedure. When that procedure has completed its service, it returns the results or other status to the stub which passes it back to the program that made the request.

style sheet

A term extended from print publishing to online media, a style sheet is a definition of a document's appearance in terms of such elements as:

- The default typeface, size, and color for headings and body text

- How front matter (preface, figure list, title page, and so forth) should look

- How all or individual sections should be laid out in terms of space (for example, two newspaper columns, one column with headings having hanging heads, and so forth).

- Line spacing, margin widths on all sides, spacing between headings, and so forth
- How many heading levels should be included in any automatically generated Table of Contents
- Any **boilerplate** content that is to be included on certain pages (for example, copyright statements)

Typically, a style sheet is specified at the beginning of an electronic document, either by embedding it or linking to it. This style sheet applies to the entire document. As necessary, specific elements of the overall style sheet can be overridden by special coding that applies to a given section of the document.

For Web pages, a style sheet performs a similar function, allowing the designer to ensure an underlying consistency across a site's pages. The style elements can be specified once for the entire document by either imbedding the style rules in the document heading or cross-referring (linking to or importing) a separate style sheet. A browser may allow the user to override some or all of the style sheet attributes.

A **cascading style sheet** is a style sheet that anticipates that other style sheets will either fill in or override the overall style sheet. This provides the designer the advantage of being able to rely on the basic style sheet when desired and overriding it when desired. The filling in or overriding can occur on a succession of "cascading" levels of style sheets. For example, one style sheet could be created and linked to from every Web page of a Web site as the overall style sheet. For any portion of a page that included a certain kind of content such as a catalog of products, another style sheet that amends the basic style sheet could be linked to. And within the span of that style sheet, yet another style sheet could be specified as applying to a particular type of product display.

When creating Web pages, the use of style sheets is now recommended by the World Wide Web Consortium. The latest version of the Hypertext Markup Language, **HTML 4.0**, while continuing to support older tags, indicates which ones should be replaced by the use of style sheet specifications. The Web's Cascading Style Sheets, level 1 (**CSSL1**) is a recommendation for cascading style sheets that has been developed by a working group of the World Wide Web Consortium (**W3C**).

stylus

A stylus (pronounced STAI-luhs, from the Latin *stilus* or "stake") is an instrument for writing and, in computers, an input device used to write text or draw lines on a surface as input to a computer. The term was first used in workstations designed for graphics applications, such as **CAD/CAM**, where the stylus was attached to an electronically-sensitive tablet or surface on which the stylus user wrote. Later, in **handheld** computers such as Apple's Newton and 3Com's PalmPilot, a stylus was provided as an instrument for

writing text characters and simple pictures. In most of today's handheld computers that accept written input, the writing instrument is referred to as a stylus or a pen.

subnet

A subnet (short for "subnetwork") is an identifiably separate part of an organization's network. Typically, a subnet may represent all the machines at one geographic location, in one building, or on the same local area network (**LAN**). Having an organization's network divided into subnets allows it to be connected to the Internet with a single shared network address. Without subnets, an organization could get multiple connections to the Internet, one for each of its physically separate subnetworks, but this would require an unnecessary use of the limited number of network numbers the Internet has to assign. It would also require that Internet routing tables on gateways outside the organization would need to know about and have to manage routing that could and should be handled within an organization.

The Internet is a collection of networks whose users communicate with each other. Each communication carries the address of the source and destination networks and the particular machine within the network associated with the user or host computer at each end. This address is called the **IP address** (Internet Protocol address). This 32-bit IP address has two parts: one part identifies the network (with the *network number*) and the other part identifies the specific machine or host within the network (with the *host number*). An organization can use some of the bits in the machine or host part of the address to identify a specific subnet. Effectively, the IP address then contains three parts: the network number, the subnet number, and the machine number.

The standard procedure for creating and identifying subnets is provided in Internet **Request for Comments** 950.

The IP Address

The 32-bit IP address (we have a separate definition of it with **IP address**) is often depicted as a **dot address** (also called *dotted quad notation*)—that is, four groups (or **quad**) of decimal digits separated by periods. Here's an example:

130.5.5.25

Each of the decimal digits represents a string of four binary digits. Thus, the above IP address really is this string of 0s and 1s:

10000010.00000101.00000101.00011001

As you can see, we inserted periods between each eight-digit sequence just as we did for the decimal version of the IP address. Obviously, the decimal version of the IP address is easier to read and that's the form most commonly used.

Some portion of the IP address represents the network number or address and some portion represents the local machine address (also known as the *host number* or address).

IP addresses can be one of several classes, each determining how many bits represent the network number and how many represent the host number. The most common class used by large organizations (Class B) allows 16 bits for the network number and 16 for the host number. Using the above example, here's how the IP address is divided:

```
<–Network address–><–Host address–>
        130.5   .    5.25
```

If you wanted to add subnetting to this address, then some portion (in this example, eight bits) of the host address could be used for a subnet address. Thus:

```
<–Network address–><–Subnet address–><–Host address–>
       130.5    .        5       .   25
```

To simplify this explanation, we've divided the subnet into a neat eight bits but an organization could choose some other scheme using only part of the third quad or even part of the fourth quad.

The Subnet Mask

Once a packet has arrived at an organization's **gateway** or connection point with its unique network number, it can be routed within the organization's internal gateways using the subnet number as well. The router knows which bits to look at (and which not to look at) by looking at a subnet mask. A mask is simply a screen of numbers that tells you which numbers to look at underneath. In a binary mask, a "1" over a number says "Look at the number underneath"; a "0" says "Don't look." Using a mask saves the router having to handle the entire 32 bit address; it can simply look at the bits selected by the mask.

Using the previous example (which is a very typical case), the combined network number and subnet number occupy 24 bits or three of the quads. The appropriate subnet mask carried along with the packet would be:

```
255.255.255.0
```

Or a string of all 1's for the first three quads (telling the router to look at these) and 0's for the host number (which the router doesn't need to look at). Subnet masking allows routers to move the packets on more quickly.

If you have the job of creating subnets for an organization (an activity called *subnetting*) and specifying subnet masks, your job may be simple or complicated depending on the size and complexity of your organization and other factors.

subnetwork

A subnetwork is a separately identifiable part of a larger **network** that typically represents a certain limited number of **host** computers, the hosts in a building or geographic area, or the hosts on an individual local area network. Companies often create subnetworks (sometimes called **subnets**) when setting up connection to the Internet as a way to manage the limited number of Internet Protocol addresses (**IP addresses**) that are available with Internet Protocol version 4.

sudo

Sudo (superuser do) is a **utility** for **UNIX**-based systems that provides an efficient way to give specific users permission to use specific system commands at the root (most powerful) level of the system. Sudo also logs all commands and arguments. Using sudo, a system administrator can:

- Give some users (or groups of users) the ability to run some (or all) commands at the root level of system operation

- Control which commands a user can use on each **host**

- See clearly from a log which users used which commands

- Using timestamp files, control the amount of time a user has to enter commands after they have entered their password and been granted appropriate privileges

The sudo configuration file is easy to create and to refer to.

suffix

A suffix is something added at the end of a word that conditions its usage or meaning. In computer system file names, a suffix is a convention for having one or more characters appended to a file name (usually separated from the file name with a dot) so that it can be distinguished from other files or grouped together with similar types of files. For example, all files created with a WordPerfect word processor can be associated with a ".wpd" suffix. That way, a user can easily distinguish it as a file created with that word processor from files created with other tools and selectively process a number of similar files.

Different operating systems have different rules about how long the suffix part of a file name can be. DOS, Windows prior to Windows 95, and OS/2 prior to OS/2 Warp limit suffix names to a maximum of three characters. UNIX systems, Windows 95, and Mac systems permit longer suffix names.

sun interference

See "solar fade"

SunOS

Since replaced by **Solaris**, SunOS was the **UNIX**-based **operating system** for the **SPARC**-based workstations and servers from Sun Microsystems.

Super Audio CD

Super Audio Compact Disc (SACD) is a high-resolution audio CD format. Version 1.0 specifications were described by Philips and Sony in March of 1999, in the Scarlet Book. SACD and DVD-Audio (**DVD-A**) are the two formats competing to replace the standard audio CD. Most of the industry is backing DVD-A, with Philips and Sony being the major exceptions.

Like SACD, DVD-A offers 5.1 channel surround sound in addition to 2-channel stereo. Both formats improve the complexity of sound by increasing the bit rate and the **sample rate**, and can be played on existing CD players, although only at quality levels similar to those of traditional CDs. SACD uses Direct Stream Digital (DSD) recording, a proprietary Sony technology that converts an **analog waveform** to a 1-bit signal for direct recording, instead of the pulse code modulation (**PCM**) and filtering used by standard CDs. DSD uses **lossless compression** (so-called because none of the data is lost in the compression process) and a **sampling rate** of 2.8MHz to improve the complexity and realism of sound. SACD can also contain extra information, such as text, graphics, and video clips.

The first SACD player was released in North America in December of 1999, with an $8000 price tag. In late 2000, Sony released a new model, priced at $1000.

supercomputer

A supercomputer is a computer that performs at or near the currently highest operational rate for computers. A supercomputer is typically used for scientific and engineering applications that must handle very large databases or do a great amount of computation (or both). At any given time, there are usually a few well-publicized supercomputers that operate at the very latest and always incredible speeds. The term is also sometimes applied to far slower (but still impressively fast) computers. Most supercomputers are really multiple computers that perform **parallel processing**. In general, there are two parallel processing approaches: symmetric multiprocessing (**SMP**) and massively parallel processing (**MPP**).

Perhaps the best-known builder of supercomputers has been Cray Research, now a part of Silicon Graphics. Some supercomputers are at "**supercomputer centers**," usually university research centers, some of which, in the United States, are interconnected on an Internet **backbone** known as **vBNS** or NSFNet. This network is the foundation for an evolving network infrastructure known as the National Technology Grid. **Internet2** is a university-led project that is part of this initiative.

At the high end of supercomputing are computers like IBM's "Blue Pacific," announced on October 29, 1998. Built in partnership with Lawrence Livermore National Laboratory in California., Blue Pacific is reported to operated at 3.9 **teraflop** (trillion operations per second), 15,000 times faster than the average personal computer. It consists of 5,800 processors containing a total of 2.6 trilllion bytes of memory and interconnected with five miles of cable. It was built to simulate the physics of a nuclear explosion. IBM is also building an academic supercomputer for the San Diego Supercomputer Center that will operate at 1 teraflop. It's based on IBM's RISC System/6000 and the **AIX** operating system and will have 1,000 microprocessors with IBM's own POWER3 chip.

At the lower end of supercomputing, a new trend, called *clustering*, suggests more of a build-it-yourself approach to supercomputing. The **Beowulf** Project offers guidance on how to "strap together" a number of off-the-shelf personal computer processors, using **Linux** operating systems, and interconnecting the processors with **Fast Ethernet**. Applications must be written to manage the parallel processing.

supercomputer center

In general, a supercomputer center is a site with a **supercomputer** that is shared by a number of other sites, usually research sites. Formerly, in the U.S., there were five supercomputer centers interconnected on the **vBNS**, a special **backbone** network financed by the National Science Foundation (NSF) and operated by MCI for the exclusive use of designated research centers. On October 1, 1997, the five supercomputer centers were replaced by two new NSF-funded programs. The new program, Partnerships for Advanced Computational Infrastructure (PACI), named two of the former supercomputer center sites as focuses for a new scientific technology infrastructure (known as the National Technology Grid) that would interconnect 50 university and scientific sites.

The first of the two NSF-funded programs is the National Computational Science Alliance (Alliance), being led by the National Center for Supercomputing Applications (NCSA) in Urbana, Illinois. The second program, the National Partnership for an Advanced Computational Infrastructure (NPACI) is led by the San Diego Supercomputer Center at the University of California at San Diego. The earlier supercomputer center program emphasized supercomputer access from researchers' desktops. The new program aims to exploit the entire World Wide Web as a new "computer-mediated center of knowledge." Part of that program is to develop a wired superstructure, referred to as the National Technology Grid, that will enable very high-bandwidth applications such as virtual reality environments. **Internet2** is a related university-led project.

superconductivity

Superconductivity is the ability of certain materials to conduct electric **current** with practically zero **resistance**. This produces interesting and potentially useful effects. For a material to behave as a superconductor, low temperatures are required.

Superconductivity was first observed in 1911 by H. K. Onnes, a Dutch physicist. His experiment was conducted with elemental mercury at 4 degrees kelvin (approximately—452 degrees Fahrenheit), the temperature of liquid helium. Since then, some substances have been made to act as superconductors at higher temperatures, although the ideal—a material that can superconduct at room temperature—remains elusive.

Superconductors have been employed in, or proposed for use in, an enormous variety of applications. Examples include:

- High-speed magnetic-levitation trains
- Magnetic-resonance-imaging (MRI) equipment
- Ultra-high-speed computer chips
- High-capacity digital **memory** chips
- Alternative energy storage systems
- Radio-frequency (**RF**) filters
- Radio-frequency **amplifier**
- Sensitive visible-light and infrared detectors
- Miniaturized **wireless** transmitting antennas
- Systems to detect submarines and underwater mines
- Gyroscopes for earth-orbiting **satellite**

Superdome

Superdome is a high-end **64-bit**, Hewlett-Packard (**HP**) PA-8600 processor-based UNIX **server** designed for e-commerce customers using very large **database**s. Superdome is available in three configurations and comes bundled with HP's **e-service** software packages and customer support options. The server is set to run on **HP-UX** 11i, HP's version of **UNIX**, but is intended to be compatible with **Windows** and **Linux** operating systems sometime in the future. One of Superdome's main features is the ability to be split into several **partition**s, each with its own operating system. Partitions defined in hardware can be further subdivided into software-based **virtual partition**s which allow resources, such as **processor** power or communication **bandwidth**, to be assigned to specific jobs.

superhet

See "superheterodyne"

superheterodyne

The term superheterodyne refers to a method of designing and building **wireless** communications or broadcast equipment, particularly radio receivers. Sometimes a receiver employing this technology is called a "superheterodyne" or "superhet."

In many wireless applications, the equipment must function over a range, or **band**, of frequencies. But it is easier to process a modulated signal at a single **frequency** than over a

band, especially if the highest frequency in the band is much different than the lowest frequency. To overcome this inherent difficulty when engineering variable-frequency wireless equipment, the desired data-carrying signal can be combined with the output of an unmodulated, variable-frequency oscillator (VFO) in a circuit called a mixer. When this is done, output is produced at a fixed frequency representing the difference between the input frequencies.

When the correct range of frequencies is chosen for the VFO, a receiver can be designed that will intercept incoming signals over a specific band. For example, if the desired input frequency range is 20 MHz to 25 MHz, a VFO can be built that generates an unmodulated carrier at 29 to 34 MHz. When the incoming signal is mixed with the VFO output, the resultant has a constant frequency of 9 MHz, representing the difference between the frequencies of the inputs. The 9-MHz output retains the **modulation** characteristics of the incoming signal. In this case, the receiver is said to have an intermediate frequency (IF) of 9 MHz. This IF signal can be amplified and filtered more easily than signals having frequencies that vary from 20 to 25 MHz.

The theory and design of superheterodyne equipment is a rather sophisticated business. Numerous books are devoted to this topic; some engineers make their entire living designing oscillators, mixers, and amplifiers that use this technology. For more information about superheterodyne engineering practice, a professional-level textbook or a formal course is recommended.

superposition

Superposition is a principle of **quantum theory** that describes a challenging concept about the nature and behavior of matter and forces at the atomic level. The principle of superposition claims that while we do not know what the state of any object is, it is actually in all possible states simultaneously, as long as we don't look to check. It is the measurement itself that causes the object to be limited to a single possibility.

In 1935, Erwin Schrodinger proposed an analogy to show how superposition would operate in the every day world: the somewhat cruel analogy of **Schrodinger's cat**. First, we have a living cat and place it in a thick lead box. At this stage, there is no question that the cat is alive. We then throw in a vial of cyanide and seal the box. We do not know if the cat is alive or if it has broken the cyanide capsule and died. Since we do not know, the cat is both dead and alive, according to quantum law—in a superposition of states. It is only when we break open the box and see what condition the cat is that the superposition is lost, and the cat must be either alive or dead.

Superposition is well illustrated by Thomas Young's double-slit experiment, developed in the early nineteenth century to prove that light consisted of waves. In fact, the noted physicist Richard Feynman claimed that the essentials of quantum mechanics could be grasped by an exploration of the implications of Young's experiment.

The Double-Slit Experiment

For this experiment, a beam of light is aimed at a barrier with two vertical slits. The light passes through the slits and the resulting pattern is recorded on a photographic plate. If one slit is covered, the pattern is what would be expected: a single line of light, aligned with whichever slit is open. Intuitively, one would expect that if both slits are open, the pattern of light will reflect that fact: two lines of light, aligned with the slits. In fact, however, what happens is that the photographic plate is entirely separated into multiple lines of lightness and darkness in varying degrees. What is being illustrated by this result is that interference is taking place between the waves/particles going through the slits, in what, seemingly, should be two non-crossing trajectories.

We would expect that if the beam of light particles or photons is slowed enough to ensure that individual photons are hitting the plate, there could be no interference and the pattern of light would be two lines of light, aligned with the slits. In fact, however, the resulting pattern still indicates interference, which means that, somehow, the single particles are interfering with themselves. This seems impossible: we expect that a single **photon** will go through one slit or the other, and will end up in one of two possible light line areas. But that is not what happens. As Feynman concluded, each photon not only goes through both slits, but simultaneously takes every possible trajectory en route to the target, not just in theory, but in fact.

In order to see how this might possibly occur, experiments have focused on tracking the paths of individual photons. What happens in this case is that the measurement in some way disrupts the photons' trajectories (in accordance with the uncertainty principle), and somehow, the results of the experiment become what would be predicted by classical physics: two bright lines on the photographic plate, aligned with the slits in the barrier. Cease the attempt to measure, however, and the pattern will again become multiple lines in varying degrees of lightness and darkness. Each photon moves simultaneously in a superposition of possible trajectories, and, furthermore, measurement of the trajectory causes the superposition of states to collapse to a single position.

superscalar

Superscalar describes a **microprocessor** design that makes it possible for more than one **instruction** at a time to be executed during a single **clock cycle**. In a superscalar design, the processor or the instruction **compiler** is able to determine whether an instruction can be carried out independently of other sequential instructions, or whether it has a dependency on another instruction and must be executed in sequence with it. The processor then uses multiple execution units to simultaneously carry out two or more independent instructions at a time. Superscalar design is sometimes called "second generation **RISC**."

superstitial

A superstitial is a Web ad format developed by Unicast, which calls itself a **rich media** company. Superstitials combine **Flash** or other animation technology with **Java** programming to deliver video-like Web commercials.

A superstitial (trademarked by Unicast as SUPERSTITIAL, but industry usage is generally lower case), like an **interstitial**, runs in the dead time between Web pages. The superstitial is delivered with what Unicast calls a "polite" cache-and-play delivery system. Designed to load invisibly into the browser's **cache** (temporary storage area) within 60 seconds (while the user is viewing the Web site containing the ad), a superstitial doesn't appear until it is completely downloaded. The ad appears in a variably-sized **pop-up** window when something the user does (such as a mouse click) triggers a move to another Web page. If the user clicks off the site before a superstitial has finished loading, the ad doesn't play.

A user can click a superstitial ad off at any time, although they can't stop them from playing altogether. Superstitials are thought to increase **stickiness** (that is, they tend to hold the viewer's attention). According to Unicast, they lead to advertising terminology on the Internet rates of up to 40%, and an average of 7.5% compared to the .3% average of banner ads.

superstring theory

Superstring theory—known less formally as "string theory"—is sometimes called *the theory of everything* (TOE), because it is a unifying physics theory that reconciles the differences between **quantum theory** and the theory of relativity to explain the nature of all known forces and matter. According to string theory, at the most microscopic level, everything in the universe is made up of loops of vibrating strings, and apparent particle differences can be attributed to variations of vibration. An object (such as an apple, for example) and a force (such as radiation, for example) can both be broken down into atoms, which can be further broken down into electrons and quarks, which can be, finally, broken down into tiny, vibrating loops of strings.

Quantum theory explains the nature and behavior of energy and matter on the microscopic scale, while the theory of relativity explains it on the macroscopic scale. Taken together, they form the basis for modern physics; nevertheless, integral aspects of the two theories conflict with each other in ways that have never been satisfactorily addressed. Although the theories work perfectly separately, equations involving both don't work at all. Einstein himself, unconvinced that nature would require entirely different

modes of behavior for differently scaled phenomena, spent thirty years searching for what he called the *unified field theory*.

Superstring theory came to the forefront in the 1980s, when Michael Green at Queen Mary College and John Schwarz at the California Institute of Technology demonstrated that it had the potential to be the unifying theory that Einstein sought: one that could be used to describe gravity as well as electromagnetic forces.

According to string theory:

- All forces and particles in nature are derived from variations in vibrations of strings. As an example, gravity is said to arise from the lowest vibration of a closed string.

- There are ten dimensions in the natural world (nine spatial dimensions plus time), rather than the four of classical science (the three spatial dimensions plus time). What causes the extra six dimensions to be largely unnoticed is that they are considered to be compacted or *curled up*.

- The reason that general relativity doesn't work at the subatomic level is because the equation mistakenly includes a figure for point-like particles. Modifying the equation to include a representation of loops of string, instead, makes the equation work.

- String theorists are currently examining the possibility that the strings themselves have multiple dimensions, and are not, as was originally thought, massless (possessing only length, and no width). The idea is that the strings may actually be membranes.

supervisor call

In computers, especially IBM **mainframe**s, a supervisor call (SVC) is a **processor instruction** that directs the processor to pass control of the computer to the **operating system**'s supervisor program. Most SVCs are requests for a specific operating system service from an application program or another part of the operating system. Application program developers usually use a language **function** or **macro instruction** to make the request (for example, to get allocated more **memory** for the program to work with). The language **compiler** or **assembler** generates the instruction that includes the specific SVC request. Each service has a preassigned SVC number. When the computer's processor executes the instruction that contains the SVC, the code representing "SVC" causes a program **interrupt** to occur, which means that control of the processor is immediately passed to the operating system supervisor program. The supervisor then passes control to programming that performs the service that goes with the specified SVC number.

An *SVC routine* is a program within the supervisor that performs the service indicated by the specific SVC instruction.

supervisory control and data acquisition

See "SCADA"

SuperZap

SuperZap is an IBM **utility** program used to install **zap**s or fixes to **MVS operating system**s or **application** program code that is causing a problem. Its file name is IMASPZAP (I M A SuPerZAP).

supplier exchange

See "e-procurement"

supply chain management

Supply chain management (SCM) is the oversight of materials, information, and finances as they move in a process from supplier to manufacturer to wholesaler to retailer to consumer. Supply chain management involves coordinating and integrating these flows both within and among companies. It is said that the ultimate goal of any effective supply chain management system is to reduce inventory (with the assumption that products are available when needed). As a solution for successful supply chain management, sophisticated software systems with Web interfaces are competing with Web-based application service providers (**ASP**) who promise to provide part or all of the SCM service for companies who rent their service.

Supply chain management flows can be divided into three main flows:

- The product flow
- The information flow
- The finances flow

The product flow includes the movement of goods from a supplier to a customer, as well as any customer returns or service needs. The information flow involves transmitting ordersand updating the status of delivery. The financial flow consists of credit terms, payment schedules, and consignment and title ownership arrangements.

There are two main types of SCM software: Planning applications and execution applications. Planning applications use advanced algorithms to determine the best way to fill an order. Execution applications track the physical status of goods, the management of materials, and financial information involving all parties.

Some SCM applications are based on open data models that support the sharing of data both inside and outside the enterprise (this is called the extended enterprise, and includes key suppliers, manufacturers, and end customers of a specific company). This shared data may reside in diverse database systems, or **data warehouse**s, at several different sites and companies.

By sharing this data "upstream" (with a company's suppliers) and "downstream" (with a company's clients), SCM applications have the potential to improve the time-to-market of products, reduce costs, and allow all parties in the supply chain to better manage current resources and plan for future needs.

Increasing numbers of companies are turning to Web sites and Web-based applications as part of the SCM solution. A number of major Web sites offer **e-procurement** marketplaces where manufacturers can trade and even make auction bids with suppliers.

surf

In using the **World Wide Web**, to surf is to either:

1) Explore a sequence of Web sites in a random, unplanned way, or

2) Simply use the Web to look for something in a questing way.

As the term is ordinarily used, if you are going to one specific site you already know about, you aren't surfing. The term suggests an analogy between surfing ocean waves with a surfboard and surfing **cyberspace**.

surge suppressor

See also **uninterruptible power supply**.

A surge suppressor (sometimes optimistically called a "surge protector") is a device inserted in the alternating current (**AC**) utility line and/or telephone line to prevent damage to electronic equipment from voltage "spikes" called transients. A more accurate term for this type of device is "transient suppressor." A typical surge suppressor is a small box with several utility outlets, a power switch, and a 3-wire cord for plugging into a wall outlet.

In most countries where electronic equipment is used, the effective AC utility voltage is 110 to 120 volts; the peak **voltage** is on the order of plus-or-minus 160 to 170 volts at a **frequency** of 60 **hertz**. But transients, which arise from various causes, commonly reach peak levels of several hundred volts. These pulses are of short duration, measured in microseconds (units of 10^{-6} second), but in that time, they can cause hardware to malfunction. The worst type of transient occurs when lightning strikes in the vicinity (it is not necessary for a power line to be directly hit). Such a "spike" can peak at thousands of volts and cause permanent damage to equipment.

A surge suppressor prevents the peak AC voltage from going above a certain threshold such as plus-or-minus 200 volts. **Semiconductor** devices are used for this purpose. The power line is effectively short-circuited to electrical ground for transient pulses exceeding the threshold, while the flow

of normal 60-Hz current is unaffected. For the suppressor to work, a 3-wire AC power connection must be used. "Cheater" adapters, which allow 3-wire appliances to be used with 2-wire outlets or extension cords, defeat the electrical ground connection and render most surge suppressors ineffective.

Surge suppressors should be used as a matter of habit with all semiconductor-based electronic and computer hardware, including peripherals such as printers, monitors, external disk drives, and **modem**s. But the suppressor should not be relied upon to provide protection against lightning-induced transients. The safest procedure, inconvenient though it be, is to ensure that all susceptible hardware is plugged into the suppressor box, and to unplug the suppressor's main power cord when the equipment is not in use if you live in a thunderstorm-prone area.

susceptance

Susceptance (symbolized B) is an expression of the ease with which alternating current (**AC**) passes through a **capacitance** or **inductance**.

In some respects, susceptance is like an AC counterpart of direct current (**DC**) **conductance**. But the two phenomena are different in important ways, and they can vary independently of each other. Conductance and susceptance combine to form **admittance**, which is defined in terms of two-dimensional quantities known as **complex number**s.

When AC passes through a component that contains a finite, nonzero susceptance, energy is alternately stored in, and released from, a magnetic field or an electric field. In the case of a magnetic field, the susceptance is inductive. In the case of an electric field, the susceptance is capacitive. Inductive susceptance is assigned negative **imaginary number** values, and capacitive susceptance is assigned positive imaginary number values.

As the inductance of a component increases, its susceptance becomes smaller negatively (that is, it approaches zero from the negative side) in imaginary terms, assuming the frequency is held constant. As the frequency increases for a given value of inductance, the same thing happens. If L is the inductance in henries (**H**) and f is the frequency in hertz (**Hz**), then the susceptance $-jB_L$, in imaginary-number **siemens**, is given by:

$$-jB_L = -j\,(6.2832fL)^{-1}$$

where 6.2832 is approximately equal to 2 times **pi**, a constant representing the number of **radian**s in a full AC cycle, and j represents the unit imaginary number (the positive square root of -1).

As the capacitance of a component increases, its susceptance becomes larger positively in imaginary terms, assuming the frequency is held constant. As the frequency increases for a given value of capacitance, the same thing happens. If C is

the capacitance in farads (**F**) and f is the frequency in Hz, then the susceptance $+jB_C$, in imaginary-number ohms, is given by:

$$+jX_C = +j \ (6.2832fC)$$

Also see **admittance**, **conductance**, **reactance**, **resistance**, **impedance**, **ohm**, **siemens**, **henry**, and **farad**.

SuSE

SuSE (pronounced soo'-sah) is a privately owned German company whose mission is to promote **Open Source** development and **GNU** General Public License distribution and to be the most reliable **Linux** distribution provider. Like **Red Hat** and Caldera, SuSE assembles open source **components** for the Linux operating system and related programs into a selection of distribution packages that can be purchased. The advantage of buying the Linux **kernel** and support programs from a distributor (rather than assembling it at no cost yourself from various sources) is that you save time by purchasing a convenient package that comes with extensive documentation and tech support. SuSE, which even has a Braille edition, has targeted users new to the Linux **operating system** and hopes to attract Windows expatriots by promoting the Personal edition of SuSE as an easy way for the average desktop user to migrate to Linux. Both the Personal Edition and the Professional Editions come with a large number of applications.

SuSE is an abbreviation for the German company "Gesellschaft f l r Software und Systementwicklung mbH", whose name loosely translates to mean "Software and System Development Company".

SVC

See "switched virtual circuit"

SVG

See "Scalable Vector Graphics"

SVGA

See "display modes"

SWAG

See "Semantic Web Agreement Group"

swap

See "swap file"

swap file

A swap file (or swap space or, in Windows NT, a pagefile) is a space on a **hard disk** used as the **virtual memory** extension of a computer's real memory (**RAM**). Having a swap file allows your computer's **operating system** to pretend that you have more RAM than you actually do. The least recently used files in RAM can be "swapped out" to your hard disk until they are needed later so that new files can be "swapped in" to RAM. In larger operating systems (such as IBM's OS/390), the units that are moved are called *pages* and the swapping is called *paging*.

One advantage of a swap file is that it can be organized as a single contiguous space so that fewer I/O operations are required to read or write a complete file.

In general, Windows and **UNIX**-based operating systems provide a default swap file of a certain size that the user or a system administrator can usually change.

Swing

Swing is a set of program **components** for **Java** programmers that provide the ability to create graphical user interface (**GUI**) components, such as buttons and scroll bars, that are independent of the **windowing systems** for specific **operating systems**. Swing components are used with the Java Foundation Classes (**JFC**).

swirl

Swirl is the term used by some people in the telecommunications industry to describe the background noise that can be present when using a **digital cellular telephone** phone. It's the equivalent of *static* on an **analog** cellular phone. Digital **wireless** phones pick up background noise just like analog phones but the background noise is different, something like the sound of air whooshing or swirling through space.

switch

Also see **bridge**, **gateway**, **hub**, and **router**.

In telecommunications, a switch is a **network** device that selects a path or circuit for sending a unit of **data** to its next destination. A switch may also include the function of the **router**, a device or program that can determine the route and specifically what adjacent network point the data should be sent to. In general, a switch is a simpler and faster mechanism than a router, which requires knowledge about the network and how to determine the route.

Relative to the layered Open Systems Interconnection (**OSI**) communication model, a switch is usually associated with **layer 2**, the **Data-Link layer**. However, some newer switches also perform the routing functions of layer 3, the **Network layer**. Layer 3 switches are also sometimes called *IP switches*.

On larger networks, the trip from one switch point to another in the network is called a **hop**. The time a switch takes to figure out where to forward a data unit is called its **latency**. The price paid for having the flexibility that switches provide in a network is this latency. Switches are found at the **backbone** and **gateway** levels of a network where one network connects with another and at the subnetwork level where data is being forwarded close to its destination or origin. The former are often known as *core switches* and the latter as *desktop switches*.

In the simplest networks, a switch is not required for messages that are sent and received within the network. For example, a local area network may be organized in a **token ring** or **bus** arrangement in which each possible destination inspects each message and reads any message with its address.

Circuit-Switching version Packet-Switching

A network's paths can be used exclusively for a certain duration by two or more parties and then switched for use to another set of parties. This type of "switching" is known as *circuit-switching* and is really a dedicated and continuously connected path for its duration. Today, an ordinary voice phone call generally uses circuit-switching.

Most data today is sent, using **digital** signals, over networks that use *packet-switching*. Using packet-switching, all network users can share the same paths at the same time and the particular route a data unit travels can be varied as conditions change. In packet-switching, a **message** is divided into packets, which are units of a certain number of bytes. The network addresses of the sender and of the destination are added to the packet. Each network point looks at the packet to see where to send it next. Packets in the same message may travel different routes and may not arrive in the same order that they were sent. At the destination, the packets in a message are collected and reassembled into the original message.

Switched Multimegabit Data Service

See "SMDS"

switched virtual circuit

SVC also stands for **supervisor call**.

In a network, a switched virtual circuit (SVC) is a temporary **virtual circuit** that is established and maintained only for the duration of a data transfer session. A permanent virtual circuit (**PVC**) is a continuously dedicated virtual circuit. A virtual circuit is one that appears to be a discrete, physical circuit available only to the user but that is actually a shared pool of circuit resources used to support multiple users as they require the connections. Switched virtual circuits are part of an **X.25** network. Conceptually, they can also be implemented as part of a **frame relay** network.

switching fabric

Switching fabric is the combination of hardware and software that moves data coming in to a network **node** out by the correct port (door) to the next node in the network. The term suggests that the near synonym, **switch**, tends to make switching seem like a simple hardware function.

Switching fabric includes the switching units (individual boxes) in a node, the integrated circuits that they contain, and the programming that allows switching paths to be controlled. The switching fabric is independent of the **bus** technology and infrastructure used to move data between nodes and also separate from the **router**. The term is sometimes used to mean collectively all switching hardware and software in a network.

The term apparently uses the woven material metaphor to suggest the possible complexity and web-like structure of switching paths and ports within a node.

The Signal Computing System Architecture (SCSA), which provides a model framework for computer telephony, uses the term. In the SCSA framework, part of the hardware model includes a Switch Fabric Controller. Asynchronous transfer mode (**ATM**) and **frame relay** are sometimes described as switching fabric technologies.

The switching fabric typically includes data buffers and the use of shared **memory**.

Sybase

Sybase is a computer software company that develops and sells database management system (**DBMS**) and **middleware** products. The company was founded in 1984, and the headquarters offices are in Emeryville, CA.

Sybase products have found extensive application, particularly in commercial, industrial, and military communications systems. Spanish telecommunications operator Airtel uses Sybase Adaptive Server IQ Multiplex (ASIQ) to standardize its business information. Telstra, an Australian telecommunications provider, uses data-visualization software powered by Sybase ASIQ Multiplex to optimize its mobile phone network management capacity. Primark uses Sybase MQSeries Integrator to maximize transaction rates, optimize reliability, and allow customization of inputs and outputs. Sybase claims that its MQSeries Integrator makes it possible to add new data formats to meet the needs of clients, and to accommodate diverse system architectures at client locations. Sybase SQL Anywhere, embedded in Geodyn FxView, is used in two-way communications between military command centers and soldiers in the field.

Also see **Oracle** and IBM's **DB2**.

symmetric communications

Compare **asymmetric communications**.

In telecommunications, the term symmetric (also symmetrical) refers to any system in which data speed or quantity is the same in both directions, averaged over time. Examples include two-way radio, standard twisted-pair telephone Internet connections, **cable modem** Internet connections in which the cable is used for transmission as well as for reception, and full-motion videoconferencing.

Symmetric communications is not necessarily the most efficient mode in a given application. Consider casual Web browsing, in which most of the bytes come downstream (from Internet servers to the user) as relatively large graphics, sound, multimedia, and HTML files, while upstream data (from user to a server) consists mainly of new link (URL) requests by the user, which, in comparison, contain few bytes. In this environment, it often makes the best use of available resources to supply the user with a more broadbanded "pipeline" in the downstream direction, as compared with the upstream direction.

The ultimate Internet connection is broadband symmetrical, such as is provided by true cable modem connections and **optical fiber** systems. At the time of this writing, symmetric broadband is not generally available outside of metropolitan areas.

symmetric multiprocessing

See "SMP"

SynchBurst SRAM

See "burst SRAM"

SynchML

SyncML is an Extensible Markup Language (**XML**) **protocol** under development as an **open** standard for the universal synchronization of data between devices, one of the most important building blocks in the development of third generation (**3G**) **wireless**. The SyncML Initiative was founded in February of 2000, with a stated goal of developing and promoting an open and **portable** standard for consistent synchronization of remote data across networks, platforms, and devices. SyncML **leverages** existing standards such as **MIME**, the **vCard**, and the *iCalendar*, in addition to XML.

Synchronization of data allows changes made to data on one device (such as a **smartphone** or a laptop computer) to be instantly reflected in data on another device (such as a networked computer). For example, if a file is edited on one device, the updates can be automatically transfered to the other device. With automatic data synchronization, a mobile worker doesn't have to worry about the coordination of data between networked computers and devices used while out of the office. This lessens the need for **sneakernet** operations; the user doesn't have to recopy data, manually transfer it from one device to another, or deal with uncoordinated information in various versions of single files. The problem with existing data synchronization protocols is that they are only compatible with some standards and some devices. Meanwhile, with a growing number of people using wireless devices, the need to synchronize data will only increase. Given the variety of hardware and technology, a universal

standard is necessary for future development of the wireless industry, which has been held back by the existing **proprietary** technologies.

Founders of the initiative (Ericsson, IBM, Lotus, Motorola, Nokia, Psion, Palm Inc. and Starfish Software) showcased devices using the protocol in September 2000 in Dublin. Initiative members report that SyncML-compliant products may be released by early 2001. SyncML Version 1.0 Alpha is currently available to the more than 470 supporting companies.

Synchronized Multimedia Integration Language

See "SMIL"

Synchronous Data Link Control

See "SDLC"

Synchronous Digital Hierarchy

See "SDH"

synchronous DRAM

See "SDRAM"

Synchronous Graphics RAM

Synchronous Graphics RAM (SGRAM) is clock-synchronized **random access memory** that is used for video memory. It is relatively low-cost video memory. It uses *masked write*, which enables selected data to be modified in a single operation rather as a sequence of read, update, and write operations. It also uses *block write*, which allows data for background or foreground image fills to be handled more efficiently. SGRAM is single-ported. Its special features are what make it a moderately fast form of video memory. The Matrox Mystique is an example of a video card that uses SGRAM.

Synchronous Optical Network

SONET is the **American National Standards Institute** standard for synchronous data transmission on optical media. The international equivalent of SONET is synchronous digital hierarchy (SDH). Together, they ensure standards so that digital networks can interconnect internationally and that existing conventional transmission systems can take advantage of optical media through tributary attachments.

SONET provides standards for a number of line rates up to the maximum line rate of 9.953 gigabits per second (**Gbps**). Actual line rates approaching 20 gigabits per second are possible. SONET is considered to be the foundation for the physical layer of the broadband ISDN (**BISDN**).

Asynchronous transfer mode runs as a layer on top of SONET as well as on top of other technologies.

SONET defines a base rate of 51.84 Mbps and a set of multiples of the base rate known as "**Optical Carrier levels (OCx).**"

synchronous

In general, synchronous (pronounced SIHN-kro-nuhs, from Greek *syn-*, meaning "with," and *chronos*, meaning "time") is an adjective describing objects or events that are coordinated in time. In information technology, the term has several different usages.

1) In telecommunication signaling within a network or between networks, synchronous signals are those that occur at the same clock rate when all clocks are based on a single reference clock. (**Plesiochronous** signals are almost but not quite in synchronization and **asynchronous** signals are those that run from different clocks or at a different transition rate.)

2) In program-to-program communication, synchronous communication requires that each end of an exchange of communication respond in turn without initiating a new communication. A typical activity that might use a synchronous protocol would be a transmission of files from one point to another. As each transmission is received, a response is returned indicating success or the need to resend. Each successive transmission of data requires a response to the previous transmission before a new one can be initiated.

Synchronous program communication is contrasted with **asynchronous** program communication.

Synclink Dynamic RAM

SyncLink SDRAM, along with Direct **Rambus** DRAM, is a **protocol**-based approach where all signals to random access memory (**RAM**) are on the same line (rather than having separate **column address strobe**, **row address strobe**, address, and data lines). Since access time does not depend on synchronizing operations on multiple lines, SLDRAM promises RAM speed of up to 800 MHz. Like Double Data Rate SDRAM, SLDRAM can operate at twice the system clock rate. SyncLink is an open industry standard that is expected to compete with Direct Rambus DRAM.

syndication

In general, syndication is the supply of material for reuse and integration with other material, often through a paid service subscription. The most common example of syndication is in newspapers, where such content as wire-service news, comics, columns, horoscopes, and crossword puzzles are usually syndicated content. Newspapers receive the content from the content providers, reformat it as required, integrate it with other copy, print it, and publish it.

For many years mainly a feature of print media, today content syndication is the way a great deal of information is disseminated across the Web. Reuters, for example, provides online news content to over 900 Web sites and portals, such as Yahoo and America Online.

Online content syndication is a growing industry sector, in terms of both content syndication and hardware and software development. In the early days, online content syndication was a cumbersome manual process: after an agreement had been reached between the supplier and their customers, the customers would simply copy the desired content from the supplier's Web site and paste it into their own. All related activities—such as content updates, for example—were also manual, and dependent upon the user to track and perform necessary tasks. Electronic content syndication can potentially automate every aspect of online content syndication.

Two crucial components for the further development of the industry built on online syndication have been cited as: the need for a standardized data exchange mechanism, and the need for a standardized **metadata** vocabulary (since suppliers and subscribers are often using different and incompatible technologies). The Information & Content Exchange (**ICE**) protocol was developed as an open standard for data exchange that enables the automation of all processes involved. An organization made up of content providers and vendors, the *Publishing Requirements for Industry Standard Metadata* (PRISM) working group is collaborating to develop a standard vocabulary.

synergy

In general, synergy (pronounced SIHN-uhr-djee, from Greek *sunergia*, meaning "cooperation," and also *sunergos*, meaning "working together") is the combined working together of two or more parts of a system so that the combined effect is greater than the sum of the efforts of the parts. In business and technology, the term describes a hoped-for or real effect resulting from different individuals, departments, or companies working together and stimulating new ideas that result in greater productivity.

The process of synergy as a way of originating new ideas or making new discoveries can be contrasted to **serendipity**, in which ideas and discoveries emerge seemingly by accident.

syntax

Syntax is the grammar, structure, or order of the elements in a language statement. (Semantics is the meaning of these elements.) Syntax applies to computer languages as well as to natural languages. Usually, we think of syntax as "word order." However, syntax is also achieved in some languages such as Latin by inflectional case endings. In computer languages, syntax can be extremely rigid as in the case of

most **assembler** languages or less rigid in languages that make use of "keyword" parameters that can be stated in any order.

C.W. Morris in his *Foundations of the Theory of Signs* (1938) organizes *semiotics*, the study of signs, into three areas: syntax (the study of the interrelation of the signs); semantics (the study of the relation between the signs and the objects to which they apply); and pragmatics (the relationship between the sign system and the user).

sysop

See "system operator"

sysplex and Parallel Sysplex

A sysplex is IBM's systems complex (the word *sysplex* comes from the first part of the word *system* and the last part of the word *complex*), introduced in 1990 as a platform for the **MVS/ESA operating system** for IBM **mainframe servers**. An enhanced version, Parallel Sysplex, was subsequently introduced for the newer operating system, **OS/390**. The sysplex consists of the multiple computers (the systems) that make up the complex. A sysplex is designed to be a solution for business needs involving any or all of the following: **parallel processing**; online transaction processing (**OLTP**); very high transaction volumes; very numerous small work units—online transactions, for example (or large work units that can be broken up into multiple small work units); or applications running simultaneously on separate systems that must be able to update to a single database without compromising data integrity.

According to IBM, the Parallel Sysplex is the end result of IBM large systems' developments over the years, from the single system uniprocessor, to tightly-coupled multiprocessors, to loosely-coupled configurations, to the sysplex, and finally to the Parallel Sysplex. A single system uniprocessor consists of a single central processor complex (CPC)—which consists of a single **central processor** (CP) and all associated system hardware and software, controlled by a single copy of the operating system. Tightly coupled multiprocessors consist of a number of CPs added to a CPC that share central storage and a single copy of the operating system. Work is assigned to an available CP by the operating system and can be rerouted to another if the first CP fails. A loosely coupled configuration has multiple CPCs (which may be tightly coupled multiprocessors) with separate storage areas, managed by more than one copy of the operating system and connected by **channel**-to-channel communications.

A sysplex is similar to a loosely coupled configuration, but differs in that it has a standard communication mechanism (the cross-system coupling facility, or XCF) for MVS system applications that enables communication between application programs on one or multiple computers. The sysplex is made up of number of CPCs that collaborate, through specialized hardware and software, to process a work load. This is what a large computer system does in general; a sysplex, through XCF, increases the number of processing units and operating systems that can be connected.

The Parallel Sysplex, IBM's latest method of configuration for CPCs, is a clustering architecture that has improved communication capabilities and supports more connected CPCs and more copies of the operating system. There are several areas of improvement over the base sysplex. The Parallel Sysplex Coupling Facility is a new processor that stores crucial system information, usually configured on a separate device. Use of the coupling facility increases the capacity for data sharing among systems and subsystems. Because it is used through both systems and subsystems, it also ensures data integrity and consistency throughout the sysplex. Another feature of the new technology is the Workload Manager (WLM), part of OS/390 that is in each system in a Parallel Sysplex configuration. WLM manages resources more responsively than the earlier schedule-based methods through dynamic workload balancing and prioritization according to user-set criteria. The data-sharing capability enables simultaneous, multiple-system access to data.

system

A system is a collection of elements or components that are organized for a common purpose. The word sometimes describes the organization or plan itself (and is similar in meaning to *method*, as in "I have my own little system") and sometimes describes the parts in the system (as in "computer system").

A computer system consists of hardware components that have been carefully chosen so that they work well together and software components or programs that run in the computer.

The main software component is itself an **operating system** that manages and provides services to other programs that can be run in the computer.

A filing system is a group of files organized with a plan (for example, alphabetical by customer).

All of nature and the universe can be said to be a system. We've coined a word, *ecosystem*, for the systems on Earth that affect life systems.

The term can be very useful because so many things can be described as systems. It can also be very unuseful when a more specific term is needed.

system operator

A sysop is the person who runs a computer **server**. In general, a sysop or system operator is one who runs the day-to-day operation of a server and the term suggests a person who is available when the system is. A related term is *administrator*. In larger computer systems, the administrator manages security and user access while a system operator monitors and performs routine operations at the computer. In smaller computer systems (for example, UNIX systems), the administrator and the system operator tend to be the same person.

system tray

The system tray (or "systray") is a section of the *taskbar*s in the Microsoft Windows **desktop** user interface that is used to display the clock and the **icon**s of certain programs so that a user is continually reminded that they are there and can easily click one of them. The system tray is a section located at the one end of the taskbar in Windows 95, 98, and NT. Icons that are often installed in the system tray include the volume control for sound, **anti-virus software**, **scanner** software, a channel viewer, player, and a system resources indicator. When more icons are installed in the system tray than can fit in the space allotted, the system tray becomes horizontally scrollable or expandable. To interact with a program in the system tray, you select an icon with your **mouse** and double-click or right-click the icon. When you minimize the program after using it, it shrinks back into the system tray instead of into the main part of the taskbar.

What makes a system tray icon special is that, when installed, it can have a customized message appear when the mouse is hovering over it; the menu that appears when you right-click it can be customized; and the action that occurs when you double-click it can also be customized. For example, the double-click action for Internet Explorer could be to launch (start, or open a window for) the program, but the double-click action for a desktop icon could be to "View desktop," simply remove the active windows and show the underlying desktop.

An icon can be placed in the system tray when a program is installed by making an entry in the system **registry** or later by creating a **shortcut** to a program and dragging the shortcut icon to the system tray. An icon can be removed by deleting the registry entry or by right-clicking it and selecting Delete on the popup menu. The clock is removed by deselecting the show clock option in the taskbar Properties.

Systems Application Architecture

See "SAA"

systems development life cycle model

(The systems development life cycle (SDLC) model is sometimes referred to as the **waterfall model**. SDLC is also an abbreviation for **Synchronous Data Link Control**.)

The systems development life cycle (SDLC) model is an approach to developing an information system or software product that is characterized by a linear sequence of steps that progress from start to finish without revisiting any previous step. The SDLC model is one of the oldest **systems development model**s and is still probably the most commonly used.

In general, these are the steps:

1. The existing system is evaluated. Deficiencies are identified. This can be done by interviewing users of the system and consulting with support personnel.

2. The new system requirements are defined. In particular, the deficiencies in the existing system must be addressed with specific proposals for improvement.

3. The proposed system is designed. Plans are be laid out concerning the physical construction, hardware, operating systems, programming, communications, and security issues.

4. The new system is developed. The new components and programs must be obtained and installed. Users of the system must be trained in its use, and all aspects of performance must be tested. If necessary, adjustments must be made at this stage.

5. The system is put into use. This can be done in various ways. The new system can phased in, according to application or location, and the old system gradually replaced. In some cases, it may be more cost-effective to shut down the old system and implement the new system all at once.

6. Once the new system is up and running for awhile, it should be exhaustively evaluated. Maintenance must be kept up rigorously at all times. Users of the system should be kept up-to-date concerning the latest modifications and procedures. Critics of the SDLC model say that it doesn't allow sufficiently for error discovery and redesign.

systems development method

A systems development method (SDM) is a work discipline that is chosen by the developers of a computer system or product as a way to ensure successful results. Typically, a systems development method specifies a series of stages that encompass requirements gathering, design, development, testing, delivery, maintenance, and enhancement of a system or product. The term *systems development model* is not used universally. Similar terms such as *process model* or *development guidelines* are sometimes used instead.

Before systems development methods came into being, the development of new systems or products was often carried out by using the experience and intuition of management and technical personnel. However, the complexity of modern systems and computer products long ago made the need clear for some kind of orderly development process.

Some of the approaches to a systems development method include:

- The **systems development life cycle model** (also known as the **waterfall model**)
- The **prototyping model**
- The **exploratory model**
- The **spiral model**
- The **reuse model**
- **Rapid application development** (RAD)

Frequently, several models are combined into some sort of hybrid process. Record-keeping is important regardless of the type of SDM chosen or devised for any application, and is usually done in parallel with the development process.

systems management

Systems management is the management of the information technology systems in an **enterprise**. This includes gathering requirements, purchasing equipment and software, distributing it to where it is to be used, configuring it, maintaining it with enhancement and service updates, setting up problem-handling processes, and determining whether objectives are being met. Systems management is usually under the overall responsibility of an enterprise's Chief Information Officer (**CIO**). The department that performs systems management is sometimes known as management information systems (**MIS**) or simply information systems (**IS**).

Network management and *database management* can be viewed as part of systems management or they may be viewed as co-equal parts of a total information system.

Trends and issues in systems management include:

- The **total cost of ownership**, which emphasizes that updating and servicing equipment is likely to be a major cost
- The right balance of resources and control between centrally-managed and network-distributed systems
- The **outsourcing** of all or part of information systems and systems management
- Tactical versus strategic purchasing decisions
- The choices between proprietary, compatible, and **Open Source** software
- Exploitation of the Internet and Web interfaces
- Graphical user interfaces for controlling the information system
- Security management, including security for mobile device users

Systems Network Architecture

SNA is a proprietary IBM architecture and set of implementing products for network computing within an **enterprise**. It existed prior to and became part of IBM's Systems Application Architecture (**SAA**) and it is currently part of IBM's **Open Blueprint**. With the advent of multi-

enterprise network computing, the Internet, and the de facto **open** network architecture of **TCP/IP**, IBM is finding ways to combine its own SNA within the enterprise with TCP/IP for applications in the larger network.

SNA itself contains several functional layers and includes an application program interface called the Virtual Telecommunications Access Method (**VTAM**), a communications **protocol** for the exchange of control information and data, and a data link layer, Synchronous Data Link Control (**SDLC**). SNA includes the concepts of **node**s that can contain both *physical units* that provide certain setup functions and *logical units*, each associated with a particular network transaction.

T

See "tesla"

T interface

In Integrated Services Digital Network (**ISDN**) service, a T interface is the electrical interface between a network terminating unit 1 (**NT1**) and a network terminating unit 2 (NT2) device, which typically is a private branch exchange (**PBE**). Like the **S interface**, the T interface has four wires, allowing up to eight devices to be addressed. In Basic Rate Interface (**BRI**) ISDN, the bits that flow from the central office through the NT1 are divided into two 64 Kbps **channels** (known as B, or bearer, channels) and one 16 Kbps channel (the D, for data or delta, channel) for control signals. The control signals allow a specific device to be addressed.

The following table summarizes the various ISDN electrical interfaces at different demarcation points or places in the traffic flow:

Electrical interface	Between what two points
U interface	Central office and NT1
T interface	NT1 and NT2 devices (such as a PBX)
S interface	NT1 or NT2 and ISDN devices (such as a telephone or terminal adapter)
R interface	Terminal adapter and non-ISDN devices (such as a computer)
V interface	Within the ISDN node at the central office; separates line termination equipment from exchange termination equipment

T1

Also see the **T-carrier system**, of which the T1 is a part.

The T1 (or T-1) carrier is the most commonly used digital line in the U.S., Canada, and Japan. In these countries, it carries 24 pulse code modulation (**PCM**) signals using time-division multiplexing (**TDM**) at an overall rate of 1.544 million bits per second (**Mbps**). T1 lines span distances within and between major metropolitan areas. A T1 Outstate System has been developed for longer distances between cities.

It's probable that your Internet **access provider** is connected to the Internet as a point-of-presence (**POP**) on a T1 line owned by a major telephone network.

T-1

See "T1"

T3

See "T-carrier system"

tablet computer

See "Tablet PC"

Tablet PC

Microsoft's Tablet PC is a design for a fully-equipped personal computer that allows a user to take notes using natural handwriting on a **stylus**- or digital pen-sensitive **touch screen** instead of requiring the use of a keyboard. The Tablet PC is similar in size and thickness to a yellow paper notepad. It will run existing Windows-based applications and is intended to be the user's primary personal computer as well as a note-taking device. Microsoft's next **operating system**, Windows XP, (code-named **Whistler**) is designed to support the Tablet PC. The first Tablet PCs will be geared toward business users.

The Tablet PC uses what is called **digital ink**. Digital ink allows the user to write a note on the screen in freehand just as the user would write on a piece of paper. Writing can be natural rather than being required to match a pattern. The note can be edited and revised using the stylus and even indexed and searched. The note stays in "ink" or handwritten form until the user translates the note into a text document. Handwritten notes can be shared via e-mail. The recognition of handwritten notes and instructions is designed to be as reliable as input from a keyboard or mouse is today.

The idea of tablet computing is generally credited to Alan Kay of Xerox who sketched out the idea in 1971. The best-known and first widely-sold tablet computer was Apple Computer's Newton, which was not a commercial success. With today's extended **battery** life, better **display resolution**, handwriting recognition software, larger **memory**, and **wireless** Internet access, the tablet computers of the early 2000's are deemed to have a better chance of being accepted as a viable computing option. Microsoft's goal is to make its tablet computers available by 2002.

TACACS and TACACS+

TACACS (Terminal Access Controller Access Control System) is an older **authentication protocol** common to **UNIX** networks that allows a remote access server to forward a user's logon password to an authentication **server** to determine whether **access** can be allowed to a given

system. TACACS is an **encryption** protocol and therefore less secure than the later TACACS+ and **Remote Authentication Dial-In User Service** protocols. A later version of TACACS is XTACACS (Extended TACACS). Both are described in **Request for Comments** 1492.

In spite of its name, TACACS+ is an entirely new protocol. TACACS+ and RADIUS have generally replaced the earlier protocols in more recently built or updated networks. TACACS+ uses the Transmission Control Protocol (**TCP**) and RADIUS uses the User Datagram Protocol (**UDP**). Some administrators recommend using TACACS+ because TCP is seen as a more reliable protocol. Whereas RADIUS combines authentication and **authorization** in a user profile, TACACS+ separates the two operations.

TACACS and XTACACS are still running on many older systems.

tag

A tag is a generic term for a language element descriptor. The set of tags for a document or other unit of information is sometimes referred to as **markup**, a term that dates to pre-computer days when writers and copy editors marked up document elements with copy editing symbols or shorthand.

Tag Image File Format

TIFF (Tag Image File Format) is a common format for exchanging **raster graphics** (**bitmap**) images between application programs, including those used for **scanner** images. A TIFF file can be identified as a file with a ".tiff" or ".tif" file name suffix. The TIFF format was developed in 1986 by an industry committee chaired by the Aldus Corporation (now part of Adobe Software). Microsoft and Hewlett-Packard were among the contributors to the format. One of the most common graphic image formats, TIFF files are commonly used in desktop publishing, faxing, 3-D applications, and medical imaging applications.

TIFF files can be in any of several classes, including gray scale, color **palette**, or RGB full color, and can include files with **JPEG**, LZW, or CCITT Group 4 standard run-length **image compression**.

talkback

A talkback is a microphone-and-receiver system installed in a recording/mixing console for communication between people in the control room and performers in the recording studio. Most semi-professional and professional consoles include such a system. The typical setup includes an internal microphone built directly into the console, and a series of switches. The switches allow the recording engineer to route the microphone signal to a variety of audio paths in the studio, such as the performer's headphones, a set of speakers in the recording area, or directly to a tape recorder. Using this tool, the engineer can communicate with a performer with headphones while they are performing in the studio

without interfering with the recording. Another use is to announce the title or other relevant information at the beginning of a recording (called a "slate").

talker

On the Internet, especially in the United Kingdom, a talker is a **Web site** that hosts online **chatting** or conversations entered at the keyboard. In the U.S., the term *chat site* is more common. Talkers and chat sites tend to be "middle-of-the-road" in terms of interests and participants. Technically, **MUDs** have conversations but these tend to be much more focused in purpose and in the intensity and dedication of participants. A special kind of talker is one that is part of an Internet Relay Chat (**IRC**).

tape

In computers, tape is an **external storage** medium, usually both readable and writable, consisting of a loop of flexible celluloid-like material that can store data in the form of electromagnetic charges that can be read and also erased. A tape drive is the device that positions, writes to, and reads from the tape. A tape cartridge is a protectively-encased tape that is portable.

In early business computers, tape was a primary storage medium and computer system operators spent a lot of time mounting and unmounting tapes for different jobs at different times of the day. With the development of the magnetic disk, tape became a medium for backing up (see **tape backup**) the large amounts of data on mainframes. Apart from any other consideration, one drawback of tape is that it can only be accessed by starting at the beginning and rolling through the tape until the desired data is located. For this reason, its main application use has been for **batch** processing of large amounts of data (payroll is the classic example).

Today, tape is still widely used on mainframes for archiving and backup. Software is provided that allows a company to easily manage automatic backup. On personal computers, tape is also used for backup.

tape backup

In computers, tape backup is the ability to periodically copy the contents of all or a designated amount of data from its usual storage device to a **tape cartridge** device so that, in the event of a **hard disk crash** or comparable failure, the data will not be lost. Tape backup can be done manually or, with appropriate software, be programmed to happen automatically.

Tape backup systems exist for needs ranging from backing up the hard disk on a personal computer to backing up large amounts of storage for **archiving** and **disaster recovery** purposes in a large enterprise as part of a storage area network (**SAN**), usually combining a hardware and software package. For personal computer tape backup, the Onstream

USB tape drive is popular. For enterprise tape backup, Linear Tape-Open (**LTO**) is an industry **open** standard from Hewlett-Packard, IBM, and Seagate.

Tape backup also includes the ability to restore data that has been backed up back to hard disk storage devices when needed.

TAPI

TAPI (Telephony Application Program Interface) is a standard program interface that lets you and your computer "talk" over telephones or video phones to people or phone-connected resources elsewhere in the world. Assuming your computer is equipped with TAPI and your setup includes the right **application** and hardware, you may be able:

- Call someone by clicking on their picture or other image

- Use a similar graphical user interface (**GUI**) to set up a conference call and then attend the call at the scheduled time

- See who you're talking to individually or at a conference call

- Add a voice note to an e-mail note you send or listen to a voice note attached to an e-mail note you receive

- Program your computer to automatically receive phone calls from certain numbers (but not from others)

- Send and receive **fax**es

- Do these things from a portable **wireless cellular telephone** telephone/computer as well as from a desktop computer

Developed jointly by Intel and Microsoft, TAPI is included with the Windows 95/98 and **Windows NT operating system**. Using TAPI, programmers can take advantage of different telephone systems, including ordinary **public switched telephone network**, **ISDN**, and **private branch exchange** without having to understand all their details. Each phone system hardware provider (for example, the **modem** maker or ISDN **card** maker) provides a specific software **driver** that interfaces directly with the hardware.

TAPI provides a high-level interface for dialing and disconnecting. Instead of having to encode an ATDT dial string and the ATH disconnect string, the programmer codes a much simpler "function call."

In addition to the interface for applications, TAPI includes a Service Provider Interface (SPI) for hardware vendors who are writing the **driver** software. The TAPI Dynamic Link Library (**DLL**) maps the API to the SPI and coordinates input/output traffic.

tar

Tar (for "Tape ARchive") is a **UNIX shell** command that creates a single file called an "**archive**" from a number of specified files or extracts the files from such an archive. A tar archive has the file suffix ".tar". The files in a tar archive are not compressed, just gathered together in one file.

The name is derived from a time when files were commonly backed up on and occasionally retrieved from magnetic tape as a permanent storage device. (They still are in some data centers.) A tar archive is perhaps more frequently used today to transfer files among UNIX systems. A popular archive handler for Windows systems, **WinZIP**, can be used to extract the files from a tar archive.

Tarball is a jargon term for a tar archive, suggesting "a bunch of files stuck together in a ball of tar."

task

In computer programming, a task is a basic unit of programming that an **operating system** controls. Depending on how the operating system defines a task in its design, this unit of programming may be an entire program or each successive invocation of a program. Since one program may make requests of other utility programs, the utility programs may also be considered tasks (or subtasks). All of today's widely-used operating systems support **multitasking**, which allows multiple tasks to run concurrently, taking turns using the resources of the computer.

In **preemptive multitasking**, each task may be assigned a priority depending on its relative importance, the amount of resources it is consuming, and other factors. The operating system then preempts (cuts short) a task having a lower priority value so that a higher priority task is given a turn. **Windows 2000**, **OS/390**, **Linux**, and **Amiga** are examples of operating systems that use preemptive multitasking. *Cooperative multitasking* is the ability for an operating system to manage multiple tasks such as application programs at the same time, but without the ability to necessarily preempt them.

Multithreading and multitasking are similar and are often confused. Multithreading is the management of multiple concurrent uses of the same program. Most operating systems and modern computer languages also support multithreading.

taxonomy

Taxonomy (from Greek *taxis* meaning arrangement or division and *nomos* meaning law) is the science of classification according to a pre-determined system, with the resulting catalog used to provide a conceptual framework for discussion, analysis, or information retrieval. In theory, the development of a good taxonomy takes into account the importance of separating elements of a group (taxon) into subgroups (taxa) that are mutually exclusive, unambiguous,

and taken together, include all possibilities. In practice, a good taxonomy should be simple, easy to remember, and easy to use.

One of the best known taxonomies is the one devised by the Swedish scientist, Carl Linnaeus, whose classification for biology is still widely used (with modifications). In Web **portal** design, taxonomies are often created to describe categories and subcategories of topics found on the Web site. The categorization of words on whatis.com is similar to any Web portal taxonomy.

T-carrier system

To see the relationship between T-carrier, E-carrier, and DS0 multiples, see **digital signal X**.

The T-carrier system, introduced by the Bell System in the U.S. in the 1960s, was the first successful system that supported digitized voice transmission. The original transmission rate (1.544 **Mbps**) in the T-1 line is in common use today in Internet service provider (**ISP**) connections to the Internet. Another level, the T-3 line, providing 44.736 Mbps, is also commonly used by **Internet service providers**. Another commonly installed service is a **fractional T-1**, which is the rental of some portion of the 24 channels in a T-1 line, with the other channels going unused.

The T-carrier system is entirely digital, using **pulse code modulation** and **time-division multiplexing**. The system uses four wires and provides **duplex** capability (two wires for receiving and two for sending at the same time). The T-1 digital stream consists of 24 64-Kbps **channels** that are **multiplexed**. (The standardized 64 Kbps channel is based on the bandwidth required for a voice conversation.) The four wires were originally a pair of **twisted pair** copper wires, but can now also include **coaxial cable**, **optical fiber**, digital microwave, and other media. A number of variations on the number and use of channels are possible.

In the T-1 system, voice signals are sampled 8,000 times a second and each sample is digitized into an 8-bit word. With 24 channels being digitized at the same time, a 192-bit **frame** (24 channels each with an 8-bit word) is thus being transmitted 8,000 times a second. Each frame is separated from the next by a single bit, making a 193-bit block. The 192 bit frame multiplied by 8,000 and the additional 8,000 framing bits make up the T-1's 1.544 Mbps data rate. The signaling bits are the least significant bits per frame.

Tcl

Tcl is an **interpreted script** language developed by Dr. John Ousterhout at the University of California, Berkeley, and now developed and maintained by Sun Laboratories. Tcl is comparable to:

- Netscape **JavaScript**
- Microsoft's **Visual Basic**

- The UNIX-derived **Perl**
- IBM's **Rexx**

In general, script languages are easier and faster to code in than the more structured, compiled languages such as **C** and **C++**. Script languages are sometimes considered good "glue" languages for tying several programs together. TclBlend is a version of Tcl that can access certain **Java** language facilities.

Tcl has a companion program, Tool Kit (**Tk**), to help create a graphical user interface with Tcl. Both Tcl and Tk can be downloaded or ordered from Sun's Web site.

TCO

TCO (total cost of ownership) is a type of calculation designed to help consumers and **enterprise** managers assess both direct and indirect costs and benefits related to the purchase of any **IT** component. The intention is to arrive at a final figure that will reflect the effective cost of purchase, all things considered. When you decide to buy a computer you may go through a TCO analysis: for example, the greater cost price of a high-end computer might be one consideration, but one that would have to be balanced by adding likely repair costs and earlier replacement to the purchase cost of the bargain brand.

TCO analysis originated with the Gartner Group several years ago and has since been developed in a number of different methodologies and software tools. TCO analysis performs calculations on extended costs for any purchase—these are called *fully burdened costs*. For the consumer's purchase of a computer, the fully burdened cost may include costs of purchase, repairs, maintenance, and upgrades. For the business purchase of a computer, the fully burdened costs can also include such things as service and support, networking, security, user training, and software licensing. The TCO has to be compared to the *total benefits of ownership* (TBO) to determine the viability of the purchase.

TCP

TCP (Transmission Control Protocol) is a set of rules (**protocol**) used along with the Internet Protocol (**IP**) to send data in the form of message units between computers over the Internet. While IP takes care of handling the actual delivery of the data, TCP takes care of keeping track of the individual units of data (called **packet**s) that a message is divided into for efficient routing through the Internet.

For example, when an **HTML** file is sent to you from a Web **server**, the Transmission Control Protocol (TCP) program layer in that server divides the file into one or more packets, numbers the packets, and then forwards them individually to the IP program layer. Although each packet has the same destination IP address, it may get routed differently through the network. At the other end (the **client** program in your computer), TCP reassembles the individual packets and waits until they have arrived to forward them to you as a single file.

TCP is known as a connection-oriented protocol, which means that a connection is established and maintained until such time as the message or messages to be exchanged by the application programs at each end have been exchanged. TCP is responsible for ensuring that a message is divided into the packets that IP manages and for reassembling the packets back into the complete message at the other end. In the Open Systems Interconnection (**OSI**) communication model, TCP is in layer 4, the Transport layer.

TCP port numbers

See "well-known port numbers"

TCP Wrapper

TCP Wrapper is a public domain computer program that provides **firewall** services for **UNIX** servers. The program was developed by Wietse Venema.

When an unprotected UNIX computer is connected to a network, the computer's system is exposed to other computer users connected to the network. For example, by using the **finger** utility, a hacker may be able to determine which users are logged on to a given server. It is also possible to find out the identities of individual computers, and various details about their users' recent Internet behavior. A hacker can determine when a workstation is likely to be idle, and then access and use that workstation when it is unattended. TCP Wrapper can act as a firewall to prevent this.

TCP Wrapper monitors incoming packets. If an external computer or host attempts to connect, TCP Wrapper checks to see if that external entity is authorized to connect. If it is authorized, then access is permitted; if not, access is denied. The program can be tailored to suit individual user or network needs.

TCP/IP

Transmission Control Protocol/Internet Protocol (TCP/IP) is the basic communication language or **protocol** of the **Internet**. It can also be used as a communications protocol in a private network (either an **intranet** or an **extranet**). When you are set up with direct access to the Internet, your computer is provided with a copy of the TCP/IP program just as every other computer that you may send messages to or get information from also has a copy of TCP/IP.

TCP/IP is a two-layer program. The higher **layer**, **Transmission Control Protocol**, manages the assembling of a message or file into smaller packets (see **packet**) that are transmitted over the Internet and received by a TCP layer that reassembles the packets into the original message. The lower layer, **Internet Protocol**, handles the **address** part of each packet so that it gets to the right destination. Each **gateway** computer on the network checks this address to see where to forward the message. Even though some packets from the same message are routed differently than others, they'll be reassembled at the destination.

TCP/IP uses the **client/server** model of communication in which a computer user (a client) requests and is provided a service (such as sending a Web page) by another computer (a server) in the network. TCP/IP communication is primarily point-to-point, meaning each communication is from one point (or **host** computer) in the network to another point or host computer. TCP/IP and the higher-level applications that use it are collectively said to be "stateless" because each client request is considered a new request unrelated to any previous one (unlike ordinary phone conversations that require a dedicated connection for the call duration). Being stateless frees network paths so that everyone can use them continuously. (Note that the TCP layer itself is not stateless as far as any one message is concerned. Its connection remains in place until all packets in a message have been received.)

Many Internet users are familiar with the even higher layer application protocols that use TCP/IP to get to the Internet. These include the World Wide Web's Hypertext Transfer Protocol (**HTTP**), the File Transfer Protocol (**FTP**), Telnet (**Telnet**) which lets you logon to remote computers, and the Simple Mail Transfer Protocol (**SMTP**). These and other protocols are often packaged together with TCP/IP as a "suite."

Personal computer users usually get to the Internet through the Serial Line Internet Protocol (**SLIP**) or the Point-to-Point Protocol (**PPP**). These protocols encapsulate the IP packets so that they can be sent over a dial-up phone connection to an access provider's modem.

Protocols related to TCP/IP include the User Datagram Protocol (**UDP**), which is used instead of TCP for special purposes. Other protocols are used by network host computers for exchanging **router** information. These include the Internet Control Message Protocol (**ICMP**), the Interior Gateway Protocol (**IGP**), the Exterior Gateway Protocol (**EGP**), and the Border Gateway Protocol (**BGP**).

TCPMAN

TCPMAN is a utility for manual or **script modem** dialing that is used when accessing the Internet. TCPMAN comes with the **shareware** program, Trumpet **Winsock**. Winsock is an **interface** between an application program in a Windows operating system and the Internet's **Transmission Control Protocol** program. (There are other Winsock programs than Trumpet's, which was one of the first and is among the most widely installed today.)

TCPMAN is the "tcpman.exe" file in Trumpet Winsock. Although the "MAN" stands for "manual," most users set up or are provided with a script of modem AT commands that is processed automatically each time you start TCPMAN. This is viewed as "scripted manual dialing." Using the information about your modem that you provide during setup, TCPMAN negotiates the actual line speed and other characteristics of the connection between your modem and the modem that is being dialed.

Typically, you will know about TCPMAN if you are with a service provider that furnishes or requires you to have the Trumpet Winsock. If not, your dialing capability is furnished by some other program.

TDM

See "time-division multiplexing"

TDMA

TDMA (time division multiple access) is a technology used in **digital cellular telephone** communication that divides each cellular channel into three time slots in order to increase the amount of data that can be carried.

TDMA is used by Digital-American Mobile Phone Service (**D-AMPS**), Global System for Mobile communications (**GSM**), and Personal Digital Cellular (PDC). However, each of these systems implements TDMA in a somewhat different and incompatible way. An alternative multiplexing scheme to FDMA with TDMA is **CDMA** (code division multiple access), which takes the entire allocated frequency range for a given service and multiplexes information for all users across the spectrum range at the same time.

TDMA was first specified as a standard in EIA/TIA Interim Standard 54 (IS-54). IS-136, an evolved version of IS-54, is the United States standard for TDMA for both the cellular (850 MHz) and **personal communications services** (1.9 GHz) spectrums. TDMA is also used for Digital Enhanced Cordless Telecommunications (**DECT**).

teach box

A teach box is a device that registers and memorizes mechanical motions or processes for later recall and execution by an electronic or computer system. The term especially applies to programmable robots.

Robot programming can be divided into levels, starting with the least complex and progressing to the equivalent of human intelligence. The table shows a four-level scheme. Level 3, just below human-equivalent artificial intelligence (**AI**), is called task-level programming. Programs at level 3 can instruct a robot to execute complete operations, such as shoveling the snow from a driveway or flying an aircraft on a reconnaissance mission.

Programming Level	Description
4	Human intelligence
3	Complete tasks
2	Sequences of motions or operations
1	Single motions or operations

An example of a level-1 teach box is a remote-control for the doors of a car. When the wireless receiver gets the signal from the remote unit, it locks or unlocks the doors. Another example of a level-1 teach box is the remote box that controls a hi-fi sound system or videocassette recorder (VCR).

An example of a level-2 teach box is the microcomputer that controls a telephone answering machine. When a call comes in, the sequence of operations is recalled from memory. The machine answers the phone, makes an announcement, takes the message, and resets for the next incoming call.

Level-3 teach boxes are used in aerospace, miliatary, and industrial applications. The intended movements of a robot are entered into memory by pressing buttons or guiding a joystick or other three-dimensional control device. The robot's path, variations in speed, rotations, and gripping/grasping movements are all programmed. Then, when the memory is recalled, the robot reproduces these movements in the exact sequence, and to the exact extent and speed in all dimensions.

Also see **artificial intelligence** and **robotics**.

technobabble

In information technology and other specialized areas, technobabble is the use of technical or "insider" terms that, to the uninitiated, have no meaning. Technobabble can be divided into (1) technical terms with some formal standing in language such as new transmission or computer communication protocols, especially in their abbreviated or acronym forms, (2) marketing terms in which terms with prior meaning are give new missions (for example, **industrial strength**), and (3) informal, colloquial, or jargon terms (of which *technobabble* itself would seem to be an example).

Although this term primarily connotes words that discourage understanding, it is not always used in a negative sense, but often in the sense that "here is some technical information expressed in the terms that have been invented for it."

Closely related terms include: **neologism**, technospeak, and geekspeak.

techno-fiend

In information technology, a techno-fiend is someone who is addicted to finding out and knowing how things work in one or more aspects of **cyberspace**. Techno-fiends frequently know about and consult the places where you can find out. Some techno-fiends also frequent **Usenet** or other online discussions. Techno-fiends usually suspect that there's some place or someone with information that they should know about but don't.

Subjects that compel the attention of techno-fiends include: Web site design and browser behavior, Web server installation and management, any new emerging standard (a techno-fiend will read the main standard and even some of the ancillary standards), and any new technology, especially hardware technologies.

In general (with some exceptions), techno-fiends tend to be lay people rather than experts (whose motivation for understanding how things work is professional and somewhat economically motivated). A techno-fiend is less dedicated to a subject or a technology than a **geek** or a **hacker**, who both tend to be among the professionals. However, you can be an expert in one area and a techno-fiend in another.

telco

In the United States and possibly other countries, "telco" is a short form for *telephone company*. Sometimes it means a local telephone company, such as a Bell operating company or an independent local telephone company. Sometimes it means any telephone company, including one offering long-distance services.

telecenter

A telecenter (U.S. spelling) or telecentre (UK spelling) is a work location usually in a different place than the organization's main office that provides convenient occasional access for **telecommuting** to work equipment that they don't have at home or on the road. For example, a home telecommuter might need to print and reproduce printed copies of a document occasionally using a high-speed printer not available at home. Or a mobile worker might occasionally check the telecenter for **fax** mail or to send a fax. A telecenter could also have teleconference facilities.

telecentre

See "telecenter"

Telecommunications Act of 1996

The Telecommunications Act of 1996, enacted by the U.S. Congress on February 1, 1996, and signed into law by President Bill Clinton on February 8, 1996, provided major changes in laws affecting cable TV, telecommunications, and the Internet. The law's main purpose was to stimulate competition in telecommunication services. The law specifies:

- How local telephone carriers can compete
- How and under what circumstances local exchange carriers (**LEC**) can provide long-distance services
- The deregulation of cable TV rates

Included with the Act was the former Communications Decency Act, which, among other provisions, makes it a crime to convey pornography over the Internet in a way that is easily accessible to children.

Telecommunications Management Network

See "TMN"

telecommuting

Telecommuting and telework are synonyms for the use of telecommunication to work outside the traditional office or workplace, usually at home (**SOHO**) or in a mobile situation. According to one study, telecommuting has been growing at 15% a year since 1990 in North America. 80% of Fortune 1000 companies are likely to introduce it within the next two to three years. Although work at the company premises is not likely to disappear, new forms of telecommunication such as voice and picture communication and groupware are likely to make telecommuting more social in the future.

Factors that will continue to affect the future of telecommuting include the availability of **bandwidth** and fast **Internet** connections in a given country; social methodologies for balancing work control and work freedom; the perceived values and economies in telecommuting; and the opportunities and need for working collaboratively across large distances, including globally.

With the arrival of the Internet and the Web as a kind of "standard" for groupware, one can join a **virtual organization** to access resources developed for members who work almost entirely through telecommunication with an occasional face-to-face meeting.

teleconference

A teleconference is a telephone meeting among two or more participants involving technology more sophisticated than a simple two-way phone connection. At its simplest, a teleconference can be an audio conference with one or both ends of the conference sharing a speaker phone. With considerably more equipment and special arrangements, a teleconference can be a conference, called a videoconference, in which the participants can see still or motion video images of each other. Because of the high **bandwidth** of video and the opportunity for larger and multiple display screens, a videoconference requires special telecommunica-

tion arrangements and a special room at each end. As equipment and high-bandwidth cabling become more commonplace, it's possible that videoconferences can be held from your own computer or even in a mobile setting. One of the special projects of **Internet2** is to explore the possibility of having teleconferences in which all participants actually appear to be in the same room together. Today's audio teleconferences are sometimes arranged over dial-up phone lines using bridging services that provide the necessary equipment for the call.

teledactyl

A teledactyl (pronounced TEHL-eh-DAK-til) is a specialized **voice recognition** system designed to produce **ASCII** text from human speech. The teledactyl can be used in conjunction with telephone lines, allowing voice-operated directory assistance, voice-operated remote control, and dictation over the Internet.

We're not familiar with this term's origin, but Greek *tele* means "far off or distant" and *daktylos*, Greek for "finger," is the source of *dactyl*, a term used in English verse for a poetic meter consisting of one accented syllable followed by two weaker ones. *Dactylography* is the analysis of fingerprints for identification. Our guess is that the term's orginators wanted to convey the idea of "writing at a distance by speaking over the telephone."

telematics

Telematics is the blending of computers and wireless telecommunications technologies, ostensibly with the goal of efficiently conveying information over vast networks to improve a host of business functions or government-related public services. The most notable example of telematics may be the Internet itself, since it depends on a number of computer networks connected globally through telecommunication **backbone**s.

The term has evolved to refer to automobile systems that combine global positioning satellite (**GPS**) tracking and other wireless communications for automatic roadside assistance and remote diagnostics. General Motors Corp. first popularized automotive telematics with its OnStar system.

Major automakers are equipping new prototype vehicles with wireless-based services controlled by voice commands. This kind of telematics could enable motorists to perform a variety of wireless functions such as accessing the Internet, receiving or sending e-mail, downloading digital audio and video files, or obtaining "smart" transportation information.

The telematics industry is not limited to automotive applications. Other applications are being studied or developed for monitoring water and air pollution, for medical informatics and health care, and for **distance**

learning. Many European countries are developing uniform policies to integrate telematics applications into government, business and education.

telemetrics

Telemetrics is the technology involving automatic measurement and transmission of data from remote sources. The process of measuring data at the source and transmitting it automatically is called *telemetry*. The two terms, *telemetry* and *telemetrics*, are often used interchangeably. Originally, data was transmitted over wires, but now telemetrics frequently refers to wireless communication. Telemetrics applications include the monitoring of space flights, meteorological data transmission, **videoconferencing**, the Global Positioning System (**GPS**), wildlife tracking, camera control robotics, and oceanography.

In the first telemetrics application, in Chicago in 1912, telephone lines were used to transmit operational data from power plants to a central office. Because telemetry was used originally in projects like this, the first telemetry systems were called *supervisory* systems. In 1960, the *interrogation-reply principle* was developed, which led to selective transmission of data, to be sent only upon request.

In general, telemetrics works in the following way: Sensors at the source measure either electrical data (such as voltage or current) or physical data (such as temperature or pressure). These are converted to specific electrical voltages and a multiplexer combines the voltages, along with timing data, into a single data stream for transmission to the distant receiver. Upon reception, the data stream is separated into its original components and the data is displayed and processed according to user specifications.

telephone jacks

In the U.S., telephone jacks are also known as registered jacks, sometimes described as RJ-XX, and are a series of telephone connection interfaces (receptacle and plug) that are registered with the U.S. Federal Communications Commission (**FCC**). They derive from interfaces that were part of AT&T's Universal Service Order Codes (USOC) and were adopted as part of FCC regulations (specifically Part 68, Subpart F. Section 68.502). The term *jack* sometimes means both receptacle and plug and sometimes just the receptacle.

RJ-11

The most common telephone jack is the RJ-11 jack, which can have six conductors but usually is implemented with four. The RJ-11 jack is likely to be the jack that your household or office phones are plugged into from the ordinary "untwisted" wire (sometimes called "gray satin" or "flat wire") people are most familiar with. In turn, the jacks connect to the "outside" longer wires known as **twisted pair** that connect to the telephone company **central office** or to a private branch exchange (**PBX**).

The four wires are usually characterized as a red and green pair and a black and white pair. The red and green pair typically carry voice or data. On an outside phone company connection, the black and white pair may be used for low-voltage signals such as phone lights. On a PBX system, they may be used for other kinds of signaling.

Your computer modem is usually connected to an RJ-11 jack.

RJ-14

The RJ-14 is similar to the RJ-11, but the four wires are used for two phone lines. Typically, one set of wires (for one line) contains a red wire and a green wire. The other set contains a yellow and black wire. Each set carries one analog "conversation" (voice or data).

RJ-45

The RJ-45 is a single-line jack for digital transmission over ordinary phone wire, either untwisted or twisted. The interface has eight pins or positions. For connecting a modem, printer, or a data PBX at a data rate up to 19.2 **Kbps**, you can use untwisted wire. For faster transmissions in which you're connecting to an Ethernet **10BaseT** network, you need to use twisted pair wire. (Untwisted is usually a flat wire like common household phone extension wire. Twisted is often round.)

There are two varieties of RJ-45: keyed and unkeyed. Keyed has a small bump on its end and the female complements it. Both jack and plug must match.

telephone network standards

See "V.xx"

Telephony Application Program Interface

See "TAPI"

telephony

Telephony is the technology associated with the electronic transmission of voice, **fax**, or other information between distant parties using systems historically associated with the telephone, a handheld device containing both a speaker or transmitter and a receiver. With the arrival of computers and the transmittal of digital information over telephone systems and the use of radio to transmit telephone signals, the distinction between *telephony* and *telecommunication* has become difficult to make.

Internet telephony is the use of the Internet rather than the traditional telephone company infrastructure and rate structure to exchange spoken or other telephone information. Since access to the Internet is available at

local phone connection rates, an international or other long-distance call will be much less expensive than through the traditional call arrangement.

On the Internet, three new services are now or will soon be available:

- The ability to make a normal voice phone call (whether or not the person called is immediately available; that is, the phone will ring at the location of the person called) through the Internet at the price of a local call

- The ability to send fax transmissions at very low cost (at local call prices) through a gateway point on the Internet in major cities

- The ability to send voice messages along with text e-mail

Some companies that make products that provide or plan to provide these capabilities include: IDT Corporation (Net2Phone), Netspeak, NetXchange, Rockwell International, VocalTec, and Voxspeak. Among uses planned for Internet phone services are phone calls to customer service people while viewing a product catalog online at a Web site.

You can now add telephone capabilities to your computer by adding a telephony board, available for under $300, that combines the functions of modem, sound board, speakerphone, and voicemail system. A telephony board is often integrated into new machines targeted for small business and home office users.

A Telephony API (**TAPI**) is available from Microsoft and Intel that allows Windows client applications to access voice services on a server and that interconnects PC and phone systems. Both Microsoft and Netscape provide or plan to provide support for voice e-mail.

teleportation

Teleportation is the duplication or re-creation of physical objects or their properties using light beams, according to researchers at the California Institute of Technology. Also calling it *quantum teleportation*, the researchers have successfully transmitted information about the properties of an object at the speed of light so that the object could theoretically be duplicated or reconstructed at the destination. The experiment takes advantage of the atomic particle property in which two particles at a great distance are in some mysterious way intertwined. Thus, an effect on one particle is almost simultaneously felt in the other particle as well. In physics, this characteristic is called **entanglement**. The CalTech researchers believe the characteristic may one day have practical applications, one of which would be a **quantum computer** in which information is moved with light using the entanglement principle rather than wires.

In their experiment, the researchers created two entangled light beams. (A light beam is a stream of photons, and photons, which have both wave and particle characteristics, are the basic units of light.) The entangled light beams carried information about the quantum state of a third light

beam over the distance of a yard (about one meter) at the speed of light. The researchers believe the concept can be applied to transmitting the physical property attributes of solid objects at the speed of light. Is there any difference between a particular solid object and the collection of its attributes reproduced at a great distance at the speed of light? The researchers say no one knows for sure.

teletypewriter

A teletypewriter (TTY) is an input device that allows alphanumeric **characters** to be typed in and sent, usually one at a time as they are typed, to a computer or a printer. The Teletype Corporation developed the teletypewriter, which was an early interface to computers. *Teletype mode* is the capability of a keyboard, computer, application, printer, display, or modem to handle teletypewriter input and output. Basically, this is a one-character-at-a-time mode of sending, receiving, or handling data, although it is often modified to handle a line of characters at a time. Since this mode requires little programming logic, it is often used where **memory** is limited. The basic input/output operating system (**BIOS**) sends messages to a PC display using teletype mode. Most printers offer a teletype mode. The simplest video display output format is text in teletype mode. Many modems today continue to include support for a TTY interface.

telework

See "telecommuting"

Telnet

Telnet is the way you can **access** someone else's computer, assuming they have given you permission. (Such a computer is frequently called a **host** computer.) More technically, Telnet is a user command and an underlying **TCP/IP protocol** for accessing remote computers. On the Web, **HTTP** and **FTP** protocols allow you to request specific files from remote computers, but not to actually be logged on as a user of that computer. With Telnet, you log on as a regular user with whatever privileges you may have been granted to the specific **application** and **data** on that computer.

A Telnet command request looks like this (the computer name is made-up):

```
telnet the.libraryat.whatis.edu
```

The result of this request would be an invitation to log on with a userid and a prompt for a password. If accepted, you would be logged on like any user who used this computer every day.

Telnet is most likely to be used by program developers and anyone who has a need to use specific applications or data located at a particular host computer.

temperature

Temperature (symbolized T) is an expression of heat energy. Temperature can mean different things in different situations.

Thermodynamic temperature is a measure of the kinetic energy in molecules or **atoms** of a substance. The greater this energy, the faster the particles are moving, and the higher the reading an instrument will render. This is the method lay people most often use.

Spectral temperature is defined according to the **wavelength** at which the **electromagnetic** (EM) energy that an object emits is greatest. The shorter the wavelength, the higher the frequency of maximum EM energy, and the higher the spectral temperature. This is the temperature scheme that astronomers use to measure the heat in distant objects such as the sun's corona or the gas and dust between stars.

There are three temperature scales in common use today: **kelvin** (K), **centigrade** or Celsius (C), and **Fahrenheit** (F). A fourth scale, known as the Rankine (R) temperature scale, is less often used. The kelvin is the unit of temperature in the International System of Units (**SI**).

One kelvin is formally defined as $1/273.16$ (3.6609×10^{-3}) of the thermodynamic temperature of the triple point of pure water (H_2O). A temperature of 0 K represents absolute zero, the absence of all heat.

In the centigrade or Celsius temperature scale, the freezing point of pure water at one atmosphere is assigned the value zero; the boiling point is +100 C. One-degree increments in the centigrade scale are the same size as those in the kelvin scale. At standard Earth-atmospheric sea-level pressure, water freezes at 0 C or +273.15 K, and boils at +100 C or +373.15 K. A temperature of 0 K thus corresponds to -273.15 C. To convert a kelvin temperature figure to Celsius, subtract 273.15. To convert a Celsius temperature figure to kelvin, add 273.15.

The Fahrenheit scale is used mostly by non-scientists. Pure water at one atmosphere (the average sea-level pressure) freezes at +32 degrees Fahrenheit (F); pure water at one atmosphere boils at +212 degrees F. Absolute zero is -459.67 degrees F. One Fahrenheit degree increment is 5/9 (0.55555) times the size of a kelvin or centigrade degree. If C is the centigrade temperature, the Fahrenheit temperature F is given by F = (1.8 × C) + 32. The Fahrenheit and centigrade scales agree at -40.

The Rankine scale is not often used. The degree increments in this temperature scheme are the same size as those of the Fahrenheit scale, but 0 R corresponds to absolute zero or 0 K. Degrees Rankine can be obtained from degrees kelvin by multiplying the kelvin temperature by 1.8. Degrees Fahrenheit are obtained from Rankine readings by subtracting 459.67.

Also see **kelvin**, and International System of Units (**SI**).

temperature, standard

See "standard temperature and pressure"

Tempest

Tempest was the name of a classified (secret) U.S. government project to study (probably for the purpose of both exploiting and guarding against) the susceptibility of some computer and telecommunications devices to emit electromagnetic radiation (**EMR**) in a manner that can be used to reconstruct intelligible data. Tempest's name is believed to have been a code name used during development by the U. S. government in the late 1960s, but at a somewhat later stage, it became an **acronym** for Telecommunications Electronics Material Protected from Emanating Spurious Transmissions. Today, in military circles, the term has been officially supplanted by Emsec (for Emissions Security); however, the term Tempest is still widely used in the civilian arena.

Exactly when it was first noticed that certain devices can emanate decipherable data is unclear. (The practice of monitoring and capturing such data is known as **Van Eck phreaking** after the author of a formal paper on the subject.) Today, cathode ray tube (**CRT**) and to a lesser extent liquid crystal display (**LCD**) monitors, microchips, and composite devices such as printers and PCs all emit EMR into space or into some conductive medium (such as power lines, communications wires, or even water piping). The EMR that is emitted contains, to varying degrees, the information that the device is displaying, creating, storing, or transmitting. With the correct equipment and techniques, it is possible to reconstruct all or a substantial portion of that data. Some equipment is far more susceptible than others. For example, some US Robotics data/fax **modem**s generate incredibly strong EMR when active, which can be read even by comparatively crude equipment. Wireless handsets and office speakerphones are other devices that generate extremely strong EMR signals.

The range in which an eavesdropper can monitor emanations varies tremendously according to conditions. In most cases, the emanations can be picked up with proper equipment from a distance of around 200-300 meters. However, in some cases where a signal has been captured by a conductive medium (such as a power line), monitoring can occur over a distance of many kilometers.

Monitoring devices include various kinds of sensitive receivers, which can monitor a wide range of frequencies, and a combination of hardware and software that is capable of processing the received signals into the original data. The data that is picked up is often corrupted by such things as external EMR interference, signal weakness over distances, and partial transmission. Advanced **algorithm**s can help provide a more complete picture of the original information.

Shielding of devices from EMR is achieved by a number of methods. The most sophisticated devices use advanced micro-components that have been designed from scratch to minimize Tempest emanations. Generally, shielding involves encompassing the device in a Faraday cage that does not permit stray emanations, along with special modifications to the power source. This usually involves a heavy metal case around an object. Tempest shielding also involves such issues as the design of a room and placement of equipment within it, to ensure that no information can escape.

For individuals who wish to be more secure against Van Eck phreaking but cannot invest in this level of equipment, some software products recommend special displays that limit the effectiveness of monitoring of emanations from a CRT monitor. National Communications Security Committee Directive 4 sets U.S. Tempest (shielding) standards. The requirements are set out in document NACSIM 5100A, which is classified. Tempest certification for private sector usage is extremely expensive and, as a result, it has led to a newer standard, called ZONE, which is more cost effective, though somewhat less secure. Approved Tempest-shielded devices are classed into 3 categories. Type 1 is extremely secure and available only to the U.S. government and approved contractors, who must undergo strict vetting. Type 2 is somewhat less secure, but still requires government approval to use. Type 3 is for general commercial use.

In the private arena, there are few individuals who are competent in Tempest technology. With only a handful of exceptions, the only qualifications of significance come from individuals who have served in either the military or intelligence communities and who have attended courses run and approved by the NSA, namely the ones held at Lackland Air Force Base, just outside San Antonio, Texas or at National Cryptologic School at Linthicum, Maryland.

As a note of warning, there is nothing illegal in the U.S. in attempting to procure equipment that is Tempest-shielded, though some devices are classified and only obtainable to authorized entities. You are free (subject to patent law and FCC guidelines for spurious admissions) to make any modifications to equipment to shield them from attack. However, securing or attempting to secure surveillance devices is illegal and can subject all individuals involved to severe penalties. Even "scam" technology that is completely ineffective will get individuals into trouble, as the law relates also to intention. Full details are available at US Code / Title 18—Crimes and Criminal Procedures / Part 1—Crimes / Chapter 119, 2510 to 2521). The only exceptions to this are related to the military, intelligence agencies, and law enforcement bodies with court orders.

Tempest-shielding

See "Tempest"

template

A template (from French *templet*, diminutive of *temple*, a part of a weaving loom for keeping it stretched transversely) is a form, mold, or pattern used as a guide to making something. Here are some examples:

- A ruler is a template when used to draw a straight line.

- A document in which the standard opening and closing parts are already filled in is a template that you can copy and then fill in the variable parts.

- An overlay that you put on your computer keyboard telling you special key combinations for a particular application is a template for selecting the right keys to press.

- Flowcharting templates (not used much now) help programmers draw flowcharts or logic sequences in preparation for writing the code.

- In programming, a template is a generic **class** or other unit of source code that can be used as the basis for unique units of code. In **C++**, an object-oriented computing language, there are Standard Template Libraries from which programmers can choose individual template classes to modify. The **Microsoft Foundation Class Library** (MFCL) is an example.

terabit

In measuring data transmission speed, a terabit is one trillion **binary digit**s, or 1,000,000,000,000 (that is, 10^{12}) bits. A terabit is used for measuring the amount of data that is transferred in a second between two telecommunication points or within network devices. For example, several companies are building a network switch that passes incoming packets through the device and out again at a terabits-per-second speed. Terabits per second is usually shortened to Tbps.

Although the bit is a unit of the binary number system, bits in data communications have historically been counted using the decimal number system. For example, 28.8 kilobits per second (**Kbps**) is 28,800 bits per second. Because of computer architecture and memory address boundaries, bytes are always some multiple or exponent of two.

terabyte

A terabyte is a measure of computer **storage** capacity and is 2 to the 40th power or approximately a thousand billion bytes (that is, a thousand gigabytes).

Also see **byte**, **gigabyte**, **teraflop**, and **petabyte**.

teraflop

A teraflop is a measure of a computer's speed and can be expressed as:

- A trillion floating point operations per second

- 10 to the 12th power **floating-point operations per second**

Today's fastest parallel computing operations are capable of teraflop speeds. Scientists have begun to envision computers operating at **petaflop** speeds.

terahertz

The terahertz, abbreviated THz, is a unit of electromagnetic (EM) wave **frequency** equal to one trillion **hertz** (10^{12} Hz). The terahertz is used as an indicator of the frequency of infrared (**IR**), visible, and ultraviolet (UV) radiation.

An EM wave having a frequency of 1 THz has a **wavelength** of 0.3 millimeters (mm), or 300 micrometers (μm). An EM wave of 540 THz is in the middle of the visible-light spectrum. Wireless transmissions and computer clock speeds are at frequencies far below 1 THz.

The terahertz is not commonly used in computer and wireless technology, although it is possible that a microprocessor with a clock speed of 1 THz might someday be developed. At present, the terahertz is of interest primarily to physicists and astronomers. More commonly-used units of frequency are the kilohertz (**kHz**), equal to 1,000 Hz or 10^{-9} THz, the megahertz (**MHz**), equal to 10^{6} Hz or 10^{-6} THz, and the gigahertz (**GHz**), equal to 10^{9} Hz or 0.001 THz.

Teraplex

Teraplex (short for Teraplex Integration Center) is the name IBM has given to its "real life" testing centers whose purpose is to allow IBM customers and business partners to test very large database (**VLDB**) applications on a full-scale basis by using actual workloads. IBM makes its Teraplex Integration Centers freely available to its customers and business partners, but sets strict criteria for what tests can be run. The tests must involve a **terabyte** or more of data (hence the name Teraplex) and they must test **business intelligence** applications (as opposed to **online transaction processing** applications). The tests must evaluate **scalability**, and they must test the feasibility of a potential business solution in a realistic time frame. Each center can test applications and products from multiple IBM divisions and from non-IBM vendors. Currently, IBM designates individual centers for each IBM platform and provides IBM and third-party developers on site to assist with the testing.

terbo

The suffix *terbo* appears in the **V.32terbo** modem protocol and indicates the third version of the **V.32** protocol. Terbo is an invented word based on the Old Latin *ter* meaning "three times" and the word *turbo* (Latin for "whirling top" or "whirlwind") meaning "speed."

Also see **bis**, a suffix used in several modern protocols that means "second version."

terminal

1) In data communications, a terminal is any device that terminates one end (sender or receiver) of a communicated signal. In practice, it is usually applied only to the extended end points in a network, not central or intermediate devices. In this usage, if you can send signals to it, it's a terminal.

2) In telephony, the term **Data Terminal Equipment** (DTE) is used to describe the computer end of the DTE-to-**DCE** (Data Communications Equipment) communication between a computer and a **modem**.

3) In computers, a terminal (sometimes qualified as a "dumb" terminal) is an end-use device (usually with display monitor and keyboard) with little or no software of its own that relies on a **mainframe** or another computer (such as a PC server) for its "intelligence." IBM's 3270 Information Display System was a widely-installed system of such terminals in corporations. Many applications designed for the 3270 or other "dumb" terminals are still in use at PCs that emulate or act like a 3270. The VT-100 from **Digital Equipment Corporation** is another example of a widely-used so-called "dumb" terminal. A variation of this kind of terminal is being revived in the idea of the **thin client** or network computer.

4) The term is sometimes used to mean any personal computer or user workstation that is hooked up to a network.

terminal adapter

A terminal adapter (TA) is a hardware **interface** between a computer and an **Integrated Services Digital Network** line. It's what replaces a **modem** when you are using an ISDN connection. Unlike "plain old telephone service," which carries **signals** in **analog** (voice) form between your computer and the telephone company's office, ISDN carries signals in **digital** form so there is no need to modulate and demodulate between analog and digital signals. The terminal adapter is what you have to install on a computer so that data can be fed directly into the ISDN line in digital form. Since ISDN service is not available from telephone companies in all areas, the terminal adapter is not usually built into a computer. You purchase and install it when you sign up for ISDN service.

Some manufacturers and telephone companies use the term *ISDN modem*, instead.

terminal emulation

Terminal emulation is the ability to make one computer terminal, typically a PC, appear to look like another, usually older type of terminal so that a user can access programs originally written to communicate with the other terminal type. Terminal emulation is often used to give PC users the ability to log on and get direct access to legacy programs in a mainframe operating system. Terminal emulation requires installing a special program in the PC or on a local area network (**LAN**) server to which it is connected. Typically, an enterprise with **mainframe** computers installs a terminal emulation program in all its workstations (or LAN servers). Workers can work locally with Windows or other PC or workstation applications and also open a window and work directly with mainframe applications. The terminal emulation program runs like any other workstation application as a separate program task providing its own window to the user. However, instead of content with a **graphical user interface** (GUI), the terminal emulation window presents some particular mainframe operating system or application interface that is text-only.

Different terminal emulation is required for specific types of **terminal**—for example, the IBM **3270** display terminal, the **AS/400**'s 5250 display terminal, or DEC's VT100 terminal. The program performing the terminal emulation must understand the data stream from the mainframe at several communication levels, including data link control and session control.

Terminal Server product

The Microsoft Windows Terminal Server (WTS) is a **server** program running on its **Windows NT** 4.0 (or higher) operating system that provides the graphical user interface (**GUI**) of the Windows **desktop** to user **terminal**s that don't have this capability themselves. The latter include the relatively low-cost **NetPC** or "**thin client**" that some companies are purchasing as alternatives to the autonomous and more expensive PC with its own operating system and applications. The Windows Terminal Server was code-named "Hydra" during development.

The Windows Terminal Server has three parts: the multiuser core server itself, the Remote Desktop Protocol that enables the Windows desktop interface to be sent to the terminals by the server, and the Terminal Server Client that goes in each terminal. Users will have access to 32-bit Windows-based applications. The new terminal devices are being made by a number of vendors, including Network Computing Devices and Wyse Technologies. In addition, users of existing PCs running Windows 95 and Windows 3.11 operating systems can also access the Server and its applications. The Terminal Server can also serve terminals and workstations that run UNIX, Macintosh, or DOS operating systems that can't be upgraded to 32-bit Windows.

Co-developed with Citrix, Microsoft's Windows NT 4.0 Terminal Server Edition together with Citrix's MetaFrame product replace Citrix's **WinFrame** product.

terminal server

Also see **Terminal Server product**, Microsoft software that serves the Windows desktop and applications to terminals.

Generally in information technology, a terminal server is a hardware device or **server** that provides **terminal**s (PCs, printers, and other devices) with a common connection point to a local or wide area network. The terminals connect to the terminal server from their **RS-232C** or RS-423 **serial port**. The other side of the terminal server connects through network interface cards (**NIC**) to a local area network (**LAN**) (usually an **Ethernet** or **token ring** LAN) through **modem**s to the dial-in/out wide area network, or to an X.25 network or a 3270 gateway. (Different makes of terminal server offer different kinds of interconnection. Some can be ordered in different configurations based on customer need.) The use of a terminal server means that each terminal doesn't need its own network interface card or modem. The connection resources inside the terminal server are usually shared dynamically by all attached terminals.

Some terminal servers can be shared by up to 128 terminals. The terminals can be PCs, terminals that emulate 3270s, printers, or other devices with the RS-232/423 interface. In some terminal servers, the terminals can use **TCP/IP** for a **Telnet** connection to a host, LAT to a **Digital Equipment Corporation** host, or TN3270 for a Telnet connection to an IBM host with 3270 applications. With some terminal servers, a given terminal user can have multiple host connections to different kinds of host operating systems (UNIX, IBM, DEC).

The term *communication server* is also sometimes used instead of *terminal server*.

terminate and stay resident

A terminate and stay resident (TSR) program is one that is set up to be loaded and then remain in computer **memory** so that it is quickly accessible when a user presses a certain keyboard combination. TSR programs are used in **Disk Operating System**s and perhaps other non-**task operating system**s. They aren't needed in multitasking systems such as Windows and **OS/2**. TSR programs typically include calculators, clocks, and notepads. When running another program in DOS, you can press the preset keyboard key or combination of keys and the TSR program will "pop up" into view.

Terrestrial Trunked Radio

See "TETRA"

tesla

The tesla (symbolized T) is the standard unit of magnetic flux density. It is equivalent to one **weber** per meter squared (1 Wb · m^{-2}). Reduced to base units in the International System of Units (SI), 1 T represents one kilogram per second squared per ampere (kg · s^{-2} · A^{-1}). The tesla was named for Nikola Tesla, the Croatian-born scientist who contributed greatly toward the development of modern-day electrical power systems.

In practice, the tesla is a large unit, and is used primarily in industrial electromagnetics. When dealing with practical magnets of the sort encountered in consumer products, a smaller unit of flux density called the **gauss** (symbolized G) is often used. There are ten thousand gauss in one tesla (1 T = 10^4 G).

Also see **magnetic field**, **gauss**, and **International System of Units**.

testing

In general, testing is finding out how well something works. In terms of human beings, testing tells what level of knowledge or skill has been acquired. In computer hardware and software development, testing is used at key checkpoints in the overall process to determine whether objectives are being met. For example, in software development, product objectives are sometimes tested by product user representatives. When the design is complete, coding follows and the finished code is then tested at the unit or module level by each programmer; at the component level by the group of programmers involved; and at the system level when all components are combined together. At early or late stages, a product or service may also be tested for **usability**.

At the system level, the manufacturer or independent reviewer may subject a product or service to one or more **performance** tests, possibly using one or more **benchmark**s. Whether viewed as a product or a service or both, a **Web site** can also be tested in various ways—by observing user experiences, by asking questions of users, by timing the flow through specific usage scenarios, and by comparing it with other sites.

testing your bandwidth

See "bandwidth test"

TETRA

TETRA (Terrestrial Trunked Radio) is a set of standards developed by the European Telecommunications Standardisation Institute (ETSI) that describes a common mobile radio communications infrastructure throughout Europe. This infrastructure is targeted primarily at the mobile radio needs of public safety groups (such as police and fire departments), utility companies, and other enterprises that provide voice and data communications services.

All of these groups have been high-end users of private/professional mobile radio (PMR) or public access mobile radio (PAMR) technology. This is especially true in the areas of law enforcement and public safety, where fast and accurate field communications to and from a central office or dispatcher are often critical. TETRA is a standard solution for groups that use both PMR and PAMR.

In recent years, when European disasters have struck, emergency response teams from several European nations had a difficult time communicating with each other, due in part to the lack of standardization in their mobile radio equipment. The TETRA standards evolved to answer this communication challenge as well as others faced or anticipated by the European Commission (EC) in its efforts to unify European countries.

Based on digital, trunked radio technology, TETRA is believed to be the next-generation architecture and standard for current, analog PMR and PAMR markets. TETRA actually takes its features from several different technological areas: Mobile radio, digital **cellular telephone**, paging, and **wireless** data.

TETRA relies on digital trunking. TETRA-based products come with built-in **encryption** features to ensure the privacy and confidentiality of sensitive data/voice communications. These products are also designed with the ability to transfer data at faster rates than seen before in mobile communications.

TETRA, which originally stood for Trans-European Trunked Radio, was renamed Terrestrial Trunked Radio after ETSI found widespread interest in the TETRA standards beyond Europe's geographic borders. ETSI has had a successful history of developing communications standards that later become accepted industry-wide, such as the Global System for Mobile Communications (**GSMC**) standard.

The TETRA Memorandum of Understanding (MoU) was created in December 1994 as a forum to represent the needs of various members of the mobile communications industry (including product manufacturers, telecommunications agencies, end users of mobile devices). Ole M. Lauridsen, chairman of the TETRA MoU, anticipates that the introduction of TETRA across Europe will not only standardize and improve mobile radio communications for current PMR/PAMR users, but it will also significantly decrease the cost of equipment and terminals by as much as 30-40% over analog equipment currently on the market.

Efforts are currently underway to introduce TETRA standards in other parts of the world, including Denmark, China and the U.S. (In the United States, another standard called APCO 25 is currently in use by public safety agencies.

TETRA standards are currently being considered along with other standards for inclusion in a later phase of the APCO 25 Project.)

ExpressNet is purported to be the first commercial development of a TETRA-based system in Europe, which integrates both data and voice mobile communications into a single network. It is planned for initial deployment throughout the UK, France, and Germany.

texel

Also see a similar term, **voxel**.

In computer graphics, a texel (texture element) represents the smallest graphical element in two-dimensional (2-D) **texture mapping** to "wallpaper" the rendition of a three-dimensional (**3-D**) object to create the impression of a textured surface. A texel is similar to a **pixel** (picture element) because it represents an elementary unit in a graphic. But there are differences between the texels in a texture map and the pixels in an image display. In special instances, there might be a one-to-one correspondence between texels and pixels in some parts of the rendition of a 3-D object. But for most, if not all, of a 3-D rendition, the texels and pixels cannot be paired off in such a simple way.

When a 3-D texture-mapped object appears close to the viewer so that the texture elements appear relatively large, there may be several pixels in each texel and the pattern of the texture map is easy to see. When the same 3-D object is removed to increasing distances, the texture-map pattern appears smaller and smaller. Eventually, each texel can become smaller than a pixel. Then an averaging process must be used; several texels are combined to form each pixel. If the object becomes distant enough, or if one of its facets appears at a sharp angle with respect to the viewer, the texels may become so small that the essence of the pattern is lost in the observed image.

text

In information technology, text is a human-readable sequence of **character**s and the words they form that can be encoded into computer-readable formats such as **ASCII**. Text is usually distinguished from non-character encoded data, such as graphic images in the form of **bitmap**s and program code, which is sometimes referred to as being in "binary" (but is actually in its own computer-readable format).

text editor

A text editor is a computer program that lets a user enter, change, store, and usually print **text** (characters and numbers, each encoded by the computer and its input and output devices, arranged to have meaning to users or to other programs). Typically, a text editor provides an "empty" display screen (or "scrollable page") with a fixed-line length and visible line numbers. You can then fill the

lines in with text, line by line. A special command line lets you move to a new page, scroll forward or backward, make global changes in the document, save the document, and perform other actions. After saving a document, you can then print it or display it. Before printing or displaying it, you may be able to format it for some specific output device or class of output device. Text editors can be used to enter program language source statements or to create documents such as technical manuals.

A popular text editor in IBM's large or **mainframe** computers is called XEDIT. In **UNIX** systems, the two most commonly used text editors are **Emacs** and **vi**. In personal computer systems, **word processor**s are more common than text editors. However, there are variations of mainframe and UNIX text editors that are provided for use on personal computers. An example is KEDIT, which is basically XEDIT for Windows.

text on nine keys

T9 (text on nine keys) is a system that lets fixed and mobile phone users send text messages by pressing a number key for each letter in the message—effectively making a keyboard out of the nine numeric phone entry keys. The system is already somewhat familiar to anyone who enters the letters of a name when checking a bank balance or looking up someone in a company's phone directory over the phone. Originated by Tegic Communications, the T9 system has been licensed for use by over 20 mobile phone manufacturers. T9 will often be used in combination with the **Short Message Service** (SMS) and the Wireless Application Protocol (**WAP**).

texture mapping

Texture mapping is a graphic design process in which a two-dimensional (2-D) surface, called a *texture map*, is "wrapped around" a three-dimensional (**3-D**) object. Thus, the 3-D object acquires a surface texture similar to that of the 2-D surface. Texture mapping is the electronic equivalent of applying wallpaper, paint, or veneer to a real object.

The simplest texture mappings involve processes such as that shown below. Three identical squares, each covered randomly with dots, are directly mapped onto the three visible facets of a 3-D cube. This distorts the sizes and shapes of the dots on the top and right-hand facets. In this mapping, the texture map covers the cube with no apparent discontinuities because of the way the dots are arranged on the squares.

In some mappings, the correspondence between the 2-D texture map and the 3-D object's surface becomes "messy." An example is the application of a pattern of squares to the surface of a sphere. It is impossible to paste checkered wallpaper onto a sphere without cutting the paper in such a way as to create discontinuities in the pattern. This problem occurs with many texture mappings.

A complex pattern can, in some cases, be seamlessly wedded to the surface of a 3-D object using a sophisticated graphics program. The pattern is generated directly on the 3-D rendition, rather than using a texture map. For example, a sphere can be given a wood-grain finish. The squares-on-a-sphere problem cannot be solved, but it is possible to fit a pattern of triangles onto a sphere by adjusting the sizes of the triangles.

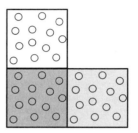
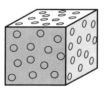

Mapping a 2-D surface onto a 3-D rendition
alters the sizes and shapes of the image elements

texture sensing

Texture sensing is the ability of a **robot end effector** to determine whether a surface is smooth or rough. There are several ways to do this; the simplest method involves reflected light.

A **laser** beam and photoreceptors can be used to tell the difference between a smooth surface and a rough or matte surface with high albedo (low light absorbtion). A shiny surface, such as a sheet of polished metal or a pane of unfrosted glass, behaves according to the principle that the angle of reflection equals the angle of incidence relative to a plane tangent to the point of incidence. A matte surface, such as a sheet of printer paper, scatters incident light rays. If several photoreceptors are set up to capture reflected light, a shiny surface will reflect the beam back only to a receptor that is positioned in the path of the beam whose reflection angle equals its incidence angle. The matte surface will reflect the beam back to all the receptors.

A laser-based texture sensor cannot accurately measure the degree of roughness of a surface that is not shiny. A piece of printer paper reflects visible light in much the same way as a layer of flour, sand, or gravel. In addition, a visible-light-based texture sensor does not work well against rough or matte surfaces with low albedo. Such a surface, such as carbon black, produces a negative response at the photoreceptors. For surfaces of this type, high-speed electrons, infrared (**IR**) rays, or ultraviolet (UV) rays sometimes work. But efficient emitters and receptors of these forms of energy are expensive.

Also see **proximity sensing**, **pressure sensing**, and **robotics**.

TFT

See "thin-film transistor"

TFTP

See "Trivial File Transfer Protocol"

The Open Group

The Open Group is a software standards organization that is sponsored by a number of major software vendors. The Open Group develops and fosters industry standards for software interfaces, often using technologies developed by one of the sponsoring companies. The Open Group originated by combining two previous organizations, X/Open and the Open Software Foundation (OSF). Standards that the Open Group maintains include the standard **UNIX** program interfaces and **Structured Query Language** (the database query language).

The speed of...

This table shows the stated data rates for the most important end-user and backbone transmission technologies.

Technology	Speed	Physical Medium	Application
GSM mobile telephone service	9.6 to 14.4 **Kbps**	**RF** in space (**wireless**)	Mobile telephone for business and personal use
High-speed circuit-switched data service (HSCSD)	Up to 56 Kbps	RF in space (wireless)	Mobile telephone for business and personal use
Regular telephone service (POTS)	Up to 56 Kbps	**Twisted pair**	Home and small business access
Dedicated 56Kbps on frame relay	56 Kbps	Various	Business e-mail with fairly large file attachments
DS0	64 Kbps	All	The base signal on a channel in the set of Digital Signal levels
General Packet Radio System (GPRS)	56 to 114 Kbps	RF in space (wireless)	Mobile telephone for business and personal use
ISDN	**BRI**: 64 Kbps to 128 Kbps **PRI**: 23 (T-1) or 30 (E1) assignable 64-Kbps channels plus control channel; up to 1.544 Mbps (T-1) or 2.048 (E1)	BRI: Twisted-pair PRI: T-1 or E1 line 128 Kbps	BRI: Faster home and small business access PRI: Medium and large enterprise access
IDSL		Twisted-pair	Faster home and small business access
AppleTalk	230.4 Kbps	Twisted pair	Local area network for Apple devices; several networks can be bridged; non-Apple devices can also be connected
Enhanced Data GSM Environment (EDGE)	384 Kbps	RF in space (wireless)	Mobile telephone for business and personal use
Satellite	400 Kbps (DirecPC and others)	RF in space (wireless)	Faster home and small enterprise access
Frame relay	56 Kbps to 1.544 **Mbps**	Twisted-pair or **coaxial** cable	Large company backbone for LANs to **ISP** ISP to Internet infrastructure

Technology	Speed	Physical Medium	Application
DS1/T-1	1.544 Mbps	Twisted-pair, coaxial cable, or **optical fiber**	Large company to ISP ISP to Internet infrastructure
Universal Mobile Telecommunications Service (UMTS)	Up to 2 Mbps	RF in space (wireless)	Mobile telephone for business and personal use (available in 2002)
E-carrier	2.048 Mbps	Twisted-pair, coaxial cable, or **optical fiber**	32-channel European equivalent of T-1
T-1C (DS1C)	3.152 Mbps	Twisted-pair, coaxial cable, or optical fiber	Large company to ISP ISP to Internet infrastructure
IBM Token Ring/802.5	4 Mbps (also 16 Mbps)	Twisted-pair, coaxial cable, or optical fiber	Second most commonly-used local area network after Ethernet
DS2/T-2	6.312 Mbps	Twisted-pair, coaxial cable, or optical fiber	Large company to ISP ISP to Internet infrastructure
Digital Subscriber Line (DSL)	512 Kbps to 8 Mbps	Twisted-pair (used as a digital, **broadband** medium)	Home, small business, and enterprise access using existing copper lines
E-2	8.448 Mbps	Twisted-pair, coaxial cable, or optical fiber	Carries four multiplexed E-1 signals
Cable modem	512 Kbps to 52 Mbps (see "Key and explanation" below)	Coaxial cable (usually uses Ethernet); in some systems, telephone used for upstream requests	Home, business, school access
Ethernet	10 Mbps	**10BASE-T** (twisted-pair); 10BASE-2 or -5 (**coaxial cable**); 10BASE-F (**optical fiber**)	Most popular business local area network (**LAN**)
IBM Token Ring/802.5	16 Mbps (also 4 Mbps)	Twisted-pair, coaxial cable, or optical fiber	Second most commonly-used local area network after Ethernet
E-3	34.368 Mbps	Twisted-pair or optical fiber	Carries 16 E-l signals
DS3/T-3	44.736 Mbps	Coaxial cable	ISP to Internet infrastructure Smaller links within Internet infrastructure
OC-1	51.84 Mbps	Optical fiber	ISP to Internet infrastructure Smaller links within Internet infrastructure
High-Speed Serial Interface (HSSI)	Up to 53 Mbps	HSSI cable	Between router hardware and WAN lines Short-range (50 feet) interconnection between slower LAN devices and faster WAN lines

Technology	Speed	Physical Medium	Application
Fast Ethernet	100 Mbps	**100BASE-T** (twisted pair); **100BASE-T** (twisted pair); **100BASE-T** (optical fiber)	Workstations with 10 Mbps Ethernet cards can plug into a Fast Ethernet LAN
Fiber Distributed-Data Interface (FDDI)	100 Mbps	Optical fiber	Large, wide-range LAN usually in a large company or a larger ISP
T-3D (DS3D)	135 Mbps	Optical fiber	ISP to Internet infrastructure Smaller links within Internet infrastructure
E–4	139.264 Mbps	Optical fiber	Carries 4 E3 channels Up to 1,920 simultaneous voice conversations
OC-3/SDH	155.52 Mbps	Optical fiber	Large company backbone Internet backbone
E-5	565.148 Mbps	Optical fiber	Carries 4 E4 channels Up to 7,680 simultaneous voice conversations
OC-12/STM-4	622.08 Mbps	Optical fiber	Internet backbone
Gigabit Ethernet	1 Gbps	Optical fiber (and "copper" up to 100 meters)	Workstations/networks with 10/100 Mbps Ethernet will plug into Gigabit Ethernet switches
OC-24	1.244 **Gbps**	Optical fiber	Internet backbone
SciNet	2.325 Gbps (15 OC-3 lines)	Optical fiber	Part of the vBNS backbone
OC-48/STM-16	2.488 Gbps	Optical fiber	Internet backbone
OC-192/STM-64	10 Gbps	Optical fiber	Backbone
OC-256	13.271 Gbps	Optical fiber	Backbone

Key and Explanation

We use the U.S. English "Kbps" as the abbreviation for "thousands of bits per second." In international English outside the U.S., the equivalent usage is "kbits s⁻¹" or "kbits/s."

Engineers use *data rate* rather than *speed*, but speed (as in "Why isn't my Web page getting here faster?") seems more meaningful for the less technically inclined. Many of us tend to think that the number of bits getting somewhere over a period of time is their speed of travel.

Relative to data transmission, a related term, **bandwidth** or "capacity," means how wide the pipe is and how quickly the bits can be sent down the channels in the pipe. (The analogy of multiple lanes on a superhighway with cars containing speed governors may help. One reason why digital traffic flows faster than voice traffic on the same copper line is because digital has managed to convert a one-lane or **narrowband** highway into a many-lane or **broadband** highway.)

These "speeds" are aggregate speeds. That is, the data on the multiple signal channels within the carrier is usually allocated by channel for different uses or among different users.

Key: "T" = T-carrier system in U.S., Canada, and Japan...."DS"= digital signal (that travels on the T-carrier or E-carrier)..."E" = Equivalent of "T" that uses all 8 bits per channel; used in countries other than U.S. Canada, and Japan...."OC" = optical carrier (**Synchronous Optical Network**)...."STM" = Synchronous Transport Modules (see **Synchronous Digital Hierarchy**)

Only the most common technologies are shown. "Physical medium" is stated generally and doesn't specify the classes or numbers of pairs of twisted pair or whether optical fiber is single-mode or multimode. The effective distance of a technology is not shown. There are published standards for many of these technologies. Some of these are indicated on pages linked to from the table.

Cable modem note: The upper limit of 52 Mbps on a cable is to an **ISP**, not currently to an individual PC. Most of today's PCs are limited to an internal design that can accomodate no more than 10 Mbps (although the **PCI** bus itself carries data at a faster speed). The 52 Mbps cable channel is subdivided among individual users. Obviously, the faster the channel, the fewer channels an ISP will require and the lower the cost to support an individual user.

theory of everything

See "superstring theory"

theory of relativity

Albert Einstein's theory of relativity is actually two separate theories: his *special theory of relativity*, postulated in the 1905 paper, *The Electrodynamics of Moving Bodies* and his *theory of general relativity*, an expansion of the earlier theory, published as *The Foundation of the General Theory of Relativity* in 1916. Einstein sought to explain situations in which Newtonian physics might fail to deal successfully with phenomena, and in so doing proposed revolutionary changes in human concepts of time, space, and gravity.

The special theory of relativity was based on two main postulates: first, that the **speed of light** is constant for all observers; and second, that observers moving at constant speeds should be subject to the same physical laws. Following this logic, Einstein theorized that time must change according to the speed of a moving object *relative* to the frame of reference of an observer. Scientists have tested this theory through experimentation—proving, for example, that an **atomic clock** ticks more slowly when traveling at a high speed than it does when it is not moving. The essence of Einstein's paper was that both space and **time** are *relative* (rather than absolute), which was said to hold true in a *special* case, the absence of a gravitational field. Relativity was a stunning concept at the time; scientists all over the world debated the veracity of Einstein's famous equation, $E=mc^2$, which implied that matter and energy were equivalent and, more specifically, that a single particle of matter could be converted into a huge quantity of energy.

However, since the special theory of relativity only held true in the absence of a gravitational field, Einstein strove for 11 more years to work gravity into his equations and discover how relativity might work generally as well.

According to the Theory of General Relativity, matter causes space to curve. It is posited that gravitation is not a force, as understood by Newtonian physics, but a curved *field* (an area of space under the influence of a force) in the space-time continuum that is actually created by the presence of mass. According to Einstein, that theory could be tested by measuring the deflection of starlight traveling near the sun; he correctly asserted that light deflection would be twice that expected by Newton's laws. This theory also explained why the light from stars in a strong gravitational field was closer to the red end of the **spectrum** than those in a weaker one.

For the final thirty years of his life, Einstein attempted to find a **unified field theory**, in which the properties of all matter and energy could be expressed in a single equation. His search was confounded by **quantum theory**'s *uncertainty principle*, which stated that the movement of a single particle could never be accurately measured, because speed and position could not be simultaneously assessed with any degree of assurance. Although he was unable to find the comprehensive theory that he sought, Einstein's pioneering work has allowed countless other scientists to carry on the quest for what some have called "the holy grail of physicists."

thermal transfer printer

A thermal transfer printer is a non-impact **printer** that uses heat to register an impression on paper. A thermal transfer printer has a printhead containing many small resistive heating pins that on contact, depending on the type of thermal transfer printer, melt wax-based ink onto ordinary paper or burn dots onto special coated paper. A microprocessor determines which individual heating pins are heated to produce the printed image. The printhead spans the entire width of the paper or medium to be printed on. Thermal transfer printers are popular for printing bar codes, labels, price tags, and other specialty print jobs. There are two types of thermal transfer printers: direct thermal and thermal wax transfer.

Direct thermal: The direct thermal printer prints the image by burning dots onto coated paper as it passes over the heated printhead. Direct thermal printers do not use ribbons. Early fax machines used direct thermal printing.

Thermal wax transfer: This type of printer uses a thermal transfer ribbon that contains wax-based ink. Heat is applied to the ribbon using a thermal printhead that melts the ink transferring it to the paper where it is permanent after it cools. A typical thermal transfer ribbon consists of three layers: the base material, the heat melting ink, and the coating on the print side of the base material. The coating and base material help keep ink from adhering to the printhead which can cause poor print quality. Monochrome and color thermal transfer ribbons are available. It is recommended that the printhead be cleaned between each ribbon change with a cotton swab and isopropyl alcohol.

The cost of a thermal transfer printer varies depending on the size of the printer and the features included. The cost of consumables such as paper, ribbons, and printheads is about the same for both types of printers. The print quality depends on the printer, the ribbon, the paper, and the environment such as where the printer is stored, the temperature, and the humidity.

Thicknet

See "Thinnet"

Thickwire

See "Thinnet"

thin client

A thin client is a low-cost, centrally-managed computer devoid of CD-ROM players, diskette drives, and expansion slots. The term derives from the fact that small computers in networks tend to be **clients** and not **servers**. Since the idea is to limit the capabilities of these computers to only essential applications, they tend to be purchased and remain "thin" in terms of the client applications they include.

The term "thin client" seems to be used as a synonym for both the **NetPC** and the network computer (**NC**), which are somewhat different concepts. The Net PC is based on Intel microprocessors and Windows software (Intel was a leader in defining the Net PC specification). The network computer (NC) is a concept backed by Oracle and Sun Microsystems that may or may not use Intel microprocessors and uses a **Java**-based operating system. The increased numbers of thin clients in today's workplace and educational facilites reflects a corporate and institutional need for low-cost computers dedicated to Internet use.

thin server

In the computer industry, a thin server is a PC that contains just enough hardware and software to support a particular function that users can share in a network, such as access to files on a storage device, access to CD-ROM drives, printing, or Internet access. According to the first companies who have used the term, a thin server can be quickly added to a network and costs less than providing the same service through a more general-purpose computer server. Usually, a thin server contains an abbreviated version of one or more operating systems, such as Windows 2000, Macintosh, or UNIX, and necessary network protocols, such as **TCP/IP** and **NetBEUI**. Typically, it also includes **Hypertext Transfer Protocol** so that it can be configured, administered, and used

through a Web browser user interface. The hardware processor sometimes uses **reduced instruction set computer** processing.

Some thin servers are designed and marketed for use on local area networks in businesses. A newer development is a thin server intended for home use. Data General makes a thin server for the home or small office that performs the single function of providing access to the Internet. Other desktop and notebook computers and possibly other electronic appliances can be hooked up as clients and share the thin server's connection or connections to the Internet.

The thin server and the **thin client** concepts arise from the same idea: why pay for the function in a computer that you don't need? Whereas the thin client is a constrained personal computer that gets applications and data the user needs from a shared and usually full-function server computer, the thin server serves the client requests of other computers and their users by doing one thing well without needing to provide any other service. A thin server is similar to a **thin client** in that both may be thought of as single application, special-purpose computers, almost always with a very limited storage capability and with "trimmed-down" operating systems.

thin-film disk

A thin-film disk is a **hard disk** storage medium with a very thin coating of a metallic alloy or glass instead of the usual carbon-based material found on other types of hard disks. The thin film lets the read/write head get closer to the surface, allowing more data to be stored in a given space.

Thin-film technology is another approach to packing more bits of data onto a disk. As the number of data bits on a disk increase, the disk drive's head must become more sensitive, getting closer to the disk to read or write the bits.

Researchers are experimenting with thin films of various materials in order to help protect the disk from the head and to help the disk have a longer life.

thin-film transistor

A display screen made with TFT (thin-film transistor) technology is a liquid crystal display (**LCD**), common in notebook and laptop computers, that has a **transistor** for each **pixel** (that is, for each of the tiny elements that control the illumination of your display). Having a transistor at each pixel means that the current that triggers pixel illumination can be smaller and therefore can be switched on and off more quickly.

TFT is also known as **active matrix display** technology (and contrasts with "passive matrix" which does not have a transistor at each pixel). A TFT or active matrix display is more responsive to change. For example, when you move your mouse across the screen, a TFT display is fast enough to

reflect the movement of the mouse cursor. (With a passive matrix display, the cursor temporarily disappears until the display can "catch up.")

A more recent development is **organic thin-film transistor** technology, which makes it possible to have flexible display surfaces.

Thinnet

Thicknet and Thinnet (sometimes called ThickWire and ThinWire) are commonly used terms for the larger and smaller size of **coaxial cable** used in **Ethernet** local area networks. Thicknet, also known as Thickwire, is 0.4 inches in diameter and has 50 ohms of electromagnetic **impedance**. Thinnet, also known as Thinwire and Cheapernet, is 0.2 inches in diameter with the same impedance as Thickwire. Thicknet was the original Ethernet wiring, but Thinnet, which is cheaper and can be installed more easily, is the more commonly installed Ethernet wire. Thicknet continues to be used for **backbone** wiring. An alternative to Thinnet on an Ethernet network is **twisted pair**.

Thinwire

See "Thinnet"

thought recognition

Thought recognition is the ability of a computer to recognize neural patterns in the brain as a form of input and control of computer processes. Computer programming and the necessary sensing devices already exist to detect other forms of biophysical activity, such as muscular activity and eye movement. Using these forms of input, paralyzed and other handicapped people have been made able to communicate with a computer. Brain waves suggest the possibility of an even more direct form of computer input—the thought command. However, thus far it has been difficult to interpret the brain waves with sufficient delineation to afford any kind of discriminatory input—for example, to sense a letter or word that a person might be thinking of.

Brain waves can be discerned in these patterns:

- Alpha waves, with large modulations and moderate frequencies, indicate unfocused brain activity

- Beta waves, with higher frequencies and small modulations, indicate focused brain activity

- Theta waves, with moderately low frequencies, indicate emotional stress

- Delta waves, with extremely low frequencies, indicate a condition of sleep

- Mu waves, have a croquet-shaped pattern of frequencies and modulation, are associated with physical activity

Scientists feel that a number of more refined distinctions about brain patterns must be made before they can be used as computer input.

thrashing

Thrashing is computer activity that makes little or no progress, usually because memory or other resources have become exhausted or too limited to perform needed operations. When this happens, a pattern typically develops in which a request is made of the operating system by a process or program, the operating system tries to find resources by taking them from some other process, which in turn makes new requests that can't be satisfied. In a virtual storage system (an operating system that manages its logical storage or memory in units called pages), thrashing is a condition in which excessive paging operations are taking place.

A system that is thrashing can be perceived as either a very slow system or one that has come to a halt.

thread

1) On the Internet in **Usenet** newsgroups and similar forums, a thread is a sequence of responses to an initial message posting. This enables you to follow or join an individual discussion in a newsgroup from among the many that may be there. A thread is usually shown graphically as an inital message and successive messages "hung off" the original message. As a newsgroup user, you contribute to a thread by specifying a "Reference" topic as part of your message.

2) In computer programming, a thread is placeholder information associated with a single use of a program that can handle multiple concurrent users. From the program's point-of-view, a thread is the information needed to serve one individual user or a particular service request. If multiple users are using the program or concurrent requests from other programs occur, a thread is created and maintained for each of them. The thread allows a program to know which user is being served as the program alternately gets re-entered on behalf of different users. (One way thread information is kept by storing it in a special data area and putting the address of that data area in a *register*. The operating system always saves the contents of the register when the program is interrupted and restores it when it gives the program control again.)

Multithreading and **multitasking** are similar and are often confused. Some computers can only execute one program instruction at a time, but because they operate so fast, they appear to run many programs and serve many users simultaneously. The computer **operating system** (for example, Windows 2000) gives each program a "turn" at running, then requires it to wait while another program gets a turn. Each of these programs is viewed by the operating system as a "task" for which certain resources are identified and kept track of. The operating system manages each application program in your PC system (spreadsheet, word processor, Web browser) as a separate task and lets you look at and control items on a "task list." If the program initiates an I/O request, such as reading a file or writing to a printer, it creates a thread so that the program will be reentered at the right place when the I/O operation completes. Meanwhile, other concurrent uses of the program are maintained on other threads. Most of today's operating systems provide support for both multitasking and multithreading. They also allow multithreading within program processes so that the system is saved the overhead of creating a new process for each thread.

The **Portable Operating System Interface**.4a **C** specification provides a set of application program interfaces that allow a programmer to include thread support in the program. Higher-level program development tools and application subsystems and "**middleware**" also offer thread management facilities. **Object-oriented programming** languages also accommodate and encourage multithreading in several ways. **Java** supports multithreading by including synchronization modifiers in the language syntax, by providing **class** developed for multithreading that can be inherited by other classes, and by doing background "garbage collection" (recovering data areas that are no longer being used) for multiple threads.

thread-safe

Thread-safe is a term used to describe a routine that can be called from multiple programming threads without unwanted interaction between the threads. **Thread** safety is of particular importance to **Java** programmers, since Java is a programming language that provides built-in support for threads. By using thread-safe routines, the risk that one thread will interfere and modify data elements of another thread is eliminated by circumventing potential data race situations with coordinated access to shared data.

It is possible to ensure that a routine is thread-safe by:

1. Making sure that concurrent threads use synchronized algorithms that cooperate with each other.
2. Confining the address of a shared object to one thread whenever an unsynchronized algorithm is active.

Three Laws of Robotics (Isaac Asimov)

See "Asimov's Three Laws of Robotics"

throughput

1) In computer technology, throughput is the amount of work that a computer can do in a given time period. Historically, throughput has been a measure of the comparative effectiveness of large commercial computers that run many programs concurrently. An early throughput measure was the number of *batch jobs* completed in a day. More recent measures assume a more complicated mixture of work or focus on some particular aspect of computer operation. While "cost per **million instructions per second** (MIPS)" provides a basis for comparing the cost of raw

computing over time or by manufacturer, throughput theoretically tells you how much useful work the MIPS are producing.

Another measure of computer productivity is **performance**, the speed with which one or a set of batch programs run with a certain workload or how many interactive user requests are being handled with what responsiveness. The amount of time between a single interactive user request being entered and receiving the application's response is known as **response time**.

A **benchmark** can be used to measure throughput.

2) In data transmission, throughput is the amount of **data** moved successfully from one place to another in a given time period.

thumbnail

Thumbnail is a term used by graphic designers and photographers for a small image representation of a larger image, usually intended to make it easier and faster to look at or manage a group of larger images. For example, software that lets you manage a number of images often provides a miniaturized version of each image so that you don't have to remember the file name of each image. A thumbnail is also used to mean a small and approximate version of an image or a brochure layout as a preliminary design step. Adobe's **Acrobat** viewer lets you show a sequence of thumbnails of viewable pages as a way to navigate among the pages in a document. Adobe's Photoshop lets you view a thumbnail version of certain kinds of images.

Web sites with many pictures, such as online stores with visual catalogs, often provide thumbnail images instead of larger images to make the page download faster. The user controls which images need to be seen in full size.

The term probably springs from the idea of "a picture the size of your thumbnail."

thunking

Thunking is the transformation between 16-bit and 32-bit instruction formats in an **operating system**. For example, Windows 95 can run application programs written in both 16-bit and 32-bit instruction sets.

THz

See "terahertz"

tier

In general, a tier (pronounced TEE-er; from the medieval French *tire* meaning rank, as in a line of soldiers) is a row or layer in a series of similarly arranged objects. In computer programming, the parts of a program can be **distributed**

among several tiers, each located in a different computer in a network. Such a program is said to be *tiered*, *multitier*, or *multitiered*.

The **3-tier application** model is probably the most common way of organizing a program in a network. **N-tier** applications (programs) are those that are tiered but the number of tiers isn't specified or may vary.

TIFF

See "Tag Image File Format"

tiger team

In the computer industry, a tiger team is a group of programmers or users who volunteer or are hired to expose errors or security holes in new software or to find out why a computer network's security is being broken. In the U.S. military, a tiger team is a group that is given the job of trying to break through security around a military base or special restricted area.

In hiring or recruiting volunteers for a tiger team, some software developers advise others to be sure that tiger team members don't include **crackers**, who might use their special knowledge of the software to disable or compromise it in the future.

tilde

A tilde (pronounced TILL-duh or TILL-day) looks like this: ~. It's a special typographic character found on most keyboards. In some operating systems, including UNIX, the tilde is used to represent the current user's home directory. On Web server systems, the tilde is frequently used by convention as the first character for any user's home directory in the file system. Since users often keep personal or business Web pages on a server under their personal home directory, you will often see the tilde as part of Web addresses.

The tilde is one of the 128 alphanumeric and special characters in **ASCII**, the most common standard for electronic text exchange. The tilde happens to be ASCII character 126. It's sometimes called a "twiddle" or a "squiggle."

Tim Berners-Lee

Tim Berners-Lee is the creator of the **World Wide Web** and director of the coordinating body for Web development, the **W3C**. Berners-Lee credits Vint Cerf and Bob Khan (who defined the Internet protocol (**IP**) that allows computers to exchange packets of information) with the invention of the Internet, but it was Tim Berners-Lee who created the most widely used part of the Internet, the part that we call the World Wide Web (often abbreviated "WWW" or called "the Web"). Its outstanding feature is **hypertext**, a method of instant cross-referencing. The introduction of Tim Berners-Lee's hypertext system revolutionized the way the Internet was used.

In 1989, Tim Berners-Lee began work at **CERN** on the first World Wide Web **server**, which he called "httpd," and the first **client**, which he called "WWW." In the beginning, WWW was a **WYSIWYG** hypertext browser/editor that ran in the **NeXTStep** environment. It is interesting to note that before choosing the name "World Wide Web" for his global hypertext system, Berners-Lee considered the name "Mine of Information" (MOI) but thought it might be "un peu egoiste" (a little egotistical). He abandoned the name "The Information Mine" (TIM) for the same reason, and didn't use "Information Mesh" because he thought it sounded too much like "mess."

By 1990, the World Wide Web was available within CERN and by 1991, it was available to anyone using the **Internet**. Tim Berners-Lee has never profited personally by creating the World Wide Web. Instead, he gave away his proprietary rights in the belief that the Web needed to be an open system if it was to grow and become universal. Berners-Lee currently occupies the 3Com Founders chair at the MIT Laboratory for Computer Science and has been the recipient of numerous awards, including a spot in Time magazine's list of the 100 greatest minds of the century.

When asked what surprised him most about how the World Wide Web has turned out thus far, Tim Berners-Lee said that he was surprised at how many ordinary people were willing to learn how to write code using the hypertext markup language he developed.

time

Time is an observed phenomenon, by means of which human beings sense and record changes in the environment and in the universe. A literal definition is elusive. Time has been called an illusion, a dimension, a smooth-flowing continuum, and an expression of separation among events that occur in the same physical location.

Time is a practical convenience in modern life. Numerous standards have been set up, allowing people to coordinate events and, in general, keep their lives running smoothly. The earth has been divided into so-called time zones that reflect the fact that high noon occurs at different times at different places on the planet. All of these time zones are referenced to the time at the longitude of Greenwich, England. A universal standard, coinciding almost exactly with the time at Greenwich, is known as Coordinated Universal Time (**UTC**). There are various other time standards.

The fundamental unit of time in the International System of Units (**SI**) is the **second** (symbolized s or sec). One second elapses during the occurrence of exactly 9,192,631,770 (9.192631770×10^9) cycles of the radiation produced by the transition between two levels of the cesium 133 **atom**. Other common units of time include the hour, the mean solar day, and the synodic year (sun-based earth year). The table below shows the relationship among the second, the hour, the mean solar day, and the synodic year.

Unit (and symbol)	To convert to seconds, multiply by:	Conversely, multiply by:
Hour (hr)	3600	2.7778×10^{-4}
Mean solar day (dy)	8.6400×10^{4}	1.1574×10^{-5}
Synodic year (yr)	3.1558×10^{7}	3.1688×10^{-8}

Isaac Newton believed that time is continuous, and that it flows at an unchanging rate everywhere in the universe. This was accepted by most scientists until the Michelson-Morley experiment around the end of the 19th century, from which it was discovered that the speed of light is the same regardless of the direction of propagation, and regardless of the motion of the source. Albert Einstein considered this result an axiom, from which he derived the special and general theories of relativity. According to relativistic physics, the rate at which time passes depends on the relative motion between observers, and also on the strength of a gravitational or acceleration field.

Time is one of three primary phenomena in the meter/kilogram/second (**mks**) and centimeter/gram/second (**cgs**) systems of measurement. It is one of seven fundamental quantities or phenomena in the International System of Units.

Also see **mks system of units**, **cgs system of units** or **small-unit metric system**, the International System of Units (**SI**), and our **Table of Physical Units**.

time division multiple access

See "TDMA"

time-division multiplexing

TDM (time-division multiplexing) is a scheme in which numerous signals are combined for transmission on a single communications line or channel. Each signal is broken up into many segments, each having very short duration.

The circuit that combines signals at the source (transmitting) end of a communications link is known as a multiplexer. It accepts the input from each individual end user, breaks each signal into segments, and assigns the segments to the composite signal in a rotating, repeating sequence. The composite signal thus contains data from all the end users. At the other end of the long-distance cable, the individual signals are separated out by means of a circuit called a demultiplexer, and routed to the proper end users. A two-way communications circuit requires a multiplexer/demultiplexer at each end of the long-distance, high-bandwidth cable.

If many signals must be sent along a single long-distance line, careful engineering is required to ensure that the system will perform properly. An asset of TDM is its flexibility. The scheme allows for variation in the number of signals being sent along the line, and constantly adjusts the time intervals to make optimum use of the available **bandwidth**. The Internet is a classic example of a communications network in which the volume of traffic can change drastically from hour to hour. In some systems, a different scheme, known as frequency-division multiplexing (**FDM**), is preferred.

time-to-live

TTL (time-to-live) is a value in an Internet Protocol (**IP**) **packet** that tells a network **router** whether or not the packet has been in the network too long and should be discarded. For a number of reasons, packets may not get delivered to their destination in a reasonable length of time. For example, a combination of incorrect routing tables could cause a packet to loop endlessly. A solution is to discard the packet after a certain time and send a message to the originator, who can decide whether to resend the packet. The initial TTL value is set, usually by a system **default**, in an 8-**binary digit** field of the packet header. The original idea of TTL was that it would specify a certain time span in seconds that, when exhausted, would cause the packet to be discarded. Since each router is required to subtract at least one count from the TTL field, the count is usually used to mean the number of router **hop**s the packet is allowed before it must be discarded. Each router that receives a packet subtracts one from the count in the TTL field. When the count reaches zero, the router detecting it discards the packet and sends an Internet Control Message Protocol (**ICMP**) message back to the originating host.

The default Windows 95/98 TTL value is 32 hops. Some users recommend changing this to 128 if you have difficulty reaching certain sites.

The **ping** and the **traceroute** utilities both make use of the TTL value to attempt to reach a given host computer or to trace a route to that host. Traceroute intentionally sends a packet with a low TTL value so that it will be discarded by each successive router in the destination path. The time between sending the packet and receiving back the ICMP message that it was discarded is used to calculate each successive hop travel time.

Using the **multicast** IP protocol, the TTL value indicates the scope or range that a packet may be forwarded. By convention:

- 0 is restricted to the same host
- 1 is restricted to the same **subnet**
- 32 is restricted to the same site
- 64 is restricted to the same region

- 128 is restricted to the same continent
- 255 is unrestricted

Tivoli

Tivoli Systems is an IBM-owned company that develops software that allows a business to manage its computing environment. In a large organization, keeping track of and upgrading computer equipment and various levels of operating systems and applications is a formidable task. Tivoli offers products and solutions in these areas:

- **E-business infrastructure** management
- E-marketplace solutions
- Industry-specific solutions
- Service provider capabilities
- Availability and application management
- Network management
- Operations management
- **OS/390** management
- Pervasive management (management of mobile devices and point-of-sale terminals)
- Storage and storage area network (**SAN**) management
- Security management
- Service management
- Web management

Tk

See "Tool Kit"

TLD

See "top-level domain"

TLS

See "Transport Layer Security"

TM

See "triplecast"

TMN

TMN (Telecommunications Management Network) originated formally in 1988 under the auspices of the International Telecommunication Union (**ITU-TS**) as a strategic goal to create or identify standard interfaces that would allow a network to be managed consistently across all network element suppliers. The concept has fostered and tracked a series of interrelated efforts at developing standard ways to define and address network elements. TMN uses the **OSI** Management Standards as its framework. TMN applies to **wireless** communications and **cable TV** as well as to private and public wired networks.

TMQL

See "Topic Map Query Language"

token ring

A token ring network is a local area network (**LAN**) in which all computers are connected in a ring or star topology and a **bit**- or token-passing scheme is used in order to prevent the collision of data between two computers that want to send messages at the same time. The token ring protocol is the second most widely-used protocol on local area networks after **Ethernet**. The IBM Token Ring protocol led to a standard version, specified as IEEE 802.5. Both protocols are used and are very similar. The IEEE 802.5 token ring technology provides for data transfer rates of either 4 or 16 megabits per second. Very briefly, here is how it works:

1. Empty information frames are continuously circulated on the ring.

2. When a computer has a message to send, it inserts a token in an empty frame (this may consist of simply changing a 0 to a 1 in the token bit part of the frame) and inserts a message and a destination identifier in the frame.

3. The frame is then examined by each successive workstation. If the workstation sees that it is the destination for the message, it copies the message from the frame and changes the token back to 0.

4. When the frame gets back to the originator, it sees that the token has been changed to 0 and that the message has been copied and received. It removes the message from the frame.

5. The frame continues to circulate as an "empty" frame, ready to be taken by a workstation when it has a message to send.

The token scheme can also be used with **bus topology** LANs.

The standard for the token ring protocol is Institute of Electrical and Electronics Engineers (**IEEE**) 802.5. The Fiber Distributed-Data Interface (**FDDI**) also uses a token ring protocol.

tool bar

See "toolbar"

Tool Command Language

See "Tcl"

Tool Kit

Tool Kit (**Tk**) is a companion program to Tool Command Language (**Tcl**) for creating graphical user interfaces. Together with Tcl, Tk is a rapid program development tool from Scriptics. Both can be ordered from the Scriptics Web site.

Tk provides a collection of standard buttons, menus, listboxes, and scrollbars and two special features, the *text widget* and the *canvas widget*, that the Tcl programmer can use to speed up program development.

toolbar

In the graphical user interface (**GUI**) for a computer, a toolbar is a horizontal row or vertical column of selectable image "buttons" that give the user a constantly visible reminder of and an easy way to select certain **desktop** or other **application** functions, such as saving or printing a document or moving pages forwards or backwards within a Web **browser**. Word processing, spreadsheet, and many other types of application programs come with one or more toolbars as part of their user interface.

In addition to the toolbars that come with a desktop or an application, some software developers or third parties provide supplementary toolbars that can be downloaded and installed. Supplementary toolbar functions may include quick access to news, sports, and weather headlines; instant form completion; instant access to favorite sites; and faster searches.

Topic Map

A Topic Map (**ISO/IEC** Standard 13250:2000) is an **SGML** or **XML** document used for navigation—by people or by machine—within an information set. A single information set can include any number of types of source data: for example, **HTML** files, **PDF** files, and databases could all be part of one information set. A Topic Map (**TM**) can be either embedded within a document, or may be, itself, a separate document. A Topic Map provides a particular view of topics within the information set. There could be, potentially, an infinite number of different TMs for any information set: for example, an information set dealing with the plays of Shakespeare could have a TM for navigation within the perspective of Elizabethan culture, or the perspective of themes throughout the plays. Each TM explicitly declares topics and provides links to relevant information.

The TAO of Topic Maps

Literally, *Tao* means *the way*; the term is expanded to mean *the underlying unifying principle of the universe*. In the case of TM, the unifying principle underlies the informational universe of the Web. The *TAO* of TMs stands for *topics, associations, and occurrences*. A topic is a subject: in terms of Shakespeare, for example, Avon, Romeo and Juliet, and Anne Hathaway would all be topics. Topics are broken down into types: "Avon" would be defined as a town, and "Romeo and Juliet" as a play, for example. The word *topic* refers to both the topic link and the topic itself. Generally, topics have three types of characteristics: Names, which explicitly identify topics; occurrences, which are topic-relevant information resources; and roles in associations, which are details of how topics are related.

TMs are being heralded as an important information management tool for the development of the **Semantic Web**, because they can enable very precise data access—they are sometimes called "the Global Positioning System (**GPS**) of the Web"—within a vast, complex, and intricately interconnected global information repository. One way of looking at the way a TM works is to think of it as similar to a book's index, and to compare seeking specific information within an indexed and an unindexed book. Although the information available on the Web now is linked, it is not linked in a systematic, standardized, and autonomously intelligent way (which explains why Web searches can often turn up so many irrelevant documents). Eventually, Topic Maps may be part of a comprehensive, user-friendly index to the body of human knowledge.

Topic Map Query Language

Topic Map Query Language (**TMQL**) is an **XML**-based extension of Structured Query Language (**SQL**), a **query** language developed for use in meeting the specialized data access requirements of Topic Maps (**TM**s). Two types of data access for Topic Maps are: information retrieval (IR), which is focused on separate search instances of a single user looking for specific information; and information filtering, which is a query process that builds up a sort of *user profile*, filtering information to construct a selection of data relevant to a particular user.

TMQL is intended to be easier to learn by developers, most of whom are likely to already be familiar with SQL. However, SQL was created to be used on the data in a **relational database**, which has a well-defined pre-existing structure; TMQL must be able to retrieve information from a vast and constantly changing body of information. A relational database may be expressed in terms of a simplified Topic Map, but TMQL will need to work with a much more complex data repository. A typical SQL *select query* (used to retrieve data from a table in a database) could be rewritten to retrieve data from a Topic Map.

top-level domain

On the Internet, a top-level domain (TLD) identifies the most general part of the **domain name** in an Internet address. A TLD is either a generic top-level domain (**gTLD**), such as "**com**" for "commercial," "**edu**" for "educational," and so forth, or a country code top-level domain (**ccTLD**), such as "fr" for France or "is" for Iceland.

topology

A topology (from Greek *topos*: place) is a description of any kind of locality in terms of its physical layout. In the context of communication networks, a topology describes pictorially the configuration or arrangement of a (usually conceptual) network, including its nodes and connecting lines.

toroid

A toroid is a coil of insulated or enameled wire wound on a donut-shaped form made of powdered iron. A toroids is used as an **inductor** in electronic circuits, especially at low frequencies where comparatively large inductances are necessary.

A toroid has more inductance, for a given number of turns, than a **solenoid** with a core of the same material and similar size. This makes it possible to construct high-inductance coils of reasonable physical size and mass. Toroidal coils of a given inductance can carry more **current** than solenoidal coils of similar size, because larger-diameter wires can be used, and the total amount of wire is less, reducing the **resistance**.

In a toroid, all the magnetic flux is contained in the core material. This is because the core has no ends from which flux might leak off. The confinement of the flux prevents external magnetic fields from affecting the behavior of the toroid, and also prevents the magnetic field in the toroid from affecting other components in a circuit.

total cost of ownership

See "TCO"

touch pad

A touch pad is a device for pointing (controlling input positioning) on a computer display screen. It is an alternative to the **mouse**. Originally incorporated in laptop computers, touch pads are also being made for use with desktop computers. A touch pad works by sensing the user's finger movement and downward pressure.

The first touch pad was invented by George E. Gerpheide in 1988. Apple Computer was the first to license and use the touch pad in its Powerbook laptops in 1994. The touch pad has since become the leading **cursor**-controlling device in laptops. Many laptops use a **trackball**. IBM ThinkPad laptops use a "pointing stick" (called a TrackPoint) that is set into the keyboard.

How the Touch Pad Works

The touch pad contains several layers of material. The top layer is the pad that you touch. Beneath it are layers (separated by very thin insulation) containing horizontal and vertical rows of *electrodes* that form a grid. Beneath these layers is a circuit board to which the electrode layers are connected. The layers with electrodes are charged with a constant alternating current (**AC**). As the finger approaches the electrode grid, the current is interrupted and the interruption is detected by the circuit board. The initial location where the finger touches the pad is registered so that subsequent finger movement will be related to that initial point. Some touch pads contain two special places where applied pressure corresponds to clicking a left or right mouse button. Other touch pads sense single or double taps of the finger at any point on the touch pad.

touch screen

A touch screen is a computer display screen that is sensitive to human touch, allowing a user to interact with the computer by touching pictures or words on the screen. Touch screens are used with information **kiosks**, computer-based training devices, and systems designed to help individuals who have difficulty manipulating a **mouse** or **keyboard**. Touch screen technology can be used as an alternative user interface with applications that normally require a mouse, such as a Web browser. Some applications are designed specifically for touch screen technology, often having larger icons and links than the typical PC application. Monitors are available with built-in touch screen technology or individuals can purchase a touch screen kit.

A touch screen kit includes a touch screen panel, a controller, and a software **driver**. The touch screen panel is a clear panel attached externally to the monitor that plugs into a serial or Universal Serial Bus (**USB**) port or a **bus** card installed inside the computer. The touch screen panel registers touch events and passes these signals to the controller. The controller then processes the signals and sends the data to the **processor**. The software driver translates touch events into mouse events. Drivers can be provided for both Windows and Macintosh operating systems. Internal touch screen kits are available but require professional installation because they must be installed inside the monitor.

There are three types of touch screen technology:

- **Resistive:** A resistive touch screen panel is coated with a thin metallic electrically conductive and resistive layer that causes a change in the electrical current which is registered as a touch event and sent to the controller for processing. Resistive touch screen panels are generally more affordable but offer only 75% clarity and the layer can be damaged by sharp objects. Resistive touch screen panels are not affected by outside elements such as dust or water.

- **Surface wave:** Surface wave technology uses ultrasonic waves that pass over the touch screen panel. When the panel is touched, a portion of the wave is absorbed. This change in the ultrasonic waves registers the position of the touch event and sends this information to the controller for processing. Surface wave touch screen panels are the most advanced of the three types, but they can be damaged by outside elements.

- **Capacitive:** A capacitive touch screen panel is coated with a material that stores electrical charges. When the panel is touched, a small amount of charge is drawn to the point of contact. Circuits located at each corner of the panel measure the charge and send the information to the controller for processing. Capacitive touch screen panels must be touched with a finger unlike resistive and surface wave panels that can use fingers and **stylus**. Capacitive touch screens are not affected by outside elements and have high clarity.

trace route

See "traceroute"

traceroute

Traceroute is a **utility** that records the route (the specific **gateway** computers at each **hop**) through the Internet between your computer and a specified destination computer. It also calculates and displays the amount of time each hop took. Traceroute is a handy tool both for understanding where problems are in the Internet network and for getting a detailed sense of the Internet itself. Another utility, **ping**, is often used prior to using traceroute to see whether a host is present on the network.

The traceroute utility comes included with a number of operating systems, including Windows and **UNIX**-based operating systems (such as IBM's AIX/6000) or as part of a **TCP/IP** package. If your system doesn't include the utility, you can install it. There are **freeware** versions that you can download.

How It Works

When you enter the traceroute command, the utility initiates the sending of a **packet** (using the Internet Control Message Protocol or ICMP), including in the packet a time limit value (known as the "time to live" (**TTL**) that is designed to be exceeded by the first **router** that receives it, which will return a Time Exceeded message. This enables traceroute to determine the time required for the hop to the first router. Increasing the time limit value, it resends the packet so that it will reach the second router in the path to the destination, which returns another Time Exceeded message, and so forth. Traceroute determines when the packet has reached the destination by including a port number that is outside the normal range. When it's received, a Port Unreachable message is returned, enabling traceroute to measure the time length of the final hop. As the tracerouting progresses, the records are displayed for you hop by hop. Actually, each hop is measured three times. (If you see an asterisk (*), this indicates a hop that exceeded some limit.)

If you have a Windows operating system, try traceroute out by clicking on Start–>Programs–>MS-DOS Prompt, and then at the C:WINDOWS prompt, enter:

```
tracert www.whatis.com
```

or whatever **domain name** for a destination host computer you want to enter. You can also enter the equivalent numeric form of the **IP address**.

trackball

A trackball is a computer **cursor** control device used in many notebook and laptop computers. The trackball is usually located in front of the **keyboard** toward the user. Essentially, the trackball is an upside-down **mouse** that rotates in place within a socket. The user rolls the ball to direct the cursor to the desired place on the screen and can click one of two buttons (identical to mouse buttons) near the trackball to select **desktop** objects or position the cursor for **text** entry.

IBM's ThinkPad series of notebook computers uses a "pointing stick," called a TrackPoint, that is integrated into the middle of the keyboard keys.

transaction

In computer programming, a transaction usually means a sequence of information exchange and related work (such as **database** updating) that is treated as a unit for the purposes of satisfying a request and for ensuring database integrity. For a transaction to be completed and database changes to made permanent, a transaction has to be completed in its entirety. A typical transaction is a catalog merchandise order phoned in by a customer and entered into a computer by a customer representative. The order transaction involves checking an inventory database, confirming that the item is available, placing the order, and confirming that the order has been placed and the expected time of shipment. If we view this as a single transaction, then all of the steps must be completed before the transaction is successful and the database is actually changed to reflect the new order. If something happens before the transaction is successfully completed, any changes to the database must be kept track of so that they can be undone.

A program that manages or oversees the sequence of events that are part of a transaction is sometimes called a *transaction monitor*. Transactions are supported by **Structured Query Language**, the standard database user and programming interface. When a transaction completes successfully, database changes are said to be *committed*; when a transaction does not complete, changes are *rolled back*. In IBM's **Customer Information Control System** product, a transaction is a unit of application data processing that results from a particular type of transaction request. In CICS, an instance of a particular transaction request by a computer operator or user is called a *task*.

Less frequently and in other computer contexts, a transaction may have a different meaning. For example, in IBM mainframe operating system **batch** processing, a transaction is a *job* or a *job step*.

Transaction Server

The Microsoft Transaction Server (MTS), called "Viper" while it was being developed, is a program that runs on an Internet or other network **server** with a **Windows NT** system and manages application and database **transaction** requests on behalf of a **client** computer user. The Transaction Server screens the user and client computer from having to formulate requests for unfamiliar **databases** and, if necessary, forwards the requests to database servers. It also manages security, connection to other servers, and transaction integrity.

The Transaction Server is Microsoft's bid to make **distributed** applications and data in a network relatively easy to create. It's one of a category of programs sometimes known as **middleware** or *multi-tier* programming for the **enterprise** market that IBM has traditionally controlled with its CICS and similar transaction management products.

Microsoft designed the Transaction Server to fit in with its overall **object-oriented programming** strategy. Using the Transaction Server, you can use a drag-and-drop interface to create a transaction model for a single user, then allow the Transaction Server to manage the model for multiple users, including the creation and management of user and task *threads* and *processes*.

MTS runs on Windows NT Server 4.0 or higher.

transactional e-mail

Transactional e-mail is a type of Web-based marketing in which e-mail recipients can buy goods and services directly from an e-mail message, without being redirected to the retailer's Web site. According to proponents, transactional e-mail leads to significantly higher conversion rates—the ratio of shoppers to buyers, which goes up when the former is converted to the latter—than regular e-mail marketing approaches. A number of different transactional e-mail products are available, from Cybuy, Radical Communication, and EActive, among others.

The transactional e-mail retail experience is easier, and minimizes the tasks involved in online shopping. Within the body of the message, an e-mail recipient can view merchandise, select items, and submit an order. Typically, the e-mail messages contain windows that change to display different products when the recipient clicks listed items. A message assuring the customer of the security of the transaction, and an order form are displayed when the customer clicks the appropriate buttons. When the order form is completed, the customer clicks the "submit" button, and resumes reading their other e-mail messages.

Zagat's, a well-known distributor of restaurant guides, tried transactional e-mail sales for the 2000 holiday season, allowing customers to buy restaurant guides directly from the body of the e-mail message, rather than just including a link to their Web site. The campaign attained conversion rates five times as high as those of regular e-mail marketing. Besides making shopping simpler for the consumer, transactional e-mail also takes into account the fact that someone who is reading e-mail is doing just that: reading their e-mail. Marketing messages, even for interesting products, may be set aside because they interfere with the task at hand. Even if the consumer wants to buy a product, they may not respond to traditional e-mail marketing messages, because the process involved (going to the retailer's Web site, going to separate pages to order, and so on) is too cumbersome. Transactional e-mail also makes impulse purchases more likely, because a transaction can be completed before the customer grows weary of the procedures involved.

transceiver

Also see **repeater** and **transponder**.

A transceiver is a combination transmitter/receiver in a single package. The term applies to **wireless** communications devices such as **cellular telephone**s, cordless telephone sets, handheld two-way radios, and mobile two-way radios. Occasionally the term is used in reference to transmitter/receiver devices in cable or **optical fiber** systems.

In a radio transceiver, the receiver is silenced while transmitting. An electronic switch allows the transmitter and receiver to be connected to the same antenna, and prevents the transmitter output from damaging the receiver. With a transceiver of this kind, it is impossible to receive signals while transmitting. This mode is called half duplex. Transmission and reception often, but not always, are done on the same **frequency**.

Some transceivers are designed to allow reception of signals during transmission periods. This mode is known as full duplex, and requires that the transmitter and receiver operate on substantially different frequencies so the transmitted signal does not interfere with reception. Cellular and cordless telephone sets use this mode. **Satellite** communications networks often employ full-duplex transceivers at the surface-based subscriber points. The transmitted signal (transceiver-to-satellite) is called the uplink, and the received signal (satellite-to-transceiver) is called the downlink.

transcendental number

A transcendental number is a **real number** that is not the solution of any single-variable **polynomial** equation whose **coefficients** are all **integers**. All transcendental numbers are **irrational numbers**. But the converse is not true; there are some irrational numbers that are not transcendental.

Examples of transcendental numbers include **pi**, the ratio of a circle's circumference to its diameter in a plane, and *e*, the base of the natural **logarithm**. The case of pi has historical significance. The fact that pi is transcendental means that it is impossible to draw to perfection, using a compass and straightedge and following the ancient Greek rules for geometric constructions, a square with the same area as a given circle. This ancient puzzle, known as *squaring the circle*, was, for centuries, one of the most baffling challenges in geometry. Schemes have been devised that provide amazingly close approximations to squaring the circle. But in theoretical mathematics (unlike physics and engineering), approximations are never good enough; a solution, scheme, or method is either valid, or else it is not.

It can be difficult, and perhaps impossible, to determine whether or not a certain **irrational number** is transcendental. Some numbers defy classification (algebraic, irrational, or transcendental) to this day. Two examples are the product of pi and *e* (call this quantity P_{pie}) and the sum of pi and *e* (call this S_{pie}). It has been proved that pi and *e* are both transcendental. It has also been shown that at least one of the two quantities P_{pie} and S_{pie} are transcendental. But as of this writing, no one has rigorously proven that P_{pie} is transcendental, and no one has rigorously proved that S_{pie} is transcendental.

transcoding

Transcoding is a technology used to adapt computer application displays and Web content so that they can be viewed on any of the increasingly diverse devices on the market. Transcoding servers and services reformat material that would otherwise have to be developed separately for display on different platforms. Working like an interpreter, the technology translates content to suitable formats for various platforms, regardless of **protocol**, application, screen size, and language used. A variant of transcoding has been used for some time in Web applications such as AltaVista's Babel Fish language translation program.

Although wireless connectivity is steadily increasing, the question of how to enable content display has been problematic. Handheld wireless devices—such as the **smartphone** and the personal digital assistant (**PDA**)—tend to have limitations in terms of power, memory, **resolution**, and screen size; this means that they have problems displaying Web content suitable for a full-sized computer. Typically, the mobile user wants to be able to access the crucial data (such as a stock quote, for example) without any extra detail or graphic display. Without transcoding, content must be written specifically (and separately) to meet the requirements and constraints of each device, and the process must be repeated every time the content is updated. Manual reauthoring of content can cause problems for a mobile workforce that depends on getting reliable information. Each

time content is rewritten, possibilities for errors exist, and updates may not always be available simultaneously for all devices.

There are two main options for those who want to automate the reformatting of content: Using a transcoding server product, such as Aether's Scout Web, AvantGo's Enterprise Server, or IBM's WebSphere Transcoding Publisher, or using a transcoding service, such as Everypath. Although the server products offer the most control over the final content, they also require in-house expertise, as developers must work directly with the original **HTML** and eXtensible Markup Language (**XML**) content. Transcoding services are application service providers (**ASPs**) that take responsibility for the entire process and deliver the reformatted content from **legacy** material.

There are a number of different ways that transcoding can take place. In one example, the original material (an HTML or XML document, for example) is analyzed by a program that then creates a separate version (rather than changing the source) that contains annotations. The annotations include information that will instruct the reformatting process, such as importance ratings of document elements, for example, so that when space is limited, non-essential elements will not be displayed. When a request for the document is sent to the hosting server, the server submits the annotated version to an authoring application. The material is reformatted there, and sent on to a transcoding **proxy server**. The proxy server accesses information about device preferences, and may adapt the material further before delivering it to the end user. The device user may also have specific display preferences, either previously set in the device, or chosen at the time that they request the document, so that the document is reformatted dynamically.

transconductance

Transconductance is an expression of the performance of a **bipolar transistor** or field-effect transistor (**FET**). In general, the larger the transconductance figure for a device, the greater the gain (amplification) it is capable of delivering, when all other factors are held constant.

Formally, for a bipolar device, transconductance is defined as the ratio of the change in collector current to the change in base **voltage** over a defined, arbitrarily small interval on the collector-current-versus-base-voltage curve. For an FET, transconductance is the ratio of the change in drain **current** to the change in gate voltage over a defined, arbitrarily small interval on the drain-current-versus-gate-voltage curve.

The symbol for transconductance is g_m. The unit is the siemens, the same unit that is used for direct-current (**DC**) **conductance**.

If *dI* represents a change in collector or drain current caused by a small change in base or gate voltage *dE*, then the transconductance is approximately:

$$g_m = dI \ / \ dE$$

As the size of the interval approaches zero—that is, the change in base or gate voltage becomes smaller and smaller—the value of dI/dE approaches the slope of a line tangent to the curve at a specific point. The slope of this line represents the theoretical transconductance of a bipolar transistor for a given base voltage and collector current, or the theoretical transconductance of an FET for a given gate voltage and drain current.

transducer

A transducer is an electronic device that converts energy from one form to another. Common examples include microphones, loudspeakers, thermometers, position and pressure sensors, and **antennas**. Although not generally thought of as transducers, photocells, LEDs (light-emitting diodes), and even common light bulbs are transducers.

Efficiency is an important consideration in any transducer. Transducer efficiency is defined as the ratio of the power output in the desired form to the total power input. Mathematically, if P represents the total power input and Q represents the power output in the desired form, then the efficiency E, as a ratio between 0 and 1, is given by:

$E = Q/P$

If $E_\%$ represents the efficiency as a percentage, then:

$E_\% = 100Q/P$

No transducer is 100-percent efficient; some power is always lost in the conversion process. Usually this loss is manifested in the form of heat. Some antennas approach 100-percent efficiency. A well-designed antenna supplied with 100 watts of radio frequency (**RF**) power radiates 80 or 90 watts in the form of an **electromagnetic field**. A few watts are dissipated as heat in the antenna conductors, the feed line conductors and dielectric, and in objects near the antenna. Among the worst transducers, in terms of efficiency, are incandescent lamps. A 100-watt bulb radiates only a few watts in the form of visible light. Most of the power is dissipated as heat; a small amount is radiated in the UV (ultraviolet) spectrum.

transient cookie

On the Web, a transient cookie, sometimes called a *session cookie*, is a small file that contains information about a user that disappears when the user's **browser** is closed. Unlike a **persistent cookie**, a transient cookie is not stored on your **hard drive** but is only stored in temporary **memory** that is erased when the browser is closed.

A transient cookie is created by simply not setting a date in the Set-Cookie option when an application creates the **cookie**. (For a persistent cookie, an expiration date is set and the cookie is stored on the user's hard drive until the expiration date or until the user deletes it.)

Transient cookies are often used to enable a site to be able to track the pages that a user has visited during a visit so that information can be customized for the user in some way. Some sites use Secure Sockets Layer (**SSL**) to **encrypt** the information contained in a cookie.

transistor

The transistor, invented by three scientists at the Bell Laboratories in 1947, rapidly replaced the vacuum tube as an electronic signal regulator. A transistor regulates **current** or **voltage** flow and acts as a switch or gate for electronic signals. A transistor consists of three layers of a **semiconductor** material, each capable of carrying a current. A semiconductor is a material such as germanium and **silicon** that conducts electricity in a "semi-enthusiastic" way. It's somewhere between a real conductor such as copper and an insulator (like the plastic wrapped around wires).

The semiconductor material is given special properties by a chemical process called *doping*. The doping results in a material that either adds extra electrons to the material (which is then called *N-type* for the extra negative charge carriers) or creates "holes" in the material's crystal structure (which is then called *P-type* because it results in more positive charge carriers). The transistor's three-layer structure contains an N-type semiconductor layer sandwiched between P-type layers (a PNP configuration) or a P-type layer between N-type layers (an NPN configuration).

As the current or voltage is changed in one of the outer semiconductor layers, it affects a larger current or voltage in the inner layer resulting in the opening or closing of an electronic gate. Today's computers use circuitry made with complementary metal oxide semiconductor (**CMOS**) technology. CMOS uses two complementary transistors per gate (one with N-type material; the other with P-type material). When one transistor is maintaining a logic state, it requires almost no power.

Transistors are the basic elements in integrated circuits (**ICs**), which consist of very large numbers of transistors interconnected with circuitry and baked into a single silicon **microchip** or "chip."

transit

Transit is the connection to and use of a telecommunication path provided by a vendor. Transit may be billed separately or, where **peering** is also provided, may be billed as part of the peering charge.

Transmeta

Transmeta is a Silicon Valley start-up company known for its recruitment of high profile talent and its **Crusoe** chip, designed for mobile Internet computing. David Ditzel (Sun UltraSparc) founded Transmeta in 1995 and recruited Linus

Torvalds, the creator of **Linux**, to be a member of Transmeta's software team. (Paul Allen, co-founder of Microsoft is a major investor.) For four and a half years, the company operated in a shroud of secrecy, causing a lot of speculation about what Transmeta actually did. In November of 2000, Transmeta went public and revealed it had developed a low-power microprocessing chip called Crusoe (named after Daniel Defoe's shipwrecked character, Robinson Crusoe). Crusoe is the first of what Transmeta hopes will be a family of smart microprocessors for mobile Internet devices.

Transmission Control Protocol

See "TCP"

Transmission Control Protocol/Internet Protocol

See "TCP/IP"

transparent GIF

A transparent GIF (**Graphics Interchange Format**) is an image file that has one color assigned to be "transparent" so that the assigned color will be replaced by the browser's background color, whatever it may be. Pretend, for example, that you have created a rectangular GIF image of a large red star on a white background. If you are only interested in having the red star appear on your Web page, and don't want to see the white background, you can transparentize the white background color so that it changes to whatever the Web page's background color is (yellow, for example). Then, when you view the Web page, you will only see a red star on a yellow background.

A single color transparent GIF can also be used as a place holder in a table cell on a Web page. Another name for this use of a transparent GIF is "spacer GIF."

transponder

A transponder is a **wireless** communications, monitoring, or control device that picks up and responds to an incoming **signal**. The term is a contraction of the words *trans*mitter and res*ponder*. Transponders can be either passive or active.

A *passive transponder* allows a computer or robot to identify an object. Magnetic labels, such as those on credit cards and store items, are common examples. A passive transponder must be used with an active sensor that decodes and transcribes the data the transponder contains. The transponder unit can be physically tiny, and its information can be sensed up to several feet away.

Simple *active transponders* are employed in location, identification, and navigation systems. An example is an RFID (radio-frequency identification) device that transmits a coded signal when it receives a request from a monitoring or control point. The transponder output signal is tracked, so the position of the transponder can be constantly monitored. The input (receiver) and output (transmitter) **frequency** are preassigned. Transponders of this type can operate over distances of thousands of miles.

Sophisticated active transponders are used in communications satellites and on board space vehicles. They receive incoming signals over a range, or **band**, of frequencies, and retransmit the signals on a different band at the same time. The device is similar to a **repeater** of the sort used in land-based cellular telephone networks. The incoming signal, usually originating from a point on the earth's surface, is called the **uplink**. The outgoing signal, usually sent to a point or region on the surface, is the **downlink**. These transponders sometimes operate on an interplanetary scale.

Transport layer

In the Open Systems Interconnection (**OSI**) communications model, the Transport layer ensures the reliable arrival of messages and provides error checking mechanisms and data flow controls. The Transport layer provides services for both "connection-mode" transmissions and for "connectionless-mode" transmissions. For connection-mode transmissions, a transmission may be sent or arrive in the form of **packet**s that need to be reconstructed into a complete message at the other end.

The **Transmission Control Protocol** portion of **TCP/IP** is a program that can be mapped to the Transport layer.

Transport Layer Security

Transport Layer Security (TLS) is a **protocol** that ensures privacy between communicating **application**s and their users on the Internet. When a **server** and **client** communicate, TLS ensures that no third party may eavesdrop or tamper with any message. TLS is the successor to the Secure Sockets Layer (**SSL**).

TLS is composed of two layers: the TLS Record Protocol and the TLS Handshake Protocol. The TLS Record Protocol provides connection security with some **encryption** method such as the Data Encryption Standard (**DES**). The TLS Record Protocol can also be used without encryption. The TLS Handshake Protocol allows the server and client to authenticate each other and to negotiate an encryption **algorithm** and cryptographic keys before data is exchanged.

The TLS protocol is based on Netscape's SSL 3.0 protocol; however, TLS and SSL are not **interoperable**. The TLS protocol does contain a mechanism that allows TLS implementation to back down to SSL 3.0. The most recent **browser** versions support TLS. The TLS Working Group, established in 1996, continues to work on the TLS protocol and related applications.

trap

1) In a **Web site**, a trap is a page that does not allow the reader to back up a previous page (the Back button on the toolbar is inoperable). A few Web site creators apparently use this technique to hold the reader and force them to read the page or to encourage them to visit other pages on their site. To exit a trap, the reader must either close the browser and open it again or enter a **URL** on the address line. Traps are highly unpopular among Web users.

2) In **assembler** language programming, a trap is a place in a program for handling unexpected or unallowable conditions—for example, by sending an error message to a log or to a program user. If a return code from another program were being checked by a calling program, a return code value that was unexpected and unplanned for could cause a branch to a trap that recorded the situation and took other appropriate action.

traveling-wave tube

A traveling-wave tube (TWT) is a specialized **vacuum tube** used in **wireless** communications, especially in **satellite** systems. The TWT can amplify or generate **microwave** signals. Two common types of TWT include the *Klystron* and the *magnetron*.

In the Klystron, a negatively charged cathode emits a beam of high-speed, high-energy **electron**s that travel through the cylindrical tube in straight lines to a positively charged anode. A coil is wound around the tube. When the coil is energized with a radio-frequency (**RF**) signal, the electrons in the beam alternately bunch up and spread out. In the magnetron, the electrons move in circles rather than in straight lines. The circular motion, produced by magnets at either end of the tube, allows the electrons to pick up energy over a greater distance.

Inside the TWT, the regions of high and low electron concentration move along or around the tube in waves. When the tube is properly operating, some of the energy from the electrons is imparted to the signal in the coil. The result is amplification of the signal.

A TWT can be made to function as an **oscillator** by coupling some of the output back into the input. This configuration is called a *backward-wave oscillator*, because the feedback is applied opposite to the direction of movement of the electrons inside the tube. Such an oscillator can generate up to approximately 0.1 watt of signal power in the microwave range.

A *parametric amplifier* is a TWT amplifier that operates from a high-frequency alternating current (**AC**) power source, rather than the usual direct current (**DC**) source. Some characteristic of the circuit, such as its **impedance**, is made to vary with time at the power-supply frequency. Parametric amplifiers are useful because they generate very little

internal **noise**. This makes it possible to obtain excellent sensitivity in receiving systems, minimizing data-transfer errors.

tree structure

A tree structure is an **algorithm** for placing and locating files (called records or keys) in a **database**. The algorithm finds data by repeatedly making choices at decision points called nodes. A node can have as few as two branches (also called children), or as many as several dozen. The structure is straightforward, but in terms of the number of nodes and children, a tree can be gigantic.

In a tree, records are stored in locations called leaves. This name derives from the fact that records always exist at end points; there is nothing beyond them. The starting point is called the root. The maximum number of children per node is called the order of the tree. The maximum number of access operations required to reach the desired record is called the depth. In some trees, the order is the same at every node and the depth is the same for every record. This type of structure is said to be balanced. Other trees have varying numbers of children per node, and different records might lie at different depths. In that case, the tree is said to have an unbalanced or asymmetrical structure.

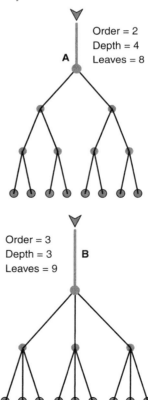

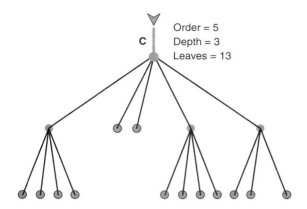

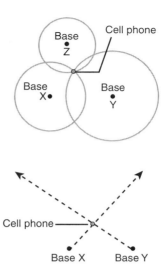

The illustration shows three examples of tree structures. (Note that the portrayals are upside-down compared to real tree plants.) Structures A and B are balanced, and structure C is unbalanced. Roots are at the top, and are represented by arrows. Nodes are shown as gray dots. Children are solid black lines. Leaves are at the bottom. As the process moves toward the leaves and away from the root, children can branch out from a node, but children never merge into a node.

In a practical tree, there can be thousands, millions, or billions of nodes, children, leaves, and records. Not every leaf necessarily contains a record, but more than half do. A leaf that does not contain data is called a null. The trees shown here are simple enough to be rendered in two dimensions, but with some large databases, three dimensions are needed to clearly depict the structure.

Also see **binary tree**, **B-tree**, **M-tree**, **quad tree**, **splay tree**, and **X-tree**.

triangulation

Triangulation is a process by which the location of a radio transmitter can be determined by measuring either the radial distance, or the direction, of the received signal from two or three different points. Triangulation is sometimes used in cellular communications to pinpoint the geographic position of a user.

The drawings below illustrate the basic principle of triangulation. In the scenario shown by the top drawing, the distance to the cell phone is determined by measuring the relative time delays in the signal from the phone set to three different base stations. In the scenario shown by the bottom drawing, directional antennas at two base stations can be used to pinpoint the location of the cell phone.

Triangulation is difficult to carry out unless the person using the cell phone wants to be located. This might be the case, for example, in an emergency situation. Triangulation is the method by which the so-called 911 cell phones work.

Triangulation apparatus can be confused by the reflection of signals from objects such as large steel-frame buildings, water towers, communications towers, and other obstructions. For this reason, at least two independent triangulation determinations should be made to confirm the position of a cell phone or other radio transmitter.

A more sophisticated form of triangulation is used by the Global Positioning System (**GPS**).

trigger

A trigger (from the Dutch *trekken*, meaning *to pull*) is a lever which, when pulled by the finger, releases the hammer on a firearm. In a database, a trigger is a set of Structured Query Language (**SQL**) statements that automatically "fires off" an action when a specific operation, such as changing data in a table, occurs. A trigger consists of an event (an INSERT, DELETE, or UPDATE statement issued against an associated table) and an action (the related procedure). Triggers are used to preserve data integrity by checking on or changing data in a consistent manner.

triplecast

A triplecast (TM) is the simultaneous broadcast of a program on television, radio, and an Internet site or channel. **NetTalk Live!** originated the term to describe its weekly program about the Internet. In addition to listening to or viewing the show on radio or television in the Dallas/Fort Worth area, you can "tune in" from a Web site, Audionet, from which you can download a RealAudio player and listen to streaming sound as the show progresses.

Trivial File Transfer Protocol

Trivial File Transfer Protocol (TFTP) is an Internet software utility for transferring files that is simpler to use than the File Transfer Protocol (**FTP**) but less capable. It is used where user **authentication** and directory visibility are not required. TFTP uses the User Datagram Protocol (**UDP**) rather than the Transmission Control Protocol (**TCP**). TFTP is described formally in Request for Comments (**RFC**) 1350.

Trojan horse

In computers, a Trojan horse is a program in which malicious or harmful code is contained inside apparently harmless programming or data in such a way that it can get control and do its chosen form of damage, such as ruining the **file allocation table** on your **hard disk**. In one celebrated case, a Trojan horse was a program that was supposed to find and destroy computer **virus**es. A Trojan horse may be widely redistributed as part of a computer virus.

The term comes from Homer's *Iliad*. In the Trojan War, the Greeks presented the citizens of Troy with a large wooden horse in which they had secretly hidden their warriors. During the night, the warriors emerged from the wooden horse and overran the city.

tropo

See "tropospheric propogation"

tropospheric propogation

Radio waves can propagate over the horizon when the lower atmosphere of the earth bends, scatters, and/or reflects the electromagnetic fields. These effects are collectively known as tropospheric propagation, or tropo for short. Tropospheric propagation can affect **wireless** communications, sometimes enhancing the usable range, but also compounding interference problems.

The most well-known form of tropo is called bending. Air reduces radio-wave propagation speed compared with the speed in a vacuum. The greater the air density, the more the air slows the waves, and thus the greater is the index of refraction. The density and index of refraction are highest near the surface, and steadily decrease with altitude. This produces a tendency for radio waves at very-high frequencies (VHF, 30 to 300 MHz) and ultra-high frequencies (UHF, 300 MHz to 3 GHz) to be refracted toward the surface. A wave beamed horizontally can follow the curvature of the earth for hundreds of miles.

The lower atmosphere scatters electromagnetic radiation over a vast range, including radio wavelengths. This effect is known as tropospheric scatter, or troposcatter. In general, troposcatter is most pronounced at UHF and microwave radio frequencies (300 MHz and above). A radio wave beamed slightly above the horizon can be scattered at altitudes up to several miles, making over-the-horizon

communication possible. The greatest communications range can be realized over flat land or over water. Scattered waves are weak, so high-power transmitters and sensitive receivers are necessary.

A less common, but often dramatic, form of tropo is called ducting or duct effect. This occurs when there is a defined, horizontal boundary between air masses having different densities. When a cool air mass is overlain by a warm air mass, as is the case along and near warm fronts and cold fronts, radio waves at VHF and UHF are reflected at the boundary if they strike it at a near-grazing angle from beneath (within the cooler air mass). Because radio waves are also reflected from the earth's surface, the result can be efficient propagation for hundreds or, in some cases, upwards of 1,000 miles, as the waves alternately bounce off the frontal boundary and the surface. Ducting can allow long-distance radio reception in the frequency-modulation (FM) broadcast band between 88 and 108 MHz. It can also affect the lower VHF television channels if receiving antennas (rather than cable networks) are used.

true color

True color is the specification of the color of a **pixel** on a display screen using a 24-bit value, which allows the possibility of up to 16,777,216 possible colors. Many displays today support only an 8-bit color value, allowing up to 256 possible colors.

The number of bits used to define a pixel's color shade is its *bit-depth*. True color is sometimes known as *24-bit color*. Some new color display systems offer a 32-bit color mode. The extra byte, called the *alpha channel*, is used for control and special effects information.

true power

True power is the **power** manifested in tangible form such as electromagnetic radiation, acoustic waves, or mechanical phenomena. In a direct current (**DC**) circuit, or in an alternating current (**AC**) circuit whose **impedance** is a pure **resistance**, the voltage and current are in phase, and the following formula holds:

$$P = E_{rms}I_{rms}$$

where P is the power in watts, E_{rms} is the **root-mean-square** voltage in volts, and I_{rms} is the rms current in amperes. But in an AC circuit whose impedance consists of reactance as well as resistance, the voltage and current are not in phase. This complicates the determination of **power**.

In the absence of reactance, this voltage-current product represents *true power*. But when there is reactance in an AC circuit, the product $E_{rms}I_{rms}$ is larger than the true power, and is known as **apparent power**.

The vector difference between the apparent and true power is called **reactive power**, and represents energy alternately stored and released by **inductor** and/or **capacitor**.

TrueType

Created at Apple Computer, TrueType was designed to fill the need for an optimized, scalable **font** format. The format uses *hinting*, a technique that preserves a font's design, even at a small scale or on a display with low resolution. It was initially developed in response to the technical limitations of Adobe's **Postscript** and Type 1 font formats.

TrueType was first introduced in the Macintosh System 7 operating system in 1990. A year later, Apple licensed TrueType to Microsoft, and it was introduced in their Windows 3.1 operating system. After making some performance improvements to the format, they released version 1.5 in Windows NT 3.1, and have continued to update the format.

In order to view and print TrueType fonts on a computer, two components are necessary: the actual TrueType font file (with the extension TTF) and the TrueType **raster graphics**. The rasterizer is built into Windows and Mac operating systems.

If you use TrueType fonts on a Web page or in Word document, it is possible to embed them into the file, so that your fonts will still be viewable by people who do not have that font installed on their machine. Also keep in mind that the Macintosh and Windows versions of TrueType fonts are not compatible. When downloading TrueType fonts from the Internet (such as from a free fonts Web site), you must select the Mac or PC version. TrueType Font converters are available if a TrueType font is only available for one platform.

Microsoft's most recent font development is called OpenType. This font format ensures that fonts are compatible across the Windows and Apple Macintosh platforms and encompasses Adobe's Type 1 and PostScript technologies.

truncate

To truncate is to shorten by cutting off. In computer terms, when information is truncated, it is ended abruptly at a certain spot. For example, if a program truncates a field containing the value of pi (3.14159265...) at four decimal places, the field would show 3.1415 as an answer. This is different from rounding, which would result in the answer of 3.1416.

For another example, consider a text entry field in an electronic form. If a program limits the size of the field to 255 characters, it may allow you to continue typing past the maxiumum number of characters. However, when the information is submitted or saved, the program truncates the data to the first 255 characters and any additional characters are disregarded.

Several operating systems or programming languages use truncate as a command or function for limiting the size of a field, data stream, or file. **Linux** includes a truncate command for rounding integers.

trunk

In telephone systems, a trunk is a line that carries multiple voice or data **channels** between two telephone exchange switching systems. In digital communications, a trunk is often a **T-carrier system**.

trusted PC

The trusted PC is an industry ideal of a PC with built-in security mechanisms that place minimal reliance on the user or administrator to keep a PC and its peripheral devices secure. Trusted personal computing devices are being developed that maximize the security of individual computers through hardware and operating system-based mechanisms rather than through add-in programs and policies. To that end, security mechanisms are being built into chips, chipsets, and motherboards, among other things, because industry consensus is that hardware-based mechanisms are inherently more trustworthy than those created with software.

The Trusted Computing Platform Alliance (TCPA) was formed in October 1999 by Compaq, HP, IBM, Intel and Microsoft. TCPA, whose membership now includes more than 140 companies, states as its goals: "To develop a specification, based on the collaboration of PC industry platform, operating system, application, and technology vendors, that delivers a set of hardware and operating system security capabilities that customers can use to enhance the trust and security in their computing environments."

Once effective mechanisms are built into the actual computer hardware, security will not be as dependent upon the vigilance of individual administrators as it has been in the past. If the trusted PC works the way it should, an inexperienced or lackadaisical administrator won't be able to unwittingly compromise system or network security through inefficient policies. The idea of a "trusted PC" is similar to the *trust relationships* that can be set up between networked computers to allow the terminals involved varying degrees of access to each other's data, depending on their requirements and level of trust. The new trusted PC uses the word in a different sense, in that its "trust" is based on hard-wired security—somewhat like trusting children to stay out of the cookie jar because it is locked in a safe.

TSR

See "terminate and stay resident"

tuple

1) In programming languages, such as Lisp, Python, Linda, and others, a tuple (pronounced TUH-pul) is an ordered set of values. The separator for each value is often a comma (depending on the rules of the particular language). Common uses for the tuple as a **data type** are (1) for passing a string of parameters from one program to another, and (2) representing a set of value attributes in a relational database. In some languages, tuples can be nested within other tuples within parentheses or brackets or other delimiters. Tuples can contain a mixture of other data types.

Here's an example of a tuple that emphasizes the different data types that may exist within a tuple data type:

17,*,2.49,Seven

The above example is sometimes referred to as a 4-tuple, since it contains four values. An n-tuple would be one with an indeterminate or unspecified number of values.

2) A tuple is analogous to a **record** in nonrelational databases.

The term originated as an abstraction of the sequence: single, double, triple, quadruple, quintuple, ... n-tuple. *Tuple* is used in abstract mathematics to denote a multidimensional coordinate system.

Tux

Tux, the penguin, is the generally accepted official logo for the **Linux operating system**. Linus Torvalds, the creator of Linux, chose Larry Ewing's design simply because he likes penguins. It is said that the name Tux was the winning entry in the "Let's Name The Penguin While Linus Is Away Contest" with the "T" standing for Torvald and the "U" and "X" for Linux.

Tuxedo

Tuxedo (which stands for *Transactions for* **UNIX**, *Enhanced for* **Distributed** *Operation*) is a **middleware** product that uses a **message**-based communications system to distribute applications across various **operating system platform**s and **databases**. Tuxedo operates as an extension of the operating system: as a platform for execution as well as development, it is designed for the creation and administration of **e-commerce** online transaction processing (OLTP) systems. Originally developed at AT&T in the 1970s, Tuxedo was subsequently owned by Unix System Laboratories (USL), and then **Novell** before it was taken over by BEA Systems, the current owners.

Tuxedo's three main functions are: as **middleware**, to relay request and response communications between servers and clients; as a transaction processing (TP) monitor, to initiate, monitor, and terminate transactions; and, as a distributed TP monitor, to enable interaction between transaction participants on different machines and associated with different databases. The Gap, E*TRADE, and Hong Kong International Terminals are some organizations that use Tuxedo for large scale transaction processing.

TWAIN

TWAIN is a widely-used program that lets you scan an **image** (using a **scanner**) directly into the application (such as PhotoShop) where you want to work with the image. Without TWAIN, you would have to close an application that was open, open a special application to receive the image, and then move the image to the application where you wanted to work with it. The TWAIN **driver** runs between an application and the scanner hardware. TWAIN usually comes as part of the software package you get when you buy a scanner. It's also integrated into PhotoShop and similar image manipulation programs.

The software was developed by a work group from major scanner manufacturers and scanning software developers and is now an industry standard. In several accounts, TWAIN was an acronym developed playfully from "technology without an important name." However, the TWAIN Working Group says that after the name chosen originally turned out to be already trademarked, an 11th hour meeting of the group came up with TWAIN, deriving it from the saying "Ne'er the twain shall meet," because the program sits between the driver and the application. The name is not intended to be an acronym.

tweak freak

A tweak freak is a person who tinkers with hardware and/or programming to a point approaching obsession. Sometimes the intent is to enhance system performance beyond the norm. But many tweak freaks engage in the activity largely because it is interesting, fun, and can be a learning experience. It can also be frustrating and at its worst, dangerous.

The term "tweak" may have originated in the early days of electronics, when tweezers were used to adjust the position of a wire on a crystal of galena in order to detect amplitude-modulated (AM) radio broadcast signals. Nowadays, hardware and programs of all kinds can (and often should) be aligned or debugged for optimum performance; technicians and programmers call the process tweaking.

The tweaking of computers, especially software and operating systems, is not for the faint-of-heart. Excessive or improper tweaking can cause computers and Web browsers to become unstable. Vulnerability to **virus** or **Trojan horse** infection may be increased. Excessive downloading and installation of tweaks and patches can increase the probability of program conflicts and crashes. Some tweaks facilitate illegal or questionable use of the Internet, and should be avoided by people who respect the law and the rights of others (and who wish to stay out of court). Let the tweaker beware.

TweakUI

TweakUI is a software **utility** that lets **Windows 9x**, **Windows NT**, and **Windows 2000** users modify the **desktop** user interface and other system characteristics to their liking. Using TweakUI, you can change the menu speed, how windows are animated, and a number of features about **Microsoft Internet Explorer**. TweakUI allows the user to change settings that are not easy to locate, including some in the system **registry**. For example, a user can speed up system startup by reducing the frequency with which the **ScanDisk** utility is run.

Microsoft includes TweakUI as one of several "Power Toys" that can be optionally installed. Users are advised to always back up their registry (for example, copy it to a new file with another name) before doing anything that might modify it.

twinaxial cable

Twinaxial cable is **coaxial cable** that contains two inner conducting wires rather than one. IBM's **AS/400** and System/3x midrange computer systems use twinaxial cable.

twip

A twip (twentieth of a point) is a measure used in laying out space or defining objects on a page or other area that is to be printed or displayed on a computer screen. A twip is 1/1440th of an inch or 1/567th of a centimeter. That is, there are 1440 twips to an inch or 567 twips to a centimeter. The twip is 1/20th of a *point*, a traditional measure in printing. A point is approximately 1/72nd of an inch.

A number of computer software programs, notably Microsoft's **Visual Basic**, as well as its rich text file format (**RTF**), require programmers to specify screen positions and image and icon sizes in twips rather than in another common measure, the **pixel**. Like the pixel, the twip can be adjusted in size as screen **resolution** is changed, but, unlike the pixel, expresses an absolute value for printing.

Since not all software development tools work with twips, a programmer may sometimes need to convert between twips and pixels, and the reverse.

twisted pair

(Also see **categories of twisted pair cabling systems** and **registered jack**.)

Twisted pair is the ordinary copper wire that connects home and many business computers to the telephone company. To reduce crosstalk or electromagnetic induction between pairs of wires, two insulated copper wires are twisted around each other. Each connection on twisted pair requires both wires. Since some telephone sets or desktop locations require multiple connections, twisted pair is sometimes installed in two or more pairs, all within a single cable. For some business locations, twisted pair is enclosed in a shield that

functions as a ground. This is known as shielded twisted pair (**STP**). Ordinary wire to the home is unshielded twisted pair (**UTP**).

Twisted pair is now frequently installed with two pairs to the home, with the extra pair making it possible for you to add another line (perhaps for **modem** use) when you need it.

Twisted pair comes with each pair uniquely color coded when it is packaged in multiple pairs. Different uses such as **analog**, **digital**, and **Ethernet** require different pair multiples.

Although twisted pair is often associated with home use, a higher grade of twisted pair is often used for horizontal wiring in LAN installations because it is less expensive than **coaxial cable**.

The wire you buy at a local hardware store for extensions from your phone or computer modem to a wall jack is not twisted pair. It is a side-by-side wire known as *silver satin*. The wall jack can have as many five kinds of hole arrangements or **pinout**, depending on the kinds of wire the installation expects will be plugged in (for example, digital, analog, or LAN) . (That's why you may sometimes find when you carry your notebook computer to another location that the wall jack connections won't match your plug.)

two-way pager

A two-way pager is a **pager** that allows you to send data as well as receive it. In some cases, a two-way pager can serve as an alternative to a cellular telephone. At least one manufacturer, Paging Network, lets you record a message and have an answering service on the machine.

Apple Computer, Hewlett-Packard, MobileMedia Corporation, Motorola, AirTouch Communications, Casio Computer, Mobile Telecommunication Technologies (Mtel), and Sharp are among companies that manufacture two-pagers or offer a two-way paging service.

typeface

A typeface is a design for a set of printer or display **font**s, each for a set of characters, in a number of specific sizes. Since *outline fonts* such as TrueType and Type 1 are scalable, a computer typeface designer must anticipate the possibility of the design being scaled through a range of sizes.

Typefaces often come as a family of typefaces, with individual typefaces for italic, bold, and other variations in the main design.

See **font** for additional information.

typosquatting

Typosquatting is a form of Internet **cybersquatting**, based on the probability that a certain number of Internet users will mistype the name of a Web site (or actually its **URL**) when surfing the Web. Typically, a typosquatter will register several possible input errors for a "brand name" Web site

known for its high traffic, and then monitor to see how many clicks a day each of their "typo" domain names receives, and use the information to sell advertising for the sites that receive a high volume of accidental traffic. Advertising revenue might come from selling ads to the original site's competitors or by providing redirect pages to related products or services.

U

A U is a standard unit of measure for designating the height in computer enclosures and rack cabinets. A U equals 1.75 inches. For example, a 4U chassis is 7 inches high. A 40U rack cabinet is 70 inches high.

U interface

In Integrated Services Digital Network (**ISDN**) Basic Rate Interface service, a U interface is the electrical interface for the single **twisted pair** wire connection from a local phone company (the **central office**) to a home or business. Unlike a regular 64 **Kbps analog** phone connection, however, the twisted-pair using ISDN carries two 64 Kbps **channels** (known as B, or bearer, channels) and an additional 16 Kbps channel (the D, for data or delta, channel) for control signals.

The U interface twisted-pair is usually connected at the home or business to a network terminator 1 (**NT1**) box, sometimes called a *network terminating unit*. (In the UK and some other countries, the NT1 is located at the central office.) The other side of the NT1 has plugs for four wires, which can be connected on a loop configuration known as an *S-bus* or **S interface** to up to eight devices (for example, two computers and six phones) or to a **T interface**. An NT1 can also be integrated into a modem or other device, in which case the ISDN connection can only serve that device.

The U-loop or U-V loop, as it is sometimes called, uses the 2B1Q line code protocol, meaning that two **binary digit**s are used to represent one quadratude—that is, four possible variations of signal level (amplitude and polarity). Communication is **full-duplex**, meaning that data can be arriving at the same time you are sending data.

The U-V loop replaces the traditional local loop. The maximum distance for the ISDN loop is 6,500 meters (about 18,000 feet).

The following table summarizes the various ISDN electrical interfaces at different demarcation points or places in the traffic flow:

Electrical interface	Between what two points
U interface	Central office and NT1
T interface	NT1 and NT2 devices (such as a PBX)
S interface	NT1 or NT2 and ISDN devices (such as a telephone or terminal adapter)
R interface	Terminal adapter and non-ISDN devices (such as a computer)
V interface	Within the ISDN node at the central office; separates line termination equipment from exchange termination equipment

UART

A UART (Universal Asynchronous Receiver/Transmitter) is the **microchip** with programming that controls a computer's interface to its attached **serial** devices. Specifically, it provides the computer with the **RS-232C** Data Terminal Equipment (**DTE**) interface so that it can "talk" to and exchange data with modems and other serial devices. As part of this interface, the UART also:

- Converts the bytes it receives from the computer along **parallel** circuits into a single **serial** bit stream for outbound transmission
- On inbound transmission, converts the serial bit stream into the bytes that the computer handles
- Adds a **parity** bit (if it's been selected) on outbound transmissions and checks the parity of incoming bytes (if selected) and discards the parity bit
- Adds start and stop delineators on outbound and strips them from inbound transmissions
- Handles **interrupt**s from the keyboard and mouse (which are serial devices with special **port**s)
- May handle other kinds of interrupt and device management that require coordinating the computer's speed of operation with device speeds

More advanced UARTs provide some amount of **buffering** of data so that the computer and serial devices data streams remain coordinated. The most recent UART, the 16550, has a 16-byte buffer that can get filled before the computer's processor needs to handle the data. The original UART was the 8250. If you purchase an internal modem today, it probably includes a 16550 UART (although you should ask when you buy it). According to modem manufacturer US Robotics, external modems do not include a UART. If you have an older computer, you may want to add an internal 16550 to get the most out of your external modem.

UCM

See "configuration management"

UDA

See "Universal Data Access"

UDDI

UDDI (**Universal Description, Discovery, and Integration**) is an **XML**-based registry for businesses worldwide to list themselves on the Internet. Its ultimate goal is to streamline online transactions by enabling companies to find one another on the Web and make their systems interoperable for e-commerce. UDDI is often compared to a telephone book's white, yellow, and green pages. The project allows businesses to list themselves by name, product, location, or the Web services they offer.

Microsoft, IBM, and Ariba spearheaded UDDI. The project now includes 130 companies, including some of the biggest names in the corporate world. Compaq, American Express, **SAP** AG, and Ford Motor Company are all committed to UDDI, as is **Hewlett-Packard**, whose own XML-based directory approach, called **e-speak**, is now being integrated with UDDI.

While the group does not refer to itself as a standards body, it does offer a framework for Web services integration. The UDDI specification utilizes World Wide Web Consortium (**W3C**) and Internet Engineering Task Force (**IETF**) standards such as XML, **HTTP**, and Domain Name System (**DNS**) protocols. It has also adopted early versions of the proposed Simple Object Access Protocol (**SOAP**) messaging guidelines for cross platform programming.

In November 2000, UDDI entered its public **beta**-testing phase. Each of its three founders—Microsoft, IBM, and Ariba—now operates a registry server that is interoperable with servers from other members. As information goes into a registry server, it is shared by servers in the other businesses. In the future, other companies will act as operators of the UDDI Business Registry.

UDDI registration is open to companies worldwide, regardless of their size.

UDF

See "Universal Disk Format"

UDP

UDP (User Datagram Protocol) is a communications protocol that offers a limited amount of service when messages are exchanged between computers in a network that uses the Internet Protocol (**IP**). UDP is an alternative to the Transmission Control Protocol (**TCP**) and, together with IP, is sometimes referred to as UDP/IP. Like the Transmission Control Protocol, UDP uses the Internet Protocol to actually get a data unit (called a **datagram**) from one computer to another. Unlike TCP, however, UDP does not provide the service of dividing a message into packets (datagrams) and reassembling it at the other end. Specifically, UDP doesn't provide sequencing of the packets that the data arrives in. This means that the application program that uses UDP must be able to make sure that the

entire message has arrived and is in the right order. Network applications that want to save processing time because they have very small data units to exchange (and therefore very little message reassembling to do) may prefer UDP to TCP. The Trivial File Transfer Protocol (**TFTP**) uses UDP instead of TCP.

UDP provides two services not provided by the IP layer. It provides **port number**s to help distinguish different user requests and, optionally, a **checksum** capability to verify that the data arrived intact.

In the Open Systems Interconnection (**OSI**) communication model, UDP, like TCP, is in layer 4, the Transport layer.

UHF

The UHF (ultrahigh frequency) range of the radio spectrum is the **band** extending from 300 **MHz** to 3 **GHz**. The wavelengths corresponding to these limit frequencies are 1 meter and 10 centimeters.

In the UHF band, signals from earth-based transmitters are not returned by the ionosphere to the surface; they always pass into space. Conversely, signals from space always penetrate the ionosphere and reach the surface. The global "shortwave" propagation familiar to users of lower frequencies is unknown at UHF. The troposphere can cause bending, ducting, and scattering at UHF, extending the range of communication significantly beyond the visual horizon. Auroral, meteor-scatter, and EME (earth-moon-earth, also called **moonbounce**) propagation are sometimes observed, but these modes do not offer reliable communication and are of interest primarily to **amateur radio** operators. In the upper portion of the band, waves can be focused or collimated by dish antennas of modest size.

The UHF band is extensively used for **satellite** communication and broadcasting, in **cellular telephone** and paging systems, and by third-generation (**3G**) **wireless** services. Because the frequency is high and the band is vast (a span of 2.7 gigahertz from the low end to the high end), **wideband modulation** and **spread spectrum** modes are practical. Channels and subbands within the UHF portion of the radio spectrum are allocated by the International Telecommunication Union (**ITU**).

UIML

UIML (User Interface Markup Language) is a descriptive language that lets you create a Web page that can be sent to any kind of **interface device**—for example, to a PC with a large display and a keyboard or to a "smart phone" with a tiny display and no keyboard. The advantage of UIML is that Web content can be created once without understanding the existing and future device types to which the content will be sent. A content developer uses the **markup** language (sometimes referred to as a set of **tag**s) to describe user interface elements such as input boxes, text messages, menus, and buttons. A programmer can then write applications that use the UIML page to generate a page appropriate to each device type, such as a PC, smart phone, or voice output device, to which the content may need to be sent.

UIML is an application of the Extensible Markup Language (**XML**). One can think of it as the XML description that describes the data structure (names of fields or elements) of a user interface. A given UIML file also describes the specific content (text, names of images, and so forth) in those fields or elements. UIML also allows you to describe possible user input events and resulting actions. The markup is described in the UIML Specification, which also includes the formal XML document type definition (**DTD**) for UIML. Since UIML requires the specification of user interface elements (often called **widget**s) in terms of names used by specific language development *toolkits* (for example, Java AWT or Microsoft Foundation Classes—**MFCL**), you need to identify the specific tookit and know the names for various elements and their properties that are used by the toolkit.

Harmonia, the software company where UIML was developed, has published it as an open source language and plans to submit it to a standards organization after comments have been received on version 2.0.

Ultra DMA

Ultra DMA (UDMA, or, more accurately, Ultra DMA/33) is a protocol for transferring data between a **hard disk** drive through the computer's data paths (or **bus**) to the computer's random access memory (**RAM**). The Ultra DMA/33 protocol transfers data in **burst** mode at a rate of 33.3 MBps (**megabyte**s per second), twice as fast as the previous Direct Memory Access (**DMA**) interface.

Ultra DMA was developed as a proposed industry standard by the Quantum Corporation, makers of hard disk drives, and Intel, makers of **chipset**s that support computer **bus** technology.

Ultra DMA support in your computer means that it will **boot** (start) and open new applications more quickly. It will also help users of graphics-intensive and other applications that require large amounts of access to data on the hard drive. Ultra DMA uses Cyclical Redundancy Checking (**CRC**), offering a new level of data protection.

Because the Ultra DMA protocol is designed to work with **legacy application PIO** and DMA protocols, it can be added to many existing computers by installing an Ultra DMA/33 **Peripheral Component Interconnect** adapter **card**. Ultra DMA uses the same 40-pin **Integrated Drive Electronics** interface cable as PIO and DMA.

ultra wideband radio

Ultra wideband radio (also known as *digital pulse wireless*) is a revolutionary **wireless** technology for transmitting large amounts of digital data over a wide spectrum of **frequency** bands with very low **power**. Ultra wideband radio not only

can carry a huge amount of data over a short distance (up to 230 feet) at very low power (less than 0.5 milliwatts), but has the ability to carry signals through doors and other obstacles that tend to reflect signals at more limited bandwidths and a higher power. Ultra wideband radio can be compared with another short-distance wireless technology, **Bluetooth**, which is a proposed standard for connecting handheld wireless devices with other similar devices and with desktop computers.

Ultra wideband radio broadcasts digital pulses that are timed very precisely on a **signal** across a very wide spectrum (number of frequency channels) at the same time. Transmitter and receiver must be coordinated to send and receive pulses with an accuracy of trillionths of a second. On any given frequency band that may already be in use, the ultra wideband signal has less power than the normal and anticipated background **noise** so theoretically no interference is possible. Time Domain, a company applying to use the technology, uses a microchip manufactured by IBM to transmit 1.25 million bits per second, but says there is the potential for a data rate in the billions of bits per second.

Ultra wideband has two main types of application:

1) **Radar**-type applications, in which the signal penetrates nearby surfaces but reflects surfaces that are farther away, allowing objects to be detected behind walls or other coverings.

2) Voice and data transmission using digital pulses, allowing a very low powered and relatively low cost signal to carry information at very high rates within a restricted range.

UML

See "Unified Modeling Language"

UMTS

UMTS (Universal Mobile Telecommunications Service) is a so-called "third-generation (3G)," **broadband**, **packet**-based transmission of text, digitized voice, video, and multimedia at data rates up to 2 megabits per second (**Mbps**) that will offer a consistent set of services to mobile computer and phone users no matter where they are located in the world. Based on the Global System for Mobile (**GSM**) communication standard, UMTS, endorsed by major standards bodies and manufacturers, is the planned standard for mobile users around the world by 2002. Once UTMS is fully implemented, computer and phone users can be constantly attached to the Internet as they travel and, as they **roaming service**, have the same set of capabilities no matter where they travel to. Users will have access through a combination of terrestrial **wireless** and **satellite** transmissions. Until UMTS is fully implemented, users can have multi-mode devices that switch to the currently available technology (such as GSM 900 and 1800) where UMTS is not yet available.

Today's **cellular telephone** systems are mainly **circuit-switched**, with connections always dependent on circuit availability. **Packet-switched** connections, using the Internet Protocol (**IP**), means that a virtual connection is always available to any other end point in the network. It will also make it possible to provide new services, such as alternative billing methods (pay-per-bit, pay-per-session, flat rate, asymmetric bandwidth, and others). The higher **bandwidth** of UMTS also promises new services, such as video conferencing. UMTS promises to realize the Virtual Home Environment (**VHE**) in which a roaming user can have the same services to which the user is accustomed when at home or in the office, through a combination of transparent terrestrial and satellite connections.

Trials of UMTS technology, using advanced mobile phone/computing device prototypes, have been conducted by Nortel Networks and BT (British Telecommunications).

The **electromagnetic radiation spectrum** for UMTS has been identified as frequency bands 1885-2025 **MHz**) for future IMT-2000 systems, and 1980-2010 MHz and 2170-2200 MHz for the satellite portion of UMTS systems.

UNC

In a network, the UNC (Universal Naming Convention) is a way to identify a shared **file** without having to specify or know the network storage drive it is on. In Windows **operating systems**, Novell **NetWare**, and possibly other operating systems, the UNC can be used instead of the local naming system (such as the DOS naming system in Windows).

In Windows operating systems, the UNC name format is:
`\\servername\sharename\path\filename`
The share name is sometimes said to logically identify the *volume* or storage device that the file is on, but the idea is to free the user from having to know this. The **path** is zero or more folder or subfolder names (in other words, the file name may exist directly under the sharename).

For example:
`\\corp1\lawdeptforms\patentap.html`
might specify on a server in the corporate main office a shared file (patentap.html) kept with other legal forms that members of a corporation's legal department might download and read or print and use. Printers and other devices can also be addressed using UNC.

uncompressing

Uncompressing (or decompressing) is the act of expanding a compression file back into its original form. Software that you download from the Internet often comes in a compressed package that can uncompress itself when you click on it. You can also uncompress files using popular tools such as PKZIP in the DOS operating system, WinZip in Windows, and MacZip in Macintosh.

Undernet

For terms frequently used in online keyboard chatting, see **chat abbreviations/IRC/BBS**.

According to its home page, the Undernet is the largest network of Internet Relay Channels (**IRCs**) on the Internet. The Undernet interconnects users from over 35 countries for Internet **chatting** on about 45 **servers** located on three continents. At any one time, as many as 20,000 people may be chatting on one of several hundred Undernet **channels**. Users must download free IRC **client** software from one of a number of possible Web sites and then register as an Undernet organization member. They will also furnish personal Web page space for members.

unicast

Unicast is communication between a single sender and a single receiver over a network. The term exists in contradistinction to **multicast**, communication between a single sender and multiple receivers, and **anycast**, communication between any sender and the nearest of a group of receivers in a network. An earlier term, *point-to-point* communication, is similar in meaning to unicast. The new Internet Protocol version 6 (**IPv6**) supports unicast as well as anycast and multicast.

Unicode

Unicode is an entirely new idea in setting up binary codes for text or script characters. Officially called the Unicode Worldwide Character Standard, it is a system for "the interchange, processing, and display of the written texts of the diverse languages of the modern world." It also supports many classical and historical texts in a number of languages.

Currently, the Unicode standard contains 34,168 distinct coded characters derived from 24 supported language scripts. These characters cover the principal written languages of the world.

Additional work is underway to add the few modern languages not yet included.

Also see the currently most prevalent script or text codes, **ASCII** and extended binary-coded decimal interchange code (**EBCDIC**).

unified field theory

Unified field theory is sometimes called the *Theory of Everything* (TOE, for short): The long-sought means of tying together all known phenomena to explain the nature and behavior of all matter and energy in existence. In physics, a *field* refers to an area under the influence of some force, such as gravity or electricity, for example. A unified field theory would reconcile seemingly incompatible aspects of various field theories to create a single comprehensive set of equations. Such a theory could potentially unlock all the secrets of nature and make a myriad of wonders possible, including such benefits as time travel and an inexhaustible source of clean energy, among many others. According to Michio Katu, a theoretical physicist at City College, City University of New York, those in pursuit of a unified field theory seek "an equation an inch long that would allow us to read the mind of God."

James Clerk Maxwell proposed the first field theory, for electromagnetism, in the middle of the 1800s. Early in the 20th century, Albert Einstein's general theory of relativity—dealing with gravitation—became the second field theory. The term *unified field theory* was coined by Einstein, who was attempting to prove that electromagnetism and gravity were different manifestations of a single fundamental field. When **quantum theory** entered the picture, the puzzle became more complex. The theory of relativity explains the nature and behavior of all phenomena on the macroscopic level (things that are visible to the naked eye); quantum theory explains the nature and behavior of all phenomena on the microscopic (atomic and subatomic) level. Perplexingly, however, the two theories are incompatible. Unconvinced that nature would prescribe totally different modes of behavior for phenomena that were simply scaled differently, Einstein sought a theory that would reconcile the two apparently irreconcilable theories that form the basis of modern physics.

Although electromagnetism and the strong and weak nuclear forces have long been explained by a single theory known as the *standard model*, gravitation does not fit into the equation. The current quest for a unified field theory (sometimes called the *holy grail of physicists*) is largely focused on **superstring theory** and, in particular, on an adaptation known as **M-theory**.

unified messaging

Unified messaging (sometimes referred to as the *unified messaging system* or *UMS*) is the handling of voice, fax, and regular text messages as objects in a single mailbox that a user can access either with a regular **e-mail** client or by telephone. The PC user can open and play back voice messages, assuming their PC has multimedia capabilities. Fax images can be saved or printed.

A user can access the same mailbox by telephone. In this case, ordinary e-mail notes in text are converted into audio files and played back.

Unified messaging is particularly convenient for mobile business users because it allows them to reach colleagues and customers through a PC or telephone, whichever happens to be available. Some services offer worldwide telephone access.

Unified Modeling Language

UML (Unified Modeling Language) is a standard notation for the modeling of real-world objects as a first step in developing an **object-oriented** design methodology. Its notation is derived from and unifies the notations of three object-oriented design and analysis methodologies:

- Grady Booch's methodology for describing a set of objects and their relationships
- James Rumbaugh's Object-Modeling Technique (OMT)
- Ivar Jacobson's approach which includes a *use case methodology*

Other ideas also contributed to UML, which was the result of a work effort by Booch, Rumbaugh, Jacobson, and others to combine their ideas, working under the sponsorship of Rational Software. UML has been fostered and now is an accepted standard of the Object Management Group (**OMG**), which is also the home of **Common Object Request Broker Architecture**, the leading industry standard for distributed object programming. Vendors of **computer-aided software engineering** products are now supporting UML and it has been endorsed by almost every maker of software development products , including IBM and Microsoft (for its Visual Basic environment).

Martin Fowler, in his book UML Distilled, observes that, although UML is a notation system so that everyone can communicate about a model, it's developed from methodologies that also describe the processes in developing and using the model. While there is no one accepted process, the contributors to UML all describe somewhat similar approaches and these are usually described along with tutorials about UML itself.

Among the concepts of modeling that UML specifies how to describe are: Class (of objects), object, association, responsibility, activity, interface, use case, package, sequence, collaboration, and state. Fowler's book provides a good introduction to UML. Booch, Rumbaugh, and Jacobson all have or soon will have published the "offficial" set of books on UML.

Uniform Resource Identifier

See "URI"

Uniform Resource Locator

See "URL"

Uniform Resource Name

A URN (Uniform Resource Name) is an Internet resource with a name that has persistent significance—that is, the user of the URN can expect that someone else (or a program) will be able to find the resource. A URN looks something like a Web page address or Uniform Resource Locator (**URL**). For example, here's a hypothetical URN:

```
urn:def://blue_laser
```
where "def://" might indicate an agency or an accessible directory of all dictionaries, glossaries, and encyclopedias on the Internet and "blue laser" was the name of a term. The result of using the agency could be the "best definition," the "longest definition," or even all definitions that the agency could find of "blue laser."

A comparable URL would need to specify one specific location for a definition such as:

```
http://www.whatis.com/bluelase.htm
```
In this case, the user has to know where the resource is located as well as how to spell the file name and suffix. With a URN, the user only needs to know the name of a resource. One or more agencies will presumably be able to locate the nearest copy of the resource and the user is freed from understanding where resources are located or relocated to.

Both URN and URL are types of a concept called the Uniform Resource Identifier (**URI**). A URN is associated with another concept called Uniform Resource Characteristics (URC), which allows descriptive information to be associated with a URN, such as author, date, length, and so forth.

It is possible to have a name that includes an address so, in some cases, a URN may also be a URL, but it doesn't have to be.

The URN is still being developed by members of the Internet Engineering Task Force (**IETF**).

uninterruptible power supply

An uninterruptible power supply (UPS) is a device that allows your computer to keep running for at least a short time when the primary power source is lost. It also provides protection from power surges. A UPS contains a **battery** that "kicks in" when the device senses a loss of power from the primary source. If you are using the computer when the UPS notifies you of the power loss, you have time to save any data you are working on and exit gracefully before the secondary power source (the battery) runs out. When all power runs out, any data in your computer's random access memory (**RAM**) is erased. When power surges occur, a UPS intercepts the surge so that it doesn't damage your computer.

Software is available that automatically backs up (saves) any data that is being worked on when the UPS becomes activated.

unipolar signaling

See also **bipolar signaling**.

Unipolar signaling, also called *unipolar transmission*, is a **baseband** method of sending **binary** data over wire or cable. There are two logic states, low and high, represented by the digits 0 and 1 respectively.

The illustration shows a unipolar signal as it might appear on the screen of an **oscilloscope**. Each horizontal division represents one **bit** (binary digit). The logic 0 state is approximately 0 volts and logic 1 is approximately +5 volts. (There is some room for error.) This is *positive logic*. Alternatively, logic 0 might be approximately +5 volts, and logic 1 might be approximately 0 volts; this would be *negative logic*.

The **bandwidth** of a unipolar signal is inversely proportional to the duration of each data bit. Typical data speeds in baseband are several megabits per second (**Mbps**); hence the duration of each bit is a fraction of a microsecond.

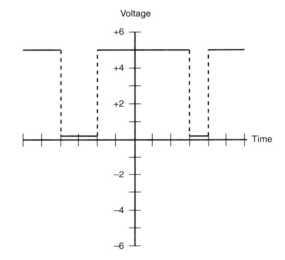

unipolar transmission

See "unipolar signaling"

universal access server

See "network access server"

Universal ADSL

See "G.lite"

Universal Asynchronous Receiver/Transmitter

See "UART"

Universal Coordinated Time

See "Coordinated Universal Time"

Universal Data Access

Universal Data Access (UDA) is Microsoft's model or framework for a single uniform application program interface to different software makers' **database**s, both **relational** and nonrelational. UDA is the database access part of Microsoft's Component Object Model (**COM**), an overall framework for creating and distributing **object-oriented programming** programs in a network. UDA consists mainly of the high-level interface, ActiveX Data Objects (**ADO**) and the lower-level services called **OLE DB**. IBM, Oracle, and other companies have provided database bridges that interface with OLE DB.

Universal Description, Discovery, and Integration

See "UDDI"

Universal Disk Format

Universal Disk Format (UDF) is a **CD-ROM** and **DVD** file system standard developed as a means of ensuring consistency among data written to various **optical media**, by facilitating both data interchange and the implementation of the **ISO/IEC 13346** standard. UDF is required for DVD-ROMs, and is used by DVD to contain **MPEG** audio/video streams. Originally developed as a replacement for the file system specifications in the original CD-ROM standard, **ISO 9660**, UDF is used by **CD-R** and **CD-RW** in a process called *packet writing* that makes CD writing more efficient in terms of the time and disk space required.

The Optical Storage Technology Association (**OSTA**) defines the UDF specification as a subset of ISO/IEC 13346, which it promotes as a single file system that overcomes limitations of **ISO 9660** and redirectors such as CDFS. UDF is used to ensure compatibility across platforms, as well as among various CD and DVD applications.

Universal Mobile Telecommunications Service

See "UMTS"

Universal Naming Convention

See "UNC"

universal network

The "universal network" is the idea of a single network that integrates the existing voice and public telecommunications network (including the Internet), cable TV, data networks, and video broadcast networks so that they work together well. Currently, each has a different kind of traffic and the older networks bear the burden of an out-of-date infrastructure. For example, the public voice network supports connections of phone-call duration and circuit-switching (although the same network also supports connectionless traffic and packet-switching for data). The video broadcast and cable TV networks deliver mainly the higher-bandwidth continous-flow traffic of streaming video and sound.

Juniper Networks planned something close to a universal network in a fiber-optic network that included very fast (multigigabit) **switch**es using microchips customized for Internet traffic. The microchips included application-specific (**ASIC**) circuits made by IBM. The switches used wave-division multiplexing (WDM).

Universal Plug and Play

See also **Plug and Play**, an earlier, proprietary Microsoft approach.

Universal Plug and Play (UPnP) is a standard that uses Internet and Web **protocol**s to enable devices such as PCs, peripherals, intelligent appliances, and wireless devices to be plugged into a network and automatically know about each other. With UPnP, when a user plugs a device into the network, the device will configure itself, acquire a **TCP/IP** address, and use a **discovery** protocol based on the Internet's Hypertext Transfer Protocol (**HTTP**) to announce its presence on the network to other devices. For instance, if you had a camera and a printer connected to the network and needed to print out a photograph, you could press a button on the camera and have the camera send a "discover" request asking if there were any printers on the network. The printer would identify itself and send its location in the form of a universal resource locator (**URL**).

The camera and printer would use Extensible Markup Language (**XML**) to establish a common language, or "protocol negotiation," to talk to each other and determine capabilities. Once a common language was established, the camera would control the printer and print the photograph you selected. Microsoft, one of 29 companies sponsoring UPnP, hopes that UPnP will make it as easy to plug a device or appliance into a home or small business data network as it is to plug a lamp into an electrical outlet.

Universal Plug and Play is an **open** industry standard that Microsoft, a leading promoter of the standard, describes as "seamless proximity networking" that provides "standardization on the wire rather than in the devices," using existing Internet standards.

Universal Serial Bus

Universal Serial Bus (USB) is a **plug-and-play** interface between a computer and add-on devices (such as audio players, joysticks, keyboards, telephones, scanners, and printers). With USB, a new device can be added to your computer without having to add an adapter **card** or even having to turn the computer off. The USB peripheral **bus** standard was developed by Compaq, IBM, DEC, Intel,

Microsoft, NEC, and Northern Telecom and the technology is available without charge for all computer and device vendors.

USB supports a data speed of 12 **megabit**s per second. This speed will accommodate a wide range of devices, including **MPEG** video devices, data gloves, and digitizers. It is anticipated that USB will easily accommodate plug-in telephones that use **ISDN** and digital **PBX**.

Since October, 1996, the Windows operating systems have been equipped with USB **driver**s or special software designed to work with specific I/O device types. USB is integrated into **Windows 98** and later versions. Today, most new computers and peripheral devices are equipped with USB.

A different plug-and-play standard, **IEEE 1394**, supports much higher data rates and devices such as video camcorders and digital video disk (**DVD**) players. However, USB and IEEE 1394 serve different device types.

Universal Time Coordinated

See "Coordinated Universal Time"

UNIX

UNIX (sometimes spelled "Unix") is an **operating system** that originated at Bell Labs in 1969 as an interactive time-sharing system. Ken Thompson and Dennis Ritchie are considered the inventors of UNIX. The name (pronounced YEW-nihks) was a pun based on an earlier system, **Multics**. In 1974, UNIX became the first operating system written in the **C** language. UNIX has evolved as a kind of large **freeware** product, with many extensions and new ideas provided in a variety of versions of UNIX by different companies, universities, and individuals.

Partly because it was not a proprietary operating system owned by any one of the leading computer companies and partly because it is written in a standard language and embraced many popular ideas, UNIX became the first **open** or standard operating system that could be improved or enhanced by anyone. A composite of the **C** language and **shell** (user command) interfaces from different versions of UNIX were standardized under the auspices of the **Institute of Electrical and Electronics Engineers** as the Portable Operating System Interface (**POSIX**). In turn, the POSIX interfaces were specified in the X/Open Programming Guide 4.2 (also known as the "Single UNIX Specification" and "UNIX 95"). Version 2 of the Single UNIX Specification is also known as UNIX 98. The "official" trademarked UNIX is now owned by the The Open Group, an industry standards organization, which certifies and brands UNIX implementations.

UNIX operating systems are used in widely-sold **workstation** products from Sun Microsystems, Silicon Graphics, IBM, and a number of other companies. The UNIX environment and the **client/server** program model were

important elements in the development of the Internet and the reshaping of computing as centered in networks rather than in individual computers. **Linux**, a UNIX derivative available in both "free software" and commercial versions, is increasing in popularity as an alternative to proprietary operating systems.

unshielded twisted pair

Unshielded twisted pair is the most common kind of copper telephone wiring. Twisted pair is the ordinary copper wire that connects home and many business computers to the telephone company. To reduce crosstalk or electromagnetic induction between pairs of wires, two insulated copper wires are twisted around each other. Each signal on twisted pair requires both wires. Since some telephone sets or desktop locations require multiple connections, twisted pair is sometimes installed in two or more pairs, all within a single cable. For some business locations, twisted pair is enclosed in a shield that functions as a ground. This is known as **shielded twisted pair** (STP).

Twisted pair is now frequently installed with two pairs to the home, with the extra pair making it possible for you to add another line (perhaps for modem use) when you need it.

Twisted pair comes with each pair uniquely color coded when it is packaged in multiple pairs. Different uses such as **analog**, **digital**, and **Ethernet** require different pair multiples.

Although twisted pair is often associated with home use, a higher grade of twisted pair is often used for horizontal wiring in LAN installations because it is less expensive than **coaxial cable**.

The wire you buy at a local hardware store for extensions from your phone or computer modem to a wall jack is not twisted pair. It is a side-by-side wire known as *silver satin*. The wall jack can have as many five kinds of hole arrangements or pinouts, depending on the kinds of wire the installation expects will be plugged in (for example, digital, analog, or LAN). (That's why you may sometimes find when you carry your notebook computer to another location that the wall jack connections won't match your plug.)

unzipping

Unzipping is the act of extracting the files from a zipped single file or similar file **archive**. If the files in the package were also compressed (as they usually are), unzipping also uncompresses them.

When you download programs from shareware or freeware companies on the Web, they almost always send you a zip file (the file name has a suffix of ".zip"). You can usually extract the files from a zipped file just by double-clicking on it since many archives include a "self-extracting" program. Several popular tools exist for zipping and unzipping: PKZIP in the DOS operating system, **WinZip** in Windows, and MacZip in Macintosh.

uplink

See "downlink and uplink"

uploading

Uploading is the transmission of a file from one computer system to another, usually larger computer system. From a network user's point-of-view, to upload a file is to send it to another computer that is set up to receive it. People who share images with others on bulletin board services (**BBS**) upload files to the BBS.

Downloading is transmission in the other direction: from one, usually larger computer to another, usually smaller computer. From an Internet user's point-of-view, downloading is receiving a file from another computer.

The File Transfer Protocol (**FTP**) is the Internet facility for downloading and uploading files. (If you are uploading a file to another site, you must usually have permission in advance to access the site and the directory where the file is to be placed.)

When you send or receive an attached file with an e-mail note, this is just an attachment, not a download or an upload. However, in practice, many people use "upload" to mean "send" and "download" to mean receive. The term is used loosely in practice and if someone says to you "Download (or upload) such–and-such a file to me" via e-mail, they simply mean "Send it to me."

In short, from the ordinary workstation or small computer user's point-of-view, to upload is to send a file and to download is to receive a file.

UPnP

See "Universal Plug and Play"

UPS

See "uninterruptible power supply"

upstream

See "downstream"

urban legend

An urban legend is a tale of contemporary folklore that purports to be true and is often designed to elicit an emotional response from the audience. On the Internet, urban legends are spread and survive over time through repeated e-mail forwardings and Web site postings. Like traditional legends, urban legends can seldom be traced to a single author. An urban legend often revolves around a strong central character or social issue of contemporary interest. Sociologists suggest that the Internet has proven to be a rich environment for urban legends because the Web allows people to share stories with each other faster than any

other medium in history. Occasionally urban legends turn out to be true, but the majority are simply Internet misinformation, sometimes entertaining, but more often annoying, as in the case of the rather common **virus hoax**.

URI

To paraphrase the World Wide Web Consortium, Internet space is inhabited by many points of content. A URI (Uniform Resource Identifier; pronounced YEW-AHR-EYE) is the way you identify any of those points of content, whether it be a page of text, a video or sound clip, a still or animated image, or a program. The most common form of URI is the Web page address, which is a particular form or subset of URI called a Uniform Resource Locator (**URL**). A URI typically describes:

- The mechanism used to access the resource
- The specific computer that the resource is housed in
- The specific name of the resource (a file name) on the computer

For example, this URI:
`http://www.w3.org/Icons/WWW/w3c_main.gif`
identifies a file that can be accessed using the Web protocol application, **Hypertext Transfer Protocol**, ("http://") that is housed on a computer named "www.w3.org" (which can be mapped to a unique Internet address). In the computer's directory structure, the file is located at "/Icons/WWW/w3c_main.gif." Character strings that identify File Transfer Protocol **FTP** addresses and e-mail addresses are also URIs (and, like the HTTP address, are also the specific subset of URI called a URL).

Another kind of URI is the Uniform Resource Name (**URN**). A URN is a form of URI that has "institutional persistence," which means that its exact location may change from time to time, but some agency will be able to find it.

The URI rules of **syntax**, set forth in the Internet Engineering Task Force (**IETF**) Request for Comments 1630, apply for all Internet addresses. In Tim Berner-Lee's original working document, URI stood for Universal Resource Identifier.

URL

A URL (Uniform Resource Locator) (pronounced YU-AHR-EHL or, in some quarters, UHRL) is the address of a file (resource) accessible on the Internet. The type of resource depends on the Internet application protocol. Using the World Wide Web's protocol, the Hypertext Transfer Protocol (**HTTP**) , the resource can be an **HTML** page, an image file, a program such as a **common gateway interface** application or Java **applet**, or any other file supported by HTTP. The URL contains the name of the protocol required to access the resource, a **domain name** that identifies a specific computer on the Internet, and a hierarchical description of a file location on the computer.

On the Web (which uses the Hypertext Transfer Protocol), an example of a URL is:

```
http://www.mhrcc.org/kingston
```

which describes a Web page to be accessed with an HTTP (Web browser) application that is located on a computer named www.mhrcc.org. The specific file is in the directory named /kingston and is the default page in that directory (which, on this computer, happens to be named index.html).

An HTTP URL can be for any Web page, not just a home page, or any individual file.

A URL for a program such as a forms-handling **common gateway interface** script written in **PERL** might look like this:

```
http://whatis.com/cgi-bin/comments.pl
```

A URL for a file meant to be downloaded would require that the "ftp" protocol be specified like this one:

```
ftp://www.somecompany.com/whitepapers/widgets.ps
```

A URL is a type of **URI** (Uniform Resource Identifier).

URL-minder

URL-minder is an **agent** or robot program (**bot**) that notifies you when a particular Web page has changed. At a URL-minder site, you specify the Uniform Resource Locator (**URL**) for the Web page and the URL-minder periodically checks the page, notices whether it has been updated, and then sends you an e-mail message when it has.

URN

See "Uniform Resource Name"

usability

Also see **human-computer interaction** and **graphical user interface**.

Usability is the measure of a product's potential to accomplish the goals of the user. In information technology, the term is often used in relation to software applications and Web sites, but it can be used in relation to any product that is employed to accomplish a task (for example, a toaster, a car dashboard, or an alarm clock). Some factors used in determining product usability are ease-of-use, visual consistency, and a clear, defined process for evolution.

Usability testing is a method by which users of a product are asked to perform certain tasks in an effort to measure the product's ease-of-use, task time, and the user's perception of the experience. Usability testing can be done formally, in a usability lab with video cameras, or informally, with paper mock-ups of an application or Web site. Changes are made to the application or site based on the findings of the usability tests. Whether the test is formal or informal, usability test participants are encouraged to think aloud and voice their every opinion. Usability testing is best used in conjunction with user-centered design, a method by which a product is designed according to the needs and specifications of users.

Within the last several years, the usability of Web sites has become a hot topic for Web developers. Many major Web sites employ usability engineers to ensure that they have an easy-to-use, friendly site that provides a positive customer experience. Major sites such as Drugstore.com and Altavista.com have recently been re-designed based on recommendations made during usability tests and evaluations.

USB

See "Universal Serial Bus"

use case

A use case is a methodology used in system analysis to identify, clarify, and organize system requirements. The use case is made up of a set of possible sequences of interactions between systems and users in a particular environment and related to a particular goal. It consists of a group of elements (for example, classes and interfaces) that can be used together in a way that will have an effect larger than the sum of the separate elements combined. The use case should contain all system activities that have significance to the users. A use case can be thought of as a collection of possible scenarios related to a particular goal, indeed, the use case and goal are sometimes considered to be synonymous.

A use case (or set of use cases) has these characteristics:

- Organizes functional requirements
- Models the goals of system/actor (user) interactions
- Records paths (called *scenarios*) from trigger events to goals
- Describes one main flow of events (also called a basic course of action), and possibly other ones, called *exceptional* flows of events (also called alternate courses of action)
- Is multi-level, so that one use case can use the functionality of another one.

Use cases can be employed during several stages of software development, such as planning system requirements, validating design, testing software, and creating an outline for online help and user manuals.

Usenet

Usenet is a collection of user-submitted notes or messages on various subjects that are posted to servers on a worldwide network. Each subject collection of posted notes is known as a **newsgroup**. There are thousands of newsgroups and it is possible for you to form a new one. Most newsgroups are hosted on Internet-connected servers, but they can also be hosted from servers that are not part of the Internet. Usenet's original protocol was UNIX-to-UNIX Copy (**UUCP**), but today the Network News Transfer Protocol (**NNTP**) is used.

Most browsers, such as those from Netscape and Microsoft, provide Usenet support and access to any newsgroups that you select. On the Web, Google and other sites provide a subject-oriented directory as well as a search approach to newsgroups and help you register to participate in them. In addition, there are other newsgroup readers, such as Knews, that run as separate programs.

User Datagram Protocol

See "UDP"

User Interface Markup Language

See "UIML"

user interface

Also see **human-computer interaction**.

In information technology, the user interface (UI) is everything designed into an information device with which a human being may interact—including display screen, keyboard, mouse, light pen, the appearance of a desktop, illuminated characters, help messages, and how an application program or a Web site invites interaction and responds to it. In early computers, there was very little user interface except for a few buttons at an operator's console. The user interface was largely in the form of punched card input and report output.

Later, a user was provided the ability to interact with a computer online and the user interface was a nearly blank display screen with a command line, a keyboard, and a set of commands and computer responses that were exchanged. This command line interface led to one in which menus (list of choices written in text) predominated. And, finally, the graphical user interface (**GUI**) arrived, originating mainly in Xerox's Palo Alto Research Center, adopted and enhanced by Apple Computer, and finally effectively standardized by Microsoft in its Windows operating systems.

The user interface can arguably include the total "user experience," which may include the aesthetic appearance of the device, response time, and the content that is presented to the user within the context of the user interface.

user profile

In **Windows NT**, a user profile is a record of user-specific data that define the user's working environment. The record can include display settings, application settings, and network connections. What the user sees on his or her computer screen, as well as what files, applications and directories they have access to, is determined by how the network **administrator** has set up the user's profile.

Roaming profiles are user profiles that are stored in the **server**. Each time the user logs on, their profile is requested and sent to whatever machine makes the request. This allows the user to move from machine to machine and still maintain a consistent personal working environment. Network administrators find roaming profiles to be especially beneficial in a work or learning environment when more than one user shares the same computer, or when a user moves from place-to-place during the course of a workday.

user session

Also see **session**, a different meaning.

In tabulating statistics for Web site usage, a user session (sometime referred to as a *visit*) is the presence of a user with a specific **IP address** who has not visited the site recently (typically, anytime within the past 30 minutes). The number of user sessions per day is one measure of how much traffic a Web site has. A user who visits a site at noon and then again at 3:30 pm would count as two user visits.

Other measures of Web site traffic in a given time period are the number of **hit**s (the number of individual files served), the number of pages served, the number of ad views, and the number of unique visitors.

UTC

See "Coordinated Universal Time"

utility

In computers, a utility is a small program that provides an addition to the capabilities provided by the **operating system**. In some usages, a utility is a special and nonessential part of the operating system. The print "utility" that comes with the operating system is an example. It's not absolutely required to run programs and, if it didn't come with the operating system, you could perhaps add it. In other usages, a utility is an **application** that is very specialized and relatively limited in capability. A good example is a **search-and-replace** utility. Some operating systems provide a limited capability to do a search-and-replace for given character strings. You can add a much more capable search-and-replace utility that runs as an application program. However, compared to a **word processor**, a search-and-replace utility has limited capability.

UTP

See "unshielded twisted pair"

UUCP

UUCP (UNIX-to-UNIX Copy Protocol) is a set of **UNIX** programs for copying (sending) files between different UNIX systems and for sending commands to be executed on another system. The main UUCP commands (each supported by a UUCP program) are:

- uucp, which requests the copying of a specific file to another specified system

- uux, which sends a UNIX command to another system where it is queued for execution

- uucico, which runs on a UNIX system as the program that carries out the copying and initiates execution of the commands that have been sent. Typically, this program is run at various times of day; meanwhile, the copy (uucp) and command (uux) requests are queued until the uucico program is run.

- uuxqt, which executes the commands sent by uux, usually after being started by the uucico program

The uucico programs are the programs that actually communicate across a network. There are several network protocols (variations on packet size and error-checking) that can be used by uucico programs, depending on the kinds of carrier networks being used.

Uuencode

Uuencode (also called Uuencode/Uudecode) is a popular utility for encoding and decoding files exchanged between users or systems in a network. It originated for use between users of **UNIX** systems (its name stood for "UNIX-to-UNIX encoding"). However, it's available or easily obtainable for use in all operating systems and most e-mail applications provide it as an encoding alternative, especially for e-mail attachments. If you're sending e-mail with an attachment and you suspect your recipient(s) may not have a **MIME**-compliant system (for example, an older PC or UNIX system), you may want to specify "Uuencode" for the attachment to an e-mail note. (In Eudora, when writing a note, look for the little box set to a default of "MIME" and change it to "Uuencode.")

Basically, what Uuencode does is to translate or convert a file or e-mail attachment (it can be an image, a text file, or a program) from its binary or bit-stream representation into the 7-bit **ASCII** set of text characters. Text can be handled by older systems that may not handle binary files well and larger files can be more easily divided into multi-part transmissions.

If your recipient is likely to be on an older Macintosh system, you may want to try sending the attachment in another format called **BinHex**.

A popular program for encoding and decoding files in Uuencode format is WinZip, which is shareware that you can download from the Winzip Web site.

V.22 – V.22bis – V.32 – V.32bis – V.32terbo – V.34 – V.34bis – V.35 – V.42

See "V.xx"

V.90

V.90 is a **standard**, approved by the International Telecommunications Union (**ITU-TS**), for transmitting data downstream to **modems** at 56 **Kbps** (thousand bits per second). The V.90 standard was arrived at by combining the **x2** technology from US Robotics (now part of 3Com) and the **K56flex** technology from Rockwell. Transmission upstream from a computer modem is slower than downstream (about 33 Kbps) since it requires **digital-to-analog conversion**.

56 Kbps transmission technologies exploit the fact that most telephone company offices are interconnected with digital lines. Assuming your Internet connection provider has a digital connection to its telephone company office, the downstream traffic from your local Internet access provider can use a new transmission technique on your regular **twisted pair** phone line that bypasses the usual **digital-to-analog conversion**. A V.90 modem doesn't need to demodulate the downstream data. Instead, it decodes a stream of multi-bit voltage pulses generated as though the line was equipped for digital information. (Upstream data still requires digital-to-analog modulation.)

Unlike **Integrated Services Digital Network**, the 56 Kbps technologies do not require any additional installation or extra charges from your local phone company. On the other hand, the maximum transmission speed of ISDN is twice that of V.90 at 128 Kbps. You also have the flexibility of combining digital and voice transmission on the same line.

V.xx

The V Series Recommendations from the **ITU-TS** are summarized in the table below. They include the most commonly used modem standards and other telephone network standards. Prior to the ITU-T standards, the American Telephone and Telegraph Company and the Bell System offered its own standards (Bell 103 and Bell 212A) at very low transfer rates. Another set of standards, the Microcom Networking Protocol, or MNP Class 1 through Class 10 (there is no Class 8), has gained some currency, but the development of an international set of standards means these will most likely prevail and continue to be extended. (Some modems offer both MNP and ITU-T standards.)

In general, when modems **handshake**, they agree on the highest standard transfer rate that both can achieve.

Beginning with V.22bis, ITU-T transfer rates increase in 2400 bps multiples. (**Bis** refers to a "second version." Terbo refers to a "third version.")

Standard	Meaning
V.22	Provides 1200 bits per second at 600 **baud** (state changes per second)
V.22bis	The first true world standard, it allows 2400 bits per second at 600 baud
V.32	Provides 4800 and 9600 bits per second at 2400 baud
V.32bis	Provides 14,400 bits per second or fallback to 12,000, 9600, 7200, and 4800 bits per second
V.32terbo	Provides 19,200 bits per second or fallback to 12,000, 9600, 7200, and 4800 bits per second; can operate at higher data rates with compression; was not a CCITT/ITU standard
V.34	Provides 28,800 bits per second or fallback to 24,000 and 19,200 bits per second and backwards compatility with V.32 and V.32bis
V.34bis	Provides up to 33,600 bits per second or fallback to 31,200 or V.34 transfer rates
V.35	The trunk interface between a network access device and a packet network at data rates greater than 19.2 Kbps. V.35 may use the bandwidths of several telephone circuits as a group. There are V.35 Gender Changers and Adapters.
V.42	Same transfer rate as V.32, V.32bis, and other standards but with better error correction and therefore more reliable
V.90	Provides up to 56,000 bits per second downstream (but in practice some-what less). Derived from the **x2** technology of 3Com (US Robotics) and Rockwell's **K56flex** technology.

VA

See "volt-ampere"

vacuum tube

Also see cathode ray tube (**CRT**), the specialized kind of vacuum tube that is in most desktop display monitors.

A vacuum tube (also called an *electron tube* or, in the UK, a *valve*) is a device sometimes used to amplify electronic signals. In most applications, the vacuum tube is obsolete, having been replaced decades ago by the **bipolar transistor** and, more recently, by the **field-effect transistor**. However, tubes are still used in some high-power amplifiers, especially at **microwave** radio frequencies and in some hi-fi audio systems.

Tubes operate at higher voltages than transistors. A typical transistorized amplifier needs 6 to 12 volts to function; an equivalent tube type amplifier needs 200 to 400 volts. At the highest power levels, some tube circuits have power supplies delivering several kilovolts.

Vacuum tubes are making a comeback among audiophiles who insist that tubes deliver better audio quality than transistors. These old-fashioned components are more electrically rugged than their solid-state counterparts; a tube can often withstand temporary overload conditions and power-line transients that would instantly destroy a transistor.

The major disadvantages of tubes include the fact that they require bulky power supplies, and the high voltages can present an electric shock hazard.

VAD

See "voice activation detection"

value chain

According to John Del Vecchio writing for Fool.com, a value chain is "a string of companies working together to satisfy market demands." The value chain typically consists of one or a few primary value (product or service) suppliers and many other suppliers that add on to the value that is ultimately presented to the buying public.

Microsoft and its Windows operating systems, the nucleus of the personal computer desktop for which much business software is developed, is often cited as a prime example of a company and product that drives a value chain. The businesses who buy personal computer software may spend far more on the add-on software than on the essential **operating system** that is the de facto standard for running the software. To the extent that companies standardize on Windows, Microsoft is said to control a value chain. This particular value chain was reported in a McKinsey study to be worth $383 billion in 1998. Although Microsoft's share of the value chain was reported to be only 4% of the total, that was still $15.3 billion.

A company that develops a product or service that engenders a value chain by providing a platform for other companies is considered more likely to increase its **market share** than a company that tries to provide the entire value chain on its own.

value-added network

VAN is also an acronym for **virtual area network**.

A value-added network (VAN) is a private network provider (sometimes called a turnkey communications line) that is hired by a company to facilitate electronic data interchange (**EDI**) or provide other network services. Before the arrival of the World Wide Web, some companies hired value-added networks to move data from their company to other companies. With the arrival of the World Wide Web, many companies found it more cost-efficient to move their data over the Internet instead of paying the minimum monthly fees and per-character charges found in typical VAN contracts. In response, contemporary value-added network providers now focus on offering EDI translation, **encryption**, secure e-mail, management reporting, and other extra services for their customers.

value-added reseller

In the computer and other industries, a value-added reseller (VAR) is a company that takes an existing product, adds its own "value" usually in the form of a specific application for the product (for example, a special computer application), and resells it as a new product or "package." For example, a VAR might take an operating system such as IBM's OS/390 with UNIX services and, adding its own proprietary UNIX application designed for architects, resell the package to architectural firms. Depending on sales and installation requirements, the VAR could choose whether or not to identify OS/390 as part of the package.

Also see **original equipment manufacturer** (OEM), a company that includes hardware components from other companies in its own product.

vampire tap

A vampire tap is a connection to a **coaxial cable** in which a hole is drilled through the outer shield of the cable so that a clamp can be connected to the inner conductor of the cable. A vampire tap is used to connect each device to Thicknet coaxial cable in the **bus** topology of an **Ethernet 10BASE-T** local area network. A different connection approach, the **BNC**, is used for the thinner coaxial cable known as **Thinnet**.

VAN

See "virtual area network"

van Eck phreaking

Van Eck phreaking is a form of eavesdropping in which special equipment is used to pick up telecommunication signals or data within a computer device by monitoring and picking up the electromagnetic fields (**EM-field**s) that are produced by the signals or movement of the data. This electromagnetic radiation is present in, and with the proper equipment, can be captured from computer displays that use cathode ray tubes (**CRT**s), from printers, and from other devices.

Here is an example: The image on a CRT is created by electron beams that scan across the screen in a series of horizontal lines from left-to-right and top-to-bottom, in the same way you read a page of text (except much faster). This occurs at a specific frequency for each individual monitor; there are only a few standard frequencies in existence, and every monitor uses one of them. The intensity of the electron beams determines the relative red, blue, and green brightness for each **pixel** (picture element) on the screen. As a result, the CRT produces a modulated EM field that contains all the information in the image displayed on the screen at any moment. This information looks like a meaningless, irregular waveform if viewed directly on an **oscilloscope**. But, like a television (TV) signal, it can be demodulated with special equipment, and the image on the screen thereby retrieved, from some distance away.

This term combines the name of Wim van Eck, who in 1985 authored an academic paper that described this form of electronic eavesdropping, with the term **phreaking**, the earlier practice of using special equipment to make phone calls without paying. Van Eck phreaking is identified in the U.S. government project known as **Tempest** and, although some information remains classified, has probably been used to spy on suspected criminals and in espionage. The Tempest project has also led to advice and some standards development for how to shield devices so that eavesdropping is not possible. However, the cost of shielding means that many commercial devices are still vulnerable and, for this and other reasons, some of the details about what equipment is required to do van Eck phreaking remains classified. Susceptibility to eavesdropping can also be minimized by designing equipment that generates little EM energy.

Depending on the type of CRT used, the sensitivity of the detection equipment, and the general level of EM energy in the area, Van Eck phreaking can be done over distances ranging from a few meters up to several hundred meters.

Also see **ELF**.

vandal

A vandal is an executable file, usually an **applet** or an **ActiveX control**, associated with a Web page that is designed to be harmful, malicious, or at the very least inconvenient to the user. Such applets or little application programs can be embedded in any **HTML** file. They can also arrive as an e-mail attachment or automatically as the result of being pushed to the user. Vandals can be viewed as **viruse**s that can arrive over the Internet stuck to a Web page. Vandals are sometimes referred to as "hostile applets."

Vandals can be harmful in two general ways:

- They can get access to sensitive information within the computer system where they execute, such as passwords and encryption keys.
- They can cause loss or denial of service within the local computer system. For example, they can flood the system with data so that it runs out of memory, or they can slow down Internet connections.

The best way to protect yourself against a hostile applet is to know who you are downloading a Web page from or who has sent you an HTML page as an e-mail attachment. Major corporate Web sites or major Web publishers are unlikely to be the source of a vandal (but it can happen).

vanilla

In information technology, vanilla (pronounced vah-NIHL-uh) is an adjective meaning plain or basic. The unfeatured version of a product is sometimes referred to as the vanilla version. The term is based on the fact that vanilla is the most popular or at least the most commonly served flavor of ice cream. Or, as Eric Raymond, editor of *The New Hacker's Dictionary*, puts it, the **default** ice cream.

IBM's BookMaster product, a text publishing system used in **mainframe** environments, provides a default way, called *vanilla*, to specify which parts of the book to publish, and another fancier way to specify it, called *mocha*.

Some Web sites with **frames** call the simpler version of their site the vanilla version.

Vannevar Bush

An electrical engineer by training, Vannevar Bush is credited with having the idea of **hypertext** or "instant cross-referencing," decades before the term itself was conceived by Ted Nelson and before the concept was widely implemented on the World Wide Web. In an article in *The Atlantic Monthly* in 1945, Bush described his proposed "memex" device, an electronic stored-information system, an aide-de-memoire for mankind. Humans, Bush argued, have associative memories where information is accessed by following a series of mental links and pathways. His hypertext system incorporated this idea, allowing users to tie information together logically as well as to annotate it and link the annotations to the body of data already present.

The bulk of Bush's career was spent at MIT's Department of Electrical Engineering where he became Dean. His mathematical work for the military during World War Two led to his invention of the first analog computer, the Rockefeller Differential Analyser, soon rendered obsolete by

the first digital computers (whose invention was spurred by the work of one of the RDA's engineers—Claude Shannon). The Differential Analyser was notable for its use of decimal rather than the binary number system. As an advisor to several presidents, Bush was arguably the most powerful scientist in the post-war U.S. He was the driving force behind the founding of the National Science Foundation.

In 1980, the National Science Board established the Vannevar Bush award to honor those scientists who make outstanding contributions to the public service. Bush's primary legacy remains that of the hypertext concept—he is remembered as a forefather of the **World Wide Web**.

vaporware

Vaporware is software or hardware that is either (1) announced or mentioned publicly in order to influence customers to defer buying competitors' products or (2) late being delivered for whatever reason. Most computer companies have from time to time delivered vaporware, either by calculation or unintentionally.

Vaporware is also the name of a company that makes games and other products for Amiga users.

variable

In programming, a variable is a value that can change, depending on conditions or on information passed to the program. Typically, a program consists of **instructions** that tell the computer what to do and **data** that the program uses when it is running. The data consists of *constants* or fixed values that never change and variable values (which are usually initialized to "0" or some default value because the actual values will be supplied by a program's user). Usually, both constants and variables are defined as certain **data types**. Each data type prescribes and limits the form of the data. Examples of data types include: An integer expressed as a decimal number, or a string of text characters, usually limited in length.

In **object-oriented programming**, each **object** contains the data variables of the **class** it is an instance of. The object's **method**s are designed to handle the actual values that are supplied to the object when the object is being used.

VAX

VAX is an established line of mid-range server computers from the Digital Equipment Corporation (DEC), which is now part of Compaq. It followed DEC's PDP-11 in 1978 and also introduced a new operating system, VMS. VAX included a 32-bit processor and **virtual memory**. Historically, VAX has competed with a number of Hewlett-Packard and IBM computers in the small enterprise and university-scientific marketplace. In earlier times, this size and price range of computer was known as the *minicomputer*.

DEC indicates that over 250,000 VAX systems are in use. Based on VMS, its operating system is called **OpenVMS**. Among other features, OpenVMS can be used with special software that facilitates its use with Windows NT servers. OpenVMS also supports the open standard **Portable Operating System Interface** set of commands and C language programming interface, effectively making it both a VMS system and a UNIX system.

Eric S. Raymond notes that the VAX running a **BSD UNIX** system was a favorite of **hackers** for its especially large and programmer-friendly set of **assembler** instructions.

VBI

See "vertical blanking interval"

vBNS

The vBNS (very high-speed Backbone Network Service) is a network that interconnects a number of **supercomputer center**s in the United States and is reserved for science applications requiring the massive computing that supercomputers can provide. Scientists at the supercomputer centers and other locations apply for time on the supercomputers and use of the vBNS by describing their projects to a committee that apportions computer time and vBNS resources. The vBNS and the supercomputer centers were initiated and are maintained by the National Science Foundation (NSF).

The vBNS began operation in April, 1995, as the successor to the NSFNet. The NSFNet itself succeeded DARPANET, the original Internet network. The vBNS is the scientific portion of the Internet that NSF continues to fund. The physical infrastructure for the original Internet is now owned and maintained by the national commercial backbone companies in the United States and worldwide.

Currently, MCI provides the backbone infrastructure for the vBNS under contract from the National Science Foundation. The backbone consists mainly of interconnected **Optical Carrier levels (OCx)** lines (operating at 155 Mbps or higher). The vBNS provides connections to the four national network access points (NAPs). The vBNS infrastructure itself is not shared with commercial companies and ordinary users.

As part of the evolution toward a commercially self-sustained Internet, the National Science Foundation continues to operate the routing arbiter, a service that the NAPs and other routers use to route and reroute **packets** and optimize traffic flow on the Internet. The routing arbiter service is managed by Merit under a contract from the NSF that expires in July, 1999.

The vBNS has recently become part of the infrastructure of **Internet2**. A new NFS-funded initiative is developing an advanced network infrastructure referred to as the National Technology Grid.

VBScript

VBScript is an **interpreted script** language from Microsoft that is a subset of its **Visual Basic** programming language. VBScript can be compared to other script languages designed for the Web, including:

- Netscape's **JavaScript**
- Sun Microsystem's **Tcl**
- The UNIX-derived **Perl**
- IBM's **Rexx**

In general, script languages are easier and faster to code in than the more structured, compiled languages such as **C** and **C++** and are ideal for smaller programs of limited capability or that can reuse and tie together existing compiled programs.

VBScript is Microsoft's answer to Netscape's popular JavaScript. Both are designed to work with an interpreter that comes with a Web **browser**—that is, at the user or **client** end of the Web **client/server** session. VBScript is designed for use with Microsoft's Internet Explorer browser together with other programming that can be run at the client, including **ActiveX controls**, automation servers, and Java **applets**. Although Microsoft does support Netscape's JavaScript (it converts it into its own **JScript**), Netscape does not support VBScript. For this reason, VBScript is best used for **intranet** Web sites that use the Internet Explorer browser only.

VC

See "venture capital"

vCalendar

vCalendar is an industry standard format for exchanging scheduling and activity-recording information electronically. If someone sends you their week's schedule in a vCalendar attachment to an e-mail note, you can drag-and drop it (or otherwise move it) to a personal information manager (PIM) type of application program and integrate with or relate it to your own schedule. vCalendar was developed along with the **vCard** electronic business card specification.

Like vCard, vCalendar was developed by a consortium founded by Apple, AT&T, IBM, and Siemens. The specification was turned over to an industry group, the Internet Mail Consortium (IMC), in 1996. Like vCard, vCalendar requires that you have an application program that supports its use. In time, it's expected that most personal information manager programs on all computer software platforms will support vCard and vCalendar as a standard exchange format.

vCard

A vCard is an electronic business (or personal) card and also the name of an industry specification for the kind of communication exchange that is done on business or personal cards. You may have seen a vCard attached to an e-mail note someone has sent you. Because vCard is a published industry specification, software application developers can create programs that process vCards by letting you view them, or drag-and-drop them to an address book or some other application. vCards can include images and sound as well as text.

vCard was developed by a consortium founded by Apple, AT&T, IBM, and Siemens, which turned the specification over to an industry group, the Internet Mail Consortium (IMC) in 1996. The vCard specification makes use of the "person" object defined by the CCITT X.500 Series Recommendation for Directory Services and can be considered an extension of it. A vCard contains a name, address information, date and time, and optionally photographs, company logos, sound clips, and geo-positioning information.

To open (look at) a vCard that someone has attached to an e-mail note, your e-mail program needs to support vCards and not all such programs do yet. However, if you have an online address book or personal information manager that supports vCards, you can move it to that program for viewing or for addition to that program's database. (If you can't open a vCard you've received, remember that its information may be repeated elsewhere in the note. It's basically just a business card.)

A promising future use of a vCard will be as a way to quickly fill in application forms on the Web. Just drag-and-drop your own vCard to the form and you won't have so many blanks to fill in. For software developers, there is a Personal Data Interchange (PDI) Software Development Kit (SDK). The specification is located at the Internet Mail Consortium's Web site where you can also find out about **vCalendar**, a similar exchange standard for personal time scheduling.

VCD

VCD (also called video CD or video compact disc) is a **compact disc** format based on **CD-ROM XA** that is specifically designed to hold **MPEG-1** video data and to include interactive capabilities. VCD has a resolution similar to that of VHS, which is far short of the resolution of **DVD**. Each VCD disc holds 72–74 minutes of video and has a data transfer rate of 1.44 **Mbps**. VCDs can be played on a VCD player connected to a television set (in the same way that video cassettes can on a VCR) or computer, on a **CD-i** player, on some **CD-ROM** drives, and some DVD players.

VCD was introduced in 1993 by JVC, Philips, SONY and Matsushita and is described in detail in the **White Book** specifications. Video data is demanding in terms of storage capacity; it requires approximately 5 **MB** of storage per second of video, which would translate to about two minutes of video on a 680 MB CD. In order to store video information on a CD in a practical fashion, the data must be compressed for storage and then decompressed for replay in real time. MPEG-1 compresses data at ratios of up to 200:1. MPEG is an international standard, and can be used by any manufacturer to create hardware for use with MPEG video. MPEG video can also be recorded on any CD. VCD formatting removes unnecessary information from MPEG-1 data, and adds specialized video authoring capabilities through inclusion of a **CD-i** (CD- Interactive) runtime application.

VCD variations include: VCD 2.0, which was introduced in 1995 and adds hi-resolution stills, fast-forward, and rewind functions to the original specifications; VCD-ROM, which was introduced in 1997 and enables the creation of hybrid VCD/CD-ROM disck; VCD-Internet, which was introduced in 1997 and is a standardized means of linking video and Internet data; and SuperVCD, which uses either high bit rate MPEG-1 or variable bit rate MPEG-2 for the use of **CD-R** drives instead of DVD drives.

VCD is more common in Asia than it is in North America, where the VCR had already cornered the home video market by the time that VCD was introduced. Because of the ease with which VCDs can be pirated, they are creating the same kind of problem for the movie industry that **MP3** caused for the music industry. Thieves may record movies from a movie screen with a camcorder, or may copy them from **laserdiscs** or DVDs. With the advent of recordable CDs (such as the **CD-R** and **CD-RW**), it became possible for the home user to create VCDs on some CD recorders.

VDT

VDT (video display terminal, or sometimes visual display terminal) is a term used, especially in **ergonomic** studies, for the computer **display**. A display is a computer output surface and projecting mechanism that shows text and often graphic images to the computer user, using a cathode ray tube (**CRT**), liquid crystal display (**LCD**), light-emitting diode, gas plasma, or other image projection technology. The display is usually considered to include the **screen** or projection surface and the device that produces the information on the screen. In some computers, the display is packaged in a separate unit called a **monitor**.

Major issues related to the VDT include the readability of content relative to other media such as paper; the effect of prolonged visual interaction with display content in terms of eye and other muscular fatigue and deterioration; proper viewing distances; and the amount and effect of exposure on users to the extremely low-frequency (**ELF**) radiation that emanates from VDTs.

vector graphics

Vector graphics is the creation of digital images through a sequence of commands or mathematical statements that place lines and shapes in a given two-dimensional or three-dimensional space. In physics, a *vector* is a representation of both a quantity and a direction at the same time. In vector graphics, the file that results from a graphic artist's work is created and saved as a sequence of vector statements. For example, instead of containing a bit in the file for each bit of a line drawing, a vector graphic file describes a series of points to be connected. One result is a much smaller file.

At some point, a vector image is converted into a **raster graphics** image, which maps bits directly to a display space (and is sometimes called a *bitmap*). The vector image can be converted to a raster image file prior to its display so that it can be ported between systems.

A vector file is sometimes called a *geometric* file. Most images created with tools such as Adobe Illustrator and CorelDraw are in the form of vector image files. Vector image files are easier to modify than raster image files (which can, however, sometimes be reconverted to vector files for further refinement).

Animation images are also usually created as vector files. For example, Shockwave's **Flash** product lets you create 2-D and 3-D animations that are sent to a requestor as a vector file and then rasterized "on the fly" as they arrive.

vector

A vector is a quantity or phenomenon that has two independent properties: magnitude and direction. The term also denotes the mathematical or geometrical representation of such a quantity.

Examples of vectors in nature are velocity, momentum, force, electromagnetic fields, and weight. (Weight is the force produced by the acceleration of gravity acting on a mass.) A quantity or phenomenon that exhibits magnitude only, with no specific direction, is called a **scalar**. Examples of scalars include speed, mass, electrical resistance, and hard-drive storage capacity.

Vectors can be depicted graphically in two or three dimensions. Magnitude is shown as the length of a line segment. Direction is shown by the orientation of the line segment, and by an arrow at one end. The illustration shows three vectors in two-dimensional rectangular coordinates (the Cartesian plane) and their equivalents in polar coordinates.

Compare **vector graphics**. Also see **scalar**.

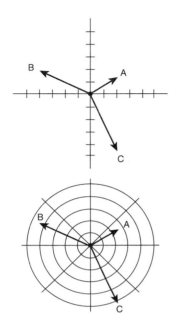

velocity

Velocity is a **vector** expression of the **displacement** that an object or particle undergoes with respect to **time**. The standard unit of velocity magnitude (also known as **speed**) is the **meter per second** (m/s or m · s^{-1}). Alternatively, the centimeter per second (cm/s or m · s^{-1}) can be used to express velocity magnitude. The direction of a velocity vector can be expressed in various ways, depending on the number of dimensions involved.

Velocity is relative. Consider a car moving at 20 m/s with respect to the surface of a highway, traveling northward. If you are driving the car, the velocity of the car relative to your body is zero. If you stand by the side of the road, the velocity of the car relative to you is 20 m/s northward. If you are driving a car at 15 m/s with respect to the road and are traveling northward, and another car moving 20 m/s with respect to the road passes you in the same direction, that other car's velocity relative to you is 5 m/s northward. But if that other car passes you going the opposite way on the road, its velocity relative to you is 35 m/s southward.

Circular motion illustrates the fundamental difference between speed and velocity. Think of yourself whirling a ball, tied to a string, around your body so the ball's tangential speed is 10 m/s. Even though the ball's speed is constant relative to your body, its velocity relative to your body constantly changes as the direction vector describes circles.

Velocity can be expressed either as an average over a period of time, or as an instantaneous value at a single moment in time. Suppose you are in a car that is not moving relative to

the road surface, and then you hit the accelerator and increase velocity uniformly from zero to 30 m/s northward in a few seconds. Your average velocity over that time frame is 15 m/s northward. However, the instantaneous velocity depends on time, and might be anything between zero and 30 m/s northward, depending on the exact moment at which it is measured.

vendor

A vendor (pronounced VEHN-duhr, from French *vendre*, meaning to sell) is any person or company that sells goods or services to someone else in the economic production chain. Parts manufacturers are vendors of parts to other manufacturers that assemble the parts into something sold to wholesalers or retailers. Retailers are vendors of products to consumers. (When you have a street fair, the people who set up booths and tables are often referred to as vendors.) In information technology as well as in other industries, the term is commonly applied to suppliers of goods and services to other companies.

A machine that takes your money and gives you a product is known as a *vending machine*.

Venn diagram

A Venn diagram is an illustration of the relationships between and among sets, groups of objects that share something in common. Usually, Venn diagrams are used to depict **set** intersections (denoted by an upside-down letter U). This type of diagram is used in scientific and engineering presentations, in theoretical mathematics, in computer applications, and in statistics.

The drawing is an example of a Venn diagram that shows the relationship among three overlapping sets X, Y, and Z. The intersection relation is defined as the equivalent of the logic AND. An element is a member of the intersection of two sets if and only if that element is a member of both sets. Venn diagrams are generally drawn within a large rectangle that denotes the *universe*, the set of all elements under consideration.

In this example, points that belong to none of the sets X, Y, or Z are white. Points belonging only to set X are a somewhat darker shade of gray in color; points belonging only to set Y are an even darker gray; points belonging only to set Z are very light gray. Points contained in all three sets are black.

Here is a practical example of how a Venn diagram can illustrate a situation. Let the universe be the set of all computers in the world. Let X represent the set of all notebook computers in the world. Let Y represent the set of all computers in the world that are connected to the Internet. Let Z represent the set of all computers in the world that have anti-virus software installed. If you have a notebook computer and surf the Net, but you are not worried about viruses, your computer is probably represented by a point in the X and Y region. If you get concerned about computer viruses and install an anti-virus program, the point representing your computer will move into the black area.

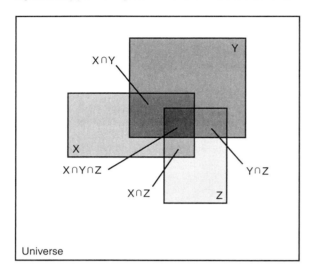

venture capital

Venture capital (VC) is funding invested, or available for investment, in an enterprise that offers the probability of profit along with the possibility of loss. Indeed, venture capital was once known also as *risk capital*, but that term has fallen out of usage, probably because investors don't like to see the words "risk" and "capital" in close conjunction. Venture capitalists often don't tend to think that their investments involve an element of risk, but are assured a successful return by virtue of the investor's knowledge and business sense. DataMerge, a financial information provider, says that VC investments in an enterprise are usually between $500,000 and $5 million, and that the investor is likely to expect an annual return of 20% to 50%.

Venture capitalists were instrumental in the enormous increase in the number of **dot-com** startups of recent years. Because the Internet was a new and untried business venue with enormous potential, many analysts feel that standard business rules were too frequently suspended in what was a very optimistic market. Internet-based enterprises were expected to enjoy unprecedented success; many venture capitalists were said to have encouraged dot-coms to focus on scaling upward rather than on realizing early profits. According to VentureWire, U.S. venture capital funding for 2000 was $105 billion, more than the total funding available in all the 15 years before that. However, in April of that same year, severe market corrections brought about a radical change in the financial climate, and since then online businesses have been failing at rates similar to the rates of startups in the early days of the dot-com boom. *Vulture capitalist*, a term coined in the volatile financial environment

of the 1980s, has been revived to refer to the venture capitalists that have recently begun to buy up failing **dot-com** enterprises at rock-bottom prices.

Venture capital is the second or third stage of a traditional startup financing sequence, which starts with the entrepreneurs putting their own available funding into a shoestring operation. Next, an angel investor may be convinced to contribute funding. Generally an angel investor is someone with spare funds and some personal or industry-related interest—angels are sometimes said to invest "emotional money," while venture capitalists are said to invest "logical money"—that is willing to help give the new enterprise a more solid footing. First-round venture capital funding involves a significant cash outlay and managerial assistance. Second-round venture capital involves a larger cash outlay and instructions to a stock or initial public offering **(IPO)** underwriter, who will sell stock in exchange for a percentage of what is sold. Finally, in the IPO stage, an investment bank is commissioned to sell shares to the public.

In the currently sober economic climate, a return to traditional business wisdom has meant that enterprises are generally expected to show a clear **path to profitability** if they want to attract investment funds.

VersaModular Eurocard bus

See "VMEbus"

vertical blanking interval

The vertical blanking interval (VBI) is a portion of a television signal that can carry information other than video or audio, such as closed-caption text and stock market data. The interval in sending a video signal is required for the time it takes the electron gun in a television monitor's cathode ray tube **(CRT)** to move back up to the top of the tube. VBI data can be inserted by a **cable TV** provider and transmitted to a special receiver that connects to a computer's **RS-232C port**.

vertical market

A vertical market is a particular industry or group of enterprises in which similar products or services are developed and marketed using similar methods (and to whom goods and services can be sold). Broad examples of vertical markets are: Insurance, real estate, banking, heavy manufacturing, retail, transportation, hospitals, and government.

Vertical market software is software aimed at a particular vertical market and can be contrasted with horizontal market software (such as word processors and spreadsheet programs) that can be used in a cross-section of industries.

vertical portal

See "vortal"

vertical solutions provider

On the Internet, a vertical solutions provider (VSP) is a company that focuses on delivering industry-specific application hosting services to customers in a specific **vertical market** such as manufacturing, health care, retailing, or financial service. A VSP is a type of application service provider (**ASP**) that enables a company in a particular vertical market to take advantage of Internet technologies and applications without having to acquire the know-how and other resources on its own. For example, a retailer could hire a VSP to configure and administer its shopping cart, inventory management and credit-card processing applications on a continuing basis, saving the company the need to hire, train, and pay its own administrators.

Companies seeking VSP services may be independent dot-coms or other start-ups or they may be companies that are launching an e-commerce branch of their existing business. Examples of VSPs include Virtual Financial Services (ViFi) and OneChem.

very high-speed Backbone Network Service

See "vBNS"

very high frequency

See "VHF"

Very Large Scale Integration

VLSI, the current level of computer microchip miniaturization, refers to microchips containing hundreds of thousands of transistors. LSI (large-scale integration) refers to microchips containing thousands of transistors. Earlier, MSI (medium scale integration) meant a microchip containing hundreds of transistors and SSI (small-scale integration) meant transistors in the tens.

very long instruction word

See "VLIW"

Very Small Aperture Terminal

See "VSAT"

VESA Local Bus

VESA Local Bus (sometimes called the VESA VL bus) is a standard interface between your computer and its expansion **slot** that provides faster data flow between the devices controlled by the expansion cards and your computer's microprocessor. A "local bus" is a physical path on which data flows at almost the speed of the **microprocessor**, increasing total system performance. VESA Local Bus is particularly effective in systems with advanced video cards

and supports 32-bit data flow at 50 **MHz**. A VESA Local Bus is implemented by adding a supplemental slot and card that aligns with and augments an **Industry Standard Architecture** (ISA) expansion card. (ISA is the most common expansion slot in today's computers.)

vestigial sideband

Vestigial sideband (VSB) is a type of amplitude modulation (**AM**) technique (sometimes called *VSB-AM*) that encodes data by varying the amplitude of a single **carrier frequency**. Portions of one of the redundant sidebands are removed to form a vestigial **sideband** signal—so-called because a *vestige* of the sideband remains.

In AM, the carrier itself does not fluctuate in amplitude. Instead, the modulating data appears in the form of signal components at frequencies slightly higher and lower than that of the carrier. These components are called *sidebands*. The lower sideband (LSB) appears at frequencies below the carrier frequency; the upper sideband (USB) appears at frequencies above the carrier frequency. The actual information is transmitted in the sidebands, rather than the carrier; both sidebands carry the same information. Because LSB and USB are essentially mirror images of each other, one can be discarded or used for a second channel or for diagnostic purposes.

VSB transmission is similar to *single-sideband* (SSB) transmission, in which one of the sidebands is completely removed. In VSB transmission, however, the second sideband is not completely removed, but is filtered to remove all but the desired range of **frequencies**.

Eight-level VSB (**8-VSB**) was developed by Zenith for inclusion in the Advanced Television Systems Committee (**ATSC**) set of digital television (**DTV**) standards.

VFAT

See "Virtual File Allocation Table"

VGA

See "display modes"

VHE

See "Virtual Home Environment"

VHF

The VHF (very high frequency) range of the radio spectrum is the **band** extending from 30 **MHz** to 300 MHz. The wavelengths corresponding to these limit frequencies are 10 meters and 1 meter.

In the VHF band, electromagnetic fields are affected by the earth's ionosphere and troposphere. Ionospheric propagation occurs regularly in the lower part of the VHF spectrum, mostly at frequencies below 70 MHz. In this mode, the communication range can sometimes extend over the entire surface of the earth. The troposphere can cause bending, ducting, and scattering, extending the range of communication significantly beyond the visual horizon. Auroral, meteor-scatter, and EME (earth-moon-earth, also called **moonbounce**) propagation take place on occasion, but these modes do not offer reliable communication and are of interest primarily to **amateur radio** operators.

The VHF band is popular for mobile two-way radio communication. A great deal of **satellite** communication and broadcasting is done at VHF. **Wideband modulation** is used by some services; the most common example is fast-scan television broadcasting. Channels and subbands within the VHF portion of the radio spectrum are allocated by the International Telecommunication Union (**ITU**).

vi

vi, pronounced by using each letter (vee-aye), is a widely-used and popular **UNIX**-based **text editor**. Like most UNIX system interfaces and other text editors, it lets you control the system by using the keyboard rather than a combination of mouse selections and keystrokes. The succinctness of the interface makes it highly useful for people who work at a computer all day, especially programmers entering or manipulating language statements. vi was invented before and is a popular alternative to Emacs, which is said to be more capable, more complicated, and somewhat slower. Like Emacs, vi is most commonly used for entering and editing program language statements and for writing short notes including e-mail. vi usually comes as part of any UNIX-based system.

video adapter

A video adapter (also called a *display adapter* or *video board*) is an integrated circuit **card** in a computer or, in some cases, a **monitor** that provides **digital-to-analog conversion**, **video RAM**, and a video controller so that data can be sent to a computer's **display**. Today, almost all displays and video adapters adhere to a common denominator de facto standard, Video Graphics Array (**VGA**). VGA describes how data—essentially red, green, blue data streams—is passed between the computer and the display. It also describes the frame refresh rates in **hertz**. It also specifies the number and width of horizontal lines, which essentially amounts to specifying the **resolution** of the **pixel**s that are created. VGA supports four different resolution settings and two related image refresh rates.

In addition to VGA, most displays today adhere to one or more standards set by the Video Electronics Standards Association (**VESA**). VESA defines how software can determine what capabilities a display has. It also identifies resolutions setting beyond those of VGA. These resolutions include 800 by 600, 1024 by 768, 1280 by 1024, and 1600 by 1200 pixels.

Video CD

See "VCD"

video display unit

A video display unit (VDU) consists of:

- A computer output device that uses a **cathode ray tube** or other technology to present visual images

- One or more input devices, such as a **keyboard**, a **mouse**, or both.

A synonym sometimes used in the United States is video display terminal (**VDT**). VDU seems to predominate elsewhere. The term is widely used in **ergonomic** discussions, guidelines, and standards related to worker safety and efficiency.

The "classic" VDU is the desktop **display** and keyboard. However, as personal computers and workstations become more portable and smaller in size, the safety and design guidelines for VDUs call for continuing reconsideration.

video or visual display terminal

See "VDT"

video RAM

Also see **RAM types**.

Video RAM (VRAM) means in general all forms of random access memory (**RAM**) used to store image data for a computer **display**. All types of video RAM are special arrangements of dynamic RAM (**DRAM**). Video RAM is really a **buffer** between the computer **processor** and the display and is often called the *frame buffer*. When images are to be sent to the display, they are first read by the processor as data from some form of main (non-video) RAM and then written to video RAM. From video RAM (the frame buffer), the data is converted by a RAM digital-to-analog converter (**RAMDAC**) into **analog** signals that are sent to the display presentation mechanism such as a cathode ray tube (**CRT**). Usually, video RAM comes in a 1 or 2 megabyte package and is located on the **video adapter card** in the computer. Most forms of video RAM are *dual-ported*, which means that while the processor is writing a new image to video RAM, the display is reading from video RAM to refresh its current display content. The dual-port design is the main difference between main RAM and video RAM.

Somewhat confusingly, the most common type of video RAM is called Video RAM (VRAM). Video RAM is the **vanilla** flavor of video RAM. It is dual-ported, allowing the processor to write to it at the same time that it is refreshing the image on the display monitor. Other forms of video RAM include:

- Synchronous Graphics RAM (**SGRAM**) is clock-synchronized RAM that is used for video memory. It is relatively low-cost video memory. It uses *masked write*, which enables selected data to be modified in a single operation rather than as a sequence of read, update, and write operations. It also uses *block write*, which allows data for background or foreground image fills to be handled more efficiently. SGRAM is single-ported. Its special features are what make it a moderately fast form of video memory. The Matrox Mystique is an example of a video card that uses SGRAM.

- Window RAM (**WRAM**), unrelated to Microsoft Windows, is very high-performance video RAM that is dual-ported and has about 25% more bandwidth than VRAM but costs less. It has features that make it more efficient to read data for use in block fills and text drawing. It can be used for very high **resolution** (such as 1600 by 1200 pixels) using **true color**. It's used in the Matrox Millenium video card.

- Multibank Dynamic RAM (**MDRAM**) is a high-performance RAM, developed by MoSys, that divides memory into multiple 32 **kilobytes** parts or "banks" that can be accessed individually. Traditional video RAM is monolithic; the entire frame buffer is accessed at one time. Having individual memory banks allows accesses to be interleaved concurrently, increasing overall performance. It's also cheaper since, unlike other forms of video RAM, cards can be manufactured with just the right amount of RAM for a given resolution capability instead of requiring it to be in multiples of megabytes.

- Rambus Dynamic RAM (**DRAM**) is a video RAM designed by Rambus that includes a proprietary **bus** that speeds up the data flow between video RAM and the frame buffer. It's optimized for video streaming.

videoconference

A videoconference is a live connection between people in separate locations for the purpose of communication, usually involving audio and often text as well as video. At its simplest, videoconferencing provides transmission of static images and text between two locations. At its most sophisticated, it provides transmission of full-motion video images and high-quality audio between multiple locations.

Videoconferencing software is quickly becoming standard computer equipment. For example, Microsoft's NetMeeting is included in Windows 2000 and is also available for free download from the NetMeeting homepage. For personal use, free or inexpensive videoconference software and a **digital camera** afford the user easy—and cheap—live connections to distant friends and family. Although the audio and video quality of such a minimal setup is not high, the combined benefits of a video link and long-distance savings may be quite persuasive.

The tangible benefits for businesses using videoconferencing include lower travel costs and profits gained from offering videoconferencing as an aspect of customer service. The intangible benefits include the facilitation of group work among geographically distant teammates and a stronger sense of community among business contacts, both within and between companies. In terms of group work, users can chat, transfer files, share programs, send and receive graphic data, and operate computers from remote locations. On a more personal level, the face-to-face connection adds non-verbal communication to the exchange and allows participants to develop a stronger sense of familiarity with individuals they may never actually meet in the same place.

A videoconference can be thought of as a phone call with pictures—Microsoft refers to that aspect of its NetMeeting package as a "web phone"—and indications suggest that videoconferencing will some day become the primary mode of distance communication.

viral marketing

On the Internet, viral marketing is any marketing technique that induces Web sites or users to pass on a marketing message to other sites or users, creating a potentially exponential growth in the message's visibility and effect. One example of successful viral marketing is Hotmail, a company, now owned by Microsoft, that promotes its service and its own advertisers' messages in every user's e-mail notes.

Sites that serve an immediate need when they are first launched seem to get the kind of viral marketing known as *buzz marketing*. Everyone simply tells everyone else. **ICQ**, a service that tells you when selected friends or colleagues are also online, is an example of a service that is viral by its nature. Its users want to tell their friends about it so that it will be more useful for them.

Some marketing people prefer terms other than *viral marketing*. In his popular e-mail newsletter about selling on the Web, John Audette asked readers to suggest alternatives, including other terms in current use. Among those suggested have been:

> avalanche marketing
> buzz marketing
> cascading style marketing
> centrifugal marketing
> exponential marketing
> fission marketing
> grass roots marketing
> organic marketing
> propogation marketing
> referral marketing (borrowing a term long used in marketing prior to the Web)
> ripple marketing

self-perpetuation marketing
self-propogation marketing
wildfire marketing

One reader suggested *word of mouse*.

virtual

In general, virtual means the quality of effecting something without actually being that something. In information technology, there seems to be a virtual version of (virtually) everything.

"Virtual" derives from the Latin "vir" ("man" in an idealized sense), from which developed the Latin "virtus" (strength, manliness, virtue). In Middle English, the adjective meant "possessed of certain physical virtues." By modern times, it had come to mean, as defined in Webster's, "being in essence or effect but not in fact."

virtual area network

A virtual area network (VAN) is a network on which users are enabled to share a more visual sense of community through high band-width connections. As conceived by PennWell Media Online, an online directory for specialized networking products, a virtual area network is something like a **metropolitan area network** (MAN) or extended local area network (**LAN**) in which all users can meet over high-bandwidth connections, enabling "face-to-face" online "coffeehouses," remote medical diagnosis and legal consultation, and online corporate or extracorporate workgroups, focus groups, and conferences. A VAN requires multi-megabyte data flow and can be implemented through the use of **Asymmetric Digital Subscriber Line** but more likely through the installation of **cable modems**. Since the high-bandwidth connections imply a common infrastructure, the first VANs are likely to be local or regional. However, a VAN can also be national or international in geographic scope, assuming all users share similar capabilities.

virtual circuit

A virtual circuit is a **circuit** or path between points in a network that appears to be a discrete, physical path but is actually a managed pool of circuit resources from which specific circuits are allocated as needed to meet traffic requirements.

A permanent virtual circuit (**PVC**) is a virtual circuit that is permanently available to the user just as though it were a dedicated or **leased line** continuously reserved for that user. A switched virtual circuit (**SVC**) is a virtual circuit in which a connection session is set up for a user only for the duration of a connection. PVCs are an important feature of **frame relay** networks and SVCs are proposed for later inclusion.

virtual community

A virtual community is a community of people sharing common interests, ideas, and feelings over the Internet or other collaborative networks. A possible inventor of this term and one of its first proponents was Howard Rheingold, who created one of the first major Internet communities, called "The Well." In his book, *The Virtual Community*, Rheingold defines virtual communities as social aggregations that emerge from the Internet when enough people carry on public discussions long enough and with sufficient human feeling to form webs of personal relationships in **cyberspace**.

Virtual communities might be thought of as subgroups within Marshall McLuhan's notion of cyberspace as a "global village." Before the Web, virtual communities existed on bulletin board services (**BBS**) and many still do. Some virtual communities or facilitators of them use the metaphor of a coffee house or something similar to help users visualize the community. In general, there are two kinds of communication among virtual community members: message postings and real-time chat. **Usenet** newsgroups are an example of the former. Many Web sites, such as Geocities, foster subject information exchanges. For real-time chat, Internet Relay Chat (**IRC**) is a system used by many Web sites that foster virtual communities.

virtual device driver

In Windows, a virtual device driver is a program for each of the computer's main hardware **device**s, including the hard disk drive controller, keyboard, and serial and parallel ports. They're used to maintain the status of a hardware device that has changeable settings. Virtual device drivers handle software **interrupt**s from the **operating system** rather than hardware interrupts.

A virtual device driver usually has a file name suffix of VXD.

Virtual File Allocation Table

Virtual File Allocation Table (VFAT) is the part of the Windows 95 and later **operating systems** that handles long file names, which otherwise could not be handled by the original **file allocation table** (FAT) programming. A file allocation table is the means by which the operating system keeps track of where the pieces of a file are stored on a hard disk. Since the original FAT for the **Disk Operating System** (DOS) assumed file names were limited to a length of eight characters, a program extension was needed to handle the longer names allowed in Windows 95. Microsoft refers to this extension as a **driver** since other operating systems may need to install and use it in order to access FAT partitions written by Windows 95 and later Windows systems. The VFAT extension runs in **protected mode**, uses 32-bit code, and uses VCACHE for disk **cache**.

Virtual Home Environment

In mobile computing, the Virtual Home Environment (VHE) is the concept that a **network** supporting mobile users should provide them the same computing environment on the road that they have in their home or corporate computing environment. VHE is part of IMT-2000 and the **Universal Mobile Telecommunications System** (UMTS). With VHE, a network (referred to as a *foreign network*) emulates the behavior of the user's *home network* and the user has the same services that they are accustomed to at home.

virtual hosting

On the Internet, virtual hosting is the provision of Web **server hosting** services so that a company (or individual) doesn't have to purchase and maintain its own Web server and connections to the Internet. A virtual hosting provider is sometimes called a Web or Internet "space provider." Some companies providing this service simply call it "hosting." Typically, virtual hosting provides a customer who wants a Web site with: **Domain name** registration assistance, multiple domain names that map to the registered domain name, an allocation of file storage and directory setup for the Web site files (**HTML** and graphic image files), e-mail addresses, and, optionally, Web site creation services. The virtual hosting user (the Web site owner) needs only to have a File Transfer Protocol (**FTP**) program for exchanging files with the virtual host.

Some virtual hosting providers make it possible for customers to have more control of their Web site file system, e-mail names, passwords, and other resources and say that they are providing each customer a **virtual server**—that is, a server that appears to be entirely their own server. When a customer does indeed want to have its very own server, some hosting providers allow the customer to rent a **dedicated server** at the hosting provider's location. If a customer is allowed to place their own purchased equipment at the provider's location, this is known as **colocation**.

Virtual Instrument file

vi (or ".vi") is the Virtual Instrument file format. It is used by National Instruments' LabVIEW development software. LABView lets you develop applications for automating and controlling processes in manufacturing and other environments. National Instruments uses a concept of "virtual "instrumentation" to generalize and accelerate the development of this kind of application.

virtual LAN

A virtual (or logical) LAN is a local area network with a definition that maps workstations on some other basis than geographic location (for example, by department, type of user, or primary application). The virtual LAN controller can change or add workstations and manage loadbalancing and bandwidth allocation more easily than with a physical picture of the LAN. Network management software keeps track of relating the virtual picture of the local area network with the actual physical picture.

VLANs are considered likely to be used with **campus** environment networks. Among companies likely to provide products with VLAN support are Cisco, Bay Networks, and 3Com.

There is a proposed VLAN standard, **Institute of Electrical and Electronics Engineers** 802.10.

virtual machine

1) Virtual machine is a term used by Sun Microsystems, developers of the **Java** programming language and runtime environment, to describe software that acts as an interface between **compiler** Java **binary** code and the **microprocessor** (or "hardware **platform**") that actually performs the program's instructions. Once a Java virtual machine has been provided for a platform, any Java program (which, after compilation, is called *bytecode*) can run on that platform. Java was designed to allow application programs to be built that could be run on any platform without having to be rewritten or recompiled by the programmer for each separate platform. Java's virtual machine makes this possible.

The Java virtual machine specification defines an abstract rather than a real "machine" (or processor) and specifies an **instruction** set, a set of registers, a **stack**, a "**garbage** heap," and a **method** area. The real implementation of this abstract or logically defined processor can be in other code that is recognized by the real processor or be built into the microchip processor itself.

The output of "compiling" a Java source program (a set of Java language statements) is called *bytecode*. A Java virtual machine can either interpret the bytecode one instruction at a time (mapping it to a real microprocessor instruction) or the bytecode can be compiled further for the real microprocessor using what is called a **just-in-time compiler**.

2) At IBM, a virtual machine is any multi-user shared-resource operating system that gives each user the appearance of having sole control of all the resources of the system.

3) At IBM, a virtual machine is also used to mean an operating system that is in turn managed by an underlying control progam. Thus, IBM's **VM/ESA** can control multiple virtual machines on an IBM S/390 system.

4) Elsewhere, virtual machine has been used to mean either an **operating system** or any program that runs a computer. We quote:

"A running program is often referred to as a virtual machine—a machine that doesn't exist as a matter of actual physical reality. The virtual machine idea is

itself one of the most elegant in the history of technology and is a crucial step in the evolution of ideas about software. To come up with it, scientists and technologists had to recognize that a computer running a program isn't merely a washer doing laundry. A washer is a washer whatever clothes you put inside, but when you put a new program in a computer, it becomes a new machine.... The virtual machine: A way of understanding software that frees us to think of software design as machine design."

From David Gelernter's "Truth, Beauty, and the Virtual Machine," *Discover Magazine*, September 1997, p. 72.

Virtual Memory System

Virtual Memory System (VMS) is an **operating system** from the Digital Equipment Corporation (DEC) that runs in its computers. VMS originated in 1979 as a new operating system for DEC's new VAX computer, the successor to DEC's PDP-11. VMS is a 32-bit system that exploits the concept of **virtual memory**.

VMS was renamed OpenVMS when it was redeveloped for the **Alpha** processor. (OpenVMS is also the name now used on the VAX computer.) The "Open" suggests the added support for the UNIX-like interfaces of the Portable Operating System Interface (**POSIX**) standard. Programs written to the POSIX standard, which includes a set of standard C language programming functions, can be ported to any POSIX-supporting computer platform.

Among other features, OpenVMS can be used with special software that facilitates its use with Windows NT servers.

virtual memory

Virtual (or logical) memory is a concept that, when implemented by a computer and its operating system, allows programmers to use a very large range of memory or storage addresses for stored data. The computing system maps the programmer's virtual addresses to real hardware storage addresses. Usually, the programmer is freed from having to be concerned about the availability of data storage.

In addition to managing the mapping of virtual storage addresses to real storage addresses, a computer implementing virtual memory or storage also manages storage swapping between active storage (RAM) and hard disk or other high volume storage devices. Data is read in units called "pages" of sizes ranging from a thousand bytes (actually 1,024 decimal bytes) up to several megabyes in size. This reduces the amount of physical storage access that is required and speeds up overall system performance.

virtual microscopy

Virtual microscopy is a method of posting microscope images on, and transmitting them over, computer networks. This allows independent viewing of images by large numbers of people in diverse locations.

Classroom viewing of microscope slides has traditionally been a cumbersome business. It is possible to set up an optical microscope with projection apparatus, but this is an inflexible scheme at best. It requires operation by a professor or instructor, and students do not have individual control over what they see. It also requires that all the students be physically present in the same classroom at the same time. These limitations also apply to the sharing of images among teams of doctors. Although closed-circuit television networks have been used for this purpose, image resolution in these systems is notoriously poor.

With the advent of computers and broadband Internet connections, microscope slide images can be digitized and posted online. Each student can use a computer to independently look at any image in a database that can contain thousands of slides. Zooming provides the equivalent of variable magnification. Using UP/DOWN/RIGHT/LEFT arrow buttons, the viewer can move the center of the field of view at will. Students can view images when and where they choose. For example, if there are 50 students in a virtual class all looking at the same image at the same time, the students can independently choose 50 different placements and magnifications of the image. Reports by users indicate that this can actually be easier than using an optical microscope in a laboratory setting.

One program used for virtual microscopy is "Virtual Slice" developed by MicroBrightField, Inc. of Colchester, Vermont. If recent tests are any indication, virtual microscopy will largely replace older instructional methods. In addition, the technology has applications in videoconferencing, and in the exchange of medical information among doctors and hospitals worldwide. This will improve the quality of patient care by increasing the quality and quantity of medical information that can be shared.

virtual organization

A virtual organization or company is one whose members are geographically apart, usually working by computer **e-mail** and **groupware** while appearing to others to be a single, unified organization with a real physical location.

Virtual PC

Virtual PC is a program that emulates Windows 95, Windows 98, Windows NT, as well as IBM OS/2, or Linux on a **Macintosh** personal computer, assuming it's equipped with a sufficiently fast **microprocessor**. With Virtual PC installed, a Mac can show the desktop for the emulated **operating system** on one part of the display or it can take up the entire screen. You can run any program that will run under the other operating systems on "regular" (Intel microprocessor-based) PCs. Virtual PC works by converting Intel x86 instructions into PowerPC instructions on the fly.

To install and use Virtual PC, the Mac must have the PowerPC 604e microprocessor, or a 603e version that runs at a minimum of 180 **MHz**. An extra 150 to 300 megabytes of **hard disk** storage is needed and you should have at least 24 megabytes of random access memory (**RAM**) with 32 megabytes recommended. Versions of Virtual PC are available that will emulate Windows 3.1 and DOS; these can run with a slower microprocessor and less storage.

Virtual PC may be helpful for Mac users who need to run a Windows program occasionally or in families where some members want to run Mac applications and other members want to run Windows applications. According to a Wall Street Journal reviewer, the emulation appears to be complete, except that the Mac mouse, which has only one button, requires the user to press an additional key when a right-hand click is required.

virtual private network

A virtual private network (VPN) is a private data network that makes use of the public telecommunication infrastructure, maintaining privacy through the use of a **tunneling protocol** and security procedures. A virtual private network can be contrasted with a system of owned or leased lines that can only be used by one company. The idea of the VPN is to give the company the same capabilities at much lower cost by using the shared public infrastructure rather than a private one. Phone companies have provided secure shared resources for voice messages. A virtual private network makes it possible to have the same secure sharing of public resources for data. Companies today are looking at using a private virtual network for both **extranet**s and wide-area **intranet**s.

Using a virtual private network involves encrypting data before sending it through the public network and decrypting it at the receiving end. An additional level of security involves encrypting not only the data but also the originating and receiving network addresses. Microsoft, 3Com, and several other companies have developed the Point-to-Point Tunneling Protocol (**PPTP**) and Microsoft has extended **Windows NT** to support it. VPN software is typically installed as part of a company's **firewall** server.

Virtual Reality Modeling Language

See "VRML"

virtual reality

Virtual reality is the simulation of a real or imagined environment that can be experienced visually in the three dimensions of width, height, and depth and that may additionally provide an interactive experience visually in full real-time motion with sound and possibly with tactile and other forms of feedback. The simplest form of virtual reality is a **3-D** image that can be explored interactively at a personal computer, usually by manipulating keys or the mouse so that the content of the image moves in some direction or zooms in or out. Most of these images require installing a **plug-in** for your browser. As the images become larger and interactive controls more complex, the perception of "reality" increases. More sophisticated efforts involve such approaches as wrap-around display screens, actual rooms augmented with wearable computers, and **haptics** joystick devices that let you feel the display images.

Virtual reality can be divided into:

- The simulation of real environments such as the interior of a building or a spaceship often with the purpose of training or education
- The development of an imagined environment, typically for a game or educational adventure

Popular products for creating virtual reality effects on personal computers include Bryce, Extreme 3D, Ray Dream Studio, trueSpace, 3D Studio MAX, and Visual Reality. The Virtual Reality Modelling Language (**VRML**) allows the creator to specify images and the rules for their display and interaction using textual language statements.

Virtual Router Redundancy

See "VRRP"

virtual server

On the Internet, a virtual server is a **server** (computer and various server programs) at someone else's location that is shared by multiple Web site owners so that each owner can use and administer it as though they had complete control of the server. Some Internet service providers (**ISP**s) offer a virtual server service instead of, or in addition to, **virtual hosting**. Using a virtual server, a company or individual with a Web site can not only have their own **domain name** and **IP address**, but can administer their own file directories, add e-mail accounts and address assignments, assign multiple domain names that resolve to a basic domain name without involvement from the ISP, manage their own logs and statistics analysis, and maintain passwords. Users of a virtual server, however, do not have to manage the hardware aspects of running a server and effectively share the cost of expensive line connections to the Internet.

Virtual Storage Access Method

See "VSAM"

Virtual Storage Portal

Virtual Storage Portal (VSP), a service mark of StorageNetworks, is a software application with a Web **browser** interface that lets a customer see how much storage is being used, predict future needs, grant access to storage administrators, view performance, and otherwise manage the **storage** that they have rented from StorageNetworks. As a leading **storage service provider**, StorageNetworks operates a network of what it calls "storage point-of-presence" data centers. An enterprise or a "**dotcom**" company with significant storage needs but a lack of expertise in buying and managing storage might choose to outsource its storage from a company like StorageNetworks. VSP allows this particular company's customers to look at its storage infrastructure and otherwise manage and forecast its rented storage resources. VSP is offered free to its customers. StorageNetworks has no immediate plans to market it independently. Like similar companies, StorageNetworks offers "plain old storage space" as well as more expensive backup service and a "zero loss" service.

virtual tape

Virtual tape is the use of a special storage device that manages less-frequently needed data so that it appears to be stored entirely on tape cartridges when some parts of it may actually be located in faster, hard disk storage. The programming for a virtual tape system is sometimes called a *virtual tape server (VTS)*. Virtual tape can be used with a hierarchical storage management (**HSM**) system in which data is moved as it falls through various usage thresholds to slower but less costly forms of storage media. Virtual tape may also be used as part of a storage area network (**SAN**) where less-frequently used or archived data can be managed by a single virtual tape server for a number of networked computers.

A virtual tape system offloads from the main computer the processing involved in deciding whether data should be available in the faster disk cache or written onto a tape cartridge. The virtual tape system also can manage data so that more of the space on a tape cartridge is actually used.

IBM and Storage Technology are well-established vendors of virtual tape systems. Sutmyn Storage sells a product that provides a virtual interface to existing IBM and other systems.

Virtual Telecommunications Access Method

See "VTAM"

virtualization

Virtualization is the pooling of physical **storage** from multiple network storage devices into what appears to be a single storage device that is managed from a central console. Virtualization is often used as part of a storage area network (**SAN**). A **virtual** storage device appears as one storage device to the **operating system**, regardless of the types of storage devices pooled. Hard disk drives are the most common storage device used. Virtualization is similar to a redundant array of independent disks (**RAID**) except that the stored data is not copied redundantly on each storage device (although this capability is sometimes provided).

The benefits of virtualization vary with each software package, but usually enable a customer to:

- Add a storage device without requiring network downtime

- Assign storage volumes from a downed server or storage device to another server or storage device within the network

- Mix hard disk drives of different sizes, speeds, and vendors

- Easily create, delete, or expand a virtual drive. For example, if a server requires more storage that its storage device allows, virtualization allows unused space from another storage device to be used. If a server needs less storage, the unused storage space is recycled or pooled back into the drive pool.

Companies that offer virtualization software include Compaq, Veritas, and XIOtech.

virus hoax

A virus hoax is a false warning about a computer **virus**. Typically, the warning arrives in an e-mail note or is distributed through a note in a company's internal network. These notes are usually forwarded using distribution lists and they will typically suggest that the recipient forward the note to other distribution lists.

If you get a message about a new virus, you can check it out by going to one of the leading Web sites that keep up with viruses and virus hoaxes. If someone sends you a note about a virus that you learn is a virus hoax, reply to the sender that the virus warning is a hoax.

virus

A virus is a piece of programming code usually disguised as something else that causes some unexpected and usually undesirable event. A virus is often designed so that it is automatically spread to other computer users. Viruses can be transmitted as attachments to an e-mail note, as downloads, or be present on a diskette or CD. The source of the e-mail note, downloaded file, or diskette you've received is often unaware of the virus. Some viruses wreak their effect as soon as their code is executed; other viruses lie dormant until circumstances cause their code to be executed by the computer. Some viruses are playful in intent and effect ("Happy Birthday, Ludwig!") and some can be quite harmful, erasing data or causing your hard disk to require reformatting.

Generally, there are three main classes of viruses:

File infectors. Some file infector viruses attach themselves to program files, usually selected .COM or .EXE files. Some can infect any program for which execution is requested, including .SYS, .OVL, .PRG, and .MNU files. When the program is loaded, the virus is loaded as well. Other file infector viruses arrive as wholly-contained programs or scripts sent as an attachment to an e-mail note.

System or boot-record infectors. These viruses infect executable code found in certain system areas on a disk. They attach to the DOS **boot sector** on diskettes or the **Master Boot Record** on hard disks. A typical scenario (familiar to the author) is to receive a diskette from an innocent source that contains a boot disk virus. When your operating system is running, files on the diskette can be read without triggering the boot disk virus. However, if you leave the diskette in the drive, and then turn the computer off or reload the operating system, the computer will look first in your A drive, find the diskette with its boot disk virus, load it, and make it temporarily impossible to use your hard disk. (Allow several days for recovery.) This is why you should make sure you have a **bootable floppy**.

Macro viruses. These are among the most common viruses, and they tend to do the least damage. Macro viruses infect your Microsoft Word application and typically insert unwanted words or phrases.

The best protection against a virus is to know the origin of each program or file you load into your computer or open from your e-mail program. Since this is difficult, you can buy **anti-virus software** that can screen e-mail attachments and also check all of your files periodically and remove any viruses that are found. From time to time, you may get an e-mail message warning of a new virus. Unless the warning is from a source you recognize, chances are good that the warning is a **virus hoax**.

viseme

A viseme is a generic facial image that can be used to describe a particular sound. A viseme is the visual equivalent of a *phoneme* or unit of sound in spoken language. Using visemes, the hearing-impaired can view sounds visually—effectively, "lip-reading" the entire human face.

visitor-based networking

Visitor-based networking (VBN) is the provision of high-speed Internet access for mobile PC users in need of temporary service in public places. A visitor-based network is most commonly established in a hotel, airport, convention center, press area, mall, university, sales center, or corporate meeting room. For years, mobile users were limited to **analog dial-up** connections through a **PBX** system or other proprietary network. Visitor-based networking goes a step further in creating a more efficient and effective work environment for them. It aims to give the on-the-go worker a productive way to temporarily connect PCs to local LANs and broadband Internet connections.

A visitor-based network usually includes hardware (such as servers, hubs, and routers), telecommunications (an Internet connection), software (a browser), and service (telephone support). Virtually any Internet-based **Ethernet LAN** can become a visitor-based network by adding a server. The server provides the necessary layer of management between public users and the gateway router to enable a seamless connection for visitors. A successful visitor-based network usually also features additional services like printing and customer support. Many ISPs are building broadband access networks in public places to enable more efficient visitor-based networks.

Technology vendors have developed ways to package their network offerings with billing and management applications that make offering temporary Internet access more than just a convenience, but also a viable business. The key commercial player in the visitor-based networking arena is 3Com; smaller vendors include Elastic Networks and Tut Systems. IT analyst Gartner Group projects the remote Internet access market will hit $31 billion by 2003. It also forecasts that by 2005 half of all remote business users will have **remote access** connections that are faster than analog modems.

Visor

Visor is the trade name of a handheld computer manufactured by **Handspring**. The Visor is similar to the **Palm** computer and uses the Palm operating system (**Palm OS**). Data can be easily transferred between the Visor and other computers, including Palm handhelds, using **HotSync** technology. Interfacing is possible with Macintosh as well as with IBM-compatible desktop and notebook computers.

The Visor can be tailored to meet the needs of the individual user. It contains an expansion slot called Springboard that allows the addition of modules, each of which is designed for a specific function. The modules are **plug-and-play** and are hot-swappable (they are automatically recognized by the Visor, and they can be exchanged without powering-down or rebooting). Data can be stored and backed up with an optional **flash memory** module.

Visual Basic

Visual Basic is a programming environment from Microsoft in which a programmer uses a graphical user interface to choose and modify preselected sections of code written in the **BASIC** programming language.

Since Visual Basic is easy to learn and fast to write code with, it's sometimes used to prototype an **application** that will later be written in a more difficult but efficient language. Visual Basic is also widely used to write working programs. Microsoft says that there are at least 3 million developers using Visual Basic.

visual computing

Visual computing is computing that lets you interact with and control work by manipulating visual images either as direct work objects or as objects representing other objects that are not necessarily visual themselves. The visual images can be photographs, 3-D scenes, video sequences, block diagrams, or simple icons. The term is generally used to describe either (or both) of these:

1. Any computer environment in which a visual paradigm rather than a conventional (text) paradigm is used

2. Applications that deal with large or numerous image files, such as video sequences and 3-D scenes

Intel's 64-bit **Merced** microprocessor has been promoted to portend a new era of visual computing at your workstation. High-bandwidth networks will help support visual computing, especially the shipping around of large amounts of video.

visual display

See "VDT"

Visual FoxPro

Visual FoxPro is a **relational database** with an **object-oriented programming** environment from Microsoft that comes with prewritten **class**es. Visual FoxPro is part of Microsoft's **Visual Studio** suite of products.

Visual FoxPro is relatively easy to learn and fast for developing reusable code. A programmer can write code to access a FoxPro database or as well as to connect to such databases as **SQL Server** and **Oracle**. Microsoft says that there are at least 500,000 developers using FoxPro.

Visual InterDev

Visual InterDev is Microsoft's development tool for building a dynamic, data-driven Web site. Whereas Microsoft's FrontPage is an **HTML** editor aimed at letting non-programmers build the pages for a Web site, Visual InterDev provides the tools for programmers to build a Web site. (FrontPage and Visual InterDev are said to be compatible.) Visual InterDev offers a user interface similar to those for **Visual Basic**, Visual J++, and Visual Studio. Using Visual InterDev, one can assemble pages that use Microsoft's **ActiveX** technologies, including **Active Server Page** (ASP) technology. The developer can build and insert **ActiveX control** or **Java applet**s. Visual InterDev includes an HTML editor and support for **dynamic HTML**. The Web site can be integrated with server programs written in any language and access to almost any **database** using Microsoft's **Universal Data Access**, including **ActiveX Data Objects**, **Open Database Connectivity**, and **OLE DB**.

visualization

Visualization is the process of representing abstract business or scientific data as images that can aid in understanding the meaning of the data.

Vital Product Data

See "VPD"

VLAN

See "virtual LAN"

VLIW

Very long instruction word (VLIW) describes a computer processing architecture in which a language **compiler** or pre-processor breaks program **instructions** down into basic operations that can be performed by the **processor** in **parallel** (that is, at the same time). These operations are put into a very long instruction **word** which the processor can then take apart without further analysis, handing each operation to an appropriate functional unit.

VLIW is sometimes viewed as the next step beyond the reduced instruction set computing (**RISC**) architecture, which also works with a limited set of relatively basic instructions and can usually execute more than one instruction at a time (a characteristic referred to as *superscalar*). The main advantage of VLIW processors is that complexity is moved from the hardware to the software, which means that the hardware can be smaller, cheaper, and require less power to operate. The challenge is to design a compiler or pre-processor that is intelligent enough to decide how to build the very long instruction words. If dynamic pre-processing is done as the program is run, performance may be a concern.

The **Crusoe** family of processors from Transmeta uses very long instruction words that are assembled by a pre-processor that is located in a **flash memory** chip. Because the processor does not need to have the ability to discover and schedule parallel operations, the processor contains only about a fourth of the **transistor**s of a regular processor. The lower power requirement enables computers based on Crusoe technology to be operated by battery almost all day without a recharge. The Crusoe processors emulate Intel's **x86** processor instruction set. Theoretically, pre-processors could be designed to emulate other processor architectures.

VLSI

VLSI (very large-scale integration), the current level of computer microchip miniaturization, refers to microchips containing in the hundreds of thousands of transistors. LSI (large-scale integration) meant microchips containing thousands of transistors. Earlier, MSI (medium scale integration) meant a microchip containing hundreds of transistors and SSI (small-scale integration) meant transistors in the tens.

VM

VM (Virtual Machine), currently embodied in a product called VM/ESA, is a widely-installed **operating system** for **mainframe**s from IBM that can host other operating systems, including **MVS** and Conversational Monitor System (**CMS**), so that each of the operating systems seems to have its own complete system of software and hardware resources (data storage, telecommunications, processor, and so forth). That is, VM gives each of these operating systems its own "virtual machine." VM, together with CMS, is popular in many large corporations as a system that can let a large number of interactive users communicate or develop and run applications at the same time. VM also provides a good test environment for MVS programs that can be run on an MVS virtual machine.

Many corporations use MVS for business applications and VM as an application development and user communication environment.

VMEbus

VMEbus (VersaModular Eurocard bus) is a **bus** (computer data path) system, designed by Motorola, Signetics, Mostek, and Thompson CSF, that is used in industrial, commercial, and military applications worldwide. VMEbuses are used in traffic control systems, weapons control systems, telecommunication switching systems, data acquisition, video imaging, and robots. VMEbus systems withstand shock, vibration, and extended temperatures better than the buses used in desktop computers, making them ideal for harsh environments.

A VMEbus system is based on the VME standard. The VME standard defines the mechanical specifications such as board dimensions, connector specifications, and enclosure characteristics, as well as the electronic specifications for sub-bus structures, signal functions, timing, signal voltage levels, and master/slave configurations. The most recent VME standard is the VME64 standard. The VME64 standard specifies a 64-bit data path for 6U cards, a 32-bit data path for 3U cards, twice the **bandwidth** for data transmission, lower **noise**, and **plug and play** features. Since the VME64 standard, an extension called the VME64x was added that supports **hot swap**. VME64 cards can be used on older VME bus systems and older VMEbus cards can be used on VME64 systems.

In 1997, a modified VME bus architecture called the VME320 was released by Arizona Digital. This architecture is designed to increase data transfer to 320 Mbps and bandwidth to 500 Mbps. The **backplane** design is different from the original VMEbus backplane.

The VMEbus system uses Eurocards. A Eurocard is a European designed circuit board that uses a 96-pin plug instead of an edge connector making it more durable. There are three sizes: 3U which is 4×6 inches, 6U which is 6×12 inches, and 9U which is 14×18 inches. 3U cards support 8- and 16-bit data paths and 6U cards support 32-bit data paths. The VME standard does not support 9U cards. Each card is plugged into a backplane. A backplane can have up to 21 slots for cards. A VMEbus system is scalable and modular, which means a card can be added when needed without having to make any other changes to the system.

A real-time operating system (**RTOS**) is included when a VMEbus system is purchased. An RTOS is better for VMEbus systems because of their ability to do a task within a certain time limit. Non real-time operating systems can be used but are not recommended.

A VMEbus system uses a master/slave architecture. A master is a device that controls another device. For example, a computer sends data to a printer. The computer is the master, and the printer is the slave because the printer cannot control the computer. A VMEbus system may have several master devices, which is why it is called a **multiprocessing** bus.

A VMEbus system has four sub-buses: the arbitration bus, the data transfer bus, the priority interrupt bus, and the utility bus.

- The arbitration bus controls the requests from various devices using an arbiter module. It gives permission to each device to use the bus and notifies requesting devices when the bus is busy. Requests are based on priority. Requests that are the same in priority are daisy-chained. The arbiter module resides in slot 1 of the backplane.

- The data transfer bus is used for reading and writing operations between modules.

- The priority interrupt bus handles **interrupt**s and monitors the interrupt request lines, which range from **interrupt request**1 to IRQ7. IRQ7 has the highest priority.

- The utility bus supports a system clock.

VMS

See "Virtual Memory System"

vocoder

A vocoder is an audio processor that captures the characteristic elements of an an audio signal and then uses this characteristic signal to affect other audio signals. The technology behind the vocoder effect was initially used in attempts to synthesize speech. The effect called vocoding can be recognized on records as a "talking synthesizer", made popular by artists such as Stevie Wonder. The basic component extracted during the vocoder analysis is called the *formant*. The formant describes the fundamental frequency of a sound and its associated noise components.

The vocoder works like this: The input signal (your voice saying "Hello, my name is Fred") is fed into the vocoder's input. This audio signal is sent through a series of parallel signal filters that create a signature of the input signal, based on the frequency content and level of the frequency components. The signal to be processed (a synthesized string sound, for example) is fed into another input on the vocoder. The filter signature created above during the analysis of your voice is used to filter the synthesized sound. The audio output of the vocoder contains the synthesized sound modulated by the filter created by your voice. You hear a synthesized sound that pulses to the tempo of your voice input with the tonal characteristics of your voice added to it.

voice activation detection

In Voice over IP (**VOiP**), voice activation detection (VAD) is a software application that allows a data network carrying voice traffic over the Internet to detect the absence of audio and conserve bandwidth by preventing the transmission of "silent packets" over the network. Most conversations include about 50% silence; VAD (also called "silence suppression") can be enabled to monitor signals for voice activity so that when silence is detected for a specified amount of time, the application informs the Packet Voice Protocol and prevents the encoder output from being transported across the network.

Voice activation detection can also be used to forward idle noise characteristics (sometimes called ambient or comfort noise) to a remote IP telephone or **gateway**. The universal standard for digitized voice, 64 Kbps, is a constant **bit rate** whether the speaker is actively speaking, is pausing between thoughts, or is totally silent. Without idle noise giving the

illusion of a constant transmission stream during silence suppression, the listener would be likely to think the line had gone dead.

Voice Markup Language

See "VoxML"

Voice over IP

See "VoIP"

voice portal

A voice portal is a Web site or other service that a user can reach by telephone for information such as weather, sport scores, or stock quotes. For example, a mobile user with a **cellular telephone** might dial in to a voice portal Web site and request information using voice or Touchtone keys and receive the requested information from a special voice-producing program at the **Web site**. Whereas a user with a **smartphone** can connect to the Internet and get information on a small visual display (perhaps with a **WAP** interface), the user of a voice portal needs only a regular cellular phone. After requesting information by speaking or pressing keys, the voice portal responds with voice information or, in some cases, with an e-mail message.

Two companies that act as voice portals are BeVocal and Tellme.

voice recognition

Voice or speech recognition is the ability of a machine or program to receive and interpret dictation, or to understand and carry out spoken commands.

For use with computers, **analog** audio must be converted into **digital** signals. This requires **analog-to-digital conversion**. For a computer to decipher the signal, it must have a digital database, or vocabulary, of words or syllables, and a speedy means of comparing this data with signals. The speech patterns are stored on the hard drive and loaded into memory when the program is run. A comparator checks these stored patterns against the output of the A/D converter.

In practice, the size of a voice-recognition program's effective vocabulary is directly related to the **random access memory** capacity of the computer in which it is installed. A voice-recognition program runs many times faster if the entire vocabulary can be loaded into RAM, as compared with searching the hard drive for some of the matches. Processing speed is critical as well, because it affects how fast the computer can search the RAM for matches.

All voice-recognition systems or programs make errors. Screaming children, barking dogs, and loud external conversations can produce false input. Much of this can be avoided only by using the system in a quiet room. There is also a problem with words that sound alike but are spelled differently and have different meanings—for example, "hear" and "here." This problem might someday be largely overcome using stored contextual information. However, this will require more RAM and faster processors than are currently available in personal computers.

Industry leaders in voice recognition include IBM and Dragon Systems.

VoiceXML

VoiceXML is an application of the Extensible Markup Language (**XML**) which, when combined with **voice recognition** technology, enables interactive access to the Web through the telephone or a voice-driven browser. An individual session works through a combination of voice recognition and keypad entry.

VoiceXML 1.0 was created through a collaboration of AT&T, IBM, Lucent Technologies, and Motorola, who were each working on their own approach but joined forces to create an **open** standard. Using XML, a programmer can enable voice recognition through the addition of a few simple **tag**s.

VXML allows people with an ordinary voice telephone to access the Internet to get and send email, check sports scores, make reservations, and so on. VXML also can support natural language, which means that the user is not locked into a limited script, but can speak naturally. In what is called a "modeless" or "conversational" mode, the user can even interrupt the system with an out-of-context question and thus redirect the session. The goal is to make the exchange as natural as possible, as if two humans were interacting.

Here's an example of what VXML would enable a user to do: Pick up a phone, dial the number of the weather Web site, and request, for example, the weekend forecast. The voice request activates an XML query and then the query result is converted back to a voice message to give the user the information requested.

VoIP

VoIP (voice over IP—that is, voice delivered using the Internet Protocol) is a term used in **IP telephony** for a set of facilities for managing the delivery of voice information using the Internet Protocol (**IP**). In general, this means sending voice information in digital form in discrete **packets** rather than in the traditional circuit-committed protocols of the public switched telephone network (**PSTN**). A major advantage of VoIP and Internet telephony is that it avoids the tolls charged by ordinary telephone service.

VoIP, now used somewhat generally, derives from the VoIP Forum, an effort by major equipment providers, including Cisco, VocalTec, 3Com, and Netspeak to promote the use of ITU-T H.323, the standard for sending voice (audio) and video using IP on the public Internet and within an **intranet**. The Forum also promotes the user of directory service

standards so that users can locate other users and the use of touch-tone signals for automatic call distribution and voice mail.

In addition to IP, VoIP uses the real-time protocol (RTP) to help ensure that packets get delivered in a timely way. Using public networks, it is currently difficult to guarantee quality of service (**QoS**). Better service is possible with private networks managed by an enterprise or by an Internet telephony service provider (ITSP).

A technique used by at least one equipment manufacturer, Netspeak, to help ensure faster packet delivery is to **Ping** all possible network **gateway** computers that have access to the public network and choose the fastest path before establishing a Transmission Control Protocol (**TCP**) **sockets** connection with the other end.

Using VoIP, an enterprise positions a "VoIP device" (such as Cisco's AS5300 access server with the VoIP feature) at a **gateway**. The gateway receives packetized voice transmissions from users within the company and then routes them to other parts of its intranet (local area or wide area network) or, using a **T-carrier system** or **E-carrier** interface, sends them over the public switched telephone network.

volatile

In general, volatile (from the Latin "volatilis" meaning "to fly") is an adjective used to describe something unstable or changeable.

In computers, volatile is used to describe **memory** content that is lost when the power is interrupted or switched off. Your computer's ordinary memory (or **RAM**) is volatile memory.

Volatile memory contrasts with **nonvolatile memory**, memory that does not lose content when power is lost, that has a continuous source of power, or does not need to have its memory content periodically refreshed.

volt

The volt (symbolized V) is the International System of Units (**SI**) unit of electric potential or electromotive force. A potential of one volt appears across a resistance of one **ohm** when a **current** of one **ampere** flows through that resistance. Reduced to SI base units, $1 \text{ V} = 1$ kg times m^2 times s^{-3} times A^{-1} (kilogram meter squared per second cubed per ampere).

Voltage can be expressed as an average value over a given time interval, as an instantaneous value at a specific moment in time, or as an effective or root-mean-square (**rms**) value. Average and instantaneous voltages are assigned a **polarity** either negative $(-)$ or positive $(+)$ with respect to a zero, or ground, reference potential. The rms voltage is a dimensionless quantity, always represented by a non-negative real number.

For a steady source of direct-current (**DC**) electric potential, such as that from a zinc-carbon or alkaline electrochemical cell, the average and instantaneous voltages are both approximately +1.5 V if the negative terminal is considered the common ground; the rms voltage is 1.5 V. For standard utility alternating current (**AC**), the average voltage is zero (the polarity constantly reverses); the instantaneous voltage ranges between approximately -165 V and +165 V; the rms voltage is nominally 117 V.

Voltages are sometimes expressed in units representing power-of-10 multiples or fractions of one volt. A kilovolt (symbolized kV) is equal to one thousand volts (1 kV = 10^3 V). A megavolt (symbolized MV) is equal to one million volts (1 MV = 10^6 V). A millivolt (symbolized mV) is equal to one-thousandth of a volt (1 mV = 10^{-3} V). A microvolt (symbolized μV) is equal to one-millionth of a volt (1 μV = 10^{-6} V).

volt per meter

The standard unit of electric field (E-field) strength is the **volt** per **meter** (V/m). An E field of 1 V/m is represented by a potential difference of 1 V existing between two points that are 1 m apart. Reduced to base **SI** units, 1 V/m is the equivalent of one meter kilogram per second cubed per ampere (m $\cdot$ kg $\cdot$ s^{-3} $\cdot$ A^{-1}).

The volt per meter, or some fractional unit based on it, is used as a means of specifying the intensity of the **electromagnetic field** (EM field) produced by a radio transmitter. Although an EM field contains a magnetic (M) component as well as an electric (E) component, the relative field strength of radio signals is easier to measure in free space by sampling only the E component. The magnitude of the E component from a distant radio transmitter is often much less than 1 V/m, and in such cases, fractional units are preferred. One millivolt per meter (mV/m) is equal to 10^{-3} V/m; one microvolt per meter (μ V/m) is equal to 10^{-6} V/m; one nanovolt per meter (nV/m) is equal to 10^{-9} V/m; one picovolt per meter (pV/m) is equal to 10^{-12} V/m.

The magnitude of the E component of a radio wave varies inversely with the distance from the transmitter in a free-space, line-of-sight link. If the distance is doubled, the E-field intensity is cut in half; if the distance increases by a factor of 10, the E-field intensity becomes 1/10 (0.1 times) as great. The E component of an EM field is measured in a single dimension, so the intensity-versus-distance relation is a straight inverse rule, not the inverse-square law.

When expressing the intensity of EM fields at infrared (**IR**), visible, ultraviolet (UV), X-ray, and gamma-ray **wavelength**s, the watt per meter squared, or one of the fractional units based on it, is more commonly used.

Also see **electromagnetic field**.

voltage

Also see **current**, **resistance**, **power**, and **Ohm's Law**.

Voltage, also called *electromotive force* (EMF), is an expression for electric potential or potential difference. If a conductive or semiconductive path is provided between the two points having a relative potential difference, an electric current flows. The common symbol for voltage is the uppercase letter V or E. The standard unit is the volt, symbolized by V. One volt is the EMF required to drive one coulomb of electrical charge (6.24 $\times$ 10^{18} charge carriers) past a specific point in one second.

Voltage can be either direct or alternating. A direct voltage maintains the same polarity at all times. In an alternating voltage, the polarity reverses direction periodically. The number of complete cycles per second is the **frequency**, which is measured in **hertz**. An example of pure direct voltage is the EMF between the terminals of an electrochemical cell. The output of a power-supply rectifier, prior to filtering, is an example of pulsating direct voltage. The voltage that appears at the terminals of common utility outlets is alternating.

A potential difference produces an electrostatic field, even if no current flows. As the voltage increases between two points separated by a specific distance, the electrostatic field becomes more intense. As the separation increases between two points having a given potential difference, the electrostatic flux density diminishes in the region between them. A single charged object is surrounded by an electrostatic field whose intensity is directly proportional to the voltage of the object relative to other objects in its vicinity.

voltage regulator module

A voltage regulator module (VRM) is an installable module that senses a computer's **microprocessor** voltage requirements and ensures that the correct voltage is maintained. If you are changing your computer's microprocessor (for example, changing from a **Pentium** to a Pentium Pro or a Pentium with **MMX**), you need to add a voltage regulator module to the existing voltage regulator in the **motherboard** so that the new voltage requirements can be detected and accommodated.

In the case of the Pentium, the original Pentium has the same voltage requirement for its core or basic operation as for its I/O operation. Both use 2.8 volts. However, the Pentium Pro and the Pentium with MMX have different voltage requirements for core (2.8 volts) and I/O (3.3 volts). Adding a VRM allows it to regulate the voltage for I/O while the original regulator built into the motherboard continues to regulate core voltage.

volt-ampere

Volt-ampere (VA) is a measurement of **power** in a direct current (**DC**) electrical circuit. The VA specification is also used in alternating current (**AC**) circuits, but it is less precise in this application, because it represents **apparent power**, which often differs from **true power**.

In a DC circuit, 1 VA is the equivalent of one **watt** (1 W). The power, P (in watts) in a DC circuit is equal to the product of the **voltage** V (in **volts**) and the **current** I (in **ampere**s):

$$P = VI$$

In an AC circuit, power and VA mean the same thing only when there is no **reactance**. Reactance is introduced when a circuit contains an **inductor** or **capacitor**. Because most AC circuits contain reactance, the VA figure is greater than the actual dissipated or delivered power in watts. This can cause confusion in specifications for power supplies. For example, a supply might be rated at 600 VA. This does not mean it can deliver 600 watts, unless the equipment is reactance-free. In real life, the true wattage rating of a power supply is $^1/_2$ to $^2/_3$ of the VA rating.

When purchasing a power source such as an uninterruptible power supply (**UPS**) for use with electronic equipment (including computers, monitors, and other peripherals), be sure the VA specifications for the equipment are used when determining the minimum ratings for the power supply. The VA figure is nominally 1.67 times (167 percent of) the power consumption in watts. Alternatively, you can multiply the VA rating of the power supply by 0.6 (60 percent) to get a good idea of its power-delivering capability in watts.

volume

Also see **volume (amount of physical bulk)**.

1) In computers, a volume is an identifiable unit of data **storage** that is sometimes (but not always) physically removable from the computer or storage system. In tape storage systems, a volume may be a tape cartridge (or, in older systems, a tape reel). In **mainframe** storage systems, a volume may be a removable hard disk. Each volume has a system-unique name or number that allows it to be specified by a user.

In some systems, the physical unit may be divided into several separately identifiable volumes.

2) In **audio**, volume is the loudness of the signal.

volume (amount of physical bulk)

Volume (symbolized V) is a three-dimensional quantity representing amount or extent of physical bulk. The standard unit of volume in the International System of Units (**SI**) is the **meter cubed** (m^3).

Volume is usually measured or defined in Euclidean (flat) three-space in Newtonian (non-relativistic) physics. We might speak of the volume of a particle, the volume of a sample of liquid or gas, or the volume of the earth. In relativistic physics, volume is determined for non-Euclidean (curved) three-space. In the case of certain complex or esoteric objects, volume might be impossible to define or measure. One example is a mathematical object having a fractional number of dimensions. Another example is an object without a well-defined surface.

When expressing large or small volumes, **prefix multipliers** are attached to the meter cubed. The table below shows the most common alternative volume units and their relationship to the meter cubed.

Unit (and symbol)	To convert to meters cubed, multiply by:	Conversely, multiply by:
Kilometer cubed (km^3)	10^9	10^{-9}
Centimeter cubed (cm^3)	10^{-6}	10^6
Millimeter cubed (mm^3)	10^{-9}	10^9
Foot cubed (ft^3)	0.0283	35.3
Micrometer cubed or micron cubed (μ^3)	10^{-18}	10^{18}
Nanometer cubed (nm^3)	10^{-27}	10^{27}
Angström squared ($Å^3$)	10^{-30}	10^{30}

Compare **displacement**, and **area**.

Also see **meter**, **meter squared**, **meter cubed**, and International System of Units (**SI**).

von Neumann, John

See "John von Neumann"

Voodoo

Voodoo is a **graphics accelerator chipset** that, depending on the version, is used either with or instead of a computer's **video adapter** for a more realistic graphics display and improved interactivity, especially for games. Voodoo, originally produced by 3Dfx, is considered to be the groundbreaking **3-D** graphics accelerator, providing better graphics quality and faster frame rates than competitors.

The original version of Voodoo was 2-D/3-D; subsequent versions are 3-D. Voodoo 3 and later versions are complete replacements for the computer's video **card**. Earlier cards are **add-on**s that don't replace the video card, but work in conjunction with it. A cable from the computer's video adapter connects to the Voodoo card and then to the monitor, blocking the signal of the original adapter when 3-D acceleration is called for, but allowing the system card to function otherwise.

Voodoo is considered to be particularly helpful for playing games on older and slower computers, allowing the graphics display to reflect user input more swiftly. However, the original version of Voodoo is not considered to offer the same degree of benefit to faster computers.

vortal

On the Web, a vortal (vertical industry portal) is a **Web site** that provides a gateway or **portal** to information related to a particular industry such as health care, insurance, automobiles, or food manufacturing. (A vertical industry is one that is focused on a relatively narrow range of goods and services, whereas a horizontal industry is one that aims to produce a wide range of goods and services. Because most industry tends to specialize, most industry tends to be vertical.) A term that might also be used is *interest community Web site* since any vertical industry brings together people sharing an interest in buying, selling, or exchanging information about that particular industry. Vortals are also seen as likely business-to-business communities—for example, small business people with home offices might be attracted to a comprehensive vortal that provided ideas and product information related to setting up and maintaining the home office.

Related terms are **infomediary** and **vertical market**.

voting online

See "e-voting"

voxel

1) A voxel is a unit of graphic information that defines a point in three-dimensional space. Since a **pixel** (picture element) defines a point in two dimensional space with its **x and y coordinates**, a third **z coordinate** is needed. In 3-D space, each of the coordinates is defined in terms of its position, color, and density. Think of a cube where any point on an outer side is expressed with an x, y coordinate and the third, z coordinate defines a location into the cube from that side, its density, and its color. With this information and 3-D rendering software, a two-dimensional view from various angles of an image can be obtained and viewed at your computer.

Medical practitioners and researchers are now using images defined by voxels and 3-D software to view X-rays, cathode tube scans, and magnetic resonance imaging (MRI) scans from different angles, effectively to see the inside of the body from outside. Geologists can create 3-D views of earth profiles based on sound echoes. Engineers can view complex machinery and material structures to look for weaknesses.

2) Voxel is also a company that makes a scanning camera that will produce 3-D images of the inside of the human body by using a patented digital holography system.

VoxML

VoxML (Voice Markup Language) is a technology from Motorola for creating a voice dialog with a Web site in which a user can call a Web site by phone and interact with it through speech recognition and Web site responses. VoxML (TM) allows a developer to create a script of the conversation a user can have with an application program run by a Web **server**. The user calling in is connected to a **client** program called a *voice browser*. The voice browser in turn passes requests on to the Web server. The **markup** defined in VoxML is consistent with the Extensible Markup Language (**XML**), the strategic data definition language for the Internet. Using VoxML is intended to be no more difficult than writing a Web page using the Hypertext Markup Language (**HTML**).

Motorola is providing VoxML as an **open** interface and potential developers can download the development kit from Motorola's Web site. Motorola has already provided the technology to some early product developers, including The Weather Channel. Typical applications might include delivering weather information, flight information, and sports scores, as well as online product and service ordering.

How the User Uses VoxML

1. The user would identify a Web site that offered phone interaction. For example, some **e-tailing** sites might allow users to order from the Web site by phone instead of by filling out a form.

2. The company with the Web site would publish a phone number to call for their Web site.

3. The user would call the number on a regular phone. (Initially—that is, making the phone connection through the Internet itself—is not supported.)

4. The user would get connected to a *voice browser* at the Web site.

5. When connected, the user would hear a recorded voice that invited the user to interact with the Web site—for example, to place an order or choose some other option.

6. As the user responded, the selected responses could trigger requests from the voice browser to a Web server application. The Web server might also send back new Web pages to the user's computer—for example, pictures of catalog items and order confirmations.

7. The user and the VoxML application would interact until the transaction was completed. Then the user would hang up, ending the session.

How the Developer Develops a VoxML Application

1. First, the developer designs and specifies the application, writing down the possible voice dialogs that will be possible.

2. Working at a regular PC that has the development software installed, the developer uses VoxML, the user dialog statements, and the names of recorded audio response files to create a file that formally defines the dialogs.

3. The developer (or someone else) records each possible voice inquiry, creating a speech file against which users' voice entries can be matched. The developer arranges for any predefined voice responses, which may be available from another application.

4. The developer has the voice client on the PC so that the VoxML script can be tested.

5. After testing, all files are put on the Web site server.

6. The developer modifies the Web site to invite users to request the voice application.

7. Once the VoxML application is set up, users can interact with the Web site through their mouse and keyboard as usual, and also, for invited purposes, over a telephone.

VPD

1) VPD (vital product data) is information about a device that is stored on a computer's hard disk (or the device itself) that allows the device to be administered at a system or network level. Typical VPD information includes a product model number, a unique serial number, product release level, maintenance level, and other information specific to the device type. Vital product data can also include user-defined information, such as the building and department location of the device. The collection and use of vital product data allows the status of a network or computer system to be understood and service provided more quickly.

2) VPD (Visual Parts Database) is a service from TEC Engineering in which a photographic database is created of a company's products and product parts.

3) VPD is also an abbreviation for "virtual printer device."

VPN

See "virtual private network"

VRAM

See "video RAM"

VRM

See "voltage regulator module"

VRML

VRML (Virtual Reality Modeling Language) is a language for describing three-dimensional (3-D) image sequences and possible user interactions to go with them. Using VRML, you can build a sequence of visual images into Web settings with which a user can interact by viewing, moving, rotating, and otherwise interacting with an apparently 3-D scene. For example, you can view a room and use controls to move the room as you would experience it if you were walking through it in real space.

To view a VRML file, you need a VRML viewer or browser, which can be a **plug-in** for a Web browser you already have. Among viewers you can download for the Windows platforms are blaxxun's CC Pro, Platinum's Cosmo Player, WebFX, WorldView, and Fountain. Whurlwind and Voyager are two viewers for the Mac.

VRRP

VRRP (Virtual Router Redundancy Protocol) is an Internet protocol that provides a way to have one or more backup **router**s when using a statically configured router on a local area network (**LAN**). Although there are other alternatives, the most common arrangement is to specify one router to serve as the router for forwarding **packet**s from a group of **host**s on a LAN. If that router fails, however, there is no way to use another router as a backup. Using VRRP, a *virtual IP address* can be specified manually or with Dynamic Host Configuration Protocol (**DHCP**) as a default. A virtual IP address is shared among the routers, with one designated as the master router and the others as backups. In case, the master fails, the virtual IP address is mapped to a backup router's IP address. (This backup becomes the master router.)

VRRP can also be used for load balancing. VRRP is part of both IPv4 (the version of IP that most networks currently use) and **IPv6**.

VSAM

VSAM (Virtual Storage Access Method) is a **file** management system for IBM's larger operating systems, including its primary **mainframe** operating system, **MVS**, now called OS/390. Using VSAM, an **enterprise** can create and access **record**s in a file in the sequential order that they were entered. It can also save and access each record with a *key* (for example, the name of an employee).

Many corporations that developed programs for IBM's mainframes still run programs that access VSAM files (also called *data sets*). VSAM succeeded earlier IBM file *access methods*, SAM (Sequential Access Method) and ISAM (Indexed Sequential Access Method). Although VSAM is still supported for legacy applications, IBM now promotes (**DB2**), a relational database management system.

VSAT

VSAT (Very Small Aperture Terminal) is a **satellite** communications system that serves home and business users. A VSAT end user needs a box that interfaces between the user's computer and an outside antenna with a **transceiver**. The tranceiver receives or sends a signal to a satellite **transponder** in the sky. The satellite sends and receives signals from an earth station computer that acts as a **hub** for the system. Each end user is interconnected with the hub station via the satellite in a star topology. For one end user to communicate with another, each transmission has to first go to the hub station which retransmits it via the satellite to the other end user's VSAT. VSAT handles data, voice, and video signals.

VSAT is used both by home users who sign up with a large service such as DirecPC and by private companies that operate or lease their own VSAT systems. VSAT offers a number of advantages over terrestrial alternatives. For private applications, companies can have total control of their own communication system without dependence on other companies. Business and home users also get higher speed reception than if using ordinary telephone service or **ISDN**.

VSP

See "Virtual Storage Portal"

VTAM

VTAM (Virtual Telecommunications Access Method) is an IBM application program interface (**API**) for communicating with telecommunication devices and their users. VTAM was the first IBM program to allow programmers to deal with devices as "logical units" without having to understand the details of line **protocol** and device operation. Prior to VTAM, programmers used IBM's Basic Telecommunications Access Method (BTAM) to communicate with devices that used the binary synchronous (BSC) and start-stop line protocols.

VTAM became part of IBM's strategic Systems Network Architecture (**SNA**) which in turn became part of the more comprehensive Systems Application Architecture (**SAA**). As the computer industry turned to **open** standard architectures, IBM began to deemphasize its proprietary architectures in favor of becoming a participant and leader in developing open standard architectures. However, most of its customer base retains a large investment in **legacy application**s and system skills based on VTAM, SNA, and SAA.

VTAM's interface consists of "macro instructions" that set up connection control blocks and then do SENDs to devices and either **synchronous** or **asynchronous** READs from them. Typically, programs written in **COBOL**, **PL/1**, and **assembler** language use VTAM to communicate with interactive devices and their users. Programs that use VTAM macro instructions are generally exchanging text strings (for example, online forms and the user's form input) and the most common interactive device used with VTAM programs was the 3270 Information Display System.

W2K

W2K stands for **Windows 2000**, which is also sometimes shortened to Win2000.

W3C

The World Wide Web Consortium (W3C) describes itself as follows:

> "The World Wide Web Consortium exists to realize the full potential of the Web.
>
> The W3C is an industry consortium which seeks to promote standards for the evolution of the Web and interoperability between WWW products by producing specifications and reference software. Although W3C is funded by industrial members, it is vendor-neutral, and its products are freely available to all.
>
> The Consortium is international; jointly hosted by the MIT Laboratory for Computer Science in the U.S. and in Europe by INRIA who provide both local support and performing core development. The W3C was initially established in collaboration with CERN, where the Web originated, and with support from DARPA and the European Commission."

Organizations may apply for membership to the Consortium; individual membership isn't offered. The W3C has taken over what was formerly called the **CERN Hypertext Transfer Protocol daemon** or Web server.

WAD

A WAD (pronounced WAHD) is a file that comes with Doom and possibly other Id Software games, containing information about game levels, game objects, creatures, graphic images, and sound. Typically, these are files in the **megabyte** range.

Many game editors allow users to create additional WAD files with their own game levels, backgrounds, creatures, and weapons. The new WAD file is loaded with the game's original WAD file and can be selected from the game's menu.

The WAD file is unique to Id Software products, but there are comparable files for other games, such as PIG and HOG files for LucasArts' Dark Forces game, MAP for Duke Nukem 3D, and PAK for Quake.

WAD is not an acronym or abbreviation. It's just "WAD."

WAIS

No longer much used, wide-area information servers (WAIS) is an Internet system in which specialized subject databases are created at multiple **server** locations, kept track of by a *directory of servers* at one location, and made accessible for searching by users with WAIS **client** programs. The user of WAIS is provided with or obtains a list of distributed **database**s. The user enters a search argument for a selected database and the client then accesses all the servers on which the database is distributed. The results provide a description of each text that meets the search requirements. The user can then retrieve the full text.

WAIS (pronounced "ways") uses its own Internet **protocol**, an extension of the Z39.50 standard (Information Retrieval Service Definition and Protocol Specification for Library Applications) of the National Information Standards Organization. Web users can use WAIS by either downloading a WAIS client and a "gateway" to the Web browser or by using **Telnet** to connect to a public WAIS client.

wait state

A wait state is a situation in which a computer **program** or **processor** is waiting for the completion of some event before resuming activity. A program or process in a wait state is inactive for the duration of the wait state. For example, an application program that communicated with one other program might send that program a message and then go into a wait state until it was "reawakened" by a message back from the other program.

When a computer processor works at a faster **clock speed** (expressed in **MHz** or millions of cycles per second) than the random access memory (**RAM**) that sends it instructions, it is set to go into a wait state for one or more clock cycles so that it is synchronized with RAM speed. In general, the more time a processor spends in wait states, the slower the **performance** of that processor.

Wake on LAN

Wake on LAN is a technology that allows a network professional to remotely power on a computer or to wake it up from *sleep mode*. Wake on LAN (**local area network**) is a part of a joint Intel-IBM Wired for Management technology. Wired for Management is designed to help network professionals save time and money on automated tasks such as software installation and upgrades, backups, and virus scans by scheduling these tasks during hours when network activity is at a minimum. By remotely triggering the computer to wake up and start these scheduled tasks, the

technician does not have to physically visit each computer to turn them on first. Wake on LAN is for use with **Ethernet** and **token ring** networks.

Wake on LAN works by sending a wake-up **frame** or **packet** to a client machine from a server machine that has remote network management software installed. The Wake on LAN network adapter installed in the client receives the wake-up frame and turns on. The scheduled tasks then begin. To use Wake on LAN technology you need a Wake on LAN network adapter, Wake on LAN-enabled motherboard, and remote management software:

- The Wake on LAN network adapter continually monitors the network looking for wake-up frames. The adapter must have a constant power source in order to boot up, which is usually from a special power supply that delivers a certain amount of power continually. The Wake on LAN adapter also decodes the wake-up frame to determine if it is a wake-up. The key to determining a wake-up frame is if the media access control (**MAC address**) address is repeated 16 times without breaks or interruptions.

- The motherboard must contain a **complementary metal-oxide semiconductor** (CMOS) that is designed to use Wake on LAN technology.

- The remote management software sends the wake-up frames. This software also enables a professional to disable Wake on LAN technology. The remote management software allows the scheduling of tasks that are needed and tells the computer to shut down or go into sleep mode when done.

walkie talkie

See "handie talkie"

walled garden

On the Internet, a walled garden is an environment that controls the user's access to Web content and services. In effect, the walled garden directs the user's navigation within particular areas, to allow access to a selection of material, or prevent access to other material. An Internet service provider (**ISP**) may or may not allow users to select some of the Web sites contained or barred from the garden. Although the walled garden does not actually prevent users from navigating outside the walls, it makes it more difficult than staying within the environment. ISPs want to fence in users for a number of reasons. In 1999, for example, America Online (AOL) UK's Kid Channel established a walled garden to prevent access to inappropriate Web sites. However, a common reason for the construction of walled gardens is for the profits they generate: vendors collaborate to direct consumer's Internet navigation to each others' Web sites and to try to keep them from accessing the Web sites of competitors.

Because **wireless** devices such as **smartphone**s are often limited to the content provided by their carriers, the portion of the Web that is available to wireless users is frequently referred to as a walled garden. Speaking of the Web as a whole, AOL is generally considered the major—and most successful—practitioner of the walled garden approach. According to a spokesperson from Disney (arguing against the recent AOL—Time Warner merger), 85% of AOL users never leave AOL territory; according to *The Economist*, almost 40% of the time Americans spend on the Web is within the confines of AOL's walled garden.

The term's creation is attributed to John Malone, former owner of Tele-Communications Inc. AT&T, who purchased Malone's company, compares the walled garden to a magazine, in which a compilation of various types of content is made available to the reader. The walled garden concept is unpopular with many consumers. Although it offers an easy-to-navigate selection of services and content, that selection includes only a very small part of what the Web has to offer. Alternate names, such as "walled prison" and "walled desert" have been proposed by some as more reflective of the confinement and lack of diversity of the walled garden.

wallet

A wallet is a small software program used for online purchase transactions. Many payment solution companies, such as CyberCash, offer free wallet software that allows several methods of payment to be defined within the wallet (for example, several different credit cards).

wallpaper

On a computer that is provided with a **desktop** kind of **user interface**, wallpaper is the background pattern or picture against which desktop menus, icons, and other elements are displayed and moved around. A wallpaper image can be in a **JPEG** or a **GIF** file format. Wallpaper is commonly used in Microsoft **Windows**, **Macintosh Mac OS**, **Linux**, and in other **operating system**s as well. Each operating system provides several pre-installed wallpaper images for the user to choose from. A user can also choose to download and install third-party wallpapers and use one of these instead.

Typically, a wallpaper image may be centered, stretched, or tiled. When an image is centered, it is placed in the middle of the desktop and is surrounded by a solid color. When an image is stretched, it is stretched to cover all of the desktop. Only certain images can be stretched or they look distorted. An image that is tiled is placed on the desktop much like tiles are placed in a shower or a tiled floor. Tiling is commonly used for patterns instead of photos because a pattern is one square image that repeats itself across and down the screen, effectively forming a single image.

WAN

See "wide area network"

WAP

WAP (Wireless Application Protocol) is a specification for a set of communication **protocol**s to standardize the way that **wireless** devices, such as cellular telephones and radio transceivers, can be used for Internet access, including e-mail, the World Wide Web, newsgroups, and Internet Relay Chat (**IRC**). While Internet access has been possible in the past, different manufacturers have used different technologies. In the future, devices and service systems that use WAP will be able to interoperate.

The WAP layers are:

- Wireless Application Environment (WAE)
- Wireless Session Layer (WSL)
- Wireless Transport Layer Security (WTLS)
- Wireless Transport Layer (WTP)

The WAP was conceived by four companies: Ericsson, Motorola, Nokia, and Unwired Planet (now Phone.com). The Wireless Markup Language (**WML**) is used to create pages that can be delivered using WAP.

There are other approaches to an industry standard besides WAP, including **i-Mode**.

war dialer

A war dialer is a computer program used to identify the phone numbers that can successfully make a connection with a computer **modem**. The program automatically dials a defined range of phone numbers and logs and enters in a database those numbers that successfully connect to the modem. Some programs can also identify the particular operating system running in the computer and may also conduct automated penetration testing. In such cases, the war dialer runs through a predetermined list of common user names and passwords in an attempt to gain access to the system.

A war dialer, usually obtained as **freeware**, is typically used by a hacker to identify potential targets. If the program does not provide automated penetration testing, the intruder attempts to hack a modem with unprotected log-ins or easily cracked passwords. Commercial war dialers, also known as modem scanners, are also used by system administrators, to identify unauthorized modems on an enterprise network. Such modems can provide easy access to a company's intranet.

warez

Warez (pronounced as though spelled "wares" or possibly by some pronounced like the city of "Juarez") is a term used by software "pirates" to describe software that has been stripped of its copy-protection and made available on the Internet for downloading. People who create warez sites sometimes call them "warez sitez" and use "z" in other pluralizations.

WASP

See "wireless application service provider"

waterfall model

(The waterfall model is also referred to as the **systems development life cycle model**.)

In software engineering, the waterfall model describes a development method that is linear and sequential. Waterfall development has distinct goals for each phase of development. Imagine a waterfall on the cliff of a steep mountain. Once the water has flowed over the edge of the cliff and has begun its journey down the side of the mountain, it cannot turn back. It is the same with waterfall development. Once a phase of development is completed, the development proceeds to the next phase and there is no turning back.

The advantage of waterfall development is that it allows for departmentalization and managerial control. A schedule can be set with deadlines for each stage of development and a product can proceed through the development process like a car in a carwash, and theoretically, be delivered on time. Development moves from concept, through design, implementation, testing, installation, troubleshooting, and ends up at operation and maintenance. Each phase of development proceeds in strict order, without any overlapping or **iterative** steps.

The disadvantage of waterfall development is that it does not allow for much reflection or revision. Once an application is in the testing stage, it is very difficult to go back and change something that was not well-thought out in the concept stage.

watermark

See "steganography"

watt

The watt (abbreviated W) is the standard unit of **power** (or **energy** per unit time) and is the equivalent of one **joule** per second. The watt is used to specify the rate at which electrical energy is dissipated, or the rate at which electromagnetic energy is radiated, absorbed, or dissipated.

In DC (direct current) and low-frequency AC (**alternating current**) electrical circuits and systems, power is the product of the **current** and the **voltage**. Power is also proportional to the ratio of the square of the voltage to the **resistance**, and to the product of the resistance and the square of the current. Consider a circuit in which the current, voltage, and resistance are all constant. If the current in amperes is represented by I, the voltage (or potential difference) in volts is represented by E, and the resistance in ohms is represented by R, then the following equations hold for power in watts, represented by P:

$$P = EI$$
$$P = E^2/R$$
$$P = I^2R$$

In radio-frequency (RF) circuits and systems, the calculation of power becomes more complex. This is because, at high frequencies, AC is affected not only by resistance, but by **reactance**. In these situations, no simple formulas exist for the calculation of power. However, dissipated or radiated RF power in can be determined by direct measurement using an instrument called an RF wattmeter.

In situations involving very high or very low power, prefix multipliers are commonly used to obtain power units. As the rate of dissipated or radiated power increases, one kilowatt (kW) is equal to 1000 W; one megawatt (MW) is equal to 10^6 W; one gigawatt (GW) is equal to 10^9 W. As power decreases, one milliwatt (mW) is equal to 0.001 W; one microwatt (W) is equal to 10^{-6} W; one nanowatt (nW) is equal to 10^{-9} W.

watt per steradian

The watt per steradian ($W \cdot sr^{-1}$) is the standard unit of radiant intensity. Reduced to base units in the International System of Units (**SI**), it is the equivalent of a **kilogram meter squared per second** cubed per **steradian** ($kg \cdot m^2 \cdot s^{-3} \cdot sr^{-1}$).

A point source of electromagnetic (EM) power that radiates equally well in all directions, and whose output is $1\ W \cdot sr^{-1}$, has a total output power of 4p (approximately 12.5664) **watts** (W). This is because there are 4p steradians in three-dimensional space with respect to a point of reference. The watt per steradian can be used to define the radiant intensity at any EM **wavelength**, from low-frequency radio waves through the gamma-ray spectrum. For visible light, in the wavelength range of approximately 390 to 770 nanometers (nm), the **lumen** is the preferred unit.

Suppose an **electromagnetic field** having P watts of total power is radiated from an isotropic emitter (that is, a point source that radiates equally well in all directions). Then the radiant intensity, P', in watts per steradian is given by the following formula:

$$P' = P\ /\ (4p)$$

Also see **electromagnetic field**, **lumen**, **power**, International System of Units (**SI**), **steradian**, and **watt**.

wav

See "Wave file"

wave division multiplexing

See "dense wavelength division multiplexing"

Wave file

A Wave file is an audio file format, created by Microsoft, that has become a standard PC audio file format for everything from system and game sounds to CD-quality audio. A Wave file is identified by a file name extension of WAV (.wav). Used primarily in PCs, the Wave file format has been accepted as a viable interchange medium for other computer platforms, such as Macintosh. This allows content developers to freely move audio files between platforms for processing, for example.

In addition to the uncompressed raw audio data, the Wave file format stores information about the file's number of tracks (mono or stereo), sample rate, and bit depth.

wave number

The term wave number refers to the number of complete wave cycles of an **electromagnetic field** (EM field) that exist in one **meter** (1 m) of linear space. Wave number is expressed in reciprocal meters (m^{-1}).

The wave number for an EM disturbance is simply the reciprocal of the **wavelength** in meters. For example, if a **microwave** radio signal has a wavelength of one centimeter (1 cm or 0.01 m), then the wave number of that signal is $1/(0.01\ m) = 100\ m^{-1}$. As the wavelength grows shorter, the wave number becomes larger.

Wave number is usually specified for EM disturbances in a vacuum, also called free space. In most situations, the air is equivalent to a vacuum. In media other than free space, the wave number for a given disturbance may increase. When a ray of light passes from air into water or glass, or a radio signal propagates through a polyethylene **dielectric** rather than air, the wavelength is shortened because the speed of propagation decreases. This causes the wave number to increase.

In free space, the wave number w (in reciprocal meters) is related to the **frequency** f (in **hertz**) according to the following formula:

$$w = f/c$$

where c is the speed of EM propagation in free space, approximately equal to 2.99792×10^8 meters per second.

In media other than free space, c must be multiplied by a velocity factor v. The velocity factor for a particular medium is the ratio of the speed of EM propagation in that medium to the speed of EM propagation in free space. As such, the velocity factor is always greater than 0 and less than or equal to 1. Taking velocity factor into account, the above formula becomes:

$$w = f/(vc)$$

See also **EM field**, **frequency**, and **wavelength**.

waveform

A waveform is a representation of how alternating current (**AC**) varies with time. The most familiar AC waveform is the *sine wave*, which derives its name from the fact that the current or voltage varies with the sine of the elapsed time. Other common AC waveforms are the square wave, the ramp, the sawtooth wave, and the triangular wave. Their general shapes are shown below.

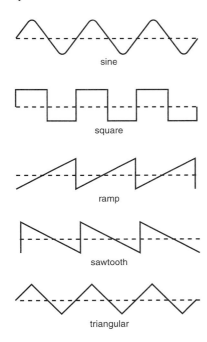

Some AC waveforms are irregular or complicated. Square or sawtooth waves are produced by certain types of electronic oscillators, and by a low-end UPS (uninterruptible power supply) when it is operating from its battery. Irregular AC waves are produced by audio amplifiers that deal with analog voice signals and/or music.

The sine wave is unique in that it represents energy entirely concentrated at a single **frequency**. An ideal, unmodulated **wireless** signal has a sine waveform, with a frequency usually measured in megahertz (**MHz**) or gigahertz (**GHz**). Household utility current has a sine waveform with a frequency of 60 Hz in most countries including the United States, although in some countries it is 50 Hz.

waveguide

A waveguide is an electromagnetic **feed line** used in **microwave** communications, broadcasting, and radar installations. A waveguide consists of a rectangular or cylindrical metal tube or pipe. The **electromagnetic field** propagates lengthwise. Waveguides are most often used with **horn antenna**s and **dish antenna**s.

An electromagnetic field can propagate along a waveguide in various ways. Two common modes are known as transverse-magnetic (TM) and transverse-electric (TE). In TM mode, the magnetic lines of flux are perpendicular to the axis of the waveguide. In TE mode, the electric lines of flux are perpendicular to the axis of the waveguide. Either mode can provide low loss and high efficiency as long as the interior of the waveguide is kept clean and dry.

To function properly, a waveguide must have a certain minimum diameter relative to the **wavelength** of the signal. If the waveguide is too narrow or the **frequency** is too low (the wavelength is too long), the electromagnetic fields cannot propagate. At any frequency above the cutoff (the lowest frequency at which the waveguide is large enough), the feed line will work well, although certain operating characteristics vary depending on the number of wavelengths in the cross section.

wavelength

Wavelength is the distance between identical points in the adjacent cycles of a waveform **signal** propagated in space or along a wire, as shown in the illustration. In **wireless** systems, this length is usually specified in meters, centimeters, or millimeters. In the case of infrared, visible light, ultraviolet, and gamma radiation, the wavelength is more often specified in nanometers (units of 10^{-9} meter) or Angstrom units (units of 10^{-10} meter).

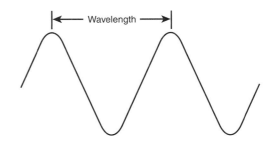

Wavelength is inversely related to **frequency**. The higher the frequency of the signal, the shorter the wavelength. If f is the frequency of the signal as measured in megahertz, and w is the wavelength as measured in meters, then

$w = 300/f$

and conversely

$f = 300/w$

Wavelength is sometimes represented by the Greek letter lambda.

wavelength switching

See "lambda switching"

wavelength-division multiplexing

In fiber optic communications, a single **laser** beam can carry millions of independent signals. A common way to get a large number of signals onto a visible-light or infrared (**infrared transmission**) laser is to assign each signal a separate radio **frequency**. At the fiber optic transmitter, the laser is **modulated** at all signal frequencies simultaneously. At the receiver, the signals are separated by a device similar to a radio receiver. This process is frequency-division multiplexing (**FDM**).

A modulated laser has a frequency far higher than that of any of the signals it carries. For visible light and IR, the **wavelength** is more often specified than the frequency. A visible-red laser might have a wavelength of 735 nanometers (nm), where 1 nm = 10^{-9} meter. A **blue laser** might produce a beam of 440 nm; an IR laser might generate energy at 1500 nm. Most fiber optic systems use lasers having wavelengths between 1300 nm and 1600 nm, in the near-IR region.

In a simple fiber optic system, the receiver is not sensitive to the wavelength of the laser. But wavelength-sensitive filters, the IR analog of visible-light color filters, can be used at the receiving end of a fiber optic system. Then, lasers of various wavelengths can be transmitted along a single fiber, and each laser can be modulated by its own set of radio-frequency signals. This is known as wavelength-division multiplexing (WDM).

The use of WDM can multiply the effective **bandwidth** of a fiber optic communications system. But its cost must be weighed against the alternative of using several separate fibers bundled into a cable. An emerging fiber optic **repeater** device called the **erbium amplifier** promises to make WDM a cost-effective technology.

wavelet

A wavelet is a mathematical function useful in **digital signal processing** and **image compression**. The use of wavelets for these purposes is a recent development, although the theory is not new. The principles are similar to those of Fourier analysis, which was first developed in the early part of the 19th century.

In signal processing, wavelets make it possible to recover weak signals from **noise**. This has proven useful especially in the processing of X-ray and magnetic-resonance images in medical applications. Images processed in this way can be "cleaned up" without blurring or muddling the details.

In Internet communications, wavelets have been used to compress images to a greater extent than is generally possible with other methods. In some cases, a wavelet-compressed image can be as small as about 25 percent the size of a similar-quality image using the more familiar **JPEG** method. Thus, for example, a photograph that requires 200 KB and takes a minute to download in JPEG format might require only 50 KB and take 15 seconds to download in wavelet-compressed format.

Wavelet compression works by analyzing an image and converting it into a set of mathematical expressions that can then be decoded by the receiver. A wavelet-compressed image file is often given a name suffix of "WIF." Either your browser must support these files or it will require a **plug-in** program to read the fles.

Wavelet compression is not yet widely used on the Web. The most common compressed image formats remain the Graphics Interchange Format (**GIF**), used mainly for drawings, and JPEG, used mainly for photographs.

wavetable

In computer technology, a wavetable is a table of stored sound waves that are digitized samples of actual recorded sound. A wavetable is stored in read-only memory (**ROM**) on a sound card **chip** but it can also be supplemented with software. Originally, computer sounds (digital versions of **analog** waveforms) were generated through frequency modulation (**FM**). Prestoring sound waveforms in a lookup table improved quality and throughput.

Today's more advanced sound cards include wavetables with 32 "voices" or instruments (that are combined during creation and playback). Some sound cards work with software that provides additional voices. Wavetables are used as part of music or sound synthesizers that use the musical instrument digital interface (**MIDI**). MIDI lets you capture sound and play it back based on the commands in files that are essentially little "scripts" to the "orchestra" (one might think of it as a written description of what the conductor is doing and which instruments are being pointed to with the baton). A wavetable sound can be enhanced or modified using reverberation or other effects before it is saved in the table. Some wavetable chips include a special section for drum sounds to support rhythmic effects.

Many sound cards take advantage of Direct Memory Access (**DMA**). Many also include an FM synthesizer in order to play back sounds from older applications or files. A full-duplex sound card lets you record and playback at the same time or, if you're using Internet telephony, talk and hear at the same time.

Wavetable sound cards use digital signal processor (**DSP**) chips.

WAX

Wireless Abstract XML (WAX) is an abstract **markup** language and associated tools that facilitate **wireless** application development. WAX comes as an integral part of **Morphis**, an **open source transcoding** platform from Kargo, Inc. Because WAX **tag**s perform at a higher level of abstraction than those of earlier wireless markup languages,

WAX translates to common languages, such as Hypertext Markup Language (**HTML**), Wireless Markup Language (**WML**), and Handheld Device Markup Language (**HDML**) through Extensible Stylesheet Language (**XSL**) **style sheet**s and XSL Transformations (**XSLT**).

The major features of WAX include: the WAX language itself; translation stylesheets, which are used to translate the WAX language into the most suitable language for the requesting device; the device registry, which includes an XML database of device particulars; dynamic image and text selection, which allows content to be written a single time for multiple transformations; and the application foundation, a WAX **servlet** that creates a foundation for WAX applications. Kargo claims that WAX transforms content for various wireless graphical user interfaces (**GUI**s) more easily and seamlessly than other wireless languages. WAX tags have complex and variable functionality: for example, a single tag can create different display options on separate devices. Because WAX is an **extensible** language, elements of other languages can easily be incorporated into applications.

WBT

See "Web-based training"

WCDMA

Also see **CDMA**, **CDMA One**, and **CDMA2000**.

WCDMA (wideband code-division multiple access), an **ITU** standard derived from code-division multiple access (**CDMA**), is officially known as IMT-2000 direct spread. WCDMA is a third-generation (**3G**) mobile wireless technology offering much higher data speeds to mobile and portable wireless devices than commonly offered in today's market.

WCDMA can support mobile/portable voice, images, data, and video communications at up to 2 **Mbps** (local area access) or 384 **Kbps** (wide area access). The input signals are digitized and transmitted in coded, spread-spectrum mode over a broad range of frequencies. A 5 **MHz**-wide carrier is used, compared with 200 **KHz**-wide carrier for narrowband CDMA.

WDM

See "dense wavelength division multiplexing"

wearable computer

Some inventors and other theorists not only believe you could wear a computer; they believe there's no reason why you shouldn't. Assuming you remembered to wear it, a wearable computer is always available. Currently, several companies sell wearables and there is a considerable literature on the subject. Some wearable computers are basically desktop or notebook computers that have been scaled down for body-wear. Others employ brand new technology. Both general and special purposes are envisioned. A number of wearables have been designed for the disabled.

Among the challenges of wearable computers are: how to minimize their weight and bulkiness, how and where to locate the display, and what kind of data entry device to provide. Some of the applications envisioned for wearable computers include:

- Augmented memory, a concept originated by Thad Starner and being developed by Bradley Rhodes at the MIT Media Lab, in which as you enter a room, your wearable computer could sense the people present and remind you of their names or personal history, or a scheduler could whisper the time of an important meeting in your ear, or a "remembrance agent" could look for related documents by observing the words you were typing

- Immediate access to important data for anyone whose occupation requires mobility, such as real estate agents, rural doctors, fire and police professionals, lawyers in courtrooms, horse bettors, military personnel, stock brokers, and many others

- The ability to take notes immediately. For example, for reporters, geologists, botanists, vendor show representatives, field service repair personnel.

Web bug

A Web bug is a file object, usually a graphic image such as a transparent one **pixel**-by-one pixel **GIF**, that is placed on a Web page or in an e-mail message to monitor user behavior, functioning as a kind of **spyware**. Unlike a **cookie**, which can be accepted or declined by a browser user, a Web bug arrives as just another **GIF** on the Web page. A Web bug is typically invisible to the user because it is transparent (matches the color of the page background) and takes up only a tiny amount of space. It can usually only be detected if the user looks at the source version of the page to find a an IMG tag that loads from a different Web server than the rest of the page.

Although proponents of Internet privacy object to the use of Web bugs in general, they also concede that Web bugs can be put to positive use, for example to track copyright violations on the Web.

According to Richard M. Smith, a Web bug can gather the following statistics:

- The IP address of the computer that fetched the Web bug
- The URL of the page that the Web bug is located on
- The URL of the Web bug image
- The time the Web bug was viewed
- The type of browser that fetched the Web bug image
- A previously set cookie value

Web farm

See "server farm"

Web hosting

Web hosting (also known as Webhosting, Web site hosting, and hosting) is the business of housing, serving, and maintaining files for one or more **Web sites**.

Web Proxy Autodiscovery

Web Proxy Autodiscovery (WPAD) is a proposed Internet **protocol** that allows a **client**, such as a Web **browser** or a **streaming media** application, to automatically locate and interface with **cache** services in a network so that information can be delivered more quickly to the user. A cache service stores copies of popular Web pages at a location closer to the users, usually on the outer edges of a network, for faster access. When a particular page is requested, the browser is directed to the cache service for that page instead of having to travel through the network to the originating site.

Cache services are maintained and offered by Internet service providers (**ISP**s) and special cache-providing services such as Akamai. The first WPAD-enabled browser was Internet Explorer 5.0. WPAD is a joint effort of Inktomi, Microsoft, Real Networks, and Sun Microsystems.

When an Internet session is started, the WPAD-enabled client automatically uses Dynamic Host Configuration Protocol (**DHCP**) to locate a cache service. If unsuccessful, WPAD then uses the Service Location Protocol (**SLP**). SLP is a protocol that allows network applications to discover the location and configuration of network services in an enterprise. If still unsuccessful, WPAD then searches through domain name system (**DNS**) records. Once a nearby cache service is located, WPAD automatically connects to that location for related page requests.

Web ring

A Web ring (or Webring) is a way of interlinking related Web **site**s so that you can visit each site one after the other, eventually (if you keep going) returning to the first Web site. Typically, users can also elect to go backwards through the ring of sites, skip a certain number at a time, visit sites randomly, or see a list of all the sites on the ring. A ring is managed from one site which includes a common gateway interface (**CGI**) application that can select random sites and bypass sites that have dropped out or aren't reachable.

The ring idea seems to have caught on as a more dynamic alternative to the list of "favorite sites" that many Web sites offer. The originator of the idea, Sage Weil (now 19 and in college), started the first ring in May, 1995. With several collaborators, Sage has created WebRing, a Web ring management system. As of April, 1998, there were over 40,000 Web rings using the system.

There are Web rings on acrobatics, quilting, mermaids, the macabre, Spanish hotels, the Chevrolet, Dixieland, medieval studies, native American sites, and Winnie the Pooh. The largest number are on computer- and game-related subjects.

Web server

A Web **server** is a program that, using the **client/server** model and the World Wide Web's Hypertext Transfer Protocol (**HTTP**), serves the files that form Web pages to Web users (whose computers contain HTTP clients that forward their requests). Every computer on the Internet that contains a Web site must have a Web server program. The most popular Web servers are Microsoft's Internet Information Server (**IIS**), which comes with the **Windows NT** server; **Netscape** FastTrack and Enterprise servers; and **Apache**, a Web server for **UNIX**-based operating systems. Other Web servers include Novell's Web Server for users of its **NetWare** operating system and IBM's family of Lotus Domino servers, primarily for IBM's **OS/390** and **AS/400** customers.

Web servers often come as part of a larger package of Internet- and intranet-related programs for serving e-mail, downloading requests for File Transfer Protocol (**FTP**) files, and building and publishing Web pages. Considerations in choosing a Web server include how well it works with the operating system and other servers, its ability to handle server-side programming, and publishing, search engine, and site building tools that may come with it.

Web server farm

See "server farm"

Web Services Description Language

The Web Services Description Language (WSDL) is an **XML**-based language used to describe the services a business offers and to provide a way for individuals and other businesses to access those services electronically. WSDL is the cornerstone of the Universal Description, Discovery, and Integration (**UDDI**) initiative spearheaded by Microsoft, IBM, and Ariba. UDDI is an XML-based registry for businesses worldwide, which enables businesses to list themselves and their services on the Internet. WSDL is the language used to do this.

WSDL is derived from Microsoft's Simple Object Access Protocol (**SOAP**) and IBM's Network Accessible Service Specification Language (**NASSL**). WSDL replaces both NASSL and SOAP as the means of expressing business services in the UDDI registry.

Web site

This definition is also listed under *presence*, *site* and *Website*.

A Web site is a related collection of World Wide Web (**WWW**) files that includes a beginning file called a **home page**. A company or an individual tells you how to get to their Web site by giving you the address of their home page. From the home page, you can get to all the other pages on their site. For example, the Web site for IBM has the home page address of http://www.ibm.com. (The home page address actually includes a specific file name like *index.html* but, as in IBM's case, when a standard default name is set up, users don't have to enter the file name.) IBM's home page address leads to thousands of pages. (But a Web site can also be just a few pages.)

Since *site* implies a geographic place, a Web site can be confused with a Web **server**. A server is a computer that holds the files for one or more sites. A very large Web site may be spread over a number of servers in different geographic locations. IBM is a good example; its Web site consists of thousands of files spread out over many servers in world-wide locations. But a more typical example is probably the site you are looking at, whatis.com. We reside on a commercial space provider's server with a number of other sites that have nothing to do with Internet glossaries.

A synonym and less frequently used term for Web site is "Web presence." That term seems to better express the idea that a site is not tied to specific geographic location, but is "somewhere in cyberspace." However, "Web site" seems to be used much more frequently.

You can have multiple Web sites that cross-link to files on each others' sites or even share the same files.

Web site hosting

Web site hosting (also known as hosting, Website hosting, Web hosting, and Webhosting) is the business of housing, serving, and maintaining files for one or more **Web sites**.

Web slate

A Web slate is a **wireless** Internet **appliance** that consists of a liquid crystal display (**LCD**) with a **touch screen** that allows the user to view and interact with Web pages.

Web Solution Platform

Web Solution Platform is a framework created by Microsoft for fitting Windows and the PC into the **3-tier application** concept. In addition to the Windows operating system (**OS**) and the Internet Explorer (IE) **browser**, Microsoft identifies a number of concepts, services, and products as part of its Web Solution Platform.

Microsoft's Web Solution Platform was formerly known as Distributed interNet Applications Architecture (DNA).

Web Standards Project

The Web Standards Project (WaSP) is a grass roots effort to encourage the main **browser** makers to create a standard implementation of the Hypertext Markup Language (**HTML**) and other Web standards and recommendations of the World Wide Consortium (**W3C**). WaSP maintains that the adoption of these standards by both manufacturers can reduce development time and budgets required for Web-based applications by up to 25%.

In spite of the existence of the W3C's recommendations almost since the beginning of Web browsers, both Microsoft's Internet Explorer and Netscape's Navigator have insisted on promoting and supporting non-standard extensions and in implementing existing recommendations differently, forcing public Web site developers to create different versions of their site, one for each browser (and often additional versions to accommodate changes in evolving browser versions).

For future versions of today's browsers, the WaSP is pushing for full support for W3C recommendations related to the Document Object Model (**DOM**), Cascading Style Sheets (**CSS**), and Extensible Markup Language (**XML**).

Web-based training

Web-based training (sometimes called e-learning) is anywhere, any-time instruction delivered over the Internet or a corporate **intranet** to browser-equipped learners. There are two primary models of Web-based instruction: synchronous (instructor-facilitated) and asynchronous (self-directed, self-paced). Instruction can be delivered by a combination of static methods (learning portals, hyperlinked pages, screen cam tutorials, streaming audio/video, and live Web broadcasts) and interactive methods (threaded discussions, chats, and desk-top video conferencing).

The ASTD (American Society for Training and Development) estimates that 75% of the U.S. workforce will need some kind of retraining within the next five years in order to keep pace with industry needs and increasingly global competition. Hewlett-Packard estimates the half-life of an bachelor's degree in engineering can be as short as 18 months. Enthusiasts feel that Web-based instruction is the perfect solution to meeting the needs of life-long learners because it is available on demand, does not require travel, and is cost-efficient. Critics point out that Web-based training is a good alternative for independent, self-motivated students but that technical issues and the need for human contact limit its usefulness for students with other learning styles.

webcam

See "cam"

Webcasting

Also see **push technology**, another usage. In both usages, *netcasting* is a synonym.

The term "Webcasting" is used to describe the ability to use the Web to deliver live or delayed versions of sound or video broadcasts. NetTalk Live! is an example of the former. They use an Internet site to deliver a RealAudio sound version of a live radio and television program at 11 pm (CST) each Sunday night. (They call this a **triplecast**.)

CNet and some other Web sites use the term "Webcast" to describe delayed or preview versions of movies, music videos, or regular radio and television broadcasts as a way to promote the live broadcasts. Each sample is known as a **Webisode**. Viewing Webcasts requires having an appropriate video viewing application such as the NetShow, RealVideo, or VXtreme streaming video players; these can usually be downloaded from any site offering a Webcast.

WebDAV

WebDAV (World Wide Web Distributed Authoring and Versioning) is the Internet Engineering Task Force (**IETF**) standard for collaborative authoring on the Web: a set of extensions to the Hypertext Transfer Protocol (**HTTP**) that facilitates collaborative editing and file management between users located remotely from each other on the Internet.

WebDAV is expected to have an impact on the development of virtual enterprises, by enabling remote groups to work together in new ways. For example, WebDAV-conforming tools could be used by a virtual organization to develop business plans, create software, or write libraries of information. The WebDAV work group is part of the applications section of the World Wide Web Consortium (**W3C**); their charter states its goal as to "define the HTTP extensions necessary to enable distributed Web authoring tools to be broadly interoperable, while supporting user needs." WebDAV is expected to fulfill early expectations of the Web's collaborative potential, by adding *write* access to the *read* access afforded by HTTP. WebDAV will enable users to collaborate over the Web in the same way as they might over a corporate **intranet**.

WebDAV features include:

- Locking (also known as *concurrency control*), which prevents accidental overwriting of files;

- **XML** properties, which facilitate operations (such as storage and retrieval) on **metadata**, so that data *about* other data can be organized;

- The DAV protocol, which enables property setting, deleting, and retrieving;

- The DASL (DAV Searching and Locating) protocol, which enables searches based on property values for locating resources on the Web;

- **Namespace** manipulation, which supports copy and move operations. Collections, which are similar to file system directories, may be created and listed.

Webification

1) Webification (sometimes seen with a lower case *w*) is the act of converting content from its original format into a format capable of being displayed on the World Wide Web. Some conversion examples are:

- A **Postscript** source file or **ASCII text** to a Hypertext Markup Language (**HTML**) file

- A Microsoft Word document to HTML (sometimes referred to as "DOC to HTML"). More recent versions of Microsoft Word include this capability.

- Hard-copy print publication pages into files in the Portable Document Format (**PDF**) for viewing on the Web with Adobe's downloadable **Acrobat** viewer

- A Lotus **Notes database** to HTML files

- An **image** in a scanned-in or other format to a Web-ready image, either a **GIF** or a **JPEG** file

- A speech or interview into a file in the **RealAudio** format for playing as **streaming sound** on the Web

- A video tape recording into a **streaming video** file

Using the File Transfer Protocol (**FTP**) from the Web browser, **text** pages (with files in the **ASCII** TXT format) can also be "Webified" for display by Web users. Many Internet Request for Comment (**RFC**) documents are available on the Web in the text format. The only Webification these files need is to simply make them available in a directory accessible to the FTP server.

2) Webification is the name of a Web site firm in Hollywood, Florida, that specializes in **internetworking** and in Web site design.

Webify

See "Webification"

Webinar

A Webinar is a live or replayed interactive multimedia presentation conducted from a **Web site**. The term combines *Web* with *seminar*. A Webinar typically uses some combination of:

- The presenter speaking (usually with **streaming audio**)

- The presenter also presented visually (**streaming video**)

- A panel of presenters

- A **chat** session that shows typed-in questions and answers as a live Webinar progresses or the entire session when it is played from an archive
- A slide presentation that can be viewed simultaneously
- For a small group, a **whiteboard** that allows the presenter and auditors to draw pictures
- For a small group, PC cameras and microphone that allow some of the auditors to talk to the presenter
- Conference telephone connections to the presenter

One type of Webinar is a chat session with an expert who delivers answers visually and aurally rather than by replying with typed-in responses. A Webinar often specifies that the auditor use or download RealPlayer or Microsoft Media Player and requires site registration. The presentation aspect of a Webinar is sometimes referred to as a Webcast.

Webisode

A Webisode is a single **push technology** episode. A Webisode can be a preview or promotion of a particular TV show, music video, or other show presented from a Web site using streaming video or other techniques. Some sites are dedicated to presenting Webisodes.

Weblog

1) A Weblog (which is sometimes written as "web log" or "weblog") is a **Web site** of personal or non-commercial origin that uses a dated log format that is updated on a daily or very frequent basis with new information about a particular subject or range of subjects. The information can be written by the site owner, gleaned from other Web sites or other sources, or contributed by users.

A Web log often has the quality of being a kind of "log of our times" from a particular point-of-view. Generally, Weblogs are devoted to one or several subjects or themes, usually of topical interest, and, in general, can be thought of as developing commentaries, individual or collective on their particular themes. A Weblog may consist of the recorded ideas of an individual (a sort of diary) or be a complex collaboration open to anyone. Most of the latter are *moderated discussions*.

Since there are a number of variations on this idea and new variations can easily be invented, the meaning of this term is apt to gather additional connotations with time. Currently, the most popular Weblog is Slashdot.org, the product of programmer and graphic artist Rob Malden and several colleagues. Slashdot.org carries discussion **thread** on many subjects including: Money, Quake (the game), Netscape, Sun Microsystems, Hardware, and **Linux**. Slashdot.org solicits and posts interesting stories reported by contributors, includes a link to the story, and manages the threads of the ensuing discussion by other users. Another well-known Weblog is Jorn Barger's Robot Wisdom Log, which is more

of collection of daily highlights from other Web sites. Jessamyn West's librarian.net is a daily log of items interesting to librarians and possibly others, too.

As a format and content approach for a Web site, the Weblog seems popular because the viewer knows that something changes every day, there is a personal (rather than bland commercial) point-of-view, and, on some sites, there is an opportunity to collaborate or respond with the Web site and its participants.

2) Weblog is the name of a software product from South Korea that analyzes a Web site's access **access log** and reports the number of visitors, views, hits, most frequently visited pages, and so forth.

WebLogic

BEA Systems' WebLogic is a **server** software application that runs on a middle **tier**, between **back-end databases** and related applications and **browser**-based **thin clients**. WebLogic is a leading **e-commerce** online transaction processing (**OLTP**) platform, developed to connect users in a **distributed** computing environment and to facilitate the integration of **mainframe** applications with distributed corporate data and applications.

WebLogic server is based on Java 2 Platform, Enterprise Edition (**J2EE**), the standard platform used to create **Java**-based multi-**tier** enterprise applications. J2EE platform technologies were developed through the efforts of BEA Systems and other vendors in collaboration with the main developer, Sun Microsystems. Because J2EE applications are standardized modules, WebLogic can automate many system-level tasks that would otherwise have demanded programming time.

The main features of WebLogic server include connectors that make it possible for any **legacy application** on any client to interoperate with server applications, Enterprise JavaBean (**EJB**) components, resource pooling, and connection sharing that make applications very scalable. An administration console with a user interface makes management tasks more efficient and features such as Secure Sockets Layer (**SSL**) support for the encryption of data transmissions, as well as **authentication** and authorization mechanisms, make applications and transactions secure.

Webmaster

A Webmaster is a person who either:
- Creates and manages the information content (words and pictures) and organization of a Web **site**
- Manages the computer server and technical programming aspects of a Web site
- Or does both.

Companies advertising for a Webmaster vary in their use of the term. In a smaller company, a Webmaster typically "does it all." In a larger company, a Webmaster tends to be

someone with either a writing and/or graphics design background who has acquired Web site creation skills (mainly knowledge and experience with **HTML**) or a more technical person with some programming skills. The "technical" Webmaster runs the **server** (for example, by managing the creation and authorization associated with file systems) and writes programs or **Perl** scripts required by the Web site.

In a very large corporation, there may be a Webmaster team of people at the top of the corporation who establish the overall corporate Web design and policies, arrange the necessary technical resources (working with the people who provide the corporation its network infrastructure), and supervise the design of the corporation's Web site (which is often done by an outside firm). At division and product levels, there may be additional Webmasters who organize and develop the Web content and programming for their division or product. In addition, there is likely to be an interrelated effort to create a Web design, organization, and content for the corporation's **intranet**.

At a small corporation, the Webmaster may be in charge of creating the site and putting it on a separate company's server or setting up one within the company. The Web design and creation may be done initially by an outside Web design firm that turns the finished site over to the company's in-house Webmaster to maintain and perhaps add content within the established design.

And if you are a firm that specializes in creating Web sites, you may refer to the overall producer or art director as the Webmaster for a site. Obviously, this term (and job) is is still defining itself. A Webmaster is what a company says one is. In general, almost any Webmaster would be expected to know the Hypertext Markup Language (**HTML**) and have a good understanding of why a company should want a Web site.

WebNFS

WebNFS is a product and proposed standard protocol from Sun Microsystems that extends its Network File System (**NFS**) to the Internet. Sun believes WebNFS offers considerable performance advantages over the current Internet protocols, the Hypertext Transport Protocol (**HTTP**) and the File Transfer Protocol (**FTP**). Netscape, Oracle, IBM, Apple, and Novell have announced support for WebNFS.

To use WebNFS, your Web browser needs a client and the Web or FTP server needs to have a WebNFS server. When requesting a file with WebNFS, your Internet address or Uniform Resource Locator (**URL**) would look something like this:

```
nfs://computer.site.com/filedirectory/file
```

WebNFS has several advantages over HTTP and FTP. The WebNFS protocol does not require the opening and closing of a connection for each requested file. Very large file downloads are supported and, because they are

downloaded in sections, they can be resent more quickly in case the download is interrupted. A WebSoft client is included with Sun's thin-client Network Computer (**NC**). Sun Microsystems suggests that WebNFS may be a technology proposal to replace or be part of the next generation of HTTP, currently being worked on by members of the World Wide Web Consortium (**W3C**).

Website

See "Web site"

WebSphere

WebSphere is a set of Java-based tools from IBM that allow customers to create and manage sophisticated business Web sites. The central WebSphere tool is the WebSphere Application Server (WAS), an **application server** that a customer can use to connect Web site users with **Java** applications or **servlet**s. Servlets are Java programs that run on the server rather than on the user's computer as Java **applet**s do. Servlets can be developed to replace traditional common gateway interface (**CGI**) scripts, usually written in **C** or **Perl**, and run much faster because all user requests run in the same **process** space.

In addition to Java, WebSphere supports **open** standard interfaces such as the Common Object Request Broker Architecture (**CORBA**) and Java Database Connectivity (**JDC**) and is designed for use across different operating system platforms. One edition of WebSphere is offered for small-to-medium size businesses and another edition for larger businesses with a higher number of transactions. WebSphere also includes Studio, a developer's environment with additional components that allow a Web site's pages to be created and managed. Both editions support **Solaris**, **Windows NT**, **OS/2**, **OS/390**, and **AIX** operating systems.

WebSphere Studio includes a copy of the **Apache** Web server so that developers can test Web pages and Java applications immediately.

webtone

Webtone is immediate and continuous **access** to the Internet in the same way that we think of dialtone when we pick up a phone receiver. To have webtone in the same way that we have dialtone, most users of the term believe that not only access is required, but also sufficient **bandwidth** to meet user demands as well as the same quality of service we expect today from the telephone system. Since the telephone system and the Internet are tending to converge, some believe that eventually webtone will include dialtone. Webtone also implies Internet access from mobile devices, supercomputers, kitchen appliances, and perhaps eventually the very walls that surround us.

WebTV

WebTV, now owned by Microsoft, was one of the first entries in the much publicized convergence of the World Wide Web with television. You buy a set-top box similar to a cable TV box, then sign up with the WebTV access service and browse Web pages using a WebTV's **browser** and a hand-held control. A keyboard is provided optionally. WebTV uses your television set as an output device; the signals arrive, however, through a **modem** and a telephone line at 33.6 **Kbps** (Classic model) or 56 Kbps (Plus model).

The most recent WebTV service includes support for **frames** (with certain limitations), **JavaScript**, **RealAudio**, Internet Relay Chat (**IRC**), and other Web technology.

weenie

1) On bullet board systems (**BBS**) and in Internet **chatting** groups, a weenie is an avid but immature participant who disrupts orderly conversation. According to cyberlorist Eric Raymond, a weenie is "typically, a teenage boy with poor social skills traveling under a grandiose handle derived from fantasy or heavy-metal rock lyrics" whose contributions are liable to consist of "marginally literate and profanity-laden **flaming**..."

2) In the context of program development and among the "hackerdom" that Raymond chronicles, the term weenie can be ascribed respectfully to someone who is highly knowledgeable, intensely committed to, or even just employed on a particular endeavor or in a particular operating system culture. For example, a "UNIX weenie" may mean someone who is an expert at using or modifying **UNIX**. But, depending on the context, it could also mean a "UNIX bigot."

3) In the popular game, Quake (and its multiplayer Internet version, QuakeWorld), a weenie is an embarrassingly new player who is usually quickly "destroyed" in some horrible way. All new Quake players apparently qualify as weenies.

weight

Weight (symbolized *w*) is a dimensionless quantity representing the force exerted on a particle or object by an acceleration field, particularly the gravitational field of the earth at the surface. The standard unit of weight in the International System of Units (**SI**) is the **kilogram** (kg), which is the force produced by gravitation on a 1-kg **mass** at the earth's surface. In the English system, the standard unit of weight is the **pound** (lb), which is the force produced by gravitational acceleration on approximately 0.454 kg of mass at the earth's surface.

Weight is not the same thing as mass. Mass is a literal representation of the amount of matter in a particle or object, and is independent of external factors such as speed, acceleration, or applied force (as long as relativistic effects are small enough to be neglected). Weight has meaning only when an object having a specific mass is placed in an acceleration field. At the earth's surface, a kilogram mass weighs about 2.2 pounds, for example. But on Mars, the same kilogram mass would weigh only about 0.8 pounds, and on Jupiter it would weigh roughly 5.5 pounds.

Also see **kilogram**, **mass**, and International System of Units (**SI**).

well-known port numbers

The well-known port numbers are the **port number**s that are reserved for assignment by the Internet Corporation for Assigned Names and Numbers (**ICANN**) for use by the application end points that communicate using the Internet's Transmission Control Protocol (**TCP**) or the User Datagram Protocol (**UDP**). Each kind of application has a designated (and thus "well-known") port number. For example, a remote job entry application has the port number of 5; the Hypertext Transfer Protocol (**HTTP**) application has the port number of 80; and the Post Office Protocol Version 3 (**POP3**) application, commonly used for e-mail delivery, has the port number of 110. When one application communicates with another application at another **host** computer on the Internet, it specifies that application in each data transmission by using its port number.

The well-known ports cover the range of possible port numbers from 0 through 1023. The **registered port**s are numbered from 1024 through 49151. The remaining ports, referred to as **dynamic port**s or **private port**s, are numbered from 49152 through 65535.

On most systems, a well-known port number can only be used by a system (**root**) **process** or by a program run by a privileged user. The well-known port numbers are administered by the Internet Internet Assigned Numbers Authority (**IANA**) on behalf of ICANN.

WetPC

WetPC (TM) is a **wearable computer** for underwater use. Developed by the Australian Institute of Marine Science, it allows a diver to gather and enter data immediately into a computer worn as part of the diver's gear. Instead of a keyboard or mouse, the diver interacts with the computer using a multi-button device worn at chest level and requiring only one hand. The display is attached to the diver's mask. The developers invented a new, easy-to-intuit human/computer interface that lets the user provide information in the form of multiple finger position combinations that are always visible on the display.

whip antenna

A whip antenna is a single-element **antenna** that can be used with an unbalanced **feed line** such as **coaxial cable**, or attached directly to a **wireless** transmitter, receiver, or transceiver. The whip resembles a **ground-plane antenna** without the radial system. The short, flexible "rubber duck"

antennas found on handheld two-way radios and cell phones are examples of whip antennas. So are the long, flexible, stainless-steel antennas used in Citizens Band mobile installations. Some portable whip antennas can be telescoped down to a length of only few inches for transport and storage, and extended to several feet for operation.

Assets of the whip antenna include electrical and mechanical simplicity. Little or no installation is necessary. But, because most whip antennas are operated with a poor electrical ground system, they are usually inefficient. A whip directly connected to a transmitter radiates radio-frequency (**RF**) energy into the immediate operating environment. This may cause nearby electronic apparatus (including medical devices) to malfunction. Whip antennas used with handheld radios and cell phones subject the human body, especially the head and hands, to strong **electromagnetic fields**. This has given rise to uncertainty about the biological safety of whip antennas directly connected to handheld transceivers.

In high-powered or long-range wireless communications, substantial outdoor antennas, used with well-engineered feed systems, work much better than whip antennas. In addition, when a transmitting antenna is placed at a distance from humans and electronic equipment, the potential electromagnetic hazard is minimized.

Whistler

See "Windows XP"

White Book

The White Book, which was released in 1993 by Sony, Philips, Matsushita, and JVC, is the specification document for Video CD (**VCD**). Like other compact disc (**CD**) standards documents, the White Book is based on the original CD specification document, Philips and Sony's **Red Book**. VCD is defined in the White Book as a particular adaptation of **CD-ROM XA** (extended architecture) that is designed to hold **MPEG**-1 video data. The CD-ROM XA sector structure (as described in the **Yellow Book** and **ISO 9660**) is used to define the physical and logical blocks, and MPEG-1 is used to compress data so that full-screen, full-motion video data can be contained on the disc—without compression, the disc could only hold about 2 minutes worth of video. VCD resolution is similar to that of VHS.

White Book specifications include the disc format (such as the use of tracks, for example), a data retrieval structure compatible with **ISO 9660**, data fields to enable fast forward and reverse, and closed captioning. VCD, **Photo CD**, and Karaoke CD are defined as *bridge discs*, a format based on CD-ROM XA to enable the discs to work in compatible **CD-ROM** and **CD-i** (CD-Interactive) drives. Following the original specifications, VCD 2.0 was released in 1995, VCD-Internet in 1997, and SuperVCD in 1998, all from extensions to the White Book. Video CD is expected to be one of the first

of all the CD formats to be completely supplanted by digital versatile disc (**DVD**) technology, which is of much higher quality.

white hat

White hat describes a **hacker** (or, if you prefer, **cracker**) who identifies a security weakness in a computer system or network but, instead of taking malicious advantage of it, exposes the weakness in a way that will allow the system's owners to fix the breach before it is can be taken advantage by others (such as **black hat** hackers.) Methods of telling the owners about it range from a simple phone call through sending an e-mail note to a Webmaster or administrator all the way to leaving an electronic "calling card" in the system that makes it obvious that security has been breached.

While white hat hacking is a hobby for some, others provide their services for a fee. Thus, a white hat hacker may work as a consultant or be a permanent employee on a company's payroll. A good many white hat hackers are former black hat hackers.

The term comes from old Western movies, where heros often wore white hats and the "bad guys" wore black hats.

white noise

White noise is a sound that contains every **frequency** within the range of human hearing (generally from 20 **hertz** to 20 **kHz**) in equal amounts. Most people perceive this sound as having more high-frequency content than low, but this is not the case. This perception occurs because each successive octave has twice as many frequencies as the one preceding it. For example, from 100 Hz to 200 Hz, there are one hundred discrete frequencies. In the next octave (from 200 Hz to 400 Hz), there are two hundred frequencies.

White noise can be generated on a sound synthesizer. Sound designers can use this sound, with some processing and filtering, to create a multitude of effects such as wind, surf, space whooshes, and rumbles.

Pink noise is a variant of white noise. Pink noise is white noise that has been filtered to reduce the volume at each octave. This is done to compensate for the increase in the number of frequencies per octave. Each octave is reduced by 6 **decibels**, resulting in a noise sound wave that has equal energy at every octave.

white paper

A white paper is an article that states an organization's position or philosophy about a social, political, or other subject, or a not-too-detailed technical explanation of an architecture, framework, or product technology. Typically, a white paper explains the results, conclusions, or construction resulting from some organized committee or research collaboration or design and development effort.

Several versions of Webster's indicate that the term arose within the past few decades in England to distinguish short government reports from longer, more detailed ones that were bound in blue covers and referred to as "blue books" (not to be confused with the blue books used when taking college exams). A shorter government publication providing a report or position about something was bound in the same white paper as the text—hence, "a white paper."

In information technology, a white paper is often a paper written by a lead product designer to explain the philosophy and operation of a product in a marketplace or technology context. Many if not most Web sites for software products include a white paper in addition to a frequently-asked questions (**FAQ**) page and more detailed product specifications.

In government, a white paper is often a policy or position paper. The U.S. Government's June, 1998 policy statement on the *Management of Internet Names and Addresses* (known generally as "The White Paper") is an example of great interest to many Internet users.

whois

whois is a program that will tell you the owner of any second-level **domain name** who has registered it with Network Solutions (formerly the only and still the most widely used of the Internet registrars of the **com**, **net**, and **org** domain names). If a Web site obtained its domain name from Network Solutions, you can look up the name of the owner of the Web site by entering (for example):

```
aol.com
```

and whois will tell you the owner of that second-level domain name.

whois can also be used to find out whether a domain name is available or has already been taken. If you enter a domain name you are considering and the search result is "No match," the domain name is likely to be available and you can apply to register it.

Recently, the Internet Corporation for Assigned Names and Numbers (**ICANN**) has opened up domain name registration to a number of other companies. To search all of these companies at the same time for registration information, you can use **BetterWhois**.

whole number

See "integer"

WHQL

See "Windows Hardware Quality Labs"

wide area network

A wide area network (**WAN**) is a geographically dispersed telecommunications **network**. The term distinguishes a broader telecommunication structure from a local area network (**LAN**). A wide area network may be privately owned or rented, but the term usually connotes the inclusion of public (shared user) networks. An intermediate form of network in terms of geography is a metropolitan area network (**MAN**).

wideband

Wideband is a transmission medium or channel that has a wider **bandwidth** than one voice channel (with a carrier wave of a certain modulated frequency). This term is usually contrasted with **narrowband**.

wideband CDMA

See "WCDMA"

wideband code-division multiple access

See "WCDMA"

widget

1) In general, widget (pronounced WIH-jit) is a term used to refer to any discrete object, usually of some mechanical nature and relatively small size, when it doesn't have a name, when you can't remember the name, or when you're talking about a class of certain unknown objects in general. (According to Eric Raymond, "legend has it that the original widgets were holders for buggy whips," but this was possibly written with tongue-in-cheek.)

2) In computers, a widget is an element of a graphical user interface (**GUI**) that displays information or provides a specific way for a user to interact with the **operating system** and **application**. Widgets include icons, pull-down menus, buttons, selection boxes, progress indicators, on-off checkmarks, scroll bars, windows, window edges (that let you resize the window), toggle buttons, forms, and many other devices for displaying information and for inviting, accepting, and responding to user actions.

In programming, a widget also means the small program that is written in order to describe what a particular widget looks like, how it behaves, and how it interacts in response to user actions. Most operating systems include a set of ready-to-tailor widgets that a programmer can incorporate in an application, specifying how it is to behave. New widgets can be created. The term was apparently applied first in **UNIX**-based operating systems and the **X Window System**. In object-oriented programming (**OOP**), each type of widget is defined as a **class** (or a subclass under a broad

generic widget class) and is always associated with a particular window. In the AIX Enhanced X-Window Toolkit, a widget is the fundamental **data type**.

Most if not all application development languages today, such as **Java** and **Tcl**, come with a ready-made library of widgets that a programmer can incorporate and modify. Using Microsoft's **Visual Basic**, a widget can be implemented as or part of an **ActiveX control**.

wildcard character

A wildcard character is a special **character** that represents one or more other characters. The most commonly used wildcard characters are the asterisk (*), which typically represents zero or more characters in a string of characters, and the questionmark (?), which typically represents any one character. For example, in searching:

    run*

would mean "any word that starts with 'run' and has any kind of ending." If you entered "run*" at a search engine that offered a wildcard character capability, you would get results for run, runs, running, runner, runners—in short, any possible word that might begin with the three letters.

Wildcard characters are used in *regular expressions* (a form of programming in which input data is modified based on specified patterns) and in searching through file directories for similar file names (for example, if all the work files on a project start with the characters "P5," you could easily locate all the project files by simply searching for "P5*").

A wildcard character is a type of **meta character**. In various games of playing cards, a wild card is a designated card in the deck of cards (for example, the two of spades) that can be used as though it were any possible card.

Willamette

See "Pentium 4"

WIMP

WIMP is an **acronym** describing the **desktop** user interface familiar to Windows and Mac computer users, significant features of which are **w**indows, **i**cons, a **m**ouse, and **p**ull-down menus. Other explanations of what the letters stand for include: window-icon-mouse-pointer and window-icon-menu-pointing device. This combination of computer-user interface ideas originated at Xerox's Palo Alto Research Laboratory, was incorporated in early Apple computers, and adopted by Microsoft in its Windows operating system, in **UNIX**'s **X Window System**, in IBM's **OS/2**, and in other operating systems. The WIMP interface is now so familiar to most of us that it may be difficult to understand that other models for a user interface are also possible. Since learning a user interface is a personal as well as a business investment, it is likely that future user interfaces will continue to include all or parts of the WIMP environment. New user interfaces

may include **speech recognition** and voice command interfaces, **haptics** devices, eye-movement detection, and new 2-D and 3-D visual models.

Win32s

Win32s is a Microsoft upgrade to the Windows 3.1 and Windows for Workgroups 3.1 **operating system**s, which run 16-bit applications, that allows them to run some 32-bit applications. Users of Windows 3.1 or Windows for Workgroups 3.1 who did not want to install Windows 95 (which was designed for 32-bit applications) could download Win32s and install it so that certain 32-bit applications would run.

The NCSA **Mosaic browser** was an example of a 32-bit application that would run on Windows 3.1 if you downloaded Win32s.

Win9x

See "Windows 9x"

WinChip

WinChip (also known as the WinChip C6) is a **microprocessor** designed for use in business computers that run Microsoft operating systems Made by IDT, the microprocessor reportedly provides comparable performance to Intel's more expensive **Pentium** microprocessors as well as to the more competitively-priced **K6** and the **Cyrix** 6X86MX. IDT designed a smaller die area for the microprocessor, making it easier and cheaper to manufacture. WinChip cites Winstone tests that show the C6 has the highest rating per square millimeter of die area among Socket 7 microprocessors. The C6 does not include branch prediction and other features of some of the other microprocessors. It is optimized for running the most frequently used **instruction**s and aims to be the most cost-effective choice for business applications such as word processing, spreadsheets, and database management.

window

A window is a separate viewing area on a computer display screen in a system that allows multiple viewing areas as part of a graphical user interface (**GUI**). Windows are managed by a *windows manager* as part of a **windowing system**.

A window can usually be resized by the user. For example, it can be stretched on any side, minimized, maximized, and closed. On today's multitasking operating systems, you can have a number of windows on your screen at the same time, interacting with each whenever you choose.

The window first came into general use as part of the Apple Macintosh. Later, Microsoft made the idea the foundation of its Windows operating system (which was actually a graphical user interface for the Disk Operating System (**DOS**) operating system on IBM-compatible PCs). The **X**

Window System was developed as an **open** cross-platform windowing system for use in networks. It allows a client application in one computer to request windowing services at a user's workstation computer.

Window RAM

Window RAM (WRAM), unrelated to Microsoft Windows, is very high-performance video RAM that is *dual-ported* and has about 25% more bandwidth than VRAM but costs less. It has features that make it more efficient to read data for use in block fills and text drawing. It can be used for very high **resolution** (such as 1600 by 1200 pixels) projection using **true color**. WRAM is used in the Matrox Millenium video card.

windowing system

A windowing system is a system for sharing a computer's graphical display presentation resources among multiple applications at the same time. In a computer that has a graphical user interface (**GUI**), you may want to use a number of applications at the same time (this is called **multitasking**). Using a separate **window** for each application, you can interact with each application and go from one application to another without having to reinitiate it. Having different information or activities in multiple windows may also make it easier for you to do your work.

A windowing system uses a *window manager* to keep track of where each window is located on the display screen and its size and status. A windowing system doesn't just manage the windows but also other forms of graphical user interface entities.

The **X Window System** is a cross-platform windowing system that uses the **client/server** model to distribute services in a network so that applications can run in a remote computer. Users of workstations or terminals using the X Window System don't need to know where the application is located. Apple's **Macintosh** and Microsoft's Windows operating systems have their own windowing systems built into the operating system.

Windows 2000

Previously called **Windows NT** 5.0, Windows 2000 is described by Microsoft as evolutionary and "Built on NT Technology." Windows 2000 is designed to appeal to small business and professional users as well as to the more technical and larger business market for which the NT was designed.

The Windows 2000 product line consists of four products:

- **Windows 2000 Professional**, aimed at individuals and businesses of all sizes. It includes security and mobile use enhancements. It is the most economical choice.

- **Windows 2000 Server**, aimed at small-to-medium size businesses. It can function as a Web server and/or a workgroup (or branch office) server. It can be part of a two-way symmetric multiprocessing system. NT 4.0 servers can be upgraded to this server.

- **Windows 2000 Advanced Server**, aimed at being a network operating system server and/or an application server, including those involving large **databases**. This server facilitates *clustering* and *load-balancing*. NT 4.0 servers with up to eight-way SMP can upgrade to this product.

- **Windows 2000 Datacenter Server**, designed for large **data warehouse**s, online transaction processing (**OLTP**), econometric analysis, and other applications requiring high-speed computation and large databases. The Datacenter Server supports up to 16-way SMP and up to 64 gigabytes of physical memory.

Windows 2000 is reported to be more stable (less apt to crash) than Windows 98/NT systems. A significant new feature is Microsoft's **Active Directory**, which, among other capabilities, enables a company to set up **virtual private network**s, to encrypt data locally or on the network, and to give users access to shared files in a consistent way from any network computer.

Windows 98

Windows 98 (called "Memphis" during development and previously called "Windows 97" based on an earlier schedule) is a widely-installed product in Microsoft's evolution of the Windows **operating system** for personal computers. Windows 98 expresses Microsoft's belief that users want and should have a global view of their potential resources and that Web technology should be an important part of the user interface. Although building Microsoft's own Web **browser** into the user **desktop** has been an issue in the U.S. Justice Department's suit, Windows 98 was released as planned with its tightly integrated browser.

In Windows 98, Microsoft's Internet Explorer is an integral part of the operating system. Using the Active Desktop of Windows 98, you can view and access desktop objects that reside on the World Wide Web as well as local files and applications. The Windows 98 desktop is, in fact, a Web page with HTML links and features that exploit Microsoft's **ActiveX control**.

With Windows 98 (or with Internet Explorer 4.0 in Windows 95), you can set up news and other content to be **push technology** to you from specified Web sites.

Windows 98 also provides a 32-bit file allocation table (**FAT**) that allows you to have a single-partition disk drive larger than 2 Gbytes. Other features in Windows 98 include:

- Support for Universal Serial Bus (**USB**), which makes it easy to plug in new devices
- Support for Digital Versatile Disc (**DVD**)
- Support for a new industry-standard form of power management called Advanced Configuration and Power Interface (ACPI)

Windows 98 is gradually being replaced by **Windows 2000**, an evolution of the Windows OS, that is designed for personal or small-office professional or business use.

Windows 9x

Windows 9x is short for "Windows 95 or **Windows 98**."

Windows CE

Windows CE is based on the Microsoft Windows **operating system** but is designed for including or embedding in mobile and other space-constrained devices. Although Microsoft does not explain the "CE," it is reported to have originally stood for "Consumer Electronics." Windows CE is used in several brands of **handheld** computers and as part of cable TV **set-top box**es built for TCI. It competes with **EPOC** and also with similar operating systems from 3Com (for its PalmPilot) and other companies. Like the full-scale Windows systems, Windows CE is a 32-bit **multitasking**, **multithreading** operating system. Microsoft emphasizes that the system was "built from scratch" while taking advantage of Windows architectural concepts and interfaces. Microsoft argues that Windows desktop system users will find that products with Windows CE provide a familiar user interface.

In addition to handheld computers and cable TV boxes, Windows CE is also offered as the operating system for the Auto PC, Microsoft's concept of controlling applications (such as selecting radio channels) while driving, using interactive speech technology.

Windows Hardware Quality Labs

Windows Hardware Quality Labs (WHQL) is a Microsoft procedure for certifying that the **hardware** for **peripherals** and other components is compatible (works as expected) with Microsoft Windows **operating system**s. WHQL provides test kits to third-party developers so that they can test their product's compatibility. Products that are submitted to and meet the tests at Microsoft are allowed to display the Microsoft Windows logo on their marketing materials and are included in Microsoft's Hardware Compatibility List (**HCL**).

A hardware developer **download**s a WHQL test kit for a specific product from Microsoft's Web site. The test kit includes a test tool, test procedures, and errata and is used throughout the development process of the hardware component. The errata shows which errors encountered during testing are not considered a failure of the component and are overlooked by WHQL. When the component is finished, the latest WHQL test kit is downloaded and used to test the final product. If the component passes, the developer submits his test to WHQL.

After WHQL receives the test submission, the developer is notified by **e-mail** within three days that the submission was received. WHQL processes the submission, which can take up to 30 days. WHQL then sends the developer a report via e-mail. If the component passed, the developer receives a signed Logo License Agreement with a logo kit containing the camera-ready logo artwork, an inclusion of the hardware component in Microsoft's Hardware Compatibility List (HCL), and a distribution of the hardware **driver**, if needed, on Microsoft's Windows Driver Library. If the component didn't pass, the developer must make the necessary changes to the component and retest.

Windows Internet Naming Service

Windows Internet Naming Service (WINS), part of the Microsoft Windows NT and 2000 Servers, manages the association of workstation names and locations with Internet Protocol addresses (**IP address**es) without the user or an administrator having to be involved in each configuration change. WINS automatically creates a computer name-IP address mapping entry in a table, ensuring that the name is unique and not a duplicate of someone else's computer name. When a computer is moved to another geographic location, the **subnet** part of the IP address is likely to change. Using WINS, the new subnet information will be updated automatically in the WINS table. WINS complements the NT Server's Dynamic Host Configuration Protocol (**DHCP**), which negotiates an IP address for any computer (such as your workstation) when it is first defined to the network. If you're a computer user on a network connected to a Windows NT/2000 Server, you may find WINS mentioned in some of your network-related programs or system messages.

Based on Microsoft's paper, DHCP and WINS have been submitted to the Internet Engineering Task Force (**IETF**) as proposed open standards in Request for Comments 1533, 1534, 1541, and 1542. New features are included in **Windows 2000**.

Windows Me

Windows Me (Millenium Edition) is an **operating system** from Microsoft, released commercially September 14, 2000. Windows Me was developed specifically for the home user, just as their Windows 2000 version was developed specifically for the business user. Microsoft claims that this Windows 98 update (which has a very similar look-and-feel

to the earlier version) combines a more intuitive interface for the new user with added functionality for the experienced user.

Designed to be **backwards compatible** with Windows 98, Windows Me works with the earlier version's applications and drivers. Improvements over Windows 98 include functions to enhance system stability and error correction (what Microsoft is calling "PC health"), as well as features designed for digital media, home networking, and online experience:

PC health features:

- System restore, which allows users to return to a prior (functioning) configuration when encountering problems

- System file protection, which prevents accidental overwriting of critical system files

- Auto-update, which automatically downloads Microsoft updates

Digital media features:

- Image acquisition, which facilitates transfer of images from digital equipment

- Movie Maker, which enables digital editing, saving and sharing of videos

- Media Player 7, which coordinates and organizes digital media operations

- DirectPlay voice chat, which enables chat between users playing games over the Web

Home networking features:

- Home Networking Wizard, which walks the user through steps to connect multiple computers in a home

- Improved technology for Internet connection-sharing

- Simplified Universal Serial Bus (**USB**) networking

- Universal **plug-and-play** technology

Online experience features:

- Internet Explorer 5.5

- NetMeeting 3.0 for conference capability

- Enhanced interoperability of Outlook and MSN Messenger Service

- Easier Web publishing

Although this is the first time that many of these features have been combined into a package, it's worthwhile to note that many—including Media Player 7.0, Internet Explorer 5.5, DirectX 7.0a and NetMeeting 3.0—are already available for free download from Microsoft's Web site. Windows Me is to be the last operating system based on the Windows 95 **kernel**.

Windows NT

Windows NT is a Microsoft Windows personal computer **operating system** designed for users and businesses needing advanced capability. NT's technology is the base for the Microsoft successor operating system, **Windows 2000**. Windows NT (which may originally have stood for "New Technology," although Microsoft doesn't say) is actually two products: Microsoft NT Workstation and Microsoft NT Server. The Workstation is designed for users, especially business users, who need faster performance and a system a little more fail-safe than Windows 95 and **Windows 98**. The Server is designed for business machines that need to provide services for network-attached computers. The Server is required, together with an Internet server such as Microsoft's Internet Information Server (**IIS**), for a Windows system that plans to serve Web pages.

Windows NT Workstation: Microsoft says that 32-bit applications run 20% faster on this system than on Windows 95 (assuming both have 32 megabytes of RAM). Since older 16-bit applications run in a separate address space, one can crash without crashing other applications or the operating system. Security and management features not available on Windows 95 are provided. The Workstation has the same desktop user interface as Windows 95.

Windows NT Server: The NT Server is probably the second most installed network server operating system after Novell's **NetWare** operating system. Microsoft claims that its NT servers are beginning to replace both NetWare and the various **UNIX**-based systems such as those of Sun Microsystems and Hewlett-Packard. NT Server 5.0. essentially became what was renamed Windows 2000. Notable features of the Windows 2000 products are:

- A fully-customizable administrative console that can be based on tasks rather than files, applications, or users:

- A new file directory approach called **Active Directory** that lets the administrator and other users view every file and application in the network from a single point-of-view.

- Dynamic Domain Name Server (DNS), which replicates changes in the network using the Active Directory Services, the Dynamic Host Configuration Protocol (**DHCP**), and the Windows Internet Naming Service (**WINS**) whenever a client is reconfigured.

- The ability to create, extend, or mirror a disk volume without having to shut down the system and to back up data to a variety of magnetic and optical storage media.

- A Distributed File System (DFS) that lets users see a distributed set of files in a single file structure across departments, divisions, or an entire enterprise.

- Close integration with and support for Microsoft's Message Queue Server, **Microsoft Transaction Server**, and Internet Information Server (**IIS**).

Windows XP

Windows XP (code named Whistler by Microsoft) is the latest version of the Windows **desktop operating system** for the PC. Microsoft and trade publication writers view Windows XP as the most important version of Windows since **Windows 95**. Windows XP is built on the **Windows 2000 kernel** but brings a new, more personalized look to the desktop that will also make it easier for users to scan or import images and to acquire music files on the Web and transfer them to portable devices. The new Windows will allow different family members to use their own desktop and personal sets of files. In addition to the "My Computer" and "My Documents" views provided in Windows 2000, Windows XP users see "My Music" and "My Pictures." The Start Menu has been redesigned to make the most-used programs easiest to find.   Windows XP will come in a Professional version and a Home Edition version.

windows, icons, mouse, and pull-down menus

See "WIMP"

WinFrame

WinFrame is a software product from Citrix that, together with a **Windows NT operating system**, allows a computer **server** to provide Windows applications and data for attached computer workstations. With Winframe, a company can install all applications and data at the server, simplifying administration, and possibly saving on application software cost. The low-cost workstations are known as **thin clients** because they are minimally-equipped and because they contain **client** software that interacts with the server. To the user, the applications and data appear to be running on the workstation. WinFrame can be compared to two other thin client approaches, the Network Computer (**NC**) and the **NetPC**.

Up to 15 workstations can be supported by a server with Windows NT and WinFrame. The NT server computer needs 32 **megabyte**s of random access memory (**RAM**) and an additional 6 to 8 MB for each attached workstation. Each user is allocated 32 MB of data storage on the server's **hard disk**.

A significant advantage of WinFrame is that it can make newer Windows applications available to older PCs. WinFrame can also handle users who dial in to the server (for example, mobile users and those working at home or in branch offices). There are two key components in the WinFrame approach:

1) The Intelligent Console Architecture (ICA) Windows Presentation Services, a **protocol** that manages the user (client) input and the server output so that the data that travels back and forth is reduced to a minimum. Data travels in **compression packet**.

2) The MultiWin Multi-User Architecture, which allows NT to manage a virtual session for each user of the same application.

Microsoft and Citrix co-developed Microsoft's **Terminal Server product** Edition of Windows NT 4.0, using WinFrame's multi-user technology. In addition, Citrix offers MetaFrame, a product that adds the thin-client/server interface to the Terminal Server. Together, the Terminal Server and MetaFrame replace WinFrame in Windows NT 4.0 and forthcoming versions.

Wingate

Wingate is a product that allows people on a small home network or a larger business network to share and control access to the Internet through a single computer connection. The Wingate program can be installed in a computer hooked up to the Internet with a dial-up, Integrated Services Digital Network (**ISDN**), Digital Subscriber Line (**DSL**), **cable modem**, or dedicated **T-carrier system** connection. The computer with Wingate acts as a **proxy server** and **firewall** for the computer users inside the home or business. All users share a common Internet connection through one computer, which does not have to be dedicated to its gateway role. Wingate requires that all computers use a Windows 95 or later operating system and include **TCP/IP**.

Wingate has a **server** component and a **client** component. The server component is installed on the computer that has the Internet connection capability. The client component is installed on the other computers in the network. The server component then routes all Internet requests from the other computers through the Internet connection. Wingate allows users to connect or disconnect to the Internet using their own computers.

The **firewall** component in Wingate prevents outsiders from accessing network computers. When Wingate receives a request for access into the local network, it compares the **IP address** of the computer requesting access with a list of those eligible. If the IP address is not recognized, the request is denied. Wingate also uses TCP port binding as a method of controlling access.

Network administrators can assign access rights to individuals or groups. For example, in a home network in which children use the Internet, a parent can prohibit access to sites that are not suitable. A history also keeps track of the Web sites visited, time spent online, and other information of each individual. This helps the administrator determine whether an individual is abusing his access rights. Wingate also provides Web page caching.

WinNuke

See "blue bomb"

WINS

See "Windows Internet Naming Service"

Winsock

Winsock is a programming interface and the supporting program that handles input/output requests for Internet applications in a Windows **operating system**. It's called Winsock because it's an adaptation for Windows of the Berkeley **UNIX** sockets interface. **Sockets** is a particular convention for connecting with and exchanging data between two program processes within the same computer or across a network.

Winsock runs between an application program such as a Netscape browser and the Internet program in your computer that uses **TCP/IP**. A request flows in the following order:

Web browser or other application
|
winsock.dll
|
TCP/IP layers
|
Modem or network card
|
The Internet and destination

Winsock provides this interface for different versions of the Windows operating system. A comparable interface exists for Mac computers. Beginning with Windows 95, Winsock came as part of the operating system, but in earlier systems, a Winsock program had to be installed. UNIX systems do not require a Winsock equivalent because TCP/IP and its use of sockets was designed to run directly with UNIX application programs.

A number of companies offer a Winsock program, sometimes along with a suite of Internet protocol programs and applications. For example, Chameleon offers a suite that includes a Web browser, an FTP utility, a mail utility, and others. The Winsock program is included. The Trumpet Winsock is another popular stand-alone version. Winsock runs as a Windows dynamic link library (**DLL**) file. That is, it is loaded into the computer when an application needs it but doesn't need to be included as part of the application.

If you have an older computer, when you initially get set up with Internet access, you may need to make sure you have the right version of Winsock for your operating system and the applications provided by the access provider. If your operating system provides one version and the application suite provided by the access provider provides another, one version of Winsock may need to be removed.

Winsock 2

Like **Winsock**, Winsock 2 is a programming interface and the supporting program that handles input/output requests for Internet applications in a Windows operating system. It's called Winsock because it's an adaptation for Windows of the Berkeley **UNIX** sockets interface. **Sockets** is a particular convention for connecting with and exchanging data between two program processes. Winsock 2 is a 32-bit version of Winsock.

Winsock 2 runs between an application program such as a Web browser and the program in your computer that handles **TCP/IP**.

Winsock 2 offers these advantages over Winsock:

- In addition to TCP/IP, it provides an interface to a variety of protocols, including IPX/SPX, **ISDN** and wireless protocols.
- An application can request **multicast** and other protocol services not supported by Winsock 1.1.
- It offers access to multiple name spaces.
- It offers an application the possibility of choosing services based on cost.

Winsock 2 is included in the latest versions of the Windows operating systems.

Wintel

Wintel is a computer trade industry term for personal computers based on the Intel **microprocessor** and one of the Windows **operating systems** from Microsoft. The term "PC" has often been used for this purpose. That is, the IBM "PC" (with the Intel chip and Windows operating system) became the prevalent personal computer in the business world and has usually been distinguished from personal computers from Apple (with a Motorola microchip and a proprietary operating system) and sometimes from **UNIX** workstations.

In most trade publication articles, Wintel implies a Pentium-level microprocessor and the Windows 95 or NT operating systems.

WinZip

WinZip is a Windows program that lets you **archive** and compress files so that you can store or distribute them more efficiently. WinZip is a more capable and easier-to-use Windows equivalent of two earlier programs commonly used in the DOS operating system, PKZIP and PKUNZIP. WinZip has a simple drag-and-drop interface that allows you to view individual files in a zip file without unzipping the file. WinZip will also launch installation programs from a zip file and automatically clean up after the installation.

When creating a zip file (or archive), you can choose from five levels of compression, including "None," for each added file. With a disk-spanning add-on, you can also create a zip file that will span multiple diskettes.

WinZip also supports other popular Internet file formats, including **tar**, gzip, Unix compress, **Uuencode**, **BinHex**, and **MIME**. ARJ, LZH, and ARC files are supported through other programs. WinZip provides an interface to most **virus** scanner programs and is available in 16-bit and 32-bit versions.

wire gauges

See "American Wire Gauge"

wire speed

Wire speed is whatever rate of data transfer a given telecommunication technology provides at the physical wire level. *Wire-speed*, an adjective, describes any hardware box or function that tends to support this data transfer rate without slowing it down. It's common to refer to functions embedded in microchips rather than in software programming as working at wire speed. **Switches,, routers**, and other devices are sometimes described by their manufacturers as operating at wire speed. Data **encryption** and decryption and hardware emulation are software functions that might run at wire speed (or close to it) when embedded in a microchip.

Wired Equivalent Privacy

Wired Equivalent Privacy (WEP) is a security mechanism, specified in the **IEEE** Wireless Fidelity (**Wi-Fi**) standard, **802.11b**. The WEP **protocol** is designed to provide a wireless local area network (**WLAN**) with a similar level of privacy to what is possible for a wired LAN. A wired local area network (**LAN** is generally protected by physical security mechanisms (controlled access to a building, for example) that are effective for a controlled physical environment, but may be ineffective for WLANs because radio waves are not necessarily bound by the walls containing the network. WEP seeks to establish similar protection to that offered by the wired network's physical security measures by encrypting data transmitted over the WLAN. Data **encryption** protects the vulnerable wireless link between **client**s and access points; once this measure has been taken, other typical LAN security mechanisms such as password protection, end-to-end encryption, virtual private networks (**VPN**s), and **authentication** can be put in place to ensure privacy.

A research group from the University of California at Berkeley recently published a report citing "major security flaws" in WEP that left WLANs using the protocol vulnerable to attacks (called *wireless equivalent privacy attacks*). In the course of the group's examination of the technology, they were able to intercept and modify transmissions and gain access to restricted networks. The Wireless Ethernet Compatibility Alliance (WECA) claims that WEP—which is included in many networking products—was never intended to be the sole security mechanism for a WLAN, and that, in conjunction with

traditional security practices, it is very effective. Nevertheless, IEEE enhancements to 802.11 security are expected to be announced by the end of 2001.

wireless

Wireless is a term used to describe telecommunications in which electromagnetic waves (rather than some form of wire) carry the signal over part or all of the communication path. Some monitoring devices, such as intrusion alarms, employ acoustic waves at frequencies above the range of human hearing; these are also sometimes classified as wireless.

The first wireless transmitters went on the air in the early 20th century using radiotelegraphy (Morse code). Later, as **modulation** made it possible to transmit voices and music via wireless, the medium came to be called "radio." With the advent of television, **fax**, data communication, and the effective use of a larger portion of the spectrum, the term "wireless" has been resurrected.

Common examples of wireless equipment in use today include:

- **Cellular** phones and pagers—provide connectivity for portable and mobile applications, both personal and business

- Global Positioning System (**GPS**)—allows drivers of cars and trucks, captains of boats and ships, and pilots of aircraft to ascertain their location anywhere on earth

- Cordless computer peripherals—the **cordless mouse** is a common example; keyboards and printers can also be linked to a computer via wireless

- Cordless telephone sets—these are limited-range devices, not to be confused with cell phones

- Home-entertainment-system control boxes—the VCR control and the TV channel control are the most common examples; some hi-fi sound systems and FM broadcast receivers also use this technology

- Remote garage-door openers—one of the oldest wireless devices in common use by consumers; usually operates at radio frequencies

- Two-way radios—this includes Amateur and Citizens Radio Service, as well as business, marine, and military communications

- Baby monitors—these devices are simplified radio transmitter/receiver units with limited range

- **Satellite** television—allows viewers in almost any location to select from hundreds of channels

- **Wireless LAN**s or local area networks—provide flexibility and reliability for business computer users Wireless technology is rapidly evolving, and is playing an increasing role in the lives of people throughout the world. In addition, ever-larger numbers of people are relying on the technology directly or indirectly. (It has been suggested that wireless is overused in some situations, creating a social nuisance.) More specialized and exotic examples of wireless communications and control include:

- Global System for Mobile Communication (**GSM**)—a digital mobile telephone system used in Europe and other parts of the world; the de facto wireless telephone standard in Europe

- General Packet Radio Service (**GPRS**)—a packet-based wireless communication service that provides continuous connection to the Internet for mobile phone and computer users

- Enhanced Data GSM Environment (**EDGE**)—a faster version of the Global System for Mobile (GSM) wireless service

- Universal Mobile Telecommunications System (**UMTS**)—a broadband, packet-based system offering a consistent set of services to mobile computer and phone users no matter where they are located in the world

- Wireless Application Protocol (**WAP**)—a set of communication protocols to standardize the way that wireless devices, such as cellular telephones and radio transceivers, can be used for Internet access

- **i-Mode**—the world's first "smart phone" for Web browsing, first introduced in Japan; provides color and video over telephone sets Wireless can be divided into:

- **Fixed wireless**—the operation of wireless devices or systems in homes and offices, and in particular, equipment connected to the Internet via specialized modems

- **Mobile wireless**—the use of wireless devices or systems aboard motorized, moving vehicles; examples include the automotive cell phone and **PCS** (personal communications services)

- **Portable wireless**—the operation of autonomous, battery-powered wireless devices or systems outside the office, home, or vehicle; examples include handheld cell phones and PCS units

- **IR wireless**—the use of devices that convey data via **IR** (infrared) radiation; employed in certain limited-range communications and control systems

Wireless Abstract XML

See "WAX"

Wireless Application Protocol

See "WAP"

wireless application service provider

WASP is also an acronym for the **Web Standards Project**.

A wireless application service provider (WASP) is part of a growing industry sector resulting from the convergence of two trends: **wireless** communications and the **outsourcing** of services. A WASP performs the same service for wireless clients as a regular application service provider (**ASP**) does for wired clients: it provides Web-based access to applications and services that would otherwise have to be stored locally. The main difference with WASP is that it enables customers to access the service from a variety of wireless devices, such as a **smartphone** or personal digital assistant (**PDA**).

Although the business world is increasingly mobile, many corporations are resisting the idea of wireless communication, because of concerns about set-up and maintenance costs and the need for in-house expertise. WASPs offer businesses the advantages of wireless service with less expense and fewer risks. Because mobile applications are subscribed to, rather than purchased, up-front costs are lower; because the WASP provides support, staffing and training costs are lower.

WASP services may include:

- Constant system monitoring

- Diagnostics and resolution

- User support

- Text formatting for various devices

- Problem detection and reporting

There are still issues to be resolved. Coverage areas remain limited, for example, and data synchronization among devices can be problematic. Nevertheless, WASPs provide an easier, safer, and cheaper way for organizations to add mobile components, and a number of major companies are opting for them. UPS, Sprint, and eBay are among the early subscribers to WASP services. Interestingly, some ASPs have begun to offer WASP services, while others are purchasing them.

wireless ASP

See "wireless application service provider"

Wireless Bitmap

A Wireless Bitmap (WBMP) is a graphic **image format** for use when sending Web content to handheld wireless devices. The format is defined as part of the Wireless Application Protocol (**WAP**), Wireless Application Environment (WAE) Specification. If you are creating Web content that is directed to handheld phones or personal digital assistants (**PDA**) that have Web access, you use the Wireless Markup Language (**WML**) to encode the page and its text. An image can be included in the form of a WBMP

file—initially, supported only in black-and-white— that you can convert from a Graphics Interchange Format (**GUI**), Tag Image File Format (**TIFF**), or other graphic formats.

The initial WAP WAE specification supports only WBMP type 0, which is an **compression** image in monochrome. Later, as the **bandwidth** for wireless transmission increases, richer images will be supported.

wireless cable

See "Multichannel Multipoint Distribution Service"

wireless LAN

A wireless LAN is one in which a mobile user can connect to a local area network (**LAN**) through a **wireless** (radio) connection. A standard, **IEEE 802.11**, specifies the technologies for wireless LANs. The standard includes an encryption method, the **Wired Equivalent Privacy algorithm**.

High-bandwidth allocation for wireless will make possible a relatively low-cost wiring of classrooms in the U.S. A similar frequency allocation has been made in Europe. Hospitals and businesses are also expected to install wireless LAN systems where existing LANs are not already in place.

A wireless LAN adapter can be made to fit on a PC card for a laptop or notebook computer.

wireless local area network

See "wireless LAN"

Wireless Markup Language

WML (Wireless Markup Language), formerly called HDML (Handheld Devices Markup Languages), is a language that allows the text portions of Web pages to be presented on **cellular telephones** and personal digital assistants (**PDAs**) via **wireless** access. WML is part of the Wireless Application Protocol (**WAP**) that is being proposed by several vendors to standards bodies. The Wireless Application Protocol works on top of standard data link protocols, such as **Global System for Mobile communication**, **code-division multiple access**, and **time division multiple access**, and provides a complete set of network communication programs comparable to and supportive of the Internet set of protocols.

WML is an open language offered royalty-free. Specifications are available at Phone.com's Web site. According to Phone.com, any programmer with working knowledge of **HTML**, **CGI**, and **Structured Query Language** should be able to write a presentation layer using WML. A **filter** program can be written or may be available from a vendor that will translate HTML pages into WML pages.

wireless service provider

A wireless service provider (WSP) is a company that offers transmission services to users of **wireless** devices (handheld computers and telephones) through radio frequency (**RF**) signals rather than through end-to-end wire communication. Generally, a WSP offers either **cellular telephone** telephone service, personal communication service (**PCS**) service, or both. The term also seems applicable to **satellite** television and Internet access providers.

Wireless Transport Layer Security

Wireless Transport Layer Security (WTLS) is the security level for Wireless Application Protocol (**WAP**) applications. Based on *Transport Layer Security* (**TLS**) v1.0 (a security layer used in the Internet, equivalent to **Secure Socket Layer** 3.1), WTLS was developed to address the problematic issues surrounding mobile network devices—such as limited processing power and memory capacity, and low **bandwidth**—and to provide adequate **authentication**, **data integrity**, and privacy protection mechanisms.

Wireless transactions, such as those between a user and their bank, require stringent authentication and encryption to ensure security to protect the communication from attack during data transmission. Because mobile networks do not provide end-to-end security, TLS had to be modified to address the special needs of wireless users. Designed to support **datagrams** in a high latency, low bandwidth environment, WTLS provides an optimized **handshake** through dynamic key refreshing, which allows **encryption keys** to be regularly updated during a secure session.

wireless Web

The wireless Web refers to use of the **World Wide Web** through a wireless device, such as a **cellular telephone** or personal digital assistant (**PDA**). Wireless Web connection provides anytime/anywhere connection to e-mail, mobile banking, instant messaging, weather and travel information, and other services. In general, sites aiming to accommodate wireless users must provide services in a format displayable on typically small wireless devices. It is estimated that 95% of wireless Internet devices being manufactured today use the Wireless Application Protocol (**WAP**) developed by Ericsson, Motorola, Nokia, and Unwired Planet (now Phone.com) for presenting content.

The wireless Web is not gaining in popularity as quickly as some have predicted. The low **bandwidth** of today's wireless service, relatively high usage charges, and small and difficult-to-use input and output devices contribute to impeding growth, a condition that has been referred to as "wapathy" (WAP apathy).

WLAN

See "wireless LAN"

WML

See "Wireless Markup Language"

word

In computer architecture, a word is a unit of data that can be moved in a single operation from storage to a processor **register**. In the most familiar architectures of the past few decades, a word has been four eight-**bit** bytes in length, or 32 bits. Both IBM's mainframe processors and Intel's processors, used in standard PCs, have used a 32-bit word. Recent processor architectures from Intel and others provide for a 64-bit word (which may be treated as though two 32-bit words can be loaded at the same time into two different registers).

In a 32-bit word system, a 16-bit unit of data is sometimes referred to as a **half-word**.

A word can contain a computer **instruction**, a storage address, or application data that is to be manipulated (for example, added to the the data in another word space).

word processor

A word processor is a computer program that provides special capabilities beyond that of a **text editor**. The term originated to distinguish editors that were "easy to use" from conventional text editors, and to suggest that the program was more than just an "editor." An early user of this term was Wang, which made a popular workstation system designed especially for secretaries and anyone else who created business letters and other documents.

In general, word processors screen the user from structural or printer-formatting **markup** (although WordPerfect and other word processors optionally let you see the markup they insert in your text). Without visible markup, it's possible to describe a word processor as having a **WYSIWYG** (what you see is what you get) user interface.

The most popular word processor is Microsoft Word. Many people still use a former favorite, WordPerfect.

work

Work is **force** applied over **distance**. Examples of work include lifting an object against the Earth's gravitation, driving a car up a hill, and pulling down a captive helium balloon. Work is a mechanical manifestation of **energy**.

The standard unit of work is the **joule** (J), equivalent to a **newton-meter** (N · m). This reduces to one kilogram-meter squared per second squared ($kg \cdot m^2/s^2$ or $kg \cdot m^2 \cdot s^{-2}$) in base International System of Units (**SI**) units. Alternatively, the **erg**, equivalent to a **dyne-centimeter** (dyn · cm), can be used to express work. One erg reduces to one gram-centimeter squared per second squared ($g \cdot cm^2/s^2$ or $g \cdot cm^2 \cdot s^{-2}$) in base SI units.

To convert from joules to ergs, mulitiply by 10,000,000 (10^7). Conversely, multiply by 0.0000001 (10^{-7}).

For a given force F (in newtons) applied over a **displacement** d (in meters), the work w (in joules) is given by:

$$w = Fd$$

If, in practice, force is not applied in the same direction as the displacement that results in actual work (this is the case for a car ascending a hill, for example), the **vector** form of the above formula must be used. For a given force vector **F** (in newtons, in a specified direction) applied to an object that undergoes displacement **d** (in meters), the work w (in joules) is given by the dot product of the force vector and the displacement vector:

$$w = \mathbf{F} \cdot \mathbf{d} = Fd \cos q$$

where q is the angle between the applied force vector and the direction of the displacement that results in actual work.

The above formulas also apply for work in ergs, force magnitude in dynes, and displacement magnitude in centimeters.

Although work is usually defined in mechanical terms, it can result from the action of electric fields, magnetic fields, thermal heating, particle bombardment, and various other phenomena.

Also see **energy**, **force**, **mass**, **newton**, **second**, **SI**, and **Table of Physical Units**.

workflow

Workflow is a term used to describe the tasks, procedural steps, organizations or people involved, required input and output information, and tools needed for each step in a business process. A workflow approach to analyzing and managing a business process can be combined with an **object-oriented programming** approach, which tends to focus on documents and **data**. In general, workflow management focuses on processes rather than documents. A number of companies make workflow automation products that allow a company to create a workflow model and components such as online forms and then to use this product as a way to manage and enforce the consistent handling of work. For example, an insurance company could use a workflow automation application to ensure that a claim was handled consistently from initial call to final settlement. The workflow application would ensure that each person handling the claim used the correct online form and successfully completed their step before allowing the process to proceed to the next person and procedural step.

A *workflow engine* is the component in a workflow automation program that knows all the procedures, steps in a procedure, and rules for each step. The workflow engine determines whether the process is ready to move to the next

step. Some vendors sell workflow automation products for particular industries such as insurance and banking or for commonly-used processes such as handling computer service calls. Proponents of the workflow approach believe that task analysis and workflow modeling in themselves are likely to improve business operations.

working draft

A working draft (sometimes called a *draft document*) is a type of technical report that is a work in progress, a preliminary form of a possible future document. A working draft indicates a commitment on the part of the issuing organization to do further work in the area outlined in the document. Several revisions of the working draft may be issued before the final document is written, or the document may be made obsolete by future developments.

The World Wide Web Consortium (**W3C**) provides extensive guidelines for their own Working Drafts, which may be followed by other groups. W3C Working Drafts must include a provision in the status section of the document specifying that it is a work-in-progress and, as such, may be updated, replaced, or made obsolete by subsequent documents and, furthermore, that it does not represent W3C or member consensus. Readers are cautioned not to use the document as a reference or, if they do cite it, to refer to it as a work in progress.

According to W3C specifications for their own technical reports, the Working Draft is the first of a minimum of four documents which may lead to a *Recommendation*. The Working Draft is a document put out by an associated Working Group. As long as the Working Group is together, the Working Draft can be maintained as such, but the group is responsible for ensuring that the document is updated every three months. If all the issues in a Working Draft have been dealt with, it receives *Last Call Working Draft* status, a (largely internal) review process which typically lasts three weeks. When the Last Call Working Draft is approved, it attains *Candidate Recommendation* status, which is a call for implementation and review from outside the organization. The next stage in the process is *Proposed Recommendation*, upon review of which, the document may achieve *Recommendation* status, which represents a consensus among the W3C members that the technology or ideas in the document should be widely implemented. At any point in the process, if the document fails to meet criteria, it reverts to Working Draft status.

Standards groups, such as the Internet Engineering Task Force (**IETF**), have similar processes for the advancement of proposed standards. IETF working drafts are called *Internet Drafts*.

workstation

1) A workstation is a computer intended for individual use that is faster and more capable than a personal computer. It's intended for business or professional use (rather than home or recreational use). Workstations and applications designed for them are used by small engineering companies, architects, graphic designers, and any organization, department, or individual that requires a faster microprocessor, a large amount of random access memory (**RAM**), and special features such as high-speed graphics adapters. Historically, the workstation developed technologically about the same time and for the same audience as the **UNIX** operating system, which is often used as the workstation operating system. Among the most successful makers of this kind of workstation are Sun Microsystems, Hewlett-Packard, DEC, and IBM.

2) In IBM and other corporations, the term "workstation" is sometimes used to mean "any individual personal computer location hooked up to a **mainframe** computer." In today's corporate environments, many workers have such workstations. They're simply **personal computers** attached to a local area network (**LAN**) that in turn shares the resources of one or more large computers. Since they are PCs, they can also be used independently of the mainframe assuming they have their own applications installed and their own hard disk storage. This use of the term "workstation" (in IBM, sometimes called a "programmable workstation") made a distinction between the earlier "terminal" or "display terminal" (or "dumb terminal") of which the 3270 Information Display System is an example.

World Wide Web

A technical definition of the World Wide Web is: all the resources and users on the Internet that are using the Hypertext Transfer Protocol (**HTTP**).

A broader definition comes from the organization that Web inventor Tim Berners-Lee helped found, the World Wide Web Consortium (**W3C**):

"The World Wide Web is the universe of network-accessible information, an embodiment of human knowledge."

World Wide Web Distributed Authoring and Versioning

See "WebDAV"

worm

1) WORM (for *write once, read many*) is a data storage technology that allows information to be written to a an optical disc a single time and prevents the drive from erasing the data. The discs are intentionally not rewritable, because they are especially intended to store data that the user does not want to erase accidentally. Because of this feature, WORM devices have long been used for the archival

purposes of organizations such as government agencies or large **enterprises**. A type of **optical media**, WORM devices were developed in the late 1970s and have been adapted to a number of different media. The discs have varied in size from 5.25 to 14 inches wide, in varying formats ranging from 140MB to more than 3 GB per side of the (usually) double-sided medium. Data is written to a WORM disc with a low-powered **laser** that makes permanent marks on the surface.

Because of a lack of standardization, WORM discs have typically been only readable by the drive on which they were written, and hardware and software incompatibility has hampered their marketplace acceptance. Other optical media, such as **CDs** and **DVDs** that can be recorded once and read an unlimited number of times are sometimes considered WORM devices, although there is some argument over whether formats that can be written in more than one session (such as the **multisession CD**) qualify as such. **CD-R** has gradually been replacing traditional WORM devices, and it is expected that some newer technology, such as **DVD-R** or **HD-ROM** will eventually replace both WORM and CD-R devices.

2) A worm is a self-replicating virus that does not alter files but resides in active memory and duplicates itself. Worms use parts of an operating system that are automatic and usually invisible to the user. It is common for worms to be noticed only when their uncontrolled replication consumes system resources, slowing or halting other tasks.

WPAD

See "Web Proxy Autodiscovery"

WRAM

Also see **RAM types**.

Window RAM (WRAM), unrelated to Microsoft Windows, is very high-performance video RAM that is *dual-ported* and has about 25% more bandwidth than VRAM but costs less. It has features that make it more efficient to read data for use in block fills and text drawing. It can be used for very high **resolution** (such as 1600 by 1200 pixels) projection using **true color**. It's used in the Matrox Millenium video card.

wrapper

In information technology, a wrapper is data that precedes or frames the main data or a program that sets up another program so that it can run successfully.

1) On the Internet, "http://" and "ftp://" are sometimes described as wrappers for the Internet addresses or Uniform Resource Locator **URL** that follow. A set of bracketing symbols (such as < and >, used here to wrap the word "and") are also sometimes referred to as wrappers .

2) In programming, a wrapper is a program or **script** that sets the stage and makes possible the running of another, more important program.

3) In data transmission, a wrapper is the data that is put in front of or around a transmission that provides information about it and may also encapsulate it from view to anyone other than the intended recipient. A wrapper often consists of a *header* that precedes the encapsulated data and the *trailer* that follows it.

4) In database technology, a wrapper can be used to determine who has access to look at or change the data that is wrapped.

write once, read many

See "worm"

writing tablet

See "Big Chief tablet"

WSDL

See "Web Services Description Language"

WTLS

See "Wireless Transport Layer Security"

WTS

See "Terminal Server product"

WYSIWYG

A WYSIWYG (pronounced "wiz-ee-wig") editor or program is one that allows an interface or content developer to create a graphical user interface (**GUI**) or page of text so that the developer can see what the end result will look like while the interface or document is being created. WYSIWYG is an acronym for "what you see is what you get." A WYSIWYG editor can be contrasted with more traditional editors that require the developer to enter descriptive codes (or **markup**) and do not permit an immediate way to see the results of the markup.

A true WYSIWYG editor, such as **Microsoft's FrontPage** or **Adobe's PageMill** or Go Live (formerly CyberStudio), conceals the markup and allows the developer to think entirely in terms of how the content should appear. (One of the trade-offs, however, is that a WYSIWYG editor does not always make it easy to fine-tune its results.)

X

X is a shortened name for the **X Window System**. X originated in the early 1980s as the result of a research collaboration between Stanford University and MIT (aided by IBM) to develop a cross-platform **windowing system**.

X (compact disc access time)

In compact disc (**CD**) and digital versatile disc (**DVD**) technology, X is a base multiplier that expresses the time it took to read data from the compact disc in its original version, which was 150 kilobytes (KB) per second. As successively faster CDs arrived, they adopted the convention of indicating the read time in terms of the original speed. Thus, a 2X CD had a read access time of 300 KB and so forth. Our table relates each common drive speed to its read access time. It also shows the range of revolutions per minute (RPM) used to make the read access time possible.

CD/DVD Drive Speed	Maximum Data Transfer Rate	RPMs (revolutions per minute)
1X CD-ROM	150 KB/sec	200—530
2X CD-ROM	300 KB/sec	400—1060
4X CD-ROM	600 KB/sec	800—2120
8X—12X CD-ROM	1.2 MB/sec	1600—4240
24X—50X	1.8—6 MB/sec	2400—6360 approximately
1X DVD-ROM	1.25 MB/sec	No exact data, but much slower than 1X CD-ROM

There are only minor increases in speed as one moves from the 24X, 32X, and 40X drives. The high rotation speeds produced can create noise and vibrations, and performance may vary from drive to drive.

It seems unlikely, because of these vibrations and performance variations, that speeds will increase much above present levels. Even though a hard drive can reach much faster speeds of rotation, its enclosure stabilizes the entire mechanism and therefore avoids much of the noise and vibration inherent in the open CD-ROM drive.

x and y coordinates

x, y coordinates are respectively the horizontal and vertical addresses of any **pixel** or addressable point on a computer display screen. The x coordinate is a given number of pixels along the horizontal axis of a display starting from the pixel (pixel 0) on the extreme left of the screen. The y coordinate is a given number of pixels along the vertical axis of a display starting from the pixel (pixel 0) at the top of the screen. Together, the x and y coordinates locate any specific pixel location on the screen. x and y coordinates can also be specified as values relative to any starting point on the screen or any subset of the screen such as an image. On the Web, each clickable area of an **image map** is specified as a pair of x and y coordinates relative to the upper left-hand corner of the image.

x coordinate

See "x and y coordinates"

X server

An X server is a **server** of connections to **X terminal**s in a distributed network that uses the **X Window System**. From the terminal user's point-of-view, the X server may seem like a server of applications in multiple windows. Actually, the applications in the remote computer with the X server are making **client** requests for the services of a windows manager that runs in each terminal. X servers (as part of the X Window System) typically are installed in a **UNIX**-based operating system in a **mainframe**, **minicomputer**, or **workstation**.

The X server may be compared to Microsoft's **Terminal Server** product except that the latter is running on a Windows-based operating system. However, there are X servers designed to run on a Microsoft Windows-based operating system.

X terminal

An X terminal is typically a diskless computer especially designed to provide a low-cost user interface for applications that run in a network **X server** as part of a distributed **X Window System**. Typically, X terminals are connected to a server running a **UNIX**-based operating system on a **mainframe**, **minicomputer**, or **workstation**.

X terminals (and the X Window System) appear to have been the forerunner for what is now generally called "network computers" or **thin client**s. The X Window System and X terminals continue to offer an alternative to Microsoft's **Terminal Server** product and their **NetPC**s.

X Window System

The X Window System (sometimes referred to as "X" or as "XWindows") is an **open**, cross-**platform**, **client/server** system for managing a **windowed** graphical user interface in a **distributed** network. In general, such systems are known as **windowing system**s. In X Window, the client-server relationship is reversed from the usual. Remote computers contain applications that make client requests for display management services in each PC or workstation. X Window is primarily used in networks of interconnected **mainframe**s, **minicomputer**s, and **workstation**s. It is also used on the **X terminal**, which is essentially a workstation with display management capabilities but without its own applications. (The X terminal can be seen as a predecessor of the network PC or **thin client** computer.)

The X Window System was the result of research efforts in the early 1980s at Stanford University and MIT, aided by IBM, to develop a platform-independent graphics protocol. The X Window System is an open standard that is managed by the X.Org consortium. Although Microsoft has its own platform-dependent windowing system (an integral part of the Windows 95/98/NT operating systems), there are vendor-supplied X Windows products that can be installed to run on these systems.

X.25

The X.25 protocol, adopted as a standard by the Consultative Committee for International Telegraph and Telephone (CCITT), is a commonly-used network **protocol**. The X.25 protocol allows computers on different public networks (such as CompuServe, Tymnet, or a TCP/IP network) to communicate through an intermediary computer at the network layer level. X.25's protocols correspond closely to the data-link and physical-layer protocols defined in the Open Systems Interconnection (**OSI**) communication model.

X.400

X.400 is the messaging (notably e-mail) standard specified by the **ITU-TS** (International Telecommunications Union— Telecommunication Standard Sector). It's an alternative to the more prevalent e-mail protocol, Simple Mail Transfer Protocol (**SMTP**). X.400 is common in Europe and Canada. It's actually a set of standards, each in the 400-number range.

Because X.400 stipulates a number of possible address characteristics that SMTP does not, an X.400 address can be long and cumbersome. On the other hand, X.400 adherents note that it is an official standard whereas SMTP is a "de facto" standard. Thus, products with X.400 implementations can be tested more rigorously than products with SMTP implementations can. X.400 offers more capabilities than SMTP does. However, many of these capabilities are seldom used.

An SMTP e-mail address that looks like this hypothetical address:

```
georg.hansen@delab.sintef.no
```

might look like this in an X.400 e-mail message:

```
G=Georg; S=Hansen; O=sintef; OU=delab; PRMD=uninett;
ADMD=uninett; C=no
```

X.400 is a complex standard that is difficult to summarize here. The arguments in favor of and against each of the opposing e-mail standards are also complicated.

X.500

X.500 Directory Service is a standard way to develop an electronic directory of people in an organization so that it can be part of a global directory available to anyone in the world with Internet access. Such a directory is sometimes called a global White Pages directory. The idea is to be able to look up people in a user-friendly way by name, department, or organization. Many enterprises and institutions have created an X.500 directory. Because these directories are organized as part of a single global directory, you can search for hundreds of thousands of people from a single place on the World Wide Web.

The X.500 directory is organized under a common "root" directory in a "tree" hierarchy of: country, organization, organizational unit, and person. An entry at each of these levels must have certain attributes; some can have optional ones established locally. Each organization can implement a directory in its own way as long as it adheres to the basic **schema** or plan. The distributed global directory works through a registration process and one or more central places that manage many directories.

Providing an X.500 directory allows an organization to make itself and selected members known on the Internet. Two of the largest directory service providers are **InterNIC**, the organization that supervises domain name registration in the U.S., and ESnet, which maintains X.500 data for all the U.S. national laboratories. ESNet and similar providers also provide access to looking up names in the global directory, using a number of different user interfaces including designated Web sites, **whois**, and **finger**. These organizations also provide assistance to organizations that are creating their own Directory Information Tree (DIT).

In X.500, each local directory is called a Directory System Agent (DSA). A DSA can represent one organization or a group of organizations. The DSAs are interconnected from the Directory Information Tree (DIT). The user interface program for access to one or more DSAs is a Directory User Agent (DUA). DUAs include whois, finger, and programs that offer a graphical user interface. X.500 is implemented as part of the Distributed Computing Environment (**DCE**) in its Global Directory Service (GDS). The University of Michigan is one of a number of universities that use X.500 as a way to route e-mail as well as to provide name lookup, using the Lightweight Directory Access Protocol (**LDAP**).

X2

x2 is a technology from US Robotics (now 3Com) for the downstream transmission of data over ordinary phone lines at 56 **Kbps** (thousands of bits per second). The 56 Kbps speed is achieved in the downstream direction only (to your

home or business). Upstream speed is at the regular maximum speed of 33.6 Kbps. (The actual achieved downstream speed is reported by users to be about 53 Kbps.) x2 provided input to and has been replaced by the **V.90 ITU-TS** standard.

56 Kbps technologies exploit the fact that most telephone company offices are interconnected with digital lines. Assuming your Internet connection provider has a digital connection to its telephone company office, the downstream traffic from your local Internet access provider can use a new transmission technique on your regular **twisted pair** phone line that bypasses the usual **digital-to-analog conversion**. A V.90-equipped modem doesn't need to demodulate the downstream data. Instead, it decodes a stream of multi-bit voltage pulses generated as though the line was equipped for digital information. (Upstream data still requires digital-to-analog modulation.)

Unlike **Integrated Services Digital Network**, the V.90 technology does not require any additional installation or extra charges from your local phone company. On the other hand, the maximum transmission speed of ISDN is twice that of V.90 at 128 Kbps. You also have the flexibility of combining digital and voice transmission on the same line.

x86

x86 is a generic name for the series of Intel **microprocessor** families that began with the 80286 microprocessor. This series has been the provider of computing for personal computers since the 80286 was introduced in 1982. x86 microprocessors include the 386DX/SX/SL family, the 486DX/SX//DX2/SL/DX4 family, and the **Pentium 3** family. The x86 line replaced Intel's previous series, the 8086/8088. Adopted by IBM for its first PCs, the 8086/8088 and the continuing x86 series have made Intel the predominant force in microprocessor design and manufacture.

Xalan

Xalan is a specification for transforming Extensible Markup Language (**XML**) documents into Hypertext Markup Language (**HTML**) or other XML document types. Xalan-Java version 1.2 is based on World Wide Web Consortium (**W3C**) recommendations for Extensible Stylesheet Language Transformations (**XSLT**) and XML Path Language (**XPL**). Xalan normally uses the **Xerces** XML parser, but it can use any **parser** that conforms to either Document Object Model (**DOM**) level 2 or Simple API for XML (**SAX**) level 1.

Xalan-Java version 2 recasts Xalan as an implementation of Transformations for XML (**TraX**) interfaces. TRaX provides a modular framework and a standard application programming interface for performing an open-ended range of XML transformations. In conjunction with TRaX, Xalan-Java 2 relies on system properties to configure its operational settings. The default settings point to the Xalan

stylesheet processor, the serializers shipped with Xalan, and the Xerces SAX parser. Xalan-Java version 2 builds on SAX level 2, DOM level 2, and the Java API for XML Parsing.

Xalan-C++ version 1.0 is an implementation of W3C recommendations for XSLT and XPath. It uses the Xerces-C++ version 1.3.0 XML parser.

LotusXSL, which used to be a specification in its own right, has been recast as a sub-specification of Xalan.

Xanadu

Xanadu (TM) is a set of ideas and a software design project for a universal system of electronic information storage and access. Its inventor, Ted Nelson, is credited with inventing the term **hypertext**, an idea that is a central part of Xanadu.

Conceived in the early 1980's or perhaps slightly earlier, Xanadu in some ways seems to have anticipated the Web and such ideas as **groupware**, group writing, **virtual organization**, and information. Nelson has described Xanadu as "an instantaneous electronic literature" and "perhaps the ultimate" hypertext system.

X-Box

X-Box is a game console being developed by Microsoft that is intended to provide players with a more realistic and immediate interactive experience than current consoles and to gain Microsoft a leadership position in the game console market. The X-Box will include a 600 **MHz** Intel processor, a custom-designed graphics processor referred to as the X-Chip, 64 **megabytes** of memory, and a built-in **digital versatile disc** movie player. Microsoft claims that the X-Box will deliver 300 million polygons per second (imagery in games is developed in uniformly-sized polygonal units) and they compare this performance with the 66 million polygons per second delivered by Sony's PlayStation 2 console. A **modem** for Internet access will be an option.

Microsoft expects to develop about 30% of the games offered for the X-Box and offers its **DirectX** graphics development interface to companies that will develop the remaining 70%. Activision is one company planning to develop or modify games for the X-Box. Existing makers of game consoles include Atari, Nintendo, Sega, and Sony.

Although Microsoft is new to the console player business, it currently is a leader in software for the PC game market. According to Microsoft, there are about 29 million console players, 11 million PC game players, and 7 million people who play both. Console games emphasize extremely fast interactive response and are described as more "visceral," whereas PC games tend to take longer to play and are more "cerebral."

At least one industry observer suggests that the X-Box may be part of a Microsoft strategy to bring a computer under another name into many living rooms that currently don't include a computer. In this view, the X-Box could later be enhanced to provide capabilities additional to game playing.

XBRL

XBRL (Extensible Business Reporting Language) is an **XML**-based language being developed specifically for the automation of business information requirements, such as the preparation, sharing, and analysis of financial reports, statements, and audit schedules. XBRL steering committee members include financial, accounting, software, and governmental communities from around the world: member organizations include Microsoft, ACCPAC, Oracle, Deloitte & Touche, IBM, Hyperion, and the American Institute of Certified Public Accountants (AICPA). The goal of the steering committee is to create a standard specification for industry-wide use.

The use of XBRL for creating financial statements will facilitate what has been a manual, repetitive, and error-prone endeavor. Statements must frequently be duplicated separately—and altered—for different uses (a Web publication and printed document, for example), and the extraction of data can be very time-consuming. XBRL will automate these processes.

In the future, XBRL is intended, among other things, to provide a standardized framework and integrated methodology for the preparation and publication of reports, as well as a consistent, automated process for the reliable extraction and exchange of financial statements.

XDMA

XDMA (Xing Distributed Media Architecture) is a network **architecture** for **multicast streaming media** transmissions. Streaming media enables live viewing of a transmission as compared to processes that require that files be completely transferred to the user's computer before their data can be viewed. Unlike prior network architectures, XDMA enables low-cost multiple access. In general, multimedia network architectures have required point-to-point connections and complex server programming, which made the multicasting of streaming media impractical, if not impossible.

XDMA was developed by Xing Technology, producers of the first **MPEG** software **encoders** and decoders. Xing was purchased by RealNetworks in 1999; the Seattle-based company's RealPlayer Plus and Microsoft's Windows Media Player are the two leading players of streaming media. The XDMA architecture supports live, on-demand multimedia transmission to multiple users over local area networks (**LAN**s) or wide area networks (**WAN**s)—such as the Internet—without requiring the use of file system applications such as **Novell**'s **NetWare** or Sun

Microsystem's Network File System (**NFS**). Because it is built on international standards such as **TCP/IP** and MPEG, XDMA is easily integrated into existing **infrastructure**s.

Xeon

Xeon (pronounced ZEE-ahn) is a **Pentium microprocessor** from Intel for use in "mid-range" **enterprise** servers and workstations. On a server motherboard from Intel, up to eight (and later even more) Xeon processors will be able to do **multiprocessing** sharing the same 100 Mhz bus. Xeon is replacing the Pentium Pro as Intel's main enterprise microchip. Xeon is designed for Internet and large transactional database servers as well as for engineering, graphics, and multimedia applications that require moving a lot of data around quickly. Xeon is the high end of the Pentium line (**Celeron** is the low end).

Xeon is based on the **Pentium** microprocessor's P6 architecture. It's designed to work with a new and faster **Peripheral Component Interconnect bus** and **Accelerated Graphics Port**. Xeon features:

- A faster **L1 and L2 cache**, either 512 Kbytes or 1 Mbyte, that runs at the same 400 Mhz **clock speed** of the processor.

- A faster **bus** to carry data between the processor, RAM, and I/O devices. The 450NX PCIset is a **chipset** that works at a 100 Mhz clock speed and supports up to 8 GB of **extended data output RAM** memory.

- A larger Accelerated Graphics Port (**AGP**) chip set called the 440GX AGPset that also runs at 100 Mhz. It supports 2 GB of 100 Mhz **SDRAM**.

- An extended server memory architecture that provide for 36-bit addresses, allowing up to 64 GB of physical memory to be addressed.

- Everything premounted in a **motherboard** package for faster manufacturing

Typically, a computer with a Xeon microprocessor would use a **Windows NT**, **NetWare**, or **UNIX** operating system. Xeon-based systems are expected to offer competition to Sun Microsystems, Silicon Graphics, and others in the workstation market, but its primary market is expected to be the mid-range server.

Xerces

Xerces (the name comes from the Xerces blue butterfly) is a set of **parser**s compatible with Extensible Markup Language (**XML**). (A parser is a program that analyzes and organizes formal language statements into a usable form for a given purpose.) Xerces parsers are available for **Java** and **C++**, implementing World Wide Web Consortium (**W3C**) XML, Document Object Model (**DOM**), and Simple API for XML (**SAX**) standards.

All of the Xerces parsers are modular and configurable. A **Perl wrapper** is provided for the C++ version; this allows access to a fully-validating XML parser from Perl. It also provides access to **Unicode** strings.

The Xerces Java Parser 1.2.0 supports XML 1.0, and can be used for building XML-compatible Web servers; building the next generation of XML-based vertical applications; creating XML editors; ensuring the integrity of XML data; and building global XML applications.

Xerces-C is an XML parser written in a portable subset of C++. Xerces-C allows applications to read and write XML data. A shared library facilitates parsing, generating, manipulating, and validating XML documents. Other features include conformity to XML 1.0; tracking of latest DOM and SAX specifications; programmatic generation and validation of XML; pluggable catalogs, validators and encodings; and customizable error handling.

XML4P includes a collection of Perl wrapper objects that internally use their XML4C counterparts for high-performance, scalable and localizable DOM parsing. Features include programmatic generation and validation of XML; conformity to DOM specifications; and customizable error handling.

XFDL

Extensible Forms Description Language (XFDL) is a use of the Extensible Markup Language (**XML**) that provides a standard way to define the data fields and layout for a complex business or government form for digital storage and display. An XFDL form can be sent to a Web user as an XML page. XFDL makes it possible to sign an XFDL page with one or more **digital certificate**s. XFDL also describes a **syntax** for inline mathematical and conditional expressions. XFDL combines the Universal Forms Definition Language (UFDL), developed earlier, with XML.

PureEdge, an e-commerce standards firm, formerly called UWI.com, and World Wide Web Consortium (**W3C**) editor Tim Bray introduced XFDL in 1998 as the world's first **open** standard for secure, legally-binding XML documents. Since then, vendors such as GTE, CommerceOne, and Verisign have moved to support or endorse XDFL in their products.

XGA

See "display modes"

XGA and XGA-2 (Extended Graphics Array)

Also see **display modes**.

XGA (Extended Graphics Array) is a high-resolution video display mode that provides screen **pixel resolution** of 1,024 by 768 in 256 colors or 640 by 480 in high (16-bit) color. XGA **monitor**s can be **interlaced display**s.

XGA-2 is a display mode that provides 1,024 by 768 resolution in high color and higher-refresh rates than XGA. XGA was introduced by IBM in 1990 as an improvement on an earlier IBM display standard, the 8514/A.

The XGA standard is used in desktop and laptop computers as well as in projection systems.

XHTML

As the World Wide Web Consortium (**W3C**) describes it, XHTML (Extensible Hypertext Markup Language) is "a reformulation of **HTML 4.0** as an application of the Extensible Markup Language (**XML**)." For readers unacquainted with either term, HTML is the set of codes (that's the "markup language") that a writer puts into a document to make it displayable on the World Wide Web. HTML 4 is the current version of it. XML is a structured set of rules for how one might define any kind of **data** to be shared on the Web. It's called an "extensible" markup language because anyone can invent a particular set of markup for a particular purpose and as long as everyone uses it (the writer and an application program at the receiver's end), it can be adapted and used for many purposes—including, as it happens, describing the appearance of a Web page. That being the case, it seemed desirable to reframe HTML in terms of XML. The result is XHTML, a particular application of XML for "expressing" Web pages.

XHTML is, in fact, the follow-on version of HTML 4. You could think of it as HTML 5, except that it is called XHTML 1.0. In XHTML, all HTML 4 **markup** elements and attributes (the language of HTML) will continue to be supported. Unlike HTML, however, XHTML can be extended by anyone that uses it. New elements and attributes can be defined and added to those that already exist, making possible new ways to embed content and programming in a Web page. In appearance, an XHTML file looks like a somewhat more elaborate HTML file.

Advantages

To quote the W3C again, the advantages are "extensibility and portability."

Extensibility means that as new ideas for Web communication and presentation emerge, they can be implemented without having to wait for the next major version of HTML and browser support. New tags or attributes can be defined to express the new possibilities and, assuming some program at the receiving end can understand and act on them, new things may happen on your Web page that never happened before. Specific sets of extensions for XHTML are planned for mathematical expressions, vector graphics, and multimedia applications.

If extensibility is likely to lead to more complicated pages and larger programs, the portability advantage means that Web pages can now be made simpler than they were before so that small devices can handle them. This is important for mobile devices and possibly household devices that contain microprocessors with embedded programming and smaller memories. XHTML defines several levels of possible markup complexity and each document states its level of complexity at the beginning. Programs in microdevices might expect XHTML-coded files that state the simplest level of complexity so that they could be handled by a small program and memory.

Differences and Distinctive Features

You can find out more by reading the specification and tutorials, but here are some distinctive features of XHTML and differences between HTML 4:

- XHTML requires strict adherence to coding rules. Notably, it requires that you use closing as well as opening elements (this is known as *well-formed* **syntax**) and that all elements be in lower case. HTML was much less rigorous about notation and browsers tended to be even more forgiving.

- This means that XHTML files will tend to be "busier" than HTML. However, they won't necessarily be harder to read because rigor may force more order in coding. In addition, the major editing and file creation tools will probably lay out pages for easier readability.

- XHTML would seem to encourage a more structured and conceptual way of thinking about content and, combined with the **style sheet**, a more creative way of displaying it.

- XHTML will make it easier for people to dream up and add new elements (and develop browsers or other applications that support them).

XIPC

XIPC is a **middleware** product that manages **interprocess communication** across programs in a network. A **process** is a unit of work associated with a particular user request (for example). Completing that work usually involves creating other processes or communicating between processes. This interprocess communication is performed using:

- Message queueing
- Semaphores
- Memory sharing

XIPC allows a programmer to use these interprocess communication methods across processes that are distributed in different locations in a network so that the programmer need not be aware of the network or individual process locations. To do this, XIPC adds **peer-to-peer** messaging to the IPC methods. The developer of XIPC, Level 8 Software, calls this "message-oriented middleware (MOM)."

XJACK

XJACK is a type of connector for notebook computer **modems** that allows a standard telephone connector to snap into the modem. Internal modems for notebook computers come on a slim PC Card. Many cards provide a connection that requires a special plug that in turn has to be plugged into a relay attachment. This plug can easily become loose in the PC Card socket, losing your connection. XJACK is a connector on the PC Card that pulls out and allows you to snap a regular wall jack connector into the modem directly. This connection is more secure.

XJACK is manufactured by Megahertz, a subsidiary of 3Com. However, a number of other modem manufacturers now build the XJACK into their mobile-size modems.

XMI

XMI (XML Metadata Interchange) is a proposed use of the Extensible Markup Language (**XML**) that is intended to provide a standard way for programmers and other users to exchange information about **metadata** (essentially, information about what a set of data consists of and how it is organized). Specifically, XMI is intended to help programmers using the Unified Modeling Language (**UML**) with different languages and development tools to exchange their data models with each other. In addition, XMI can also be used to exchange information about data warehouses. Effectively, the XMI format standardizes how any set of metadata is described and requires users across many industries and operating environments to see data the same way.

XMI is a proposal from the Object Management Group (**OMG**) that builds on and extends these industry standards or recommendations:

- Extensible Markup Language (**XML**), a standard from the World Wide Web Consortium (**W3C**)

- Unified Modeling Language (**UML**), a standard from OMG

- Meta Object Facility (MOF), another standard from the OMG for a metamodeling and metadata repository

Ideally, XMI will allow different cooperating companies a way to use each other's data repositories. XMI is described as similar to, yet competing with, Microsoft's Open Information Model.

XML

XML (Extensible Markup Language) is a flexible way to create common **information** formats and share both the format and the **data** on the World Wide Web, intranets, and elsewhere. For example, computer makers might agree on a standard or common way to describe the information about a computer product (processor speed, memory size, and so forth) and then describe the product information format

with XML. Such a standard way of describing data would enable a user to send an intelligent agent (a program) to each computer maker's Web site, gather data, and then make a valid comparison. XML can be used by any individual or group of individuals or companies that wants to share information in a consistent way.

XML, a formal recommendation from the World Wide Web Consortium (**W3C**), is similar to the language of today's Web pages, the Hypertext Markup Language (**HTML**). Both XML and HTML contain **markup** symbols to describe the contents of a page or file. HTML, however, describes the content of a Web page (mainly text and graphic images) only in terms of how it is to be displayed and interacted with. For example, the letter "p" placed within markup tags starts a new paragraph. XML describes the content in terms of what data is being described. For example, the word "phonenum" placed within markup tags could indicate that the data that followed was a phone number. This means that an XML file can be processed purely as data by a program or it can be stored with similar data on another computer or, like an HTML file, that it can be displayed. For example, depending on how the application in the receiving computer wanted to handle the phone number, it could be stored, displayed, or dialed.

XML is "extensible" because, unlike HTML, the markup symbols are unlimited and self-defining. XML is actually a simpler and easier-to-use subset of the Standard Generalized Markup Language (**SGML**), the standard for how to create a document structure. It is expected that HTML and XML will be used together in many Web applications. XML markup, for example, may appear within an HTML page.

Early applications of XML include Microsoft's Channel Definition Format (**CDF**), which describes a **channel**, a portion of a Web site that has been downloaded to your hard disk and is then is updated periodically as information changes. A specific CDF file contains data that specifies an initial Web page and how frequently it is updated. Another early application is ChartWare, which uses XML as a way to describe medical charts so that they can be shared by doctors. Applications of XML have also been created for banking, e-commerce ordering, personal preference profiles, purchase orders, litigation documents, part lists, and many others.

XML Pointer Language

See "XPointer"

XML Query Language

See "XQL"

XMLNews

XMLNews is a set of specifications for exchanging news objects such as stories, images, or audio clips in a standard format across different applications and operating systems.

XMLNews uses Extensible Markup Language (**XML**) and industry standards developed by the International Press Telecommunications Council and the Newspaper Association of America. XMLNews has two parts: XMLNews-Story and XMLNews-Meta.

XMLNews-Story is an XML document type for text-based news and information. It defines the format of a news story's content and is a subset of News Industry Text Format (NITF), the XML document type definition (**DTD**) designed to mark up and deliver news content in a variety of ways, including print, wireless devices, and the Web. XMLNews-Meta defines the format of any **metadata** associated with a story (or any other kind of news object) and is based on the World Wide Web Consortium's Resource Description Framework (**RDF**).

Xmodem

Xmodem is an error-correcting **protocol** for **modem** that was created in 1978 by Ward Christensen and became a de facto standard. Modems that agree on using the Xmodem protocol send data in 128-byte blocks. If a block is received successfully, a positive (ACK) acknowledgement is returned. If an error is detected, a negative (NAK) acknowledgement is returned and the block is resent. Xmodem uses the **checksum** method of error checking.

X-modem

See "modem error-correcting protocols"

Xon/Xoff

Xon/Xoff (sometimes written "X-on/X-off" or "XON/XOFF" and pronounced eks-AWN eks-AWF) is a protocol for controlling the flow of data between computers and other **device**s on an **asynchronous serial** connection. For example, a computer typically sends data to a printer faster than the printer can print. The printer contains a buffer where data is stored until the printer catches up with the computer. If the buffer becomes full before the printer catches up, a small microprocessor in the printer sends back an X/off signal to stop sending data. When enough data is printed and buffer storage becomes free, the printer sends an X/on signal telling the computer to resume sending data.

The "X" stands for "transmitter" so the X/on and X/off are signals to turn a transmitter on or off. The actual signal for X/on is the same bit configuration as the **ASCII** Ctrl-Q keyboard combination. The X/off signal is the Ctrl-S character.

When you define your **modem** to your computer's operating system, you may need to specify the use of flow control with X/on/Xoff or with CTS/RTS (Clear to Send/Ready to Send). When sending binary data, Xon/Xoff may not be recognized because it is character-encoded.

XOR

See "logic gate"

XPath

XPath is a language that describes a way to locate and process items in Extensible Markup Language (**XML**) documents by using an addressing **syntax** based on a path through the document's logical structure or hierarchy. This makes writing programming expressions easier than if each expression had to understand typical XML **markup** and its sequence in a document. XPath also allows the programmer to deal with the document at a higher level of **abstraction**. XPath is a language that is used by and specified as part of both the Extensible Stylesheet Language Transformations (**XSLT**) and by **XPointer** (SML Pointer Language). It uses the information abstraction defined in the XML Information Set (**Infoset**). Since XPath does not use XML syntax itself, it could be used in contexts other than those of XML.

XPath uses a syntax something like an informal set of directions for finding a particular geographic location. When telling someone how to find the Minneapolis campus of the University of Minnesota within the United States, for example, you might write:

`US/MN/Mpls/SE/WashingtonAve/bridge`

which would put the user in the middle of the campus.

The key difference between XPath and earlier languages is that XPath specifies a route, rather than pointing to a specific set or sequence of characters, words, or other elements.

XPath uses the concepts of the *concept node* (the point from which the path address begins), the *logical tree* that is inherent in any XML document, and the concepts expressing logical relationships that are defined in the XML Information Set, such as *ancestor*, *attribute*, *child*, *parent*, and *self*. XPath includes a small set of expressions for specifying mathematics functions and the ability to be extended with other functions.

XPointer

XPointer is a language for locating data within an Extensible Markup Language (**XML**) document based on properties such as location within the document, character content, and attribute values. XPointer consists of a description that comes after the # symbol in a Uniform Resource Locator (**URL**). XPointer can be used alone or together with **XPath**, another language for locating data within an XML document.

In Hypertext Markup Language (**HTML**), the # symbol enables linking to a specific marked point within an HTML page. XPointer allows linking to a point based on content as well. In this way, a reader can, for example, be enabled to link to the next instance of a certain word, phrase, or sequence of characters within an XML document.

XQL

XQL (XML Query Language) is a way to locate and filter the elements (data fields) and text in an Extensible Markup Language (**XML**) document. XML files are used to transmit collections of **data** between computers on the Web. XQL provides a tool for finding and/or selecting out specific items in the data collection in an XML file or set of files. It is based on the pattern **syntax** used in the Extensible Stylesheet Language (**XSL**) and is proposed as an extension to it.

The XSL pattern language is a declarative way to indicate specific elements for processing. It uses simple **directory** notation. For example, book/author means: Select all author elements in all book elements in a particular context (for example, within an XML file or a set of files). XQL adds to this directory pattern notation the ability to use **boolean** logic, to filter out elements, to index into a collection of elements, and to do some other things. Using XQL, a program could be written to search repositories of XML files, to provide hypertext links to specific elements, and for other applications.

For more information, we recommend reading the XQL proposal at the World Wide Web Consortium (**W3C**) Web site.

XSL

XSL (Extensible Stylesheet Language), formerly called Extensible Style Language, is a language for creating a **style sheet** that describes how data sent over the Web using the Extensible Markup Language (**XML**) is to be presented to the user. For example, in an XML page that describes the characteristics of one or more automobiles for an insurance company, a set of open and close **tags** might contain the name of an auto manufacturer. Using XSL, you could tell the Web **browser** that the auto manufacturer name should be displayed, where to display it on a page, and that it should be displayed in a bold **font**. XSL is based on and extends the Document Style Semantics and Specification Language (**DSSSL**) and the Cascading Style Sheet, level 1 (**CSS1**) standards.

Think of an XML page as similar to an HTML page (like the one you are reading now), but containing data in identified fields rather than text and graphics. XSL gives a developer the tools to describe exactly which data fields in an XML file to display and exactly where and how to display them. Like any style sheet language, XSL can be used to create a style definition for one XML document or reused for many other XML documents.

XSL is being developed under the auspices of the World Wide Web Consortium (**W3C**) and is currently in the working draft stage.

XSL Transformations

XSL Transformations (XSLT) is a standard way to describe how to transform (change) the structure of an **XML** (Extensible Markup Language) document into an XML document with a different structure. XSLT is a Recommendation of the World Wide Web Consortium (**W3C**).

XSLT can be thought of as an extension of the Extensible Stylesheet Language (**XSL**). XSL is a language for formatting an XML document (for example, showing how the data described in the XML document should be presented in a Web page). XSLT shows how the XML document should be reorganized into another data structure (which could then be presented by following an XSL **style sheet**).

XSLT is used to describe how to transform the *source tree* or data structure of an XML document into the *result tree* for a new XML document, which can be completely different in structure. The coding for the XSLT is also referred to as a style sheet and can be combined with an XSL style sheet or be used independently.

XSLT

See "XSL Transformations"

xSP

xSP is a generic term for any kind of service provider on the Internet. The two main kinds of service provider are the Internet service provider (**ISP**), which provides users with connection to the Internet and sometimes offers **hosting** and other services, and the application service provider (**ASP**), which provides remote access to one or more computer **application**s.

An application service provider may be one of these kinds of xSP:

- A storage service provider (**SSP**)
- A management service provider (**MSP**)
- A business service provider (BSP)
- A security application service provider (SASP)
- A wireless application service provider (**WASP**)
- And so forth

XTACACS

See "TACACS"

XUL

XUL (Extensible User-interface Language) is a standard way to exchange data that describes a program's **user interface**, or at least the portion of it that can be controlled by programming. Historically, user interfaces have been difficult to customize so they would work across various operating platforms such as Windows and Macintosh. Netscape and Mozilla, an open group that develops Netscape, have jointly developed XUL to solve this problem. (XUL developers say that XUL is pronounced ZOOL, rhyming with "rule.")

One of the main assets of XUL is simplicity. XUL is easier to work with than the interface programming tools of the past. A few lines of XUL can accomplish what previously required many lines of code. One need not be a professional programmer to build a basic Web browser interface using XUL. This fact may ultimately translate into lower cost for the development of user interfaces.

Flexibility is another asset of XUL. It is an application of Extensible Markup Language (**XML**), Cascading Style Sheets (**CSS**), the Document Object Model (**DOM**), and the Hypertext Markup Language (**HTML**). Portions of some XUL documents must be platform-specific, because platforms have different default preferences concerning the arrangement of "widgets" such as mail-inbox icons and dialog buttons.

Y

See "admittance"

y coordinate

See "x and y coordinates"

Y2K

See "2000"

Yagi antenna

A Yagi antenna, also known as a *Yagi-Uda array* or simply a *Yagi*, is a unidirectional **antenna** commonly used in communications when a **frequency** is above 10 **MHz**. This type of antenna is popular among Amateur Radio and Citizens Band radio operators. It is used at some surface installations in **satellite** communications systems.

A basic Yagi consists of two or three straight elements, each measuring approximately $^1/_2$ electrical **wavelength**s. The **antenna** can be balanced or unbalanced. The Yagi is inherently a balanced antenna, but it can be fed with **coaxial cable** and a device called a *balun* at the point where the feed line joins the *driven element*.

The driven element of a Yagi is the equivalent of a center-fed, half-wave **dipole antenna**. Parallel to the driven element, and approximately 0.2 to 0.5 wavelength on either side of it, are straight rods or wires called *reflectors* and *directors*. A reflector is placed behind the driven element and is slightly longer than $^1/_2$ wavelength; a director is placed in front of the driven element and is slightly shorter than $^1/_2$ wavelength. A typical Yagi has one reflector and one or more directors. The antenna propagates **electromagnetic field** energy in the direction running from the driven element toward the director(s), and is most sensitive to incoming **electromagnetic field** energy in this same direction.

The Yagi antenna not only has a unidirectional radiation and response pattern, but it concentrates the radiation and response. The more directors a Yagi has, the greater the so-called *forward gain*. As more directors are added to a Yagi, it becomes longer. Some Yagi antennas have as many as 10 or even 12 directors in addition to the driven element and one reflector. Long Yagis are rarely used below 50 MHz, because at these frequencies the structure becomes physically unwieldy.

Yahoo

Yahoo! is a directory of World Wide Web sites organized in a hierarchy of topic categories. As a directory, it provides both new and seasoned Web users the reassurance of a structured view of hundreds of thousands of Web sites and millions of Web pages. It also provides one of the best ways to search the Web for a given topic. Since Yahoo is associated with the most popular Web search sites, if a search argument doesn't lead to a Yahoo topic page, it will still lead to results from Google or the six or seven other popular search engine sites Yahoo links to.

Yahoo! began as the bookmark lists of two Stanford University graduate students, David Filo and Jerry Yang. After putting their combined bookmark lists organized by categories on a college site, the list began to grow into an Internet phenomenon. It became the first such directory with a large following. Filo and Yang postponed their graduate work and became part of a public offering for a multimillion dollar corporation.

Yellow Book

The Yellow Book is the informal name for Philips and Sony's ECMA-130 standard specification for compact disc, read-only-memory (**CD-ROM**). Published by the two companies in 1988, the Yellow Book is an extension of the **Red Book** that enables the CD to contain data other than audio data. In 1989, the Yellow Book was issued by the International Organization for Standardization (**ISO**) as *ISO/IEC 10149, Data Interchange on Read-Only 120mm Optical Discs (CD-ROM)*. Because the Yellow Book only defines the physical arrangement of the data on the disc, other standards are used in conjunction with it to define directory and file structures. They include **ISO 9660**, HFS (Hierarchical File System, for Macintosh computers), and Hybrid HFS-ISO.

In addition to the disc specification, optical stylus parameters, the control/display system, and sector structure, the Yellow Book includes modulation and error correction data. Definitions include two data modes, mode 1 and mode 2.

CD-ROM, Mode 1 is the standard data storage mode used by almost all standard data CDs (CD-ROMs). Of the 2,352 bytes of data in each block, 2048 are allocated for the data that the user sees. The remaining 304 bytes are used for added error detection and correction code.

CD-ROM, Mode 2 can contain 2336 bytes of user data. It is the same as Mode 1, except that the error detection and code correction bytes are not included. The Mode 2 format offers a flexible method for storing graphics and video. It allows different kinds of data to be mixed together, and became the

basis for another standard known as **CD-ROM XA** (Extended Architecture). The specification for CD-ROM XA was published as an extension to the Yellow Book in 1991.

Ymodem

Ymodem is an error-correcting **protocol** for a **modem** that uses larger data blocks for greater efficiency. Modems that agree on using the Ymodem protocol send data in 1024-byte blocks. Blocks received successfully are not acknowledged. Blocks with errors are acknowledged (with a NAK or negative acknowledgement) and the blocks are retransmitted. Ymodem is similar to Xmodem-1K except that a batch mode is provided. In batch mode, a number of files can be sent with a single command. Ymodem uses **cyclic redundancy checking** as the method of error detection.

z coordinate

A z coordinate is the third-dimensional coordinate in a volume **pixel**, or **voxel**. Together with **x and y coordinates**, the z coordinate defines a location in a three-dimensional space.

See **voxel** for more information.

Z Object Publishing Environment

See "Zope"

z/OS

z/OS is the computer **operating system** for IBM's **zSeries 900** (z900) line of large (**mainframe**) **servers**. z/OS is a renamed and upgraded version of **OS/390**, which in turn evolved from the **MVS** operating system. IBM's renamed servers and operating systems reflect a strategy to realign its products more closely with the Internet and its own **e-business** initiatives.

z/OS is described as an extremely **scalable** and secure high-performance operating system based on the **64-bit z/Architecture**. Like its predecessor, OS/390, z/OS lays claim to being highly reliable for running mission-critical applications. The operating system supports Web- and **Java**-based applications.

Z39.50

Z39.50 is a standard communications **protocol** for the search and retrieval of bibliographic data in online databases. Z39.50 is used on the Internet to search the Online Public Access Catalogues (**OPAC**) of library holdings. It is also sometimes used to link disparate OPACs into a single "union" OPAC. Z39.50 is an American National Standards Institute (**ANSI**/NISO) standard.

zap

In general usage, zap (noun) is spiciness, kick, or a powerful force. Dishes with chili pepper have zap. This term may be traceable to a comic book convention in which the hurling of an electronic beam or bolt of electricity by a hero (or anti-hero) using a ray gun is often accompanied by a sound balloon that says "ZAP!!!" The term is also used in Paintball and in some computer games.

In information technology, zap has several meanings:

1) In programming, a zap (noun) is a precise and immediate correction for a computer code problem. Most proprietary software programs are distributed to customers as **compiler** code in the form of an unreadable string of computer **binary digit**s. When a bug is detected after the software is released, the only way to fix the already compiled code is to overlay the bad code with a sequence of good code. This overlaying is known as zapping and the fix itself is a zap. IBM provides its mainframe software customers with a special program for applying zaps that is called **SuperZap**.

2) In computers, to zap (verb) can also mean to erase or get rid of something. On a **Macintosh** computer, to "zap the PRAM" is to erase PRAM so that the system can rebuild its contents. (See **parameter RAM** for this procedure.)

3) Relative to computer hardware, to zap (verb) can mean to ruin something electrically. Thus, a power surge when you don't have a surge protector can zap a computer's electronic components.

z-buffering

Z-buffering is an **algorithm** used in 3-D graphics to ensure that perspective works the same way in the virtual world as it does in the real one: a solid object in the foreground will block the view of one behind it. You've seen this illustrated in the real world when someone stands between you and the television screen. Z-buffering is a type of algorithm known as a Visual Surface Determination (VSD) algorithm.

Z-buffering works by testing **pixel** depth and comparing the current position (z coordinate) with stored data in a **buffer** (called a *z-buffer*) that holds information about each pixel's last postion. The pixel in the closer position to the viewer is the one that will be displayed, just as the person in front of the television is what the viewer sees rather than the screen.

Z-buffering is one of three VSD algorithms commonly used for this purpose. The other two, BSP trees and depth sorting, work with polygons and consequently are less effective for portrayal of movement and overlap. Since it works at the pixel level, z-buffering can be demanding in terms of memory and processing time. Nevertheless, its more complex and life-like simulation of real-world object dynamics ensures its continuing popularity as a 3-D graphics development tool.

Zero Administration

Zero Administration for Windows is Microsoft's initiative to help make its **operating system** easier to install and manage. The goal is to reduce the ownership costs of PCs, particularly in large corporations with many thousands of desktop computers to support.

Microsoft introduced Zero Administration in November 1996, at a time when Oracle and Sun were touting their own approach of "network computers" as a new way of doing corporate applications with less overhead than traditional PCs. Microsoft responded with its concept of Zero Administration. The idea was to include in all of Microsoft's

Windows operating systems features that would simplify the time it took to install and maintain the system on thousands of machines—and at the same time reduce the costs of keeping PCs in corporate America.

Microsoft provides Zero Administration packs for **Windows NT** and **Windows 98**. These packs include features to automatically send out operating-system and application software updates throughout the company from one workstation, and having these updates roll back to the previous version if something goes wrong during the process.

For **Windows 2000**, Zero Administration's Group Policy feature lets administrators set rights and permissions for network and application access on the group level instead of having to do it for each individual user. If everyone in the legal department needs the same permissions and rights to applications, administrators need set this up only once for all the employees in the department.

ZIF

A ZIF (Zero Insertion Force) socket is the physical way that Intel's 486 and Pentium microprocessors up to Pentium II connect on the computer **motherboard** to the data **bus**. As its name implies, the ZIF socket is designed for ease of manufacture and so that the average computer owner will be able to upgrade the microprocessor. The ZIF socket contains a lever that opens and closes, securing the microprocessor in place.

The ZIF interface evolved through eight variations, each with a differing number of pins and pin layout arrangements. Currently, the best-known is Socket 7, the configuration used in the Pentium microprocessor. (However, the Pentium Pro uses Socket 8.) With the Pentium II microprocessor, which is based on Intel's new P6 micro architecture, Intel has changed to a new connection configuration called **Slot 1**. In this configuration, the microprocessor comes packaged in a cartridge that fits into a 242-contact or 330-contact slot in the motherboard.

The following table summarizes the Zero Insertion Force (ZIF) socket characteristics for different Intel processors.

Socket	Pins	Layout	Processor(s)	Voltage
0	168	Inline	486DX	5 V
1	169	Inline	486DX,SX	5 V
2	238	Inline	486DX, SX,DX2	5 V
3	237	Inline	486DX, SX,DX2, DX4	3V or 5 V
4	273	Inline	60 or 66 MHz Pentium	5 V
5	320	Staggered	Pentium	3 V
6	235	Inline	486DX4	3 V

Socket	Pins	Layout	Processor(s)	Voltage
7	321	Staggered	Pentium	3 V
8	387	Staggered	Pentium Pro	3 V

zine

See "ezine"

ZIP codes

ZIP (Zoning Improvement Plan) codes are postal codes in the United States that identify preassigned geographic boundaries and make mail sorting and delivery more efficient. Other countries have similar designations, usually referred to as *post codes* or *postal codes*.

Zip drive

Also see **zipping**.

A Zip drive is a small, portable disk drive used primarily for backing up and archiving personal computer files. The trademarked Zip drive was developed and is sold by Iomega Corporation. Zip drives and disks come in two sizes. The 100 **megabyte** size actually holds 100,431,872 bytes of data or the equivalent of 70 floppy diskettes. There is also a 250 megabyte drive and disk. The Iomega Zip drive comes with a software utility that lets you copy the entire contents of your hard drive to one or more Zip disks.

In addition to data backup, Iomega suggests these additional uses:

- Archiving old e-mail or other files you don't use any more but may want to access someday
- Storing unusually large files, such as graphic images that you need infrequently
- Exchanging large files with someone
- Putting your system on another computer, perhaps a portable computer
- Keeping certain files separate from files on your hard disk (for example, personal finance files)

The Zip drive can be purchased in either a **parallel** or a Small Computer System Interface (**SCSI**) version. In the parallel version, a printer can be chained off the Zip drive so that both can be plugged into your computer's parallel port.

SyQuest makes a similar product and also makes larger and more expensive removable (portable) disk drives that are worth considering if you have a more professional system.

zipping

A **Zip drive** is something different.

Zipping is the act of packaging a set of files into a single file or **archive** that is called a zip file. Usually, the files in a zip file are compressed so that they take up less space in storage or take less time to send to someone. There are several popular tools that can be used for zipping files: PKZIP for the DOS operating system, **WinZip** and **NetZIP** for Windows, MacZip for Macintosh users, and Zip and UnZip for UNIX systems. The result of zipping is a single file with a ".zip" **suffix**. After you receive a zip file, you may have to extract and decompress the file by using the same kind of tool that was used to zip the original file.

Most software that you download from the Internet will arrive as a self-extracting zip file. Typically, by double-clicking on a self-extracting zip file, it will automatically extract, decompress, and store the individual files. One of these files is usually called the "setup.exe" file. Double-clicking on this file will cause the software to be installed as a selectable program in your operating system.

Zmodem protocol

Zmodem is an error-correcting **protocol** for **modem**s. Modems that agree on using the Zmodem protocol send data in 512-byte blocks. If a block arrives and an error is detected, a "NAK" (negative acknowledgement) is returned and the block is resent.

Z-modem

See "modem error-correcting protocols"

Zoetrope

The Zoetrope (pronounced ZOH-uh-trohp), invented in 1834 by William George Horner, was an early form of motion picture projector that consisted of a drum containing a set of still images, that was turned in a circular fashion in order to create the illusion of motion. Horner originally called it the Daedatelum, but Pierre Desvignes, a French inventor, renamed his version of it the Zoetrope (from Greek word root *zoo* for animal life and *trope* for "things that turn.")

A Zoetrope is relatively easy to build. It can be turned at a variable rate to create slow-motion or speeded-up effects. Like other motion simulation devices, the Zoetrope depends on the fact that the human retina retains an image for about a tenth-of-a-second so that if a new image appears in that time, the sequence was seem to be uninterrupted and continuous. It also depends on what is referred to as the Phi phenomenon, which observes that we try to make sense out of any sequence of impressions, continuously relating them to each other.

The visual effect created by a Zoetrope (or **Zoopraxiscope**) is still used today to create **animated GIF**s and video display technologies such as **streaming video**, which essentially create an effect of motion by presenting discrete but closely-related images one after the other.

zombie

In the West Indies, a zombie is a will-less, automaton-like person who is said to have been revived from the dead and must now do the will of the living. There are at least three usages of the term related to computers and the Internet.

1) In the **UNIX operating system** world, developers sometimes use the term to refer to a program **process** that has died but hasn't yet given its process table entry back to the system.

2) On the World Wide Web, a zombie is an abandoned and sadly out-of-date **Web site** that for some reason has been moved to another Web address. It's a **ghost site** that appears to have moved. Zombies contribute to **linkrot**.

3) In at least one form of **denial of service**, one or more insecure Web servers are compromised by **hackers** who place code in each Web server that, when triggered, will launch an overwhelming number of requests toward an attacked Web site, which will soon be unable to service legitimate requests from its users. A compromised Web site that is used as an attack launch point is known as a zombie.

zoo

A zoo is a **Web site** that holds collections of Internet **viruses**. These sites may be illegal in certain countries.

Zoopraxiscope

The Zoopraxiscope (pronounced ZOH-uh-PRACKS-uh-scohp), invented by British photographer Eadweard Muybridge and first shown in 1879, was a primitive motion picture device that worked by showing a sequence of still photographs in rapid succession. Muybridge, perhaps best known today for his sequence of photographs of a race horse in motion (which proved for the first time that at top speed all feet leave the ground), studied photography in the early 1860s with daguerrotypist Silas Selleck and later achieved recognition for his photographs of the Yosemite Valley and other scenes of the American Far West. The Zoopraxiscope emerged out of his studies of motion as shown in sequences of still photographs. His 11-volume work, *Animal Locomotion*, published in 1887, contained over 100,000 photographs. In 1893, he lectured at "Zoopraxigraphical Hall" at the World's Columbian Exposition in Chicago.

The Zoetrope, along with the Zoopraxiscope and the Thaumatrope, are forerunners of the **animated GIF** and video display technologies such as **streaming video**, which essentially create an effect of motion by presenting discrete but closely-related images one after the other.

Zope

Zope (Z Object Publishing Environment) is a Web site builder and **application server** that uses the idea that it is serving (or "publishing") **object**s rather than merely providing content that will be added to a Web page. Zope's proponents believe that it is competitive with site builders and application servers such as **ColdFusion** and the Netscape Application Server. Zope software is free and uses **Open Source** code.

Zope programmers describe Zope as "object publishing software." They propose that users are interacting directly with "real objects" rather than with dynamically updated files that are being served. Zope consists of a "publisher" that publishes the objects using Zope's Persistent CGI protocol; a framework for the folders, files, and images that Zope views as "built-in objects"; an object database; a template for dynamic Web page generation; and **Structured Query Language methods** and database adapters so that Zope can interact with data in popular database servers, such as Microsoft's SQL Server. By default, Zope's object database uses the operating system's **file system** to manage data. However, it can also work with relational database management systems. Specifically, Oracle, Sybase, MySQL, and **Open Database Connectivity** are supported.

Zope was created by Digital Creations and has been used by the U.S. government, U.S. newspapers, and many company Web sites. The software is written in Python, an interpreted, interactive, **object-oriented programming** language similar to **Java**, with small pieces written in **C** for better performance. Web site developers using Zope do not need to use Python, however. Zope runs on all major operating system platforms.

Zulu

Zulu (short for "Zulu time") is used in the military and in navigation generally as a term for Universal Coordinated Time (UCT), sometimes called Universal Time Coordinated (UTC) or Coordinated Universal Time (but abbreviated UTC), and formerly called Greenwich Mean Time. In military shorthand, the letter Z follows a time expressed in Greenwich Time. Greenwich Time, now called Universal Coordinated Time, is the time at longitude 0 degrees 0 minutes—the prime meridian or longitudinal line that separates East from West in the world geographical coordinate system. This line of longitude is based on the location of the British Naval Observatory in Greenwich, England, near London. "Zulu" is the radio transmission articulation for the letter Z.

Traditionally, ship and airplane navigation is conducted using Zulu time. Zulu time is usually expressed in terms of a 24-hour clock using the **Gregorian calendar** time divisions of hours and minutes.

ZV port

The Zoomed Video port (ZV port) is a technology that supports the delivery of full-screen motion video and multimedia to notebook computers. The ZV port allows special software and a version of the **PC Card** called a ZV Port Card to provide a separate dedicated, point-to-point **bus** or path from continuously arriving video signals directly to the display controller so that they do not need to be handled by the main bus or the **central processing unit**. ZV ports are provided in IBM, Toshiba, and other manufacturers' notebook computers.

With the ZV port technology, video signals are sent in compressed files using the **MPEG** standard. The ZV Port Card decompresses the files and sends the data directly to the video **frame buffer** managed by the display controller. The technology can also be used for capturing images sent to the display from a video camera and storing them on a hard disk. Combining user input from the computer's regular **PCI** bus with the video from the ZV port, notebook users can play interactive MPEG-based games.

The specification for the ZV port is an industry standard sponsored by the **Personal Computer Memory Card International Association**.